Student CD-ROM

Included with every new copy of *Statistical Techniques in Business and Economics*, First Canadian Edition, is a student CD-ROM containing:

- **Added Content:**   Chapter 19: *An Introduction to Decision Making*
                         Chapter 20: *Statistical Quality Control*
                         Presentation of Statistics
                         Supplementary Chapter Appendices
- **Data sets in Excel and Minitab formats** for all the computer data exercises in the text
- **Data Appendices:**   1. *Factors for Control Charts*
                           2. *Poisson Distribution*
                           3. *Areas under the Normal Curve*
                           4. *Student's* t *Distribution*
                           5. *Wilcoxon T Values*

- Fully worked-out **solutions** to all odd-numbered exercises in the text
- Easy reference **Formula Sheet** in printable PDF format
- Screencam software **tutorials** for Excel, MegaStat, and Minitab
- **PowerPoint** walkthroughs of statistical techniques using Excel and Minitab
- **MegaStat 9.0 Software:** Written by J.B. Orris, the MegaStat add-in dramatically enhances the power of Excel to perform statistical analysis. Used in examples throughout the text, MegaStat has been designed for ease of use by students and instructors alike.
- **Visual Statistics 2.0 Software:** Written by Doanne, Tracy, and Mathieson, Visual Statistics 2.0 is a program designed for teaching and learning statistics through interactive experimentation and visualization. The software consists of 21 topics that are typically covered in business statistics. This unique tool fosters "interactive learning" through competency-building exercises, individual and team experiments, relevant examples, and built-in databases.

The **McGraw·Hill** Companies

McGraw-Hill
Ryerson

STATISTICAL TECHNIQUES IN BUSINESS AND ECONOMICS
First Canadian Edition

ISBN: 0-07-088044-1

1 2 3 4 5 6 7 8 9 10 TCP 0 9 8 7 6 5 4

Printed and bound in Canada

Vice President and Editorial Director: *Pat Ferrier*
Senior Sponsoring Editor: *Catherine Koop*
Developmental Editor: *Darren Hick*
Marketing Manager: *Kim Verhaeghe*
Senior Supervising Editor: *Margaret Henderson*
Copy Editor: *Janet (JJ) Wilson*
Production Coordinator: *Paula Brown/Jennifer Wilkie*
Composition: *SR Nova Private Limited, Bangalore, India*
Cover Design: *Sharon Lucas*
Interior Design: *Sharon Lucas*
Printer: *Transcontinental Printing Group*

National Library of Canada Cataloguing in Publication

Statistical techniques in business and economics/Douglas A. Lind ... [et al.].—1st Canadian ed.

Includes bibliographical references and index.
ISBN 0-07-088044-1

1. Social sciences—Statistical methods.   2. Economics—Statistical methods.   3. Commercial statistics. I. Lind, Douglas A.

HA29.S73 2003   519.5   C2003-901914-4

First Canadian Edition

Statistical Techniques
in Business and Economics

Douglas A. Lind
Coastal Carolina University and The University of Toledo

William G. Marchal
The University of Toledo

Robert D. Mason
Late of The University of Toledo

Satya Dev Gupta
St. Thomas University

Santosh Kabadi
University of New Brunswick—Fredericton

Jineshwar Singh
George Brown College

Toronto   Montréal   Boston   Burr Ridge, IL   Dubuque, IA   Madison, WI   New York
San Francisco   St. Louis   Bangkok   Bogotá   Caracas   Kuala Lumpur   Lisbon   London
Madrid   Mexico City   Milan   New Delhi   Santiago   Seoul   Singapore   Sydney   Taipei

CONTENTS IN BRIEF

Visit our Web site at www.mcgrawhill.ca/college/lind and you'll find more material!

CONTENTS

Chapter 18 Time Series and Forecasting 786

Chapter 19 An Introduction to Decision Making
Available in PDF format on CD-ROM

Chapter 20 Statistical Quality Control
Available in PDF format on CD-ROM

Visit our Web site at www.mcgrawhill.ca/college/lind and you'll find more material!

PREFACE TO THE CANADIAN EDITION

Today, data is everywhere. CNN, *The Globe and Mail*, and Yahoo! have Web sites that can track stock prices with a delay of less than 20 minutes. Federal and provincial organizations, large companies, and research institutions maintain a wealth of statistical data on their Web sites. Statistics Canada tracks everything from grocery sales to unemployment rates to national egg production. Someone is even out there keeping track of the popularity of five-pin bowling! However, skills are needed to *deal with* all of this numerical information. We need to be able to reduce large amounts of data into a meaningful form so that we can make effective interpretations, judgments, and decisions. Furthermore, we need to be critical consumers of this information. A good understanding of the statistical techniques is *sine qua non* for this purpose.

One of the major problems with most textbooks on the subject of statistics is that they either present the subject matter accurately but in a language impenetrable to students, or they oversimplify the material to the point where concepts are presented either inaccurately or in so vague a manner as to lead to misinterpretation by students. The goal of the Canadian edition of *Statistical Techniques in Business and Economics* has been to present the concepts and usage of statistical techniques accurately and in a language within the reach of all students.

Most statistics textbooks include an explanation of the "how" and "what" of the statistical techniques without an adequate attention to "why" (the *roots*) of the techniques. In our view, an explanation of the "why" of the statistical techniques is equally important for students to gain a more comprehensive and deeper understanding of these concepts and techniques, to develop their critical thinking, and to motivate them for further study of the discipline. We have therefore placed an equal emphasis on all three aspects throughout the textbook.

Our aim in this book is not to leave students with mere familiarity with statistical techniques, but to enhance their understanding of the concepts and the techniques through history, reasoning, and a variety of examples from the real world of business and economics. Our objectives throughout the text have been to give students the ability to apply the correct techniques to a variety of problems, and to give them a long-lasting feeling of "ownership" of the statistical techniques for a lifelong study of the real world. We have achieved our goals of producing a *unique* book for Canadian students by keeping the widely appreciated, easy-to-understand pedagogy of the 11th US edition by Lind, Marchal, and Mason, and then adding, adapting, and sometimes heavily revising the text, examples, exercises, and other material to suit the aims and objectives of the Canadian edition.

In this book, statistical concepts and techniques are introduced through problems relating to Canadian business and economy, and supplemented by exercises based on real-life problems to further students' grasp of the techniques. We hope this will help motivate students to learn statistical techniques and enhance their knowledge of Canadian economy and business—knowledge that will provide a *grounding* for the techniques they are learning and an understanding that will prove helpful in their careers. The range of data is wide, and the types of problems chosen are generic and can be applied to economics and business in a variety of settings.

AN OVERVIEW OF NEW FEATURES IN THE CANADIAN EDITION

Content The text has been thoroughly adapted for Canadian students, with new and revised material in every chapter. Several chapters in the text have been heavily revised for the Canadian edition, including Frequency Distribution and Graphic Presentation (2), Sampling Methods, Confidence Intervals, and Tests of Hypothesis (8–10), Linear Regression and Correlation (13), Multiple Regression Analysis (14), and Decision Making (20). Other chapters have undergone major revisions to reflect our aims and objectives in producing this Canadian edition of the book. We have also added several techniques, such as remedies to problems encountered in multiple regression analysis, to enable an interested student to gain a comprehensive understanding of the subject. Material of an advanced nature has been placed in chapter notes, chapter appendices, and/or the CD-ROM to allow a smooth flow of the primary material.

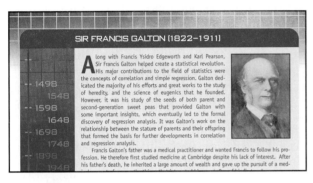

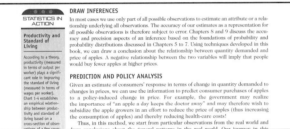

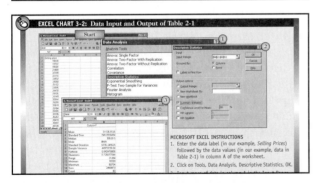

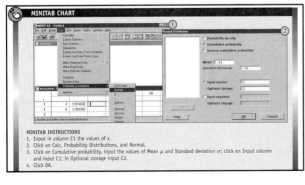

"Pioneers" Vignettes Each chapter opens with a "Pioneers" vignette introducing the background to the material being studied in the chapter, focusing on a pioneer in the development of the major statistical techniques discussed in the chapter, and illustrating the importance and pedigree of the technique or concept. Additional vignettes also appear in selected chapters. We hope the origin of and the struggle in the development of the concepts and the lives of the pioneers will inspire students and develop their sense of appreciation of the subject.

"Statistics in Action" Vignettes Thoroughly reworked for the Canadian edition, each chapter contains a number of Statistics in Action vignettes. Each vignette includes brief notes from published material that feature real-life usage of concepts and techniques covered in the chapter. These interesting applications, we believe, will enable students to realize the importance of the concepts/techniques in real-life situations and their long-lasting impact on the world around us. It will also enhance their understanding of the concepts.

Excel/MegaStat and Minitab Minitab is an easy-to-use and comprehensive software for statistical techniques. It is available on networks at many colleges and universities as well as in a student-edition version that is available to students for a nominal price. Microsoft® Excel® is widely used in business settings. We have therefore integrated the usage of these packages throughout the text. Inputs, outputs, and in-between steps are presented visually and are accompanied by step-by-step instructions for students to facilitate ease of use. This will enable instructors to focus on teaching concepts and techniques rather than spending an enormous amount of time explaining the usage of the computer software to students.

However, Microsoft Excel does not contain a number of statistical techniques. We have therefore included a separately written software package called MegaStat, which adds to the functionality of Excel for statistical techniques not covered by Excel. MegaStat version 9.0 is available on the CD-ROM packaged with this book and can easily be downloaded into Excel by Excel users.

*A **Canadian Focus*** Real-life examples from Canadian economy and business are used throughout the text, in introducing the subject, in examples and problems, and in many end-of-chapter exercises and case studies. This will motivate students learning statistical techniques by relating them to real life around them as well as contributing to their understanding of the Canadian economy and business.

Caveats Each concept and technique must be used with caution to avoid a misunderstanding and misinterpretation. For this reason, we have inserted caveats after the discussion on the concepts and techniques where such possibilities exist. This will enable students to become critical consumers of information and avoid a misunderstanding of the concepts/techniques.

Internet Exercises To familiarize students with the sources of data on Canadian economy and business and to satisfy their appetite for exploratory data analysis, each chapter contains a number of exercises that guide students to explore and obtain data on aspects of the Canadian economy and business. Most of these Internet exercises are of a comprehensive nature for the material covered in that chapter and therefore can also be assigned as case studies. As case studies, these exercises will provide students a great deal of satisfaction in terms of a sense of ownership in their work.

Computer Data Exercises In most chapters, the last few exercises refer to large business data sets. A complete listing of the data sets used is available on the CD-ROM (easily downloadable in both Excel® and Minitab) included with the text. Many of the exercises associated with these data sets are of a comprehensive nature for the material covered in the chapter, and therefore enable the instructor to assign them as case studies for the material associated with the chapter.

Case Studies Each section (a group of related chapters) contains a number of case studies that will allow students to gain a comprehensive understanding of the material covered in the group of related chapters.

Attractive Diagrams/Figures Concepts and techniques are illustrated by attractive diagrams and figures interspersed throughout the text. These enhance readability, enabling students to grasp the meaning of the more difficult concepts.

SOME CAVEATS

How good is the value of r? While the value of the correlation coefficient can be very useful in analyzing the underlying relationship between variables, we must, however, use extreme caution when drawing conclusions from a value of the coefficient of correlation obtained from a particular sample data set. As we have noted earlier, a different sample data set may yield a different value of the coefficient of correlation. If the sample data is not fully representative of the underlying population, our conclusions may be erroneous. We shall learn how to test the correlation coefficient in the population based on sample values in the following section. However, even if the sample is representative of the population, a value of the correlation coefficient may lead us to make erroneous conclusions in the following circumstances.

OUTLIERS AND AVERAGING

The coefficient of correlation is the arithmetic mean of the product of two "standardized" variables. Note, we do not imply normality in every case when we standardize a variable. We saw in Chapter 3, how conclusions based on arithmetic means can be misleading in the presence of some extremely large or small observations in a data set. The value of the

---

www.exercises.ca 9-63 TO 9-64

9-63. An excellent site for information on houses for sale in Canada is www.homestore.ca. Suppose you want to obtain a 95-percent confidence interval estimate for the average sale price of *single family* houses currently on sale in Burnaby, B.C. Go to this site, and click on Province: British Columbia, Area: Vancouver, Burnaby. Select a random sample of sale prices of 10 houses using SRR. (Use the random number table in Appendix B to select the numbers.) Assuming that the population distribution is approximately normal, obtain a 95-percent confidence interval for the population mean.

9-64. An excellent site for information on Canadian business is www.strategis.gc.ca. Suppose we are interested in obtaining a 95-percent confidence interval estimate for the mean monthly business bankruptcy rate in Canada during the last 6 years. Randomly select a sample of 6 of these months using SRR. (Number these months from 1 to 72. Randomly select a sample of 10 numbers from 1 to 72 using a random number table.) Now, go to the page strategis.ic.gc.ca/engdoc/alpha.html#A. Find the number of business bankruptcies during each of the months in the sample. Assuming that the data are approximately normally distributed, find a 95-percent confidence interval estimate of the population mean.

■ **COMPUTER DATA EXERCISES 9-65 TO 9-67**

9-65. Refer to Real Estate Data.xls on the CD, which reports sample information on the homes sold in Victoria, B.C., in 2001.
(a) Develop a 95-percent confidence interval estimate for the mean selling price of the homes.
(b) Develop a 90-percent confidence interval estimate for the fraction of homes that were sold for more than $240 000.
(c) Develop a 98-percent confidence interval estimate for the population mean of the number of bedrooms.

■ **CASE STUDY A**

Future Mutual Fund Inc. received a telephone call from a new customer. The customer is 45 years old and is thinking of placing part of her total investment in a sports fund.

Alex Robinson brought up historical year-year rates of return data of two funds. Assume that the history of the data of two funds is a useful guide to making decisions for the long run. Standard deviation of the returns measures the risk involved in investing. Below are the historical data for two funds:

Year	Canadian Growth Annual Return (%)	International Fund Annual Return (%)
1973	0.40	
1974	−10.20	
1975	−12.00	
1976	40.09	
1977	44.25	
1978	28.35	
1979	26.45	
1980	22.50	
1981	25.25	
1982	12.34	
1983	30.56	
1984	31.67	
1985	15.67	
1986	10.34	
1987	26.78	
1988	5.68	6.90
1989	10.56	−1.50
1990	12.34	25.60
1991	−15.45	21.15
1992	28.90	48.35
1993	14.50	5.20
1994	30.40	12.20
1995	2.50	21.50
1996	10.4	15.80

Use Excel or Minitab for your calculations. The client's questions are:
1. What are the standard deviations of Canadian Growth and International Fund?
2. Which of the two funds involves less risk? What statistic would you use to compare the relative dispersion of returns of the two funds?
3. Find the value of any extreme return (outlier) in each fund.

■ **CASE STUDY B**

Kimuyen Pham has lived in Scarborough, Ontario, for the last three years. She is planning to move to Clarington, east of Toronto in Durham Region, to stay close to her parents. She asked the manager of a real estate company to provide a list of houses. The manager asked one of his brokers to provide the price list of a sample of 55 houses with a price range of $99 000 to $759 900. Kimuyen would like to know the average price of houses and the variation in the price of houses. She would like to see a graphical display of the prices for a quick overview, the first and third quartile prices, and the prices that can be considered statistically extreme. As Kimuyen's broker, you provide the following information.

1. Group the data set into 12 classes with a class width of $60 000 and draw a relative frequency histogram. Use MegaStat software.
2. What percent of house prices are in the range $180 000 to $240 000?
3. Is the distribution of house prices skewed to the right or left?
4. Draw a suitable graph that will show the first, second, and third quartile prices, and also any extreme values

New Design The book has been thoroughly redesigned to enhance readability, to make key elements—such as definitions and formulae—easier to find, and to incorporate new visual elements into the text.

OTHER FEATURES

Learning Objectives Along with each opening vignette is a set of learning objectives. These are designed to provide focus for the chapter, to motivate learning, and to indicate what students should be able to do after completing the chapter.

Introduction At the start of each chapter, we review the important concepts of the previous chapter(s) and describe how they link to what the current chapter will cover.

Definitions Definitions of new terms or terms unique to the study of statistics are set apart from the text in boxes and indicated by icons. This allows easy reference and review.

Formulae Whenever a formula is used for the first time it is shaded and numbered for easy reference. In addition, a formula card that summarizes the key formulae can be found in easily-printable PDF format on the Student CD-ROM and Online Learning Centre.

Examples/Solutions We include numerous examples with solutions. These are designed to show immediately in detail how the concepts can be applied to business situations.

Self-Reviews Self-reviews are interspersed throughout each chapter to help monitor progress and provide immediate reinforcement for that particular technique. The answers and methods of solution are located at the end of the chapter.

Exercises We include exercises within the chapter for each technique/concept, after the Self-Reviews, and at the end of the chapter. Brief answers for all odd-numbered exercises are given at the end of the book. Detailed solutions, together with guidance for interpreting results, are included in CD-ROM packaged with the book.

Chapter Outline As a summary, each chapter includes a chapter outline. This learning aid provides an opportunity to review material, particularly vocabulary, and to see and review formulae again.

Section Reviews After each selected group of related chapters, a section review is included. This review also includes a brief review of the chapters, a glossary of the key terms, case studies, and a practice examination of the material covered. This review also includes cases that let students make decisions using tools and techniques from a variety of related chapters.

SUPPLEMENTS AND FEATURES

FOR THE INSTRUCTOR

i-Learning Sales Specialist Your Integrated Learning Sales Specialist is a McGraw-Hill Ryerson representative who has the experience, product knowledge, training, and support to help you assess and integrate any of the below-noted products, technology, and services into your course for optimum teaching and learning performance. Whether it's how to use our test bank software, helping your students improve their grades, or how to put your entire course online, your *i*-Learning Sales Specialist is there to help. Contact your local *i*-Learning Sales Specialist today to learn how to maximize all McGraw-Hill Ryerson resources!

Instructor's CD-ROM (ICD) The ICD contains the Instructor's Manual, Computerized Test Bank, and Microsoft PowerPoint® Presentation, chapters 19 "An Introduction to Decision Making" and 20 "Statistical Quality Control" in PDF format, and a host of other tools:

- **Instructor's Manual** contains complete solutions to all even-numbered problems in the text, and solutions to assignments in the Student Study Guide.
- **Computerized Test Bank,** written by Ed Zuke, Red River College, contains almost 1500 questions and problems for exams.
- **PowerPoint Presentations,** prepared by Colleen Quinn and Ron Thornbury of Seneca College, draw on the highlights of each chapter and provide an opportunity for instructors to emphasize the most relevant visuals in class discussions, or for students to brush up on key features for tests.

Instructor's Online Learning Centre (OLC) The OLC at http://www.mcgrawhill.ca/college/lind includes a password-protected Web site for Instructors, and offers downloadable supplements and access to PageOut, the McGraw-Hill Ryerson Web site development centre, as well as a host of tools for students and instructors alike to use in the classroom or at home.

PowerWeb (Optional Package) Self-grading quizzes, interactive exercises, and a discipline-specific search engine with instant access to articles, essays, and daily news for your class.

PageOut Development centre for course Web sites. Faculty can create online courses complete with assignments, quizzes, links to relevant sites, and more—in a matter of minutes, and free to instructors.

FOR THE STUDENT

Student CD-ROM Packaged free with the text, the CD features detailed solutions to all odd-numbered exercises, software tutorials, PowerPoint slides, data files in Excel, Minitab, and ASCII formats, and MegaStat for Excel, by J.B. Orris, software that enhances the power of Excel in statistical analysis. Visual Statistics is also included—a software program for teaching and learning statistics through interactive experimentation and visualization. Also included is additional content on Hypergeometric Distribution, Definition and Properties of *F*-distribution, Statistical Quality Control and more. See a complete list of contents on the inside front cover of this text.

Study Guide Written by Walter Lange of the University of Toledo and Ed Zuke of Red River College. Each chapter includes objectives, a brief summary of the chapter, problems and their solutions, self-review exercises, and assignment problems.

Student Online Learning Centre (OLC) The OLC at www.mcgrawhill.ca/college/lind contains chapter quizzes, chapters on Linear Programming and Statistical Quality Control, WWW links to chapter exercises, sample chapter from the Study Guide, data files, appendices, Glossary, chapter goals, PowerPoint Presentation, link to Σ-STAT, and more!

ACKNOWLEDGMENTS

Statistical Techniques in Business and Economics, First Canadian Edition is the product of many people: students, colleagues, reviewers, and the staff at McGraw-Hill Ryerson and McGraw-Hill/Irwin. First of all, we wish to express our sincere gratitude to the reviewers of this Canadian edition as well as the reviewers for the 11th US edition for their thorough reviews and many helpful suggestions for enriching the text.

REVIEWERS OF THE FIRST CANADIAN EDITION

Leslie Brailsford, *George Brown College*; Wendy Brown, *Southern Alberta Institute of Technology*; Ross Bryant, *Conestoga College*; Felix Ernst, *Camosun College*; Blake Friesen, *Saskatchewan Institute of Applied Science and Technology*; Diane Huysmans, *Fanshawe College*; Marc Jerry, *Mount Royal College*; Dave Jobson, *University of Alberta*; Dennis Kira, *Concordia University*; Gillian Leek, *Mohawk College*; John Marasigan, *Kwantlen University College*; Peter Miller, *University of Windsor*; Colleen Quinn, *Seneca College*; Stephen Reid, *British Columbia Institute of Technology*; Judith Skuce, *Georgian College*; Maurice Tugwell, *Acadia University*; Carol Ann Waite, *Sheridan College*; Ed Zuke, *Red River College*.

REVIEWERS OF THE 11th US EDITION

Douglas Barrett, *University of North Alabama*; Darl Bien, *University of Denver*; Wendy Brown, *Southern Alberta Institute of Technology*; Mary Elizabeth Camp, *Indiana University*; Sharad Chitgopekar, *Illinois State University*; Gopal Dorai, *William Paterson University*; Bernice Evans, *Morgan State University*; Burdette Hansen, *University of Phoenix*; Clifford B. Hawley, *West Virginia University*; Lloyd R. Jaisingh, *Morehead State University*; Valerie M. Jones, *Tidewater Community College*; Creig Kronstedt, *Cardinal Stritch University*; Denise Kummer, *St. Louis Community College*; Jack Muryn, *Cardinal Stritch University*; Julia A. Norton, *California State University—Hayward*; Louis A. Patille, *University of Phoenix—Colorado*; Christopher W. Rogers, *Miami-Dade Community College*; Charlene Robert, *Louisiana State University*; Linda Stephanchick, *DeVry Institute of Technology*; Andrew Welki, *John Carroll University*; Kathleen Whitcomb, *University of South Carolina*; Charles W. Williams, *Troy State University*.

We further wish to acknowledge our colleagues at St. Thomas University, University of New Brunswick, and George Brown College for their encouragement and support for this project. Thanks are also due to Mr. B. Pramujati for help in preparing the manuscript, and to Joe Bellomo and Dr. L. Brailsford of George Brown College, Dr. J.K. Singh (FRCPC), Dr. M. Storoszczuk, and Endu and John Gentles.

Finally, we wish to thank Catherine Koop (Senior Sponsoring Editor), Darren Hick (Developmental Editor), Margaret Henderson (Senior Supervising Editor), Kelly Dickson (Manager of Editorial Services), Kim Verhaeghe (Marketing Manager), Megan Farrell (Sales Manager), and many other McGraw-Hill Ryerson staff, whom we do not know personally, but who made valuable contributions to the development and production of this text.

Satya Dev Gupta
Santosh Narayan Kabadi
Jineshwar Singh

Online LearningCentre

www.mcgrawhill.ca/college/lind

FOR THE STUDENT

- Want to get higher grades?

- Want instant feedback on your comprehension *and* retention of the course material?

- Want to know how ready you *really* are to take your next exam?

- Want the extra help at *your* convenience?

Of course you do!

Then check out your
Online Learning Centre!

- Online Quizzes
- Additional and Expanded Content
- Data Files

- Microsoft® PowerPoint® Presentations
- Problems and Exercises
- Link to Σ-Stat

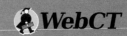

Statistical Techniques
in Business and Economics

First Canadian Edition

FOR THE INSTRUCTOR

- Want an easy way to test your students prior to an exam that *doesn't* create more work for you?

- Want to access your supplements *without* having to bring them all to class?

- Want to integrate current happenings into your lectures *without* all the searching and extra work?

- Want an *easy* way to get your course on-line?

- Want to *free up more time* in your day to get more done?

Of course you do!

Then check out your
Online Learning Centre!

- Downloadable Supplements
- PageOut
- Online Resources

McGraw-Hill Ryerson

Higher Learning. Forward Thinking.™

CHAPTER 1

What is Statistics?

GOALS

When you have completed this chapter, you will be able to:

- Explain what is meant by statistics

- Identify the role of statistics in the development of knowledge and everyday life

- Explain what is meant by descriptive statistics and inferential statistics

- Distinguish between a qualitative variable and a quantitative variable

- Distinguish between a discrete variable and a continuous variable

- Collect data from published and unpublished sources

- Distinguish among nominal, ordinal, interval, and ratio levels of measurement

- Identify abuses of statistics

- Gain an overview of the art and science of statistics. We recommend that you read this chapter at least twice, once at the beginning and once at the end of your course!

"God does not play dice with Nature," said Einstein, but what about His creation?

What do games, gods, and gambling have to do with statistics? Interestingly enough, human pursuits in games of chance, divinity, and gambling have served as the sources of inspiration for the development of modern statistics.

Games of chance date back to antiquity. Archaeologists have found dice and dice-like bones in many early civilizations dating back from 1000 to 3000 B.C., including regions in the Indus valley, Babylonia, Mesopotamia, Greece, and Rome. The great Vedic epic *The Mahabharata*, written about 1000 B.C., describes how gambling among the princes resulted in the Great War and an eventual fall of the great empire. Augustus (63 B.C.–A.D. 14), the first Roman emperor, once wrote to his daughter: "I send you 250 *denarii*, the sum I gave to each of my guests in case they wished to play at dice or at odd and even during dinner"![1] Claudius (10 B.C.–A.D. 54) is known to have published a book on the art of dicing, and is known "to play while driving, having the board game fitted to his carriage in such a way as to prevent his game from being disturbed."[2]

Chance outcomes have been used as an indication of divine will in many ancient religions. The goddess Fortuna (Roman and Greek: see the picture above) and the goddess Laxmi (Hindu) were (and still are, by many) often prayed to for a favourable lot at games of chance. In the Old Testament, "the lot is cast into the lap; but the whole disposing thereof is of the Lord" (Proverbs 16:33). In ancient Assyria, the king gave his own name to the first year of his reign; the names of subsequent years were determined by lot. On a die found in Assyria (from the year 833 B.C.), it is inscribed: "O great lord, Assur! O great lord, Adad! This is the lot of Jahali,... king of Assyria,... make prosper the harvest of Assyria.... May his lot come up!"[3] The Chinese used *I Ching* (one of the five books written by Confucius) together with coins or milfoil to create an oracle that they believed to be the result of a partnership between god and humans.

The search for formal methods for experimental knowledge did not begin until the 15th century. Often inspired by games of chance and problems in gambling, efforts in this direction were pioneered by Leonardo da Vinci and Cardano from Italy, and Fermat and Pascal from France. Some of the reasons speculated for such a late development of the experimental methods include the prevalence of an Aristotelian (deterministic) mindset and an opposition of the Church to all types of games of chance and casting of lots.

INTRODUCTION

More than 100 years ago, H.G. Wells, an English author and historian, noted that statistical thinking will one day be as necessary for efficient citizenship as the ability to read. He made no mention of business, because the Industrial Revolution was just beginning. Were he to comment on statistical thinking today, he would probably say that "statistical thinking is necessary not only for effective citizenship but also for effective decision making in various facets of business."

The late W. Edwards Deming, a noted statistician and quality control expert, insisted that statistics education should begin before high school. He liked to tell the story of an 11-year-old who devised a quality control chart to track the on-time performance of his school bus. Deming commented, "He's got a good start in life." We hope that this book will give you a solid foundation in statistics for your future studies and work in economics and business related fields.

Almost daily we apply statistical concepts to our lives. For example, to start the day you turn on the shower and let it run for a few moments. Then you put your hand in the shower to sample the temperature and decide to add more hot water or more cold water. You then conclude that the temperature is just right and enter the shower. As a second example, suppose you are at the grocery store looking to buy a frozen pizza. One of the pizza makers has a sample stand, and they offer a small wedge of their pizza. After sampling the pizza, you decide whether to purchase the pizza or not. In both the shower and pizza examples, you make a decision and select a course of action based on a sample.

Businesses are faced with similar problems. The Kellogg Company must ensure that the average amount of Raisin Bran in the 25.5 g package meets the label specifications. To do so, they select periodic random samples from the production area and weigh the contents. In politics, a candidate for the position of Member of Parliament wants to know what percentage of the voters in his riding will support him in the upcoming election. There are several ways he could go about answering this question. He could have his staff call all those people in his riding who plan to vote in the upcoming election and ask for whom they plan to vote. He could go out on a street in his riding, stop 10 people who look to be of voting age, and ask them for whom they plan to vote. He could select a random cross-section of about 1000 voters from his riding, contact these voters and, based on this cross-section, make an estimate of the percentage who will vote for him in the upcoming election. In this text we will show you why the third choice is the best course of action.

1.1   WHAT IS MEANT BY STATISTICS?

The word *statistics* owes its origin to the German word *statistik*, used to describe numerical information on economic, social, political, cultural, or other characteristics of a nation state. In popular usage, the word is still used to express some numerical information not necessarily related to the characteristics of a state. Examples include the number of Lotto 6/49 tickets sold before the next draw, the number of students enrolled at Concordia University this year, the value of donuts sold at Tim Hortons in Calgary last week, the number of tourists visiting PEI last summer, or the change in the value of the Toronto Stock Exchange Index last Friday. In these examples, statistics is a single number.

Likewise, the word *statistics* is also used to describe a large amount of information through summary measures, called *descriptive statistics*. Examples include the average income of all households in Canada, the average driving speed of cars on Highway 401, and the variation (say, minimum and maximum values) in Bell Canada stock prices during the last week. More examples are given below.

- In 1998, 45 percent of Canadian households owned a computer and 25 percent were connected to the Internet.
- In 2000, 358 870 adults and 113 598 youths were charged in criminal incidents in Canada.
- In 1998, there were 54 763 police officers and 58 198 teachers in universities and community colleges in Canada.
- On average, Canadians spend 1.3 hours per day commuting, and 1.5 hours per day with their children.
- In July 2000, average weekly earnings (all employees) of Canadians were $665.41.
- In 2000, John Roth, president and CEO of Nortel Networks Corp., was the best paid ($71 million) Canadian company executive.
- On average, Canadians listen to the radio for nearly 21 hours per week.

Larger amounts of information can also be organized in tabular form or as graphical displays (see Table 1-1 and Chart 1-1) to describe patterns in the data. The graphical display of a large quantity of information allows easier interpretation than the tabular form. We study these methods in the next chapter.

While descriptive or numerical methods have played a significant role in the early development of statistics, it is the interplay of numerical methods and theories underlying probability and probability distributions that constitute the core of modern statistics. This enables us to draw inferences about the *whole* from information on only a *part* of that whole. This is called *statistical inference*. For example, we can draw inferences about average income and/or variations in the incomes of about 12 million Canadian households based on information on only, say, 1200 or 12 000 households. Consistent with the inferential aspects of statistics, statisticians define the word *statistic* as an estimator of a certain attribute (average, variation, etc.) of the entire

Index of Provincial Well-Being and Improvement in the Level of Well-Being

TABLE 1-1	CHART 1-1: Improvement in the Level of Well-Being (1971–97, 1971=100)

Province	Well-Being
CAN	112.53
NF	106.98
PEI	125.26
NS	107.12
NB	114.09
QC	106.89
ON	113.78
MB	120.74
SK	119.53
AB	120.05
BC	113.67

CHART 1-1: Improvement in the Level of Well-Being (1971–97, 1971=100). Canada and the Provinces

CHART 1-2: Types of Statistics

```
                        Types of Statistics
            ┌───────────────────────┴───────────────────────┐
   Descriptive Statistics                      Inferential Statistics
 Methods of collecting, organizing,           Science of making inferences
   presenting and analyzing data                 about a population
                                             based on a sample of information
```

data (called a "population") based on only a small part of that data (called a "sample"). In other words, statistics is a method of inquiry that enables us to make scientific generalizations about the world from the knowledge of only a small part of that world. We shall discuss this process in some detail in the next section. Thus, the field of statistics includes both descriptive statistics and inferential statistics. Further, statistical methods can be used for prediction and policy analysis. For a visual representation of the types of statistics, see Chart 1-2 above.

 Statistics   The art and science of collecting, organizing and presenting data, drawing inferences from a sample of information about the entire population, as well as prediction and policy analysis.

Statistics is both an art and a science. It is a science inasmuch as it depends on scientific theories underlying inference. It is an art in the sense that it requires a good understanding of how to bring various statistical techniques together to understand real-world phenomena and use them for prediction and policy analysis.

Note the words "population" and "sample" in the definition of inferential statistics. We often make reference to the population of 31 million people in Canada, or more than 1 billion people in China. However, in statistics the word *population* has a broader meaning. A population may consist of *individuals*, such as all the students enrolled at the University of Toronto, all the students in Accounting 2001, or all the inmates at the Kingston prison. A population may also consist of *objects*, such as copies of this book printed by McGraw-Hill Ryerson this year, or all the $100 bills in circulation in Canada. A population may also consist of a group of *measurements*, such as all the weights of the defensive linemen on the University of British Columbia's football team or all the heights of the basketball players at Memorial University of Newfoundland. Thus, a population in the statistical sense of the word does not necessarily refer to people.

POPULATION AND PARAMETER

A *population* is defined as a collection or as a set of all elements (individuals, objects, or measurements) of interest in an investigation. A *parameter* is a summary measure of some characteristic such as an average, a proportion, or a variation in all elements of a population.

To infer something about a population, we usually take a sample from the population.

SAMPLE AND STATISTIC

A *sample* is a portion, or subset, of all elements in a population. A statistic is an estimator of parameter of interest in population.

REASONS FOR SAMPLING

Why take a sample instead of studying every member (element) of the population?

- *Costs of surveying the entire population may be too large or prohibitive:* A sample of registered voters is necessary because of the prohibitive cost of contacting millions of voters before an election.
- *Destruction of elements during investigation:* If Sylvania tried to estimate the life of all its 60-watt light bulbs by actually using them until they burned out, there would be nothing left to sell. Testing wheat for moisture content destroys the wheat, thus making sampling imperative.
- *Accuracy of results:* Assuming proper techniques of sampling are used, results based on samples may be close in accuracy to the results based on populations. Further, as discussed in Chapter 8, we can identify the extent of error due to sampling in most cases.

As noted, taking a sample to learn something about a population is done extensively in business, economics, agriculture, politics, and government. Example 1-1 illustrates the use of a sample in relation to a population (compare the relative sizes of the sample and the population) by Statistics Canada.

Example 1-1

Internet Shopping

The HIUS (Household Internet Use Survey) is administered by Statistics Canada to a sub-sample of dwellings included in the Labour Force Survey (LFS), and therefore its sample design is closely tied to the LFS. The LFS is a monthly household survey whose sample is representative of households with a civilian, non-institutionalized population, 15 years of age or older, in Canada's 10 provinces.

In total, 43 034 households were eligible for the HIUS survey. Interviews were completed for 36 241 of these households for a response rate of 84.2 percent. Results were weighted to the entire count of households in Canada. The annual estimate for the number of households in Canada is projected from the census of population. The HIUS used a population projection based on the 1996 Census of population (11.632 million households).

Based on the information collected on 36 241 households, the authors of the report conclude:

> In 1999, 1.8 million households indicated that at least one member of their household had engaged in some aspect of Internet shopping from home, either using the Internet as part of their buying process by researching characteristics and prices of goods and services (window shopping) or placing orders for purchases on line.... There were 806 000 households that took the extra step and actually engaged in e-commerce (*those Internet shoppers that did place at least one order over the Internet from home*).[4]

Some additional examples of the use of a sample in relation to a population are provided below.

- Television networks constantly monitor the popularity of their programs by hiring Nielsen and other organizations to sample the preferences of TV viewers. These program ratings are used to set advertising rates and to cancel programs.
- A public accounting firm selects a random sample of 100 invoices and checks each invoice for accuracy. There were errors on five of the invoices; hence, the accounting firm estimates that 5 percent of the entire population of invoices contains an error.
- A random sample of 260 accounting graduates from community colleges showed that the mean starting salary was $32 694. We therefore conclude that the mean starting salary for all accounting graduates from community colleges is $32 694.

- In the week after the terrorist attacks on New York and Washington on September 11, 2001, Prime Minister Jean Chrétien's personal approval rating for his political performance shot up from 57 to 65 percent. The results are based on polls conducted jointly by *The Globe and Mail*, CTV, and Ipsos-Reid. The calculated margin of error for these polls is 3.1 percent.

In the above examples, the mean starting salary of $32 694 and Jean Chrétien's approval ratings of 57 and 65 percent are estimates of mean starting salary and approval rating (parameters) in the respective populations. Actual values of the parameters will not be known unless we calculate the mean starting salary or approval rating based on all elements in each population. Since it is too costly or time-consuming to collect information on all elements in the population, we use statistics to draw inferences about the population parameters. Statistical techniques enable us to estimate parameters and draw inferences with a level of confidence such as a maximum of 3.1 percent margin of error (in the pollsters' estimate of the parameter) mentioned in the approval rating case.

1.2 THE ROLE OF STATISTICS IN THE DEVELOPMENT OF KNOWLEDGE

The development of knowledge, since antiquity, has proceeded through a number of methods such as intuition, revelation, abstraction, and experimentation. However, abstraction and experimentation have been the most popular methods of advancing the frontiers of knowledge in the material world.

THE METHOD OF ABSTRACTION

The method of abstraction involves *deducing* a hypothesis about a phenomenon in the real world from a set of definitions and assumptions and following the rules of logic. For example, suppose you are interested in understanding why people buy more apples at lower prices. A theorist may explain (deduce) this phenomenon as follows:

DEFINITIONS AND ASSUMPTIONS

1. People are rational. That is, they have well-defined preferences and always prefer more of a commodity to less of that commodity.

2. Except for the price of apples, all other factors that may influence purchases of apples (such as people's incomes, prices of substitutes for apples, people's tastes for apples) remain unchanged.

3. Each additional apple they buy/consume gives them a lower level of satisfaction. Thus, if we could define satisfaction in terms of some imaginary units such as *utils* (short for utility), then we might assume that the first apple gives them 50 *utils*, the second apple 35 *utils*, and the third apple 22 *utils* of satisfaction, and so on.

4. Parting with money yields dissatisfaction. Suppose that each penny spent gives them one *util* of dissatisfaction. Thus, if they spend 50 cents it gives them 50 *utils* of dissatisfaction (negative 50 *utils*).

REASONING

Since people derive lower satisfaction from each additional apple, and since they lose one unit of satisfaction from each penny spent, the maximum they would be willing to pay for the first apple is 50 cents; for the second apple 35 cents; for the third apple 22 cents, and so on.

IMPLICATIONS/HYPOTHESES

People will buy more apples at lower prices. This is also called the *law of demand*. You can even make a prediction that a tax on apples that increases the price of apples would result in lower sales/purchases of apples.

Thus, in this method, we start from our observation of a general pattern in some real-world phenomenon and draw a particular conclusion about that phenomenon. Our journey in this method is therefore *from general to particular*. Since in this method we deduce a particular conclusion/hypothesis based on a general pattern, we call it the *deductive* method.

THE METHOD OF EXPERIMENTATION

The method of experimentation, on the other hand, proceeds in the opposite direction. For example, in the case of demand for apples we would need to decide how the relevant information on the quantity and price of apples would be collected (the design of the experiment), collect data for the experiment, use statistical methods to analyze the data, and then draw inferences about the buying behaviour of apple consumers in the real world.

In this method, we induce a relation based on the information from the real world. In this method, in general, we proceed as follows:

DEFINE THE EXPERIMENTAL GOAL OR A WORKING HYPOTHESIS

The goal or the working hypothesis may be based on some theory or experience. For example, we may have seen people buying a lower quantity of apples at a higher price, or we may use the law of demand derived by an economist.

DESIGN AN EXPERIMENT

We develop a method of collection of data for the relevant information on the variables of interest in a way that is consistent with both the theoretical hypothesis and the statistical techniques. For example, to verify the law of demand we would need to collect data in a way that, except for the price of apples, all other forces including income, tastes, prices of substitutes for apples, and so on remain unchanged. We could also use an experimental design that would enable us to isolate the effects of changes in price on quantity demanded. In general, the nature of experimental design is determined by the objective(s) of investigation. We discuss this aspect in Chapters 8 and 12.

COLLECT DATA

Given the experimental design, we collect data and check for its adequacy and accuracy. Application of proper survey methods is an essential part of data collection. Data may be collected from published sources, if available and reliable.

ESTIMATE THE VALUES/RELATIONS

We use a suitable statistical technique to estimate the value of an attribute, such as average, for a single variable or a relationship for multiple variables. By using the technique of two-variable regression analysis (Chapter 13), we can estimate the relationship between quantity and price of apples. Techniques for estimating certain attributes of a single variable, such as an average or variation, are discussed in Chapters 3 and 4.

STATISTICS IN ACTION

Productivity and Standard of Living

According to a theory, productivity (measured in terms of output per worker) plays a significant role in improving the standard of living (measured in terms of wages per worker). Chart 1-4 establishes an empirical relationship between productivity and standard of living based on a cross-section of observations of a few countries. Countries with higher productivity in general are seen with a higher standard of living. The scatter of observations (and the line going through these observations) shows a strong relationship between productivity and standard of living (see Chart 1-4). To improve the Canadian standard of living, Canadian policy-makers can use this relationship as a guide to devise policies that would result in improvements in productivity.

DRAW INFERENCES

In most cases we use only part of all possible observations to estimate an attribute or a relationship underlying all observations. The accuracy of our estimates as a representation for all possible observations is therefore subject to error. Chapters 8 and 9 discuss the accuracy and precision aspects of an inference based on the foundations of probability and probability distributions discussed in Chapters 5 to 7. Using techniques developed in this book, we can draw a conclusion about the relationship between quantity demanded and price of apples. A negative relationship between the two variables will imply that people would buy fewer apples at higher prices.

PREDICTION AND POLICY ANALYSIS

Given an estimate of consumers' response in terms of change in quantity demanded to changes in prices, we can use the information to predict consumer purchases of apples to a policy-induced change in price. For example, the government may realize the importance of "an apple a day keeps the doctor away" and may therefore wish to subsidize the apple growers in an effort to reduce the price of apples (thus increasing the consumption of apples) and thereby reducing health-care costs!

Thus, in this method, we start from particular observations from the real world and draw conclusions about the general patterns in the real world. Our journey in this method is therefore from the *particular to the general*. Since in this method we induce a conclusion/hypothesis based on a particular set of observations, we call it the **inductive method**. *In practice, the two methods are often complementary in advancing the frontiers of knowledge.* Apples falling from trees (rather than rising from the ground) can give an idea to a person like Newton to develop a theory of gravitation, and the hypotheses on gravitational forces can further be confirmed/corroborated through experimental methods. These ideas on the construction of knowledge based on two methods, as outlined above, are shown through a simplified diagram in Chart 1-3.

However, we should caution you against jumping to the conclusion of proving or disproving a theory based on statistical evidence. While theories are based on definitions, assumptions, and tight rules of logic, statistical evidence is based on accuracy of experimental design, a particular set of observations produced by the experiment, and continuously evolving methods of estimation and the science of measurement of uncertainty.

CHART 1-3: Characteristics of Abstraction and Experimentation

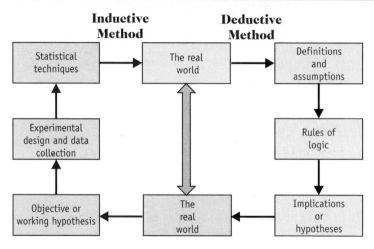

CHART 1-4: High Productivity Is Key to a High Standard of Living

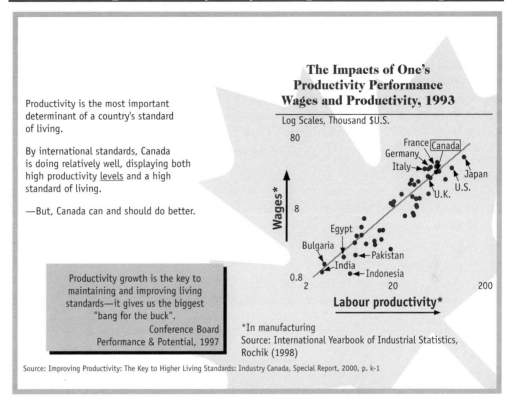

Productivity is the most important determinant of a country's standard of living.

By international standards, Canada is doing relatively well, displaying both high productivity <u>levels</u> and a high standard of living.

—But, Canada can and should do better.

> Productivity growth is the key to maintaining and improving living standards—it gives us the biggest "bang for the buck".
>
> Conference Board
> Performance & Potential, 1997

The Impacts of One's Productivity Performance Wages and Productivity, 1993

Log Scales, Thousand $U.S.

*In manufacturing
Source: International Yearbook of Industrial Statistics, Rochik (1998)

Source: Improving Productivity: The Key to Higher Living Standards: Industry Canada, Special Report, 2000, p. k-1

1.3 THE ROLE OF STATISTICS IN EVERYDAY LIFE

If you look through your college/university catalogue, you will find that statistics is a required course for many programs. Why is this so? What are the differences in the statistics courses taught in engineering, psychology, sociology, or business? The biggest difference is the examples used; the course content is basically the same. In engineering we may be interested in how many units are manufactured on a particular machine; in psychology or sociology we are interested in test scores; and in business we are interested in such things as profits, hours worked, and wages. However, all three are interested in what is a typical value and how much variation there is in the data. There may also be a difference in the level of mathematics required. An engineering statistics course usually requires calculus. Statistics courses in colleges of business and education usually teach the course at a more applied level. You should be able to handle the mathematics in this text if you have completed high-school algebra.

So why is statistics required in so many programs? The *first reason* is that numerical information is everywhere; look in newspapers (*The Globe and Mail* or your local newspaper), news magazines (*TIME, Newsweek*), business magazines (*The Economist, BusinessWeek*, or *Forbes*), general-interest magazines (*MACLEAN'S*), women's magazines (*Chatelaine, Canadian Living*), or sports magazines (*Sports Illustrated*), and you will be bombarded by numerical information. Here are some examples.

- Alberta's oil sands, by most estimates, contain more oil in the so-called "tar sands" than there is in all of Saudi Arabia, or about 300 billion barrels that are recoverable using existing technology. That's enough to supply the United States for more than 40 years—plus there are another 1.5 to 2 trillion barrels on top of that, which would be harder to extract. That's 10 times what Saudi Arabia has.

- The Canadian Radio-Television Commission's (CRTC) first annual report on competition in Canadian telecommunications markets, released September 28, 2001, said this country's telecom-services industry was worth $28.7 billion in 2000 and has grown at an average of 9 percent a year since 1996.

- Golfer Tiger Woods turned pro in mid-1996 and racked up $2.7 million in tournament winnings in his first year on the Tour. At that rate, he was a bargain: according to one estimate, Woods generated $650 million in new revenues for television networks, equipment manufacturers, and other businesses in that first year. He now earns $20 million a year from his endorsement of Nike.

- Graduates of McGill University's Master's of Business Administration Program had a mean starting salary of $54 000 and 91 percent were employed within three months of graduation.

- On July 20, 2001, DaimlerChrysler reported a second-quarter loss of $125 million ($US), much better than the expected loss of $700 million ($US) and a big improvement from the first-quarter loss of $1.2 billion ($US).

How are we to determine if the conclusions reported are reasonable? Were the samples large enough? How were the sampled units selected? To be an educated consumer of this information, we need to be able to read charts and graphs and understand discussions of numerical information. An understanding of the concepts of basic statistics will be a big help.

The *second reason* for taking a statistics course is that statistical techniques are used to make decisions that affect our daily lives. That is, they affect our personal welfare. Here are a few examples.

- Insurance companies use statistical analysis to set rates for home, automobile, life, and health insurance. Tables are available that summarize the probability of an auto accident by a 20-year-old female and a 20-year-old male. The differences in the probabilities are revealed in the differences in their insurance premiums.

- Air Canada slashed 5000 jobs at the end of September 2001 and cautioned that passengers will face less frequent service as it implements plans to ground 84 planes and cut one fifth of its capacity.

- As a result of the technology "meltdown" in 2001, Nortel slashed 30 000 jobs by September 2001 and planned to cut 20 000 more jobs in the remainder of the year.

- About 15 000 forestry workers in B.C. have been laid off as a result of the 19.3-percent US duty imposed on Canadian softwood lumber.

- Medical researchers study the cure rates for diseases, based on the use of different drugs and different forms of treatment. For example, what is the effect of treating a certain type of knee injury surgically or with physical therapy? If you take an Aspirin each day, does that reduce your risk of a heart attack?

A *third reason* for taking a statistics course is that the knowledge of statistical methods will help you understand how decisions are made and give you a better understanding of how they affect you. No matter what line of work you select, you will find yourself faced with decisions where an understanding of data analysis is helpful.

To make informed decisions, you will need to be able to:

- Define the objective (or hypothesis) of your inquiry/investigation.
- Determine the method and framework (design of experiment) for collection of the required information.
- Collect the required data from published and/or unpublished sources as necessary.
- Determine the adequacy and accuracy of the collected data and make changes as necessary.
- Estimate the required characteristics of the population as identified in the objective of your inquiry.
- Analyze the results.
- Draw inferences while assessing the risk of an incorrect conclusion.

The statistical methods presented in the text will provide you with a framework for the decision-making process.

In summary, there are at least three reasons for studying statistics: (1) data are everywhere, (2) statistical techniques are used to make many decisions that affect our lives, and (3) no matter what your future line of work, you will make decisions that involve data. An understanding of statistical methods will help you make these decisions more effectively.

■ SELF-REVIEW 1-1

Halifax-based Market Facts asked a sample of 1960 consumers to try a newly developed frozen fish dinner by Morton Foods called Fish Delight. Of the 1960 sampled, 1176 said they would purchase the dinner if it was marketed.
   (a) What would Market Facts report to Morton Foods regarding acceptance of Fish Delight in the population?
   (b) Is this an example of descriptive statistics or inferential statistics? Explain.

1.4   TYPES OF VARIABLES

QUALITATIVE VARIABLES

When the characteristic or variable being studied is non-numeric, it is called a *qualitative variable* or an *attribute*. Examples of qualitative variables are gender, religious affiliation, type of automobile owned, province of birth, and eye colour. When the data being studied are qualitative, we are usually interested in how many or what proportion falls into each category. For example, what percentage of the population has blue eyes? How many Catholics and how many Protestants are there in Canada? What percentage of the total number of cars sold last month were Buicks? Qualitative data are often summarized in charts and bar graphs (see Chapter 2).

QUANTITATIVE VARIABLES

When the variable studied can be reported numerically, the variable is called a *quantitative variable*. Examples of quantitative variables are the balance in your chequing account, the ages of company presidents, the life of a battery, the speeds of automobiles travelling along a highway, and the number of children in a family.

CHART 1-5: The Types of Variables

Examples:
Colours of pens in a drawer (1)
Distance between Winnipeg and Bangkok (2b)
Gender (1)
Kilometres driven between oil changes (2b)
Number of children (2a)
Number of employees (2a)
Number of TV sets sold last year (2a)
Type of car owned (1)
Weight of a shipment (2b)

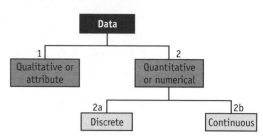

Quantitative variables are either discrete or continuous. **Discrete variables** can assume only certain values, and there are usually "gaps" between the values. Examples of discrete variables are the number of bedrooms in a house (1, 2, 3, 4, etc.), the number of cars arriving at a Tim Hortons drive-through in downtown Fredericton during an hour (16, 19, 30, etc.), and the number of students in each section of a statistics course (25 in section A, 42 in section B, and 18 in section C). Notice that a home can have 3 or 4 bedrooms, but it cannot have 3.56 bedrooms. Thus, there is a "gap" between possible values. Typically, discrete variables result from counting. We count, for example, the number of cars arriving at the Tim Hortons, and we count the number of students in each section in a statistics course.

Observations on a **continuous variable** can assume any value within a specific range. Examples of continuous variables are the air pressure in a tire and the weight of a shipment of grain (which, depending on the accuracy of the scales, could be 15.0 tonnes, 15.01 tonnes, 15.03 tonnes, etc.). The amount of Raisin Bran in a box and the time it takes to fly from Fredericton to Toronto are other variables of a continuous nature. The Fredericton to Toronto flight could take 1 hour and 50 minutes; or 1 hour, 45 minutes, and 45 seconds; or 1 hour, 55 minutes, and 45.1 seconds, depending on the accuracy of the timing device. Typically, continuous variables result from measuring something.

For analytical purposes, it is often useful to remember a distinction between flow variables and stock variables. **Stock variables** refer to variables measured at a point in time. **Flow variables**, on the other hand, are variables measured over a specific period of time (a function of time). For example, the amount of water entering or leaving a reservoir per period (per minute, per day, per week, etc.) is a flow variable, whereas the amount of water in the reservoir at any particular point in time (December 31 at noon) is a stock variable. Thus, the flow variable represents a rate of change in stock over a period of time. Variables such as capital goods, wealth, or government debt are measured at a point in time (such as October 24, 2001), and are therefore called *stock variables*. Investment, savings, or government budget deficit are measured over a period of time (such as per month, per quarter, or per year) and are therefore called *flow variables*.

The types of variables are summarized in Chart 1-5 above.

1.5 LEVELS OF MEASUREMENT

Data can be classified according to levels of measurement. The level of measurement of data often dictates the calculations that can be done to summarize and present the data. It will also determine the appropriate statistical tests to be performed.

For example, there are six colours of candies in a bag of M&M's. Suppose we assign the brown candy a value of 1, yellow 2, blue 3, orange 4, green 5, and red 6. From a bag of M&M's, we add the assigned colour values and divide by the number of candies and report that the mean colour is 3.56. Does this mean that the average colour is blue or orange? As a second example, in a high-school track meet there are 8 competitors in the 400-metre run. We report the order of finish and that the mean finish is 4.5. What does the mean finish tell us? In both of these instances, we have not properly used the level of measurement.

There are actually four levels of measurement: nominal, ordinal, interval, and ratio. The "lowest" or the weakest measurement is the nominal level. The highest, or the level that gives us the most information about the observation, is the ratio level of measurement.

NOMINAL LEVEL DATA

In the nominal level of measurement, observations can be only classified or counted. There is no particular order to the labels. The classification of the six colours of M&M's is an example of the nominal level of measurement. We simply classify the candies by colour. There is no natural order. That is, we could report the brown candies first, the orange first, or any of the colours first. Gender is another example of the nominal level of measurement. Suppose we count the number of students entering a football game with a student ID and report how many are male and how many are female. Or, we could report how many are single or married or divorce or widowed. There is no order implied in the presentation. For the nominal level of measurement there is no measurement involved, only counts. Table 1-2 shows the breakdown of Canadians (15 years and over) by their marital status. This is the nominal level of measurement because we placed the number of people according to the category in which they belonged.

Note that the variable in this case is status, and not the numbers belonging to each status. Numbers are just counts of people falling under one of the status categories. These categories are **mutually exclusive**, meaning that a person cannot belong to more than one category. The categories in Table 1-2 are also **exhaustive**, meaning that every member of the population, or sample, must appear in one of the categories.

 Mutually exclusive   An individual, object, or measurement is included in only one category.

 Exhaustive   Each individual, object, or measurement must appear in one of the categories.

TABLE 1-2: Marital Status in Canada, 1999

(Population 15 years and over)		
Status	Number	%
Single (never married)	7 114 681	29.0
Married*	14 535 881	59.2
Divorced	1 417 136	5.8
Widowed	1 506 231	6.1
Total	24 573 929	100.0

*Includes persons legally married and separated and persons living in common-law unions
Source: Statistics Canada: Canada at a Glance, 2nd edition

To process data on telephone usage, gender, and employment by industry, and so forth, the categories are often coded 1, 2, 3, and so on, with 1 representing single, 2 representing married, and so on. This facilitates counting by computer. However, because we have assigned numbers to the various categories, this does not give us licence to manipulate the numbers. For example, $1 + 2$ does not equal 3; that is, single plus married does not equal divorced. To summarize, nominal level data have the following properties:

1. Data categories are mutually exclusive, so an object belongs to only one category.
2. Data categories are exhaustive, so that all observations are included in one of the categories.
3. Data categories have no logical order, nor can be they compared with each other.

In brief, nominal level data does not imply any order.

ORDINAL LEVEL DATA

Ordinal level data implies order. Each data point can be expressed in terms of the arithmetic operation > or <. In other words, each data point can be compared to other data points. Table 1-3 lists the student ratings of Professor James Brunner in an Introduction to Finance course. Each student in the class answered the question, "Overall, how did you rate the instructor in this class?" This illustrates the use of the ordinal scale of measurement. One category is "higher" or "better" than the next one. That is, "superior" is better than "good," "good" is better than "average," and so on. However, we are not able to distinguish anything about the magnitude of the differences between groups. Is the difference between superior and good the same as the difference between good and average? We cannot tell. If we substitute a 5 for superior and a 4 for good, we can conclude that the rating of superior is better than the rating of good, but we cannot add or subtract a ranking of superior and a ranking of good with the result being meaningful. Further, we cannot conclude that a rating of good (rating is 4) is necessarily twice as good as a "poor" (rating is 2). We can only conclude that a rating of good is better than a rating of poor. We cannot conclude how much better the rating is. Note that the variable is rating and not frequency (the number of students providing the rating).

In summary, the properties of ordinal level data are:

1. The data categories are mutually exclusive and exhaustive.
2. Data categories are ranked or ordered according to the particular trait they possess.
3. Only the rating values are comparable, but not the differences between the rating values.
4. We cannot do any arithmetic operation on the data other than set up inequalities. Arithmetic operations of subtraction and addition are not meaningful. However, it is not unusual to see such operations being done in practice! You are familiar with

TABLE 1-3: Rating of a Finance Professor	
Rating	**Frequency**
5. Superior	6
4. Good	28
3. Average	25
2. Poor	12
1. Inferior	3

your grades being averaged. All it means is that users of information have decided to use the data as interval-level data.

INTERVAL-LEVEL DATA

The interval level of measurement is the next highest level. In addition to the setting up of inequalities, interval-level data allows arithmetic operations of subtraction and addition. It includes all the characteristics of the ordinal level, and in addition, the differences between values are now meaningful. Numerical differences of equal size between any two pairs of values represent equal changes in the attribute being measured. Examples of the interval level of measurement are temperature (Fahrenheit and Celsius), calendar time, and potential energy. Suppose temperatures on three consecutive winter days in Toronto are $-5°C$, $-2°C$, and $1°C$. These temperatures can be easily ranked, but we can also determine the difference between temperatures. This is possible because $1°C$ represents a constant unit of measurement. Equal differences between two temperatures mean the same amount of change in the temperature (the attribute), regardless of their position on the scale. That is, the difference between $10°C$ and $15°C$ represents the same amount of change in the temperature as the difference between $20°C$ and $25°C$. However, we cannot say that $20°C$ indicates twice the amount of heat compared to $10°C$. This happens because both the Celsius scale and the Fahrenheit scale of measurement have artificial origins (0). You can convince yourself by converting these values to Fahrenheit (F). Since $F = 32 + 1.8°C$; $10°C = 50°F$; and $20°C = 68°F$. Obviously, 20/10 on the Celsius scale is not equal to 68/50 on the Fahrenheit scale. For another example of interval scale, see Table 1-1 on the Index of Provincial Well Being.

The properties of interval scale data are:

1. Data categories are mutually exclusive and exhaustive.
2. Equal differences in the characteristics are represented by equal differences in the numbers assigned to the categories.
3. Arithmetic operations of addition and subtraction are meaningful, but ratios of two values are *not* meaningful.

RATIO-LEVEL DATA

The ratio level is the "highest" level of measurement. The ratio level of measurement has all the characteristics of the interval level, but in addition, the 0 (zero) point is meaningful and the ratio between two numbers is meaningful. Examples of the ratio scale of measurement include wages, units of production, weight, height, area, pressure, density, and so on. Money is a good illustration. If you have zero dollars, then you have no money. Weight is another example. If the dial on the scale is at zero, then there is a complete absence of weight. The ratio of two numbers is now meaningful. If Jim earns $30 000 per year selling insurance and Rob earns $60 000 per year selling cars, then Rob earns twice as much as Jim.

The properties of the ratio level are that:

1. Data categories are mutually exclusive and exhaustive.
2. Data categories are scaled according to the amount of the characteristic they possess.
3. Equal differences in the characteristic are represented by equal differences in the numbers assigned to the categories.
4. The point 0 reflects the absence of the characteristic. All arithmetic operations are possible.

TABLE 1-4: The World's 10 Most Valuable Athletes (2000)

Rank	Name	Money ($US millions)	Performance Last Season	Sport
1	Tiger Woods	63.1	A+	Golf
2	Michael Schumacher	59	A+	Motor Sport
3	Shaquille O'Neal	24	A+	Basketball
4	Alex Rodríguez	35.2	B+	Baseball
5	Mike Tyson	48	B+	Boxing
6	Allen Iverson	14.3	A−	Basketball
7	Marion Jones	2.7	A	Track
8	Vince Carter	4.2	B	Basketball
9	David Beckham	10.6	B	Soccer
10	Ken Griffey Jr.	11.3	B	Baseball

(Source: www.robmagazine.com, October 7, 2001.)

In Table 1-4, money earned by each athlete illustrates the use of the ratio scale of measurement. Unlike the interval scale, the ratio level allows us to carry out multiplication and division operations as well. Thus, we can say that Mike Tyson earned twice as much money as Shaquille O'Neal.

Chart 1-6 summarizes the characteristics of various levels of measurement through an organizational chart.

In brief, nominal scales are good for displaying data consisting of names, ordinal scales for order, interval scales for meaningful intervals, and ratio scales for meaningful ratios. A higher level of measurement scale possesses properties of all lower-level scales.

CHART 1-6: Characteristics of Levels of Measurement

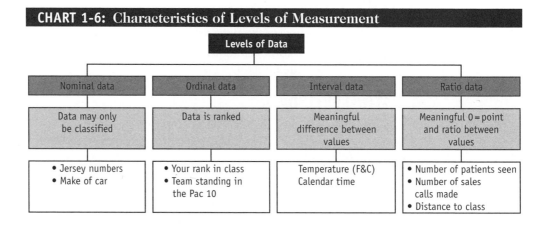

■ SELF-REVIEW 1-2

Data relating to five students (out of 25) in Stats 2163 are given below. Identify the level of measurement in each case.

(a) Students' ID numbers are:

911992   912345   913465   915429   913978

(b) Students' ranks in their class are:

3   8   15   6   11

(c) Students' annual GPAs (for all courses taken that year) are:

    3.9   3.6   2.5   3.5   3.0

(d) Amounts of student loans (in $) owed by the students are:

    10 500   5450   12 200   0   8300

EXERCISES 1-1 TO 1-5

1-1. In Table 1-4, what is the level of measurement for
(a) Ranks for the athletes?
(b) Sports?
(c) Performance?

1-2. What is the level of measurement for each of the following variables?
(a) Student IQ ratings.
(b) Distance students travel from home (or residence) to school.
(c) Student scores on the first statistics test.
(d) A classification of students by province of birth.
(e) A ranking of students by first-year, second-year, third-year, and fourth-year.
(f) Number of hours students study per week.

1-3. What is the level of measurement for these items related to the newspaper business (*The Globe and Mail*)?
(a) The number of Saturday copies of *The Globe and Mail* sold last week.
(b) The number of employees in each department (editorial, advertising, sports, etc.).
(c) A summary of the number of papers sold by county.
(d) The number of years employed by the paper for each employee.

1-4. Look in the latest edition of *The Globe and Mail* or your local newspaper and find examples of each level of measurement. Write a brief memo summarizing your findings.

1-5. For each of the following, determine whether the group is a sample or a population.
(a) The participants in a study of a new diabetes drug.
(b) All the drivers who received a speeding ticket on Highway 401 last month.
(c) All families below the income of $20 000 per year in York-Sunbury county (Fredericton).
(d) Ten of the top 50 athletes in the world (by earnings per year).

1.6 SOURCES OF STATISTICAL DATA

Statistical data are available from two types of sources. Data collected by an investigator that are not available in published form are called *primary data*. Data available in published form are called *secondary data*.

PUBLISHED DATA

Conducting research on problems involving such topics as crime, health, imports and exports, production, and hourly wages generally requires published data. We may want information on the total number of housing starts in Canada in 2000 (151 700), the total value of retail trade in 2000 ($277 billion), the total number of persons in the Canadian labour force (15 and over) in a particular month, such as April 2001 (16 271 700), the unemployment rate in each of the Canadian provinces, the inflation rate this month, employment and average weekly earnings by industry, and so on.

Almost every country has a statistical agency responsible for collecting and publishing data on social, economic, business, and other aspects of life in the country. In Canada, our statistical agency is called Statistics Canada. Statistics Canada collects both micro-level (individual businesses and households, communities) data and macro-level (economy as a whole) data. Published data in hard copy are available in libraries. However, increasing amounts of data are now available in the form of electronic files on Statistics Canada's Web site (www.statcan.ca). Federal government and provincial government departments also collect data relevant to their objectives. These data can be accessed from their respective Web sites. Often these data are also available from Statistics Canada; the Statistics Canada site has links to most governmental Web sites as well as many international Web sites. In addition to Statistics Canada, the most important governmental sources for Canadian business, industry, trade, and financial data are:

- Industry Canada: www.strategis.gc.ca (for data on Canadian business, industry, and trade).
- Bank of Canada: www.bankofcanada.ca (for data on Canadian monetary conditions).
- Links to all provincial Web sites are available from www.gc.ca and www.statcan.ca
- Links for several international statistical Web sites are also available from www.statcan.ca

For US data, see www.census.gov. Summary data on other countries are available from:

- United Nations: www.un.org and its sub-sites.
- Organization for Economic Co-operation and Development: www.oecd.org
- International Monetary Fund: www.imf.org
- World Bank: www.worldbank.org

In addition to regularly published data, daily/weekly publications such as financial data of a daily, weekly, or monthly nature are available on www.globeandmail.com and its sub-sites, such as www.globefund.com, www.globeinvestor.com, and www.robmagazine.com, all available by links from www.globeandmail.com. Further, most chartered banks also have a wealth of financial data on their own Web sites. Other business-related Web sites are www.fortune.com, www.forbes.com, and www.economist.com. Sports-related data can be obtained from www.sportserver.com and www.canadiansport.com and from links available from these Web sites.

LEARNING RESOURCES AT STATISTICS CANADA (Σ-STAT)

Statistics Canada maintains a Web site called Σ-Stat that is freely available to all educational institutions in Canada (see Chart 1-7). There are more than 700 000 series of data on socio-economic conditions in Canada. We refer you to this Web site several times in this book. If your educational institution is not a registered user of the site, it can register and make the services available to all students. Alternatively, McGraw-Hill Ryerson, the publisher of this textbook, would provide an ID and PIN to access this Web site for all students who are using this textbook in their course.

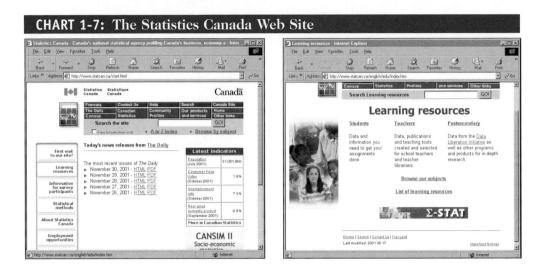

CHART 1-7: The Statistics Canada Web Site

To collect data from this Web site, first go to the Statistics Canada Web site at www.statcan.ca, then to Learning Resources, then to Σ-Stat. At this point, you will be asked to accept a licence agreement. Say yes. You will then be presented with a small screen requesting your ID and password. Enter the ID and password provided to you by your educational institution or instructor. Select Enter. Now you have access to the wealth of information that Statistics Canada has to offer! You can access data either by series number, if you know it, or by finding data on the topic of your interest through a search engine. There is a user guide and an animated tutorial on the Web site. We strongly advise you to at least go through the animated tutorial to avoid frustrations.

UNPUBLISHED DATA

Like the sources for published data, there are sources for unpublished data collected and analyzed by researchers working at universities and research institutes. Often such data are contained in working papers, discussion papers, and dissertations. You can access all Canadian universities and their business, economics, and statistics departments through the Association of Universities and Colleges of Canada Web site at www.aucc.ca. You can access a wide variety of resources on statistics including data, texts, animated lectures/tutorials on selected topics, universities around the world, and even jokes (http://noppa5.pc.helsinki.fi/links.html).

Published data are not always available on every subject of interest. Individuals may be contacted in a shopping mall, at their homes, over the telephone, or by mail. The respondents' answers are usually tabulated either by hand or using a computer. You have probably seen and completed many questionnaires. You can often see a poll conducted on *The Globe and Mail* Web site on a current topic of public interest. Perhaps you will be presented with such a questionnaire at the end of this course. Here are the results from a survey conducted by *Working Mother* magazine.

Working Mother commissioned Gallup to study how satisfied working mothers are with their dual role. Gallup polled 1000 working mothers nationwide. Some of the findings are listed below.

1. Seven out of 10 women said they work to feel good about themselves, regardless of the job they do or the amount of money they make.

2. Eight out of 10 working mothers were "extremely satisfied" or "very satisfied" with the job they are doing as mothers.

3. Ninety percent said their children are happy.

4. Three-quarters said they "like" or "love" their jobs.

5. Four percent said they "hate" their work.

1.7   USES AND ABUSES OF STATISTICS

LIES, DAMN LIES, AND STATISTICS

"It ain't so much the things we don't know that get us into trouble. It's the things we know that just ain't so."—Artemus Ward

You have probably heard the old saying that there are three kinds of lies: lies, damn lies, and statistics. This saying is attributable to Benjamin Disraeli, a British Prime Minister, nearly a century ago. It has also been said that "Charts don't lie: liars chart." Both of these statements refer to the abuses of statistics in which data are presented in ways that are misleading. Many abusers of statistics are simply ignorant or careless, while others have an objective to mislead the reader by emphasizing data that support their position while leaving out data that may be detrimental to their position. *One of our major goals in this text is to make you a critical consumer of information.* When you see charts or data in a newspaper, in a magazine, or on TV, always ask yourself these questions: What is the person trying to tell me? Does that person have an agenda? The following are several examples of the abuses of statistical analysis.

AN AVERAGE MAY NOT BE REPRESENTATIVE OF ALL THE DATA

The term *average* refers to several different measures of central tendency that we discuss in Chapter 3. To most people, an average is found by adding the values in the data set and then dividing the total by the number of values in the data. So if a real estate developer tells a client that the average home in a particular subdivision sold for $150 000, we assume that $150 000 is a representative selling price for all the homes. But suppose there are only five homes in the subdivision and they sold for $50 000, $50 000, $60 000, $90 000, and $500 000. We can correctly claim that the average selling price is $150 000, but does $150 000 really seem like a "typical" selling price? Would you like to also know that the same number of homes sold for more than $150 000 as sold for less than $150 000? Or that $150 000 is the selling price that occurred most frequently? So what selling price really is the most "typical"? This example illustrates how a reported average can be misleading. We will discuss averages, or measures of central tendency, in Chapter 3.

GRAPHS CAN BE MISLEADING

Pictographs are often used as a visual aid for an easy interpretation. However, if they are not drawn carefully, they can lead to misinterpretation of information. Suppose the cost of heating a typical home in Toronto increased from $100 a month to $200 a month over the past 20 years; that is, the heating cost per month doubled. To show this change, the dollar sign on the right in Chart 1-8a is twice as tall as the one on the left. It is also twice as wide, making the area of the dollar sign on the right four times (not twice) that of the one on the left. When we double the dimensions of a two-dimensional

CHART 1-8a: Cost of Heating in Toronto

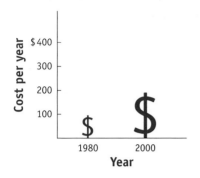

CHART 1-8b: Full Economy Standards for Autos Set by Congress and Supplemented by the Transportation Department. In miles per gallon

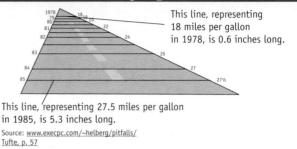

This line, representing 18 miles per gallon in 1978, is 0.6 inches long.

This line, representing 27.5 miles per gallon in 1985, is 5.3 inches long.

Source: www.execpc.com/~helberg/pitfalls/
Tufte, p. 57

object, we increase the area by a factor of four. The chart is misleading because visually the increase seems much larger than it really is. In Chart 1-8b, the line representing 27.5 miles per gallon in 1985 was 5.3 inches long and the line for 18 miles per gallon only 0.6 inches long in the original presentation.

Edward R. Tufte, in his book *The Visual Display of Qualitative Information* (Cheshire, CT: Graphics Press, 1983) has given many examples of how to recognize misleading graphs and how to construct a good graph. In his book, Tufte introduces a concept called the "**lie factor**". It can be defined as the percentage change in the graphic elements divided by the percentage change in the actual quantities represented by those graphic elements. By this definition, the value of the lie factor should equal 1 for an accurate and informative graph. In Chart 1.8b, the lie factor can be calculated as $\dfrac{(5.3-0.6)/0.6}{(27.5-18)/18} = 14.8$. Thus, the lie factor is 14.8!

Graphs and charts of data, such as histograms, line charts, and bar charts, can also be misleading if they are not drawn appropriately. We cover these graphs and charts in detail in the next chapter. A misleading visual interpretation in the context of charts arises often due to a presentation of only part of the data, or using the horizontal and/or vertical axis inappropriately.

Chart 1-9 is designed to show a relationship between unemployment rate (in percent) and crime rate (in thousands, per year) in Canada in three different ways based on the same data for the years 1986 to 1999. In Chart 1-9a, we have broken the vertical axis at 2000, and thus show a strong relation between unemployment rate and crime. In Chart 1-9b, we have broken the horizontal axis at a 7-percent rate of unemployment.

CHART 1-9: Unemployment Rate and Crime Rate in Canada, 1986–99

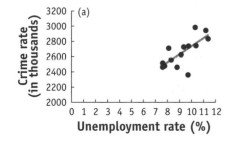

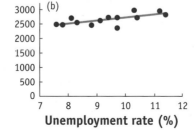

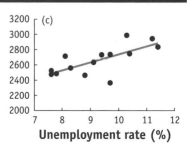

In this graph, we get an impression of a weaker relation between unemployment rate and crime. A more accurate depiction of the relationship can be obtained by using values near the minimum values of the variables as starting points on each axis. Thus, a break on the vertical axis at 2000 and on the horizontal axis at 7 percent will give you a more accurate picture of the relationship as shown in Chart 1-9c.

There are many graphing techniques, but there are no hard and fast rules about drawing a graph. It is therefore both a science and an art. Your aim should always be a truthful representation of the data. The objectives and the assumptions underlying the data must be kept in mind and mentioned briefly along with graphs. The visual impressions conveyed by the graphs must correspond to the underlying data. The graphs should reveal as much information as possible with the greatest precision and accuracy. *Graphical excellence is achieved when a viewer can get the most accurate and comprehensive picture of the situation underlying the data set in the shortest possible time.* In brief, a graph should act like a mirror between the numerical data and the viewer. According to a popular saying, "*Numbers speak for themselves.*" This is true for small data sets. For large data sets, it may be difficult to discern any patterns by looking at numbers alone. We therefore *need accurate portrayal of data through graphs that can speak for numbers*, and can give a quick overview of the data. We discuss graphic techniques in detail in the next chapter.

STUDIES BASED ON INADEQUATE SURVEYS CAN BE MISLEADING

Several years ago, a series of TV advertisements reported that "2 out of 3 dentists surveyed indicated they would recommend Brand X toothpaste to their patients." The implication is that 67 percent of all dentists would recommend the product to their patients. What if they surveyed only three dentists? It would certainly not be a true representation of the real situation. The trick is that the manufacturer of the toothpaste could take *many* surveys of three dentists and report *only* the surveys of three dentists in which two dentists indicated they would recommend Brand X. This is concealing the information to mislead the public. Further, a survey of more than three dentists is needed, and it must be unbiased and representative of the population of all dentists. We discuss sampling methods in Chapter 8.

Example 1-2	**Professor Best's Encounter with Bad Statistics**[5]

A graduate student started his dissertation with a quote (possibly to impress his dissertation committee): "Every year since 1950, the number of American children gunned down has doubled." When Professor Best, a member of the student's dissertation committee, read the quotation, he did not believe it. He went to the library and looked up the article the student had cited. In the journal's 1995 volume, he found exactly the same sentence.

"What makes this statistic so bad?" asks Professor Best. "Just for the sake of argument, let's assume that the number of American children gunned down in 1950 was one. If the number doubled each year, there must have been two children gunned down in 1951, four in 1952, eight in 1953, and so on. By 1970, the number would have passed one million; by 1980, one billion (more than four times the total US population in that year). By 1995, when the article was published, the annual number of victims would have been over 35 trillion—a really big number...." Professor Best asked the article's author about the source of this statistic. The author's response was that he had seen the statistic in a document published by the Children's Defense Fund, a well-known advocacy group for children. The CDF's *The State of America's Children Yearbook, 1994* does state that: "The number of American children killed each year by guns has doubled since 1950." Note the difference in wording—the CDF claimed there were twice as many deaths in 1994 as in 1950; the article's author reworded that claim and created a very different meaning.

It is worth examining the history of this statistic. It began with the CDF noting that child gunshot deaths had doubled from 1950 to 1994. This is not quite as dramatic an increase as it might seem. Remember that the US population also rose throughout this period; in fact, it grew about 73 percent, or nearly double. Therefore, we might expect all sorts of things—including the number of child gunshot deaths to increase—to nearly double, just because the population grew. Before we can decide whether twice as many deaths indicate that things are getting worse, we'd have to know more. The CDF statistic raises other issues as well: Where did the statistics come from? Who counts child gunshot deaths, and how? What is meant by a "child"? (Some CDF statistics about violence include everyone under age 25.) What is meant by "killed by guns"? (Gunshot-death statistics often include suicides and accidents, as well as homicides.) But people rarely ask questions of this sort when they encounter statistics. Most of the time, most people simply accept statistics without question.

Certainly, the article's author didn't ask many probing, critical questions about the CDF's claim. Impressed by the statistic, the author repeated it—well, meant to repeat it. Instead, by rewording the CDF's claim, the author created a mutant statistic, one garbled almost beyond recognition.

ASSOCIATION DOES NOT NECESSARILY IMPLY CAUSATION

Another area where there can be a misrepresentation of data is the association between variables. In statistical analysis often we find there is a strong *association* between variables. We find there is a strong negative association between outside work and grade point average. The more outside work a student is engaged in, the lower will be his or her grade point average. Does it mean that more outside work causes a lower grade point average? Not necessarily. It is also possible that the lower grade point average does not make the student eligible for a scholarship and therefore the student is required to engage in outside work to finance his or her education. Alternatively, both outside work and lower GPA could be a result of the social circumstances of the student. Unless we have used an experimental design that has successfully controlled the influence of all other factors on grade point average except the outside work, or vice versa, we are not justified in establishing any causation between variables based on statistical evidence alone. In general, *association based on observational (non-experimental) data is neutral with regard to causation*. We study the association between variables in Chapters 13 and 14.

BECOME A BETTER CONSUMER AND A BETTER PRODUCER OF INFORMATION

There are many other ways that statistical information can be deceiving. It may be because (1) The data are not representative of the population; (2) Appropriate statistics have not been used; (3) The data do not satisfy the assumptions required for inferences; (4) The prediction is too far out from the range of observed data; (5) Policy analysis does not meet the requirements of either data or theory or both; (6) Ignorance and/or carelessness on the part of the investigator; (7) A deliberate attempt to introduce bias has been made to mislead the consumer of information. Entire books have been written about the subject. The most famous of these is *How to Lie with Statistics* by Darrell Huff. Understanding the art and science of statistics will make you both a better consumer of information as well as a better producer of information (statistician). This is our aim in writing this book.

1.8 COMPUTER APPLICATIONS

Computers are now available for student use at most colleges and universities. Spreadsheets, such as Microsoft Excel, which have many statistical functions, are also available in most computer labs and on most home computers. We have selected Excel and Minitab for most of the statistical applications in the text. We also use an Excel add-in called MegaStat, software bundled free on the CD-ROM included with this book. This add-in gives Excel the capability to produce additional statistical results. With statistical software such as Excel and Minitab, we can get most of the descriptive and inferential statistics at the click of a few buttons! The statistical software can save an enormous amount of time required for computations, and thereby enable us to devote more of our valuable time to analytical aspects.

The following example shows the wide application of computers in statistical analysis. In Chapters 2, 3, and 4 we illustrate methods for summarizing and describing data. Chart 1-10 shows a sample of 19 of the top 100 Canadian companies computing most of the descriptive statistics for profits (in 2000). The Excel output reveals, among other things, that the mean (average) profit was $583 million, and ranged between $122 million and $2274 million. Many other descriptive statistics of data are also shown.

The Minitab output in Chart 1-11 contains much of the same information, although it is arranged somewhat differently. Minitab is user-friendly statistics software. It is versatile software for most of the needs of statistical analysis. If your institution does not have this software on its network, you may purchase or rent the software or download free for a month (on a trial basis) from Minitab's Web site (www.minitab.com). An introductory guide to Minitab, called *Meet Minitab*, is also available (free) as a PDF file that you can download and print. This guide, together with the Minitab Help Menu, will help you in using the software.

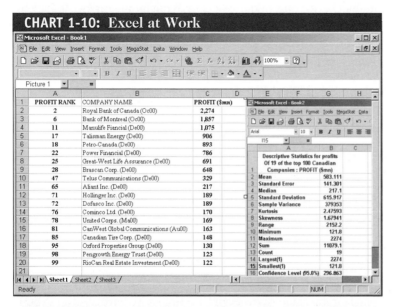

CHART 1-10: Excel at Work

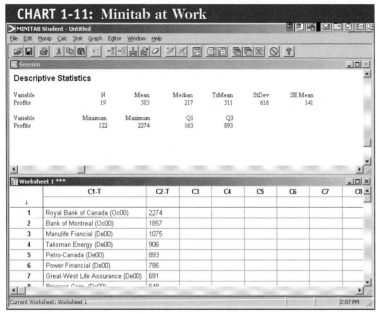

CHART 1-11: Minitab at Work

CHAPTER OUTLINE

I.   Statistics is the art and science of collecting, organizing, and analyzing data; making inferences from the part about the whole; and prediction and policy analysis.

II. There are two types of statistics:

   A. *Descriptive statistics* are procedures used to organize and summarize data.

   B. *Inferential statistics* involve taking a sample from a population and making inferences about a population based on the sample results.

   C. Statistical methods can also be used for prediction and policy analysis.

   D. A *population* is the total collection of individuals or objects. A summary measure that describes some characteristic of a population is called a *parameter*.

   E. A *sample* is a part of the population. A summary measure used to estimate a given characteristic of a population from a sample is called a *statistic*.

III. Statistics plays a significant role in the development of knowledge as well as in everyday life.

IV. There are two types of variables:

   A. A *qualitative variable* is non-numeric.
      1. Usually we are interested in the number or percentage of the observations in each category.
      2. Qualitative data are usually summarized in graphs and bar charts.

   B. A *quantitative variable* is numeric. There are two types of quantitative variables and they are usually reported numerically.
      1. Discrete variables can assume only certain values, and there are usually gaps between values.
      2. A continuous variable can assume any value within a specified range.

V.   There are four levels of measurement:

   A. With the *nominal* level, the data are sorted into categories with no particular order to the categories.

   B. The *ordinal* level of measurement presumes that one category is ranked higher than another.

   C. The *interval* level of measurement has the ranking characteristic of the ordinal level of measurement plus the characteristic that the distance between values is meaningful.

   D. The *ratio* level of measurement has all the characteristics of the interval level as well as a zero point. The ratio of two values is meaningful.

VI. Statistical data can be collected either through surveys or from published sources. Most published data are available in electronic form.

VII. Statistical methods, if not used appropriately, can result in grossly misleading information.

CHAPTER EXERCISES 1-6 TO 1-18

1-6. Explain the difference between qualitative and quantitative data. Give an example of qualitative and quantitative data.

1-7. List the four levels of measurement and give an example (different from those used in the book) of each level of measurement.

1-8. Explain the difference between a sample and a population, and a statistic and a parameter.

1-9. (a) Define the lie factor in graphical presentations. Find the lie factor in Chart 1-8a. Assume the smaller dollar figure is 1 cm wide and 2 cm tall, and the larger dollar figure is 2 cm wide and 4 cm tall.
    (b) Explain the possible reasons for misuses of statistics.

1-10. Using data from Statistics Canada and such publications as *The Economist*, *Newsweek*, *The Globe and Mail*, or your local newspaper, give examples of the nominal, ordinal, interval, and ratio level of measurement.

1-11. A random sample of 300 executives out of 2500 employed by a large firm showed that 270 would move to another location if it meant a substantial promotion. Based on these findings, write a brief note to management regarding all executives in the firm.

1-12. A random sample of 500 customers was asked to test a new toothpaste. Of the 500 customers, 400 said it was excellent, 32 thought it was fair, and the remaining customers had no opinion. Based on these sample findings, make an inference about the reaction of all customers to the new toothpaste.

1-13. What is the measurement scale in the following graph? Are scales the same or different in the right-hand and left-hand graphs? Write a brief report on the information contained in the graph.

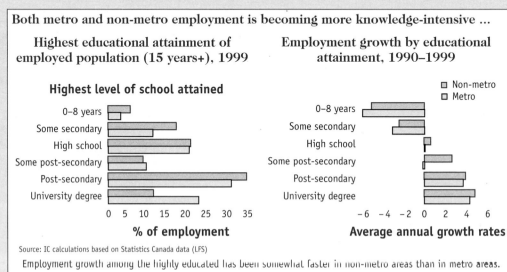

Both metro and non-metro employment is becoming more knowledge-intensive ...

Highest educational attainment of employed population (15 years+), 1999

Employment growth by educational attainment, 1990–1999

Highest level of school attained

% of employment

Average annual growth rates

Source: IC calculations based on Statistics Canada data (LFS)

Employment growth among the highly educated has been somewhat faster in non-metro areas than in metro areas.

Still, non-metro Canada has a much smaller share of workers with a university degree and a larger share of workers with less than high school graduation.

– Job growth trends over the 1990–99 period demonstrate the influence of education on employment. Employment growth was faster for those with university and post-secondary education.

Source: MEPA, Industry Canada

1-14. What is the level of measurement in the following graph? Write a brief note on the information contained in the graph. (Source: Statistics Canada, Adapted.)

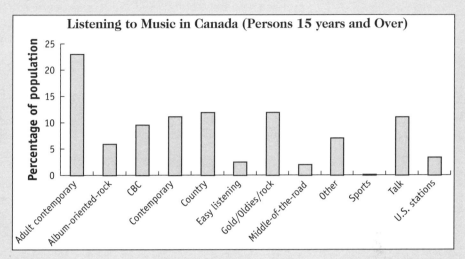

COMPUTER DATA EXERCISES 1-15 TO 1-18

1-15. Refer to the file Real Estate Data.xls on the CD-ROM and the text Web site, which reports information on homes sold in Victoria, B.C., last year.
(a) Which of the variables are qualitative and which are quantitative?
(b) Determine the level of measurement for each of the variables.

1-16. Refer to the file BASEBALL-2000.xls on the CD-ROM and the text Web site. Consider the following variables: team salary, attendance, and number of errors.
(a) Which of the variables are qualitative and which are quantitative?
(b) Determine the level of measurement for each of the variables.

1-17. Refer to the file 100 of the Top 1000 Companies.xls on the CD-ROM and the text Web site. Answer the following questions:
(a) Which of the variables are qualitative and which are quantitative?
(b) Determine the level of measurement for each of the variables.

1-18. Refer to the file Youth Unemployment in Canada.xls on the CD-ROM and the text Web site.
(a) Which of the variables are qualitative and which are quantitative?
(b) Determine the level of measurement for each of the variables.

www.exercises.ca 1-19 TO 1-21

In these exercises, you are required to go on the Web sites indicated, collect data as required, and write a brief report including the measurement scale of variables, type of statistic, and so on.

1-19. Go to www.statcan.ca and click on Community Profiles (located on the top of the screen). Collect data in your community on the following variables and write a brief report: population (male and female), immigrant population, persons who have completed university degrees, average income of males and females, proportion of married and common-law families, average value of owner-occupied dwellings, and ratio of male to female birth rate and death rate.

1-20. On the same Web site as in Exercise 1-19, go to Daily and read about the labour force characteristics in your province. Write a brief report.

1-21. Go to the Web site www.globefund.com. Choose the stocks of five companies and look at the variation in prices over the last 30 days. Write a brief report.

CHAPTER 1   ANSWERS TO SELF-REVIEW

1-1. (a) Based on the sample of 1960 consumers, we estimate that, if it is marketed, 60 percent of all consumers will purchase Fish Delight (1176/1960) × 100 = 60 percent.

(b) Inferential statistics, because a sample was used to make an inference about how all consumers in the population would react if Fish Delight were marketed.

1-2. (a) Nominal

(b) Ordinal

(c) Ordinal but often used as interval

(d) Ratio

CHAPTER 2

Describing Data: Frequency Distributions and Graphic Presentation

GOALS

When you have completed this chapter, you will be able to:

- Organize raw data into a *frequency distribution*

- Produce a *histogram*, a *frequency polygon*, and a *cumulative frequency polygon* from quantitative data

- Develop and interpret a *stem-and-leaf display*

- Present qualitative data using such graphical techniques as a *clustered bar chart*, a *stacked bar chart*, and a *pie chart*

- Detect graphic deceptions and use a graph to present data with clarity, precision, and efficiency.

FLORENCE NIGHTINGALE (1820–1910)

1498
1548
1598
1648
1698
1748
1898
1948
2000

The tendency to graphically represent information seems to be one of the basic human instincts. As such, identification of the oldest such representation is an elusive- task, the earliest known being the map of Konya, Turkey, dated 6200 B.C. The earliest known bar chart is the one by Bishop N. Oresme (1350).

Most of the modern forms of statistical graphic techniques were invented between 1780 and 1940. In 1786, William Playfair used time-series graphs to depict the amount of import and export to and from England, and in 1801, he published a pie chart to show graphically that the British paid more tax than other countries. The first stacked bar chart, cumulative frequency polygon, and histogram were published, respectively, by A. Humboldt (1811), J.B.J. Fourier (1821), and A.M. Guerry (1833). The same period saw development of non-trivial applications of these techniques to real-world problems. One of the most significant contributors in this regard was *the lady with a lamp*, Florence Nightingale.

Florence Nightingale was born in Florence, Italy in 1820, but was raised mostly in Derbyshire, England. In spite of resistance from society and her mother, her father educated her in Greek, Latin, French, German, Italian, history, philosophy, and, her favourite subject, mathematics.

When she was 17 years old, Florence had a spiritual experience. She felt herself called by God to His service. Since that time, she made up her mind to dedicate her life to some social cause. She refused to marry several suitors and at the age of twenty-five, stunned her parents by informing them that she had decided to be a nurse, a profession considered low class at that time.

During the 1854 British war in Crimea, stirred by the reports of primitive sanitation methods at the British barracks' hospital, she volunteered her services, and set out to Scutari, Turkey with a group of 38 nurses. Here, mainly by improving the sanitary conditions and nursing methods, she managed to bring down the mortality rate at the hospital from 42.7 percent to about 2 percent.

On her return to England after the war as a national hero, she dedicated herself to the task of improving the sanitation, and quality of nursing in military hospitals. In this, she encountered strong opposition from the establishment. But with the support of Queen Victoria, and more importantly, with shrewd use of graphic methods (such as stacked bar charts and a new type of polar bar chart that she developed on her own), she succeeded in bringing forth reforms. She was one of the first to use graphical methods in a prescriptive, rather that merely a descriptive way, to bring about social reform.

Over the subsequent 20 years, she applied statistical methods to civilian hospitals, midwifery, Indian public health, and colonial schools. She briefly served as an adviser to the British war office on medical care in Canada. Her mathematical activities included determining "the average speed of transport by sledge," and "the time to transport the sick over immense distances in Canada."

Nightingale revolutionized the use of mathematical techniques to study social phenomena. Karl Pearson acknowledged her as "prophetess" in the development of applied statistics.

Nightingale held strong opinions on women's rights, and fought for the removal of restrictions that prevented women from having careers. In 1907 she became the first woman to receive the Order of Merit, an order established by King Edward VII for meritorious service.

INTRODUCTION

Rob Whitner is the owner of Whitner Pontiac. Rob's father founded the dealership in 1964, and for more than 30 years they sold exclusively Pontiacs. In the early 1990s Rob's father's health began to fail, and Rob took over more of the dealership's day-to-day operations. At the same time, the automobile business began to change—dealers began to sell vehicles from several manufacturers—and Rob was faced with some major decisions. The first came when another local dealer, who handled Volvos, Saabs, and Volkswagens, approached Rob about purchasing his dealership. After considerable thought and analysis, Rob made the purchase. More recently, the local Jeep Eagle dealership got into difficulty and Rob bought it out. So now, on the same lot, Rob sells the complete line of Pontiacs; the expensive Volvos and Saabs; Volkswagens; and Chrysler products including the popular Jeep line. Whitner Pontiac employs 83 people, including 23 full-time salespeople. Because of the diverse product line, there is quite a bit of variation in the selling price of the vehicles. A top-of-the-line Volvo sells for more than twice the price of a Pontiac Grand Am. Rob would like to develop some charts and graphs that he could review monthly to see where the selling prices tend to cluster, to see the variation in the selling prices, and to note any trends. In this chapter we present techniques that will be useful to Rob or someone like him in managing his business.

2.1   CONSTRUCTING A FREQUENCY DISTRIBUTION OF QUANTITATIVE DATA

Recall from Chapter 1 that we refer to techniques used to describe a set of data as *descriptive statistics*. To put it another way, we use descriptive statistics to organize data in various ways to point out where the data values tend to concentrate and to help distinguish the largest and the smallest values. The first method we use to describe a set of data is a **frequency distribution**. Here our goal is to summarize the data in a table that reveals the shape of the data.

> ***i*** **Frequency distribution**   A grouping of data into non-overlapping classes (mutually exclusive classes or categories) showing the number of observations in each class. The range of classes includes all values in the data set (collectively exhaustive categories).

How do we develop a frequency distribution? The first step is to tally the data into a table that shows the classes and the number of observations in each class. The steps in constructing a frequency distribution are best described using an example. Remember that our goal is to make a table that will quickly reveal the shape of the data.

Example 2-1 | In the introduction to this chapter, we described a case where Rob Whitner, owner of Whitner Pontiac, is interested in collecting information on the selling prices of vehicles sold at his dealership. What is the typical selling price? What is the highest selling price? What is the lowest selling price? Around what value do the selling prices tend to cluster? To answer these questions, we need to collect data. According to sales records, Whitner Pontiac sold 80 vehicles last month. The price paid by the customer for each vehicle is shown in Table 2-1. Summarize the selling prices of the vehicles sold last month. Around what value do the selling prices tend to cluster?

TABLE 2-1: Selling Prices ($) at Whitner Pontiac Last Month

31 373	26 879	31 710	36 442	37 657	21 969	23 132
39 552	42 923	25 544	31 060	50 596	25 026	26 252
32 778	32 839	33 277	39 532	19 320	19 920	25 984
34 266	38 552	33 160	37 642	26 009	26 186	22 109
26 418	34 306	25 699	31 812	36 364	27 558	26 492
31 978	35 085	36 438	45 086	27 169	29 231	32 420
35 110	19 702	23 505	50 719	22 175	23 050	26 728
28 400	28 831	25 149	30 518	25 819	27 154	27 661
30 561	35 859	38 339	40 157	45 417	24 470	28 859
29 836	33 219	34 571	39 018	27 168	31 744	32 678
42 588	29 940	22 932	27 439	35 784	26 865	28 576
28 704	32 795	31 103				

Solution

Table 2-1 contains *quantitative data* (recall from Chapter 1). These data are *raw* or *ungrouped data*. With a little searching, we can find the lowest selling price ($19 320) and the highest selling price ($50 719), but that is about all. It is difficult to get a feel for the shape of the data by mere observation of the raw data. The raw data are more easily interpreted if they are organized into a frequency distribution. The steps for organizing data into a frequency distribution are outlined below.

1. **Decide how many classes you wish to use.** The goal is to use just enough groupings or **classes** to reveal the shape of the distribution. Some judgment is needed here. Too many classes or too few classes might not reveal the basic shape of the set of data. In the vehicle selling price problem, for example, three classes would not give much insight into the pattern of the data (see Table 2-2).

TABLE 2-2: An Example of Too Few Classes

Vehicle Selling Price	Number of Vehicles
19 000 up to 32 900	53
32 900 up to 46 800	25
46 800 up to 60 700	2
Total	80

A useful recipe to determine the number of classes is the "2 to the k rule." This guide suggests you select the smallest number (k) for the number of classes such that 2^k (in words, 2 raised to the power of k) is greater than the number of data points (n).

In the Whitner Pontiac example, there were 80 vehicles sold. So $n = 80$. If we try $k = 6$, which means we would use 6 classes, then $2^6 = 64$, somewhat less than 80. Hence, 6 classes are not enough. If we let $k = 7$, then $2^7 = 128$, which is greater than 80. So the recommended number of classes is 7.

2. **Determine the class width.** Generally, the class width should be the same for all classes. At the end of this section, we shall briefly discuss some situations where unequal class widths may be necessary. All classes taken together must cover at least the distance from the lowest value in the raw data up to the highest value.

Expressing these words in a formula:

$$\text{Class width} > \frac{H - L}{k}$$

where H is the highest observed value, L is the lowest observed value, and k is the number of classes.

In the Whitner Pontiac case, the lowest value is \$19 320 and the highest value is \$50 719. If we wish to use 7 classes, the class width should be greater than (\$50 719 − \$19 320)/7 = \$4485.571. In practice, this class width is usually rounded up to some convenient number, such as a multiple of 10 or 100. We round this value up to \$4490.

3. **Set up the individual class limits.** We should state class limits very clearly so that each observation falls into only one class. For example, classes such as \$19 000–\$20 000 and \$20 000–\$21 000 should be avoided because it is not clear whether \$20 000 is in the first or second class. In this text, we will use the format \$19 000 up to \$20 000 and \$20 000 up to \$21 000 and so on. With this format it is clear that \$19 999 goes into the first class and \$20 000 in the second.

Because we round the class width up to get a convenient class width, we cover a larger than necessary range. For example, seven classes of width \$4490 in the Whitner Pontiac case result in a range of (\$4490)(7) = \$31 430.

The actual range is \$31 399, found by (H − L = 50 719 − 19 320). Comparing this value to \$31 430, we have an excess of \$31. It is natural to put approximately equal amounts of the excess in each of the two tails. As we have said before, we should also select convenient multiples of 10 for the class limits. We shall use \$19 310 as the lower limit of the first class. The upper limit of the first class is then 23 800, found by (19 310 + 4 490 = 23 800). Hence, our first class is from \$19 310 up to \$23 800. We can determine the other classes (in dollars) similarly (from \$23 800 up to \$28 290), (from \$28 290 up to \$32 780), (from \$32 780 up to \$37 270), (from \$37 270 up to \$41 760), (from \$41 760 up to \$46 250), and (from \$46 250 up to \$50 740).

4. **Tally the selling prices into the classes.** To begin, the selling price of the first vehicle in Table 2-1 is \$31 373. It is tallied in the \$28 290 up to \$32 780 class. The second selling price in the first column is \$39 552. It is tallied in the \$37 270 up to \$41 760 class. The other selling prices are tallied in a similar manner. When all the selling prices are tallied, we get Table 2-3(a).

TABLE 2-3: Construction of a Frequency Distribution of Whitner Pontiac Data

(a) Tally Count

Classes ($)	Tally
19 310 up to 23 800	╫╢ ╫╢
23 800 up to 28 290	╫╢ ╫╢ ╫╢ ╫╢ I
28 290 up to 32 780	╫╢ ╫╢ ╫╢ ╫╢
32 780 up to 37 270	╫╢ ╫╢ ╫╢
37 270 up to 41 760	╫╢ III
41 760 up to 46 250	IIII
46 250 up to 50 740	II

(b) Frequency Distribution

Selling Prices ($ thousands)	Frequency
19.310 up to 23.800	10
23.800 up to 28.290	21
28.290 up to 32.780	20
32.780 up to 37.270	15
37.270 up to 41.760	8
41.760 up to 46.250	4
46.250 up to 50.740	2
Total	80

5. **Count the number of items in each class.** The number of observations in each class is called the *class frequency*. In the $19 310 up to $23 800 class, there are 10 observations; in the $23 800 up to $28 290 class there are 21 observations. Therefore, the class frequency in the first class is 10 and the class frequency in the second class is 21. The sum of frequencies of all the classes equals the total number of observations in the entire data set, which is 80.

Often it is useful to express the data in thousands, or some convenient units, rather than the actual data. Table 2-3(b) reports the frequency distribution for Whitner Pontiac's vehicle selling prices where prices are given in thousands of dollars rather than dollars.

Now that we have organized the data into a frequency distribution, we can summarize the patterns in the selling prices of the vehicles for Rob Whitner. These observations are listed below:

1. The selling prices ranged from about $19 310 to $50 740.
2. The largest concentration of selling prices is in the $23 800 up to $28 290 class.
3. The selling prices are concentrated between $23 800 and $37 270. A total of 56 (70 percent) of the vehicles are sold within this range.
4. Two of the vehicles sold for $46 250 or more, and 10 sold for less than $23 800.

By presenting this information to Rob Whitner, we give him a clearer picture of the distribution of the selling prices for the last month.

We admit that arranging the information on the selling prices into a frequency distribution does result in the loss of some detailed information. That is, by organizing the data into a frequency distribution, we cannot pinpoint the exact selling price (such as $23 820, or $32 800), and we cannot tell that the actual selling price of the least expensive vehicle was $19 320 and of the most expensive vehicle was $50 719. However, the lower limit of the first class and the upper limit of the largest class convey essentially the same meaning. Whitner will make the same judgment if he knows the lowest price is about $19 310 that he will make if he knows the exact selling price is $19 320. The advantage of condensing the data into a more understandable form more than offsets this disadvantage.

■ SELF-REVIEW 2-1

The commissions earned for the first quarter of last year by the 11 members of the sales staff at Master Chemical Company are $1650, $1475, $1510, $1670, $1595, $1760, $1540, $1495, $1590, $1625, and $1510.
  (a) What are the values such as $1650 and $1475 called?
  (b) Using $1400 up to $1500 as the first class, $1500 up to $1600 as the second class, and so forth, organize data on commissions earned into a frequency distribution.
  (c) What are the numbers in the right column of your frequency distribution called?
  (d) Describe the distribution of commissions earned based on the frequency distribution. What is the largest amount of commission earned? What is the smallest?

CLASS INTERVALS AND CLASS MIDPOINTS

We will use two other terms frequently: **class midpoint** and **class interval**. The midpoint, also called the **class mark**, is halfway between the lower and upper class limits. It can be computed by adding the lower class limit to the upper class limit and dividing by 2. Referring to Table 2-3 for the first class, the lower class limit is $19 310 and the upper limit is $23 800. The class midpoint is $21 555, found by ($19 310 + $23 800)/2. The midpoint of $21 555 best represents, or is typical of, the selling prices of the vehicles in that class.

To determine the class interval, subtract the lower limit of the class from its upper limit. The class interval of the vehicle selling price data is $4490, which we find by subtracting the lower limit of the first class, $19 310, from its upper limit; that is, $23 800 − $19 310 = $4490. You can also determine the class interval by finding the distance between consecutive midpoints. The midpoint of the first class is $21 555 and the midpoint of the second class is $26 045. The difference is $4490.

A SOFTWARE EXAMPLE: FREQUENCY DISTRIBUTION USING MEGASTAT

Chart 2-1 shows the frequency distribution of the Whitner Pontiac data produced by MegaStat. The form of the output is somewhat different than the frequency distribution in Table 2-3(b), but overall conclusions are the same.

■ SELF-REVIEW 2-2

The following table includes the grades of students who took Math 1021 during Fall 2002.

| 40 | 55 | 50 | 55 | 28 | 60 | 25 | 55 | 60 | 65 | 70 | 64 |
| 62 | 70 | 50 | 65 | 55 | 48 | 69 | 25 | 64 | 58 | 55 | 71 |

(a) How many classes would you use?
(b) How wide would you make the classes?
(c) Create a frequency distribution table.

RELATIVE FREQUENCY DISTRIBUTION

It may be desirable to convert class frequencies to relative class frequencies to show the fraction of the total number of observations in each class. In our vehicle sales example, we may want to know what percentage of the vehicle prices are in the $28 290 up to $32 780 class.

To convert a frequency distribution to a relative frequency distribution, each of the class frequencies is divided by the total number of observations. Using the distribution of vehicle sales again (Table 2-3(b), where the selling prices are reported in thousands of dollars), the relative frequency for the $19 310 up to $23 800 class is 0.125, found by dividing 10 by 80. That is, the price of 12.5 percent of the vehicles sold at Whitner Pontiac is between $19 310 and $23 800. The relative frequencies for the remaining classes are shown in Table 2-4.

EXCEL CHART 2-1: Frequency Distribution of Data in Table 2-1

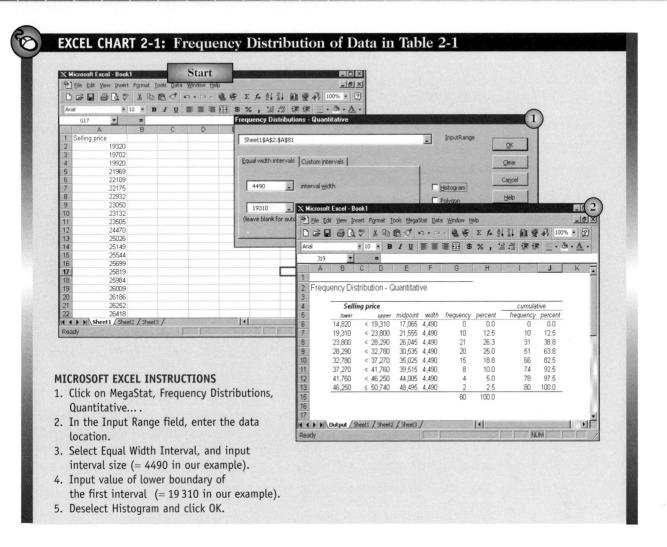

MICROSOFT EXCEL INSTRUCTIONS

1. Click on MegaStat, Frequency Distributions, Quantitative... .
2. In the Input Range field, enter the data location.
3. Select Equal Width Interval, and input interval size (= 4490 in our example).
4. Input value of lower boundary of the first interval (= 19 310 in our example).
5. Deselect Histogram and click OK.

TABLE 2-4: Relative Frequency Distribution of Selling Prices at Whitner Pontiac Last Month

Selling Price ($ thousands)	Frequency	Relative Frequency		Found by
19.310 up to 23.800	10	0.1250	«———	10/80
23.800 up to 28.290	21	0.2625	«———	21/80
28.290 up to 32.780	20	0.2500	«———	20/80
32.780 up to 37.270	15	0.1875	«———	15/80
37.270 up to 41.760	8	0.1000	«———	8/80
41.760 up to 46.250	4	0.0500	«———	4/80
46.250 up to 50.740	2	0.0250	«———	2/80
Total	80	1.0000		

■ SELF-REVIEW 2-3

Refer to Table 2-4, which shows the relative frequency distribution for the vehicles sold last month at Whitner Pontiac.
   (a) How many vehicles sold for $23 800 up to $28 290?
   (b) What percentage of the vehicles sold for a price from $23 800 up to $28 290?
   (c) What percentage of the vehicles sold for $37 270 or more?

EXERCISES 2-1 TO 2-8

2-1. A set of data consists of 38 observations. How many classes would you recommend for the frequency distribution?

2-2. A set of data consists of 45 observations. The lowest value is $0 and the highest value is $29. What size would you recommend for the class interval?

2-3. A set of data consists of 230 observations. The lowest value is $235 and the highest value is $567. What class interval would you recommend?

2-4. A set of data contains 53 observations. The lowest value is 42 and the highest is 129. The data are to be organized into a frequency distribution.
   (a)   How many classes would you suggest?
   (b)   What would you suggest as the lower limit of the first class?

2-5. The Wachesaw Outpatient Centre, designed for same-day minor surgery, opened last month. Below are the numbers of patients served during the first 16 days.

27	27	23	24	25	28	35	33
34	24	30	30	24	33	23	23

   (a) How many classes would you recommend?
   (b) What class interval would you suggest?
   (c) What lower limit would you recommend for the first class?

2-6. The Quick-Change Oil Company has a number of outlets in Hamilton, Ontario. The numbers of oil changes at the Oak Street outlet in the past 20 days are listed below. The data are to be organized into a frequency distribution.

65	98	55	62	79	59	51	90	72	56
70	62	66	80	94	79	63	73	71	85

   (a) How many classes would you recommend?
   (b) What class interval would you suggest?
   (c) What lower limit would you recommend for the first class?
   (d) Organize the number of oil changes into a frequency distribution.
   (e) Comment on the shape of the frequency distribution. Also determine the relative frequency distribution.

2-7. The local manager of Food Queen is interested in the number of times a customer shops at her store during a two-week period. The responses of 51 customers were:

5	3	3	1	4	4	5	6	4	2	6	6	6	7	1
1	14	1	2	4	4	4	5	6	3	5	3	4	5	6
8	4	7	6	5	9	11	3	12	4	7	6	5	15	1
1	10	8	9	2	12									

    (a) Starting with 0 as the lower limit of the first class and using a class interval of 3, organize the data into a frequency distribution.
    (b) Describe the distribution. Where do the data tend to cluster?
    (c) Convert the distribution to a relative frequency distribution.

2-8. Moore Travel, a nationwide travel agency, offers special rates on certain Caribbean cruises to senior citizens. The president of Moore Travel wants additional information on the ages of those people taking cruises. A random sample of 40 customers taking a cruise last year revealed these ages:

77	18	63	84	38	54	50	59	54	56	36	26	50	34
44	41	58	58	53	51	62	43	52	53	63	62	62	65
61	52	60	60	45	66	83	71	63	58	61	71		

    (a) Organize the data into a frequency distribution, using 7 classes and 15 as the lower limit of the first class. What class interval did you select?
    (b) Where do the data tend to cluster?
    (c) Describe the distribution.
    (d) Determine the relative frequency distribution.

FREQUENCY DISTRIBUTION WITH UNEQUAL CLASS INTERVALS

In constructing frequency distributions of quantitative data, generally, equal class widths are assigned to all classes. This is because unequal class intervals present problems in graphically portraying the distribution and in doing some of the computations, as we will see in later chapters. Unequal class intervals, however, may be necessary in certain situations to avoid a large number of empty, or almost empty, classes. Such is the case in Table 2-5. Canada Customs and Revenue Agency (CCRA) used unequal-sized class intervals to report the adjusted gross income on individual tax returns. Had the CCRA used an equal-sized interval of, say, $1000, more than 1000 classes would have been required to describe all the incomes. A frequency distribution with 1000 classes would be difficult to interpret. In this case, the distribution is easier to understand in spite of the unequal classes. Note also that the number of income tax returns or "frequencies" is reported in thousands in this particular table. This also makes the information easier to digest.

TABLE 2-5: Adjusted Gross Income for Individuals Filing Income Tax Returns

Adjusted Gross Income ($)	Number of Returns (in thousands)
Under 2 000	135
2 000 up to 3 000	3 399
3 000 up to 5 000	8 175
5 000 up to 10 000	19 740
10 000 up to 15 000	15 539
15 000 up to 25 000	14 944
25 000 up to 50 000	4 451
50 000 up to 100 000	699
100 000 up to 500 000	162
500 000 up to 1 000 000	3
1 000 000 and over	1

2.2   STEM-AND-LEAF DISPLAYS

In Section 2.1, we showed how to organize quantitative data into a frequency distribution so we could summarize the raw data into a meaningful form. The major advantage of organizing the data into a frequency distribution is that we get a quick visual picture of the shape of the distribution without doing any further calculation. That is, we can see where the data are concentrated and also determine whether there are any extremely large or small values. However, it has two disadvantages: (1) we lose the exact identity of each value, and (2) we are not sure how the values within each class are distributed. To explain, consider the following frequency distribution of the number of 30-second radio advertising spots purchased by the 45 members of the Toronto Automobile Dealers' Association in 2001. We observe that 7 of the 45 dealers purchased at least 90 but less than 100 spots. However, is the number of spots purchased within this class clustered near 90, spread evenly throughout the class, or clustered near 99? We cannot tell.

Number of Spots Purchased	Frequency
80 up to 90	2
90 up to 100	7
100 up to 110	6
110 up to 120	9
120 up to 130	8
130 up to 140	7
140 up to 150	3
150 up to 160	3
Total	45

For a mid-sized data set, we can eliminate these shortcomings by using an alternative graphic display called the **stem-and-leaf display**. To illustrate the construction of a stem-and-leaf display using the advertising spots data, suppose the seven observations in the 90 up to 100 class are 96, 94, 93, 94, 95, 96, and 97.

Let us sort these values to get: 93, 94, 94, 95, 96, 96, 97. The **stem** value is the leading digit or digits, in this case 9. The **leaves** are the trailing digits. The stem is placed to the left of a vertical line and the leaf values to the right. The values in the 90 up to 100 class would appear in the stem-and-leaf display as follows:

9 | 3 4 4 5 6 6 7

With the stem-and-leaf display, we can quickly observe that there were two dealers who purchased 94 spots and that the number of spots purchased ranged from 93 to 97. A stem-and-leaf display is similar to a frequency distribution with more information (i.e., data values instead of tallies).

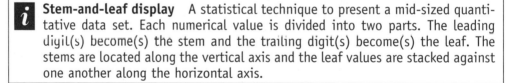 **Stem-and-leaf display**   A statistical technique to present a mid-sized quantitative data set. Each numerical value is divided into two parts. The leading digit(s) become(s) the stem and the trailing digit(s) become(s) the leaf. The stems are located along the vertical axis and the leaf values are stacked against one another along the horizontal axis.

The following example will explain the details of developing a stem-and-leaf display.

Example 2-2   Table 2-6 lists the number of 30-second radio advertising spots purchased by each of the 45 members of the Toronto Automobile Dealers' Association last year. Organize the data into a stem-and-leaf display. Around what values do the number of advertising spots tend to cluster? What is the smallest number of spots purchased by a dealer and the largest number purchased?

Solution   From the data in Table 2-6 we note that the smallest number of spots purchased is 88. So we will make the first stem value 8. The largest number is 156, so we will have the stem values begin at 8 and continue to 15. The first number in Table 2-6 is 96, which will have a stem value of 9 and leaf value of 6. Moving across the top row, the second value is 93 and the third is 88. After the first three data values are considered, the display is shown opposite.

Stem	Leaf
8	8
9	6 3
10	
11	
12	
13	
14	
15	

TABLE 2-6: Number of Advertising Spots Purchased during 2001 by Members of the Toronto Automobile Dealers' Association

96	93	88	117	127	95	113	96	108	94
148	156	139	142	94	107	125	155	155	103
112	127	117	120	112	135	132	111	125	104
106	139	134	119	97	89	118	136	125	143
120	103	113	124	138					

Organizing all the data, the stem-and-leaf display would appear as shown in Chart 2-2(a).

The usual procedure is to sort the leaf values from smallest to largest. The last line, the row referring to the values in the 150s, would appear as:

15 | 5 5 6

The final table would appear as shown in Chart 2-2(b), where we have sorted all of the leaf values.

CHART 2-2: Stem-and-Leaf Display

a.

Stem	Leaf
8	8 9
9	6 3 5 6 4 4 7
10	8 7 3 4 6 3
11	7 3 2 7 2 1 9 8 3
12	7 5 7 0 5 5 0 4
13	9 5 2 9 4 6 8
14	8 2 3
15	6 5 5

b.

Stem	Leaf
8	8 9
9	3 4 4 5 6 6 7
10	3 3 4 6 7 8
11	1 2 2 3 3 7 7 8 9
12	0 0 4 5 5 5 7 7
13	2 4 5 6 8 9 9
14	2 3 8
15	5 5 6

You can draw several conclusions from the stem-and-leaf display. First, the lowest number of spots purchased is 88 and the highest is 156. Two dealers purchased less than 90 spots, and three purchased 150 or more. You can observe, for example, that the three dealers who purchased more than 150 spots actually purchased 155, 155, and 156 spots. The concentration of the number of spots is between 110 and 139. There were nine dealers who purchased between 110 and 119 spots and eight who purchased between 120 and 129 spots. We can also tell that within the 120 up to 130 group, the actual number of spots purchased was spread evenly throughout. That is, two dealers purchased 120 spots, one dealer purchased 124 spots, three dealers purchased 125 spots, and two dealers purchased 127 spots.

We can also generate this information using Minitab. We have named the variable *Spots*. The Minitab output is given below.

The Minitab stem-and-leaf display provides some additional information regarding cumulative totals. In Chart 2-3, the column to the left of the stem values has numbers such as 2, 9, 15, and so on. The number 9 indicates that there are 9 observations of value less than the upper limit of the current class, which is 100. The number 15 indicates that there are 15 observations less than 110. About halfway

MINITAB CHART 2-3: Stem-and-Leaf Display of Data in Table 2-6

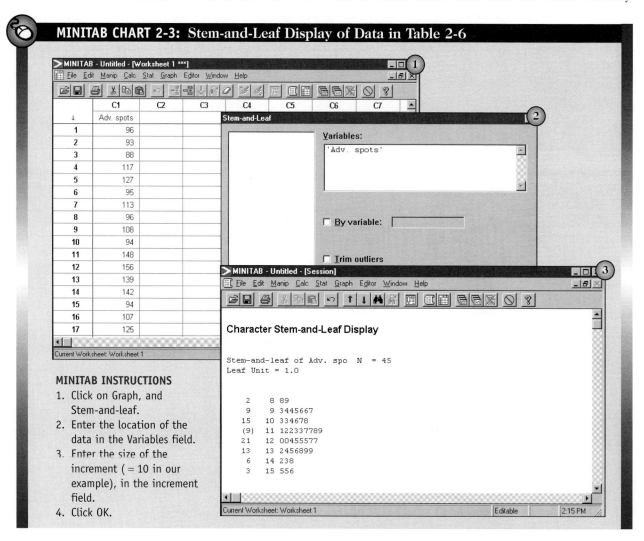

	C1	C2	C3
↓	Adv. spots		
1	96		
2	93		
3	88		
4	117		
5	127		
6	95		
7	113		
8	96		
9	108		
10	94		
11	148		
12	156		
13	139		
14	142		
15	94		
16	107		
17	125		

Current Worksheet: Worksheet 1

Stem-and-Leaf

Variables:
'Adv. spots'

☐ By variable:

☐ Trim outliers

MINITAB - Untitled - [Session]

Character Stem-and-Leaf Display

```
Stem-and-leaf of Adv. spo   N  = 45
Leaf Unit = 1.0

    2     8 89
    9     9 3445667
   15    10 334678
   (9)   11 122337789
   21    12 00455577
   13    13 2456899
    6    14 238
    3    15 556
```

Current Worksheet: Worksheet 1   Editable   2:15 PM

MINITAB INSTRUCTIONS
1. Click on Graph, and Stem-and-leaf.
2. Enter the location of the data in the Variables field.
3. Enter the size of the increment (= 10 in our example), in the increment field.
4. Click OK.

down the column the number 9 appears in parentheses. The parentheses indicate that the middle value appears in that row; hence, we call this row the *median row*. In this case, we describe the middle value as the value that divides the total number of observations into two equal parts. There are a total of 45 observations, so the middle value, if the data were arranged from smallest to largest, would be the 23rd observation. After the median row, the values begin to decline. These values represent the "more than" cumulative totals. There are 21 observations of value greater than or equal to the lower limit of this class, which is 120; 13 of 130 or more, and so on.

In the stem-and-leaf display for Example 2-2, the leading digits (stems) take the values from 8 to 15 and thus have 8 stems (8, 9, 10, 11, 12, 13, 14, 15) in units of 10. However, in some data sets, stems assume only two or three values. Generating a stem-and-leaf display in these situations is not as easy as in Example 2-2. Let us look at the sample of marks of 20 students in Math 2010:

50　52　54　53　65　60　45　43　57　62
56　58　51　61　46　44　69　55　64　59

The leading digits (units of 10) in this example assume only three values: 4, 5, and 6. Following the above procedure for drawing a stem-and-leaf display, the stem-and-leaf display of the above data set looks like the one given below.

Stem	Leaf
4	3 4 5 6
5	0 1 2 3 4 5 6 7 8 9
6	0 1 2 4 5 9

As we can see, this stem-and-leaf display has only three stems and does not display the characteristics of the data set as well as if there were more stems. We can improve the stem-and-leaf display by *splitting* each stem. For example, stem 4 can be split as

4	3 4
4	5 6

The first stem 4 contains leaves less than 5 and the second stem 4 contains leaves 5 and above.

The revised stem-and-leaf display is given below.

Stem	Leaf
4	3 4
4	5 6
5	0 1 2 3 4
5	5 6 7 8 9
6	0 1 2 4
6	5 9

Other data sets may require even more splitting. The question of how much splitting is necessary can be answered by the rule suggested by Tukey et al.[1] For a sample size ≤ 100, the number of stems should be the integer part of $2\sqrt{n}$, where n is the sample size; for $n \geq 100$, the number of stems should be the integer part of $10 \log_{10} n$. In our example of 20 students' marks, the number suggested by the rule is 8. However, we have 6 stems in our example, which is close to 8. Remember, the rule provides a guideline for selecting the number of stems.

Stem-and-leaf display is useful only for a mid-sized data set. When we use a stem-and-leaf display for a large data set, we produce a large number of stems and/or leaves and are not able to see the characteristics of a large data set.

■ SELF-REVIEW 2-4

The price–earnings ratios for 21 stocks in the retail trade category are:

8.3	9.6	9.5	9.1	8.8	11.2	7.7	10.1	9.9	10.8	10.2
8.0	8.4	8.1	11.6	9.6	8.8	8.0	10.4	9.8	9.2	

Organize this information into a stem-and-leaf display.
  (a) How many values are less than 9.0?
  (b) List the values in the 10.0 up to 11.0 category.
  (c) What are the largest and the smallest price–earnings ratios?

EXERCISES 2-9 TO 2-14

2-9. The first row of a stem-and-leaf display appears as follows: 62 | 1 3 3 7 9.
      Assume whole number values.
      (a) What is the range of the values in this row?
      (b) How many data values are in this row?
      (c) List the actual values in this row.

2-10. The third row of a stem-and-leaf display appears as follows: 21 | 0 1 3 5 7 9.
      Assume whole number values.
      (a) What is the range of the values in this row?
      (b) How many data values are in this row?
      (c) List the actual values in this row.

2-11. The following stem-and-leaf display shows the number of units produced
      per day in a factory.

1	3	8
1	4	
2	5	6
9	6	0 1 3 3 5 5 9
(7)	7	0 2 3 6 7 7 8
9	8	5 9
7	9	0 0 1 5 6
2	10	3 6

      (a) How many days were studied?
      (b) How many observations are in the first class?
      (c) What are the largest and the smallest values in the data set?
      (d) List the actual values in the fourth row.
      (e) List the actual values in the second row.
      (f) How many values are less than 70?
      (g) How many values are 80 or more?
      (h) How many values are between 60 and 89?

2-12. The following stem-and-leaf display reports the number of movies rented per day at Video Connection.

3	12	6 8 9
6	13	1 2 3
10	14	6 8 8 9
13	15	5 8 9
15	16	3 5
20	17	2 4 5 6 8
23	18	2 6 8
(5)	19	1 3 4 5 6
22	20	0 3 4 6 7 9
16	21	2 2 3 9
12	22	7 8 9
9	23	0 0 1 7 9
4	24	8
3	25	1 3
1	26	
1	27	0

(a) How many days were studied?
(b) How many observations are in the last class?
(c) What are the largest and the smallest values in the entire set of data?
(d) List the actual values in the fourth row.
(e) List the actual values in the next to the last row.
(f) On how many days were fewer than 160 movies rented?
(g) On how many days were 220 or more movies rented?
(h) On how many days were between 170 and 210 movies rented?

2-13. A survey of the number of calls received by a sample of Southern Phone Company subscribers last week revealed the following information. Develop a stem-and-leaf display. How many calls did a typical subscriber receive? What were the largest and the smallest number of calls received?

52   43   30   38   30   42   12   46   39   37   34   46   32
18   41   5

2-14. Aloha Banking Co. is studying the number of times a particular automated teller machine (ATM) is used each day. The following is the number of times it was used during each of the last 30 days. Develop a stem-and-leaf display. Summarize the data on the number of times the machine was used: How many times was the ATM used on a typical day? What were the largest and the smallest number of times the ATM was used? Around what values did the number of times the ATM was used, tend to cluster?

83   64   84   76   84   54   75   59   70   61   63   80   84
73   68   52   65   90   52   77   95   36   78   61   59   84
95   47   87   60

2.3 GRAPHIC PRESENTATION OF A FREQUENCY DISTRIBUTION

Sales managers, stock analysts, hospital administrators, and other busy executives often need a quick picture of the trends in sales, stock prices, or hospital costs. These trends can often be depicted by the use of charts and graphs. The charts that depict a frequency distribution graphically are the histogram, the stem-and-leaf display, the frequency polygon, and the cumulative frequency polygon.

HISTOGRAM

One of the most common graphical methods of displaying the frequency distribution of a quantitative data is a **histogram**.

 Histogram   A graph in which classes are marked on the horizontal axis and class frequencies on the vertical axis. The class frequencies are represented by the heights of the rectangles, and the rectangles are drawn adjacent to each other without any space between them.

Thus, a histogram describes a frequency distribution using a series of adjacent rectangles. Since the height of each rectangle equals the frequency of the corresponding class, and all the class widths are equal, the area of each rectangle is proportional to the frequency of the corresponding class.

Example 2-3   Refer to the data in Table 2-7 on life expectancy of males at birth in 40 countries. Construct a frequency distribution and a histogram. What conclusions can you reach based on the information presented in the histogram?

TABLE 2-7: Life Expectancy of Males at Birth					
Country	**Life Expectancy (years)**	**Country**	**Life Expectancy (years)**	**Country**	**Life Expectancy (years)**
Afghanistan	45	Bhutan	59.5	Egypt	64.7
Albania	69.9	Botswana	46.2	France	74.2
Angola	44.9	Brazil	63.1	Germany	73.9
Argentina	69.6	Bulgaria	67.6	Hungary	66.8
Armenia	67.2	Cambodia	51.5	India	62.3
Australia	75.5	Canada	76.1	Iran	68.5
Austria	73.7	Chad	45.7	Japan	76.8
Bahamas	70.5	Chile	72.3	Kenya	51.1
Bahrain	71.1	China	67.9	Nepal	57.6
Bangladesh	58.1	Congo	48.3	UK	74.5
Barbados	73.7	Cuba	74.2	USA	73.4
Belarus	62.2	Czech		Venezuela	70
Belgium	73.8	Republic	70.3	Zambia	39.5
Bermuda	71.7	Denmark	73		

Source: Life Expectancy at Birth (Males), United Nations Statistics Divisions, 1996–2000

Solution   The data in Table 2-7 is a quantitative data. Therefore, the first step is to construct a frequency distribution using the method discussed in Section 2.1 This is given in Table 2-8. (In Table 2-8, we also give relative frequencies. These will be discussed later.)

TABLE 2-8: Frequency and Relative Frequency Distribution of Life Expectancy Data

Life Expectancy	Frequency	Relative Frequency		Found by
36 up to 43	1	0.025	→	1/40
43 up to 50	5	0.125	→	5/40
50 up to 57	2	0.050	→	2/40
57 up to 64	6	0.150	→	6/40
64 up to 71	11	0.275	→	11/40
71 up to 78	15	0.375	→	15/40
Total	40	1.000		

To construct a histogram, class frequencies are scaled along the vertical axis (y-axis) and either the class limits or the class midpoints are scaled along the horizontal axis (x-axis).

From the frequency distribution, the frequency of the class 36 up to 43 is 1. Therefore, the height of the column for this class is 1. Make a rectangle whose width spreads from 36 to 43 with the height of one unit. Repeat the process for the remaining classes. The completed histogram should resemble the graph presented in Chart 2-4. The double slant on the x-axis indicates that the class limits did not start at zero. That is, the division between 0 and 36 is not linear. In other words, the distance between 0 and 36 is not the same as the distance between 36 and 43, between 43 and 50, and so on.

CHART 2-4: Histogram of Life Expectancy for Males at Birth

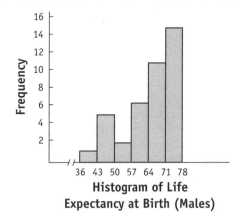

Histogram of Life
Expectancy at Birth (Males)

From Chart 2-4, we conclude that:

- the lowest life expectancy is about 36 years and the highest is about 78 years.
- the class with the highest frequency (15) is 71 up to 78. That is, 15 countries have a life expectancy from 71 up to 78 years.
- the class with the lowest frequency (1) is 36 up to 43 years. That is, there is only one country with a life expectancy from 36 up to 43.
- the histogram is j-shaped. There is a tail on the left side of the class with the highest frequency (mode), and no tail on its right side.

COMMON DISTRIBUTION SHAPES

According to the shapes of histograms, distributions can be classified into (i) symmetrical and (ii) skewed.

A symmetrical distribution is one in which, if we divide its histogram into two pieces by drawing a vertical line through its centre, the two halves formed are mirror images of each other. This is displayed in Chart 2-5(a).

A distribution that is not symmetrical is said to be skewed.

For a skewed distribution, it is quite common to have one tail of the distribution longer than the other. If the longer tail is stretched to the right, the distribution is said to be *skewed to the right*. If the longer tail is stretched to the left, it is said to be *skewed to the left*. These are displayed in Charts 2-5(b) and (c) below.

CHART 2-5: Common Distribution Shapes

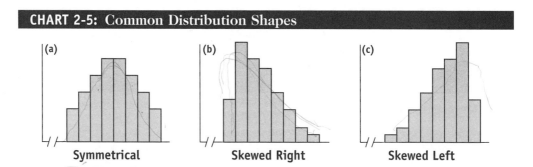

For a symmetrical distribution, the centre, or the typical value, of the distribution is well defined. For a skewed distribution, however, it is not that easy to define the centre. We shall discuss this in detail in the next chapter.

Another commonly used classification of distributions is according to its number of peaks. When the histogram has a single peak, the distribution is called *unimodal*. A *bimodal distribution* is one in which the histogram has two peaks not necessarily equal in height.

RELATIVE FREQUENCY HISTOGRAM

A relative frequency histogram is a graph in which classes are marked on the horizontal axis and the relative frequencies (frequency of a class/total frequency) on the vertical axis. Let us refer again to the data in Table 2-7 on life expectancy of males at birth in 40 countries. In Table 2-8 we also give a relative frequency distribution corresponding to this data. For example, the relative frequency of the class 43 up to 50 is 0.125 (5/40). We follow the procedure used in drawing a histogram to draw a relative frequency histogram. Chart 2-6 shows the relative frequency histogram of the life expectancy data.

A relative frequency histogram has the following important properties:

- The shape of a relative frequency histogram of a data set is identical to the shape of its histogram. (Verify this for the life expectancy data.)

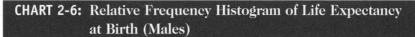

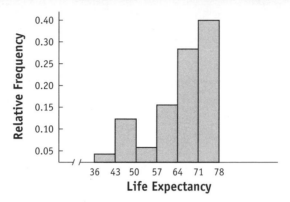

CHART 2-6: Relative Frequency Histogram of Life Expectancy at Birth (Males)

- It is useful in comparing shapes of two or more data sets with different total frequencies. (Note that when total frequencies of two data sets are different, histograms of these data sets cannot be compared. For example, total frequency of one data set may be 1000, while that of the other data set may be 100. But relative frequencies of any data set add up to 1.0.)

- The area of the rectangle corresponding to a class interval equals (relative frequency of the class) × (class width). For example, the relative frequency of class 43 up to 50 is 0.125 (12.5 percent of the countries listed in Table 2-7 have life expectancy in this class). The area of the corresponding rectangle is $(0.125)(50 - 43) = 0.875$.

The total area under the entire relative frequency histogram is therefore (class width) × (sum of relative frequencies of all the classes) = class width. (This is because the sum of the relative frequency of all classes equals 1.)

If we scale the height of each rectangle by 1/(class width), then the total area under each rectangle of the scaled relative frequency histogram will be equal to its relative frequency, and the total area under the entire scaled relative frequency histogram will be equal to 1.

A histogram provides an easily interpreted visual representation of the frequency distribution of given raw data. The shape of the histogram is the same whether we use the actual frequency distribution or the relative frequency distribution. We shall see in later chapters the importance of shapes in determining the appropriate method of statistical analysis.

HISTOGRAM USING EXCEL AND MINITAB

We can plot a histogram using MegaStat by following the same instructions as those for the construction of a frequency distribution, except that in this case, we do *not* deselect "histogram." We give below instructions for plotting a histogram using Excel (without MegaStat) and Minitab.

EXCEL CHART 2-7: Histogram of Life Expectancy

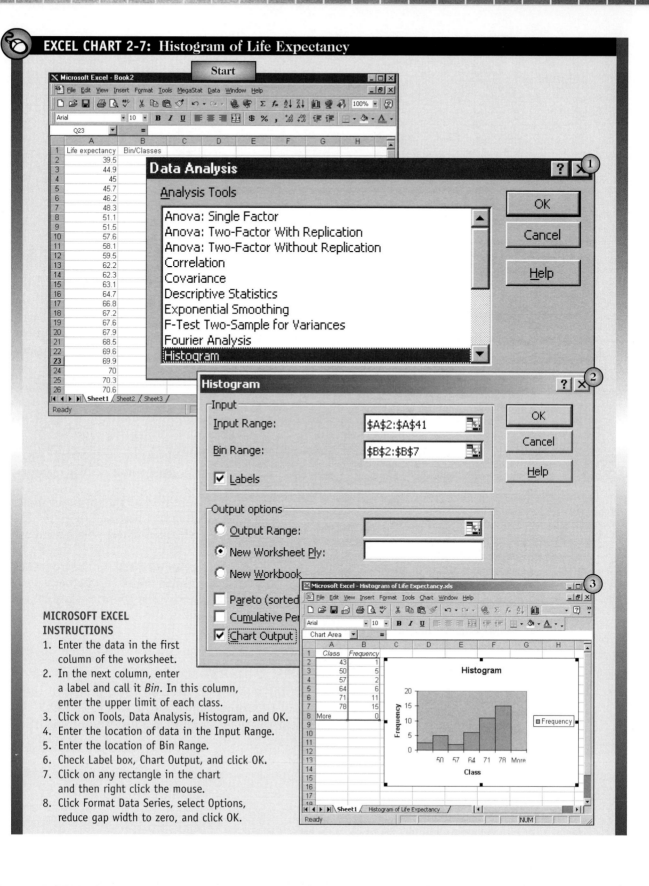

MICROSOFT EXCEL INSTRUCTIONS

1. Enter the data in the first column of the worksheet.
2. In the next column, enter a label and call it *Bin*. In this column, enter the upper limit of each class.
3. Click on Tools, Data Analysis, Histogram, and OK.
4. Enter the location of data in the Input Range.
5. Enter the location of Bin Range.
6. Check Label box, Chart Output, and click OK.
7. Click on any rectangle in the chart and then right click the mouse.
8. Click Format Data Series, select Options, reduce gap width to zero, and click OK.

MINITAB CHART 2-8: Histogram of Life Expectancy

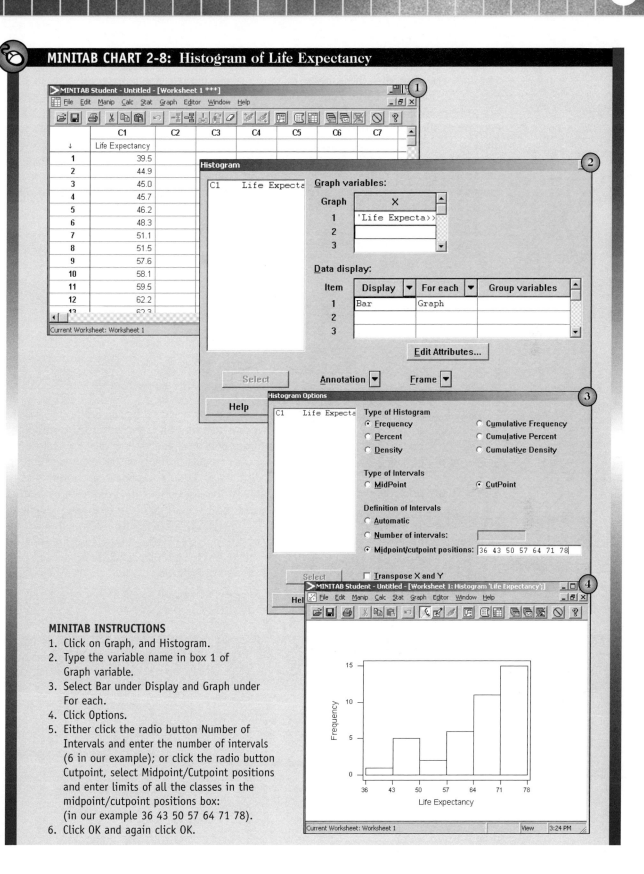

MINITAB INSTRUCTIONS

1. Click on Graph, and Histogram.
2. Type the variable name in box 1 of Graph variable.
3. Select Bar under Display and Graph under For each.
4. Click Options.
5. Either click the radio button Number of Intervals and enter the number of intervals (6 in our example); or click the radio button Cutpoint, select Midpoint/Cutpoint positions and enter limits of all the classes in the midpoint/cutpoint positions box: (in our example 36 43 50 57 64 71 78).
6. Click OK and again click OK.

FREQUENCY POLYGON

The construction of a frequency polygon is similar to the construction of a histogram. It consists of line segments connecting the points formed by the intersections of the class midpoints and the class frequencies. The construction of a frequency polygon is illustrated in Chart 2-9. We use the vehicle prices for the cars sold last month at Whitner Pontiac. The midpoint of each class is scaled on the x-axis and the class frequencies on the y-axis. Recall that the class midpoint is the value at the centre of a class and represents the values in that class. The *class frequency* is the number of observations in a particular class. The frequency distribution of the vehicle selling prices at Whitner Pontiac is reproduced below.

Selling Price ($ thousands)	Midpoint	Frequency
19.310 up to 23.800	21.555	10
23.800 up to 28.290	26.045	21
28.290 up to 32.780	30.535	20
32.780 up to 37.270	35.025	15
37.270 up to 41.760	39.515	8
41.760 up to 46.250	44.005	4
46.250 up to 50.740	48.495	2
Total		80

As noted earlier, the 19.310 up to 23.800 class is represented by the midpoint 21.555. To construct a frequency polygon, we move horizontally on the graph to the midpoint 21.555 and then vertically to 10, the class frequency, and place a dot. The x and y values of this point are called the *coordinates*. The coordinates of the next point are x = 26.045 and y = 21. The process is continued for all classes. Then the points are connected in order. That is, the point representing the lowest class is joined to the one representing the second class, and so on. Note in Chart 2-9 that to complete the frequency polygon, two additional points with x co-ordinates 17.065 and 52.985 and with 0 frequencies (that is, points on the x-axis), are added to *anchor* the polygon. These two values are derived by subtracting the class width of 4.49 from the lowest midpoint (21.555) and adding 4.49 to the highest midpoint (48.495) in the frequency distribution.

CHART 2-9: Frequency Polygon of the Selling Prices of 80 Vehicles at Whitner Pontiac

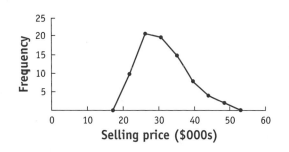

CHART 2-10: Distribution of Selling Prices at Whitner Pontiac and Midtown Cadillac

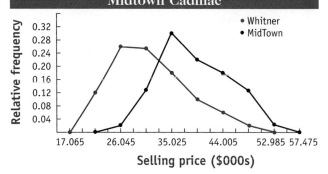

Both the histogram and the frequency polygon allow us to get a quick picture of the main characteristics of the data (highs, lows, points of concentration, etc.). Although the two representations are similar in purpose, the histogram has the advantage of depicting each class as a rectangle, with the height of the rectangular bar representing the number of frequencies in each class. The frequency polygon, in turn, has an advantage over the histogram. It allows us to directly compare two or more frequency distributions. Suppose Rob, the owner of Whitner Pontiac, wants to compare the sales last month at his dealership with those at Midtown Cadillac. To do this, two frequency polygons are constructed, one on top of the other, as shown in Chart 2-10. It is clear from the chart that the total sales volume at each dealership is more or less the same.

■ SELF-REVIEW 2-5

The annual imports of a selected group of electronic suppliers are shown in the following frequency distribution.

Imports ($ millions)	Number of Suppliers
2 up to 5	6
5 up to 8	13
8 up to 11	20
11 up to 14	10
14 up to 17	1

(a) Draw a histogram.
(b) Draw a frequency polygon.
(c) Summarize the important features of the distribution (such as low and high values, concentration, etc.).

EXERCISES 2-15 TO 2-18

2-15. Molly's Candle Shop has several retail stores in Vancouver. Many of Molly's customers ask her to ship their purchases. The following chart shows the number of packages shipped per day for the last 100 days.

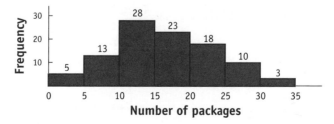

(a) What is this chart called?
(b) What is the total number of frequencies?
(c) What is the class interval?
(d) What is the class frequency for the 10 up to 15 class?

(e) What is the relative frequency for the 10 up to 15 class?

(f) What is the midpoint for the 10 up to 15 class?

(g) On how many days were there 25 or more packages shipped?

2-16. The following chart shows the number of patients admitted daily to Memorial Hospital through the emergency room.

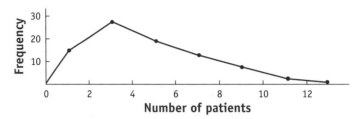

(a) What is the midpoint of the 2 up to 4 class?

(b) On how many days were 2 up to 4 patients admitted?

(c) Approximately how many days were studied?

(d) What is the class interval?

(e) What is this chart called?

2-17. The following frequency distribution represents the number of days during a year that employees at J. Morgan Manufacturing Company were absent from work due to illness.

Number of Days Absent	Number of Employees
0 up to 3	5
3 up to 6	12
6 up to 9	23
9 up to 12	8
12 up to 15	2
Total	50

(a) Construct a relative frequency histogram.

(b) What proportion of the total area under the relative frequency histogram is contained above the interval 3 up to 12?

2-18. A large retailer is studying the lead time (elapsed time between when an order is placed and when it is filled) for a sample of recent orders. The lead times are reported in days.

Lead Time (days)	Frequency
0 up to 5	6
5 up to 10	7
10 up to 15	12
15 up to 20	8
20 up to 25	7
Total	40

(a) How many orders were studied?

(b) What is the midpoint of the first class?

(c) What are the coordinates of the point on the frequency polygon corresponding to the first class?

(d) Draw a histogram.

(e) Draw a frequency polygon.

(f) Interpret the lead times using the two charts.

CUMULATIVE FREQUENCY DISTRIBUTIONS

Let us consider again the distribution of the selling prices of vehicles at Whitner Pontiac. Suppose we were interested in the number of vehicles that sold for less than $28 290. These numbers can be approximated by developing a **cumulative frequency distribution** and portraying it graphically in a **cumulative frequency polygon**, which is also called an *ogive*.

Example 2-4

Refer to Table 2-4 on page 39. Construct a less than cumulative frequency polygon. Fifty percent of the vehicles were sold for less than what amount? Twenty-five of the vehicles were sold for less than what amount?

Solution

As the name implies, a cumulative frequency distribution and a cumulative frequency polygon require cumulative frequencies. The cumulative frequency of a class is the number of observations fewer than the upper limit of that class. For example, in Table 2-9, the frequency distribution of the vehicle selling prices at Whitner Pontiac is repeated from Table 2-4 on page 39. The cumulative frequency of the class 23.800 up to 28.290 is 31. How did we get it? We added the number of vehicles sold for less than $23 800 (which equals 10) to the 21 vehicles sold in the next higher class. Thus the number of vehicles sold for *less than* $28 290 is 31. Similarly, the cumulative frequency of the next higher class is $10 + 21 + 20 = 51$. The process is continued for all the classes.

To plot a cumulative frequency distribution, scale the upper limit of each class along the x-axis and the corresponding cumulative frequencies along the y-axis. We label the vertical axis on the left in units and the vertical axis on the right in percent. In the Whitner Pontiac example, the vertical axis on the left is labelled from 0 to 80 (vehicles sold) and on the right from 0 to 100 percent. The value of 50 percent corresponds to 40 vehicles sold.

TABLE 2-9: **Cumulative Frequency Distribution for Selling Prices at Whitner Pontiac Last Month**

Selling Price ($ thousands)	Frequency	Cumulative Frequency		Found by
19.310 up to 23.800	10	10	«——	$(10 + 0)$
23.800 up to 28.290	21	31	«——	$(10 + 21)$
28.290 up to 32.780	20	51	«——	$(10 + 21 + 20)$
32.780 up to 37.270	15	66		
37.270 up to 41.760	8	74		
41.760 up to 46.250	4	78		
46.250 up to 50.740	2	80		
Total	80			

To begin the plotting, 10 vehicles sold for less than $23 800, so the first point in the plot is at $x = 23.80$ and $y = 10$. The coordinates of the next point are $x = 28.29$ and $y = 31$. The rest of the points are plotted and then the dots are connected to form Chart 2-11. Close the lower end of the graph by extending the line to the lower limit of the first class. To find the selling price below which half the cars sold, we draw a line from the 50-percent mark on the right-hand vertical axis over to the polygon, then drop down to the x-axis and read the selling price. The value of the x-axis is about

$30 300. To find the price below which 25 of the vehicles sold, we locate the value of 25 on the left-hand vertical axis. Next, we draw a horizontal line from the value of 25 to the polygon, and then drop down to the x-axis and read the price; it is about 27. So, we estimate that 25 of the vehicles sold for less than $27 000. We can also estimate the percentage of vehicles sold for less than $39 000. We begin by locating the value of 39 on the x-axis, then moving vertically to the polygon and then horizontally to the vertical axis on the right. The value is about 88.5 percent. We therefore conclude that 88.5 percent of the vehicles sold for less than $39 000.

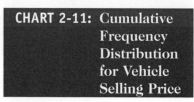

CHART 2-11: Cumulative Frequency Distribution for Vehicle Selling Price

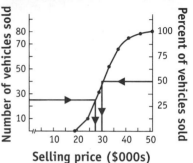

SELF-REVIEW 2-6

The following table provides information on the annual net profits of 34 small companies.

Annual Net Profits ($ thousands)	Number of Companies
65 up to 75	1
75 up to 85	6
85 up to 95	7
95 up to 105	12
105 up to 115	5
115 up to 125	3

(a) What is the table called?
(b) Develop a cumulative frequency distribution and draw a cumulative frequency polygon for the distribution.
(c) Based on the cumulative frequency polygon, find the number of companies with annual net profits of less than $105 000.

EXERCISES 2-19 TO 2-22

2-19. The following table lists the salary distribution of full-time instructors in a community college.

Salary ($)	Number of Instructors
28 000 up to 33 000	5
33 000 up to 38 000	6
38 800 up to 43 000	4
43 000 up to 48 000	3
48 000 up to 53 000	7

(a) Develop a cumulative frequency distribution.
(b) Develop a cumulative relative frequency distribution.
(c) How many instructors earn less than $33 000?
(d) Seventy-two percent of instructors earn less than what amount?

2-20. Active Gas Services mailed statements of payments due to 70 customers.
The following amounts are due:

Amount ($)	Number of Customers
70 up to 80	5
80 up to 90	20
90 up to 100	10
100 up to 110	11
110 up to 120	14
120 up to 130	10

(a) Draw a cumulative frequency polygon.
(b) What number of customers owes less than $100?

2-21. Refer to the frequency distribution of the annual number of days
the employees at the J. Morgan Manufacturing Company were absent from
work due to illness, given in Exercise 2-17.
(a) How many employees were absent less than three days annually?
How many were absent less than six days due to illness?
(b) Convert the frequency distribution to a less than cumulative frequency
distribution.
(c) Portray the cumulative distribution in the form of a less than cumulative
frequency polygon.
(d) From the cumulative frequency polygon, calculate the number of days
during which about three out of four employees were absent due to
illness?

2-22. Refer to the frequency distribution of the lead time to fill an order given in
Exercise 2-18.
(a) How many orders were filled in less than 10 days? In less than 15 days?
(b) Convert the frequency distribution to a less than cumulative frequency
distribution.
(c) Develop a less than cumulative frequency polygon.
(d) About 60 percent of the orders were filled in fewer than how many days?

2.4   GRAPHICAL METHODS FOR DESCRIBING QUALITATIVE DATA

The histogram, the stem-and-leaf display, the frequency polygon, and the cumulative
frequency polygon all are used to display a frequency distribution of quantitative data
and all have visual appeal. In this section, we will examine the simple bar chart, the
clustered bar chart, the stacked bar chart, the pie chart, and the line chart for
depicting frequency distribution of qualitative data.

SIMPLE BAR CHART

A bar chart can be used to depict any level of measurement: nominal, ordinal, interval, or ratio. (Recall our discussion of the levels of measurement of data in Chapter 1.) Let us look at the following example.

Example 2-5 | The following table shows the number of students enrolled in each of the five business programs in a certain community college in the year 2000.

Program	Students
Accounting	200
Industrial Relations	150
Financial Planning	250
Marketing	290
Management Studies	275

Represent this data using a bar chart.

Solution | The qualitative variable contains five categories: Accounting, Industrial Relations, Financial Planning, Marketing, and Management Studies. The frequency (number of students) for each category is given. As the variable is qualitative, we select a bar chart to depict the data. To draw the bar chart, we place categories on the horizontal axis at regular intervals. We mark the frequency of each category on the vertical axis. Above each category, we draw a rectangle whose height corresponds to the frequency of the category. With this chart, it is easy to see that the highest enrollment is in Marketing and the lowest is in the Industrial Relations program. This chart is vertical, but a horizontal bar chart can also be drawn by hand or using software such as Excel or Minitab. Horizontal bars are preferred for large category labels.

Chart 2-12 is produced using the data from Example 2-5 in Excel.

CLUSTERED BAR CHART

A clustered bar chart is used to summarize two or more sets of data. Consider Example 2-6.

Example 2-6 | The following table shows the number of students enrolled in five business programs in a community college in 2000 and 2001.

Program	Students (2000)	Students (2001)
Accounting	200	300
Industrial Relations	150	200
Financial Planning	250	230
Marketing	290	230
Management Studies	275	304

Construct a clustered bar chart for this data.

EXCEL CHART 2-12: Bar Chart for Enrollment in Different Programs

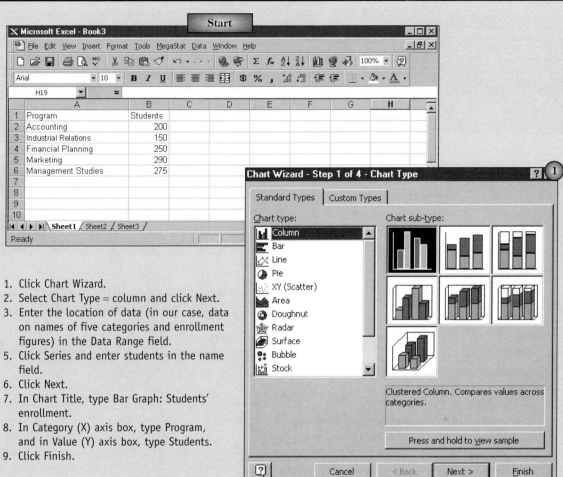

1. Click Chart Wizard.
2. Select Chart Type = column and click Next.
3. Enter the location of data (in our case, data on names of five categories and enrollment figures) in the Data Range field.
5. Click Series and enter students in the name field.
6. Click Next.
7. In Chart Title, type Bar Graph: Students' enrollment.
8. In Category (X) axis box, type Program, and in Value (Y) axis box, type Students.
9. Click Finish.

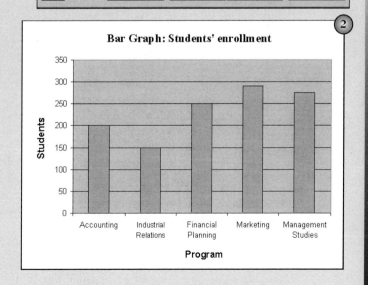

EXCEL CHART 2-13: Clustered Bar Chart of Enrollment in 2000 and 2001

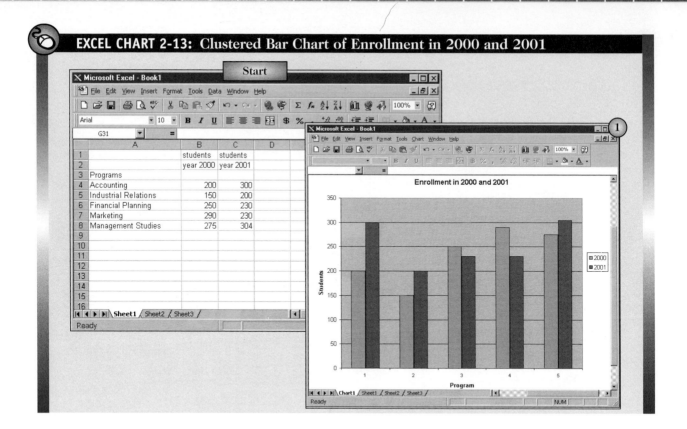

Solution

As there are two sets of data (data series) for each category, we can summarize both sets of data simultaneously using a clustered bar chart. Steps to draw a clustered bar chart are the same as for the bar chart, except that for each category we draw two rectangles: one for 2000 and the other for 2001. The height of the Accounting rectangle for 2000 shows the frequency in that program for 2000 and the height of the Accounting rectangle for 2001 shows the frequency in that program for 2001. Both rectangles are side by side without any space between them. We repeat the process for each category.

We use Excel again to draw a clustered bar chart (see Chart 2-13). The instructions are almost the same as those in the case of a simple bar chart. The only difference is that, we enter the location of the entire data (data on names of categories and enrollment figures for 2000 and 2001) in the data range field. Then when we click on Series, we give a name to each of the series (in our case, we give names *year 2000* and *year 2001*). The computer output shows enrollment in 2000 and 2001 in one frame. The frequencies (number of students) in 2000 and 2001 for each program are shown side by side with no space between bars. We can see that enrollment in three programs (Accounting, Industrial Relations, and Management Studies) increased in 2001, while enrollment in Marketing and Financial Planning has decreased in 2001,

STACKED BAR CHART

In a stacked bar chart, the values in different data sets corresponding to the same category are stacked in a single bar. For example, an Excel output for stacked bar chart for data in Example 2-6 is shown in Chart 2-14.

EXCEL CHART 2-14: Stacked Bar Chart Enrollments in 2000 and 2001

MICROSOFT EXCEL INSTRUCTIONS

1. Click Chart Wizard, then select chart subtype Stacked Column, and click Next.
2. Enter the data location in the Data Range field.
3. Click Series and type *2000* in the Name field; click Series 2 and type *2001* in the name field.
4. Click Next.
5. In the Chart Title field, type *Stacked Bar Chart of Enrollment in 2000 and 2001*.
6. Type *Program* in Category (*x*) field and *Enrollment* in the Value (*y*) field. Click on Data Label and then click the Show Value radio button.
7. Click Finish.

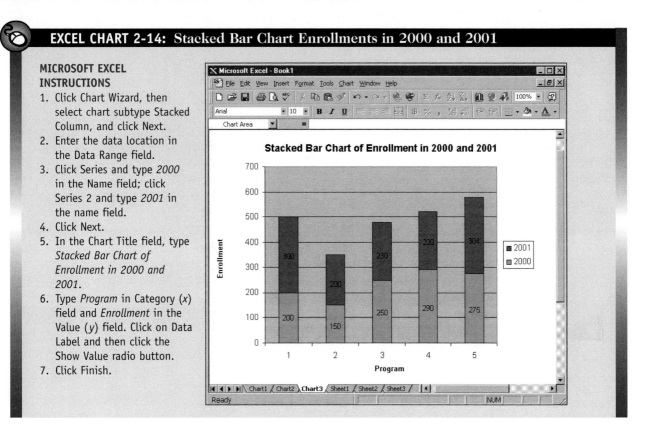

The total height of the Accounting bar is 500, which equals total number of students in Accounting for the years 2000 and 2001 combined. This is divided into two parts: the bottom part (of height 200) shows enrollment during the year 2000, and the top part (of height 300) shows enrollment during 2001. We can compare the enrollments in 2000 and 2001 for each program. We can also compare the enrollments in different programs for 2000 because the baselines of bars representing programs are all anchored to the horizontal axis. For example, the enrollment in 2000 is highest in the Marketing program and lowest in the Industrial Relations program. Due to the floating baselines of bars for 2001, we are not able to visualize the difference in the enrollments for programs in 2001.

In a variation of the stacked bar chart called a 100-percent stacked bar chart, the corresponding data sets for each category are stacked as a percentage of the total. For example, in the data from Example 2-6, the percentage enrollment in Accounting for 2000 is 40 percent (200/500)(100) of the total enrollment in Accounting. The percentage enrollment for Accounting in 2001 is 60 percent.

To produce a 100-percent stacked bar chart, the menu sequence is the same except that we select Chart *Subtype 100-percent stacked column.*

PIE CHART

A pie chart, like a bar chart, is also used to summarize qualitative data. It is used to display the percentage of relative frequency of each category by partitioning a circle into sectors. The size of a sector is proportional to the percentage of relative frequency of the corresponding category.

Example 2-7   Draw a pie chart for the data in Example 2-5 (see page 60).

Solution   To draw a pie chart, we first calculate the percentage of relative frequency for each category.

Program	Percentage Relative Frequency
Accounting	(200/1165)(100) = 17.1
Industrial Relations	(150/1165)(100) = 12.9
Financial Planning	(250/1165)(100) = 21.5
Marketing	(290/1165)(100) = 24.9
Management Studies	(275/1165)(100) = 23.6

An entire circle corresponds to 360 degrees; therefore, a one-percent relative frequency observation corresponds to 3.6 degrees (360/100). Therefore, the sector angle for the Accounting program is (3.60)(17.1) = 61.6 degrees. Using a protractor, we mark 0 degrees, 90 degrees, 270 degrees, and 360 degrees on a circle. To plot 17.1

EXCEL CHART 2-15: Pie Chart of the Enrollment in Programs

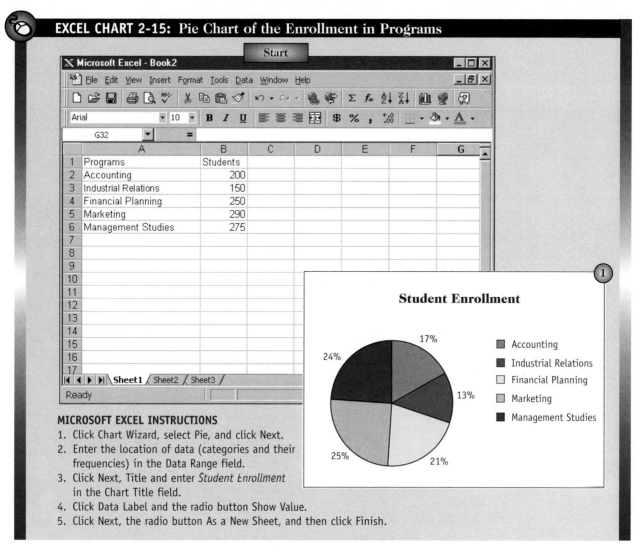

MICROSOFT EXCEL INSTRUCTIONS
1. Click Chart Wizard, select Pie, and click Next.
2. Enter the location of data (categories and their frequencies) in the Data Range field.
3. Click Next, Title and enter *Student Enrollment* in the Chart Title field.
4. Click Data Label and the radio button Show Value.
5. Click Next, the radio button As a New Sheet, and then click Finish.

percent for Accounting, we draw a line from the centre of the circle to 0 degrees on the circle and then from the centre of the circle to 61.6 degrees on the circle. The area of this "slice" represents 17.1 percent of total students enrolled in the Accounting program. Next we add 17.1 percent of students enrolled in the Accounting program to 12.9 percent of students enrolled in the Industrial Relations program; the result is 30.0 percent. The angle corresponding to 30.0 percent is (3.60)(30.0) = 108 degrees. We draw a line from the centre of the circle to 108 degrees. Now the sector formed by joining the line from the centre of the circle to 61.8 degrees and from the centre of the circle to 108.2 degrees on the circle represents 12.9 percent of students enrolled in the Industrial Relations program. We continue the process for the other programs.

Because the areas of the sectors, or "slices," represent the relative frequencies of the categories, we can quickly compare them.

We can use Excel and Minitab to draw a pie chart. The instructions for this are given in Charts 2-15 and 2-16.

MINITAB CHART 2-16: Pie Chart of the Enrollment in Programs

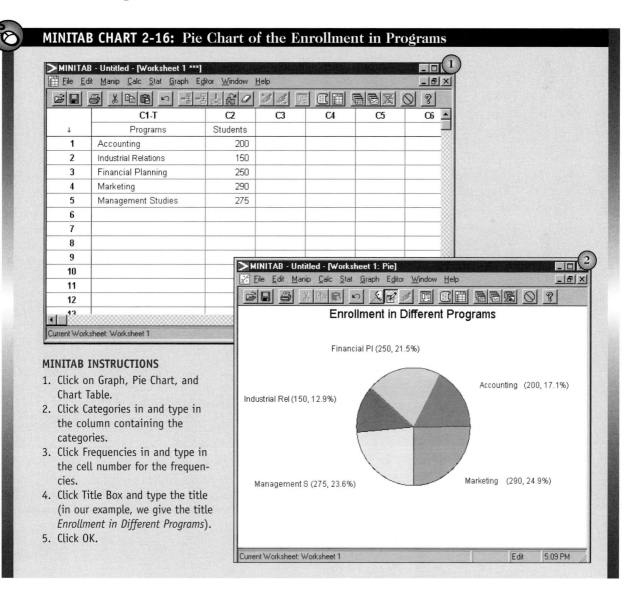

MINITAB INSTRUCTIONS
1. Click on Graph, Pie Chart, and Chart Table.
2. Click Categories in and type in the column containing the categories.
3. Click Frequencies in and type in the cell number for the frequencies.
4. Click Title Box and type the title (in our example, we give the title *Enrollment in Different Programs*).
5. Click OK.

It may be noted that in Excel, percentage values are rounded off to the nearest whole number. In Minitab, the percentage values are rounded off to one decimal place.

From the pie charts, we see that the highest enrollment is in the Marketing program and the lowest is in the Industrial Relations program. In addition, we also observe that the enrollment in Marketing is almost twice the enrollment in the Industrial Relations program. (The sector corresponding to Marketing is almost twice as big.)

A pie chart is meaningful when we do not use more than six or seven different data values. If we do, we lose clarity and cannot interpret the pie chart correctly. The other limitation of the pie chart is that we can use it for only one data series.

■ SELF-REVIEW 2-7

The total consumer credit (excluding mortgages) for the year 2000 is given below.

Financial Institution	Consumer Credit ($ millions)
Chartered Banks	119 837
Trust and Mortgage	1 959
Credit Unions	15 345
Life Insurance Companies	4 443
Finance Companies	12 734
Special-Purpose Corporations	29 008

(a) Draw a pie chart.   (b) Interpret the pie chart.

LINE CHART

A line chart is often used to depict changes in the value of a variable over a period. Time values are labelled chronologically across the horizontal axis and values of the variable along the vertical axis. A line is drawn through data points. This line chart is also nown as a time-series chart. It is widely used in newspapers and magazines to show the variation of data over a given period, for example to depict the changing values over different periods of the Dow Jones Industrial Average, the Toronto Stock Exchange S&P/TSX composite index, and the NASDAQ. The line chart is also used to display two or more data series simultaneously for a given period, for example share price and price–earning ratios, (the return on shares of a company), versus the S&P/TSX. Chart 2-17 shows the Dow Jones Industrial Average and the NASDAQ, the two most reported measures of business activity, on June 6, 2000.

CHART 2-17: Market Summary on June 6, 2000

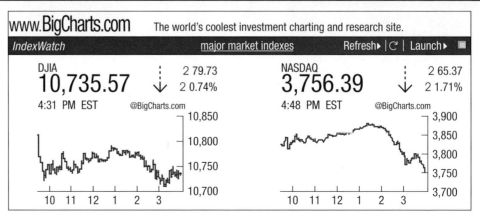

2.5   MISLEADING GRAPHS

When you purchase a computer for your home or office, it usually includes some graphics and spreadsheet software, such as Excel. This software will produce effective charts and graphs; however, you must be careful not to mislead readers or misrepresent the data. In this section we present several examples of charts and graphs that are misleading. Whenever you see a chart or graph, study it carefully. Ask yourself what the writer is trying to show you. Could the writer have any bias?

One of the easiest ways to mislead the reader is to make the range of the y-axis very small in terms of the units. A second method is to begin at some value other than 0 on the y-axis. In Chart 2-18(a), it appears there has been a dramatic increase in sales from 1989 to 2000. However, during that period, sales increased only 2 percent (from $5.0 million to $5.1 million)! In addition, observe that the y-axis does not begin at 0.

The vertical axis does not have to start at zero. It can start at some value other than zero. If we cannot detect the variation in data with zero as the starting point on the vertical axis, we should consider some value other than zero so that we can see the variation.[2]

Chart 2-18(b) gives the correct impression of the trend in sales. Sales are almost flat from 1989 to 2000; that is, there has been practically no change in sales during the 10-year period.

Without much comment, we ask you to look at each of the scenarios on page 68 and carefully decide whether the intended message is accurate.

CHART 2-18: Sales of Matsui Nine-Passenger Vans, 1989–2000

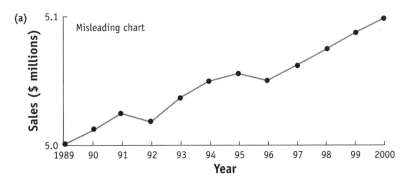

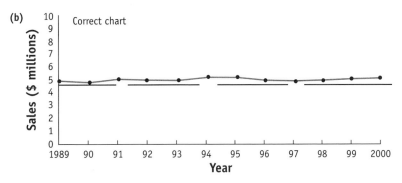

Scenario 1

The following chart was adapted from an advertisement for the new Wilson Ultra Distance golf ball. The chart shows that the new ball gets the longest distance, but what is the scale for the horizontal axis? How was the test conducted?

Maybe everybody can't hit a ball like John Daly. But everybody wants to. That's why Wilson © is introducing the new Ultra © Distance ball. Ultra Distance is the longest, most accurate ball you'll ever hit.

ULTRA © DISTANCE	540.4 m
DUNLOP © DDH IV	534.3 m
MAXFLI MD ©	522.1 m
TITLEIST © HVC	520.3 m
TOP-FLITE © Tour 90	517.2 m
TOP-FLITE © MAGNA	515.8 m

Combined yardage with a driver, #5 iron, and #9 iron, Ultra Distance is clearly measurably longer.

Wilson has totally redesigned this ball from the inside out, making Ultra Distance a major advancement in golf technology.

Scenario 2

Fibre Glass Inc., based in Red Deer, Alberta, makes and installs Fibre Tech, fibreglass coatings for swimming pools. The following chart was included in a brochure. Is the comparison fair? What is the scale for the vertical axis? Is the scale in dollars or in percent?

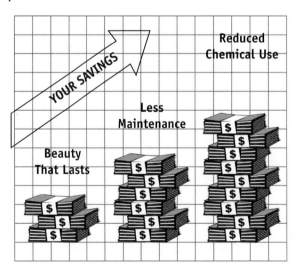

Fibre Tech Reduces Chemical Use, Saving You Time and Money.

- Saves up to 60 percent on chemical costs alone.
- Reduces water loss, which means less need to replace chemicals and up to 10-percent warmer water (reducing heating costs, too).
- Fibre Tech pays for itself in reduced maintenance and chemical costs.

   Misleading information may be given by an improper scaling used in a chart or graph where an attempt is made to change all the dimensions simultaneously in response to a change in one-dimensional data.

Again, we caution you. When you see a chart or graph, particularly as part of an advertisement, be careful. Look at the scales used on the *x*-axis and the *y*-axis.

Guidelines for Selecting a Graph to Summarize Data

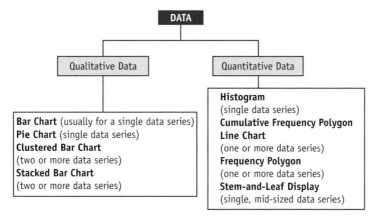

Bar and pie charts both are used to display qualitative data (single data series). Generally, a bar chart is preferred to display a single data series because it is easier to visualize changes within a data set. According to psychologists who have studied visual preferences,[3] it is more complicated to interpret the relative size of angles in a pie chart than to judge the length of the rectangles in a bar chart.

To compare two or more qualitative data sets, both clustered bar charts and stacked bar charts are used; however, in the case of stacked bar charts, it is difficult to compare data *visually* due to the floating baselines of rectangles that are stacked on the bottom rectangles.

The histogram is a more popular graphic to summarize a large, quantitative, single-data set. It is not used to compare two or more quantitative data series. Instead, frequency polygons, cumulative frequency polygons and line charts are used to compare two or more data series in a single graphic frame. The stem-and-leaf display is very convenient for mid-sized quantitative data.

EXERCISES 2-23 TO 2-28

2-23. A small-business consultant is investigating the performance of several companies. The sales in 2000 (in thousands of dollars) for the selected companies are listed below. The consultant wants to include a chart in a report comparing the sales of the six companies. Use a bar chart to compare the fourth-quarter sales of these corporations and write a brief report summarizing the bar chart.

Corporation	Fourth-Quarter Sales ($ thousands)
Hoden Building Products	1 645.2
J & R Printing, Inc.	4 757.0
Long Bay Concrete Construction	8 913.0
Mancell Electric and Plumbing	627.1
Maxwell Heating and Air Conditioning	24 612.0
Mizella Roofing & Sheet Metal	191.9

2-24. The Gentle Corporation in Montreal, Quebec sells fashion apparel for men and women and a broad range of other related products. It serves customers in the United States and Canada by mail. Listed below are the net sales from 1996 to 2001. Draw a line chart depicting the net sales over the period.

Year	Net Sales ($ millions)
1996	525.00
1997	535.00
1998	600.50
1999	625.80
2000	645.70
2001	758.75

2-25. The following are long-term business credit amounts ($ millions) from 1996 to 2000 (Canada). Draw a line chart depicting the long-term business credit for the period.

Year	Long-Term Business Credit ($ millions)
1996	357 946
1997	392 846
1998	432 909
1999	470 250
2000	504 850

Source: Adapted from Statistics Canada, Bank of Canada, CANSIM, Matrix 2567

2-26. The following are the unemployment rates in Canada from 1996 to 2000. Draw a line chart for the unemployment rate for the period 1996 to 2000. Describe the trend for the unemployment rate.

Year	Unemployment Rate (%)
1996	9.6
1997	9.1
1998	8.3
1999	7.6
2000	6.8

Source: Adapted from Statistics Canada, CANSIM, Matrix 3472; and Catalogue No. 71-529-XPB

2-27. The following are gross domestic products (GDP) at market prices from 1990 to 2000. Draw a line chart to show the highest and lowest GDP at market prices.

Year	GDP at market prices ($ millions)
1990	705 464
1991	692 247
1992	698 544
1993	714 583
1994	748 350
1995	769 082
1996	780 916
1997	815 013
1998	842 002
1999	880 254
2000	921 485

Source: The Centre for the Study of Living Standards: www.csls.ca

2-28. The following table shows the gross domestic product (GDP) for eight countries in 2000. Develop a bar chart and summarize the results.

Country	GDP ($ trillions)
USA	9.3
Japan	3.9
Germany	2.2
France	1.5
UK	1.4
Italy	1.2
Canada	0.7

CHAPTER OUTLINE

I.   A *frequency distribution* is a grouping of data into mutually exclusive categories showing the number of observations in each category.
   A. The steps in constructing a frequency distribution are:
       1. Decide how many classes you need.
       2. Determine the class width or interval.
       3. Set the individual class limits.
       4. Tally the raw data into classes.
       5. Count the number of tallies in each class.
   B. The *class frequency* is the number of observations in each class.
   C. The *class interval* is the difference between the lower limit and the upper limit of a class.
   D. The *class midpoint* is halfway between the lower limit and the upper limit of a class.

II. A *relative frequency distribution* shows the fraction of the observations in each class.

III. A *stem-and-leaf display* provides a frequency distribution of a data set and at the same time shows a graphic similar to a histogram.
   A. The leading digit is the stem and the trailing digits are the leaves.
   B. The advantages of the stem-and-leaf display over a frequency distribution include:
      1. The identity of each observation is not lost.
      2. The digits themselves give a picture of the distribution.

IV. There are two methods for graphically portraying a frequency distribution.
   A. A *histogram* portrays the number of frequencies in each class in the form of rectangles.
   B. A *frequency polygon* consists of line segments connecting the points formed by the intersections of the class midpoints and the class frequencies.

V. A *cumulative frequency polygon* shows the number of observations below a certain value.

CHAPTER EXERCISES 2-29 TO 2-51

2-29. A data set consists of 83 observations. How many classes would you recommend for a frequency distribution?

2-30. A data set consists of 145 observations that range from 56 to 490. What size class interval would you recommend?

2-31. The following is the number of minutes it takes to commute from home to work for a group of automobile executives.

| 28 | 25 | 48 | 37 | 41 | 19 | 32 | 26 | 16 | 23 | 23 | 29 | 36 |
| 31 | 26 | 21 | 32 | 25 | 31 | 43 | 35 | 42 | 38 | 33 | 28 | |

(a) How many classes would you recommend?
(b) What class interval would you suggest?
(c) What would you recommend as the lower limit of the first class?
(d) Organize the data into a frequency distribution.
(e) Comment on the shape of the frequency distribution.

2-32. The following data are the weekly amounts (in dollars) spent on groceries for a sample of households. This data is also found on the accompanying CD in Exercise 2-32.xls.

271	363	159	76	227	337	295	319	250	279	205	279
266	199	177	162	232	303	192	181	321	309	246	278
50	41	335	116	100	151	240	474	297	170	188	320
429	294	570	342	279	235	434	123	325			

(a) How many classes would you recommend?
(b) What class interval would you suggest?
(c) What would you recommend as the lower limit of the first class?
(d) Organize the data into a frequency distribution.

2-33. The following stem-and-leaf display shows the number of minutes spent per week watching daytime TV for a sample of university students.

2	0	0 5
3	1	0
6	2	1 3 7
10	3	0 0 2 9
13	4	4 9 9
24	5	0 0 1 5 5 6 6 7 7 9 9
30	6	0 2 3 4 6 8
(7)	7	1 3 6 6 7 8 9
33	8	0 1 5 5 8
28	9	1 1 2 2 3 7 9
21	10	0 2 2 3 6 7 8 9 9
12	11	2 4 5 7
8	12	4 6 6 8
4	13	2 4 9
1	14	5

(a) How many students were studied?
(b) How many observations are in the second class?
(c) What is the smallest value? the largest value?
(d) List the actual values in the fourth row.
(e) How many students watched less than 60 minutes of TV?
(f) How many students watched 100 minutes or more of TV?
(g) What is the middle value?
(h) How many students watched at least 60 minutes but less than 100 minutes?

2-34. The following stem-and-leaf display reports the number of orders received per day by a mail-order firm.

1	9	1
2	10	2
5	11	2 3 5
7	12	6 9
8	13	2
11	14	1 3 5
15	15	1 2 2 9
22	16	2 2 6 6 7 7 8
27	17	0 1 5 9 9
(11)	18	0 0 0 1 3 3 4 6 7 9 9
17	19	0 3 3 4 6
12	20	4 6 7 9
8	21	0 1 7 7
4	22	4 5
2	23	1 7

(a) How many days were studied?
(b) How many observations are in the fourth class?
(c) What is the smallest value and what is the largest value?

(d) List the actual values in the sixth class.
(e) How many days did the firm receive less than 140 orders?
(f) How many days did the firm receive 200 or more orders?
(g) On how many days did the firm receive 180 orders?
(h) What is the middle value?

2-35. The following histogram shows the scores on the first statistics exam.

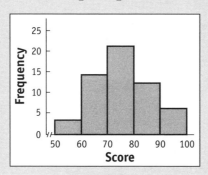

(a) How many students took the exam?
(b) What is the class interval?
(c) What is the class midpoint for the first class?
(d) How many students earned a score of less than 70?

2-36. The following chart summarizes the selling price of homes sold last month in Victoria, B.C.

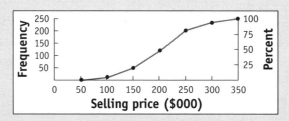

(a) What is the chart called?
(b) How many homes were sold during the last month?
(c) What is the class interval?
(d) About 75 percent of the homes sold for less than what amount?
(e) 175 of the homes sold for less than what amount?

2-37. A chain of ski and sportswear shops catering to beginning skiers, headquartered in Banff, Alberta, plans to conduct a study of how much a beginning skier spends on his or her initial purchase of equipment and supplies. Based on these figures, they want to explore the possibility of offering combinations, such as a pair of boots and a pair of skis, to induce customers to buy more. A sample of their cash-register receipts revealed these initial purchases (in dollars):

140	82	265	168	90	114	172	230	142	86	125	235
212	171	149	156	162	118	139	149	132	105	162	126
216	195	127	161	135	172	220	229	129	87	128	126
175	127	149	126	121	118	172	126				

(a) Arrive at a suggested class interval. Use five classes, and let the lower limit of the first class be $80.
(b) What would be a better class interval?
(c) Organize the data into a frequency distribution.
(d) Interpret your findings.

 2-38. The numbers of shareholders for a selected group of large companies (in thousands) are listed in Exercise 2-38.xls on the CD-ROM accompanying the text.
    The numbers of shareholders are to be organized into a frequency distribution and several graphs drawn to portray the distribution.
(a) Using seven classes and a lower limit of 130, construct a frequency distribution.
(b) Portray the distribution in the form of a frequency polygon.
(c) Portray the distribution in a less than cumulative frequency polygon.
(d) Based on the polygon, three out of four (75 percent) of the companies have how many shareholders or fewer?
(e) Write a brief analysis of the number of shareholders based on the frequency distribution and graphs.

2-39. The following is the list of top-selling drugs in 2002. Draw an appropriate chart to portray the data.

Products	Sales ($ billions)
Lipitor (cholesterol-reducing)	5.7
Zocor (cholesterol-reducing)	5.3
Claritin-family (anti-histamine)	4.2
Norvasc (calcium-antagonist)	4.1
Losec (anti-ulcerant)	3.6

2-40. The Midland National Bank selected a sample of 40 student chequing accounts. Below are their end-of-the-month balances.

404	74	234	149	279	215	123	55	43	321	87	234
68	489	57	185	141	758	72	863	703	125	350	440
37	252	27	521	302	127	968	712	503	489	327	608
358	425	303	203								

(a) Tally the data into a frequency distribution using $100 as a class interval and $0 as the starting point.
(b) Draw a cumulative frequency polygon.
(c) The bank considers any student with an ending balance of $400 or more a "preferred customer." Estimate the percentage of preferred customers.
(d) The bank is also considering a service charge to the lowest 10 percent of the ending balances. What would you recommend as the cut-off point between those who have to pay a service charge and those who do not?

2-41. The following are grades of students in Math 1021 in 2002.

57	81	47	87	21	47	57	64	86	41	84	48	80	58	88
73	30	64	84	77	28	95	40	42	10	72	61	13	56	47
55	48	60	99	88	86	95	49							

(a) Construct a stem-and-leaf display.
(b) Summarize your conclusion.

2-42. A recent study of home technologies reported the number of hours of personal computer usage per week for a sample of 60 persons. Excluded from the study were people who worked out of their homes and used the computer as a part of their work.

9.3	5.3	6.3	8.8	6.5	0.6	5.2	6.6	9.3	4.3	6.3	2.1	2.7	0.4
3.7	3.3	1.1	2.7	6.7	6.5	4.3	9.7	7.7	5.2	1.7	8.5	4.2	5.5
5.1	5.6	5.4	4.8	2.1	10.1	1.3	5.6	2.4	2.4	4.7	1.7	2.0	6.7
1.1	6.7	2.2	2.6	9.8	6.4	4.9	5.2	4.5	9.3	7.9	4.6	4.3	4.5
9.2	8.5	6.0	8.1										

(a) Organize the data into a frequency distribution. How many classes would you suggest? What value would you suggest for a class interval?
(b) Draw a histogram. Interpret your result.

2-43. Merrill Lynch recently completed a study regarding the size of investment portfolios (stocks, bonds, mutual funds, and certificates of deposit) for a sample of clients in the 40 to 50 age group. Listed below are the values of all the investments for the 70 participants in the study.

669.9	7.5	77.2	7.5	125.7	516.9	219.9	645.2
301.9	235.4	716.4	145.3	26.6	187.2	315.5	89.2
136.4	616.9	440.6	408.2	34.4	296.1	185.4	526.3
380.7	3.3	363.2	51.9	52.2	107.5	82.9	63.0
228.6	308.7	126.7	430.3	82.0	227.0	321.1	403.4
39.5	124.3	118.1	23.9	352.8	156.7	276.3	23.5
31.3	301.2	35.7	154.9	174.3	100.6	236.7	171.9
221.1	43.4	212.3	243.3	315.4	5.9	1002.2	171.7
295.7	437.0	87.8	302.1	268.1	899.5		

(a) Organize the data into a frequency distribution. How many classes would you suggest? What value would you suggest for a class interval?
(b) Draw a histogram. Interpret your result.

2-44. The following are gross domestic products (GDP) per head in the following European countries (in dollars). Develop a bar chart depicting this information.

Country	GDP per head ($)
Austria	26 740
Denmark	32 576
France	24 956
Germany	27 337
Greece	11 860
Norway	35 853
Turkey	3 120

2-45. Care Heart Association reported the following percentage breakdown of expenses. Draw a pie chart depicting the information. Interpret the results.

Category	Percent
Research	32.3
Public Health Education	23.5
Community Service	12.6
Fundraising	12.1
Professional and Educational Training	10.9
Management and General	8.6

2-46. In its 2002 annual report, Schering-Plough Corporation reported the income, in millions of dollars, for 1995 to 2002 as listed below. Develop a line chart depicting the results and comment on your findings.

Year	Income ($ millions)
1995	1053
1996	1213
1997	1444
1998	1756
1999	2110
2000	2900
2001	3595
2002	4550

2-47. The following table shows Canada's exports in merchandise trade with its principal trading partners:

Principal Trading Partner	December 1999 ($ millions)	December 2000 ($ millions)
USA	27 243	31 876
Japan	764	824
European Union	1 616	1 896
Other OECD Countries	728	682
All Other Countries	1 510	1 572

Source: Adapted from Statistics Canada, CANSIM, Matrix 3618

(a) Draw a clustered bar graph.
(b) Name the trading partner to whom we exported more than any other trading partner in 2000.

2-48. The following is the population distribution of Canada by sex from 1996 to 2000. Draw a stacked bar graph and comment on your findings.

Year	Male	Female
1996	14 691 777	14 980 115
1997	14 850 874	15 136 340
1998	14 981 482	15 266 467
1999	15 104 717	15 388 716
2000	15 232 909	15 517 178

Source: Adapted from Statistics Canada, CANSIM, Matrix 6213

2-49. Cash receipts from milk and cream sold from farms in six provinces in 2001 are given below. Draw a pie chart to display the data set.

Province	Cash Receipts ($ thousands)
Alberta	318 454
B.C.	336 977
Manitoba	154 029
N.B.	69 041
Nova Scotia	90 368
P.E.I.	50 987

Source: Adapted from Statistics Canada, CANSIM, Matrices 5650–5651; and Catalogue No. 23-001-XIB

2-50. The following are exports of goods to the Organization for Economic Co-operation and Development (OECD[4]) from 1995 to 2000. Draw a line chart and describe the trend in exports of goods to the OECD.

Year	Export of Goods ($ millions)
1995	4563.4
1996	5087.8
1997	8033.5
1998	7560.4
1999	7160.9
2000	8159.3

Source: Adapted from Statistics Canada, CANSIM, Matrices 3651 and 3685

2-51. The following table shows the volume (in kilolitres) of milk and cream sold from farms in 2001 in six Canadian provinces. Draw a simple bar chart to depict the data.

Province	Volume of Milk and Cream Sold from Farms (kL)
NFLD	33 583
P.E.I.	94 472
Nova Scotia	173 985
N.B.	134 428
Manitoba	294 674
Alberta	208 198

Source: Adapted from Statistics Canada, CANSIM, Matrices 5650–5651; and Catalogue No. 23 001 XIB

www.exercises.ca 2-52 TO 2-53

2-52. Go to the Web site: www.statcan.ca. Click English, Canadian Statistics, Education, Graduates, and Secondary School Graduates. Draw a bar chart depicting the number of school graduates in each province. Summarize your findings.

2-53. Go to the Statistics Canada Web site (www.statcan.ca) and click English / Canadian Statistics / Labour, Employment, and Unemployment / Earnings. Select two data series for a given category and draw a clustered bar graph.

■━━ COMPUTER DATA EXERCISES 2-54 TO 2-57

2-54. The file Exercise 2-32.xls contains the amount spent on groceries by households.
(a) How many classes would you recommend?
(b) What class interval or width would you suggest?
(c) Organize the data into a frequency distribution.
(d) Use Excel to draw a histogram. Use the number of classes you recommended. Describe the shape of the histogram.
(e) Draw the histogram using Excel. Let Excel decide the number of classes. Describe the shape of the histogram.

2-55. Use the data in the file Exercise 2-32.xls to draw a stem-and-leaf diagram. Use Minitab. Use the same data to draw a histogram. Do you find the stem-and-leaf diagram more informative than the histogram? Explain.

2-56. Refer to the data in file OECD.xls on the CD, which reports information on census, economic, and business data for 29 countries. Develop a stem-and-leaf diagram for the variable regarding the percentage of the workforce that is over 65 years of age. Are there any outliers? Briefly describe the data.

2-57. The file Exercise 2-57.xls contains the amount of money spent by beginning skiers on the purchase of equipment and supplies.
(a) Draw a cumulative frequency polygon using Excel. Do not specify the Bin.
(b) Estimate the proportion of the amount of money spent on the purchase of equipment and supplies that is less than $143.
(c) How many skiers spent less than $173.50 on the purchase of equipment and supplies?

CHAPTER 2   ANSWERS TO SELF-REVIEW

2-1. (a) The raw data.

(b)

Commission	Number of Salespeople
1400 up to 1500	2
1500 up to 1600	5
1600 up to 1700	3
1700 up to 1800	1
Total	11

(c) Class frequencies.
(d) The largest concentration of commissions is in the class $1500 up to $1600. The smallest commission is about $1400 and the largest is about $1800.

2-2. (a) 5, ($2^4 = 16$, less than 24, and $2^5 = 32$, more than 24. Hence, $k = 5$ is suggested).

(b) 10, found by rounding up $\left[\dfrac{71-25}{5}\right] = 9.2$.

(c)

Class	Frequency
23 up to 33	3
33 up to 43	1
43 up to 53	3
53 up to 63	9
63 up to 73	8
Total	24

2-3. (a) 21
(b) 26.3 percent
(c) 17.5 percent (found by $(0.1 + 0.05 + 0.025) \times 100$)

2-4.

7	7
8	0 0 1 3 4 8 8
9	1 2 5 6 6 8 9
10	1 2 4 8
11	2 6

(a) 8
(b) 10.1, 10.2, 10.4, 10.8
(c) 11.6 and 7.7

2-5. (a)

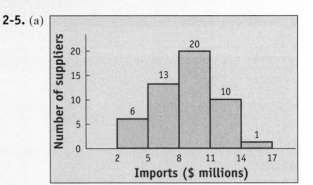

(b)

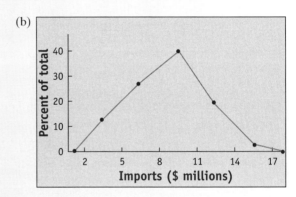

(c) The smallest annual sales volume of imports by a supplier is about $2 million, the highest about $17 million. The concentration is between $8 million and $11 million.

2-6. (a) A frequency distribution.

(b)

Annual Net Profits ($000)	Cumulative Number
65 up to 75	1
75 up to 85	7
85 up to 95	14
95 up to 105	26
105 up to 115	31
115 up to 125	34

(c)

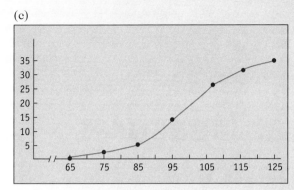

The number of companies with annual net profits of less than \$105 000 is about 26.

2-7. (a)

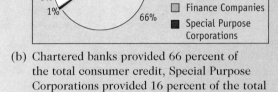

(b) Chartered banks provided 66 percent of the total consumer credit, Special Purpose Corporations provided 16 percent of the total consumer credit, and so on.

CHAPTER 3

Describing Data: Measures of Central Tendency

GOALS

When you have completed this chapter, you will be able to:

- Calculate the arithmetic mean, the weighted mean, the median, the mode, and the geometric mean of a given data set

- Identify the relative positions of the arithmetic mean, median, and mode for both symmetric and skewed distributions

- Point out the proper uses and common misuses of each measure

- Explain your choice of the measure of central tendency of data

- Explain the result of your analysis.

ARISTOTLE (384–322 B.C.)

Aristotle, the scientist and philosopher, was born in Stagirus in northern Greece. His father, Nicomachus, a family physician of Amyntas II, the King of Macedonia, died when Aristotle was only 10 years old. Aristotle was educated at Plato's Academy in Athens, and later became tutor to Alexander the Great. He is said to have written more than 150 treatises, only 50 of which have been found. He wrote extensively on a variety of subjects including philosophy and logic, physics and metaphysics, biology and psychology, and ethics and political science. Historians of science and philosophy consider Aristotle one of the greatest philosophers and scientists, the man who determined the orientation and content of Western intellectual history. We encourage you to explore the magnitude of Aristotle's achievements at www.utm.edu or www.wsu.edu.

The concept of averages is likely to have existed from antiquity. Buddha's "Middle Path" and Aristotle's "golden"[1] means for a "happy life" provide ample evidence of existence of the concept in 400–600 B.C. Aristotle used the concept of mean to justify a balance of the extremes in real life for leading a happy life. In his *Nicomachean Ethics* (Moral Virtues, Lecture VI), he advocates the use of relative means (means of ratios): "means in regards to us" of qualitative variables. According to Aristotle, "Virtue is a mean between two vices: of that which is according to excess and of that which is according to defect." He therefore advocates courage as the mean of rashness and cowardice; liberality as the mean of extravagance and stinginess and temperance as the mean of pleasure and pain. Aristotle similarly discusses arithmetic mean for quantitative variables: "For example, if ten be taken as many and two as few, then six will be the mean on the part of things because six both exceeds and is exceeded by an equal amount."

Modern pioneers responsible for advancing the concept of averages include Simpson (1710–1757), Lagrange (1736–1813), Quetelet (1796–1874), and Cournot (1801–1877). The interested reader is referred to Stigler (1986), Johnson and Kotz (ed.) 1997, and Hald (1998).

■ INTRODUCTION

Chapter 2 began our study of descriptive statistics. To transform raw or ungrouped quantitative data into a meaningful form, we organized the data into a frequency distribution and portrayed it graphically in a histogram or a frequency polygon. We also discussed other tools for describing data, such as stem-and-leaf displays, line charts, bar charts, and pie charts.

In this chapter we develop methods to describe data by a single value. We refer to this single value as a **measure of central tendency**.

> **Measure of central tendency**   A single value that summarizes a set of data; it locates the centre of the data values.

You are familiar with the concept of an average—the sports world is full of them. Toronto Raptor Vince Carter's scoring average in 2000 was 28.5. Toronto Blue Jay Carlos Delgado's batting average in 2001 was 0.279. Some other averages are:

- Average expenditure per household in Canada on food (1999): $6101
- Average price of a house in Ottawa (2000): $136 000
- Average highway fuel consumption of the mid-size Honda Accord (model year 2001): 7.6 L/100 km

There is not just one measure of central tendency; in fact, there are many. We will consider five: the arithmetic mean, the weighted mean, the median, the mode, and the geometric mean. We will begin by discussing the most widely used and widely reported measure of central tendency, the arithmetic mean.

■ 3.1   THE ARITHMETIC MEAN

POPULATION MEAN

Many studies involve all the values in a population. As an example, suppose our population, (the entire data of interest) is the placement-test marks of all students in a local community college in the fall of 2001. Suppose the arithmetic mean of the marks of *all* these students in the fall of 2001 is 67.8. Then the value 67.8 is the arithmetic mean of the population, or the *population mean*. As another example, suppose our population (the entire data of interest) is the amount of tips earned by *all* 15 waiters employed by a local restaurant during December 2001. Suppose the arithmetic mean of the tips they earned during December 2001 was $4500. This is again a population mean because it is the arithmetic mean of the entire population data.

For raw data—that is, data that have not been grouped in a frequency distribution—the population mean is the sum of all the values in the population divided by the number of values in the population. To find the population mean, we use the following formula.

$$\text{Population mean} = \frac{\text{Sum of all the values in the population}}{\text{Number of values in the population}}$$

Instead of writing out in words the full directions for computing the population mean (or any other measure), it is more convenient to use the shorthand symbols of

STATISTICS IN ACTION

The Average Canadian

Have you met the average Canadian man? Well, his name is Michael Baldwin. He is 38 years old, 177 cm tall, and weighs 78 kg. The average man exercises three or more times per week, earns $24 340 per year, drinks about 682 mL of beer per day, and believes that married couples divorce due to the abusive behaviour of their partners.

Sara Stewart is the average Canadian woman. She is 38 years old, 163 cm tall, and weighs 72 kg. The average woman exercises three or more times per week, earns $18 399 per year, drinks 142 mL of red wine per day, and believes that married couples divorce due to the abusive behaviour of their partners.

Is Michael or Sara really an "average" man or an "average" woman, or would it be better to refer him or her as a "typical" Canadian person? Would you expect to find a person with all these characteristics?

mathematics. The mean of a population using mathematical symbols is:

Population Mean	$\mu = \dfrac{\Sigma x}{N}$	**3-1**

where:

μ represents the population mean. It is the Greek lower case letter *mu*.

N is the number of items in the population.

x represents any particular value in the population.

Σ is the Greek capital letter *sigma* and indicates the operation of adding.

Σx is the sum of all the values, x, in the population.

Any descriptive measure of a population characteristic is called a **parameter**. The mean of a population is a parameter.

 Parameter   A descriptive measure of population characteristics.

Example 3-1

Suppose our entire data of interest is the annual salaries of all the five deans in a local community college which are $89 000, $80 000, $78 000, $82 000, and $92 000.

Are the data a sample or a population? What is the arithmetic mean salary?

Solution

The data are a population, because it is our entire data of interest. We add the salaries of all the deans. The total salary is $421 000. Divide the total salary by the number of deans; the arithmetic mean is $84 200. Using Formula 3-1:

$$\mu = \frac{89\ 000 + 80\ 000 + 78\ 000 + 82\ 000 + 92\ 000}{5} = \$84\ 200$$

The average salary of deans is $84 200. Because we considered the salaries of *all* deans in the community college, the value is considered a population parameter.

SAMPLE MEAN

A researcher does not always have access to all the values in a population. In such a case, if one is interested in the value of any population parameter, then this value has to be estimated from a sample of observations drawn from the population. The quality-assurance department, for example, needs to be assured that the ball bearings being produced have an acceptable outside diameter. Therefore, a sample of five bearings might be selected and the outside diameters of the five bearings calculated. We are now interested in obtaining from this sample data a value that is a good estimate of the arithmetic mean of the outside diameters of all the bearings being produced (the population mean). One such value obtained from the sample is the mean of the sample, or the *sample mean*.

For a raw—that is, ungrouped—sample data, *the sample mean is the sum of all the values in the data divided by the total number of values in the sample*.

$$\text{Sample mean} = \frac{\text{Sum of all the values in the sample}}{\text{Number of values in the sample}}$$

The mean of a sample and the mean of a population are computed in the same way, but the shorthand notation used is different. The formula for the mean of a *sample* is:

| Sample Mean | $\bar{x} = \dfrac{\Sigma x}{n}$ | 3-2 |

Where $\bar{x}$ stands for the sample mean. It is read "*x*-bar." The lower case n is the number of data values in the sample.

The sample mean calculated from sample data is used as an estimate of the population mean. Any descriptive measure of sample data that is used to estimate the value of a population parameter is called a **statistic**. If the mean of the outside diameters of a sample of ball bearings is 1.525 cm, then 1.525 cm is the value of the sample mean, which is a *statistic*.

 Statistic   A descriptive measure of sample data that is used to estimate the value of a population parameter.

Example 3-2

The Merrill Lynch Global Fund specializes in the long-term obligations of foreign countries. We are interested in the interest rate on these obligations. A random sample of six bonds revealed the following:

Issue	Interest Rate (%)
Australian government bonds	9.50
Belgian government bonds	7.25
Canadian government bonds	6.50
French government "B-TAN"	4.75
Buoni Poliennali de Tesora (Italian government bonds)	12.00
Bonos del Estado (Spanish government bonds)	8.30

What is the arithmetic mean of this sample of interest rates on long-term obligations?

Solution

Using Formula 3-2, the sample mean is:

$$\text{Sample mean} = \frac{\text{Sum of all the values in the sample}}{\text{Number of all the values in the sample}}$$

$$\bar{x} = \frac{\Sigma x}{n} = \frac{9.50 + 7.25 + \cdots + 8.30}{6} = \frac{48.3}{6} = 8.05$$

The arithmetic mean of the sample of interest rates on long-term obligations is 8.05 percent.

PROPERTIES OF THE ARITHMETIC MEAN

The arithmetic mean is the most widely used measure of central tendency. It has five important properties:

1. Every set of interval-level and ratio-level data has a mean. (Recall from Chapter 1 that interval- and ratio-level data include such data as ages, incomes, and weights.)
2. All the values are included in computing the mean.

3. A set of data has only one mean. The mean is unique.

4. The mean is a useful measure for comparing two or more populations.

5. The arithmetic mean is the only measure of location where *the sum of the deviations of data values from the mean is always zero*. Expressed symbolically: $\sum(x - \bar{x}) = 0$ (for sample data) and $\sum(x - \mu) = 0$ (for population data).

   As an example, the mean of 3, 8, and 4 is 5. Then:

$$\sum(x - \bar{x}) = (3 - 5) + (8 - 5) + (4 - 5)$$
$$= -2 + 3 - 1$$
$$= 0$$

MEAN AS A BALANCE POINT

We can consider the mean as a balance point for a set of data. To illustrate, suppose we had a long board with the numbers $1, 2, 3, \ldots, n$ evenly spaced on it. Suppose three gold bars of equal weight were placed on the board at numbers 3, 4, and 8, and the balance point was set at 5, the mean of the three numbers. We would find that the board balanced perfectly! The deviations below the mean (-3) are equal to the deviations above the mean $(+3)$. Shown schematically:

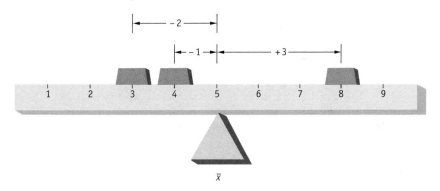

DISADVANTAGES OF THE MEAN

Mean is unduly affected by unusually large or small values. Recall that the arithmetic mean uses all values of a population or sample in its computation. If one or more values are either extremely large or small, the mean might not be an appropriate average to represent the data set. Let us take an example. The earnings (in $US) of a sample of five of the world's 50 most valuable athletes are $1.4 million, $1.5 million, $1.4 million, $1.2 million, and $63.1 million. The sample mean earning is $13.72 million. Obviously, this sample mean earning is not a representative earning of the five athletes. The earning of one athlete ($63.1 million) is unduly affecting the mean earning. A value such as $63.1 million is known as an *outlier*. The presence of an outlier in a data set may be due to incorrect recording; we should first check the data set. If the recording is incorrect, we should remove the incorrect data from the data set and then conduct the statistical analysis. If the recording is correct, we must *not remove* the extreme value from the data set. It does provide important information. For example, in this case it tells us that one of the athletes is earning much more than the rest of the athletes. In preparing a summary report, we can say that the earning of one athlete in the data set has significantly affected the mean.

The size of our data set in this case is small (five). However, when we have a large data set, the effect of an outlier on the mean is less significant.

■ SELF-REVIEW 3-1

1. The annual incomes of a sample of four middle management employees at Westinghouse Communications Canada are $62 900, $69 000, $58 300, and $76 800.
   (a) Write the formula for the sample mean.
   (b) Find the sample mean.
   (c) Is the mean you calculated in (b) a statistic or a parameter? Why?
   (d) What is your best estimate of the population mean?

2. The course grades of all the students in advanced Computer Science 411, which forms our population, are 95, 87, 66, 98, 56, and 12.
   (a) Write the formula for the population mean.
   (b) Calculate the population mean.
   (c) Is the mean you calculated in (b) a statistic or a parameter? Why?
   (d) Do you think that the mean is an appropriate measure of central tendency for this data set? Justify your answer.

3. Do you think that the arithmetic mean calculated in (1) has all the properties of the arithmetic mean discussed in this chapter? Explain.

EXERCISES 3-1 TO 3-10

3-1.   Compute the mean of the following population data: 6, 3, 5, 7, 6.

3-2.   Compute the mean of the following population data: 7, 5, 7, 3, 7, 4.

3-3.   (a) Compute the mean of the following sample data: 5, 9, 4, 10.
       (b) Show that $\sum(x - \bar{x}) = 0$.

3-4.   (a) Compute the mean of the following sample data: 1.3, 7.0, 3.6, 4.1, 5.0.
       (b) Show that $\sum(x - \bar{x}) = 0$.

3-5.   Compute the mean of the following sample data: 16.25, 12.91, 14.58.

3-6.   Compute the mean hourly wage paid to carpenters who earned the following hourly wages: $15.40, $20.10, $18.75, $22.76, $30.67, $18.00.

3-7.   The weekly earnings of a sample of five employees in a logging and forestry company are: $775.70, $1025.51, $702.50, $825.67, $1112.94.

       (a) Calculate the arithmetic mean of the data.
       (b) Is the calculated mean a statistic or a parameter?

3-8.   The accounting department at a mail-order company counted the following numbers of daily incoming calls to the company's toll-free number during the first seven days in May 1998: 14, 24, 19, 31, 36, 26, 17.
       (a) Calculate the arithmetic mean of the data.
       (b) Is the mean calculated in part (a) a statistic or a parameter?

3-9. In 2000, five families in each of Toronto and Ottawa were randomly selected and requested to keep a record of the amount (to the nearest dollar) spent on food for 2001. The data obtained were as follows:

Toronto Food Expenses ($)	Ottawa Food Expenses ($)
6010	7050
6050	8075
5900	6500
4000	7500
8000	7008

(a) Calculate the arithmetic mean of each of the sample data for Toronto and Ottawa.

(b) Are the means statistics or parameters?

(c) If household expenditure were the only criterion for selecting a city in which to work, would you prefer Toronto or Ottawa? Explain.

3-10. Statistics Canada reported that in Prince Edward Island in 1999 the sample mean expenditure on household repairs and renovations was $1811. The sample size was 37 880. In Nova Scotia, the sample mean expenditure on household repairs and renovations was $1654 and the sample size was 255 620. In New Brunswick, the sample mean expenditure on household repairs and renovations was $1332 and the sample size was 212 870. (Source: Statistics Canada, Catalogue No. 62-201-XIB 1999.)

(a) Based on the sample data, which province seems to have the highest mean expenditure on household repairs and renovations?

(b) Calculate the total expenditure on household repairs and renovations in the sample for each province. Describe the property of the mean used in this case.

(c) Write the formula you used in (b).

3.2   THE WEIGHTED MEAN

We shall now generalize the concept of arithmetic mean to that of *weighted mean*. Let us start with an example. Suppose the nearby Burger King sold small, medium, and large-sized soft drinks for $0.99, $1.39, and $1.59, respectively. During the last one hour, 10 drinks were sold—3 small, 4 medium and 3 large. To find the mean selling price of the 10 drinks sold during the last one hour, we could use Formula 3-1.

$$\mu = \frac{0.99 + 0.99 + 0.99 + 1.39 + 1.39 + 1.39 + 1.39 + 1.59 + 1.59 + 1.59}{10} = 1.33$$

The mean selling price of the 10 drinks sold during the last one hour is $1.33.

An easier way to compute the above mean selling price is as follows: we multiply each observation by the number of times it happens. Thus,

$$\mu = \frac{3(\$0.99) + 4(\$1.39) + 3(\$1.59)}{10} = \frac{\$13.30}{10} = \$1.33$$

We shall refer to this as a weighted mean of the values $0.99, $1.39, and $1.59, with weights 3, 4, and 3, respectively, and we shall denote it by μ_w.

In general, the weighted mean of a set of numbers designated $x_1, x_2, x_3, \ldots, x_n$ with the corresponding weights $w_1, w_2, w_3, \ldots, w_n$ is computed by:

Weighted Mean	$$\mu_w = \frac{w_1 x_1 + w_2 x_2 + \cdots + w_n x_n}{w_1 + w_2 + w_3 + \cdots + w_n}$$	3-3

This may be shortened to:

$$\mu_w = \frac{\Sigma(wx)}{\Sigma w}$$

3-3a

Example 3-3

Roman Concrete Ltd. pays its hourly employees $12.50, $13.56, and $14.25 per hour. There are 20 hourly employees; 7 are paid at the $12.50 rate, 8 at $13.56, and 5 at $14.25. What is the mean hourly rate paid?

Solution

To find the mean hourly rate, we multiply each hourly rate by the number of employees earning that rate and then divide it by the total number of employees working at these rates. Using Formula 3-3, the mean hourly rate is

$$\mu_w = \frac{7(\$12.50) + 8(\$13.56) + 5(\$14.25)}{20} = \frac{\$267.23}{20} \approx \$13.36$$

The weighted mean hourly wage is rounded to $13.36.

There are circumstances when the weight given to each item depends on the importance of the item in the data set. For example, when we need to calculate a grade point average for a number of courses that include some courses worth six credit hours and some courses worth three credit hours, we use credit hours as weights to arrive at the grade point average of all courses taken during a year.

Suppose Melody, a first-year student, took 7 courses during 2001–02. Her grades (A = 4.0, B = 3.0, C = 2.0, D = 1.0, F = 0.0) for each course are given below. The last digit of the course number indicates the number of credit hours associated with the course.

Biology 1003: A
English 1006: B
Math 1006: A
Statistics 1013: A
Accounting 1006: B
Chemistry 1016: C
Computer Science 1003: A

In this case, the weighted mean is:

$$\frac{3(4) + 6(3) + 6(4) + 3(4) + 6(3) + 6(2) + 3(4)}{(3 + 6 + 6 + 3 + 6 + 6 + 3)} = \frac{108}{33} = 3.27$$

whereas the simple arithmetic mean is $\dfrac{4 + 3 + 4 + \cdots + 4}{7} = \dfrac{24}{7} = 3.43!$

STATISTICS IN
ACTION

The Weighted Mean

The weighted mean is used to calculate market indexes such as S&P/TSX Composite Index. Each of the stocks in the index and the 14 industry groups representing the different sectors of Canadian industry are **weighted** to reflect their influence on trading activities. A weighted index is used as not all companies carry out the same type of business or issue the same number of shares. In addition, changes in stock prices of some companies have a greater influence on the share prices of other companies. The formula used to calculate S&P/TSX Composite Index is: S&P/TSX Composite Index = {[(Aggregate Float Quoted Market value)/(Trade-weighted average float quoted market value for original index stocks for the year 1975)] × (1000)}.

The aggregate float quoted market value = (outstanding shares − control blocks) (price).

Control blocks = any individual or group of related individuals who control 20% or more of the outstanding shares.

1000 = a multiplier chosen so that the start-up of the index level would be approximately 1000 in 1977.

One of the problems with the weighted mean is that the assignment of weights to each item may not be so obvious or agreeable to all. In such cases, we obtain different values of weighted means depending on the choice of weights. For example, the Centre for the Study of Living Standards (CSLS) (Ottawa) computes the index for overall well-being in Canada and each of the provinces. The index for overall well-being is computed as a weighted mean of four component indices (with their weights in parentheses): consumption (0.4), wealth stock (0.1), income equality (0.25), and economic security (0.25). For example, the CSLS computes indices for these components for 1997 for Prince Edward Island as ($C = 1.3152$, $W = 1.3870$, $I = 1.4482$, $E = 0.9029$), and for Ontario as ($C = 1.3192$, $W = 1.2233$, $I = 1.0880$, $E = 0.8180$). This yields the index of overall well-being for Prince Edward Island = 1.2526 and Ontario = 1.1265. Obviously, if you were to assign a higher weight to consumption and a lower weight to economic security you would achieve different results. We encourage you to visit the CSLS Web site (see www.csls.ca) for a wealth of information on the Canadian economy.

■ SELF-REVIEW 3-2

Harry Rosen sold 95 suits for the regular price of $500 each. For the spring sale, the price of suits was reduced to $300 each and 126 were sold. At the final clearance, the price was reduced to $250 each and the remaining 79 suits were sold.

What was the weighted mean price of the suits sold?

EXERCISES 3-11 TO 3-14

3-11. In June an investor purchased 300 shares of Oracle stock at $20 per share. In August she purchased an additional 400 shares at $25 per share. In November she purchased an additional 400 shares, but the stock price had declined to $23 per share. What is the weighted mean price per share?

3-12. A specialty bookstore concentrates mainly on used books. Paperbacks are $1.00 each, and hardcover books are $3.50. Of the 50 books sold last Tuesday morning, 40 were paperback and the rest were hardcover. What was the weighted mean price of the books sold last Tuesday?

3-13. The average hourly salaries of registered nurses in Ontario, Quebec, and New Brunswick for the year 2001 were $25.37, $21.29, and $22.02, respectively; the number of registered nurses employed in Ontario, Quebec, and New Brunswick during 2001 were 81 679, 58 750, and 7 776, respectively. Calculate the weighted mean hourly salary of nurses for the three provinces combined.

3-14. Andrews and Associates specialize in corporate law. They charge $100 an hour for researching a case, $75 an hour for consultations, and $200 an hour for writing a brief. Last week one of the associates spent 10 hours consulting with her client, 10 hours researching the case, and 20 hours writing the brief. What was the weighted mean hourly charge for her legal services?

3.3 THE MEDIAN

We pointed out in the previous section, that for data containing one or two very large or very small values, the arithmetic mean may not be representative. The centre point for such problems can be better described using a measure of central tendency called the **median**.

> **Median**   The midpoint of the data values after they have been ordered from the smallest to the largest.

To illustrate the need for a measure of central tendency other than the arithmetic mean, suppose you are seeking to buy a condominium in Huntsville, Ontario. Your real estate agent says that the average price of the five units currently available is $189 000. Would you still want to look? If you have budgeted a maximum purchase price between $150 000 and $170 000, you might think the condos are out of your price range. However, after checking the individual prices of the units you might change your mind. They are $140 000, $150 000, $160 000, $170 000, and $325 000 (for a super-deluxe penthouse). The arithmetic mean price is $189 000, as the real estate agent reported, but one price ($325 000) is pulling the arithmetic mean price upward, causing it to be a non-representative average. It does seem that a price around $160 000 is a more typical or representative average, and it is. In cases such as this, the median provides a more accurate measure of central tendency.

Median is the middle value of an ordered data set.

The median price of the units available is $160 000. To determine this, we arrange the prices from low ($140 000) to high ($325 000) and select the middle value ($160 000).

Price Ordered from Low to High
$140 000
$150 000   Median
$160 000   □⟸———
$170 000
$325 000

Note that there are the same number of prices below the median of $160 000 as there are above it. The median is, therefore, unaffected by extremely low or high observations. Had the highest price been $400 000—or even $1 million—the median price would still be $160 000. Likewise, had the lowest price been $90 000, the median price would still be $160 000.

In the previous illustration there is an *odd* number of observations (five). How is the median determined for an *even* number of observations? As before, the observations are ordered. Then the usual practice is to find the arithmetic mean of the two middle observations. Note that for an even number of observations, the median may not be one of the given values.

Example 3-4

The three-year compound annual returns of the six top-performing mutual funds are listed below. What is the median annualized return?

Fund Name	Three-Year Compound Annual Returns (%)
MB American Equity	17.4
Spectrum America Growth	23.8
AIC Advantage	5.1
Investors U.S. Large Cap Value	13.9
Formula Growth Fund	8.5
Teachers' RSP-Equity Section	18.7

Source: *The Globe and Mail*, Thursday, February 1, 2001

Solution

Note that the number of returns is even (6). As before, the returns are first ordered from low to high. Then the two middle returns are identified. The arithmetic mean of the two middle observations gives us the median return. Arranging from low to high:

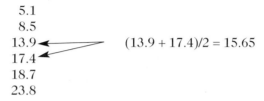

5.1
8.5
13.9
17.4   (13.9 + 17.4)/2 = 15.65
18.7
23.8

Thus, the median three-year compound annual return is 15.65 percent. Notice that in this case, the median is not one of the data values. Also, half of the returns are above it and half are below it.

The population median is the value of the $((N + 1)/2)th$ *item* in an ordered data set; N is the number of observations in the population. In the case of an even number of observations in the population, the value of the $((N + 1)/2)th$ *item* is the mean of the values of $(N/2)th$ and $((N/2) + 1)th$ *items* in the ordered data set.

The sample median is the value of the $((n + 1)/2)th$ *item* in an ordered data set; n is the number of observations in a sample. In the case of an even number of observations, the value of the $((n + 1)/2)th$ *item* is the mean of the values of $(n/2)th$ and $((n/2) + 1)th$ *items* of the ordered data set.

The population median serves the same purpose for the population data as the sample median does for the sample data.

The major properties of the median are listed below. The median:

- is unique; that is, like the mean, there is only one median for a given data set.

- is unaffected by extremely large or small values and is therefore a valuable measure of central tendency when such values do occur.

- can be calculated for ratio-level, interval-level and ordinal-level data. (Recall from Chapter 1 that ordinal-level data can be ranked from low to high, such as the responses "excellent," "very good," "good," "fair," and "poor" to a question on a marketing survey.) To use a simple illustration, suppose five people rated a new fudge bar. One person thought it was excellent, one rated it very good, one called it good, one rated it fair, and one considered it poor. The median response is "good." There are the same number of responses above "good" as there are below "good."

3.4   THE MODE

The **mode** is another measure of central tendency.

> **Mode**   The value of the observation that appears most frequently.

The mode is especially useful in describing nominal and ordinal levels of measurement. As an example of its use for nominal-level data, a company has developed five bath oils. Chart 3-1 shows the results of a marketing survey designed to find out which bath oils consumers prefer. The largest number of respondents favoured Lamoure, as evidenced by the highest bar. Thus, Lamoure is the mode.

CHART 3-1: Number of Respondents Favouring Various Bath Oils

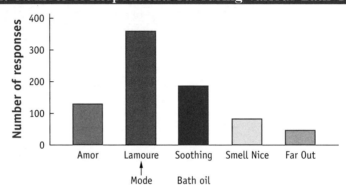

Example 3-5   Three-year returns on a sample of 8 funds of Templeton Funds-Class A are given below (period ending March 31, 2001). (Source: www.templeton.ca/prices/perf_open.html)

What is the mode of this data set?

Solution   When you browse the data set, you notice that Templeton Treasury Bill and Templeton Balanced funds report 3-year returns of 4.4%. The rest of the funds report different values. Therefore, the mode of the data set is 4.4%.

TABLE 3-1

Funds	3-Year Return (%)	Funds	3-Year Return (%)
Templeton Growth	2.9	Templeton Treasury Bill	4.4
Templeton Canadian Stock	2.7	Templeton Canadian Asset	
Templeton Intl Stock	2.8	Allocation	4.3
Templeton Balanced	4.4	Templeton Global-Smaller	
Templeton Canadian Bond	2.5	Companies	4.5

ADVANTAGES AND DISADVANTAGES OF THE MODE

We can determine the mode for all levels of data—nominal, ordinal, interval, and ratio. The mode has the advantage of not being affected by a few extremely high or low values. The mode does have a number of disadvantages, however, that cause it to be used less frequently than the mean or median.

For many sets of data, more than one data value has the same maximum frequency, and thus, there is more than one mode. For example, suppose the ages of workers in a company are 22, 27, 30, 30, 30, 30, 34, 58, 60, 60, 60, 60, and 65. Both ages 30 and 60 appear four times each, and thus, are modes. Such a data set is referred to as *bimodal* (having two modes). If the data set has more than two modes, the distribution is referred to as being *multimodal*.

Presence of multiple modes often implies that the data is not homogeneous. In the above example, the population might be composed of two distinct groups—one a group of relatively young workers who have been recently hired to meet the increased demand for a product, and the other a group of older employees who have been with the company for a long time.

In some cases, all of the data values occur the same number of times. In such a case, we say that the data set has no mode. For example, there is no mode for the set of price data: $19, $21, $23, $20, and $18.

For data with multiple modes it is often inappropriate to use mode(s) as representative of the central value of the data.

■ SELF-REVIEW 3-3

Below are the grades of a random sample of 11 students enrolled in a Quantitative Methods Course in a local community college during Fall 2002.

89, 71, 86, 66, 55, 89, 80, 56, 96, 72, 70.

(a) Find the mode of the grades of the 11 students.
(b) Find the median grade of students. How many grades are above the median? How many grades are below it?

We can use computer software to find the values of the mean, median and mode of a given data set. Charts 3-2 and 3-3 show the inputs and outputs of Excel and Minitab based on the Whitner Pontiac example from Table 2-1 (refer to Chapter 2). It may be noted that the outputs give some additional information, such as the values of kurtosis, skewness, and standard deviation. These will be discussed in detail in the next chapter.

From the computer outputs we see that the mean selling price is about $31 136 and the median is about $30 540. These two values are about $596 apart. What can we conclude from this? The typical vehicle is sold for about $31 000. Mr. Whitner might use this value in his revenue projections. For example, if the dealership could increase the number sold in a month from 80 to 90, this would result in an additional revenue of around $310 000, found by (10)($31 000).

EXCEL CHART 3-2: Data Input and Output of Table 2-1

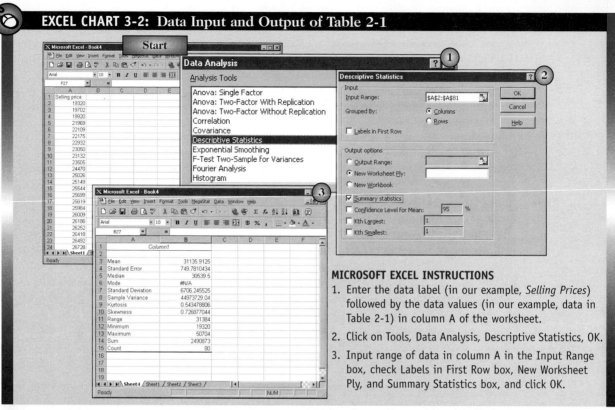

MICROSOFT EXCEL INSTRUCTIONS

1. Enter the data label (in our example, *Selling Prices*) followed by the data values (in our example, data in Table 2-1) in column A of the worksheet.

2. Click on Tools, Data Analysis, Descriptive Statistics, OK.

3. Input range of data in column A in the Input Range box, check Labels in First Row box, New Worksheet Ply, and Summary Statistics box, and click OK.

MINITAB CHART 3-3: Data Input and Output of Table 2-1

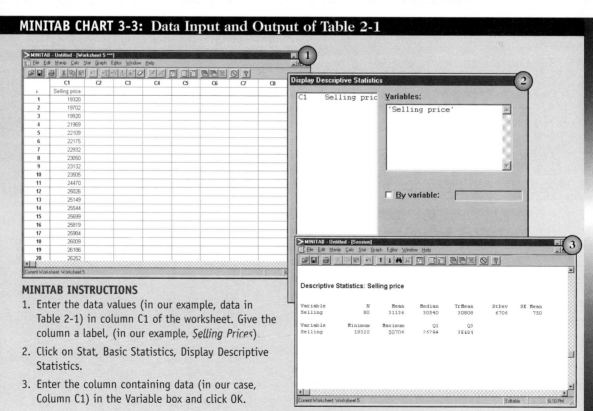

MINITAB INSTRUCTIONS

1. Enter the data values (in our example, data in Table 2-1) in column C1 of the worksheet. Give the column a label, (in our example, *Selling Prices*).

2. Click on Stat, Basic Statistics, Display Descriptive Statistics.

3. Enter the column containing data (in our case, Column C1) in the Variable box and click OK.

EXERCISES 3-15 TO 3-20

3-15. What would you report as the modal value for a set of observations if there were a total of:
(a) 10 observations and no two values were the same?
(b) 6 observations and they were all the same?
(c) 6 observations and the values were 1, 2, 3, 3, 4, and 4?

For Exercises 3-16 to 3-20, determine (a) the median and (b) the mode.

3-16. The number of oil changes done during the last seven days at Canadian Tire, Scarborough are:

| 41 | 15 | 39 | 54 | 31 | 15 | 33 |

3-17. The percentages of seven visible minorities (1996 Census) as defined by the *Employment Equity Act* as part of the total Canadian population (Source: Census of Canada, Statistics Canada) are:

| 3.0 | 2.4 | 0.6 | 2.0 | 0.6 | 0.2 | 0.2 |

3-18. The annual rates (in percentage) of changes in economic indicators for Canada for 2000–2001 (Source: *The Economist*, December 9–15, 2000) are:

GDP	5	Consumer prices	2.8
Industrial production	4.3	Produce prices	4.4
Retail sales (volume)	4.6	Wages/earnings	5.5
Unemployment rate	6.9		

3-19. The ages (rounded to the nearest year) of students in an advanced Statistics course are:

| 24 | 26 | 20 | 27 | 26 | 22 | 22 | 22 |

3-20. The expenditures by Canadians in the top six countries they visited in 1999 (Source: Statistics Canada, Culture, Tourism, and the Centre for Education Statistics, 1999) are:

Countries	Spending (in $millions)
United States	8401
Mexico	557
United Kingdom	1009
France	506
Italy	283
Cuba	265

3.5 THE GEOMETRIC MEAN

The geometric mean is useful in finding the average of percentages, ratios, indices, or growth rates. It has a wide application in business and economics because we are often interested in finding the percentage change in sales, salaries, or economic figures, such as the gross national product. The geometric mean of a set of n positive numbers is defined as the nth root of the product of the n values. The formula for the geometric mean is written:

Geometric Mean
$$GM = \sqrt[n]{(x_1)(x_2)\cdots(x_n)}$$
3-4

The geometric mean is never greater than the mean.

The geometric mean will always be less than or equal to—never more than—the arithmetic mean. Note also that all the data values must be positive to determine the geometric mean.

As an example of the interpretation of the geometric mean, suppose you received a 5-percent increase in salary in 2000 and a 15-percent increase in 2001. Recall that a 5-percent increase in salary in 2000 will raise your salary during the year to $\left(1 + \dfrac{5}{100}\right)$ times the (salary during 1999, that is, to (1.05)(salary during 1999). A 15-percent increase in 2001 will raise your salary to (1.15)(1.05)(salary during 1999). The average annual increase in salary during these two years can be calculated from the geometric mean of 1.05 and 1.15 as follows:

$$GM = \sqrt{(1.05)(1.15)} = 1.098863$$

Hence, average annual growth rate during the two-year period is 1.098863 – 1 = 0.098863 or 9.8863%. This can be verified by assuming that your monthly earning was $3000 during 1999 and you received two consecutive increases of 5 percent and 15 percent.

- Monthly salary during 2000 will be $3000(1.05) = $3150.00
- Monthly salary during 2001 will be $3150(1.15) = $3622.50

If instead you received a raise of 9.8863 percent during each of the years, then your monthly salary during 2000 would be $3000(1.098863) = $3296.589, and your monthly salary during 2001 would be $3296.589(1.098863) = $3622.50.

AN ALTERNATIVE APPROACH

It should be noted that (1.05)(1.15) = 3622.50/3000 = (salary at the end)/(salary at the beginning). Thus, the geometric mean of 1.05 and 1.15 is

$$\sqrt{\frac{3622.50}{3000}} = 1.098863$$

Hence, average annual growth rate during the period is 1.098863 – 1 = 0.098863 or 9.8863%. This gives us an alternative formula for calculating the average percentage increase over time.

$$\text{Average Annual Increase Over Period} = \sqrt[n]{\frac{\text{Value at end of period}}{\text{Value at beginning of period}}} - 1 \quad \textbf{3-5}$$

To further understand the importance of the geometric mean, consider Example 3-6.

Example 3-6

A mutual fund recorded annual growth rates of 100 percent and – 50 percent during 1999 and 2000, respectively. Find the average annual growth rate during this period.

Solution

The geometric mean of $\left(1 + \dfrac{100}{100}\right) = 2$ and $\left(1 - \dfrac{50}{100}\right) = 0.5$ is

$$GM = \sqrt{(2)(0.5)} = 1$$

Hence, the average growth rate is 1 – 1 = 0.

Let us check whether this makes sense. Suppose Charlie invested $1000 in the fund at the beginning of 1999. The value of his investment at the end of 1999 was $1000(2) = $2000; the value of his investment at the end of 2000 was $2000(0.5) = $1000. Thus, the end value is the same as the starting value, and the total growth is zero.

Note that if we use the arithmetic mean, we get the arithmetic mean = (2 + 0.5)/2 = 1.25, which would give us a growth rate of 1.25 – 1 = 0.25, or 25 percent. This would be misleading.

Example 3-7

The population of Canada in 1996 was 29 671 900; in 2000, it was 30 750 100. What was the average annual rate of percentage increase during the period? (Source: Statistics Canada, CANSIM Matrices 6367-6378 and 6408-6409.)

Solution

There are four increments (2000 – 1996 = 4). So, $n = 4$. Using Formula 3-5, we find the average percentage increase over the period:

$$\text{Average Annual Rate of Increase} = \sqrt[4]{\frac{\text{Value at end of period}}{\text{Value at beginning of period}}} - 1$$

$$\sqrt[4]{\frac{30750100}{29671900}} - 1 = 0.00896 \text{ or } 0.896\%$$

Therefore, the average annual rate of increase in the population was 0.896 percent.

Examples 3-6 and 3-7 illustrate applications of geometric mean for time-series data. Example 3-8 shows a case of cross-sectional data where we can use the geometric mean.

Example 3-8

The profits earned by Atkins' Construction Company on four recent projects were 3 percent, 2 percent, 4 percent, and 6 percent. What is the geometric mean profit? Assume the total cost of each project was the same.

Solution

The geometric mean is 3.46 percent, found by:

$$GM = \sqrt[n]{x_1 x_2 \ldots x_n} = \sqrt[4]{(3)(2)(4)(6)} = \sqrt[4]{144} = 3.46$$

■ SELF-REVIEW 3-4

1. The annual dividends, in percent, of four oil stocks are 4.91, 5.75, 8.12, and 21.60.
   (a) Find the geometric mean dividend.
   (b) Find the arithmetic mean dividend.
   (c) Is the arithmetic mean equal to or greater than the geometric mean?

2. Production of Cablos trucks increased from 23 000 units in 1988 to 120 520 units in 2000. Find the average annual percentage increase.

EXERCISES 3-21 TO 3-28

3-21. Compute the geometric mean of the following values: 8, 12, 14, 26, and 5.

3-22. Compute the geometric mean of the following values: 2, 8, 6, 4, 10, 6, 8, and 4.

3-23. Listed below is the percentage increase in sales for the MG Corporation over the last five years. Determine the average annual increase in sales over the period.

9.4   13.8   11.7   11.9   14.7

3-24. Total health-care spending in Canada in 1995 was $74 223.3 million. In 1998, this amount had increased to $79 879.8 million. What was the average annual percentage increase during this period? (Source: Adapted from Canadian Institute for Health Information.)

3-25. Failure to stop or remain at the site of an accident (hit and run incidents) in Canada decreased from 54 180 in 1995 to 37 484 in 1999. Calculate the average annual percentage decrease during this period. (Source: Statistics Canada, CANSIM, Matrix 310.)

3-26. Listed below is the percentage increase in sales for ABC.com over the last six years. Determine the average annual increase in sales over the period.

56   87   45   67   65   14

3-27. A store is divided into four departments: hardware, paint and wallpaper, kitchen and bathroom, and sporting goods. Profits earned in the four departments in 2000 are 12.5 percent, 32.5 percent, 10.25 percent, and 12.6 percent, respectively.
   (a) Would you use an arithmetic mean or a geometric mean to calculate the average profit? Explain.
   (b) Calculate the mean based on your decision in (a).

3-28. The number of strikes and lockouts in Canada in 1991 was 463 and the number of strikes and lockouts in Japan in 1991 was 310. The number of strikes and lockouts for Canada and Japan in 1996 were 279 and 193, respectively. (The number of strikes and lockouts does not include work stoppages involving less than 10 work days in Canada. In Japan, the number of strikes and lockouts does not include work stoppages lasting less than half a day.)
   (a) Calculate the average annual percentage decrease in the number of strikes and lockouts for both countries for the period 1991 to 1996.
   (b) Is the comparison for the number of strikes and lockouts for the two countries correct?

3.6   THE MEAN, MEDIAN, AND MODE OF GROUPED DATA

Quite often, data on income, age, health care, and so on are grouped and presented in the form of a frequency distribution. It is usually impossible to secure the original raw data. Thus, if we are interested in a typical value to represent the data, we must calculate it based on the frequency distribution.

The sample mean and the population mean of data organized in a frequency distribution are computed by:

Population Mean of Grouped Data	$\mu = \dfrac{\sum fx}{N}$	3-6
Sample Mean of Grouped Data	$\bar{x} = \dfrac{\sum fx}{N}$	3-7

where,

$\bar{x}$ denotes the sample mean.
μ denotes the population mean.
x is the mid-value, or midpoint, of each class.
f is the frequency of each class.
fx is the frequency of each class times the midpoint of the class.
n is the total number of data values in the sample (= sum of frequencies).
N is the total number of data values in the population (= sum of frequencies).

The population mean of grouped population data gives us an approximate value of the population mean of the corresponding raw population data. Similarly, the sample mean of grouped sample data gives us an approximate value of the sample mean of the corresponding raw sample data. If the sample data are available in grouped form and we do not have access to raw sample data, then the sample mean of the grouped data is used as an estimate of the population mean.

We shall illustrate the computations of the arithmetic mean of data grouped into a frequency distribution using the frequency distribution for Whitner Pontiac data that we constructed in Table 2-3 in Chapter 2.

Example 3-9 | Using the frequency distribution for the vehicle selling prices at Whitner Pontiac, given in Table 2-3, (page 36), obtain an approximate value of the arithmetic mean vehicle selling price.

Solution | We shall use the arithmetic mean of the data grouped into a frequency distribution as an approximate value of the arithmetic mean of the corresponding raw data. This grouped data in Table 2-3 is reproduced in Table 3-2.

We assume the midpoint of each class as representative of the data values in that class. Recall that the midpoint of a class is halfway between the upper and lower class limits, and is found by adding the upper and lower class limits and dividing by 2. Midpoints of all the classes are given in Table 3-2 under the column labelled x.

TABLE 3-2: Price of 80 Vehicles Sold Last Month at Whitner Pontiac (Frequency Distribution)

Selling Price ($ thousands)	Frequency f	Midpoint x	fx
19.310 up to 23.800	10	21.555	215.55
23.800 up to 28.290	21	26.045	546.95
28.290 up to 32.780	20	30.535	610.70
32.780 up to 37.270	15	35.025	525.38
37.270 up to 41.760	8	39.515	316.12
41.760 up to 46.250	4	44.005	176.02
46.250 up to 50.740	2	48.495	96.99
Total	80		2487.71

Using Formula 3-6, we get:

$$\mu = \frac{\Sigma\, fx}{N} = \frac{2487.71}{80} = \$31.096\ (thousands)$$

So, we conclude that the mean vehicle selling price of all vehicles is approximately $31 096.

The mean of data grouped into a frequency distribution may be different from that of the raw data. The grouping results in some loss of information. In the vehicle-selling-price problem, the mean of the raw data is $31 135.91. This value is quite close to the mean of the same data grouped into a frequency distribution that we just computed. The difference is $35.91, or 0.13 percent.

■ SELF-REVIEW 3-5

The net incomes of a sample of large importers of antiques were organized into the following table:

Net Income ($ millions)	Number of Importers
2 up to 6	1
6 up to 10	4
10 up to 14	10
14 up to 18	3
18 up to 22	2

    (a) What is the table called?
    (b) Based on the sample data, what is the estimate of the arithmetic mean net income?

EXERCISES 3-29 TO 3-34

3-29. Is the value of the arithmetic mean of raw data the same as the value of the arithmetic mean computed from the same data grouped into a frequency distribution? Explain.

3-30. Determine the mean of the following frequency distribution:

Class	Frequency
0 up to 5	2
5 up to 10	7
10 up to 15	12
15 up to 20	6
20 up to 25	3

3-31. Determine the mean of the following frequency distribution:

Class	Frequency
20 up to 30	7
30 up to 40	12
40 up to 50	21
50 up to 60	18
60 up to 70	12

3-32. The selling prices of a sample of 60 antiques sold in Toronto, Ontario, last month were organized into the following frequency distribution. Estimate the mean selling price.

Selling Price ($ thousands)	Frequency
70 up to 80	3
80 up to 90	7
90 up to 100	18
100 up to 110	20
110 up to 120	12

3-33. FM radio station WLQR recently changed its format from easy-listening to contemporary. A recent sample of 50 listeners revealed the following age distribution. Estimate the mean age of the listeners.

Age	Frequency
20 up to 30	1
30 up to 40	15
40 up to 50	22
50 up to 60	8
60 up to 70	4

3-34. Listed below is a frequency distribution of the advertising expenditures of 30 small companies located in Vancouver.

Advertising Expenditures ($ thousands)	Number of Companies
25 up to 35	10
35 up to 45	5
45 up to 55	8
55 up to 65	4
65 up to 75	3

(a) Obtain an approximate value of the mean of the advertising expenditures.
(b) Explain why the solution in part (a) is an approximate value of the mean.

THE MEDIAN OF GROUPED DATA

Recall that the **median** is defined as the midpoint of the data values after they have been ordered from the smallest to the largest. If the raw data is organized into a frequency distribution, some of the information is not identifiable. As a result, we cannot determine the exact value of the median. It can be approximated, however, by (1) locating the class in which the median lies, and then (2) calculating the location of the median within this median class. The rationale for this approach is that the members of the median class are assumed to be evenly spaced throughout the class. The formula is:

Median Of Grouped Data	$Median = L + \dfrac{\dfrac{N}{2} - CF}{f}$ (i)	3-8

where:

L	is the lower limit of the class containing the median.
N	is the total number of data values (sum of all frequencies).
f	is the frequency in the median class.
CF	is the cumulative number of frequencies in all the classes preceding the class containing the median.
i	is the width of the class in which the median lies.

In Example 3-10 we shall first calculate the approximate value of the median by locating the class in which it falls and interpolating. Then Formula 3-8 will be applied to check our answer.

Example 3-10

Using the frequency distribution for the vehicle selling prices at Whitner Pontiac, given in Table 2-3, (page 36), obtain an approximate value of the median selling price of the vehicles.

Solution

The frequency distribution for the vehicle selling prices in Table 2-3 is reproduced below in Table 3-3. Here, we have included an additional column of the cumulative frequencies, (CF), which will be needed for computing the approximate value of the median selling price.

To find the median selling price of this grouped sample data, we need to locate the 40th observation (there are a total of 80 observations) when the data are arranged from smallest to largest. Why the 40th? Recall that the median is the midpoint of the data values after they have been ordered from smallest to largest. So if we thought of arranging all the selling prices from smallest to largest, the midpoint of the 40th and 41st would be the median. However, because the number of observations is usually large for data grouped into a frequency distribution, we usually ignore the small difference.

The class containing the selling price of the 40th vehicle is located by referring to the right-hand column of Table 3-3, which is the cumulative frequency. There are 31 vehicles that sold for less than $28 290 and 51 that sold for less than $32 780. Hence, the 40th vehicle price must be in the range $28 290 up to $32 780. We have located the median selling price as somewhere between the two limits of $28 290 and $32 780.

To locate the median more precisely, we need to interpolate in this class containing the median. Recall that there are 20 vehicles sold in the $28 290 up to $32 780 class. Assume the selling prices are evenly distributed between the lower ($28 290) and the upper ($32 780) class limits. There are nine vehicle selling prices between the 31st

TABLE 3-3: Price of 80 Vehicles Sold Last Month at Whitner Pontiac (Median)

Selling Price ($ thousands)	Frequency f	Cumulative Frequency CF
19.310 up to 23.800	10	10
23.800 up to 28.290	21	31
28.290 up to 32.780	**20**	**51**
32.780 up to 37.270	15	66
37.270 up to 41.760	8	74
41.760 up to 46.250	4	78
46.250 up to 50.740	2	80
Total	80	

CHART 3-4: Location of the Median

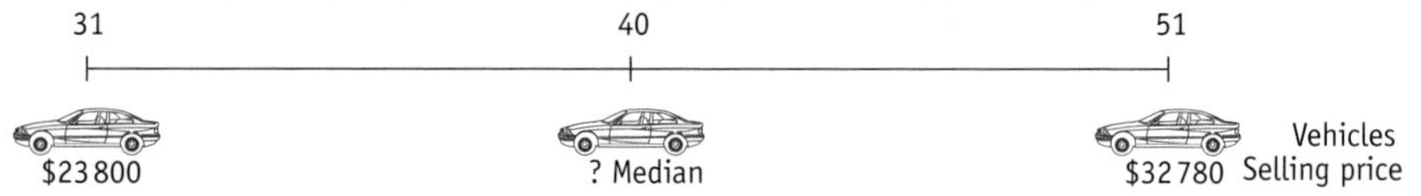

and 40th vehicle. The median is, therefore, 9/20 of the distance between $28 290 and $32 780. The class width is $4490. Therefore (9/20)(4490) = 2020.50. We add $2020.5 to the lower class limit of $28 290. Thus, the approximate value of the median vehicle selling price is $30 310.50.

We could use Formula 3-8 to determine the median of data grouped into a frequency distribution, where L is the lower limit of the class containing the median, which is $28 290. There are 80 selling prices, so $N = 80$. CF is the cumulative number of selling prices preceding the median class (31); f is the frequency of the number of observations in the median class (20) and i is the width of the class containing the median ($4490). Subsituting these values:

$$\text{Median} = L + \frac{\frac{N}{2} - CF}{f}(i)$$

$$= 28\,290 + \frac{\frac{80}{2} - 31}{20}(4490)$$

$$= 28\,290 + 2020.5 = 30\,310.5$$

The assumption underlying the approximation of the median—that the frequencies in the median class are evenly distributed between $28 290 and $32 780—may not be exactly correct. Therefore, it is safer to say that about half of the selling prices are less than $30 310.50 and about half are more. The median obtained from the grouped data and the median determined from raw data are usually not exactly equal. In this case, the median computed from the raw data using Excel is $30 539.50 and the value obtained from the frequency distribution is $30 310.50. The difference between the two values is $243, or about 1 percent.

THE MODE

Recall that the mode of a data set is defined as the value that occurs most often in the data set. For data grouped into a frequency distribution, the mode can be approximated by the midpoint of the class containing the largest class frequency. Thus,

> **i** Class midpoint of the modal class of a grouped data gives an approximate value of the mode of the corresponding raw data.

For the frequency distribution of the data on selling prices at Whitner Pontiac, given in Table 3-2 (page 101), an approximate value of the modal selling price is found by first locating the class containing the largest frequency. It is the $23 800 up to $28 290 class, because it has the largest frequency (21). The midpoint of that class $\left(\frac{23\,800 + 28\,290}{2} = \$26\,045\right)$ is an approximate value of the mode.

■ SELF-REVIEW 3-6

1. The data on daily production of transistors at Scott Electronics for the last 50 days was organized into the following distribution. Obtain an approximate value of the median daily production during the 50 days.

Daily Production	Frequency
80 up to 90	5
90 up to 100	9
100 up to 110	20
110 up to 120	8
120 up to 130	6
130 up to 140	2

2. The net sales of a sample of small stamping plants were organized into the following percentage frequency distribution. Obtain an approximate value of the mode of the sample data.

Net Sales ($ millions)	Percentage of Total
1 up to 4	13
4 up to 7	14
7 up to 10	40
10 up to 13	23
13 and greater	10

EXERCISES 3-35 TO 3-40

3-35. Refer to Exercise 3-30. Compute the median and the mode of the grouped data.

3-36. Refer to Exercise 3-31. Compute the median and the mode of the grouped data.

3-37. The chief accountant at Betts Machine, Inc. wants to prepare a report on the company's accounts receivable. Below is a frequency distribution showing the amount outstanding.

Amount	Frequency
$0 up to $2 000	4
$2 000 up to $4 000	15
$4 000 up to $6 000	18
$6 000 up to $8 000	10
$8 000 up to $10 000	4
$10 000 up to $12 000	3

(a) Obtain an approximate value of the median amount.
(b) Obtain an approximate value of the modal amount owed.

3-38. The following is the length of service distribution of 70 professors in a community college in Quebec. Find the approximate values of the median and modal lengths of services.

Length of Service	Number of Professors
0 up to 6	10
6 up to 12	15
12 up to 18	20
18 up to 24	25

3-39. The following table provides the income of a random sample of 64 families living in Fraser Valley, B.C. Calculate the approximate median income of the sample data.

Income ($ thousands)	Number of Families
30 up to 40	11
40 up to 50	18
50 up to 60	12
60 up to 70	14
70 up to 80	9

3-40. The following is the distribution of ages of males heading single-parent families in 1998. (Source: Statistics Canada, *Canadian Global Almanac*, 2000.)

Age	Families
15–25	1 696
25–35	21 092
35–45	64 898
45–55	65 029
55–65	25 270
65+	26 535

(a) Find the median and modal classes.
(b) Find an approximate value of the median and modal ages.
(c) Find an approximate value of the difference between the median and modal ages.

3.7 THE RELATIVE POSITIONS OF THE MEAN, MEDIAN, AND MODE

Recall that a distribution is said to be symmetrical if *its frequency polygon has the same shape on either side of the centre*. For example, Chart 3-5 shows a frequency polygon of a symmetrical distribution. For a symmetrical distribution, the mean and the median

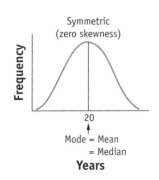

CHART 3-5: A Symmetrical Distribution

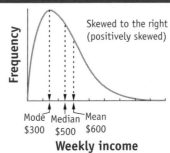

CHART 3-6: A Positively Skewed Distribution

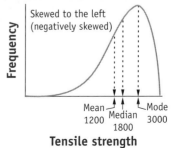

CHART 3-7: A Negatively Skewed Distribution

are located at the centre of the distribution and are always equal. If the distribution is symmetrical and has only one peak, then the mode is also located at the centre of the distribution.

A distribution that is not symmetrical is said to be a skewed distribution.

Let us refer to the distribution in Chart 3-5. It is symmetrical and has a single peak. The number of years corresponding to the highest point of the curve is the *mode* (20 years). Because the frequency curve is symmetrical, the *median* corresponds to the point where the distribution is cut in half (20 years). The total number of frequencies representing many years is offset by the total number representing few years, resulting in an *arithmetic mean* of 20 years. Logically, any of the three measures would be appropriate to represent this distribution.

If the frequency polygon of the data has only one peak and it is skewed, the relationship among the three averages changes. In a **positively skewed distribution** (that is, skewed to the right), the arithmetic mean is the largest of the three averages. Why? Because the mean is influenced more than the median or mode by a few extremely high values. The median is generally the next largest average in a positively skewed frequency distribution. The mode is the smallest of the three averages.

Conversely, in a distribution that is **negatively skewed** (that is, skewed to the left), the mean is the lowest of the three averages. The median is greater than the arithmetic mean, and the modal value is the largest of the three averages.

In moderately skewed distributions, data sets normally satisfy the relationship:

$$\text{Mean} - \text{Mode} \approx 3(\text{Mean} - \text{Median})$$

If the distribution is highly skewed, such as the distribution of weekly income in Chart 3-6 and the distribution of tensile strength in Chart 3-7, the mean should not be used to represent the data. The median and mode would be more representative.

■ SELF-REVIEW 3-7

The weekly sales from a sample of Hi-Tec electronic supply stores were organized into a frequency distribution. The mean of weekly sales was computed to be $105 900, the median $105 000, and the mode $104 500.

(a) Sketch a possible shape of the frequency polygon of the sales data. Note the location of the mean, median, and mode on the x-axis.
(b) Is the distribution symmetrical, positively skewed, or negatively skewed? Explain.

PROPERTIES OF DIFFERENT MEASURES OF AVERAGE

A preferred choice for an average should depend on some criteria. Most statisticians agree that the chosen average should possess most of the properties listed in the first column of the table given below. The rest of the columns list the properties satisfied by each of the averages (AM = Arithmetic Mean, WM = Weighted Mean, GM = Geometric Mean, Med = Median, and Mode).

Based on the above information, it is obvious that the arithmetic mean satisfies more criteria than any other average. This is the reason why *arithmetic mean is the most popular of all averages*.

Properties	AM	WM[1]	GM	Med	Mode
Well-defined and gives a unique value	Yes	No	Yes	Yes	?[2]
Based on all observations in the data	Yes	Yes	Yes	?[3]	?[3]
Easy to understand and interpret	Yes	No	No	Yes	Yes
Easy to calculate	Yes	Yes	No	Yes	Yes
Has good mathematical properties that are often required for a further analysis of the data	Yes	Yes	Yes	No	No
Value is relatively stable from one sample to another obtained from the same population	Yes	No	Yes	No	No

Notes:

[1] Where weight given to each data item is based on considerations other than the frequency associated with each item. Recall that when weights are based on the frequencies, AM and WM are identical.

[2] There may be more than one value of the mode in a given data.

[3] If you decrease (increase) the value of an observation below (above) the median value in a given data set, the value of the median will be unaffected. Similarly, for some changes in the values in the data set, mode is also unaffected. Try it yourself!

Where the nature of data dictates a choice:

- *Nominal Data:* In this case, our only choice is to compute the mode.
- *Ordinal Data:* In this case, we can calculate both median and mode and choose the one depending on the objective of our analysis. GM is the desired average if we need to calculate average growth rates, and particularly if we have only two values of a variable for the initial year and the final year over a long period of time.
- *Extreme Values:* If a data set contains unusually large or small values, we should compute the median or mode. Alternatively, if the arithmetic mean is used, we should supplement our analysis with the values of the median and mode. Think of mean income of all households on your street with and without a hockey superstar in the family!
- *Open-ended Class Intervals:* Since it may be difficult to determine a reasonable mid-value of an open-ended class interval, we have to compute the value of median or mode and use the one depending on the objective of our analysis.

CHAPTER OUTLINE

I. A measure of location is a value used to describe the centre of a data set.
   A. The arithmetic mean is the most widely reported measure of location.
      1. It is calculated by adding the values of the observations and dividing by the total number of observations.
      (a) The formula for a population mean of ungrouped or raw data is:

$$\mu = \frac{\sum x}{N}$$

3-1

(b) The formula for the mean of a sample is

$$\bar{x} = \frac{\sum x}{n} \qquad \text{3-2}$$

(c) For population data grouped into a frequency distribution, the formula for the arithmetic mean is:

$$\mu = \frac{\sum fx}{N} \qquad \text{3-6}$$

2. The major characteristics of the arithmetic mean are:
   (a) At least the interval scale of measurement is required.
   (b) All the data values are used in the calculation.
   (c) A set of data has only one mean. That is, it is unique.
   (d) The sum of the deviations from the mean equals 0.

B. The weighted mean is found by multiplying each observation by its corresponding weight.
   1. The formula for determining the weighted mean is:

   $$\mu_w = \frac{w_1 x_1 + w_2 x_2 + w_3 x_3 + \cdots + w_n x_n}{w_1 + w_2 + w_3 + \cdots + w_n} \qquad \text{3-3}$$

   2. The arithmetic mean is a special case of the weighted mean.

C. The geometric mean is the nth root of the product of n positive values.
   1. The formula for the geometric mean is:

   $$GM = \sqrt[n]{(x_1)(x_2)(x_3)\cdots(x_n)} \qquad \text{3-4}$$

   2. The geometric mean is also used to find the average annual rate of change over an n year period.

   $$\text{Average Annual Rate of Change} = \sqrt[n]{\frac{\text{Value at end of period}}{\text{Value at beginning of period}}} - 1 \qquad \text{3-5}$$

   3. The geometric mean is always equal to or less than the arithmetic mean.

D. The median is the value in the middle of a set of ordered data.
   1. To find the median, sort the observations from smallest to largest and identify the middle value.
   2. The formula for estimating the median from grouped data is:

   $$\text{Median} = L + \frac{\frac{N}{2} - CF}{f}(i) \qquad \text{3-8}$$

   3. The major characteristics of the median are:
      (a) At least the ordinal scale of measurement is required.
      (b) It is not influenced by extreme values.
      (c) There is an equal number of observations on either side of the median.
      (d) It is unique to a set of data.

E. The *mode* is the value that occurs most often in a set of data.

1. The mode can be found for nominal- or higher-level data.

2. A set of data can have more than one mode.

CHAPTER EXERCISES 3-41 TO 3-66

3-41. The accounting firm of Crawford and Associates has five senior partners. Yesterday the senior partners saw six, four, three, seven, and five clients, respectively.
(a) Compute the mean number and median number of clients seen by a partner.
(b) Is the mean a sample mean or a population mean?
(c) Verify that $\Sigma(x - \mu) = 0$.

3-42. Owens' Orchards sells apples in a large bag by weight. A sample of seven bags contained the following numbers of apples: 23, 19, 26, 17, 21, 24, 22.
(a) Compute the mean number and median number of apples in a bag.
(b) Verify that $\Sigma(x - \bar{x}) = 0$.

3-43. A sample of households that subscribe to the Bell Phone Company revealed the following numbers of calls received last week. Compute the sample mean and the sample median number of calls received.

52	43	30	38	30	42	12	46
39°	37	34	46	32	18	41	5

3-44. The Citizens' Banking Company is studying the number of times the automated teller located in a particular supermarket is used per day.
Following are the numbers of times the ATM was used over each of the last 30 days. Determine the mean number of times the ATM was used per day.

83	64	84	76	84	54	75	59	70	61
63	80	84	73	68	52	65	90	52	77
95	36	78	61	59	84	95	47	87	60

3-45. The profits (in $ millions) of the world's 15 largest corporations (1998) are given below. (Source: *Canadian Global Almanac*, 2000, p. 257.)

2956.0	5656.0	22071.0	4430.0	233.0
−266.7	244.0	6370.0	9296.0	2786.5
350.0	−921.0	−102.3	6328.0	1702.4

(a) Find the mean profit.
(b) Find the median profit.

3-46. Trudy Green works for the True-Green Lawn Company. Her job is to solicit lawn-care business via the telephone. Listed below are the number of appointments she made in each of the last 25 hours of calling. What is the arithmetic mean number of appointments she made per hour? What is the median number of appointments per hour? Write a brief report summarizing the findings.

9	5	2	6	5	6	4	4	7
2	3	6	3	4	4	7	8	4
4	5	5	4	8	3	3		

3-47. Quality Fencing Company in Hamilton, Ontario sells three types of fences to homeowners. Grade A costs $7.50 per running metre to install, Grade B costs $8.50 per running metre, and Grade C costs $10.00 per running metre. The company installed 300 metres of Grade A, 270 metres of Grade B, and 100 metres of Grade C. What is the mean cost per metre of fence installed?

3-48. Josephine Palmer is a full-time student in a community college. Last semester she took a course in Statistics and a course in Accounting and earned a C in each. She earned a B in Business Mathematics, an A in Speaking with Confidence, a B in Financial Accounting, and a C in E-Business. What was her GPA for the semester? Assume that she receives 4 points for an A, 3 points for a B, and 2 points for a C, and that each course is a 3-credit-hour course. What measure of central tendency did you just calculate?

3-49. The following is the list of total number of tax filers and percentage of tax filers who gave charitable donations for four provinces in Canada in 1999. (Source: Statistics Canada CANSIM, Matrix 10-300; percentage calculated from the data.) Calculate the average percent of donors for four provinces.

Tax Filers	Percent Donors
381 320	21.32
96 350	27.06
650 340	24.42
538 910	23.27

3-50. The following distribution provides the annual net profits of 34 small companies:

Annual Net Profits ($000)	Number of Companies
65 up to 75	1
75 up to 85	6
85 up to 95	7
95 up to 105	12
105 up to 115	5
115 up to 125	3

(a) Find the median annual net profit.
(b) Find the arithmetic mean annual net profit.

3-51. The following are the hours the nine employees of Hick Inc. worked during a certain week in 2001. Calculate the median, arithmetic mean, and mode of the data.

45   42   45   24   39   40   22   36   49

3-52. The following are the marks of students for Test 1 (out of a possible score of 20) in Math 1021 during February 2001:

17   11   13   14   8   2   20   13
9   12   15   16   18   16   19   9

(a) Calculate the mean, the median, and the mode of the marks.
(b) Is the distribution symmetrical, positively skewed, or negatively skewed? Explain.

3-53. The following table shows the expenditures of Canadians in 15 countries they visited in 1999. (Source: Statistics Canada, Tourism and the Centre for Education Statistics.)

Countries Visited	Expenditures ($ Cdn millions)
Australia	227
Cuba	265
Dominican Rep.	122
France	506
Germany	183
Hong Kong	138
Ireland	114
Italy	283
Japan	150
Mexico	557
Netherlands	107
Spain	105
Switzerland	91
United Kingdom	1009
United States	8401

(a) Find the mean and the median expenditures.

(b) What are the highest and the lowest expenditures?

3-54. The population of Canada will increase from 30 679 000 in 2000 to 36 633 000 in 2030. (Source: *Canadian Global Almanac 2000*, p. 255.)

(a) To find the average rate of growth, which measure of central tendency would you use? Explain.

(b) Based on your selection of measure of central tendency, calculate the value of the central tendency.

3-55. The year-by-year returns of one of the funds of ABC Capital Group from 1999 to 2001 are 11.55 percent, 16.7 percent, and 10.3 percent.

(a) Find the average rate of return over the period 1999–2001.

(b) Find the arithmetic mean of returns.

(c) Is the arithmetic mean greater than the average rate of return calculated in part (a)?

3-56. A recent article suggested that if you earn $25 000 a year today and the inflation rate continues at 3 percent per year, you'll need to make $33 598 in 10 years to have the same buying power. You would need to make $44 771 if the inflation rate jumped to 6 percent. Confirm that these statements are accurate.

3-57. The gross domestic product of Canada at market prices increased from $833 070 (millions) in 1996 to $1 038 794 (millions) in 2000. Calculate the annual percentage increase for the period 1996 to 2000. (Source: Adapted from Statistics Canada, CANSIM, Matrix 6547.)

3-58. The 12-month returns on five aggressive-growth mutual funds were 32.2 percent, 35.5 percent, 80.0 percent, 60.9 percent, and 92.1 percent. Determine the arithmetic mean and the geometric mean rates of return.

3-59. Endu made the following payments to Visa Gold on each due date in 2001.

$2231.61	$2516.08	$1215.97	$2809.45
$1983.08	$1983.08	$487.91	$2381.72
$791.55	$791.55	$2381.72	$461.36

(a) Find the mean payment.
(b) Find the median payment.

3-60. Census of Canada, Statistics Canada reported the following information on family size in 1996. (Source: *Canadian Global Almanac 2000*, p. 72.)

Families with Children at Home	No. of Families
1 child	2106
2 children	2047
3 children	729
4 children	175
5 children or more	51

(a) What was the median number of children per family in 1996?
(b) What was the modal number of children per family in 1996?

3-61. ARS Services Inc. employs 40 electricians, providing service to both residential and commercial accounts. ARS has been in business since the early 1960s and has always advertised prompt and reliable service. Of concern in recent years is the number of days employees are absent. Below is a frequency distribution of the number of days missed by the 40 electricians last year:

Number of Days Missed	Number of Electricians
0 up to 3	17
3 up to 6	13
6 up to 9	7
9 up to 12	3
Total	40

(a) Determine an approximate value of the mean number of days missed per employee.
(b) Determine an approximate value of the median number of days missed per employee.

3-62. In recent years there has been intense competition for the long-distance phone service of residential customers. In an effort to study the actual phone usage of residential customers, an independent consultant gathered the following data on the number of long-distance phone calls per household for a sample of 50:

Number of Phone Calls	Frequency
3 up to 6	5
6 up to 9	19
9 up to 12	20
12 up to 15	4
15 up to 18	2
Total	50

(a) Obtain an estimate of the mean number of phone calls per household.
(b) Determine the median number of phone calls per household for the sample data.

3-63. The following is the frequency distribution of size (in mm) of 100 Dover sole fish taken randomly from catches obtained in Morro Bay and Port San Luis, California: (Source: Donald Sanders et al., *Statistics: A First Course*, McGraw-Hill Ryerson, 2001.)

Length (mm)	Number of Fish
275 up to 300	1
300 up to 325	1
325 up to 350	14
350 up to 375	24
375 up to 400	30
400 up to 425	22
425 up to 450	6
450 up to 475	2

(a) Estimate the mean size of Dover sole fish.
(b) Find an approximate value of the median of the sample of fish sizes.
(c) Find an approximate modal value of the sample of fish sizes.

3-64. A sample of 50 antique dealers in St. John's revealed the following sales last year:

Sales ($ thousands)	Number of Firms
100 up to 120	5
120 up to 140	7
140 up to 160	9
160 up to 180	16
180 up to 200	10
200 up to 220	3

(a) Estimate the mean sales.
(b) Obtain an approximate value of the median of sample data.
(c) Obtain an approximate value of the modal sales amount.

3-65. The following are the numbers of people granted Canadian citizenship from 1980 to 1999. (Source: *Canadian Global Almanac 2000*, p. 65, Citizenship and Immigration.)

118 590	94 457	87 468	90 328	109 504
126 466	103 800	73 638	58 810	87 478
104 267	118 630	115 757	150 543	217 320
227 720	166 627	140 241	134 485	180 000

(a) Find the mean, median, and mode.
(b) Write in complete sentences the meaning of median number of persons granted Canadian citizenship.
(c) In what year was the number of persons granted Canadian citizenship the highest?

3-66. (a) Use five classes to group the data in Exercise 3-65 and find the mean.
(b) Is the mean of the grouped data the same as found in Exercise 3-65?
(c) Comment on the two values of the mean of grouped and ungrouped data.

www.exercises.ca 3-67 TO 3-68

3-67. Go to www.canoe.ca/BaseballMoneyMatters/salaries_players.html. Select Toronto Blue Jays and Montreal Expos from Baseball Salaries. Compute the average salaries of both major league teams. Is the average salary of a Toronto Blue Jays' player higher than the average salary of a Montreal Expos' player?

3-68. One of the most famous averages, the Dow Jones Industrial Average (DJIA), is not really an average. Below is a listing of the 30 stocks that make up the DJIA and their selling prices on July 11, 2000. Compute the mean of the 30 stocks. Compare this to the closing price on July 11, 2000, of 10 727.19. Then go to the Dow Jones Web site and read about the history of this average and the stocks that are currently included in its calculation. To obtain this information go to www.dowjones.com: in the bottom left corner click on About Dow Jones/Dow Jones Industrial Average/Stocks. The output can be found on the CD-ROM accompanying this text under the file name Exercise 3-68.xls. Compute the mean of the 30 stocks included in the DJIA today with the DJIA of July 11, 2000. Has there been a change?

▶ COMPUTER DATA EXERCISES 3-69 TO 3-72

Use Excel or Minitab for the following questions.

3-69. File Exercise 3-69.xls contains names of companies, names of countries, and sales in millions of dollars. (Source: *Canadian Almanac 2000*, p. 257.)
   (a) Find the name of the country that is listed most often (mode) in the top 25 world's largest corporations. Name the level of measurement of the variable.
   (b) Find the mean and median sales (round off the figures to two decimal places).
   (c) Which of the two measures of central tendency is the better measure? Explain.
   (d) Find the frequency distribution of sales (in millions of dollars).

3-70. File Exercise 3-70.xls contains the numbers of students in different counties of Ontario. (Source: Statistics Canada, 1996 Census of Population, Education, Mobility and Migration.)
   (a) Find the mean and median number of students.
   (b) Find the difference between the mean and median.
   (c) Is the median a better measure of central tendency? Explain.

3-71. File Exercise 3-71.xls contains marks of students in Test 1.
   (a) Find the mean, median, and mode of the Test 1 mark.
   (b) Is the mark distribution skewed to the left or right?
   (c) Why is the distribution skewed in one direction? Explain.

3-72. File Exercise 3-72.xls contains the number of reported bicycle deaths over a 22-year period. (Source: David Sanders et al., *Statistics: A First Course*, McGraw-Hill, p. 87.)
   (a) Calculate the mean and the median.
   (b) Create a frequency distribution and find the mean and the median of the grouped data.
   (c) Compare the mean of grouped and ungrouped data. Explain the differences between the two mean values.

CHAPTER 3   ANSWERS TO SELF-REVIEW

3-1. 1. (a) $\bar{x} = \dfrac{\Sigma x}{n}$

(b) $\bar{x} = \dfrac{\$267\,000}{4} = \$66\,750$

(c) Statistic, because it is a value calculated from a sample to estimate a population parameter.

(d) $66 750. The sample mean is our best estimate of the population mean.

2. (a) $\mu = \dfrac{\Sigma x}{N}$

(b) $\mu = \dfrac{414}{6} = 69$

(c) Parameter, because it was computed using all the population values.

(d) No. The data value 12 is an extreme value.

3. Yes. The data are ratio level; all the data values are considered in calculating the mean; the sum of deviations of all the values from the mean is zero.

3-2. (a) 350.17, found by:

$$\mu_w = \frac{\Sigma wx}{\Sigma w}$$

$$= \frac{(95 \times \$500) + (126 \times \$300) + (79 \times \$250)}{95 + 126 + 79}$$

$$= \$350.17$$

3-3. (a) The modal grade is 89 because it is the only value that appears twice in the data set. Every other value appears once.

(b) The median grade is 72, which is the middle (6th) grade of the ordered data set: 55, 56, 66, 70, 71, 72, 80, 86, 89, 89, 96. Five grades are above the median and five grades are below it.

3-4. 1. (a) Approximately 8.39 percent, found by

$$\sqrt[4]{(4.91)(5.75)(8.12)(21.60)} \approx 8.39$$

(b) 10.095 percent, found by

$$\frac{4.91 + 5.75 + 8.12 + 21.60}{4} = 10.095$$

(c) Arithmetic mean is greater than the geometric mean.

2. 14.8 percent, found by
$$\sqrt[12]{(120520)/(23000)} - 1 = 0.148$$

3-5. (a) Frequency distribution

(b)

f	x	fx
1	4	4
4	8	32
10	12	120
3	16	48
2	20	40
20		244

$$\bar{x} = \frac{\Sigma fx}{n} = \frac{\$244}{20} = \$12.20$$

3-6. 1.

Production	Frequency	CF
80 up to 90	5	5
90 up to 100	9	14
100 up to 110	20	34
110 up to 120	8	42
120 up to 130	6	48
130 up to 140	2	50
	50	

$$\text{Median} = 100 + \frac{25 - 14}{20}(10)$$

$$= 100 + 5.5 = 105.5$$

2. The modal class of $7 million up to $10 million. An approximate value of

$$\text{mode} = \frac{7 + 10}{2} = \$8.5 \text{ million.}$$

3-7. (a)

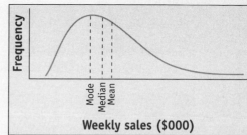

Weekly sales ($000)

(b) Positively skewed, because the mean is the largest average and the mode is the smallest.

CHAPTER 4

Other Descriptive Measures

GOALS

When you have completed this chapter, you will be able to:

- Compute and interpret the range, the mean deviation, the variance, the standard deviation, and the coefficient of variation of ungrouped data

- Compute and interpret the range, the variance, and the standard deviation of grouped data

- Explain the characteristics, uses, advantages, and disadvantages of each measure

- Describe Chebyshev's theorem and the normal or empirical rule, as it relates to a set of observations

- Compute and interpret percentiles, quartiles and the interquartile range

- Construct and interpret box plots

- Compute and describe the coefficients of skewness and kurtosis of a data distribution.

JOHN W. TUKEY (1915–2000)

John W. Tukey was born in New Bedford, Massachusetts on June 16, 1915. He was schooled at home by his parents up to pre-college and his formal education began when he entered Brown University to study mathematics and chemistry. He earned a bachelor's and a master's degree in chemistry at Brown University and, after receiving a PhD degree in mathematics from Princeton University in 1939, he joined the mathematics faculty at Princeton.

During World War II, he joined the Fire Control Research Office as his contribution to the war effort. Here, he had to deal with statistical problems and his academic interest shifted permanently from abstract mathematics to statistics. For the rest of his career he worked as a statistician within the mathematics department at Princeton University and also at the AT&T Bell Laboratories at Murray Hill.

One of his major contributions to statistics is in the area of data analysis. His work on data analysis changed the paradigm and language of statistics. A critical part of this work was the development of methods, both numerical and graphical, that are effective in studying patterns in the data. Among the graphics he developed are the *stem-and-leaf display* (see Chapter 2) and the *box-and-whisker plot* (*also known as Boxplot*), which is commonly used in scientific presentations. He also developed the field of dynamic graphics to study multidimensional data. Some of his other great contributions to statistics are (i) development of a statistical tool called *Jackknife*, which is now accepted as a very important statistical tool, and (ii) re-invention of Fast Fourier Transforms.

From 1960 to 1980, Tukey headed the statistical division of NBC's election night vote projection team. He became renowned in 1960 for preventing an early call for victory for Richard Nixon in the presidential election which Nixon lost.

Tukey was also an active member of public service work. He was a member of the US delegations to the conference on discontinuance of nuclear weapons tests in Geneva in 1959, and to the UN conference on human environment in Stockholm in 1972. Between 1950 and 1954, he served on a committee to advise the National Research Council for Research in Problems of Sex. He also served on the President's Science Advisory Committee, and various President's task forces on environmental and nuclear disarmament issues.

Tukey was known for his fondness for coining terms that reflected new ideas or techniques. He is credited with introducing the terms *linear programming*, *bit* (*for binary digit*), *ANOVA*, and was first in print with the word *software*.

Among many awards and honours, Tukey received the National Medal of Science from President Nixon in 1973. He was a member of the National Academy of Sciences and the Royal Society of England.

1498
1548
1598
1648
1698
1748
1898
1948
2000

INTRODUCTION

Chapter 2 began our study of descriptive statistics. We organized a mass of raw quantitative data into a table called a *frequency distribution* and then portrayed the distribution graphically in a histogram or a frequency polygon. This allowed us to visualize where the data values tended to cluster and the general shape of the distribution. In Chapter 3 we computed several measures of central tendency, or *averages* as they are commonly called. This allowed us to define a typical value in a set of observations. In this chapter we continue to develop measures to describe a set of data, concentrating on measures that describe the **dispersion** or variability of the data set.

4.1   WHY STUDY DISPERSION?

A measure of dispersion can be used to evaluate the reliability of two or more averages.

An average, such as the mean or the median, only locates the centre of the data. It is valuable from that standpoint, but an average does not tell us anything about the spread of the data. For example, if your nature guide told you that the river ahead averaged 1.2 m in depth, would you cross it without additional information? Probably not. You would want to know something about the variation in the depth. Is the maximum depth of the river 1.3 m and the minimum 1.1 m? If that is the case, you would probably agree to cross. What if you learned the river depth ranged from 0.4 m to 3.5 m? Your decision would probably be not to cross. Before making a decision about crossing the river, you would want information on both the typical depth and the variation in the depth of the river.

A small value for a measure of dispersion indicates that the data are clustered closely around, say, the arithmetic mean. The mean is therefore considered rep-

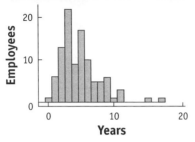

CHART 4-1: Histogram of Years of Employment at Struthers and Wells Inc.

resentative of the data. Conversely, a large measure of dispersion indicates that the mean is not reliable. Refer to Chart 4-1: the data on the number of years of employment with the company of 100 employees of Struthers and Wells Inc., a steel fabricating company, are organized into a histogram. The mean is 4.9 years, but the spread of the data is from 6 months to 16.8 years. The mean of 4.9 years is not very representative of all the employees.

A second reason for studying the dispersion in a set of data is to compare the spread in two or more distributions. Suppose, for example, that the new PDM/3 computers are assembled in Ottawa and also in Montreal. The arithmetic mean daily output in the Ottawa plant is 50, and in the Montreal plant the mean output is also 50. Based on the two means, one might conclude that the distributions of the daily outputs are identical. Production records for nine days at the two plants, however, reveal that this conclusion is not correct (see Chart 4-2). Ottawa's production varies from 48 to 52 assemblies a day. Production at the Montreal plant is more erratic, ranging from 40 to 60 a day.

4.2   MEASURES OF DISPERSION

We will consider several measures of dispersion. The range is based on the location of the largest and the smallest values in the data set. The mean deviation, the variance, and the standard deviation are all based on deviations from the mean.

RANGE

The simplest measure of dispersion is the **range**. It is the difference between the highest and the lowest values in a data set. In the form of an equation:

$$\text{Range} = \text{Highest value} - \text{Lowest value} \qquad \textbf{4-1}$$

The range can be a useful measure of dispersion for a small data set. It is generally used in statistical process control (SPC) applications. For these applications, see the chapter on statistical quality control on the CD-ROM or the Online Learning Centre. However, in many applications, the range is not used because there are other measures that provide better information about the dispersion of a data set.

Example 4-1 | Refer to Chart 4-2. Find the range in the number of computers produced for the Ottawa and the Montreal plants. Interpret the two ranges.

Solution | The range of the daily production of computers at the Ottawa plant is 4, found by the difference between the largest daily production of 52 and the smallest of 48. The range of the daily production for the Montreal plant is 20 computers, found by 60 – 40. We therefore conclude that (1) there is less dispersion in the daily production in the Ottawa plant than in the Montreal plant because a range of 4 computers is less than a range of 20 computers, and (2) the production is clustered more closely around the mean of 50 at the Ottawa plant than at the Montreal plant (because a range of 4 is less than a range of 20). Thus, the mean production in the Ottawa plant (50 computers) is a more representative average than the mean of 50 computers for the Montreal plant.

CHART 4-2: Daily Production of Computers at the Ottawa and Montreal Plants

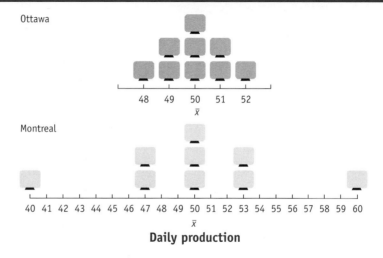

Daily production

MEAN DEVIATION

A serious defect of the range is that it is based on only two data values, the highest and the lowest; it does not take into consideration all of the values. The **mean deviation** does. It measures the mean amount by which the values in a population, or sample, vary from their mean.

> **Mean deviation** The average of the absolute values of the deviations of the data values from the arithmetic mean of the data set.

In terms of a formula, the mean deviation for the population is computed by:

Population Mean Deviation	$MD = \dfrac{\sum|x - \mu|}{N}$	4-2

where:

x is the value of an observation in the population.
μ is the arithmetic mean of the population.
N is the number of observations in the population.
$||$ indicates the absolute value. For example, the absolute value of -5 is $|-5| = 5$, while the absolute value of $+4$ is $|4| = 4$.

Example 4-2

The salaries of the five deans in a community college are $90 000, $84 000, $86 000, $90 000, and $82 000. Calculate the population mean deviation.

Solution

Calculating the value of the mean deviation of salaries of the five deans involves three steps:

1. We find the arithmetic mean of the salaries of the five deans. The arithmetic mean is ($90 000 + $84 000 + $86 000 + $90 000 + $82 000)/5 = $86 400.

2. We calculate the difference between the salary of each dean and the arithmetic mean of the deans' salaries.

3. We add these differences, ignoring the signs, and then divide the sum by the number of deans. The details of the calculations using Formula 4-2 are shown in tabular form.

Salaries ($) ($x$)	($x - \mu$) ($)	Absolute Deviation ($) ($|x-\mu|$)
90 000	(90 000 − 86 400) = 3600	3600
84 000	(84 000 − 86 400) = −2400	2400
86 000	(86 000 − 86 400) = −400	400
90 000	(90 000 − 86 400) = 3600	3600
82 000	(82 000 − 86 400) = −4400	4400
Total	$\sum(x - \mu) = 0$	$\sum|x - \mu| = 14\,400$

$$MD = \frac{\sum|x - \mu|}{N} = \frac{14\,400}{5} = 2880$$

The mean deviation is $2880. The salary of a dean deviates, on average, by $2880 from the mean salary of $86 400.

In terms of a formula, the mean deviation for a sample, designated *md*, is computed by:

Sample Mean Deviation	$md = \dfrac{\sum|x - \bar{x}|}{n}$	4-3

where:

x is the value of each observation.

$\bar{x}$ is the arithmetic mean of the sample data (or sample mean).

n is the number of observations in the sample.

Why do we ignore the signs of the deviations from the mean? If we didn't, the positive and negative deviations from the mean would exactly offset each other, and the mean deviation would always be zero. Such a measure (zero) would be useless. Because we use absolute deviations, the mean deviation is also called the **mean absolute deviation**, or **MAD**.

Example 4-3

The numbers of patients seen in the emergency room at St. Luke's Memorial Hospital for a sample of five days last year were 103, 97, 101, 106, and 103. Determine the sample mean deviation and interpret it.

Solution

To find the mean deviation of a set of data, we begin by finding the sample mean. The sample mean is 102, found by $(103 + 97 + 101 + 106 + 103)/5$. Next, we find the amount by which each observation differs from the mean. Then we sum these differences, ignoring the signs, and divide the sum by the number of observations. Below are the details of the calculations using Formula 4-3.

Number of Cases (x)	($x - \bar{x}$)	Absolute Deviation
103	$(103 - 102) = 1$	1
97	$(97 - 102) = -5$	5
101	$(101 - 102) = -1$	1
106	$(106 - 102) = 4$	4
103	$(103 - 102) = 1$	1
		Total 12

$$md = \frac{\sum|x - \bar{x}|}{n} = \frac{12}{5} = 2.4$$

The mean deviation is 2.4 patients per day. The number of patients per day deviates, on average, by 2.4 from the mean of 102 patients per day.

The mean deviation has two advantages. First, all the values in the given data set are used in the computation of the mean deviation. Recall that the range uses only the highest and the lowest values. Second, it is easy to understand—it is the average amount by which values deviate from the mean. However, its major drawback is the use of absolute values. Generally, absolute values are difficult to work with, so the mean deviation is not used as frequently as other measures of dispersion, such as the standard deviation which we shall discuss shortly.

■ SELF-REVIEW 4-1

1. The weights of a sample of eight crates being shipped to Ireland are (in kg) 43, 47, 48, 50, 48, 48, 51, and 41.
   (a) What is the range of the weights?
   (b) Compute the sample mean weight.
   (c) Compute the sample mean deviation of the weights.

2. Endu made the following payments to Visa Gold on each due date in 2001:

$2231.61	$2516.08	$1215.97	$2809.45	$1983.08	$1983.08
$487.91	$2381.72	$791.55	$791.55	$2381.72	$461.36

   (a) Calculate the arithmetic mean of Endu's monthly payments.
   (b) Calculate the mean deviation of Endu's monthly payments.

EXERCISES 4-1 TO 4-6

For Exercises 4-1 through 4-6, calculate (a) the range, (b) the arithmetic mean, (c) the mean deviation, and (d) interpret the range and the mean deviation.

4-1. There were five customer-service representatives on duty at the Electronic SuperStore during last Friday's sale. The numbers of VCRs these representatives each sold were 5, 8, 4, 10, and 3.

4-2. The department of statistics at a local university offers eight sections of Basic Statistics. The following are the numbers of students enrolled in these sections: 34, 46, 52, 29, 41, 38, 36, and 28.

4-3. One-year returns (%) on the common equity of a list of 15 companies are:

29.56	15.73	8.54	11.88	4.47	0.45	−21.76	−13.09
25.87	−9.42	5.85	15.95	10.21	22.87	−0.99	

4-4. Eight companies in the aerospace industry were surveyed as to their return on investment last year. The results are (in percent): 10.6, 12.6, 14.8, 18.2, 12.0, 14.8, 12.2, and 15.6.

4-5. The following are the weekly share prices of BCE Inc. from March 23 to June 22, 2001.

$36.05	$35.44	$34.65	$37.02	$38.75	$39.38	$39.20
$39.34	$41.35	$39.75	$39.50	$39.20	$38.25	$39.65

4-6. The personnel files of all eight male employees employed by Acme Carpet revealed that, during a six-month period, they lost the following numbers of days due to illness: 2, 0, 6, 3, 10, 4, 1, and 2.

VARIANCE AND STANDARD DEVIATION

Variance and **standard deviation** are based on squared deviations from the mean.

Population Variance is the arithmetic mean of the squared deviations from the population mean. For ungrouped data—that is, data not tabulated into a frequency distribution—the population variance is found by:

Population Variance	$\sigma^2 = \dfrac{\Sigma(x - \mu)^2}{N}$	4-4

where:

σ^2 is the symbol for the population variance.

x is the value of an observation in the population.

μ is the arithmetic mean of the population.

N is the total number of observations in the population.

$\Sigma(x-\mu)^2$ is the sum of squared deviations from the population mean.

Note in the definition of population variance that the deviations from the population mean are squared. Squaring the deviations from the mean eliminates the effect of negative signs.

Example 4-4

The ages of all the patients in the isolation ward of Willowstone Hospital are 38, 26, 13, 41, and 22 years. What is the population variance?

Solution

Age (x)	$x - \mu$	$(x - \mu)^2$
38	+10	100
26	-2	4
13	-15	225
41	+13	169
22	-6	36
140	0*	534

$$\mu = \frac{\Sigma x}{N} = \frac{140}{5} = 28$$

$$\sigma^2 = \frac{\Sigma(x-\mu)^2}{N}$$

$$= \frac{534}{5} = 106.8$$

* Sum of the deviations from mean must equal zero

Like the range and the mean deviation, the variance can be used to compare the dispersion in two or more sets of observations. For example, the variance of the ages of the patients in the isolation ward was just computed to be 106.8. If the variance of the ages of all the cancer patients in the hospital is 342.9, we conclude that (1) there is less dispersion in the distribution of the ages of patients in the isolation ward than in the age distribution of all cancer patients (because 106.8 is less than 342.9), and (2) the ages of the patients in the isolation ward are clustered more closely about their mean value than are the ages of those in the cancer ward. Thus, the mean age of the patients in the isolation ward is a more representative average than the mean of ages of cancer patients.

Standard deviation is in the same units as the data.

Population Standard Deviation Both the range and the mean deviation are easy to interpret. The *range* is the difference between the high and low values of a set of data, and the *mean deviation* is the average of the absolute values of deviations of the data values from the arithmetic mean of the data set. However, the variance is difficult to interpret for a single set of observations. The variance of 106.8 for the ages of the patients in the isolation ward is not in terms of years, but rather "years squared."

There is a way out of this dilemma. By taking the positive square root of the population variance, we can transform it to the same unit of measurement used for the original data. The square root of 106.8 years squared is 10.3 years.

The positive square root of the population variance is called the **population standard deviation**. In terms of a formula for ungrouped data:

Population Standard Deviation	$\sigma = \sqrt{\dfrac{\Sigma(x - \mu)^2}{N}}$	4-5

PROPERTIES OF STANDARD DEVIATION

- Calculation of standard deviation is based on *all* observations.
- It is reasonably easy to calculate.
- It has nice mathematical properties and lends itself readily to algebraic manipulations.
- It is a key parameter of an important class of distribution called *normal distribution*, which we shall learn later.

■ SELF-REVIEW 4-2

Marge Cold Storage employs six workers. The ages of the workers are 28, 20, 34, 19, 60, and 25.
   (a) Compute the mean age of the workers.
   (b) Compute the variance of the ages of the workers.
   (c) Compute the standard deviation of the ages of the workers.

EXERCISES 4-7 TO 4-12

4-7.   The salaries of the five accountants working in a small accounting firm are:

   $58 100 $69 990 $36 500 $77 000 $43 050

   (a) Compute the mean salary.
   (b) Compute the standard deviation of salaries of the accountants.

4-8.   Consider the following population data: 13, 3, 8, 10, 8, and 6.
   (a) Determine the mean of the population.
   (b) Determine the variance.

4-9.   The annual report of Dennis Industries cited these primary earnings per common share for the past five years: $2.68, $1.03, $2.26, $4.30, and $3.58. If we assume these are population values, what is:
   (a) the arithmetic mean primary earnings per share of common stock?
   (b) the variance?

4-10. Refer to Exercise 4-9. The annual report of Dennis Industries also gave these returns on shareholder equity for the same five-year period (in percent): 13.2, 5.0, 10.2, 17.5, and 12.9.
   (a) What is the arithmetic mean return?
   (b) What is the variance?

4-11. Plywood, Inc. reported these returns on shareholder equity for the past five years: 4.3, 4.9, 7.2, 6.7, and 11.6. Consider these as population values. Compute the range, the arithmetic mean, the variance, and the standard deviation.

4-12. One-year returns (%) on common equity of the 13 biotechnology and pharmaceutical companies listed in the top 1000 companies in the year 2000 are given below.

Company	One-Year Returns on Common Equity (%)	Company	One-Year Returns on Common Equity (%)
Glyko Biomedical	63.12	AngioTech Pharma	−1.94
Lorus Therap.	−24.33	Drug Royalty Corp.	5.52
Cangene Corp.	20.21	SignalGene Inc.	−22.01
AnorMED Inc.	−15.80	Aeterna Lab.	1.53
Axcan Pharma	6.20	Draxis Health	−8.99
Patheon Inc.	13.31	Paladin Labs	11.28
QLT Inc.	3.00		

Source: *Report on Business* magazine, Bell Globemedia Publishing Inc., June 29, 2001.

(a) Compute the range and standard deviation of one-year returns on common equity of the biotechnology and pharmaceutical companies.

(b) Why is the range not suitable to measure the variability in the above data set? Give two reasons.

SAMPLE VARIANCE

The formula for the population mean given in Chapter 3 is $\mu = \Sigma x / N$. We just changed the symbols for the sample mean; that is $\bar{x} = \Sigma x / n$. Unfortunately, the conversion from the population variance to the sample variance is not as direct. It requires a change in the denominator. Instead of substituting n (number of data values in the sample) for N (number of data values in the population), the denominator is $n - 1$. Thus, the formula for the **sample variance** is:

Sample Variance, Conceptual Formula	$s^2 = \dfrac{\Sigma(x - \bar{x})^2}{n - 1}$	**4-6**

where:
s^2 is the symbol for the sample variance.
x is the value of each observation in the sample.
$\bar{x}$ is the sample mean.
n is the total number of observations in the sample.

Why is this seemingly insignificant change made in the denominator? The primary use of a sample statistic (s^2) is to obtain a *good estimate* of the population parameter (σ^2). Although the use of n in the denominator looks logical, it tends to underestimate the population variance, σ^2. The use of ($n - 1$) in the denominator provides the appropriate correction for this tendency. Therefore ($n - 1$) is preferred to n when defining the sample variance.

COMPUTATIONAL FORMULA FOR SAMPLE VARIANCE

It can be shown that

$$\sum(x - \bar{x})^2 = \sum x^2 - \frac{(\sum x)^2}{n}$$

Using this, we get the following alternative formula for the sample variance:

Sample Variance, Computational Formula	$s^2 = \dfrac{\sum x^2 - \dfrac{(\sum x)^2}{n}}{n - 1}$	4-7

The computational Formula 4-7 is faster and much easier to calculate than Formula 4-6, even with a hand calculator, because it requires only one subtraction. It also generates less rounding error. However, to a beginning student it does not provide much insight into the concept of variance. Therefore, we recommend using Formula 4-6, which is more intuitive and insightful. However, chances of rounding error are high in this formula. We suggest prudence in rounding the value of the sample mean and the values of squared deviations. The resulting value of the sample variance can then be rounded off to fewer digits as required in a question.

Example 4-5

Employees at Fruit Packers Inc. are paid on a per unit basis of 10 cents per box packed. In one hour, a sample of 5 employees had earned $2, $10, $6, $8, and $9. What is the sample variance?

Solution

The sample variance is computed using two methods. On the left is the conceptual method, using Formula 4-6. On the right is the computational method, using Formula 4-7.

$$\bar{x} = \frac{\sum x}{n} = \frac{\$35}{5} = \$7$$

Conceptual Formula (Formula 4-6)

Hourly Wage (x)	$x - \bar{x}$	$(x - \bar{x})^2$
$2	$-\$5$	25
10	3	9
6	-1	1
8	1	1
9	2	4
$35	0	40

Computational Formula (Formula 4-7)

(x)	x^2
$2	4
10	100
6	36
8	64
9	81
$35	285

$$s^2 = \frac{\sum(x - \bar{x})^2}{n - 1} = \frac{40}{5 - 1}$$

$$= 10 \text{ in dollars squared}$$

$$s^2 = \frac{\sum x^2 - \frac{(\sum x)^2}{n}}{n - 1}$$

$$= \frac{285 - \frac{(35)^2}{5}}{5 - 1} = \frac{40}{5 - 1}$$

$$= 10 \text{ in dollars squared}$$

SAMPLE STANDARD DEVIATION

The sample standard deviation is used to estimate the value of the population standard deviation.

It is the positive square root of the sample variance. Hence, from the Formulae 4-6 and 4-7 for the sample variance, we get the following formulae for the sample standard deviation:

Sample Standard Deviation, Conceptual Formula	$s = \sqrt{\dfrac{\sum(x - \bar{x})^2}{n-1}}$	**4–8**
Sample Standard Deviation, Computational Formula	$s = \sqrt{\dfrac{\sum x^2 - \dfrac{(\sum x)^2}{n}}{n-1}}$	**4–9**

Example 4-6 | In Example 4-5, the sample variance of the sample data on hourly wages was computed to be 10. What is the sample standard deviation?

Solution | The sample standard deviation is $3.16, found by $\sqrt{10}$. Note again that the sample variance is in terms of dollars squared, but taking the square root of 10 gives us $3.16, which is in the same units (dollars) as the original data.

We use MegaStat to find the standard deviation of population data in Example 4-4.

EXCEL CHART 4-3: Variance and Standard Deviation of Population

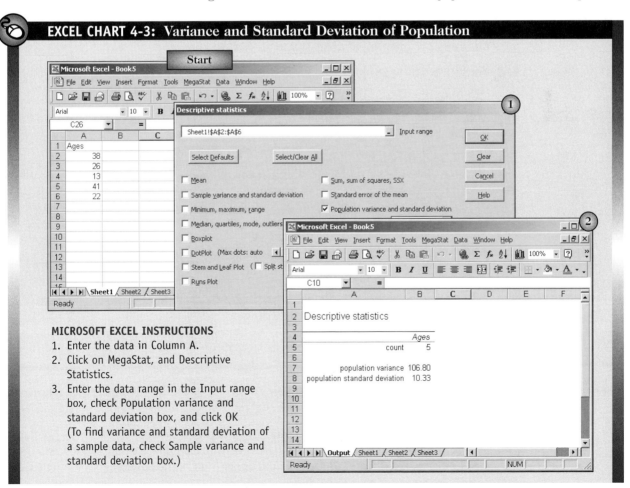

MICROSOFT EXCEL INSTRUCTIONS
1. Enter the data in Column A.
2. Click on MegaStat, and Descriptive Statistics.
3. Enter the data range in the Input range box, check Population variance and standard deviation box, and click OK
   (To find variance and standard deviation of a sample data, check Sample variance and standard deviation box.)

The population standard deviation can also be obtained in Excel by selecting f_x (Paste function) and then the function name STDEVP. The values of the sample standard deviation and variance can be found using Excel by following the same instructions as on page 96 of Chapter 3.

The sample standard deviation can be calculated using Minitab by following instructions given on page 96 in Chapter 3. It may be noted that Minitab does not compute population standard deviation.

■ SELF-REVIEW 4-3

A random sample of annual rates of returns (%) of six mutual funds is given below.

13.34,   16.62,   21.44,   2.23,   7.15,   −6.46.

(a) Compute the sample variance.
(b) Compute the sample standard deviation.

EXERCISES 4-13 TO 4-18

For each of Exercises 4-13 to 4-17, (a) compute the sample variance by conceptual formula; (b) compute the sample variance by computational formula; and (c) determine the sample standard deviation.

4-13. Consider the sample data: 7, 2, 6, 2, and 3.

4-14. Consider the sample data: 11, 6, 10, 6, and 7.

4-15. Treat the data in Exercise 4-3 on one-year returns (%) on common equity of 15 companies as sample data.

4-16. Treat the data in Exercise 4-4 on return on investment last year of eight companies in the aerospace industry as sample data.

4-17. Trout Inc. feeds fingerling trout in special ponds and markets them when they attain a certain weight. A sample of 10 trout were isolated in a pond and fed a special food mixture, designated RT-10. At the end of the experimental period, the weights of the trout were (in grams): 124, 125, 125, 123, 120, 124, 127, 125, 126, and 121.

4-18. Refer to Exercise 4-17. Another special mixture, AB-4, was used in another pond. The mean of a sample was computed to be 126.9 grams, and the standard deviation 1.2 grams. Which food results in a more uniform weight?

4.3 MEASURES OF DISPERSION FOR DATA GROUPED INTO A FREQUENCY DISTRIBUTION

RANGE

Recall that the range is defined as the difference between the highest and lowest values. To estimate the range from data already grouped into a frequency distribution, subtract the lower limit of the smallest class from the upper limit of the largest class. For example, suppose a sample of 47 hourly wages was grouped into this frequency distribution:

Hourly Earnings	Number
$5 up to $10	6
10 up to 15	12
15 up to 20	19
20 up to 25	7
25 up to 30	3

The range is $25, found by $30 – $5.

STANDARD DEVIATION

For a sample data given in frequency form, the conceptual Formula 4-8 for the sample standard deviation can be modified to the Formula 4-10 below:

$$s = \sqrt{\frac{\sum f(x - \bar{x})^2}{n - 1}} \qquad \text{4–10}$$

where:

f is the frequency of each observation.
x is the value of each observation in the sample.
$\bar{x}$ is the sample mean.
n is the number of observations and is equal to the sum of all frequencies.

Example 4-7   Listed below is the data (in frequency form) on weekly earnings of a sample of 30 employees of Grand Day Hotel. Compute the value of the sample standard deviation.

Weekly Earnings ($)	Number of Employees (f)
500	10
700	5
560	10
750	4
1000	1
	30

Solution

Step 1   To find the arithmetic mean of the frequency data, we use the formula $\left(\bar{x} = \dfrac{\sum fx}{n} \right)$ discussed in Chapter 3.

$$\sum fx = 18\,100 \qquad \text{(see Table 4-1 below)}$$

So, $\left(\bar{x} = \dfrac{\sum fx}{n} \right) = \dfrac{18\,100}{30} = 603.33$

This value is shown in the fourth column of Table 4-1.

Step 2   The value of $(x - \bar{x})^2$ for the first row is $(500 - 603.33)^2 = 10\,677.09$, for the second row $(700 - 603.33)^2 = 9345.09$, and so on.

Step 3   The value of $f(x - \bar{x})^2$ for the first row is $(10)(10\,677.09) = 106\,770.90$, for the second row, $(5)(9345.09) = 46\,725.45$, and so on.

TABLE 4-1: Calculation for the Sample Standard Deviation

Weekly Earnings ($) (x)	Number of Employees (f)	fx	$\bar{x}$	$(x - \bar{x})^2$	$f(x - \bar{x})^2$
500	10	5000	603.33	10 677.09	106 770.90
700	5	3500	603.33	9 345.09	46 725.45
560	10	5600	603.33	1 877.49	18 774.90
750	4	3000	603.33	21 512.09	86 048.36
1000	1	1000	603.33	157 347.09	157 347.09
Total	30	18 100			415 666.70

Step 4   Add entries in the $f(x - \bar{x})^2$ column. Their sum is 415 666.7. Substitute this in Formula 4-10 to get:

$$s = \sqrt{\frac{\sum f(x - \bar{x})^2}{n - 1}} = \sqrt{\frac{415\,667.7}{29}} = \$119.72$$

Thus, the sample standard deviation is $119.72

In the case of a grouped data set, the sample standard deviation can be approximated by using the conceptual Formula 4-10 where x represents the midpoint of each class and f represents the frequency of a class.

Example 4-8   A sample of the semi-monthly amounts invested in the Dupree Paint Company's profit-sharing plan by employees was organized into a frequency distribution for further study and it is given in the first two columns of Table 4-2. Calculate the sample variance and the sample standard deviation.

Solution   Following the same procedure used in Example 3-9 in Chapter 3 (page 101) for computing the arithmetic mean of grouped data, x represents the midpoint of each class. For example, the midpoint of the $30 up to $35 class is $32.50 (see Table 4-2). It is assumed that the three amounts invested in the $30 up to $35 class, average about $32.50. Similarly, the seven amounts in the $35 up to $40 class are assumed to average about $37.50, and so on. To find the standard deviation of these data using the conceptual formula, we develop Table 4-2 by following the steps outlined below.

TABLE 4-2: Calculation for the Sample Standard Deviation

Amount Invested ($)	Frequency f	Midpoint x	fx	$\bar{x}$	$f(x - \bar{x})^2$
30 up to 35	3	32.5	97.5	51.5	1083
35 up to 40	7	37.5	262.5	51.5	1372
40 up to 45	11	42.5	467.5	51.5	891
45 up to 50	22	47.5	1 045.0	51.5	352
50 up to 55	40	52.5	2 100.0	51.5	40
55 up to 60	24	57.5	1 380.0	51.5	864
60 up to 65	9	62.5	562.5	51.5	1089
65 up to 70	4	67.5	270.0	51.5	1024
Total	120		6185		6715

Step 1 | Each class frequency is multiplied by its class midpoint. That is, multiply f times x. Thus, for the first class $(3)(\$32.5) = \$97.50$, for the second class $fx = (7)(\$37.5) = \$262.50$, and so on.

Step 2 | Add the entries in the fx column. The total is 6185. Add the entries in the f column and the result is $n = 120$ (see Table 4-2). To find the value of $\bar{x}$, we divide the sum of the fx column (6185) by the sum of the f column (120).

The quotient $(6185/120) = 51.5$ is the approximate value of the sample mean and is placed in the $\bar{x}$ column (Table 4-2).

Step 3 | Calculate values of the $f(x-\bar{x})^2$ column. This could be written as (f) times $(x-\bar{x})^2$. For the first class, it would be $(3)(32.5 - 51.5)^2 = 1083$, for the second class $(7)(37.5 - 51.5)^2 = 1372$, and so on. Add the entries in this column. The sum is 6715. Substituting these values in Formula 4–10, we get:

$$s = \sqrt{\frac{\sum f(x-\bar{x})^2}{n-1}} = \sqrt{\frac{6715}{119}} = 7.51$$

Thus, the sample standard deviation is approximately $7.51. The sample variance is approximately $(\$7.51)^2 = 56.40$ (in dollars squared).

Formula 4-9 is a computational formula for the sample standard deviation of an ungrouped sample data. For sample data given in the form of a frequency distribution, a computational formula for an approximate value of the sample standard deviation can be obtained from Formula 4-9 by substituting $\sum fx^2$ for $\sum x^2$ and $\sum fx$ for $\sum x$. We provide it below.

Sample Standard Deviation, Grouped Data $\qquad s = \sqrt{\dfrac{\sum fx^2 - \dfrac{(\sum fx)^2}{n}}{n-1}}$ $\qquad$ **4-11**

where,

s is the symbol for the sample standard deviation.
x is the midpoint of a class.
f is the class frequency.
n is the total number of sample observations.

Example 4-9 | Consider again the frequency distribution, in the first two columns of Table 4-2, for the sample data on the semi-monthly amounts invested in the Dupree Paint Company's profit-sharing plan by its employees. Calculate approximate values of sample standard deviation and sample variance using the computational formula.

Solution | As in the previous example, we denote by x the midpoint of each class. For example, the midpoint of the $30 up to $35 class is $32.50 (see Table 4-2).

It is assumed that the amounts invested in the $30 up to $35 class average about $32.50. Similarly, the seven amounts in the $35 up to $40 class are assumed to average about $37.50, and so on.

TABLE 4-3: Calculations Needed for the Sample Standard Deviation

Amount Invested	Frequency, f	Midpoint, x	fx	$fx \times x$ or fx^2
$30 up to $35	3	$32.50	$97.50	3 168.75
35 up to 40	7	37.50	262.50	9 843.75
40 up to 45	11	42.50	467.50	19 868.75
45 up to 50	22	47.50	1 045.00	49 637.50
50 up to 55	40	52.50	2 100.00	110 250.00
55 up to 60	24	57.50	1 380.00	79 350.00
60 up to 65	9	62.50	562.50	35 156.25
65 up to 70	4	67.50	270.00	18 225.00
Total	120		$6 185.00	325 500.00

The grouped data is reproduced in the first two columns of Table 4-3.

Step 1

Each class frequency is multiplied by its class midpoint. That is, we multiply f times x. Thus, for the first class, $3 \times \$32.50 = \$97.50$; for the second class, $fx = 7 \times \$37.50 = \$262.50$, and so on.

Step 2

Calculate fx^2. This could be written $fx \times x$. For the first class it would be $\$97.50 \times \$32.50 = 3168.75$, for the second class $\$262.50 \times \$37.50 = 9843.75$, and so on.

Step 3

Sum up the entries in each of the fx and the fx^2 columns. The totals are $6185 and 325 500, respectively.

Inserting these sums in Formula 4-11, we get:

$$s = \sqrt{\frac{\sum fx^2 - \frac{(\sum fx)^2}{n}}{n-1}} = \sqrt{\frac{325\,500 - \frac{(6185)^2}{120}}{119}} = \$7.51$$

The sample standard deviation is approximately $7.51. The sample variance is approximately $(\$7.51)^2$, or about 56.40 (in dollars squared).

Therefore, we see that we get the same value of the sample standard deviation ($7.51) from the conceptual and computational formulae.

■ SELF-REVIEW 4-4

The following is the income distribution of a random sample of 64 families living in Fraser Valley, B.C.

Income ($ thousands)	Number of Families
30 up to 40	11
40 up to 50	18
50 up to 60	12
60 up to 70	14
70 up to 80	9

(a) Compute the range of the distribution of the data set.
(b) Compute the sample standard deviation using the conceptual formula.

EXERCISES 4-19 TO 4-22

For Exercises 4-19 to 4-22, compute approximate values of the range, the sample standard deviation, and the sample variance.

4-19. Refer to the following frequency distribution of sample data:

Class	Frequency
0 up to 5	2
5 up to 10	7
10 up to 15	12
15 up to 20	6
20 up to 25	3

4-20. Refer to the following frequency distribution of sample data:

Class	Frequency
20 up to 30	7
30 up to 40	12
40 up to 50	21
50 up to 60	18
60 up to 70	12

4-21. The following is the frequency distribution of profits of a sample of 46 of the top 1000 companies listed in *Report on Business* magazine, June 2001.

Profit ($ millions)	Number of Companies
154 up to 236.1	7
236.1 up to 318.2	11
318.2 up to 400.3	8
400.3 up to 482.4	5
482.4 up to 564.5	1
564.5 up to 646.6	4
646.6 up to 728.7	4
728.7 up to 810.8	4
810.8 up to 892.9	1
892.9 up to 975.0	1
	46

4-22. The following is the frequency distribution of the lengths of service of a sample of 70 professors in a university.

Length of service (years)	Number of Professors
0 up to 6	10
6 up to 12	15
12 up to 18	20
18 up to 24	25
Total	70

4.4 INTERPRETATION AND USES OF THE STANDARD DEVIATION

The standard deviation is commonly used to compare the spread in two or more sets of observations. For example, the standard deviation of the semi-monthly amounts invested in the Dupree Paint Company profit-sharing plan was just computed to be $7.51. Suppose these employees are located in Quebec. If the standard deviation for a group of employees in Alberta is $10.47, and the means are about the same, it indicates that the amounts invested by the employees in Quebec are not dispersed as much as those in Alberta (because $7.51 < $10.47). Since the amounts invested by the employees in Quebec clustered more closely about the mean, the mean for the Quebec employees is a more reliable measure than the mean for employees in Alberta.

PAFNUTY LVOVICH CHEBYSHEV (1821–1894)

Pafnuty Chebyshev was born in Okatovo, Russia on May 16, 1821. He graduated with a degree in mathematics from Moscow University in 1841, and received his doctorate in mathematics from Petersburg University in 1849. In 1850, he was elected extraordinary professor of mathematics at Petersburg University where he became a full professor in 1860.

Chebyshev made deep contributions to various branches of mathematics. He is particularly well known for his contributions to number theory. His monograph *Teoria Sravneny* ("Theory of Congruences") is considered a classic work in this area. He is best known to beginning students of statistics for his theorem, which gives a lower bound on the fraction of data values that lie within a certain standard deviation of the mean.

To supplement his modest salary as a university professor, Chebyshev often had to take private clients. One such task he accepted was to develop a more economical means of cutting fabrics for army uniforms. He perceived the fabric as a kind of net and developed a profound mathematical theory of cable nets, which he published in the form of a book.

Chebyshev is known not only for his discoveries in mathematics and sciences but also for the foundation of a scientific school, the Petersburg Mathematical School. He became a foreign associate of the Institut de France and also of the Royal Society.

CHEBYSHEV'S THEOREM

We have stressed that a small standard deviation for a data set indicates that these data values are located close to the mean. Conversely, a large standard deviation reveals that the observations are widely scattered about the mean. The Russian mathematician P.L. Chebyshev (1821–1894) developed a theorem that allows us to determine a lower bound on the proportion of the values that lie within a specified number of standard deviations of the mean. For example, based on **Chebyshev's theorem**, at least three out of four values, or 75 percent, must lie between the mean plus two standard deviations and the mean minus two standard deviations. This relationship applies regardless of the shape of the distribution. Further, at least eight of nine values, or 88.9 percent, will lie between plus three standard deviations and minus three standard deviations of the mean. At least 24 of 25 values, or 96 percent, will lie between plus and minus five standard deviations of the mean.

> i **Chebyshev's theorem**   For any population data, the proportion of the data values that lie within k standard deviations of the population mean is at least $1 - \dfrac{1}{k^2}$, where k is any constant number greater than one.

If we replace the population mean and the population standard deviation by the sample mean and the sample standard deviation, then for a large sample of data the result is approximately valid.

Example 4-10   The arithmetic mean salary of all professors in a community college is $60 000. The standard deviation of salaries is $1500.

      (a) At least what percentage of the salaries lie within plus 1.5 standard deviations and minus 1.5 standard deviations of the arithmetic mean?

      (b) What is the range of salaries that fall within plus 1.5 standard deviations of the mean and minus 1.5 standard deviations of the mean?

Solution   (a) We are given that $k = 1.5$.

The proportion of salaries within plus 1.5 standard deviations and minus 1.5 standard deviations of the population mean is

$$1 - \frac{1}{k^2} = 1 - \frac{1}{1.5^2} = 1 - \frac{1}{2.25} = 0.555, \text{ which is } 55.5\%$$

      (b) 1.5 standard deviations of the population mean is $(1.5)(1500) = 2250$. Thus, the range of salaries is from $(60 000 − 2250) = $57 750$ to $(60 000 + 2250) = $62 250$.

THE EMPIRICAL RULE

Chebyshev's theorem is true for any data set, that is, the distribution of data values can have any shape (symmetrical, skewed, etc.). However, many sets of data in real life, such as heights, weights, and blood pressures (for people), linear dimensions (for manufactured articles), and percent daily changes (for stock markets), have distributions that are approximately symmetrical and bell-shaped. A symmetrical, bell-shaped distribution is therefore of great significance in statistical inferences, and we shall discuss it in detail in Chapter 7. For such a distribution, we can use the following empirical rule to obtain a more precise value of the proportion of data values that lie within a specified number of standard deviations of the mean.

> ℹ️ **Empirical rule**   If the population distribution is symmetrical and bell-shaped, then approximately 68 percent of the data values will lie within plus and minus one standard deviation of the population mean. About 95 percent of the data values will lie within plus and minus two standard deviations of the population mean, and practically all (99.7 percent) will lie within plus and minus three standard deviations of the population mean.

CHART 4-4: Distribution of Data Values in a Symmetrical, Bell-Shaped Curve

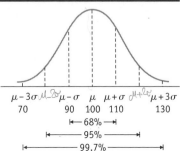

If we substitute the sample mean and sample standard deviation of a large sample in the empirical rule, we get an approximation.

These relationships are portrayed graphically in Chart 4-4 for a symmetrical, bell-shaped distribution with a mean of 100 and a standard deviation of 10.

We saw that if a distribution is symmetrical and bell-shaped, practically all of the observations lie between the mean plus and minus three standard deviations. Thus, if $\mu = 100$ and $\sigma = 10$, practically all the observations lie between $100 + 3(10)$ and $100 - 3(10)$, or 70 and 130. The range is therefore approximately 60, found by $130 - 70$, or by $6\sigma = 6(10) = 60$.

Conversely, if we know that the range is 60, we can approximate the standard deviation by dividing the range by 6. For this illustration: range ÷ 6 = 60 ÷ 6 = 10, the standard deviation.

Example 4-11 | The distribution of monthly amounts spent on food by all senior citizens living alone in a particular region of Canada approximates a bell-shaped distribution. The population mean and standard deviation are $150 and $20, respectively. Use the empirical rule.

1. Find an interval symmetrical about the population mean containing the monthly food expenditures of about 68 percent of the senior citizens in the region.

2. Find an interval symmetrical about the population mean containing the monthly food expenditures of about 95 percent of the senior citizens in the region.

3. Find an interval symmetrical about the population mean containing the monthly food expenditures of almost all the senior citizens in the region.

Solution

1. About 68 percent of the data values lie between $130 and $170, found by $\mu - 1\sigma$ $= (150 - 1(20)) = \$130$, and $\mu + 1\sigma = (150 + 1(20)) = \$170$.

2. About 95 percent of the data values lie between $110 and $190, found by $\mu - 2\sigma$ $= (150 - 2(20)) = \$110$, and $\mu + 2\sigma = (150 + 2(20)) = \$190$.

3. Almost all (99.7 percent) of the data values are between $90 and $210, found by $\mu - 3\sigma = (150 - 3(20)) = \$90$, and $\mu + 3\sigma = (150 + 3(20)) = \$210$.

■ SELF-REVIEW 4-5

Engel Canada Inc. is one of several domestic manufacturers of PVC pipe. The quality control department sampled 600 3 m lengths. For each pipe, they measured the outside diameter at a point 0.3 m from the end of the pipe. The sample mean was 35.6 cm and the sample standard deviation 0.25 cm.

  (a) If the shape of the distribution is unknown, at least what percentage of the observations will be between 35.3 cm and 35.9 cm?

  (b) If the distribution of diameters is symmetrical and bell-shaped, find an interval symmetrical about the mean containing about 95 percent of the observed values of diameters.

EXERCISES 4-23 TO 4-26

4-23. According to Chebyshev's theorem, at least what percentage of population data will be within 1.8 standard deviations of the mean?

4-24. The average of the marks of all 65 students in a Quantitative Methods II class of Winter 2002 was 70.4. The standard deviation was 2.4. The distribution of marks approximated a bell-shaped distribution.

  (a) About what percentage of students' marks were between 68 and 72.8?

  (b) About what percentage of students' marks were between 65.6 and 75.2?

4-25. The weights of cargo containers are found to be somewhat normally distributed. Based on the empirical rule, approximately what percentage of the weights will lie:

  (a) Between $\mu - 2\sigma$ and $\mu + 2\sigma$?

  (b) Between μ and $\mu + 2\sigma$? Below $\mu - 2\sigma$?

4-26. The following figure portrays the symmetrical appearance of a sample distribution of efficiency ratings. Assuming that the sample size is large, answer the following:

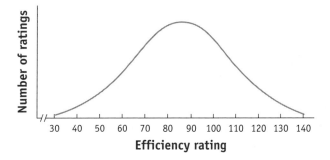

(a) Estimate the mean efficiency rating.
(b) Estimate the standard deviation to the nearest whole number.
(c) Find an interval of values, symmetrical about the sample mean, containing about 68 percent of the efficiency ratings.
(d) Find an interval of values, symmetrical about the sample mean, containing about 95 percent of the efficiency ratings.

4.5   RELATIVE DISPERSION

A direct comparison of the values of the same measure of dispersion for two different data sets—say, the standard deviation of a distribution of annual incomes and the standard deviation of a distribution of absenteeism for the same group of employees—is impossible. Can we say that the standard deviation of $1200 for the income distribution is greater than the standard deviation of 4.5 days for the distribution of absenteeism? Obviously not, because we cannot directly compare dollars and days absent from work. To make a meaningful comparison of the dispersion in incomes and absenteeism, we need to convert each of these measures to a *relative* value. Karl Pearson (1857–1936), developed one such relative measure called the **coefficient of variation** (*CV*). It is a very useful measure when:

1. The data are in different units (such as dollars and days absent).
2. The data are in the same units, but the means are far apart (such as the incomes of top executives and the incomes of unskilled employees).

> i **Coefficient of variation**   The ratio of the standard deviation to the arithmetic mean, expressed as a percentage.

In terms of a formula for a population:

Coefficient of Variation	$CV = \dfrac{\sigma}{\mu}(100)$	**4-12**

In terms of a formula for a sample:

Coefficient of Variation	$CV = \dfrac{s}{\bar{x}}(100)$	**4-13**

Example 4-12   A study of the size of bonus paid and the years of service of employees resulted in the following statistics. (1) The mean bonus paid was $200; the standard deviation was $40. (2) The mean number of years of service was 20 years; the standard deviation was 2 years. Compare the relative dispersions in the two distributions using the coefficient of variation.

Solution   The distributions are in different units (dollars and years of service). Therefore, they are converted to coefficients of variation.

For the bonus paid	For years of service
$CV = \dfrac{s}{\bar{x}}(100)$	$CV = \dfrac{s}{\bar{x}}(100)$
$= \dfrac{40}{200}(100)$	$= \dfrac{2}{20}(100)$
$= 20$ percent	$= 10$ percent

There is more dispersion relative to the mean in the distribution of bonuses paid compared with the distribution of years of service (because 20 percent > 10 percent).

The same procedure is used when the data are in the same units but the means are far apart.

Example 4-13 | Mina is teaching two general education courses in a community college: Speaking with Confidence and Personal Finance. The mean and standard deviation of marks of all the students in Speaking with Confidence are 70.5 and 5.6, respectively. The mean and standard deviation of marks of all the students in Personal Finance are 90 and 6.4, respectively. She would like to compare the relative dispersion of marks in these two courses using the coefficient of variation.

Solution

Speaking with Confidence	Personal Finance
$CV = \dfrac{\sigma}{\mu}(100)$	$CV = \dfrac{\sigma}{\mu}(100)$
$= \dfrac{5.6}{70.5}(100) = 7.94$	$= \dfrac{6.4}{90}(100) = 7.11$

The higher coefficient of variation for Speaking with Confidence indicates more dispersion (relative to the mean) of marks in this course than in Personal Finance.

■ SELF-REVIEW 4-6

The average amount of money earned by the world's 50 most valuable athletes in 2000 was 18.7 ($millions) and the standard deviation of their earnings was 19.4 ($millions). The average amount of money earned by the 50 best-paid executives in 2000 was 14.4 ($millions) and the standard deviation of their earnings was 12.7 ($millions).

Compare the relative dispersions in the earnings of the world's 50 most valuable athletes and the 50 best-paid executives.

EXERCISES 4-27 TO 4-30

4-27. The average annual return of a fund over a period of six years (1994–2000) is 15.50 percent and the standard deviation is 12.17 percent. Compute the coefficient of variation of the annual returns of the fund.

4-28. Following are percentage one-year returns on common equity for a sample of 15 mining companies and 15 biotechnology and pharmaceutical companies in 2000.

One-Year Return on Common Equity (%)			
Mining	Biotechnology and Pharmaceuticals	Mining	Biotechnology and Pharmaceuticals
8.54	63.12	0.39	−24.33
16.41	20.21	0.09	−15.80
11.38	3.00	−0.75	13.31
86.04	5.52	−2.90	6.20
13.58	1.53	−1.42	11.28
4.98	−8.99	−3.36	−1.94
14.54	20.21	−4.44	13.78
		4.82	6.20

(a) Estimate the standard deviation of each group of stocks.
(b) Which statistical measure would you use to compare the relative variability of the two groups of stocks?
(c) The coefficient of variation is used as a measure of risk in investment. Keeping this in mind, which of the two groups of stocks should be preferred by investors who have an aversion to taking risk in investment? Show your calculations.

4-29. Below are the price–earnings ratios and returns on common equity of a sample of 13 stocks of companies listed in the top 1000 companies for 2000.

Companies	Price–Earnings Ratio	Return (One-year) on Common Equity
BCE Inc.	5.83	29.56
Royal Bank	13.68	19.36
Imperial Oil	11.60	32.44
Manu Life	21.15	15.73
Bombardier Inc.	33.07	28.10
Alberta Energy	11.18	23.74
Magna Intl.	6.02	15.64
Cdn Natl.Resources	6.19	31.35
Power Corp.	12.63	18.53
Sun Life Finl	21.05	10.00
Telus Corp	22.46	8.64
Investors Group	19.19	27.53
Manitoba Telecom Services	24.77	17.68

(a) Why should the coefficient of variation be used to compare the variations in the price–earnings ratio and return on common equity?
(b) Compare the relative variation for the price–earnings ratios with the variation in the returns on common equity of the top 1000 companies in 2000.

4-30. The spread in the annual prices of stocks selling for under $10 and the spread in prices of those selling for more than $60 are to be compared. The mean price of the stocks selling for under $10 is $5.25 and the standard deviation is $1.52. The mean price of those stocks selling for more than $60 is $92.50 and the standard deviation is $5.28.

(a) Why should the coefficient of variation be used to compare the dispersion in the prices?

(b) Compute the coefficients of variation. What is your conclusion?

SKEWNESS AND KURTOSIS

Chapter 3 numerically describes the central tendency of a set of observations using the mean, the median, and the mode. The current chapter describes measures that show the amount of spread or variation in a set of data, such as the range and the standard deviation.

Another characteristic of a data set is the shape of its histogram or frequency polygon. The shape of a distribution is either unimodal or multimodal. It is said to be unimodal if it has only one peak, while a multimodal distribution has two or more peaks. As we saw in Chapter 3 (page 107), the shapes of distributions can also be categorized as symmetrical and non-symmetrical (or skewed). In the case of a symmetrical curve, if we cut it at its centre, the left side obtained is a mirror image of the right. In a symmetrical distribution of a data set, mean and median are equal. If, in addition, it is unimodal, then the mean, median, and mode are all equal.

SKEWNESS

The degree of non-symmetry in the shape of a distribution is called its **coefficient of skewness**. So, ideally, the value of the coefficient of skewness of a distribution should be defined in such a way that it will be zero for symmetrical distributions and it will be non-zero for non-symmetrical distributions.

Karl Pearson proposed the following simple expression for the coefficient of skewness:

$$SK_1 = \frac{3(\text{Mean} - \text{Median})}{\sigma} \qquad \text{4-14a}$$

For a sample of observations, SK_1 can be estimated by:

$$\overline{SK_1} = \frac{3(\text{Mean} - \text{Median})}{s} \qquad \text{4-14b}$$

Distributions with a positive value of SK_1 are said to be *positively skewed*, while distributions with a negative value of SK_1 are said to be *negatively skewed*. The value of SK_1 can vary from -3 to 3. A value near ± 3 or -3, such as -2.57, indicates considerable skewness. A value such as 1.63 indicates moderate skewness.

For a symmetrical distribution, mean and median are equal and hence the value of SK_1 is zero. In the case of a unimodal distribution with a long tail to the right, the mean is greater than the median and, thus, the distribution is *positively skewed*. We observe such distributions commonly in the real world. For example, salaries often follow this pattern. Think of the salaries of those employed in a small company of about 100 people. The president and a few top executives would have very large salaries relative to the other workers and hence the distribution of salaries would show positive skewness. A unimodal distribution with a long tail to the left has a mean smaller than the median. Such a distribution is thus negatively skewed.

CHART 4-5: Shapes of Frequency Polygons

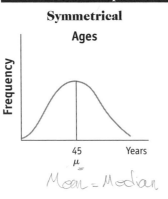

Symmetrical

Ages

Mean = Median

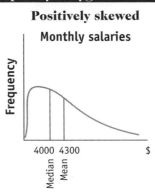

Positively skewed

Monthly salaries

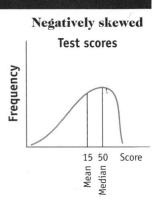

Negatively skewed

Test scores

These are summarized in Chart 4-5.

Various more sophisticated measures of skewness have been proposed by statisticians for general distributions. The statistical software packages Minitab and Excel use the following formula for a sample estimate of the coefficient of skewness:

$$\overline{SK}_2 = \frac{n}{(n-1)(n-2)}\left[\Sigma\left(\frac{x-\overline{x}}{s}\right)^3\right] \qquad \textbf{4-15}$$

For a symmetrical data set, the sum of the cubed expression is zero and therefore the value of SK_2 is zero. In the presence of many large values in the data, the sum of the cubed values in the expression gives a large positive value. On the other hand, the presence of several small values results in a negative cubed sum.

Example 4-14

Earnings per share for a sample of 15 software companies for the year 2000 are arranged in ascending order below:

$0.09 $0.13 $0.41 $0.51 $1.12 $1.20 $1.49 $3.18 $3.50
$6.36 $7.83 $8.92 $10.13 $12.99 $16.40

(a) Compute the sample mean, median, and standard deviation.
(b) Find estimates of the coefficient of skewness using Pearson's expression and the software method. Comment on the shape of the distribution.

Solution

As the sample data set is ungrouped, we use Formula 3-2 to compute the mean:

$$\overline{x} = \frac{\Sigma x}{n} = \frac{\$74.26}{15} = \$4.95$$

The median is the middle value of the data set. In this case, it is $3.18. Using Formula 4-9 calculate the sample standard deviation.

$$s = \sqrt{\frac{\Sigma x^2 - \frac{(\Sigma x)^2}{n}}{n-1}} = \sqrt{\frac{749.372 - \frac{(74.26)^2}{15}}{15-1}} = 5.22$$

Using Formula 4-14b, we obtain the following estimate of Pearson's coefficient of skewness:

$$\overline{SK}_1 = \frac{3(\text{Mean} - \text{Median})}{s} = \frac{3(4.95 - 3.18)}{5.22} = 1.017.$$

Let us now obtain an estimate of the coefficient of skewness using computer software. For Excel (MegaStat), we follow the same instructions as on page 129 for standard deviation, except that in Step 3, we check the *Skewness*, *Kurtosis*, and *CV* box. The MegaStat output is given below.

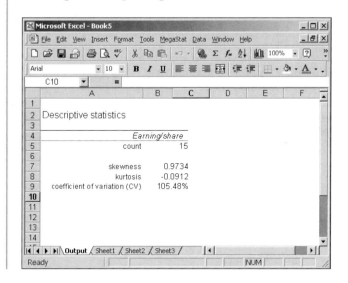

The instructions, as well as screen shots for Minitab are given below:

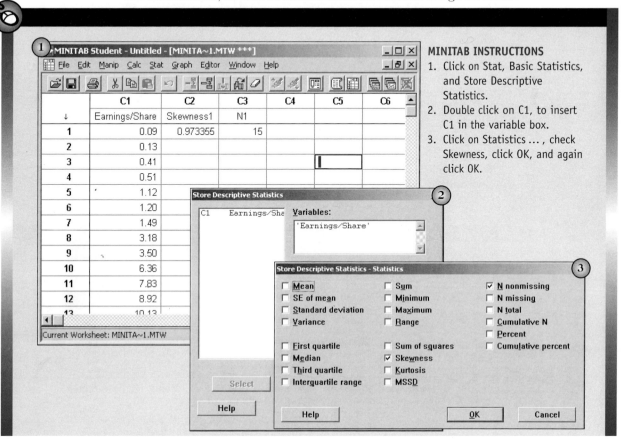

MINITAB INSTRUCTIONS

1. Click on Stat, Basic Statistics, and Store Descriptive Statistics.
2. Double click on C1, to insert C1 in the variable box.
3. Click on Statistics ... , check Skewness, click OK, and again click OK.

It may be noted that since Excel and Minitab use Formula 4-15, the estimate of the coefficient of skewness obtained from the computer outputs ($= 0.9734$) is slightly different from the one we obtained above using Formula 4-14b ($= 1.017$).

KURTOSIS

Kurtosis (Greek word, *kyrtösis*) refers to the flatness or peakedness of the shape of a data distribution. Generally, the peakedness of a distribution is compared to that of a very important distribution called the *normal distribution*, which we shall study in detail in Chapter 7. A distribution that is more peaked compared to the normal distribution, is known as *leptokurtic* (Greek *lepto*: long thin peak), and a distribution that is flat-topped, compared to the normal distribution is known as *platykurtic* (Greek *platu*: broad, flat expanse). Charts 4-6a and 4-6b show respectively, a leptokurtic and a platykurtic distribution.

HOW TO MEASURE KURTOSIS

The kurtosis of a population data set is measured by:

$$K = \frac{\sum(x-\mu)^4}{N\sigma^4} - 3 \qquad\qquad 4\text{-}16$$

where:
K is the kurtosis.
x is the values of the population data.
μ is the population mean.
N is the number of data values in the population data set.
σ is the standard deviation of the population.
The value of kurtosis for a normal curve is 0. Hence, for a *leptokurtic* distribution the value of kurtosis is positive, for a *platykurtic* distribution, the value of kurtosis is negative.

    Example 4-15 illustrates the calculation of the value of kurtosis.

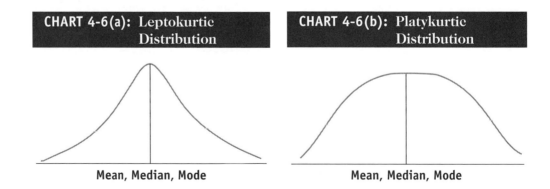

CHART 4-6(a): Leptokurtic Distribution

Mean, Median, Mode

CHART 4-6(b): Platykurtic Distribution

Mean, Median, Mode

Example 4-15   The following are the marks of all 10 students enrolled in an advanced level computer science course in fall 2002. Calculate the value of kurtosis.

74   54   94   100   60   44   74   58   53   32

Solution   The calculations for the value of kurtosis are shown in tabular form below.

Marks (x)	Population Mean (μ)	$(x - \mu)^4$	Population Standard Deviation (σ)
74	64.3	8 852.93	20.23
54	64.3	11 255.09	
94	64.3	778 082.77	
100	64.3	1 624 324.76	
60	64.3	341.88	
44	64.3	169 818.17	
74	64.3	8 852.93	
58	64.3	1 575.30	
53	64.3	16 304.74	
32	64.3	1 088 454.02	
Total		3 707 862.59	

$$\sigma = \sqrt{\frac{\Sigma(x - \mu)^2}{N}} = \sqrt{409.21} = 20.23$$

Now, we can substitute the values in Formula 4-16:

$$K = \frac{\Sigma(x - \mu)^4}{N\sigma^4} - 3 = \frac{3\ 707\ 862.59}{10(20.23)^4} - 3 = -0.79$$

As the value of the kurtosis is negative, the shape of the distribution is flat-topped.

The kurtosis of the population can be estimated from given sample data using the following formula for a sample

$$K_1 = \frac{n(n+1)}{(n-1)(n-2)(n-3)} \frac{\Sigma(x - \bar{x})^4}{s^4} - \frac{3(n-1)^2}{(n-2)(n-3)} \qquad \text{4-17}$$

where:
K_1 is the kurtosis for a sample.
$\bar{x}$ is the sample mean.
s is the sample standard deviation.
n is the number of data values in a sample.

The value of the kurtosis for a given data set can be obtained using computer software. In the case of MegaStat, the instructions for this are the same as those for finding the skewness, given on page 145. Also, in the case of Minitab, the instructions are the same as the ones for skewness, (see page 145), except that we check the *Kurtosis* box in place of the *Skewness* box in *Store Descriptive Statistics-statistics* window.

■ SELF-REVIEW 4-7

A sample of five data-entry clerks employed in the Canada Customs and Revenue Office in Vancouver revised the following numbers of tax records yesterday:

73   98   60   92   84

(a) Find the sample mean, median, and the sample standard deviation.
(b) Obtain an estimate of the coefficient of skewness using Pearson's method.
(c) Obtain an estimate of the coefficient of skewness using the software method.
(d) What is your conclusion regarding the skewness of the data?
(e) Obtain an estimate of kurtosis of the data.

EXERCISES 4-31 TO 4-34

4-31. The price–earnings ratios (P/E) of the stocks of a sample of 15 companies listed in the top 1000 companies were published in *Report on Business* magazine on June 29, 2001. The values are given below.

5.83   10.67   10.23   8.68   15.99   6.44   22.98   13.05
8.28   16.14   9.26   9.25   20.21   3.04   13.60

(a) Find the sample mean, median, and standard deviation of the data set.
(b) Obtain an estimate of the coefficient of skewness using Pearson's method.
(c) Obtain an estimate of the coefficient of skewness using the software method.
(d) Is the distribution skewed to the right? Justify your answer.

4-32. Listed below are the salaries ($ thousands) for a sample of 15 executives from the list of the 50 best-paid executives in 2000.

297   655   450   746   475   900   480   629
900   817   419   149   814   575   763

(a) Calculate the sample mean, median, and standard deviation of the data set.
(b) Obtain an estimate of the coefficient of skewness of the distribution of salaries using the software method.
(c) Is the distribution of salaries skewed to the right? Justify your answer. Based on the summary data, which measure of central tendency would you recommend to describe the executives' salaries?

4-33. Listed below are the commissions earned ($ thousands) last year by all the sales representatives at the Furniture Patch.

3.9   5.7   7.3   10.6   13.0   13.6   15.1   15.8   17.1
17.4   17.6   22.3   38.6   43.2   87.7

(a) Calculate the mean, median, and the standard deviation.
(b) Determine the coefficient of skewness using Pearson's method.

4-34. The share prices of a sample of 30 companies for 2000 are listed below.

$1.60	$1.28	$0.81	$1.13	$3.70	$1.01	$0.77	$1.50
$1.59	$0.92	$0.63	$0.99	$0.15	$1.90	$1.42	$1.30
$1.97	$1.64	$3.17	$1.08	$1.67	$1.05	$0.94	$1.56
$1.11	$0.32	$1.36	$0.39	$0.73	$0.82		

(a) Compute the sample mean, median, and standard deviation of the share prices.

(b) Obtain an estimate of the coefficient of skewness of the share prices using Pearson's method.

(c) Obtain an estimate of the coefficient of skewness of the share prices using the software method.

(d) Is the distribution of the share prices skewed to the left or to the right?

(e) Obtain an estimate of the value of kurtosis for the data set.

4.6 OTHER SUMMARY MEASURES OF DISPERSION

QUARTILES, DECILES, AND PERCENTILES

Quartiles divide a set of observations into four equal parts. To explain further, think of any set of values arranged from smallest to largest. In Chapter 3, we called the midpoint of the data values after they have been ordered from smallest to largest, the *median*. The median is a measure of location because it pinpoints the centre of the data. In a similar fashion, quartiles divide a set of observations into four equal parts. The first quartile, usually labelled Q_1, is the value of an ordered data set such that at most, one-quarter of the data is below it and at most three-quarters of the data are above it. The third quartile, usually labelled Q_3, is the value of the ordered data set such that at most three-quarters of the data are below it and at most one-quarter of the data is above it. Q_2 is the median. The values corresponding to Q_1, Q_2, and Q_3 divide a set of data into four equal parts. Q_1 can be thought of as the "median" of the lower half of the data and Q_3 the "median" of the upper half of the data.

In a similar fashion, *deciles* divide a set of observations into 10 equal parts, and *percentiles* into 100 equal parts. So, if you found that your GPA was in the 8th decile at your university, you could conclude that at most 80 percent of the students had a GPA lower than yours and at most 20 percent of the students had a GPA higher than yours. A GPA in the 33rd percentile means that at most 33 percent of the students have a lower GPA and at most 67 percent have a higher GPA. Percentile scores are frequently used to report results on such national standardized tests as the SAT, ACT, GMAT (used to judge entry into many MBA programs), and LSAT (used to judge entry into law school).

COMPUTATION OF QUARTILES, DECILES, AND PERCENTILES

To find a percentile value of a population data set, first we arrange the data set in ascending order and then create an index $L = \dfrac{NP}{100}$, where N is the number of data values in the data set and P is the required percentile. If L is a whole number, then the midpoint of the Lth and $[L + 1]$th values of the ordered data set is the required percentile value. If L is not a whole number, then the value corresponding to the next whole number greater than L in the ordered data set is the required percentile value. Example 4-16 illustrates.

Example 4-16

The following are the marks of all 20 students enrolled in Math 1015 in 2002.

74   54   94   100   100   44   74   58   42   97
81   88   99   100   86   100   82   52   53   32

Find the values of the 25th and 28th percentiles of the above data set.

STATISTICS IN ACTION

Ranking Mutual Funds

(Continued)

The Fraser Institute of British Columbia ranks its provincial secondary schools on the basis of teaching and counselling techniques used to help students to succeed in their lives.

The standard deviation is the most widely used measure of dispersion. However, there are other ways of describing the variation or spread in a set of data. One method is to determine the *location* of values that divide a set of observations into equal parts. These measures include *quartiles*, *deciles*, and *percentiles*.

Solution

First, we arrange the marks of students in ascending order:

32   42   44   52   53   54   58   74   74   81
82   86   88   94   97   99   100   100   100   100

To calculate the 25th percentile, we first calculate $L = \dfrac{NP}{100} = \dfrac{(20)(25)}{100} = 5$.

As 5 is a whole number, the 25th percentile value is the midpoint of the 5th and 6th values of the ordered data set; that is, $\left(\dfrac{53+54}{2}\right) = 53.5$. The value of the 25th percentile is 53.5.

To calculate the 28th percentile, we first calculate $L = \dfrac{NP}{100} = \dfrac{(20)(28)}{100} = 5.6$.

The value of L is *not* a whole number, and the next higher whole number is 6. Hence, the 28th percentile is the value in the 6th position in the ordered data set, which is 54. Thus, the 28th percentile value is 54.

A good estimate of the value of the population percentile that we can obtain from a sample data is the sample percentile. It is the value in the ordered sample data, located in position, given by Formula 4-18 below.

Location of Sample *P*th Percentile L_p	$L_p = (n+1)\dfrac{P}{100}$	**4-18**

Where:

L_p is the location of a desired percentile.
n is the number of observations in the sample.
P is the required percentile.

The value of L_p obtained using Formula 4-18 could be a fraction. In this case, the value of the sample percentile is a weighted mean of the data values in the two adjacent locations in the ordered sample data. For example, if we obtain $L_p = 5.2$, then the value of the sample percentile is (0.2)(the sixth value) $+ (1 - 0.2)$(the fifth value).

Example 4-17

The following is the list of the price per share of a sample of 15 companies in *Report on Business* magazine for 2000.

$1.60 $0.81 $3.70 $0.77 $0.99 $1.90 $1.30 $1.64
$1.56 $0.32 $0.39 $1.50 $0.92 $3.17 $1.67

Find the sample median, first quartile, third quartile, and sixtieth percentile of the above data set.

Solution

We organize the data from the smallest price per share to the largest·

$0.32 $0.39 $0.77 $0.81 $0.92 $0.99 $1.30 $1.50
$1.56 $1.60 $1.64 $1.67 $1.90 $3.17 $3.70

The median value of the data set is the value in the centre of the ordered data set. It is therefore the same as the 50th percentile. Similarly, recall that quartiles divide a set of data values into four equal parts. Hence, the first quartile is the same as the 25th percentile and the third quartile is the same as the 75th percentile. Thus, we are required to find the 50th, 25th, 75th, and 60th sample percentiles.

Using Formula 4-18, we find their locations in the ordered sample data:

for the median: $$L_p = (n+1)\frac{P}{100} = (15+1)\frac{50}{100} = 8;$$

for the first quartile: $$L_p = (n+1)\frac{P}{100} = (15+1)\frac{25}{100} = 4;$$

for the third quartile: $$L_p = (n+1)\frac{P}{100} = (15+1)\frac{75}{100} = 12;$$

for the sixtieth percentile: $$L_p = (n+1)\frac{P}{100} = (15+1)\frac{60}{100} = 9.6.$$

Therefore, the sample median, first and third quartiles are values in the locations 8, 4, and 12 in the ordered sample data, which are \$1.50, \$0.81, and \$1.67, respectively.

For the sixtieth percentile, we get $L_p = 9.6$. Hence,

The sample sixtieth percentile = (0.6)(the 10th value) + (1 − 0.6)(the 9th value)
$$= (0.6)(1.60) + (0.4)(1.56)$$
$$= 1.584$$

Q_1 median

\$0.32   \$0.39   \$0.77   \$0.81   \$0.92   \$0.99   \$1.30   \$1.50

\$1.56   \$1.60   \$1.64   \$1.67   \$1.90   \$3.17   \$3.70

60th percentile Q_3

It is quite easy to find the percentile values using a computer software package. In the example we will illustrate two percentile values, the 25th percentile (first quartile) and the 75th percentile (third quartile).

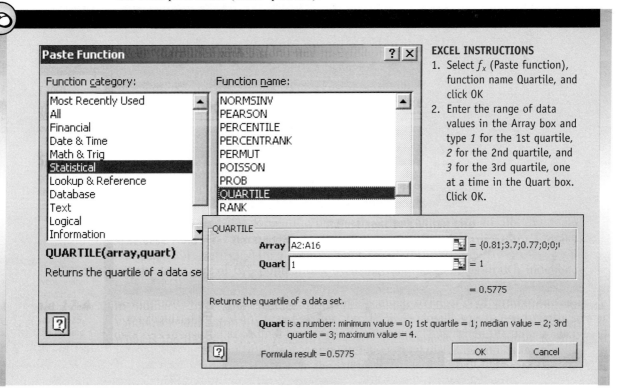

EXCEL INSTRUCTIONS
1. Select f_x (Paste function), function name Quartile, and click OK
2. Enter the range of data values in the Array box and type *1* for the 1st quartile, *2* for the 2nd quartile, and *3* for the 3rd quartile, one at a time in the Quart box. Click OK.

Paste Function   ? X

Function category: Function name:

Most Recently Used   NORMSINV
All   PEARSON
Financial   PERCENTILE
Date & Time   PERCENTRANK
Math & Trig   PERMUT
Statistical   POISSON
Lookup & Reference   PROB
Database   QUARTILE
Text   RANK
Logical
Information

QUARTILE(array,quart)

Returns the quartile of a data se

QUARTILE

Array A2:A16   = {0.81;3.7;0.77;0;0;

Quart 1   = 1

                                 = 0.5775

Returns the quartile of a data set.

Quart is a number: minimum value = 0; 1st quartile = 1; median value = 2; 3rd quartile = 3; maximum value = 4.

Formula result = 0.5775   OK   Cancel

The instructions for finding the first and third quartiles using Minitab are the same as those described on page 96 in Chapter 3.

In MegaStat, we use the same instructions to calculate quartiles as those on page 129, for calculation of standard deviation, except that in Step 3, we check the *Median, Quartiles, Mode, Outliers* box.

The instructions for finding the values of quartiles using Excel are given on the previous page.

■ SELF-REVIEW 4-8

The following are the amounts of money earned (in $US millions) by 13 of the world's 50 most valuable athletes in the year 2000.

63.1	24.0	48.0	2.7	10.6	18.0	17.0
20.0	7.0	17.5	10.0	3.0	6.5	

(a) Calculate the sample median salary of the data set.
(b) Calculate the sample first and the third quartiles of the data set and interpret the meanings in the context of the question.

EXERCISES 4-35 TO 4-38

4-35. The market capitalization ($ millions) of a sample of 14 companies in the list of top 1000 companies in Canada in 2000 are given below. Determine the sample median and first and third quartile values and interpret their meanings in the context of the question.

35 067	29 096	18 254	21 661	35 919	18 421
12 277	15 771	22 630	10 665	26 119	31 324
10 759	16 325				

4-36. Below are the sale prices ($ thousands) of a sample of 16 houses in Clarington, Ontario, in 2000. Determine the sample median and first and third quartile values of the sale prices of the houses in Clarington. Explain the value of the sample third quartile.

295.0	475.0	549.0	739.9	759.9	99.8	129.0	182.5
138.9	149.9	154.9	157.9	174.9	174.9	179.8	179.9

4-37. Anderson Inc. is a distributor of small electrical motors. As with any business, the length of time customers take to pay their invoices is important. Listed below, arranged from smallest to largest, is the time in days to pay for a sample of Anderson Inc. invoices.

13	13	13	20	26	27	31	34	34	34	35	35	36
37	38	41	41	41	45	47	47	47	50	51	53	54
56	62	67	82									

(a) Determine the sample first and third quartiles.
(b) Determine the sample second decile and the eighth decile.
(c) Determine the sample 67th percentile.

4-38. Rajnee Singh is the national sales manager for National Textbooks Inc. She has a sales staff of 40 who visit professors all over Canada. Each Saturday morning she requires her sales staff to send her a report. This report includes, among other things, the number of professors visited during the previous week. Listed below, ordered from smallest to largest, are the number of visits last week.

38	40	41	45	48	48	50	50	51	51	52	52
53	54	55	55	55	56	56	57	59	59	59	62
62	62	63	64	65	66	66	67	67	69	69	71
77	78	79	79								

(a) Determine the median number of calls.
(b) Determine the first and third quartiles.
(c) Determine the first decile and the ninth decile.
(d) Determine the 33rd percentile and explain its meaning.

BOX PLOTS

A box plot is a graphical display of a data set based on its minimum, maximum, and quartiles. It helps us to see if the data distribution is symmetrical or skewed; we are also able to detect outliers in the data sets.

   To draw a box plot, we need five values: the minimum value, Q_1 (the first quartile), Q_2 (the second quartile or median), Q_3 (the third quartile), and the maximum value. Example 4-18 illustrates.

Example 4-18 | Alexander's Pizza offers free delivery within 24 km. Alex, the owner, wants some information on the time it takes for delivery. How long does a typical delivery take? Within what range of times will most deliveries be completed? He determined the following information for the data on the delivery times this month:

Minimum value = 13 minutes
Q_1 = 15 minutes
Median = 18 minutes
Q_3 = 22 minutes
Maximum value = 30 minutes

Develop a box plot for the delivery times. What conclusions can you make about the delivery times?

Solution | The first step in drawing a box plot is to create an appropriate scale along the horizontal axis. Next, we draw a box that starts at Q_1 (15 minutes) and ends at Q_3 (22 minutes). Inside the box we place a vertical line to represent a median (18 minutes). Finally, we extend horizontal lines from the box out to the minimum value (13 minutes) and the maximum value (30 minutes). These horizontal lines outside of the box are sometimes called "whiskers," because they look a bit like a cat's whiskers.

   The box plot shows that the middle 50 percent of the deliveries takes between 15 minutes and 22 minutes. The distance between the ends of the box, 7 minutes, is called the **interquartile range** (IQR). The IQR is the distance between the first and the third quartile (= $Q_3 - Q_1$). One half of the IQR, that is, $(Q_3 - Q_1)/2$ is known as the **quartile deviation**.

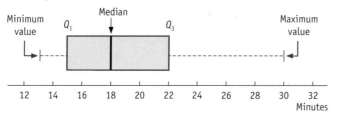

The box plot also reveals that the distribution of delivery times is positively skewed. How do we know this? In this case there are actually two pieces of information that suggest that the distribution is positively skewed. First, the dashed line to the right of the box (right whisker) from 22 minutes (Q_3) to the maximum time of 30 minutes is longer than the dashed line (left whisker) from the left of 15 minutes (Q_1) to the minimum value of 13 minutes. To put it another way, the 25 percent of data larger than the third quartile are more spread out than the 25 percent smaller than the first quartile. A second indication of positive skewness is that the median is not in the centre of the box.

The distance from the first quartile to the median is smaller than the distance from the median to the third quartile. We know that the number of delivery times between 15 minutes and 18 minutes is the same as the number of delivery times between 18 minutes and 22 minutes.

To find outliers, we define two values called a *lower fence* and an *upper fence*. Any data value smaller than the lower fence or greater than the upper fence is called an *outlier*.

The lower fence is defined as $Q_1 - (1.5)(IQR)$. (That is, in the box plot, it is a point at a distance of (1.5)(width of the box) to the left of the box.) In Example 4-18, $IQR = (22 - 15) = 7$. So, the lower fence is $15 - (1.5)(7) = 4.5$ minutes.

The upper fence is defined as $Q_3 + (1.5)(IQR)$. (In the box plot, it is a point at a distance of (1.5)(width of the box) to the right of the box.) In Example 4-18, the upper fence is $22 + (1.5)(7) = 32.5$ minutes.

In Example 4-18, no data value is less than 4.5 minutes or greater than 32.5 minutes. Therefore, we conclude that there are no outliers.

Example 4-19

The following are the marks of students in Math 1021 in 2002.

60	75	80	80	14	68	86	33	38	69	81
70	89	58	64	77	44	71	84	56	72	63
61	86

Draw a box plot and show any outlier present in the data set.

Solution

Minimum mark = 14; maximum mark = 89; median = 69.5; $Q_1 = 58.5$; $Q_3 = 80$.

As explained in Example 4-18, we create an appropriate scale (10 to 120) along the horizontal axis. We draw a box that starts at Q_1 (58.5) and ends at Q_3 (80). We draw a vertical line to represent the median (69.5).

Now we calculate the values of the lower and upper fences. The value of IQR is $(Q_3 - Q_1) = (80 - 58.5) = 21.5$. The lower fence is $Q_1 - (1.5)(IQR) = 58.5 - (1.5)(21.5) = 26.3$, and the value of the upper fence is $Q_3 + (1.5)(IQR) = 80 + (1.5)(21.5) = 112.3$.

We have only one data value (14) that is below the lower fence value (26.3) and no data value above 112.3. Therefore, the value 14 is the only outlier.

We extend lines from either side of the box. The line on the left extends from Q_1 (= 58.5) to the smallest value in the data set that is not an outlier, (which is 33). The line on the right extends from Q_3 (=80) to the largest data value that is not an outlier, (which is 89). Finally, each outlier (in our example, 14 is the only outlier), is marked with an asterisk (*).

The box plot is displayed in Chart 4-7. We see that the left whisker is larger than the right whisker, and the median is located at almost the centre of the box. This indicates almost symmetry in the middle 50 percent of the marks. But overall, the distribution of marks is skewed to the left.

We will draw a box plot, using Minitab, for the data set in Example 4-19 (see Chart 4-8).

CHART 4-7: Box Plot of Marks in Math 1021

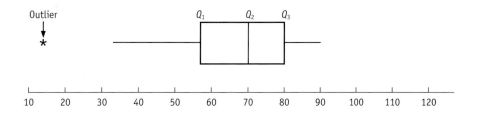

MINITAB CHART 4-8: Box Plot of Example 4-19

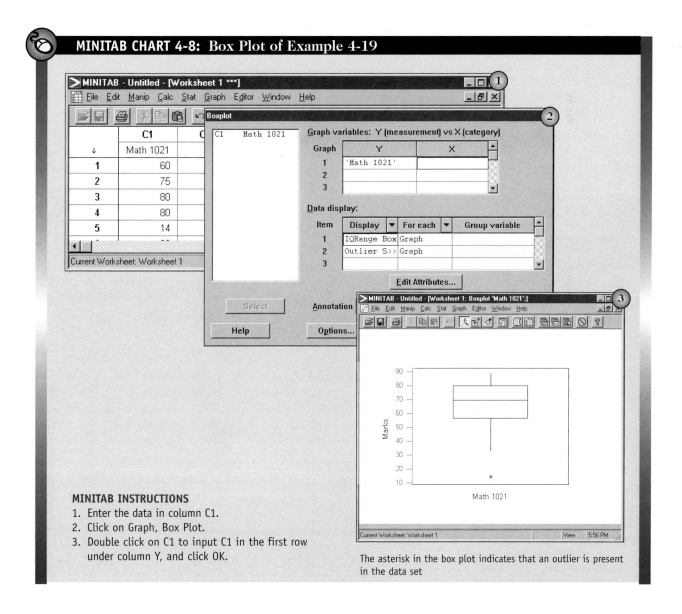

MINITAB INSTRUCTIONS
1. Enter the data in column C1.
2. Click on Graph, Box Plot.
3. Double click on C1 to input C1 in the first row under column Y, and click OK.

The asterisk in the box plot indicates that an outlier is present in the data set

Example 4-20

The student marks in Stat 2011 during 2002 are given below. Draw a single graph containing box plots for both the data on marks in Math 1021 (considered in Example 4-19) and the marks in Stat 2011.

72	61	75	71	61	89	85	80	59	73	75
78	71	59	73	72	70	59	75	60	23	95
44	86	91	97	93	66	76	87	54	78	47
74	26	66	64	6	89	69	66	63	80	91
74	91	72	85	58	77	57	83	62	91	

Solution

The Minitab instructions and output are given in Chart 4-9.

We can see that there are three outliers in Stat 2011 and only one outlier in Math 1021. The values of the first, second, and third quartiles for each data set are also different. Thus, a box plot in Minitab is an excellent tool to compare the data distributions of two or more data sets.

MINITAB CHART 4-9: Box Plot of Example 4-20 and Example 4-21

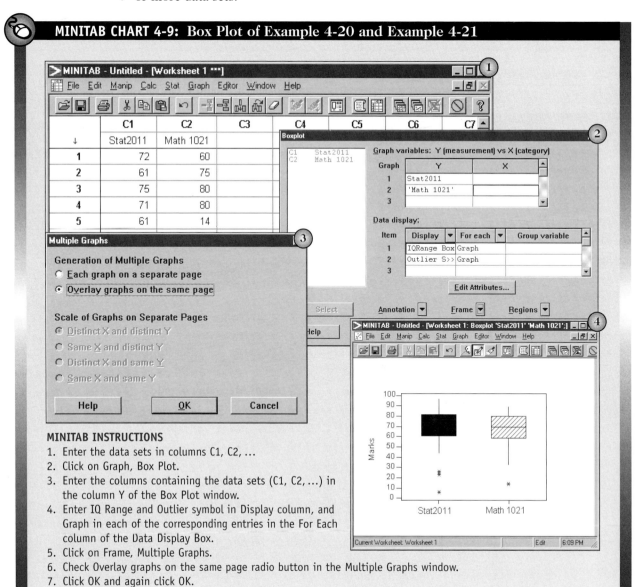

MINITAB INSTRUCTIONS

1. Enter the data sets in columns C1, C2, ...
2. Click on Graph, Box Plot.
3. Enter the columns containing the data sets (C1, C2, ...) in the column Y of the Box Plot window.
4. Enter IQ Range and Outlier symbol in Display column, and Graph in each of the corresponding entries in the For Each column of the Data Display Box.
5. Click on Frame, Multiple Graphs.
6. Check Overlay graphs on the same page radio button in the Multiple Graphs window.
7. Click OK and again click OK.

■ SELF-REVIEW 4-9

The following box plot is given.

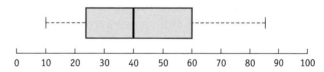

(a) What are the median, the largest and smallest values, and the first and third quartiles? Would you agree that the distribution is symmetrical?
(b) Is there any outlier in the box plot?

EXERCISES 4-39 TO 4-42

4-39. Refer to the box plot below.

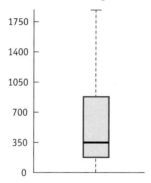

(a) Find approximate values of the median and first and third quartiles.
(b) Determine the interquartile range.
(c) Beyond what point is a value considered an outlier? Identify all other outliers.
(d) Is the distribution symmetrical or positively or negatively skewed?

4-40. Refer to the box plot.

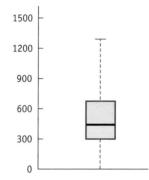

(a) Find approximate values of the median and first and third quartiles.
(b) Determine the interquartile range.
(c) Beyond what point is a value considered an outlier? Identify all other outliers.
(d) Is the distribution symmetrical or positively or negatively skewed?

4-41. In a study of fuel efficiency of automobiles manufactured in 2000, the mean number of litres per 100 km (on the highway) was found to be 8.8 and the median was 8.6. The smallest value in the study was 4.7 L/100 km and the largest was 18.5. The first and third quartiles were 6.6 and 13.1 L/100 km respectively. Develop a box plot and comment on the distribution. Is it a symmetrical distribution?

4-42. The following are the salaries of 20 accountants working in an accounting firm.

$58 100	$63 500	$69 990	$48 950	$54 120
$62 000	$60 200	$63 500	$68 750	$61 900
$69 950	$77 000	$43 340	$47 860	$50 990
$38 930	$43 050	$45 960	$36 500	$37 430

(a) Construct a box plot to show the salary distribution of the accountants. Identify the first, second, and third quartiles and comment on the shape of the salary distribution.
(b) Find the lower and upper fences. Are there any outliers in the data set?

CHAPTER OUTLINE

I. The **dispersion** is the variation in a set of data.
   A. The **range** is the difference between the largest and the smallest values in a set of data.
      1. The formula for the range is:

$$\text{Range} - (\text{Highest value} - \text{Lowest value}) \qquad \textbf{4-1}$$

      2. The major characteristics of the range are:
         (a) Only two values are used in its calculation.
         (b) It is influenced by outliers.
         (c) It is easy to compute and to understand.
   B. The *mean absolute deviation* is the sum of the absolute deviations from the mean divided by the total number of observations.
      1. The formula for computing the population mean deviation is

Population Mean Deviation $\qquad MD = \dfrac{\Sigma |x - \mu|}{N} \qquad$ **4-2**

      2. The formula for computing the sample mean absolute deviation is

Sample Mean Absolute Deviation $\qquad md = \dfrac{\Sigma |x - \bar{x}|}{n} \qquad$ **4-3**

      3. Its major characteristics are:
         (a) It is not unduly affected by large or small values.
         (b) All values are used in the calculation.
         (c) The absolute values are somewhat difficult to work with.
   C. The *variance of population* is the mean of the squared deviations from the arithmetic mean.

1. The formula for the population variance is

$$\sigma^2 = \frac{\Sigma(x - \mu)^2}{N}$$

4-4

2. The formula for the sample variance is

$$s^2 = \frac{\Sigma(x - \bar{x})^2}{n - 1}$$

4-6

3. Dividing the sum of squared variations from the sample mean by $(n - 1)$ provides a better estimate of the *population variance*.

D. The following are conceptual formulae for population and sample standard deviations, respectively.

$$\sigma = \sqrt{\frac{\Sigma(x - \mu)^2}{N}}$$

4-5

$$s = \sqrt{\frac{\Sigma(x - \bar{x})^2}{n - 1}}$$

4-8

II. The major characteristics of the standard deviation are:
   (a) It is in the same units as the original data.
   (b) It is the positive square root of the average squared distance from the mean.
   (c) It cannot be negative.
   (d) It is the most widely reported measure of dispersion.
   (e) It has nice mathematical properties and lends itself readily to algebraic manipulations.

III. For population data, Chebyshev's theorem states that regardless of the shape of the distribution at least $1 - \frac{1}{k^2}$ of the observations will be within k standard deviations of the mean. If we replace the population mean and the population standard deviation by the sample mean and the sample standard deviation, then for a large sample of data the result is approximately valid.

IV. Empirical Rule: For a bell-shaped distribution of population data:
   (a) Approximately 68 percent of the data values will lie within plus and minus one standard deviation of the population mean.
   (b) About 95 percent of the data values will lie within plus and minus two standard deviations of the population mean.
   (c) Practically all (99.7 percent) of the data values will lie within plus and minus three standard deviations of the population mean.
   A. If we substitute the mean standard deviation of a large sample in the empirical rule, the result is approximately true.

V. The formulae for the coefficient of variation for population and sample data are:

$$CV = \frac{\sigma}{\mu}(100)$$

4-12

$$CV = \frac{s}{\bar{x}}(100)$$

4-13

   A. It reports the variation relative to the mean.
   B. It is useful for comparing distributions with different units.

VI. The *coefficient of skewness* measures the symmetry of a distribution.
     A. Pearson's coefficient of skewness is:

For Population Data $$SK_1 = \frac{3(\text{Mean} - \text{Median})}{\sigma}$$ 4-14a

For Sample Data $$\overline{SK}_1 = \frac{3(\text{Mean} - \text{Median})}{s}$$ 4-14b

The value of SK_1 varies from -3 to 3.

     B. Minitab and Excel use the following formula to estimate skewness from sample data.

$$\overline{SK}_2 = \frac{n}{(n-1)(n-2)}\left[\Sigma\left(\frac{x-\bar{x}}{s}\right)^3\right]$$ 4-15

     C. If the value of the coefficient of skewness is zero, the distribution is symmetrical. For a non-zero value, the distribution is non-symmetrical.

     D. In a data skewed to the right, the coefficient of skewness is positive.

     E. In a data skewed to the left, the coefficient of skewness is negative.

VII. Measures of location also describe the spread in a set of observations.
      A. Quartiles divide a set of observations into four equal parts.

          1. The first quartile, usually labelled Q_1, is the value of an ordered data set such that, at most, one-quarter of the data is below it and, at most, three-quarters of the data are above it. The third quartile, usually labelled Q_3, is the value of the ordered data set such that at most, three-quarters of the data set are below it and at most, one-quarter of the data is above.

          2. The interquartile range is the difference between the third and the first quartiles.

      B. Deciles divide a set of observations into 10 equal parts.

      C. Percentiles divide a set of observations into 100 equal parts.

VIII. A box plot is a graphic display of a set of data.
       A. A box plot is based on five statistics: the largest and smallest observations, the first and third quartiles, and the median.

       B. A box is drawn connecting the first and third quartiles.

          1. A vertical line through the inside of the box shows the median.

       C. Dotted line segments from the third quartile to the largest value and from the first quartile to the smallest value show the range of the largest 25 percent of the observations and the smallest 25 percent.

       D. A box plot identifies outliers in a data set. Data below the lower fence and above the upper fence are outliers.

CHAPTER EXERCISES 4-43 TO 4-72

Exercises 4-43 through 4-51 are based on the following data.

The quality control department at Clegg Industries constantly monitors three assembly lines that produce ovens for private homes. The oven is designed to preheat to 104°C in four minutes and then shut off. However, the oven may not reach 104°C in the allotted time because of improper installation of the insulation or for other reasons. Likewise, the temperature might go beyond 104°C during the four-minute preheating cycle. A large sample from each of the three production lines revealed the following information.

Temperature (°C)			
Statistical Measures	Line 1	Line 2	Line 3
Sample Mean	103.0	104.0	105.5
Sample Median	104.0	104.0	104.0
Sample Mode	104.8	104.0	103.5
Sample Standard Deviation	3.0	0.4	3.9
Sample Quartile Deviation	1.0	0.1	1.7

4-43. Which of the lines do not have a symmetrical, bell-shaped distribution?

4-44. Which line has the most variation in temperature? How do you know?

4-45. According to the empirical rule, about 95 percent of the temperature readings for line 2 are between what values?

4-46. The distribution of temperatures for which line is positively skewed?

4-47. For line 2, obtain estimates of the values of the first and third quartiles.

4-48. Let us assume that the values of the sample standard deviation are close to the values of the population standard deviations. Then, for line 3, according to Chebyshev's theorem, what interval, symmetrical about the mean, will contain at least 89 percent of the temperatures?

4-49. Obtain an estimate of the coefficient of variation for line 3.

4-50. Obtain an estimate of the coefficient of skewness for line 1.

4-51. Determine the sample variance for line 1.

4-52. In a study of data from the personnel files of a large company, the coefficient of variation for the number of years with the company is 20 percent and the coefficient of variation for the amount of commission earned last year is 30 percent. Comment on the relative dispersion of the two variables.

4-53. In the same study discussed in Exercise 4-52, the coefficient of skewness for the age of the employees is -2.25. Comment on the shape of the distribution. Which measure of central tendency is the largest? Which direction is the longer tail? What would you conclude about the ages of the employees?

4-54. The following are one-year returns (%) of a sample of 15 companies from the top 1000 companies in Canada in 2000.

22.99	3.03	14.54	37.51	15.22	14.10	9.77	7.39
10.89	6.88	0.61	-0.42	3	2.37	-8.46	

(a) Compute the sample standard deviation using the computational method.

(b) Use an appropriate graphical display to detect outliers and list the number of outliers in the data set.

(c) Comment on the value of the sample standard deviation.

4-55. The ages of a sample of Canadian tourists flying from Toronto to Hong Kong were 32, 21, 60, 47, 54, 17, 72, 55, 33, and 41.

(a) Compute the range.

(b) Compute the sample mean.

(c) Compute the sample standard deviation.

4-56. The weights (kg) of a sample of five boxes being sent by UPS are 5.4, 2.7, 3.2, 1.4, and 4.5

(a) Compute the range.

(b) Compute the sample mean deviation.

(c) Compute the sample standard deviation.

4-57. There are 19 universities in one of the provinces in Canada. The number of volumes (in thousands) held in their libraries are:

146	510	133	125	601	147	123	850	320	200
435	210	250	300	450	200	230	300	249	

(a) Is this data set a sample or a population?

(b) Compute the standard deviation and interpret its meaning.

(c) Compute the coefficient of variation. Why is the coefficient of variation used to measure the variability of two or more data sets?

4-58. The following is the distribution of amount of money ($US) earned by the world's 50 most valuable athletes in 2000.

Amount of Money ($US millions)	Number of Athletes
1 up to 11	32
11 up to 21	12
21 up to 31	2
31 up to 41	1
41 up to 51	1
51 up to 61	1
61 up to 71	1

(a) Compute an approximate value of the mean amount of money earned by the world's 50 most valuable athletes

(b) Compute an approximate value of the standard deviation of money earned by the world's 50 most valuable athletes.

4-59. The Greater Toronto Area Chamber of Commerce surveyed a sample of 95 employees working in the downtown area to determine how far from home the employees must travel to work. The frequency distribution of the responses of the survey is given below.

Distance (km)	Frequency
0 up to 8	11
8 up to 16	15
16 up to 24	31
24 up to 32	20
32 up to 40	18
Total	95

(a) Compute the range of the distance distribution and explain its meaning.
(b) Obtain an estimate of the population standard deviation of the distance distribution.

4-60. Listed below is the frequency distribution of advertising expenditures for a sample of 30 small companies located in Vancouver.

Advertising Expenditures ($ thousands)	Number of Companies
25 up to 35	10
35 up to 45	5
45 up to 55	8
55 up to 65	4
65 up to 75	3

(a) Calculate the approximate values of the range and the sample standard deviation of the distribution of the advertising expenditures.
(b) Which of the two measures of variation in the data set is better? Explain.
(c) List four properties of the standard deviation.

4-61. The following are the amounts of money (in $US millions) earned by the world's 50 most valuable athletes in 2000.

63.1	59.0	24	35.2	48	14.3	2.7	4.2	4.7	10.0
10.6	11.3	18	18.9	17.0	1.4	20.0	7.9	7.3	1.4
7.0	10.0	17.5	11.4	10.0	23.0	3.0	11.0	5.0	7.5
6.5	7.1	6.5	15.0	3.0	16.0	15.3	9.5	9.0	5.1
6.3	15.7	7.5	4.8	7.5	7.0	1.5	1.4	1.2	5.6

(a) Develop a box plot of the data values in the data set.
(b) Is the data distribution skewed or symmetrical?
(c) How many outliers are present in the data set?
(d) What is the value of the interquartile range? Explain its meaning.

4-62. The National Muffler Company claims it will change your muffler in less than 30 minutes. An undercover consumer reporter for CTOL Channel 11 monitored 30 consecutive muffler changes at the National outlet on Liberty Street. The number of minutes to perform changes is reported below.

44	12	22	31	26	22	30	26	18	28	12
40	17	13	14	17	25	29	15	30	10	28
16	33	24	20	29	34	23	13			

(a) Develop a box plot for the time to change a muffler.
(b) Does the distribution show any outliers?
(c) Summarize your findings in a brief report.

4-63. The following box plot displays the salaries of a sample of 15 executives from the list of the 50 best-paid executives in 2000.

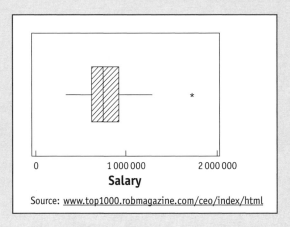

Source: www.top1000.robmagazine.com/ceo/index/html

(a) Estimate the values of the population median and the first and third quartiles.
(b) Is the distribution skewed to the right? Justify your answer.

4-64. The box plot below shows the final grades of students in Math 1015. Summarize the students' performance in Math 1015. Be sure to include the values of the first, second, and third quartiles, and whether there is any skewness. Find the approximate value of the outlier displayed by an asterisk.

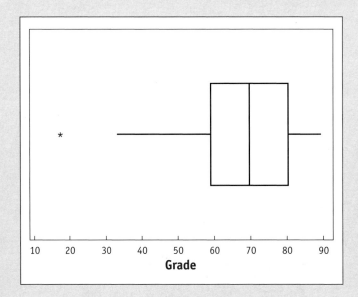

4-65. The previous problem presented a box plot of grades of students in Math 1015 using Minitab. Listed below is a summary from Minitab showing statistics for the same data set.

		Box Plot Grade			
		Descriptive Statistics: Grade			
Variable	N	Mean	Median	StDev	SE Mean
Grade	24	65.79	69.50	18.49	3.77
Variable	Min	Max	Q1	Q3	
Grade	14.00	89.00	58.50	80.00	

(a) Using Chebyshev's theorem, between what values, symmetrical about the mean, would you expect about at least 55.5 percent of the grades to occur?
(b) Determine the coefficient of variation.
(c) Determine Pearson's coefficient of skewness. Does this value indicate a positive or negative skewness?

4-66. Danfoss Electronics Inc. has 150 suppliers throughout the United States and Canada. Listed below are Minitab summary statistics on the sales volume to its suppliers.

Variable	N	Mean	Median	Tr Mean	StDev	SE Mean
Sales	150	128.1	81.0	102.2	162.7	13.3
Variable	Min	Max	Q1	Q3		
Sales	2.0	1019.0	38.7	138.2		

(a) What is the range?
(b) Determine the interquartile range.
(c) Determine the coefficient of variation.
(d) Determine Pearson's coefficient of skewness.
(e) Draw a box plot.

4-67. The following data are the estimated market values ($ millions) of 50 companies in Canada and the U.S. in the auto parts business.

26.8	8.6	6.5	30.6	15.4	18.0	7.6	21.5	11.0	10.2
28.3	15.5	31.4	23.4	4.3	20.2	33.5	7.9	11.2	1.0
11.7	18.5	6.8	22.3	12.9	29.8	1.3	14.1	29.7	18.7
6.7	31.4	30.4	20.6	5.2	37.8	13.4	18.3	27.1	32.7
6.1	0.9	9.6	35.0	17.1	1.9	1.2	16.6	31.1	16.1

(a) Determine the mean and the median of the market values.
(b) Determine the standard deviation of the market values.
(c) Using Chebyshev's theorem, between what values, symmetrical about the mean, would you expect at least 60 percent of the market values to occur?
(d) Using the empirical rule, about 95 percent of the values would occur between what values symmetrical about the mean?
(e) Determine the coefficient of variation.
(f) Determine Pearson's coefficient of skewness.
(g) Draw a box plot.
(h) Write a brief report summarizing the results.

4-68. Below are the one-year and five-year rates of return for the 20 best-performing stocks in 2000. Assume the data are a sample.

Stocks	1-year (%)	5-year (%)
CGI Group (Se00)	8.98	14.57
C-Mac Industries (De00)	9.91	11.99
Velvet Exploration (De00)	20.71	4.98
Bonavista Petroleum (De00)	44.08	15.70
Baytex Energy (De00)	14.37	3.85
Ballard Power Systems (De00)	−11.13	−6.49
Meota Resources (De00)	54.04	21.64
Patheon Inc. (Oc00)	13.31	12.19
Compton Petroleum (De00)	29.19	13.48
BCE Emergis (De00)	−39.99	−57.17
Home Capital Group (De00)	23.24	16.99
ATS Automation Tooling System (Ma00)	10.79	14.55
Stratos Global (De00)	−16.74	−6.92
SureFire Commerce (Ma00)	−22.16	−20.71
Vermillion Resources (De00)	33.90	17.79
Mount Real Corp (De00)	25.31	29.29
Gauntlet Energy (De00)	16.87	−0.06
BakBone Software (Ap00)	−6.83	−14.41
Cognos Inc. (Fe00)	26.98	32.87
C.I. Fund Management (Ma00)	−1.00	10.90

(a) Compute the mean, median, and standard deviation for one-year and five-year rates of return. Compare the standard deviations of both of the rates of return. Comment on your findings.

(b) Use an appropriate statistical measure to compare the levels of risk of the two returns.

(c) Compute the coefficient of skewness for one-year and five-year rates of return. Which of the two is skewed more?

(d) Draw a single box plot depicting the one-year and five-year rates of return. Comment on the results. Are there any outliers?

4-69. Following are the amounts ($) spent by a sample of 14 customers in a grocery store in a day:

$42.94 $67.45 $52.08 $85.64 $105.10 $56.67
$50.25 $75.34 $87.34 $46.65 $90.45 $95.90
$54.56 $99.34

(a) Compute the values of the sample mean, median, and standard deviation of the amounts spent by the customers in the store.

(b) Find the sample 45th and 80th percentiles of the data set.

(c) Draw a box plot and comment on your findings.

4-70. The following table shows the expenditures of Canadians in 13 countries they visited in 1999.

Countries Visited	Spending ($ millions)	Countries Visited	Spending ($ millions)
Mexico	557	Netherlands	107
Hong Kong	138	Australia	227
France	506	Spain	105
Dominican Rep.	122	Japan	150
Italy	283	Switzerland	91
Ireland	114	Germany	183
Cuba	265		

(a) Find the mean, median, Q_1, and Q_3.
(b) Find the 15th and 90th percentiles.
(c) Find Pearson's coefficient of skewness and interpret the result.
(d) Construct a box plot. Is there any outlier in the data set?

4-71. The following are the total revenues earned ($ thousands) by 15 companies listed in *Report on Business* magazine, June 20, 2001. Assume the data set is a sample.

$18 209 000	$18 996 000	$16 152 900	$10 934 800	$20 075 000
$10 720 000	$21 405 000	$15 267 000	$17 159 000	$16 376 000
$22 377 000	$24 917 000	$31 401 000	$31 299 000	$11 006 149

(a) Find the mean, median, Q_1, and Q_3 of the total revenue distribution. Interpret the meanings of the first and third quartiles.
(b) Find Pearson's coefficient of skewness. Is the total revenue distribution skewed to the right? Explain.
(c) Construct a box plot. Is there any outlier in the data set?

4-72. The following is a list of weekly share prices ($) of BCE Inc. from July 2, 1999 to July 14, 2000.

17.805	17.795	18.665	17.535	18.23	17.075	17.22	17.005
17.55	6.81	17.975	18.0	16.71	17.45	19.845	18.73
19.43	21.52	22.47	23.61	24.775	26.475	25.955	27.51
28.42	32.305	31.855	30.825	29.695	33.69	34.555	41.535
41.44	42.0	39.17	40.66	43.115	42.12	47.67	42.965
42.63	33.765	37.19	41.66	41	38.15	33.8	32.65
34.9	37.95	35.05	35.45	35.1	37.0	37.0	

(a) Construct a box plot.
(b) What are the values of the median and the first and third quartiles?
(c) What is the value of the coefficient of skewness? Is the distribution of the share prices symmetrical or non-symmetrical? Explain.

www.exercises.ca 4-73 TO 4-77

4-73. Go to the Web site http://unstats.un.org/unsd/demographic/ww2000/table3a.htm. Take the life expectancy at birth data, 2000–2005 of women and men of the first forty countries.
(a) Construct a single box plot depicting box plots of life expectancies of males and females for the first 40 countries listed in the data set. Are the distributions symmetrical? Explain.

(b) Which of the life expectancy distributions shows more variations in its data values?

(c) Estimate the value of the median for each distribution from each box plot.

4-74. Go to the Web site www.globefund.com. Select "globe-fund-mutual funds" from "other globeandmail.com sites" and click Go. Type " Dividend" in "Enter Fund Name" and click Go. View the three-year returns of the first 35 funds.

(a) Find the standard deviation of three-year returns of the first 35 funds.

(b) Find the first and third quartiles of the three-year returns of the first 35 funds.

(c) Draw a box plot. Are there any outliers in the data set?

(d) Determine the coefficient of skewness of the distribution of the data set.

4-75. Go to www.canoe.ca/BaseballMoneyMatters/salaries_players.html. Under the heading "Baseball Salaries," look for *Montreal Expos.*

(a) Draw a box plot. Are there any outliers in the data set?

(b) What are the values of the standard deviation and the coefficient of variation?

(c) Is the data distribution symmetrical or skewed? If skewed, is the data distribution skewed to the right or left? Explain.

4-76. Go to the Web site www.oecd.org/std. Collect data on the gross domestic product (GDP) for the latest quarter and the quarter before that.

(a) Find the mean, median, and the standard deviation of the GDP for the latest quarter.

(b) Find the mean, median, and the standard deviation of the GDP for the previous quarter.

(c) Comment on the values you calculated in (a) and (b).

(d) Determine the coefficient of variation for the two data sets. Which of the two data sets shows more variability?

(e) Determine the coefficient of skewness for the two data sets and comment on your results.

4-77. Go to the Web site www.forbes.com/tool/toolbox/forbes500s, select "Forbes International 500" from the company list and click Go. Click revenues ($ millions). Use the first 25 data for the data analysis.

(a) Draw a box plot. List the number of outliers in the data set and show their values.

(b) Find the mean, median, and the standard deviation. Calculate Pearson's coefficient of skewness.

CHAPTER 4   ANSWERS TO SELF-REVIEW

4-1. 1. (a) 10, found by (51 – 41)

(b) $\bar{x} = \dfrac{376}{8} = 47$

(c)

x	$x - \mu$	$|x - \mu|$
43	−4	4
47	0	0
48	1	1
50	3	3
48	1	1
48	1	1
51	4	4
41	−6	6
		20

$md = \dfrac{20}{8} = 2.5$

2. (a) $\mu = \dfrac{20\,035.08}{12} = 1669.59$

(b)

x	$x - \mu$	$|x - \mu|$
2 231.61	562.02	562.02
2 516.08	846.49	846.49
1 215.97	−453.62	453.62
2 809.45	1 139.86	1 139.86
1 983.08	313.49	313.49
1 983.08	313.49	313.49
487.91	−1 181.68	1 181.68
2 381.72	712.13	712.13
791.55	−878.04	878.04
791.55	−878.04	878.04
2 381.72	712.13	712.13
461.36	−1 208.23	1 208.23
		9 199.4

$MD = \dfrac{\$9199.4}{12} = \$766.62$

4-2. (a) $\mu = \dfrac{186}{6} = 31$

(b) $\sigma^2 = \{[(28 - 31)^2 + (20 - 31)^2 + (34 - 31)^2$
$+ (19 - 31)^2 + (60 - 31)^2 + (25 - 31)^2]/6\}$
$= 193.3$ years

(c) $\sigma = \sqrt{193.3} = 13.9$ years

4-3. (a) Sample variance is 103.98, found by

$\bar{x} = \dfrac{\sum x}{n} = \dfrac{54.32}{6} = 9.05$

$s^2 = \dfrac{\sum (x - \bar{x})^2}{n-1}$ or $\dfrac{\sum x^2 - \dfrac{(\sum x)^2}{n}}{n-1}$

$= \dfrac{519.89}{6-1} = 103.98$ or $\dfrac{1011.67 - \dfrac{(54.32)^2}{6}}{6-1}$

$= 103.98$

x	$\bar{x}$	$x - \bar{x}$	$(x - \bar{x})^2$	x^2
13.34	9.05	4.29	18.4	177.96
16.62	9.05	7.57	57.3	276.22
21.44	9.05	12.39	153.51	459.67
2.23	9.05	−6.82	46.51	4.97
7.15	9.05	−1.9	3.61	51.12
−6.46	9.05	−15.51	240.56	41.73
54.32			519.89	1011.67

(b) The sample standard deviation is 10.20, found by $\sqrt{103.98} = 10.20$

4-4. (a) 50, found by (80 – 30)

$s = \sqrt{\dfrac{f(x - \bar{x})^2}{n-1}} = \sqrt{\dfrac{11\,100.01}{63}} = 13.3$

(b)

Income ($000)	f	x	fx	$\bar{x}$	$f(x - \bar{x})^2$
30–40	11	35	385	53.75	3 867.19
40–50	18	45	810	53.75	1 378.13
50–60	12	55	660	53.75	18.75
60–70	14	65	910	53.75	1 771.88
70–80	9	75	675	53.75	4 064.06
Total	64		3440		11 100.01

4-5. The sample size is large. So, Chebyshev's theorem will hold approximately, if we replace μ by $\bar{x}$ and σ by s.

(a) $35.9 - \bar{x} = 35.9 - 35.6 = 0.3$; and $35.3 - \bar{x}$
$= 35.3 - 35.6 = -0.3$. So, the interval from 35.3 to 35.9 is symmetrical about the mean.

$k = \dfrac{35.9 - \bar{x}}{s} = \dfrac{35.9 - 35.6}{0.25} = 1.2$

$1 - \dfrac{1}{k^2} = 1 - \dfrac{1}{(1.2)^2} = 0.306$. So, at least 30.6 percent of the observations will lie between 35.3 cm and 35.9 cm.

(b) 35.1 to 36.1, found by $35.6 \pm 2(0.25)$

4-6. CV for World's 50 most valuable athletes
= 103.7 percent, found by,

$$\frac{\$19.4 \text{ millions}}{\$18.7 \text{ millions}}(100)$$

CV for the 50 best-paid executives
= 88.19 percent, found by,

$$\frac{\$12.7 \text{ millions}}{\$14.4 \text{ millions}}(100)$$

The earnings of athletes have more dispersion (relative to the mean).

4-7. (a) $\bar{x} = \dfrac{407}{5} = 81.4$, median $= 84$

$$s = \sqrt{\frac{34\,053 - \dfrac{(407)^2}{5}}{5-1}} = 15.19$$

(b) $\overline{SK}_1 = \dfrac{3(81.4 - 84.0)}{15.19} = -0.51$

(c)

x	$\dfrac{x - \bar{x}}{s}$	$\left[\dfrac{x - \bar{x}}{s}\right]^3$	
73	-0.5530	-0.1691	$\overline{SK}_2$
98	1.0928	1.3050	
60	-1.4085	-2.7961	$= \dfrac{5}{(4)(3)}[-1.3154]$
92	0.6978	0.3398	
84	0.1712	0.0050	$= -0.5481$
		-1.3154	

(d) The distribution is somewhat negatively skewed.

(e)

x	$\dfrac{x - \bar{x}}{s}$	$\left[\dfrac{x - \bar{x}}{s}\right]^4$
73	-0.5530	0.0935
98	1.0928	1.4261
60	-1.4085	3.9357
92	0.6978	0.2371
84	0.1712	0.0009
		5.6993

$$K_1 = \frac{(5)(6)}{(4)(3)(2)}(5.6933) - \frac{3(4)^2}{(3)(2)} = -0.8834$$

4-8. (a) $L_p = (n+1)\dfrac{P}{100} = (14)\dfrac{50}{100} = 7.$

So, sample median is the 7th value = $17.0 million.

(b) For the first sample quartile,

$$L_p = (n+1)\frac{25}{100} = (14)\frac{25}{100} = 3.5.$$

So, the first sample quartile
= $(0.5)(4\text{th } value) + (0.5)(3\text{rd } value)$
= $(0.5)(7.0) + (0.5)(6.5)$
= $6.75 million.
For the third sample quartile,

$$L_p = (n+1)\frac{75}{100} = (14)\frac{75}{100} = 10.5.$$

So, the third sample quartile
$= (0.5)(11\text{th } value) + (0.5)(10\text{th } value)$
$= (0.5)(24.0) + (0.5)(20.0)$
$= \$22.0$ million.
At most one-quarter of the athletes earn less than $6.75 million and at most three-quarters earn more than it. At most three-quarters of the athletes earn less than $22 million and at most one-quarter earn more than it.

4-9. (a) The smallest value is 10 and the largest 85; the first quartile is 25 and the third 60. About 50 percent of the values are between 25 and 60. The median value is 40. The distribution is somewhat positively skewed.

(b) There are no outliers.

A REVIEW OF   CHAPTERS 1–4

This section is a review of the major concepts and terms introduced in Chapters 1 through 4. These chapters focussed on describing a set of data by organizing it into a *frequency distribution* and then portraying the distribution in the form of a *histogram*, a *frequency polygon*, and a *cumulative frequency polygon*. The purpose of these graphs is to visually reveal the important characteristics of the data.

Computing a central value to represent the data is a numerical way of summarizing a mass of observations. Chapter 3 looked at several measures of central tendency, including the *mean*, *weighted mean*, *geometric mean*, *median*, and *mode*. Chapter 4 described the *dispersion*, or *spread*, in the data by computing the *range*, *standard deviation*, and other measures. Further, *skewness*, or lack of symmetry in the data, was described by determining the *coefficient of skewness*.

We stressed the importance of computer software packages, including Excel and Minitab. Several computer outputs in these chapters demonstrated how quickly and accurately a mass of raw data can be organized into a frequency distribution and a histogram. Also, we noted that the computer outputs present a large number of descriptive measures, including the mean, the variance, and the standard deviation.

■ GLOSSARY

Chapter 1

Descriptive statistics   The techniques used to describe the important characteristics of a data set. These may include organizing the values into a frequency distribution, depicting the data set as graphics, and computing measures of central tendency, measures of spread, and skewness.

Inferential statistics, also called *statistical inference* or *inductive statistics*.   This facet of statistics deals with estimating or testing a hypothesis about the characteristics of a population based on a sample statistic. For example, if 2 out of 10 hand calculators sampled are defective, we might infer, based on the statistical evidence, that 20 percent of the production is defective.

Interval measurement   If one observation is greater than another by a certain amount, and the zero point is arbitrary, the measurement is on an interval scale. For example, the difference between temperatures of 70 degrees and 80 degrees is 10 degrees. Likewise, a temperature of 90 degrees is 10 degrees more than a temperature of 80 degrees, and so on.

Mutually exclusive categories   An observation cannot fall into more than one category if the categories are mutually exclusive.

Nominal measurement   The "lowest" level of measurement. If data are classified into categories and the order of those categories is not important, it is the nominal level of measurement. Examples are gender (male, female) and political affiliation (Canadian Alliance, Liberal, NDP, Progressive Conservative). If it makes no difference whether male or female is listed first, the data are *nominal level*.

Ordinal measurement   Data that can be logically ranked are referred to as ordinal measures. For example, consumer response to the sound of a new speaker might be excellent, very good, fair, or poor.

Population   The collection, or set, of all individuals, objects, or measurements whose properties are being studied.

Ratio measurement   If the distances between numbers are of a known constant size and *there is a true zero point*, and the ratio of two values is meaningful, the measurement is ratio scale. For example, the distance between $200 and $300 is $100, and in the case of money there is a true zero point. If you have zero dollars, there is an absence of money (you have none). Also, the ratio between $200 and $300 is meaningful.

Sample   A portion, or subset, of the population being studied.

Statistics   The science of collecting, organizing, analyzing, and interpreting numerical data for the purpose of making more effective decisions.

Chapter 2

Charts   Special graphical formats used to portray a frequency distribution, including histograms, frequency polygons, and cumulative frequency polygons. Time series data were depicted into graphics to reveal any trend in a data set and compare two or more data sets. Frequency distributions of qualitative data were depicted as a simple bar chart, cluster chart, and stacked bar chart to visualize and compare one or more sets of data.

Class   The interval in which the data are tallied. For example, $4 up to $7 is a class; $7 up to $11 is another class.

Class frequency   The number of observations in each class. If there are 16 observations in the $4 up to $6 class, 16 is the class frequency.

Frequency distribution   A grouping of data into categories showing the number of observations in each of the non-overlapping classes. For example, data are organized into classes, such as $1000 up to $2000, $2000 up to $3000, and so on, to summarize the information.

Midpoint   The value that divides the class into two equal parts. For the classes $10 up to $20 and $20 up to $30, the midpoints are $15 and $25, respectively.

Chapter 3

Measure of central tendency   A number that describes the central tendency of the data. There are several such measures, including arithmetic mean, weighted mean, median, mode, and geometric mean.

Arithmetic mean   The sum of the values divided by the number of values. The symbol for a sample mean is $\bar{x}$, and the symbol for a population mean is μ.

Geometric mean   The nth root of the product of all the values. It is especially useful for averaging rates of change and index numbers. It minimizes the importance of extreme values. A second use of the geometric mean is to find the mean annual percentage change over a period of time. For example, if gross sales were $245 million in 1985 and $692 million in 2000, what is the average annual percentage increase?

Median   The value of the middle observation after all the observations have been arranged from low to high. For example, if observations 6, 9, 4 are rearranged to read 4, 6, 9, the middle value is 6, the median.

Mode   The value that appears most frequently in a set of data. For grouped data, it is the *midpoint* of the class containing the largest number of values.

Weighted mean   Each value is weighted according to its relative importance. For example, if 5 shirts cost $10 each and 20 shirts cost $8 each, the weighted mean price is $8.40: $[(5 \times \$10) + (20 \times \$8)]/25 = \$210/25 = \$8.40$.

Chapter 4

Dispersion or spread   A measure of central tendency pinpoints a single value that is typical of the data. A measure of dispersion indicates how close or far apart the values are from the mean or other measure of central tendency.

Coefficient of skewness   A measure of the lack of symmetry in a distribution. For a symmetrical distribution there is no skewness, so the coefficient of skewness is zero. Otherwise it is either positive or negative, with the limits at ± 3.0.

Coefficient of variation   The standard deviation divided by the mean, expressed as a percentage. It is especially useful for comparing the relative dispersion in two or more sets of data where (1) they are in different units or (2) one mean is much larger than the other mean.

Interquartile range   The distance between the third quartile and the first quartile.

Mean deviation   The mean of the deviations of actual observations from the mean of those observations, disregarding signs. It is abbreviated as *MD*. Also called *mean absolute deviation*.

Range   Difference between the highest and lowest values.

Standard deviation   The positive square root of the variance.

Variance   Mean of the squared deviations of actual observations from the mean of those observations.

Quartiles   Values that divide a set of data into four equal parts.

■ EXERCISES

1. A small number of employees were selected from all the employees at NED Electronics and their hourly rates recorded. The rates were $9.50, $9.00, $11.70, $14.80, and $13.00.
    a. Are the hourly rates a sample or a population?
    b. What is the level of measurement?
    c. What is the arithmetic mean hourly rate?
    d. What is the median hourly rate? Interpret.
    e. What is the variance?
    f. What is the coefficient of skewness? Interpret.

2. The weekly overtime hours worked by all the employees at the Public Market are 1, 4, 6, 12, 5, and 2.
    a. Is this a sample or a population?
    b. What is the mean number of overtime hours worked?
    c. What is the median? Interpret.
    d. What is the mode?

e. What is the mean deviation?
f. What is the standard deviation?
g. What is the coefficient of variation?

3. The Tourist Bureau of Vancouver surveyed a sample of tourists as they left to return to the United States. One of the questions was: how many rolls of film did you expose when visiting our island? The responses were:

8	6	3	11	14	8	9	16	9	10
5	11	7	8	8	10	9	12	13	9

a. Using five classes, organize the sample data into a frequency distribution.
b. Portray the distribution in the form of a frequency polygon.
c. What is the mean number of rolls exposed? Use the actual raw data.
d. What is the median? Use the actual raw data.
e. What is the mode? Use the actual raw data.
f. What is the range? Use the actual raw data.
g. What is the sample variance? Use the actual raw data.
h. What is the sample standard deviation? Use the actual raw data.
i. Assuming that the distribution is symmetrical and bell-shaped, about 95 percent of the tourists exposed between _____ and _____ rolls.

4. The annual amounts spent on research and development for a sample of electronic component manufacturers located in North America are (in $ millions):

8	34	15	24	15	28	12	20	22	23
14	26	18	23	10	21	16	17	22	31
13	25	20	28	6	20	19	27	16	22

a. What is the level of measurement?
b. Using six classes, organize the expenditures into a frequency distribution.
c. Portray the distribution in the form of a histogram.
d. Portray the distribution in the form of a less-than-cumulative frequency polygon.
e. Based on the less-than-cumulative frequency polygon, what is the *estimated* median amount spent on research and development? Interpret.
f. What is the mean amount spent on research and development?
g. Based on the less-than-cumulative frequency polygon, what is the interquartile range?

5. The rates of growth of Bardeen Chemicals for the past five years are 5.2 percent, 8.7 percent, 3.9 percent, 6.8 percent, and 19.5 percent.
a. What is the arithmetic mean annual growth rate?
b. What is the geometric mean annual growth rate?
c. Should the arithmetic mean or geometric mean be used to represent the average annual growth rate? Why?

6. The Currin Manufacturing Co. noted in its 2000 second-quarter report that as of June 30, 2000, notes payable amounted to $284.0 million. For the same date in 1990, they were $113.0 million. What is the geometric mean yearly percentage increase from June 1990 to June 2000?

7. In its annual report, BFI revealed that working capital was (in $ billions) $4.4, $3.4, $3.0, $4.8, $7.8, and $8.3 consecutively for the years 1995–2000. Present these figures in either a simple line chart or a simple bar chart.

8. Refer to the following diagram.

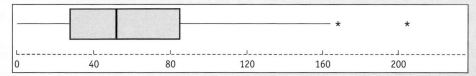

a. What is the graph called?
b. What are the median and the first and third quartile values?
c. Is the distribution positively skewed? Explain how you know.
d. Are there any outliers? If yes, estimate these values.
e. Can you determine the number of observations in the study?

FOR EXERCISES 9–18, FILL IN THE BLANKS

9. Employees were asked to rate a company training course as either outstanding, very good, good, fair, or poor. The level of measurement is _____.

10. A sample of senior citizens revealed that their mean annual retirement income is $16 900. Since the mean is based on a sample, the $16 900 is called a _____.

11. Refer to the following picture. It is called a _____. The third quartile is about _____, the first quartile _____, the interquartile range _____, and the range _____.

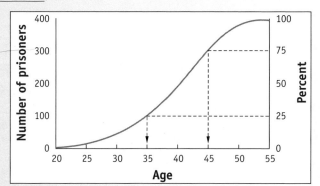

12. Refer to the following picture, which is based on a frequency distribution. It is called a _____. Describe the skewness in the distribution. Explain.

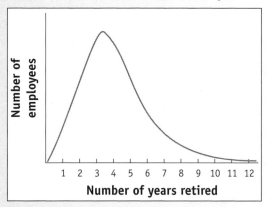

13. For a set of observations, we have the following information: mean = $64, median = $61, mode = $60, standard deviation = $6, and range = $40. The coefficient of variation is _____.

14. Refer to Exercise 13. The coefficient of skewness is _____.

15. A useful measure to compare the relative dispersion in two or more distributions, if they are in different units, is the _____.

16. For a set of observations we have the following information: mean = 100, median = 100, mode = 100, and s = 4, The range is about _____.

17. Refer to Exercise 16. About 95 percent of the values lie between _____ and _____.

18. Fine Furniture Inc. produced 2460 desks in 1990 and 6520 in 2000. To find the average annual percentage increase in production, the _____ should be used.

19. The amounts (in $) that customers deposited at a newly opened branch of a national bank are:

124	14	150	289	52	156	203	82	27	248
39	52	103	58	136	249	110	298	251	157
186	107	142	185	75	202	119	219	156	78
116	152	206	117	52	299	58	153	219	148
145	187	165	147	158	146	185	186	149	140

Using the preceding raw data and a statistical package such as Minitab or Excel,
a. Organize the data into a frequency distribution.
b. Calculate the mean, median, and other descriptive measures. Include charts, if available. Decide on the class interval.
c. Interpret the computer output, that is, describe the central tendency, spread, skewness, and other measures.

20. If a computer is not available, organize the chequing accounts into a frequency distribution. Decide on the class interval. Portray the distribution in chart form, and compute the measure of central tendency, spread, and skewness. Then interpret the important characteristics of the chequing accounts.

21. Professor Sunita Sen teaches Stat 444 in a community college. The following are the grades of students in her class. She uses these 54 grades as a data set for an assignment she hands out to her students in Stat 432.

72	61	75	71	61	89	85	80	59
73	75	60	78	71	59	73	72	70
59	75	23	95	54	78	44	86	91
97	93	66	76	87	63	47	80	91
74	26	66	64	66	89	69	66	62
91	74	91	72	85	58	77	57	83

She gives the following assignment:
a. Construct a stem-and-leaf display. Use leaf unit equal to 1.
b. How many students received grades between 70 and 78?
c. Is the grade distribution skewed to the left or right?

22. The following are per capita incomes of countries in $US (1998) as of November 2000.

Per Capita GDP			
Country	($US 1998)	Country	($US 1998)
Algeria	1 689	Greece	11 463
Australia	20 125	Hong Kong	24 581
Austria	25 911	Hungary	4 644
Bahamas	11 395	Iceland	29 946
Belgium	24 692	India	422
Bolivia	1 077	Ireland	23 098
Brazil	4 673	Israel	17 041
Canada	19 642	Italy	20 659
China	777	Japan	29 956
Cyprus	11 631	Mexico	4 324
Denmark	33 085	Singapore	24 577
Egypt	1 211	Sweden	6 790
Finland	24 934	Switzerland	35 910
France	24 739	U.K.	23 934
Germany	26 183	USA	31 746

a. Organize the data into a frequency distribution.

b. What is the arithmetic mean of GDP per capita values in the data set?

c. Find Pearson's coefficient of skewness and indicate if the distribution is skewed to the left or right.

23. ABC Technology is planning to restructure and would like to review the age distribution of its employees. The following are the ages of a sample of 30 employees.

34	45	56	44	57	28	33	44	46	52
64	55	30	35	60	61	59	44	56	63
63	28	30	32	33	45	54	48	45	56

a. Construct a stem-and-leaf display.

b. Compute the median age of the employees.

■ CASE STUDY A

Future Mutual Fund Inc. received a telephone call from a new customer. The customer is 45 years old and is thinking of placing part of her total investment in a growth fund.

Alex Robinson brought up historical year-year rates of return data of two funds. Assume that the history of the data of two funds is a useful guide to making decisions for the long run. Standard deviation of the returns measures the risk involved in investing. Below are the historical data for two funds:

Year	Canadian Growth Annual Return (%)	International Fund Annual Return (%)
1973	0.40	
1974	−10.20	
1975	−12.00	
1976	40.09	
1977	44.25	
1978	28.35	
1979	26.45	
1980	22.50	
1981	25.25	
1982	12.34	
1983	30.56	
1984	31.67	
1985	15.67	
1986	10.34	
1987	26.78	
1988	−5.68	6.90
1989	10.56	−1.50
1990	12.34	25.60
1991	−15.45	21.15
1992	28.90	48.35
1993	14.50	5.20
1994	30.40	12.20
1995	2.50	21.50
1996	10.4	15.80
1997	12.5	8.10
1998	11.4	21.20
1999	−8.2	−0.65
2000	29.4	10.5
2001	−4.6	12.54

Use Excel or Minitab for your calculations. The client's questions are:

1. What are the standard deviations of Canadian Growth and International Fund?

2. Which of the two funds involves less risk? What statistic would you use to compare the relative dispersion of returns of the two funds?

3. Find the value of any extreme return (outlier) in each fund.

■ CASE STUDY B

Kimuyen Pham has lived in Scarborough, Ontario, for the last three years. She is planning to move to Clarington, east of Toronto in Durham Region, to stay close to her parents. She asked the manager of a real estate company to provide a list of houses. The manager asked one of his brokers to provide the price list of a sample of 55 houses with a price range of $99 000 to $759 900. Kimuyen would like to know the average price of houses and the variation in the price of houses. She would like to see a graphical display of the prices for a quick overview, the first and third quartile prices, and the prices that can be considered statistically extreme. As Kimuyen's broker, you provide the following information.

1. Group the data set into 12 classes with a class width of $60 000 and draw a relative frequency histogram. Use MegaStat software.

2. What percent of house prices are in the range $180 000 to $240 000?

3. Is the distribution of house prices skewed to the right or left?

4. Draw a suitable graph that will show the first, second, and third quartile prices, and also any extreme values in the list of house prices.

5. Write a brief report outlining a suitable measure of central tendency and variations in the data set. Include the price range in which the highest percentages of the houses are listed, the extreme values, and the first and third quartile values. Explain the meaning of extreme

values and quartile values so that Kimuyen can interpret the prices of houses in the list.

The following is the price list ($ thousands) of houses in Clarington in 2001.

295.0	475.0	549.9	739.9
759.9	99.8	129.0	138.9
259.9	265.0	269.9	279.0
149.9	154.9	157.9	174.9
174.9	179.8	179.9	182.5
279.9	309.9	309.9	319.9
183.9	183.9	184.9	187.9
189.9	189.9	194.9	196.0
329.9	339.9	339.9	359.0
199.5	199.7	199.9	199.9
204.9	219.0	219.9	219.9
369.9	399.9	399.9	219.9
229.0	229.9	237.9	247.7
249.9	249.9	249.9	

■ CASE STUDY C

Rafiq reads in his local newspaper that the demand for new employees will grow across Canada. He would like to sponsor his brother Abdul and sister Nidha. Rafiq examines the labour statistics prepared by Statistics Canada and wonders if it is the right time to bring them to Canada. The table below shows the labour force and unemployment rates for 10 Canadian provinces. The unemployment rate is the proportion of unemployed individuals in the labour force.

Labour Force and Unemployment Rates (2000)

Province	Labour Force (in thousands)		Unemployment Rates (%)	
	Men	Women	Men	Women
NF	132.3	113.3	17.8	15.4
PE	38.3	35.0	13.1	10.9
NS	244.0	217.5	9.9	8.2
NB	200.0	171.7	11.1	8.9
PQ	2 061.9	1 691.3	8.6	8.1
ON	3 330.2	2 897.7	5.5	5.9
MB	315.2	268.0	5.1	4.7
SK	279.9	231.8	5.8	4.5
AB	920.9	750.5	5.0	5.0
BC	1 126.6	973.1	7.6	6.7

Rafiq would like to know:

1. The weighted mean rate of unemployment (men) for 10 Canadian provinces. Use Excel.

2. The weighted mean rate of unemployment (women) for 10 Canadian provinces. Use Excel.

3. Which of the two rates is higher?

4. He would like you to prepare a clustered bar graph displaying labour force and the number of unemployed in Alberta, Nova Scotia, Ontario, and New Brunswick. Use Excel.

5. Based on the reported unemployment rate, Rafiq would like to know which province offers equal opportunity to his siblings for employment.

CHAPTER 5

A Survey of Probability Concepts

GOALS

When you have completed this chapter, you will be able to:

- Explain the terms *experiment, event, outcome, sample space permutations,* and *combinations*

- Define *probability*

- Describe the *classical, empirical,* and *subjective* approaches to probability

- Explain and calculate *conditional probability* and *joint probability*

- Calculate probabilities using the *rules of addition* and the *rules of multiplication*

- Use a *tree diagram* to organize and compute probabilities

- Calculate a probability using Bayes' theorem.

BLAISE PASCAL (1623–1662)

Historical evidence of well-developed games of chance has been found as far back as 2750 B.C. in contemporary civilizations in ancient India (The Indus Valley) and Iraq (ancient Mesopotamia). In fact a game of chance plays a major role in the Vedic epic *Mahabharata*, which is dated 850 B.C. However, the foundation of the modern mathematical theory of probability was laid, around 1654, by the two famous mathematicians, Blaise Pascal and Pierre de Fermat. Since then, a large number of mathematicians have contributed towards the development of the theory in its present form. Some of the major contributors were Jacob Bernoulli, Thomas Bayes, Pierre de Laplace, Chebyshev, Markov, Von Mises, and Kolmogorov.

Blaise Pascal was born in Clermont-Ferrand, France on June 19, 1623. He was a man of extraordinary intellect but very delicate health. He wrote his first mathematical research paper at the age of sixteen and went on to make significant contributions to mathematics, physics, philosophy, and literature in his short life of 39 years.

As a mathematician, Pascal is perhaps best known for his correspondence with Pierre de Fermat in 1654 in the context of the following problem proposed to him by a gamester, the Chevalier de Mere. *Two players of equal skill want to leave the table before finishing their game. It is desired to find, based on their scores at the time of leaving, in what proportion they should divide the stakes*. The two developed basic principles of *the theory of probability* to answer the problem, and Pascal went on to apply probability theories to other games of chance and making decisions under uncertainty. Today, this area is extended to decision-making in investment, risk management, and other fields.

His other significant contributions included the inventions of the first digital calculator, the modern syringe and the hydraulic press. His *Provincial Letters*, written in defense of Jansenism in their struggle against the Jesuits, have greatly influenced French prose. He is accounted as the father of modern French prose. His work, *Pensées*, which includes many commentaries on religions, human nature, and ways to achieve happiness in life, was a precursor to existentialist thought. Here, he wrote:

> *There are but three classes of men: Those who have found God and serve Him, those who busily seek Him but find Him not, those who pass their lives neither seeking nor finding. The first are reasonable and happy, the last are senseless and wretched, and the middle class are wretched and reasonable.*[1]

Pascal was somewhat of a mystic. In the night of November 23, 1654, he had an ecstatic spiritual experience that was decisive for the rest of his life. He wrote an account of the incident on a small piece of parchment, sewed it to the inner lining of his jacket, and wore it for the rest of his life, transferring it from garment to garment.

1498
1548
1598
1648
1698
1748
1898
1948
2000

INTRODUCTION

The emphasis in Chapters 2 through 4 is on descriptive statistics. In Chapter 2, we saw how to organize a given data set into a frequency distribution, showing the lowest and highest values and where the largest concentration of data occurs. In Chapter 3, we introduced a number of measures of central tendency, such as the arithmetic mean, median and mode, to locate a typical value representing the entire data set. In Chapter 4, we introduced measures of dispersion, such as the range and the standard deviation, to examine the spread in the data. Descriptive statistics is concerned with summarizing a data set that is explicitly available to us.

We now turn to the second facet of statistics, namely, *computing the chance that something will occur in the future*. This facet is called **statistical inference** or **inferential statistics**.

Seldom does a decision maker have complete information from which to make a decision. For example:

- Toys and Things, a toy and puzzle manufacturer, recently developed a new game based on sports trivia. They want to know whether sports buffs will purchase the game. "Slam Dunk" and "Home Run" are two of the names under consideration. One way to minimize the risk of making the wrong decision is to hire pollsters to take a sample of, say, 2000 from the population and ask each respondent for a reaction to the new game and its proposed titles.

- The quality assurance department of a steel mill must assure management that the 0.635-cm wire being produced has an acceptable tensile strength. Obviously, not all the wire produced can be tested for tensile strength, because testing requires the wire to be stretched until it breaks—thus destroying it. So, a random sample of 10 pieces is selected and tested. Based on the test results, all the wire produced is deemed to be either satisfactory or unsatisfactory.

Statistical inference deals with conclusions about a population based on a random sample taken from that population. (The populations for the preceding illustrations are the reactions of all the sports buffs, and the strengths of all the pieces of 0.635-cm steel wire produced.)

Other questions involving uncertainty include the following: should the daytime drama *Days of Our Lives* be discontinued immediately? Will the S&P/TSX Composite Index pass 14 000 by the end of 2004? Will a newly developed mint-flavoured cereal be profitable if marketed? Should I marry Jean? Should I buy a new Rolls-Royce? Should I buy high-tech stocks?

Because there is uncertainty in decision making, it is important that all the known risks involved be scientifically evaluated. Helpful in this evaluation is *probability theory*, which has often been referred to as the science of uncertainty. The use of probability theory allows the decision maker with only limited information, to analyze the risks and minimize the gamble, inherent for example, in marketing a new product or accepting an incoming shipment possibly containing defective parts.

Because probability concepts are so important in the field of statistical inference (to be discussed starting in Chapter 8), this chapter introduces the basic language of probability theory, including such terms as *random experiment*, *event*, *probability*, and *addition* and *multiplication rules*.

5.1 CONCEPTS OF RANDOMNESS AND PROBABILITY

The words *probability*, *chance*, and *likelihood* are often used interchangeably in everyday conversation as a measure of one's belief in the occurrence of an uncertain event. To develop a theory that can be effectively applied to statistical problems in business and economics, we need a more rigorous definition. A precise definition of the term *probability* is beyond the scope of this book. In this section, we shall give a definition that is rigorous enough for the applications considered in this book.

If we toss a coin, the outcome cannot be predicted in advance with certainty. It could be a *head* or a *tail*. It is uncertain. It has been observed that if we ask a group of people to each toss the same coin a large number of times (say a thousand or a million times), the fractions of heads obtained by the different individuals will all be more or less the same. In fact, all these fractions will cluster around a constant number, the value of which will depend on the coin. For most average coins, this constant is around 0.5. Thus, if John and Martha each toss such a coin say a thousand times each, John may get 510 heads (that is, a fraction of 0.51), and Martha may get 495 heads, (that is, a fraction of 0.495). It is very, very unlikely that one of them will get only about 200 heads. It is said that the renowned statistician, Karl Pearson, tossed a coin 24 000 times and obtained 12 012 heads, (a fraction of 0.501). If the selected coin is heavy on one side, then the value of the constant fraction for such a coin will be different than 0.5. It may be 0.2 or 0.4 or 0.9. In this case, if the coin is tossed a large number of times the fraction of heads will be close to this constant.

The *outcome of a coin toss* is therefore said to be *random*, the *process of a coin toss* is said to be a *random experiment*, and the constant number around which the values of the fraction of heads clusters in the long term is called *the probability of head*, and is denoted by $P(Head)$. It is used as a measure of chance or likelihood that the outcome will be a head in any one toss. If we assume that the only possible outcomes when we toss the coin are head and tail, then the probability of tail will be $P(\text{Tail}) = (1 - P(\text{Head}))$.

In general, we define a **random experiment** as:

> *i* **Random experiment** A process (i) that is (at least conceptually) repetitive in nature, (ii) for which the outcome of any trial which is uncertain and is always one of a well-defined set of possible outcomes, and (iii) that has associated with each of its outcomes, a number called the probability of the outcome, such that if we conduct a large number of trials of the experiment, the fraction of times an outcome will occur will, on the average, be equal to its probability.

A toss of a six-sided die is another example of a random experiment. In this case, the outcome (number observed on the upper face) in a trial can be any one of 1, 2, 3, 4, 5, 6. A large number of examples of random experiments have been observed in nature. The example of gender of a newborn child is similar to that of a toss of a coin. In this case, the outcome of any trial (that is, gender of a newborn child) is uncertain and can be either male or female. It is generally accepted among demographers that the gender of a newborn child is random, with $P(\text{Male})$ around 0.516, under normal conditions. As one more example, let the random experiment entail observing the total sale (number of items sold) of washing machines, of a particular brand, in Calgary over a three-day period. The possible outcomes are no sale (zero), 1, 2, 3, 4, and so on. There are many possible outcomes in this experiment.

> **i** | **Outcome** A particular result of a random experiment.

In the example of coin toss, the possible **outcomes** are head or tail.

> **i** | **Sample space** A collection or set of *all* the possible outcomes of a random experiment.

For example, when we toss a coin, there are only two possible outcomes: head (*H*) or tail (*T*). Thus, in this case, the **sample space** (*S*) consists of two outcomes and is expressed by: $S = \{H, T\}$. Similarly, when we toss a six-sided die, there are six possible outcomes: a 1, 2, 3, 4, 5, 6; we express it by: $S = \{1, 2, 3, 4, 5, 6\}$.

■ SELF-REVIEW 5-1

Investors are waiting to see the behaviour of the stock price of Rogers' Wireless Communications Inc. on the next trading day at the Toronto Stock Exchange.
    (a) Is this a random experiment? Explain.
    (b) What is the sample space for the experiment?

TREE DIAGRAM

The random experiments we encounter in the real world are complex. But, often they can be broken down into a sequence of simpler random experiments. In such a case, a graphical device called a *tree diagram* provides a very useful pictorial representation of all the possible outcomes of the experiment. A tree diagram consists of heavy dots, which represent starting or ending points of simpler experiments, and lines, known as branches, that represent outcomes of the simpler experiments. Each of the outcomes of a simpler experiment, starting at a heavy dot, is represented by a branch starting from this heavy dot and going to the right. Let us draw a tree diagram for a random experiment that involves tossing two fair coins once each (see Chart 5-1). We break this into a sequence of two coin tosses: a toss of coin number 1 (which we call stage 1), followed by a toss of coin number 2 (which we call stage 2).

We start with a heavy dot (·) to the left, known as the trunk of the tree. This represents the start of the first simple random experiment (toss of coin 1). The two lines starting from this dot represent the two possible outcomes (head or tail) of the first coin toss. The heavy dots at the tip of these lines represent the start of the second stage. For example, suppose the outcome of the first coin toss is a head. Then we are at the dot at the tip of the stage 1 branch marked "*H*." The two branches starting from this dot represent the two possible outcomes, head and tail, of the second coin toss. Similarly, if the outcome of the first coin toss is a tail, then we are at the dot at the tip of the stage 1 branch marked "*T*." The two branches starting from this dot represent the possible outcomes, head and tail, of the second coin toss.

CHART 5-1: Tree Diagram for the Toss of Two Coins

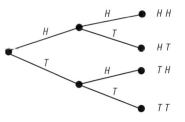

The tree thus has four end dots. Each path from the trunk of the tree to an end dot represents an outcome of the complex experiment. For example, a path traversed through the blue coloured branches represents the outcome *H H*. All four possible outcomes of the experiment are displayed to the right of the tree diagram.

A sample space for this experiment can be indicated by:

$$S = \{HH, HT, TH, TT\}$$

The total number of possible outcomes is (total number of outcomes in stage 1 experiment) × (total number of outcomes in stage 2 experiment) = (2)(2) = 4.

Let us take another example not related to a game of chance.

Example 5-1

A 24-hour restaurant is offering, for the special price of $3.50, a breakfast with choice of eggs, pancakes, or oatmeal, served with either orange juice or apple juice. Coffee is served with every order.

A new customer has just arrived. In how many ways can the customer order the breakfast?

Solution

To draw a tree diagram showing the total number of possible ways for ordering breakfast, we follow the steps used in the tree diagram for tossing a pair of coins. In stage 1, three branches appear: (i) eggs, (ii) pancakes, and (iii) oatmeal. In stage 2, two branches: orange juice and apple juice appear from each of the heavy dots at the end of (i), (ii), and (iii). Thus, there are (3)(2) = 6 ways to order the breakfast.

The complete diagram is shown in Chart 5-2.

CHART 5-2: Tree Diagram for Ordering Breakfast in a 24-hour Restaurant

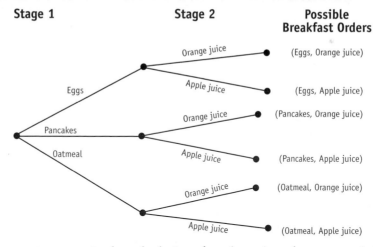

A pattern seems to appear in the calculation of total number of outcomes. In both cases considered above, we are multiplying the number of outcomes in the first stage experiment by the number of outcomes in the second stage experiment. This leads us to the rule of multiplication for counting. We will discuss this and other rules of counting in Section 5-5.

■ SELF-REVIEW 5-2

Out of 20 students in an advanced course in statistics, 16 passed and 4 failed. Two students are randomly selected from the class list, as follows: the name of one student is drawn from the list of 20 and then the name of a second student is drawn from the list of remaining 19 students. The performances of these two students are recorded. Draw a tree to represent this random experiment.

EVENTS OF A RANDOM EXPERIMENT

In applications of probability theory, we are often interested in not just individual outcomes, but in certain collections of outcomes. For example, in the tossing of a die, we may be interested whether the outcome of a toss will be an even number, that is, it will be one of the numbers 2, 4, and 6. Thus, in this case, we are interested in the collection of outcomes {2, 4, 6}.

We call any collection of one or more outcomes of a random experiment an event.

 Event   A collection of one or more outcomes of a random experiment.

In the tossing of a die, **event** A may be *observing a 1* on the upper face; event B may be *observing an even number* on the upper face, which includes a 2, 4, or 6; event C may be *observing an odd number* on the upper face, which includes a 1, 3, or 5, event D may be *observing a number less than 3*, which includes a 1 or 2, and so on.

The event such as observing a 1 is known as a *simple event*. A simple event consists of only one outcome of the random experiment. Each of the events B, C, and D consists of more than one outcome. Such an event is known as a *compound event*.

We shall denote by S the event that includes all the elements of the sample space.

We say that an *event has occurred* if the outcome of a trial of the experiment belongs to the event. For example, in a toss of a die, we say that an event *observing an even number* has occurred if the outcome is one of 2, 4, and 6.

A collection of events, such that *at the most one* of these events can occur at one time, is called a **mutually exclusive** set of events.

 Mutually exclusive set of events   A collection of events such that the occurrence of one of the events excludes the occurrence of other events in the collection at the same time.

In the die-tossing experiment, the pair of compound events *observing an even number* and *observing an odd number* are mutually exclusive. If one of them has occurred, then the other could not occur at the same time. However, the events *observing an even number* and *observing a number less than 3* are *not* mutually exclusive. If the outcome is a 2, then both these events will have occurred. If a student is selected randomly for an interview, the student is either male or female, but cannot be both. The pair of events *selecting a male student* and *selecting a female student* is mutually exclusive.

If a set (collection) of events is such that at least one of the events in the set must occur in any trial of the experiment, then the set of events is called **collectively exhaustive**. For example, in the die-tossing experiment, every outcome is either an odd number or an even number. The pair of events *observing an even number* and *observing an odd number* is thus collectively exhaustive.

 Collectively exhaustive set of events   At least one of the events must occur in any trial of the experiment.

■ SELF-REVIEW 5-3

Consider the problem in Self-Review 5-2.
   (a) What is the event *at least one of the two selected students passed?*
   (b) What is the event *at the most one of the two selected students passed?*

(c) Are the events in (a) and (b) mutually exclusive? Are they collectively exhaustive?

Justify your answers.

PROBABILITY

The **probability** of an event of a random experiment is the fraction of times the event will occur, on average, in a large number of repetitive trials of the random experiment. It is used as a measure of chance or likelihood of the event occurring in one trial of the experiment.

 Probability of an event It is the fraction of times the event will occur, on average, in a large number of repetitive trials of the random experiment.

A probability can assume any value from 0 to 1 inclusive. We usually express it as a decimal, such as 0.70, 0.27, or 0.50, or as a fraction, such as 7/10, 27/100, or 1/2. If a company has only five sales regions and each region's name is written on a separate slip of paper, and the slips are put in a hat, and a slip is drawn from the hat, the probability of selecting a slip of paper containing the name of any one of the five regions is 1. The probability of selecting from the hat a slip of paper not having the name of any region written on it is 0. Thus,

 An event that is certain to happen has a probability of 1, and an event that cannot happen has a probability of 0. In particular, $P(S)$, probability of the entire sample space, equals 1.

The closer a probability is to 0, the more improbable it is that the event will happen. The closer the probability is to 1, the more sure we are it will happen. The relationship is shown in the following diagram along with a few of our personal beliefs. You might, however, select a different probability for Gandria's chance to win the Queen's Plate or for an increase in federal taxes.

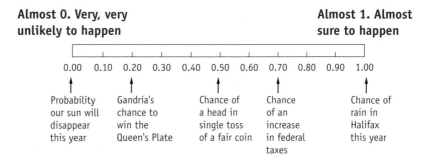

PROBABILITY AND DECISION MAKING

What role does probability have in decision making? This question can be answered by citing two cases:

CASE 1

Based on past experience, a publishing company determined that at least 20 percent of the target group must subscribe to a monthly magazine to make it a financial success. The company is considering a monthly magazine for bird-watchers. A special issue was designed and mailed to a sample of 1000 bird-watchers. In response, 190 out of 1000, or 19 percent, said they would subscribe to the magazine if it were published.

Should we state that this proportion is less than 20 percent and make an immediate decision not to publish the magazine? Or, could the difference between the required percentage (20) and the sample percentage (19) be attributed to sampling, that is, chance? Probability will help us arrive at a decision for this type of situation, which will be discussed in Chapter 10.

CASE 2

A large construction project requires thousands of concrete blocks. Specifications state that the blocks must stand up to a pressure of 7237.5 kPa. Two firms manufacturing these blocks submitted samples for testing. The arithmetic mean strength, measured by ability to withstand pressure, of the Strong Block Company's blocks was 7375.4 kPa; those from the Taylor Company tested at 7320.2 kPa. Strong Block thinks it should be awarded the contract because its blocks have a higher mean strength. Taylor disagrees, saying that the difference of only 55.1 kPa could be due to sampling (chance). If Strong Block's claim is correct, it will be awarded the contract. If Taylor's statement is correct, the contract will be divided between the two companies. Probability will help us reach a decision for a case such as this in Chapter 11.

5.2   APPROACHES TO ASSIGNING PROBABILITY

Two approaches to probability will be discussed: namely, the *objective* and the *subjective* viewpoints. **Objective probability** can be subdivided into (1) *classical probability* and (2) *empirical probability*.

OBJECTIVE PROBABILITY

CLASSICAL PROBABILITY

Classical probability is based on the assumption that the outcomes of an experiment are *equally likely*. Using the classical viewpoint, the probability of an event happening is computed by dividing the number of favourable outcomes by the total number of possible outcomes.

Definition of Classical Probability	
$\text{Probability of an event} = \dfrac{\text{Number of favourable outcomes}}{\text{Total number of possible outcomes}}$	**5-1**

Example 5-2   Consider a random experiment of rolling a six-sided fair die. What is the probability of the event that "an even number of dots appear face up?"

Solution   There are three "favourable" outcomes (a 2, 4 and a 6) in the collection of six equally likely possible outcomes. Therefore:

$$\text{Probability of an Even Number} = \frac{\text{Number of favourable outcomes}}{\text{Total number of possible outcomes}} = \frac{3}{6} = 0.5$$

Let us consider another example:

Example 5-3

A survey of all 200 executives of a company measured their loyalty to the company. One of the questions asked was, "If you were given an offer by another company equal to or slightly better than your present position, would you remain with the company or take the other position?" The responses of the 200 executives were cross-classified with their length of service with the company (see Table 5-1). That is, the response of each executive was included in the column corresponding to his or her length of service, and the row corresponding to loyalty (would remain or would not remain with the company). The type of table that resulted is usually referred to as a *contingency table*.

A company executive is randomly selected. Let A_1 be the event *the selected executive will be loyal to the company*, (that is, his/her answer is "would remain"), let A_2 be the event *the selected executive will not be loyal*. Also, let B_1, B_2, B_3 and B_4 be the events *the selected executive will have less than one year of service, 1–5 years of service, 6–10 years of service, and more than 10 years of service*, respectively.

    (a) Find the value of $P(A_1)$, the probability that the selected executive will be loyal to the company.
    (b) Find the value of $P(B_1)$, the probability that the selected executive will have less than one year of service.
    (c) Find the value of $P(A_1$ and $B_1)$, the probability that the selected executive will be loyal to the company and will have less than one year of service; similarly, find the values of $P(A_1$ and $B_2)$, $P(A_1$ and $B_3), \ldots, P(A_2$ and $B_4)$.

Solution

(a) We note in Table 5-1 that there are $(10 + 30 + 5 + 75 =)$ 120 executives out of the 200 in the survey who would remain with the company. So, the probability that a randomly selected executive will be loyal to the company is the same as the probability that the selected executive will be one of these 120 executives.

$$P(A_1) = \frac{\text{Number of favourable outcomes}}{\text{Total number of possible outcomes}} = \frac{120}{200} = 0.6$$

(b) We note in Table 5-1 that $(10 + 25 =)$ 35 executives out of the 200 have less than one year of service. So the probability that a randomly selected executive will have less than one year of service with the company is the same as the probability that the selected executive will be one of these 35 executives.

$$P(B_1) = \frac{\text{Number of favourable outcomes}}{\text{Total number of possible outcomes}} = \frac{35}{200} = 0.175$$

TABLE 5-1: Loyalty of Executives and Length of Service with Company

Loyalty	Less than 1 Year	1–5 Years	6–10 Years	More than 10 Years
Would remain	10	30	5	75
Would not remain	25	15	10	30

TABLE 5-2: Joint Probability Distribution of Loyalty and Years of Service

Loyalty	Length of Service			
	Less than 1 Year (B_1)	1–5 Years (B_2)	6–10 Years (B_3)	More than 10 Years (B_4)
Yes (A_1)	10/200 = 0.05	30/200 = 0.15	5/200 = 0.025	75/200 = 0.375
No (A_2)	25/200 = 0.125	15/200 = 0.075	10/200 = 0.05	30/200 = 0.15

(c) We note in Table 5-1, that out of the total of 200 executives, 10 are loyal ("would remain") and have less than one year of service. So,

$$P(A_1 \text{ and } B_1) = \frac{\text{Number of favourable outcomes}}{\text{Total number of possible outcomes}} = \frac{10}{200} = 0.05$$

Similarly, we get $P(A_1 \text{ and } B_2) = \frac{30}{200} = 0.15$, and so on. These are displayed in Table 5-2.

The probability $P(A_1 \text{ and } B_1) = 0.05$ is called *the joint probability of events* A_1 *and* B_1. It is the probability that both the events A_1 and B_1 will occur together, (that is, the selected executive will be loyal and will also have less than one year of service). Similarly, $P(A_1 \text{ and } B_2)$, the joint probability of events A_1 and B_2, equals 0.150, and so on.

Historically, the classical approach to probability was developed and applied in the 17th and 18th centuries to games of chance, such as cards and dice. Note that it is unnecessary to do an experiment to determine the probability of an event occurring using the classical approach; we can logically arrive, for example, at the probability of getting a tail on the toss of one coin or three heads on the toss of three coins. Nor do we have to conduct an experiment to determine the probability that your income tax return will be audited if there are 2 million returns mailed to your area of the Canada Customs and Revenue Agency and 2400 are to be audited. Assuming that each return has an equal chance of being audited, your probability is 0.0012—found by 2400 divided by 2 million. Obviously, the chance of your return being audited is rather remote.

EMPIRICAL CONCEPT

Another way to estimate probability is based on **relative frequencies**. The probability of an event happening is estimated by observing what fraction of the time similar events have happened in repeated trials of a random experiment in the past. In terms of a formula:

Definition of Empirical Probabilities

$$\text{Estimate of Probability of an Event Happening} = \frac{\text{Number of times the event occurred in repeated trials in the past}}{\text{Total number of trials}} \qquad \textbf{5-2}$$

Example 5-4 An automatic Shaw machine fills plastic bags with a mixture of beans, broccoli, and other vegetables. Most of the filled bags meet the weight specification, but because of the slight variation in the size of the beans and other vegetables, a package might be slightly underweight or overweight. A check of 4000 packages selected randomly from those filled in the past month revealed the following data:

Weight	Number of Packages
Underweight	100
Satisfactory	3600
Overweight	300

$\frac{100}{4000} = 0.025$

What is the probability that the next package filled will be underweight? What is the probability that its weight will be satisfactory? What is the probability it will be overweight?

Solution

Let A be the event: *the next package is underweight*. An estimate of $P(A)$, the probability of the event A is

$$\frac{\text{Number of times the event } A \text{ occurred in repeated trials in the past}}{\text{Total number of trials}}$$

Since 100 of the 4000 packages selected in the past were underweight, an estimate of

$$P(A) \text{ is } \frac{100}{4000} = 0.025$$

Let B be the event: *the weight of the next package is satisfactory*. An estimate of $P(B)$ is

$$\frac{\text{Number of times the event } B \text{ occurred in repeated trials in the past}}{\text{Total number of trials}} = \frac{3600}{4000} = 0.9$$

Finally, let C be the event: *the next package is overweight*. An estimate of $P(C)$ is

$$\frac{\text{Number of times the event } C \text{ occurred in repeated trials in the past}}{\text{Total number of trials}} = \frac{300}{4000} = 0.075$$

In other words, based on past experience, the probability that the next package filled will be underweight is 0.025, that its weight will be satisfactory is 0.9, and that it will be overweight is 0.075.

SUBJECTIVE PROBABILITY

If there is little or no past experience on which to base a probability, it may be arrived at subjectively. Essentially, this means evaluating the available opinions and other information and then estimating or assigning the probability. This probability is aptly called a **subjective probability**.

 Subjective probability The likelihood of a particular event happening assigned by an individual based on whatever information is available.

Some illustrations of subjective probability are: estimating the likelihood that Gustav Schickedanz will win the Queen's Plate in the next horse racing event; estimating the probability that General Motors will lose its number-one ranking in total units sold to Ford or DaimlerChrysler within two years; estimating the likelihood you will earn an A in this course.

■ SELF-REVIEW 5-4

1. One card will be randomly selected from a standard 52-card deck. What is the probability the card will be a queen? Which approach to probability did you use to answer this question?

2. To estimate the probability that a randomly chosen New Brunswicker prefers Pepsi to all other soft drinks, a New Brunswicker was randomly selected and his preference was noted. The process was repeated 500 times. It was observed that 210 times the person chosen preferred Pepsi. Obtain an estimate of the desired probability.

3. In a soft drink taste test, each of 1000 consumers was asked to choose between two colas, Cola 1 and Cola 2,[2] and also state whether he or she preferred the cola drink *sweet* or *very sweet*. The results are summarized in the following contingency table:

	Taste	
Cola	Sweet	Very Sweet
Cola 1	527	156
Cola 2	93	224

   (a) Estimate the probability of a randomly selected customer preferring very sweet cola drinks.
   (b) Construct the table of joint probabilities.
   (c) Do the joint probabilities total 1.00? Why?

EXERCISES 5-1 TO 5-14

5-1.   A statistician has decided to randomly select two residents of Ottawa and ask each of them the following question: "Do the Members of Parliament deserve a raise?" List the possible outcomes.

5-2.   A quality control inspector selects a part to be tested. The part is then declared acceptable, repairable, or scrapped. Then another part is tested. List all of the possible outcomes of this experiment regarding two parts.

5-3.   The annual enrollment of part-time students in a community college in the Greater Toronto Area in 2002 is 30 000. Of the 30 000 students, 22 800 are taking courses for career improvement. A person in the registrar's office has decided to randomly select a part-time student from the database for an interview. Estimate the probability that she will select a student enrolled in courses for career improvement.

5-4.   The world's 50 most valuable athletes in 2000 participate in one of the sports listed in the table below. (The number in the column "Athletes" corresponding to each sports category refers to the number of athletes out of 50 who engage in that sport.) (Source: *Report on Business* Magazine, Globemedia Publishing Inc., June 21, 2001.) An athlete is selected randomly from this list.

Sport	Athletes
Golf	4
Basketball	5
Baseball	8
Hockey	5
Tennis	5
Other	23
Total	50

(a) What is the probability that the selected athlete plays tennis?

(b) What is the probability that the selected athlete plays baseball?

(c) Which concept of probability did you use to compute the probabilities in (a) and (b)?

5-5.   In each of the following cases, indicate whether a classical, empirical, or subjective approach to assigning probability will be suitable.

   (a) A basketball player makes 30 out of 50 foul shots. What is the probability that she will make the next attempted foul shot?

   (b) A seven-member committee of students is formed to study environmental issues. One of the seven is to be randomly selected as a spokesperson for the committee. What is the likelihood that a particular member of the committee will be chosen as the spokesperson?

   (c) You purchase one of 4 million tickets sold for Lotto 6/49. What is the probability you win the jackpot of $2 million?

   (d) What is the probability of an earthquake in Eastern Canada in the next 10 years?

5-6.   An investor buys 100 shares of BCE Inc. stock and records its price change daily.

   (a) List several possible events for this experiment.

   (b) How would you estimate the probability for each event you described in (a)?

5-7.   There are 52 cards in a standard deck.

   (a) What is the probability that the first card selected is a spade?

   (b) What is the probability that the first card selected is the jack of spades?

   (c) What approaches to assigning probability have you used in (a) and (b)?

5-8.   A company wants to market a new product. The market response to the product will be either favourable or unfavourable. Before marketing the product, the company will conduct a market survey. The result of the survey will be either a forecast that the market response will be favourable, or a forecast that the response will be unfavourable. Construct a tree diagram for this random experiment.

5-9.   A sample of 40 executives is randomly selected to test a questionnaire. One question about legislation of environmental issues requires a yes or no answer.

   (a) What is the random experiment? What is its sample space?

   (b) List two events that are mutually exclusive but *not* collectively exhaustive.

   (c) List two events that are collectively exhaustive, but *not* mutually exclusive.

   (d) Ten of the 40 favoured the legislation. Based on these sample responses, estimate the probability that a randomly selected executive will be in favour of the legislation.

   (e) What approach to assigning probability did you follow in part (d)?

5-10.   A sample of 2000 licensed drivers revealed the following number of violations.

Number of Violations	Number of Drivers
0	1910
1	46
2	18
3	12
4	9
5 or more	5
Total	2000

(a) What is the probability that a randomly selected driver will have exactly two violations?
(b) What is the probability that the number of violations of a randomly selected driver will be between 2 and 4 (including 2 and 4)?
(c) What approach to assigning probability have you used?

5-11. A study of 100 independent grocery chains revealed these incomes after taxes:

Income after Taxes	Number of Grocery Chains
Under $180 000	60
$180 000 to $1 million	25
$1 million or more	15
Total	100

(a) What is the probability that a randomly selected grocery chain has under $180 000 in income after taxes?
(b) What is the probability that a grocery chain selected at random has either an income between $180 000 and $1 million or an income of $1 million or more?
(c) What approach for assigning probability have you used in (a) and (b)?

5-12. A study of the opinions of designers with respect to the paint colour most desirable for use in executive offices showed the following. (Let us assume that each designer has a unique most preferred colour.)

Colour	Number of Opinions	Colour	Number of Opinions
Red	92	Blue	37
Orange	86	Indigo	46
Yellow	46	Violet	2
Green	91		

(a) What is the experiment?
(b) What is the probability that for a randomly selected designer, the most preferable colour for executive offices will be red or green?
(c) What is the probability that for a randomly selected designer the most preferable colour will not be yellow?

5-13. A brokerage firm studied the stock performance of a randomly selected set of 26 companies in the forest products sector and 106 companies in the technology sector and used the risk-adjusted ranking system. The finding of the brokerage house is shown in the following contingency table.

Grouping of Company	Low Risk Stocks	Moderate-to- High Risk Stocks	Total
Forest Products	18	8	26
Technology	50	56	106
Total	68	64	132

(a) Find the probability that a randomly selected company's stock will be low risk.
(b) Find the probability that a randomly selected company will be from the forest products sector and its stock will be low risk.

5-14. Three defective electric toothbrushes were accidentally shipped to a drugstore by Clean-Brush Products along with 17 non-defective ones.
(a) What is the probability that out of these 20 toothbrushes, the first toothbrush sold will be a defective one?
(b) What is the probability that the first electric toothbrush sold will not be defective?

5.3 SOME RULES OF PROBABILITY

Now that we have defined probability and described the different approaches to computing (or estimating) probability, we turn our attention to computing probabilities of combinations of events by applying rules of addition and multiplication.

RULES OF ADDITION

SPECIAL RULE OF ADDITION

To apply the special rule of addition, the events must be mutually exclusive. Recall that a *mutually exclusive* set of events means that when one event occurs, none of the other events in the set can occur at the same time. An illustration of mutually exclusive events in the die-tossing experiment is the pair of events "a number 4 or larger," and "a number 2 or smaller." If the outcome is in the first group {4, 5, and 6}, then it cannot also be in the second group {1 and 2}. Similarly, a product coming off the assembly line cannot be defective and satisfactory at the same time.

If two events A and B are mutually exclusive, the special rule of addition states that the probability of one *or* the other event occurring, equals the sum of their probabilities. This rule is expressed in the following formula:

Special Rule of Addition	$P(A \text{ or } B) = P(A) + P(B)$	5-3

For three mutually exclusive events designated A, B, and C, the rule is written:

$$P(A \text{ or } B \text{ or } C) = P(A) + P(B) + P(C) \qquad \textbf{5-4}$$

Example 5-5

In Example 5-4, concerning weights of plastic bags filled with a mixture of beans, broccoli, and other vegetables, we calculated that the probability, $P(A)$, of the event A, *the next bag filled will be underweight*, is 0.025, and the probability, $P(C)$, of the event C, *the next bag will be overweight*, is 0.075. Using this information, find the probability that the next bag filled will be either underweight or overweight.

Solution

The events A and C are mutually exclusive, meaning that a package cannot be both underweight and overweight at the same time.
Hence, applying the special rule of addition, we get:

$$P(A \text{ or } C) = P(A) + P(C) = 0.025 + 0.075 = 0.10$$

VENN DIAGRAMS

A Venn diagram is a useful tool to depict addition or multiplication rules.

English logician J. Venn (1834–1884) developed a diagram to portray graphically a sample space, events, and relationships among events. The set operators "and," "or," and "not" are used to show the relationships among events. The mutually exclusive concept and various rules for combining probabilities of events can be illustrated using Venn diagrams. They are also called *Euler's circles*, after Leonhard Euler (1707–1783). To construct a Venn diagram, a space is first enclosed representing the total of all possible outcomes. This space is usually in the form of a rectangle. An event is then represented by a circular area that is drawn inside the rectangle proportional to the probability of the event. The schematic Venn diagram to the left represents the *mutually exclusive* concept. The three events do not overlap, meaning that the events are mutually exclusive.

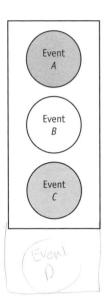

Let us consider again Example 5-3 concerning the survey of 200 executives of a company. The joint probabilities in Table 5-2 are reproduced in Table 5-3 below.

The events A_1 and A_2 are mutually exclusive, (an executive cannot be both loyal and disloyal) and they are collectively exhaustive, (every executive is either loyal or disloyal).

Hence, the events (A_1 and B_1), and (A_2 and B_1) are also mutually exclusive, and the event $B1$ is the same as ((A_1 and B_1) or (A_2 and B_1)). (Every executive with less than one year of service will belong to precisely one of these two categories.) So, using the special rule of addition, we find that,

$$P(B_1) = P(A_1 \text{ and } B_1) + P(A_2 \text{ and } B_1) = 0.05 + 0.125 = 0.175$$

This gives us the same value of $P(B_1)$ as in the solution to Example 5-3. We call it the **marginal probability of B_1**. It is displayed in the last row of Table 5-3, under column "(B_1)". We see that the marginal probability of B_1 is the sum of all the joint probabilities in column "(B_1)".

Similarly, the events B_1, B_2, B_3, and B_4 are mutually exclusive and collectively exhaustive. Hence, the events (A_1 and B_1), (A_1 and B_2), (A_1 and B_3), and (A_1 and B_4) are mutually exclusive, and the event A_1 is the same as ((A_1 and B_1) or (A_1 and B_2) or (A_1 and B_3) or (A_1 and B_4)). So, using the special rule of addition, we get,

$$P(A_1) = P(A_1 \text{ and } B_1) + P(A_1 \text{ and } B_2) + P(A_1 \text{ and } B_3) + P(A_1 \text{ and } B_4)$$
$$= 0.05 + 0.15 + 0.025 + 0.375 = 0.6$$

Hence, the marginal probability of A_1 is $P(A_1) = 0.6$. It is displayed in Table 5-3 in the last column under the row labelled "(A_1)", and is the sum of all the joint probabilities in that row.

TABLE 5-3: Joint and Marginal Probabilities of Loyalty and Years of Service

| Loyalty | Length of Service | | | | |
	Less than 1 Year (B_1)	1–5 Years (B_2)	6–10 Years (B_3)	More than 10 Years (B_4)	Marginal Probabilities
Yes (A_1)	10/200 = 0.05	30/200 = 0.15	5/200 = 0.025	75/200 = 0.375	0.6
No (A_2)	25/200 = 0.125	15/200 = 0.075	10/200 = 0.05	30/200 = 0.15	0.4
Marginal Probabilities	0.175	0.225	0.075	0.525	

$$P(A) + P(B) + P(C) = 1 \qquad \frac{1}{6} + \frac{1}{6} + \frac{1}{6} + \frac{1}{6} + \frac{1}{6} + \frac{1}{6} = \frac{6}{6} = 1$$

Marginal Probability

$$P(A_1) = P(A_1 \text{ and } B_1) + P(A_1 \text{ and } B_2) + P(A_1 \text{ and } B_3) + P(A_1 \text{ and } B_4) \qquad \textbf{5-5}$$

given events B_1, B_2, B_3, and B_4 are mutually exclusive and collectively exhaustive.

The marginal probabilities of A_2, B_2, B_3, and B_4 can be obtained the same way and are displayed in the last row/column of Table 5-3. They equal the sum of all the probabilities in the corresponding row/column.

The complement of an Event A, denoted by ($\sim A$), is the collection of all outcomes of a sample space not included in the event A. For example, in rolling a six-sided die if the event A is getting a 1, then the complement of the event A—that is, $\sim A$—is getting a 2, 3, 4, 5, or 6. Recall that in rolling a die, the sample space is $S = \{1, 2, 3, 4, 5, 6\}$. An event and its complement form a mutually exclusive pair of events. These two events make up the entire sample space. This, together with the fact that the probability of the entire sample space equals 1, gives us the following equality:

$$P(S) = P(A) + P(\sim A) = 1$$

This can be revised to read:

Complement Rule

$$P(A) = 1 - P(\sim A) \qquad \textbf{5-6}$$

The complement rule is used to determine the probability of an event occurring by subtracting the probability of the event *not* occurring from 1. A Venn diagram illustrating the complement rule might appear as shown in the margin.

Example 5-6

Reconsider the problem in Example 5-4. Recall that the probability of an underweight bag of mixed vegetables is 0.025 and that the probability of an overweight bag is 0.075. Use the complement rule to show that the probability of a satisfactory bag is 0.900.

Solution

B is the event: *the weight of the bag is satisfactory*. So, the event: *weight is unsatisfactory*, (that is, $\sim B$), is the same as the event: *the bag is overweight or underweight*, (that is, A or C). The probability that the bag is unsatisfactory (that is, $P(\sim B)$) equals $P(A$ or $C)$ $= P(A) + P(C) = 0.025 + 0.075 = 0.100$. Hence, $P(B) = 1 - P(\sim B) = 1 - 0.1 = 0.9$. This is the same as the answer we obtained in Example 5-4.

The complement rule is important in the study of probability. Often it is easier to calculate the probability of an event happening by determining the probability of it not happening and subtracting the result from 1.

■ SELF-REVIEW 5-5

1. From the table of joint probabilities constructed for problem 3 in Self-Review 5-4, find the marginal probability of the event a randomly selected customer prefers very sweet cola drink, using the special rule of addition. Is the answer the same as the one you obtained in Self-Review 5-4?

2. The list of the top 1000 companies in Canada in 2002 was analyzed and the probabilities of a randomly selected company in the list belonging to different categories were calculated and are given below:

Category	Financial Services	Oil and Gas	Food and Beverage	Precious Metal	Mining	Other Services
Probability	0.33	0.19	0.12	0.13	0.10	0.13

A company is selected randomly from the list.
   (a) What is the probability that the selected company will be from either financial services or mining?
   (b) What is the probability that the selected company will be from neither financial services nor mining?
   (c) Draw a schematic Venn diagram illustrating your answers in (a) and (b).

GENERAL RULE OF ADDITION

Suppose that the Regional Municipality of Niagara selected a sample of 200 tourists who visited the municipality during 2001. The survey showed that 120 tourists went to Niagara Falls and 100 went to Niagara-on-the-Lake. A tourist is selected randomly from those who visited the municipality. What is the probability that the selected tourist visited Niagara Falls or Niagara-on-the-Lake?

For convenience, let us denote the event *visited Niagara Falls* by simply *Falls*, and the event *visited Niagara-on-the-Lake* by simply *Lake*. If the special rule of addition discussed earlier is used, then $P(Falls) = 120/200 = 0.60$; and $P(Lake) = 100/200 = 0.50$. The sum of these probabilities is 1.10. We know, however, that the desired probability, $(P(Falls \text{ or } Lake))$, cannot be greater than one. Therefore, the special rule of addition does not apply. An explanation is that many tourists visited both places and are being counted twice! A check of the survey responses revealed that 60 out of 200 sampled did, in fact, visit both places. The events *Falls* and *Lake* are *not* mutually exclusive.

To find the probability $P(Falls \text{ or } Lake)$, (1) add $P(Falls)$ and $P(Lake)$; and (2) subtract the probability of visiting both. Thus,

$$P(Falls \text{ or } Lake) = P(Falls) + P(Lake) - P(Falls \text{ and } Lake)$$
$$= \frac{120}{200} + \frac{100}{200} - \frac{60}{200}$$
$$= \frac{160}{200} = 0.80$$

In summary, the general rule of addition is used to combine events that are not mutually exclusive. This rule for any two events designated A and B is written as follows:

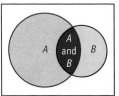

General Rule of Addition $P(A \text{ or } B) = P(A) + P(B) - P(A \text{ and } B)$ **5-7**

The Venn diagram to the left depicts this general situation.

Example 5-7 | What is the probability that a card chosen at random from a standard deck of cards will be a king or a heart?

Solution | Let us denote by A the event, *the chosen card is a king*, and by B the event, *the chosen card is a heart*. Thus, we want to find $P(king \text{ or } heart) = P(A \text{ or } B)$. We may be inclined to use *the special rule of addition* (5-3). But this would be improper since the events A and B are not mutually exclusive. A chosen card can be a *king* and also a *heart* at the same time. Hence, we use *the general rule of addition* (5-7).

Card	Probability	Explanation
King (A)	$P(A) = 4/52$	4 kings in a deck of 52 cards
Heart (B)	$P(B) = 13/52$	13 hearts in a deck of 52 cards
King and (of)		
heart (A *and* B)	$P(A \text{ and } B) = 1/52$	1 king of heart in a deck of 52 cards

Using Formula 5-7:

$$P(A \text{ or } B) = P(A) + P(B) - P(A \text{ and } B)$$
$$= 4/52 + 13/52 - 1/52$$
$$= 16/52, \text{ or } 0.3077$$

■ SELF-REVIEW 5-6

A study of the claim forms submitted to an insurance company by the employees of a community college in the Greater Toronto Area revealed the following: 8 percent of the employees submitted claims for major prescription drugs, 15 percent submitted claims for major dental work, and 3 percent submitted claims for both major prescription drugs and dental work. What is the probability that an employee selected at random submitted claims for major prescription drugs or major dental work?

EXERCISES 5-15 TO 5-28

5-15. Events A and B are mutually exclusive. Suppose $P(A) = 0.30$ and $P(B) = 0.20$. What is the probability of A or B occurring? What is the probability that neither A nor B will happen?

5-16. Events X and Y are mutually exclusive. Suppose $P(X) = 0.05$ and $P(Y) = 0.02$. What is the probability of either X or Y occurring? What is the probability that neither X nor Y will happen?

5-17. The chair of a company's board of directors says that "There is a 50-percent chance this company will earn a profit, a 30-percent chance it will break even, and a 20-percent chance it will lose money next quarter."
   (a) Use an addition rule to find the probability they will not lose money next quarter.
   (b) Use the complement rule to find the probability they will not lose money next quarter.

5-18. 9500 students are enrolled in a community college in the Greater Toronto Area in 2001. Of 9500 students, 3350 have a Visa, 2200 have a MasterCard, and 860 have both credit cards. Find the probability that a student selected randomly:
   (a) Has a Visa.
   (b) Has a MasterCard.
   (c) Has both a Visa and a MasterCard.
   (d) Has a Visa or a MasterCard.

5-19. A single die is rolled. Let *A* be the event *the die shows 4*, *B* be the event *the die shows an even number*, and *C* be the event *the die shows an odd number*. Consider each pair of these events and describe whether they are mutually exclusive. Then identify whether they are complementary.

5-20. Two coins are tossed. If *A* is the event *two heads* and *B* is the event *two tails*, are *A* and *B* mutually exclusive? Are they complementary events?

5-21. A survey of 150 investors reveals that 110 of them invest in oil and gas stocks, 60 of them in technology stocks, and 45 in both types. What is the probability that an investor selected at random invested in oil and gas or in technology stocks?

5-22. Let $P(A) = 0.55$ and $P(B) = 0.35$. Assume the probability that they both occur is 0.20. What is the probability of *A* or *B* occurring?

5-23. Suppose the two events *A* and *B* are mutually exclusive. What is the probability of their joint occurrence?

5-24. A student is taking two courses, history and math. The probability that the student will pass the history course is 0.60, and the probability of passing the math course is 0.70. The probability of passing both is 0.50. What is the probability of passing at least one?

5-25. A survey of top executives showed 35 percent of them regularly read *The Globe and Mail,* 20 percent read the *Calgary Herald*, and 40 percent read the *Halifax Daily News*. Ten percent read both *The Globe and Mail* and the *Halifax Daily News*.
   (a) What is the probability that a randomly selected executive reads *The Globe and Mail* or the *Halifax Daily News*?
   (b) Are the events *an executive reads The Globe and Mail regularly* and *an executive reads The Halifax Daily News regularly* mutually exclusive?
   (c) Are the events *an executive reads The Globe and Mail regularly*, an *executive reads The Calgary Herald regularly* and an *executive reads The Halifax Daily News regularly* collectively exhaustive?

5-26. A study by the National Park Services revealed that 50 percent of vacationers in Alberta visit Banff National Park, 40 percent visit Jasper National Park, and 35 percent visit both.
   (a) What is the probability that a vacationer in Alberta will visit at least one of these parks?
   (b) What is the probability 0.35 called?
   (c) Are the events mutually exclusive? Explain.

5-27. A local bank reports that 80 percent of its customers maintain a chequing account, 60 percent have a savings account, and 50 percent have both. A customer is chosen at random.
   (a) What is the probability the selected customer has a chequing or a savings account?
   (b) What is the probability the selected customer does not have either a chequing or a savings account?

(c) What is the probability the selected customer has a chequing account but does not have a savings account?

(d) What is the probability the selected customer has a savings account but does not have a chequing account?

(e) What is the probability the selected customer has exactly one of the two types of accounts?

5-28. All Seasons Plumbing has two service trucks that frequently break down. The probability the first truck is available is 0.75, the probability the second truck is available is 0.50, and the probability that both trucks are available is 0.30.

(a) What is the probability neither truck is available?

(b) What is the probability that the first truck is the only truck available?

(c) What is the probability that the second truck is the only truck available?

(d) What is the probability that exactly one of the two trucks is available?

RULES OF MULTIPLICATION

SPECIAL RULE OF MULTIPLICATION

The special rule of multiplication requires that two events A and B, be independent. Two events are **independent** if the occurrence of one does not alter the probability of the other. So if the events A and B are independent, the occurrence of A does not alter the probability of B.

> **Independent** A set of events is independent if the probability of occurrence of any one of the events in the set is *not* affected by the occurrence of any collection of the other events in the set.

For two independent events A and B, the probability that A and B will both occur is found by multiplying the two probabilities. This is called the special rule of multiplication and is written symbolically as: $\frac{1}{6} \times \frac{1}{6} = \frac{1}{36}$

Special Rule of Multiplication	$P(A \text{ and } B) = P(A)\,P(B)$	5-8

To illustrate what is meant by independence of events, suppose two coins are tossed. The outcome of one coin (head or tail) is unaffected by the outcome of the other coin (head or tail). To put it another way, two events are independent if the occurrence of the second event does not depend on the occurrence of the first event.

For three independent events A, B, and C, the special rule of multiplication used to determine the probability that all three events will occur is:

$$P(A \text{ and } B \text{ and } C) = P(A)P(B)P(C) \qquad \text{5-9}$$

Example 5-8 A survey by the Canadian Automobile Association (CAA) revealed that 60 percent of its members made airline reservations last year. Two members are selected at random. What is the probability that both made airline reservations last year? $.60 = P(R)$

Solution The probability that the first member made an airline reservation last year is 0.60, written $P(R_1) = 0.60$ where R_1 refers to the fact that the first member made a reservation. The probability that the second member selected made a reservation is also 0.60,

$.60 \times .60$

STATISTICS IN ACTION

Probability in Our Technological Society

The theory of probability, which started some 600 years ago, is playing a pivotal role in our technological society. It is used in the design of games in casinos, the premiums charged by insurance companies, and investment decisions made by professionals in investment industries.

Other factors aside, the mortality rate determines life insurance premiums, the probability of being disabled controls long-term disability premiums, and the probability of having an auto accident determines auto insurance premiums.

The mortality rate for a male is higher than the mortality rate for a female. For example, the mortality rate for a 30-year-old male during the next 10 years is 0.009, whereas for a female of the same age it is 0.0051.[3] The probability of a 30-year-old female being disabled within a year is higher than the probability of a 30-year-old male being disabled within a year. Males pay higher premiums for life insurance because the mortality rates are higher than that of females. Females pay higher premiums for disability insurance because the probability of being disabled is higher than that of males.

so $P(R_2) = 0.60$ also. Since the total number of CAA members is very large, R_2 is almost independent of R_1. Hence, using Formula 5-8, the probability that they both made a reservation is 0.36, found by:

$$P(R_1 \text{ and } R_2) = P(R_1)\,P(R_2) = (0.60)(0.60) = 0.36$$

■ SELF-REVIEW 5-7

1. From long experience, Teton Tire knows the probability is 0.80 that their XB-70 model will last 96 000 km before it becomes bald or fails. An adjustment is made on any tire that does not last 96 000 km. You purchase four XB-70s. What is the probability that all four tires will last at least 96 000 km?

2. As cited in Example 5-4, an automatic Shaw machine fills mixed vegetables into a plastic bag. Past experience revealed that some packages were underweight and some overweight, but most of them had a satisfactory weight. We estimate from the past data the following values of probabilities: $P(\text{underweight}) = 0.025$, $P(\text{satisfactory weight}) = 0.90$, and $P(\text{overweight}) = 0.075$.
   (a) What is the probability of selecting three packages from the food processing line today and finding that all three of them are underweight?
   (b) What does this probability mean?

DEPENDENT EVENTS

If two events are not independent, they are referred to as *dependent*. To illustrate dependency, suppose there are 10 rolls of film in a box, and it is known that 3 are defective. A roll of film is selected from the box. Obviously, the probability of selecting a defective roll is 3/10, and the probability of selecting a good roll is 7/10. Then a second roll is selected from the box without the first one being returned to the box. The probability that this second roll is defective *depends on* whether the first roll selected was defective or good. The probability that the second roll is defective is,

    2/9, if the first roll was defective (only two defective rolls remain in the box containing nine rolls); or

    3/9, if the first roll selected was good (all three defective rolls are still in the box containing nine rolls).

    The fraction 2/9 (or 3/9) is aptly called a **conditional probability** because its value is conditional on (dependent on) whether a defective or a good roll of film is chosen in the first selection from the box.

> ℹ **Conditional probability** The probability of a particular event occurring given that another event has occurred.

Symbolically, it is expressed by:

$$P(B|A) = \frac{P(A \text{ and } B)}{P(A)}, \quad \text{if } P(A) > 0 \qquad \textbf{5-10}$$

Where $P(B|A)$ stands for the probability of the event B given that event A has occurred. The vertical line between B and A is read as "given that."

    Let us take another example.

Example 5-9

A manager of a self-service gas station has noticed over a period of six months that 8 percent of drivers check windshield washer fluid, 3 percent check fluid nozzles on the hood, and 2 percent check both windshield washer fluid and fluid nozzles on the hood. If a randomly selected driver checked the windshield washer fluid, what is the probability that fluid nozzles on the hood were also checked?

Solution

Event A = *driver checks windshield washer fluid*
Event B = *driver checks fluid nozzles on the hood*
$P(A) = 0.08$
$P(B) = 0.03$
$P(A \text{ and } B) = 0.02$
　　We are required to find $P(B|A)$

$$P(B|A) = \frac{P(A \text{ and } B)}{P(A)} = \frac{0.02}{0.08} = 0.25$$

How can we describe this value of $P(B|A)$?
Of the drivers who check windshield washer fluid, 25 percent also check fluid nozzles on the hood.
　　Note that the unconditional probability of event B—that is, $P(B) = 0.03$—and the conditional probability of B—that is, $P(B|A) = 0.25$—are *different*. That is, the value of the unconditional probability $P(B)$ is revised.

Example 5-10

Let us consider again the joint and marginal probabilities of loyalty and years of service of executives in a company given in Table 5-2. Suppose a randomly selected executive of the company has 1–5 years of service. What is the probability that the executive is loyal?

Solution

We have denoted the event 1–5 *years of service* by B_2, and the event *loyal* by A_1. Using Formula 5-10 with A_1 in the place of B and B_2 in the place of A, we get,

$$P(A_1|B_2) = \frac{P(B_2 \text{ and } A_1)}{P(B_2)} = \frac{0.15}{0.225} = 0.67$$

(It may be noted that $P(B_2 \text{ and } A_1)$ is the same as $P(A_1 \text{ and } B_2)$).

GENERAL RULE OF MULTIPLICATION

We use the general rule of multiplication to find the joint probability of occurrence of two events such as selecting 2 defective rolls from a box of 10 rolls, one after the other. In general, the rule states that for two events A and B, the joint probability of occurrence of both of the events is found by multiplying the probability of event A occurring by the conditional probability of event B occurring, given that A has occurred.

General Rule of Multiplication	$P(A \text{ and } B) = P(A)P(B|A)$	**5-11**

Example 5-11

To illustrate the formula, let's use the problem regarding 10 rolls of film in a box, three of which are defective. Two rolls are to be selected from the box, one after the other. What is the probability of selecting a defective roll followed by another defective roll?

Solution

Event A is that the first roll of film selected from the box will be defective. $P(A) = 3/10$ because 3 out of the 10 are defective. Event B is that the second roll selected will be defective. Therefore, $P(B|A) = 2/9$, because after the first selection is found to be defective, only 2 defective rolls of film will remain in the box containing 9 rolls. Determining the probability of two defectives (see Formula 5-11):

$$P(A \text{ and } B) = P(A)P(B|A)$$
$$= \left(\frac{3}{10}\right)\left(\frac{2}{9}\right) = \frac{6}{90}, \text{ or about } 0.067$$

Incidentally, it is assumed that this experiment was conducted *without replacement*—that is, the defective roll of film was not thrown back in the box before the next roll was selected.

It should also be noted that the general rule of multiplication can be extended to more than two events. For three events A, B, and C, the formula would be:

$$P(A \text{ and } B \text{ and } C) = P(A)P(B|A)P(C|A \text{ and } B) \qquad \textbf{5-12}$$

$P(A \text{ and } B \text{ and } C)$ is the product of the probability of the first event, the probability of the second event given the first event has occurred, and the probability of the third event given that the first two events have occurred.

For illustration, the probability that the first three rolls chosen from the box without replacement will all be defective is 0.00833, found by:

$$P(A \text{ and } B \text{ and } C) = P(A)P(B|A)P(C|A \text{ and } B)$$
$$= \left(\frac{3}{10}\right)\left(\frac{2}{9}\right)\left(\frac{1}{8}\right) = \frac{6}{720} = 0.00833$$

■ SELF-REVIEW 5-8

1. The board of directors of Tarbell Industries consists of eight men and four women. A four-member search committee is to be chosen at random to recommend a new company president.
   (a) What is the probability that all four members of the search committee will be women?
   (b) What is the probability that all four members will be men?
   (c) Does the sum of the probabilities for the events described in (a) and (b) equal 1? Explain.

2. From the table of joint probabilities constructed for problem 3 in Self-Review 5-4, find the probability of a randomly selected consumer preferring Cola 1, given that he or she prefers very sweet cola drinks.

TREE DIAGRAMS

As we pointed out before, the random experiments we encounter in the real world are complex. But, often they can be broken down into a sequence of simpler experiments. In such a case, a *tree diagram* is very useful in calculating probabilities of various events. For illustration, let us consider again the problem in Example 5-11. Thus, two rolls of film are to be selected from a box containing 10 rolls, of which three are defective.

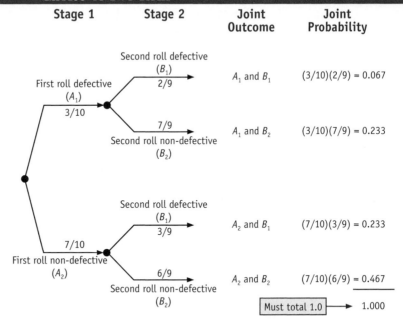

CHART 5-3: Tree Diagram Showing Different Outcomes of Choice of Two Rolls

	Stage 1	Stage 2	Joint Outcome	Joint Probability
	First roll defective (A_1) 3/10	Second roll defective (B_1) 2/9	A_1 and B_1	$(3/10)(2/9) = 0.067$
		7/9 Second roll non-defective (B_2)	A_1 and B_2	$(3/10)(7/9) = 0.233$
	7/10 First roll non-defective (A_2)	Second roll defective (B_1) 3/9	A_2 and B_1	$(7/10)(3/9) = 0.233$
		6/9 Second roll non-defective (B_2)	A_2 and B_2	$(7/10)(6/9) = 0.467$
			Must total 1.0	1.000

Steps in constructing a tree diagram.

1. To construct a tree diagram, we begin by drawing a heavy dot on the left to represent the trunk of the tree (see Chart 5-3).

2. For this problem, the two main branches go out from the trunk, the upper one representing *First roll defective*, which we have denoted by event A_1, and the lower one *First roll non-defective*, which we have denoted by event A_2. Their probabilities are written on the branches; namely, 3/10 and 7/10. These are $P(A_1)$ and $P(A_2)$.

3. From the heavy dot at the end of each of these two main branches, two branches go out, representing the events *Second roll defective*, (which we have denoted by B_1), and *Second roll non-defective*, (which we have denoted by B_2). The conditional probabilities for the two branches emerging from the upper heavy dot are $P(B_1|A_1) = 2/9$, and $P(B_2|A_1) = 7/9$. Similarly, the conditional probabilities for the two branches emerging from the lower heavy dot are $P(B_1|A_2) = 3/9$, and $P(B_2|A_2) = 6/9$. These are all written on the respective branches.

4. Finally, joint probabilities that *As* and *Bs* will occur together are shown on the right side. For example, the joint probability of randomly selecting *first roll defective* (A_1) and *second roll defective* (B_1), using Formula 5-11, is:

$$P(A_1 \text{ and } B_1) = P(A_1)\, P(B_1|A_1) = (3/10)(2/9) = 0.0667$$

■ SELF-REVIEW 5-9

Superimpose probabilities on the branches of the tree diagram constructed in Self-Review 5-2, and find the probabilities of all the outcomes.

EXERCISES 5-29 TO 5-38

5-29. Suppose $P(A) = 0.40$ and $P(B|A) = 0.30$. What is the joint probability of A and B?

5-30. A sample of 225 companies was randomly selected from the list of the top 1000 Canadian companies during 2000. These companies were grouped according to their areas of industrial activity and whether they made profit or incurred loss in 2000. The data are summarized in the contingency table below.

Area of Activity	Profit	Loss	Total
Oil and gas	100	19	119
Technology	35	71	106
Total	135	90	225

Source: Adapted from the list of top 1000 companies, *Report on Business*, Globemedia Publishing Inc., June 29, 2001

(a) Compute the probability that a randomly selected company made a profit in 2000.
(b) Compute the probability that a randomly selected company is from the oil and gas sector.
(c) Compute the probability that a randomly selected company belonged to the oil and gas sector, given that the company made a profit in 2000.
(d) Label the event in (a) and (b) A and B, respectively. Are these events independent? Explain.

5-31. Refer to Exercise 5-27. A randomly chosen customer is found to have a chequing account. What is the probability that the customer also has a savings account?

5-32. Refer to Exercise 5-28.
(a) Find the probability that the second truck is available given that the first truck is not available.
(b) Find the probability that the first truck is available given that the second truck is not available.
(c) Find the probability that the first truck is available given that at least one of the two trucks is available.

5-33. Refer to Exercise 5-13. Find the probability that a randomly selected stock is from the forest products' sector, given that it is a low-risk stock.

5-34. Refer to Exercise 5-14. What is the probability that both the first two toothbrushes sold will be defective ones given that at least one of them was defective?

5-35. Each salesperson at Stiles-Compton is rated either below average, average, or above average with respect to sales ability. Each salesperson is also rated with respect to his or her potential for advancement—either fair, good, or excellent. These traits for the 500 salespeople were cross-classified into the following table.

| | Potential for Advancement | | |
Sales Ability	Fair	Good	Excellent
Below average	16	12	22
Average	45	60	45
Above average	93	72	135

(a) What is this table called?

(b) What is the probability a salesperson selected at random will have above-average sales ability and excellent potential for advancement?

(c) A randomly selected salesperson was rated *excellent* in potential for advancement. What is the probability that the rating of his/her sales ability was *above average*?

5-36. An investor owns three common stocks. Each stock, independently of the other, has equally likely chances of (1) increasing in value, (2) decreasing in value, or (3) remaining the same value. Construct a tree diagram for the problem. List the possible outcomes of this experiment. Estimate the probability that at least two of the stocks increase in value.

5-37. The board of directors of a small company consists of five people. Three of them are "strong leaders." If they buy an idea, the entire board will agree. The other "weak" members have no influence. Three salespeople are scheduled, one after the other, to make a sales' presentation to a board member of the salesperson's choice. The salespeople are convincing but do not know who the "strong leaders" are. However, they will know to whom the previous salespeople spoke. The first salesperson to find a strong leader will win the account. Do the three salespeople have the same chance of winning the account? If not, find their respective probabilities of winning.

5-38. If you randomly select three strangers on campus, what is the probability that: (a) All were born on a Wednesday? (b) All were born on different days of the week? (c) None were born on a Saturday?

5.4   BAYES' THEOREM

We shall illustrate Bayes' theorem through an example.

Example 5-12

Suppose that 5 percent of the population of a certain country is known to have a particular disease. There is a medical diagnostic test for detecting the disease. But the test is not very accurate. Historical evidence shows that if a person has the disease, the probability that his or her test result will be positive is 0.9. However, the probability is 0.15 that the test result will be positive for a person who does not have the disease. For a randomly selected citizen of the country, the test result was positive. What is the probability that the person has the disease?

THOMAS BAYES (1702–1761)

Thomas Bayes (1702–1761) was born into a non-conformist family in England. He was educated privately, as was deemed suitable for the son of a nonconformist minister at that time. He worked for his father at the Presbyterian Church in Holborn, London and then became minister of the Presbyterian chapel in Tunbridge Wells, England. Being a nonconformist, he did not accept most of the rituals of the Church of England.

He was elected a Fellow of the Royal Society of London in 1742. His pamphlet *Divine Benevolence* in 1731 addressed the main religious controversy of the day: "God was not compelled to create the Universe. Why did He do so?" Some theologians cited God's rectitude for creating the universe, but Bayes stated God's benevolence behind creating the universe. His paper *An Essay Towards Solving a Problem in the Doctrine of Chances* was posthumously published in 1763.[4] Many statisticians consider this the first effort to lay the groundwork for statistical inference, the great issue first raised by Jacob Bernoulli (1759–1789). Bayes introduced a new technique in the decision-making process where new information is used to modify probabilities of events based on old information.

1498
1548
1598
1648
1698
1748
1898
1948
2000

Solution

We shall denote by A_1 the event *the person has the disease*, and we shall denote by A_2, the event *the person does not have the disease*.

Then the events A_1 and A_2 are mutually exclusive, and collectively exhaustive. (For any selected person exactly one of these two is true—he or she either has the disease or does not have the disease.) Since 5 percent of the population has the disease, $P(A_1) = 0.05$. Also, $A_2 = \sim A_1$. Therefore, $P(A_2) = 1 - P(A_1) = 1 - 0.05 = 0.95$.

Let B denote the event *the medical test result is positive*. Then we are given that:

$$P(B|A_1) = 0.90 \text{ and } P(B|A_2) = 0.15$$

We want to find $P(A_1|B)$, (that is the probability that the person has the disease given the additional information that he or she tested positive).

This can be calculated using Bayes' theorem which can be stated as:

Bayes' Theorem
$$P(A_1|B) = \frac{P(A_1)P(B|A_1)}{P(A_1)P(B|A_1) + P(A_2)P(B|A_2)}$$
5-13

The above theorem can be derived using the rules of addition and multiplication we saw before. We provide the details in the Chapter 5 Appendix A on the CD-ROM.

Thus, by applying Bayes' theorem to our problem we get,

$$P(A_1 \mid B) = \frac{P(A_1)P(B \mid A_1)}{P(A_1)P(B \mid A_1) + P(A_2)P(B \mid A_2)}$$

$$= \frac{(0.05)(0.9)}{(0.05)(0.9) + (0.95)(0.15)} = \frac{0.0450}{0.1875} = 0.24$$

How do we interpret the probability value = 0.24? If a person is selected randomly from the population, the probability that the person has the disease is 0.05. If the person is tested and the test result is positive, the probability that the person actually has the disease is increased from 0.05 to 0.24.

The initial probability value (0.05) is known as **prior probability** and is based on the initial level of information.

The probability value (0.24) is known as **posterior probability** because it is based on additional information.

> **ℹ Posterior Probability**   A revised probability based on additional information.

The tree diagram in Chart 5-4 shows the probabilities of the events in Example 5-12, and Table 5-4 summarizes the calculation of the probabilities.

CHART 5-4: Tree Diagram of Example 5-12

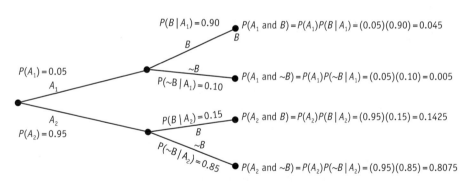

Joint Event

$P(B \mid A_1) = 0.90$ $P(A_1 \text{ and } B) = P(A_1)P(B \mid A_1) = (0.05)(0.90) = 0.045$

$P(\sim B \mid A_1) = 0.10$ $P(A_1 \text{ and } \sim B) = P(A_1)P(\sim B \mid A_1) = (0.05)(0.10) = 0.005$

$P(A_1) = 0.05$

$P(B \mid A_2) = 0.15$ $P(A_2 \text{ and } B) = P(A_2)P(B \mid A_2) = (0.95)(0.15) = 0.1425$

$P(A_2) = 0.95$ $P(\sim B \mid A_2) = 0.85$ $P(A_2 \text{ and } \sim B) = P(A_2)P(\sim B \mid A_2) = (0.95)(0.85) = 0.8075$

TABLE 5-4: Probability Distribution of Events in Example 5-12

Event	Prior Probability	Conditional Probability	Joint Probability	Posterior Probability
A_i	$P(A_i)$	$P(B \mid A_i)$	$P(A_i \text{ and } B)$	$P(A_i \mid B)$
A_1 (Disease)	0.05	0.90	0.045	$\dfrac{0.0450}{0.1875} = 0.24$
A_2 (No Disease)	0.95	0.15	0.1425	$\dfrac{0.1425}{0.1875} = 0.76$
Total			0.1875	1.00

Marginal Probability: $P(B)$

In the preceding problem, the two events A_1 and A_2 formed a set of mutually exclusive and collectively exhaustive set of events. If there are n events, say $A_1, A_2, \ldots, A_n$, in such a set of mutually exclusive and collectively exhaustive events, the Bayes' theorem formula becomes:

$$P(A_i|B) = \frac{P(A_i)P(B|A_i)}{P(A_1)P(B|A_1) + P(A_2)P(B|A_2) + \cdots + P(A_n)P(B|A_n)} \qquad \text{5-14}$$

where A_i refers to any of the n possible outcomes.

Example 5-13

A manufacturer of VCRs purchases a particular microchip, called the LS-24, from three suppliers: Hall Electronics, Schuller Sales, and Crawford Components. Thirty percent of the LS-24 chips are purchased from Hall Electronics, 20 percent from Schuller Sales, and the remaining 50 percent from Crawford Components. The manufacturer has extensive histories on the three suppliers and knows that 3 percent of the LS-24 chips from Hall Electronics are defective, 5 percent of chips from Schuller Sales are defective, and 4 percent of the chips purchased from Crawford Components are defective.

When the LS-24 chips arrive at the manufacturer, they are placed directly in a bin and not inspected or otherwise identified by the supplier. A worker selects a chip for installation in a VCR and finds it defective. What is the probability that it was manufactured by Schuller Sales?

Solution

As a first step, let's summarize some of the information given in the problem statement.

There are three events, that is, three suppliers.
A_1 The LS-24 was purchased from Hall Electronics.
A_2 The LS-24 was purchased from Schuller Sales.
A_3 The LS-24 was purchased from Crawford Components.

The prior probabilities are:
$P(A_1) = 0.30$ The probability the LS-24 was manufactured by Hall Electronics;
$P(A_2) = 0.20$ The probability the LS-24 was manufactured by Schuller Sales;
$P(A_3) = 0.50$ The probability the LS-24 was manufactured by Crawford Components.

The additional information can be:
B_1 The LS-24 is defective;
B_2 The LS-24 is not defective;

The following conditional probabilities are given.
$P(B_1|A_1) = 0.03$ The probability that an LS-24 chip produced by Hall Electronics is defective.
$P(B_1|A_2) = 0.05$ The probability that an LS-24 chip produced by Schuller Sales is defective.
$P(B_1|A_3) = 0.04$ The probability that an LS-24 chip produced by Crawford Components is defective.

A chip is selected from the bin. Because the chips are not identified by supplier, we are not certain which supplier manufactured the chip. We want to determine the probability that the defective chip was purchased from Schuller Sales. The probability is written

$$P(A_2|B_1)$$

Look at Schuller's quality record. It is the worst of the three suppliers. Now that we have found a defective LS-24 chip, we suspect that $P(A_2|B_1)$ is greater than $P(A_2)$. That is, we expect the revised probability to be greater than 0.20. But how much greater? Bayes' theorem can give us the answer. As a first step, consider the tree diagram in Chart 5-5.

The events are dependent, so the prior probability in the first branch is multiplied by the conditional probability in the second branch to obtain the joint probability. The joint probability is reported in the last column of Chart 5-5. To construct the tree diagram of Chart 5-5, we used a time sequence that moved from the supplier to the determination of whether the chip was acceptable or unacceptable.

What we need to do is reverse the time process. That is, instead of moving from left to right in Chart 5-5, we need to move from right to left. We have a defective chip, and we want to determine the likelihood that it was purchased from Schuller Sales. How is that accomplished? We first look at the joint probabilities as relative frequencies out of 1000 cases. For example, the likelihood of a defective LS-24 chip that was produced by Hall Electronics is 0.009. So, of 1000 cases we would expect to find 9 defective chips produced by Hall Electronics. We observe that in 39 of 1000 cases the LS-24 chip selected for assembly will be defective, found by $9 + 10 + 20$. Of these 39

CHART 5-5: Tree Diagram of VCR Manufacturing Problem

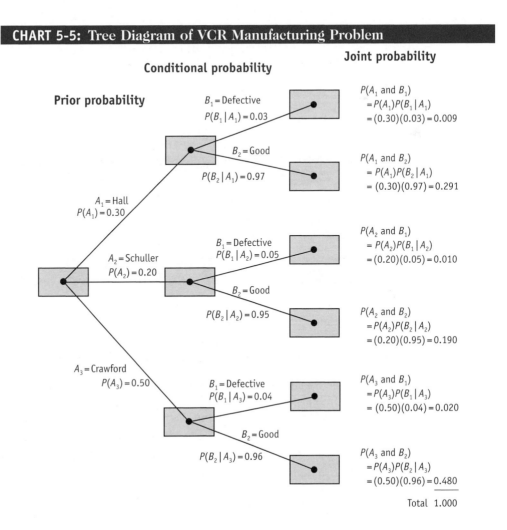

Conditional probability

Joint probability

Prior probability

$B_1 = $ Defective
$P(B_1|A_1) = 0.03$

$P(A_1 \text{ and } B_1)$
$= P(A_1)P(B_1|A_1)$
$= (0.30)(0.03) = 0.009$

$B_2 = $ Good
$P(B_2|A_1) = 0.97$

$P(A_1 \text{ and } B_2)$
$= P(A_1)P(B_2|A_1)$
$= (0.30)(0.97) = 0.291$

$A_1 = $ Hall
$P(A_1) = 0.30$

$A_2 = $ Schuller
$P(A_2) = 0.20$

$B_1 = $ Defective
$P(B_1|A_2) = 0.05$

$P(A_2 \text{ and } B_1)$
$= P(A_2)P(B_1|A_2)$
$= (0.20)(0.05) = 0.010$

$B_2 = $ Good
$P(B_2|A_2) = 0.95$

$P(A_2 \text{ and } B_2)$
$= P(A_2)P(B_2|A_2)$
$= (0.20)(0.95) = 0.190$

$A_3 = $ Crawford
$P(A_3) = 0.50$

$B_1 = $ Defective
$P(B_1|A_3) = 0.04$

$P(A_3 \text{ and } B_1)$
$= P(A_3)P(B_1|A_3)$
$= (0.50)(0.04) = 0.020$

$B_2 = $ Good
$P(B_2|A_3) = 0.96$

$P(A_3 \text{ and } B_2)$
$= P(A_3)P(B_2|A_3)$
$= (0.50)(0.96) = 0.480$

Total 1.000

defective chips, 10 were produced by Schuller Sales. Thus, the probability that the defective LS-24 chip was purchased from Schuller Sales is $10/39 = 0.2564$. We have now determined the revised probability of $P(A_2|B_1)$. Before we found the defective chip, the likelihood that it was purchased from Schuller Sales was 0.20. This likelihood has been increased to 0.2564.

This information is summarized in the following table:

Event A_i	Prior Probability $P(A_i)$	Conditional Probability $P(B_1|A_i)$	Joint Probability $P(A_i \text{ and } B_1)$	Posterior Probability $P(A_i|B_1)$
Hall	0.30	0.03	0.009	$0.009/0.039 = 0.2308$
Schuller	0.20	0.05	0.010	$0.010/0.039 = 0.2564$
Crawford	0.50	0.04	0.020	$0.020/0.039 = 0.5128$
			$P(B_1) = 0.039$	1.0000

The probability the defective LS-24 chip came from Schuller Sales can be formally found by using Bayes' theorem. We compute $P(A_2|B_1)$, where A_2 refers to Schuller Sales and B_1 to the fact that the selected LS-24 chip was defective.

$$P(A_2|B_1) = \frac{P(A_2)P(B_1|A_2)}{P(A_1)P(B_1|A_1) + P(A_2)P(B_1|A_2) + P(A_3)P(B_1|A_3)}$$

$$= \frac{(0.20)(0.05)}{(0.30)(0.03) + (0.20)(0.05) + (0.50)(0.04)} = \frac{0.010}{0.039} = 0.2564$$

This is the same result obtained from Chart 5-5 and from the conditional probability table.

■ SELF-REVIEW 5-10

Refer to Example 5-13 and its solution using Bayes' theorem.
Compute the probability that the part selected came from Crawford Components, given that it was a good chip.

EXERCISES 5-39 TO 5-44

5-39. $P(A_1) = 0.60$, $P(A_2) = 0.40$, $P(B_1|A_1) = 0.05$, and $P(B_1|A_2) = 0.10$. Use Bayes' theorem to determine $P(A_1|B_1)$.

5-40. $P(A_1) = 0.20$, $P(A_2) = 0.40$, and $P(A_3) = 0.40$. $P(B_1|A_1) = 0.25$. $P(B_1|A_2) = 0.05$, and $P(B_1|A_3) = 0.10$. Use Bayes' theorem to determine $P(A_3|B_1)$.

5-41. The Ludlow Wildcats' baseball team, a minor-league team in the Manitoba Indians' organization, plays 70 percent of their games at night and 30 percent during the day. The team has won 50 percent of their night games and 90 percent of their day games. According to today's newspaper, they won yesterday. What is the probability the game was played at night?

5-42. Dr. Stallter has been teaching basic statistics for many years. She knows that 80 percent of the students complete the assigned problems. She has also determined that among those who do their assignments, 90 percent pass the course. Among those students who do not do their homework, 60 percent pass. Mike Fishbaugh took statistics last semester from Dr. Stallter and received a passing grade. What is the probability that he completed the assignments?

5-43. The credit department of Lion's Department Store in Vancouver, B.C., reported that 30 percent of their sales are cash, 30 percent are paid by cheque at the time of purchase, and 40 percent are charged. Twenty percent of the cash purchases, 90 percent of the cheques, and 60 percent of the charges are for more than $50. A new dress costing $120 has just been purchased by one Tina Stevens. What is the probability that she paid cash?

5-44. One-fourth of the residents of the Courtice Area leave their garage doors open when they are away from their homes. The local chief of police estimates that 5 percent of the garages with open doors will have something stolen, but only 1 percent of those closed will have something stolen. If a garage is raided, what is the probability the door was left open?

5.5   PRINCIPLES OF COUNTING

If the number of possible outcomes in an experiment is small, it is relatively easy to count all of the possible events. There are six possible events, for example, resulting from the roll of a die, namely 1, 2, 3, 4, 5, and 6.

However, if there were a large number of possible outcomes, such as the number of ways a family of six could sit around the dining table, it would be cumbersome to count all possibilities. To facilitate counting, three counting formulae will be examined: the multiplication formula (not to be confused with the *multiplication rule*, described earlier in the chapter), the permutation formula, and the combination formula.

THE MULTIPLICATION FORMULA

> **ⅈ   Multiplication Formula**   If an activity can be done m ways and a second can be done n ways, then there are $(m)(n)$ ways of doing both activities.

Example 5-14 explains the formula.

Example 5-14

An automobile dealer wants to advertise that for $46 199 you can buy a convertible, a two-door, or a four-door model with your choice of either wire wheel covers or solid wheel covers. How many different arrangements of models and wheel covers can the dealer offer?

Solution

A tree diagram, discussed in the beginning of the chapter, can also display the total number of arrangements of the models and wheel covers the dealer can offer. See Chart 5-6.

The sequence of blue lines in Chart 5-6 shows one arrangement: convertible wire wheel cover.

The other ways are convertible solid wheel cover, two-door wire wheel cover, two-door solid wheel cover, four-door wire wheel cover, and four-door solid wheel cover.

We can employ the multiplication formula as a check (where m is the number of models and n the number of wheel cover types). Using the multiplication formula,

$$\text{Total possible ways} = (m)(n) = (3)(2) = 6$$

CHART 5-6: Tree Diagram of Models and Wheel Covers

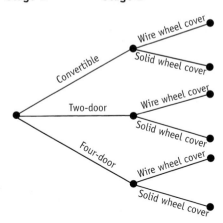

It was not difficult to count all the possible model and wheel cover combinations in Example 5-14. Suppose, however, that the dealer decided to offer eight models and six types of wheel covers. It would be tedious to draw a tree diagram to count all possible alternatives. Instead, the multiplication formula can be used. In this case, $(m)(n) = (8)(6) = 48$ possible ways.

■ SELF-REVIEW 5-11

1. Stiffin Lamps has developed five lamp bases and four lampshades that can be used together. How many different ways can a base and shade be offered?

2. An electronics company manufactures three models of stereo receivers, two cassette decks, four speakers, and three CD carousels. When the four types of components are sold together, they form a "system." How many different systems can the electronics firm offer?

THE PERMUTATION FORMULA

As noted, the multiplication formula is applied to find the number of possible ways of choosing elements, one from each group, of two or more groups. The permutation formula is applied to find the possible number of ways of choosing some elements from a single group. As illustrations of this type of problem:

• Three electronic parts are to be assembled into a plug-in unit for a television set. The parts can be assembled in any order. The question involving counting is: in how many different ways can the three parts be assembled?

• A machine operator must make four safety checks before starting his machine. It does not matter in which order the checks are made. In how many different ways can the operator make the checks?

One order for the first illustration might be the transistor first, the LEDs second, and the synthesizer third. This arrangement is called a **permutation**.

 Permutation   Any arrangement of *r* objects selected from a single group of *n* possible objects.

Note that the arrangements a, b, c, and b, a, c are *different* permutations. The formula to count the total number of different permutations is:

Permutation Formula	$$_nP_r = \frac{n!}{(n-r)!}$$	5-15

where
n is the total number of objects
r is the number of objects selected
$_nP_r$ is the total number of permutations of r objects taken from n objects.

Before we solve the two problems illustrated, note that permutations and combinations (to be discussed shortly) use a notation called n factorial. It is written $n!$ and it means the product of $n(n-1)(n-2)(n-3)...(1)$. This product is the total number of permutations of n objects taken all together. When we substitute n for r in Formula 5-15, $_nP_n = \frac{n!}{(n-n)!} = \frac{n!}{0!}$ where $_nP_n$ indicates the total number of permutations of n objects taken n together; that is, the total number of permutations of n objects taken *all* together. Here, 0! is equal to 1 (by definition). For example, to find the total number of permutations of five objects taken all five together = 5! = (5)(4)(3)(2)(1) = 120.

As shown below, numbers can be cancelled when the same numbers are included as factors in the numerator and denominator.

$$\frac{6!3!}{4!} = \frac{(6)(5)(\cancel{4})(\cancel{3})(\cancel{2})(\cancel{1})(3)(2)(1)}{(\cancel{4})(\cancel{3})(\cancel{2})(\cancel{1})} = 180$$

4, 3, 2, and 1 in the numerator and 4, 3, 2, and 1 in the denominator are cancelled out.
Another way of solving the above expression is:

$$\frac{6!3!}{4!} = \frac{(6)(5)\cancel{4!}(3)(2)(1)}{\cancel{4!}} = 180$$

We write 6! = (6)(5) 4! and then cancel 4! in the numerator and 4! in the denominator.

Most scientific calculators contain factorial (!), $_nP_r$, and $_nC_r$ keys. We advise you to consult your calculator manual for the use of these keys.

By definition, zero factorial, written 0!, is 1. That is, 0! = 1.

Example 5-15 | Referring to the group of three electronic parts that are to be assembled in any order, in how many different ways can they be assembled?

Solution | Because there are three electronic parts to be assembled, $n = 3$. Because all three are to be inserted in the plug-in unit, $r = 3$. Solving using Formula 5-15:

$$_nP_r = \frac{n!}{(n-r)!} = \frac{3!}{(3-3)!} = \frac{3!}{0!} = \frac{3!}{1} = 6$$

A check can be made to the number of permutations arrived at using the permutation formula. To check, we merely determine how many "spaces" have to be filled and the possibilities for each "space" and apply the multiplication formula. In the problem involving three electronic parts, there are three locations in the plug-in unit for the three parts. There are three possibilities for the first place, two for the second (one has been used up), and one for the third, as follows:

$$(3)(2)(1) = 6 \text{ permutations}$$

The six ways in which the three electronic parts, lettered A, B, C, can be arranged are:

ABC BAC CAB ACB BCA CBA

In the previous example we selected all the objects. In many cases we select only r of the n possible objects. We explain the details of this application in the following example.

Example 5-16

The Betts' Machine Shop has eight screw machines but only three spaces available in the production area for the machines. In how many different ways can the three spaces be filled with three machines?

Solution

There are eight possibilities for the first available space in the production area, seven for the second space (one has been used up), and six for the third space. Then:

$$(8)(7)(6) = 336$$

There are 336 different possible arrangements. This may also be expressed mathematically using Formula 5-15, where the number of machines is n and the number of spaces available is r. So in this example $n = 8$ and $r = 3$.

$$_nP_r = \frac{n!}{(n-r)!} = \frac{8!}{(8-3)!} = \frac{8!}{5!} = \frac{(8)(7)(6)5!}{5!} = 336$$

THE COMBINATION FORMULA

To qualify as a *permutation*, the order for each of the outcomes is different. For three objects a, b, and c the order abc is one permutation, the order acb is another, and the order cba is a third permutation.

If the order of the objects is not important, an outcome is called a **combination**. The formula to count the total number of combinations of r objects from a set of n objects is:

Combination Formula	$_nC_r = \dfrac{n!}{r!(n-r)!}$	5-16

For example, if executives Able, Baker, and Chauncy are to be chosen as a committee to negotiate a merger, there is only one possible combination of these three; the committee of Able, Baker, and Chauncy is the same as the committee of Baker, Chauncy, and Able. Using the combination formula:

$$_nC_r = \frac{n!}{r!(n-r)!} = \frac{3 \cdot 2 \cdot 1}{3 \cdot 2 \cdot 1(1)} = 1$$

Example 5-17

The marketing department has been given the assignment of designing colour codes for the 42 different lines of compact discs sold by Goody Records. Three colours are to be used on each CD, but a combination of three colours used for one CD cannot be rearranged and used to identify a different CD. This means that if green, yellow, and violet were used to identify one line, then yellow, green, and violet (or any other combination of these three colours) cannot be used to identify another line. Would seven colours, taken three at a time, be adequate to colour-code the 42 lines?

Solution | Using Formula 5-16, there are 35 combinations, found by

$$_7C_3 = \frac{n!}{r!(n-r)!} = \frac{7!}{3!(7-3)!} = \frac{7!}{3!4!} = 35$$

The seven colours taken three at a time (i.e., three colours to a line) would not be adequate to colour-code the 42 different lines because they would provide only 35 combinations. Eight colours taken three at a time would give 56 different combinations. This would be more than adequate to colour-code the 42 different lines.

Example 5-18 | Lotto 6/49 consists of selecting six numbers from numbers 1 to 49. The order of the numbers is not important.
      (a) If a player selects one combination of six numbers, what is the probability that the player's selection of six numbers is the winning combination of six numbers?
      (b) What is the probability that the player will match exactly three of the six winning numbers?

Solution | (a) Number of ways (combinations) of choosing 6 numbers out of 49 is

$$_{49}C_6 = \frac{49!}{6!(49-6)!} = 13\,983\,816.$$

$$\text{Probability of winning} = \frac{\text{Number of favourable outcomes}}{\text{Total number of outcomes}}$$

$$= \frac{1}{13\,983\,816} = 0.000000072$$

(b) Number of ways (combinations) of choosing three out of the six winning

numbers $= {_6C_3} = \dfrac{6!}{3!(6-3)!} = 20.$

Number of ways (combinations) of choosing three out of the remaining

$(49-6) = 43$ numbers $= {_{43}C_3} = \dfrac{43!}{3!(43-3)!} = 12\,341.$

The total number of favourable outcomes (number of ways of choosing six numbers containing exactly three of the six winning numbers $= 20\,(12\,341) = 246\,820.$

$$P(\text{matching exactly three numbers}) = \frac{\text{Number of favourable outcomes}}{\text{Total number of outcomes}}$$

$$= \frac{246\,820}{13\,983\,816} = 0.01765$$

■ SELF-REVIEW 5-12

1. A market research company would like to ask customers at local malls about the quality of stores in the malls. An employee of the company selects four malls from a total of nine malls in a given area. The order is not important. How many groupings of malls are possible?

2. The 10 digits 0 through 9 are to be used in code groups of four to identify an item of clothing. Code 1083 might identify a blue blouse, size medium; the code group 2031 might identify a pair of pants, size 18; and so on. Repetitions of digits are not permitted. That is, the same digit cannot be used twice (or more) in a total sequence. For example, 2256, 2562, or 5559 would not be permitted. How many different code groups can be designed?

3. The president of a local university considers six professors suitable for serving on a committee for the Centre for Excellence. Of the six professors, two are to be selected: one to serve as a chairperson and the other as an assistant to the chairperson. How many different ways can this selection be made by the president of the university?

EXERCISES 5-45 TO 5-52

5-45. Solve the following:

(a) $\dfrac{40!}{(35!)0!}$

(b) $_7P_4$

(c) $_5C_2$

5-46. Solve the following:

(a) $20!/17!$

(b) $_9P_3$

(c) $_7C_2$

5-47. Dr. Sunil Dutt teaches psychology in a community college. He needs a group of five students for testing his latest personality tests. There are 30 students in his class. How many different ways can he form a group of five students?

5-48. A telephone number consists of seven digits, the first three representing the exchange. How many different telephone numbers are possible within the 537 exchange?

5-49. An overnight express delivery company must include five cities on its route. How many different routes are possible, assuming that it does not matter in which order the cities are included in the routing?

5-50. A representative of Environment Canada wants to select samples from 10 landfills. The director has 15 landfills from which she can collect samples. How many different samples are possible?

5-51. An investment adviser must create a mutual fund portfolio for her client. She has decided to include eight funds in the portfolio. How many different ways are there to choose a mutual fund portfolio of eight funds from a list of 40 funds?

5-52. A company is creating three new divisions and seven managers are eligible to be appointed head of a division. How many different ways could the three new heads be appointed?

CHAPTER OUTLINE

I.   A random experiment is a process having the following three characteristics: (i) it is (at least conceptually) repetitive in nature; (ii) the outcome of any trial of the process is uncertain and is always one of a well-defined set of possible outcomes; and (iii) associated with each of its outcomes, is a number called the probability of the outcome, such that if we conduct a large number of trials of the process, the fraction of times an outcome will occur will on the average be equal to its probability.

    A. An outcome is a particular result of a random experiment.

    B. A sample space is the collection of all possible outcomes of a random experiment.

    C. An event is the collection of one or more outcomes of a random experiment.

    D. A probability is a value between 0 and 1 inclusive, which represents the likelihood a particular event will happen.

    E. A tree diagram is a graphic device to visualize all possible outcomes of a random experiment.

II.   There are three ways of assigning probability to events.

    A. In the classical approach, all the n possible outcomes of the random experiment are assumed to be equally likely.

    B. In the empirical approach, probability is estimated as the number of times an event happened in past trials divided by the total number of trials.

    C. A subjective probability is based on whatever information is available.

III. Two events are mutually exclusive when the occurrence of one event excludes the occurrence of the other event at the same time.

IV. A set of events is independent if the probability of occurrence of any one of the events in the set is not affected by the occurrence of any subset of the other events.

V.   The complement of an event $A(\sim A)$ is the collection of all outcomes of a sample space not contained in the event A.

VI. A Venn diagram portrays graphically a sample space, events, and relationships among events. Set operators, "and," "or," and "not" are used to show the relationships among events.

VII. The rules of addition are used to combine events.

    A. The special rule of addition is used to combine events that are mutually exclusive.

$$P(A \text{ or } B) = P(A) + P(B) \qquad \textbf{5-3}$$

    B. The general rule of addition is

$$P(A \text{ or } B) = P(A) + P(B) - P(A \text{ and } B) \qquad \textbf{5-7}$$

    C. The complement rule is used to determine the probability of an event happening by subtracting the probability of the event not happening from 1.

$$P(A) = 1 - P(\sim A) \qquad \textbf{5-6}$$

VIII. The rules of multiplication are also used to combine events.

    A. The special rule of multiplication is used to combine events that are independent.

$$P(A \text{ and } B) = P(A)P(B) \qquad \textbf{5-8}$$

B. The general rule of multiplication is

$$P(A \text{ and } B) = P(A)P(B|A)$$ **5-11**

C. A joint probability is the likelihood that two or more events will happen at the same time.

D. A conditional probability is the likelihood that an event will happen, given that another event has already happened.

IX. Bayes' theorem is a method of revising a probability, given that additional information is obtained. For two events:

$$P(A_1|B) = \frac{P(A_1)P(B|A_1)}{P(A_1)P(B|A_1) + P(A_2)P(B|A_2)}$$ **5-13**

X. There are three counting rules that are useful in determining the total number of ways in which events can occur.
A. The multiplication rule states that if there are m ways one event can happen and n ways another event can happen, then there are mn ways the two events can happen.

$$\text{Number of ways} = (m)(n)$$

B. A permutation is a selection in which the order of the objects selected from a specific pool of objects is important.

$$_nP_r = \frac{n!}{(n-r)!}$$ **5-15**

C. A combination is an arrangement where the order of the objects selected from a specific pool of objects is not important.

$$_nC_r = \frac{n!}{r!(n-r)!}$$ **5-16**

■ CHAPTER EXERCISES 5-53 TO 5-102

5-53. Ten percent of the accounts at an accounting firm are mismanaged. An auditor randomly chooses two of the accounts for auditing.
(a) What is the sample space of this random experiment?
(b) Given the events (i) at least one of the two accounts selected is mismanaged, (ii) none of the accounts selected is mismanaged, and (iii) at the most, one of the two accounts selected is mismanaged, are the three events mutually exclusive? Are they collectively exhaustive?

5-54. The number of times a particular event occurred in the past is divided by the total number of occurrences. What is this approach to probability called?

5-55. The probability that the cause and the cure of all cancers will be discovered before 2010 is 0.20. What viewpoint of probability does this statement illustrate?

5-56. Is it true that, if there is absolutely no chance a person will recover from 50 bullet wounds, the probability assigned to this event is -1.00? Why?

5-57. On the throw of one die, what is the probability that a one-spot or a two-spot or a six-spot will appear face up? What definition of probability is being used?

5-58. One-year returns (%) of 50 Canadian dividend funds published on June 30, 2001 on *The Globe and Mail* Web site (www.globefund.com) are grouped below.

One-Year Returns of Canadian Dividend Funds	
Class (Return in %)	Frequency
−9 up to −4	2
−4 up to 1	1
1 up to 6	7
6 up to 11	9
11 up to 16	9
16 up to 21	18
21 up to 26	2
26 up to 31	2
Total	50
Source: Adapted from www.globefund.com	

(a) What is the probability that a randomly selected dividend fund posted a one-year return of 26 percent up to 31 percent?
(b) Are "−9 up to −4," "−4 up to 1," and so on considered mutually exclusive?
(c) If the probabilities associated with each outcome were totalled, what would that be?
(d) What is the probability of selecting a fund with a one-year return of up to 11 percent?
(e) Compute the probability of selecting a fund with a one-year return of less than 1 percent.

5-59. Define each of these terms:
(a) Conditional probability.
(b) Event.
(c) Joint probability.

5-60. The first card selected from a standard 52-card deck was a king.
(a) If it is returned to the deck, and the deck is shuffled well, what is the probability that a king will be drawn on the second selection?
(b) If the king is not replaced, what is the probability that a king will be drawn on the second selection?
(c) What is the probability that a king will be selected on the first draw from the deck and another king on the second draw (assuming that the first king was not replaced)?

5-61. Advance Signal Control Inc., a manufacturer of traffic light systems, found that under accelerated-life tests, 95 percent of the newly developed systems lasted three years before failing to change signals properly.
(a) If a city purchased four of these systems, what is the probability that all four systems would operate properly for at least three years?
(b) Which rule of probability does this illustrate?
(c) Using letters to represent the four systems, design an equation to show how you arrived at the answer to (a).

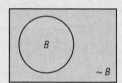

5-62. Refer to the picture at left.
   (a) What is the picture called?
   (b) What rule of probability is illustrated?
   (c) If B represents the event of mutual funds posting positive returns, what does $P(B) + P(\sim B)$ equal?

5-63. Dr. Usha Patnaik is teaching Fluid Mechanics and an elective course, How to Lie with Statistics, in a community college. She asks students to complete a questionnaire to know their academic qualifications. The following table shows the distribution of students' qualifications. (No student is enrolled in both of the courses.)

Course	Ontario Secondary School Diploma	University Degree
Fluid Mechanics	58	7
How To Lie with Statistics	85	15

   (a) Find the probability that a student selected for a personal interview with Dr. Patnaik is enrolled in Fluid Mechanics, given that the student holds an Ontario Secondary School Diploma.
   (b) Compute the probability that a student selected for the interview is enrolled in Fluid Mechanics.

5-64. Assume that the likelihood that a randomly selected Air Canada flight arrives within 15 minutes of the scheduled time is 0.90. We randomly select four flights from yesterday for study.
   (a) What is the likelihood that all four of the selected flights arrived within 15 minutes of the scheduled time?
   (b) What is the likelihood that none of the selected flights arrived within 15 minutes of the scheduled time?
   (c) What is the likelihood that at least one of the selected flights did not arrive within 15 minutes of the scheduled time?

5-65. Of 100 houses listed for sale in Burnaby, B.C. in 2001, the number of 2-bedroom, 3-bedroom, 4-bedroom, and more than 4-bedroom houses was 12, 27, 28, and 33, respectively. (Source: Adapted from www.homestore.ca.)
   A house is selected randomly from those listed for sale in Burnaby.
   (a) What is the probability that the selected house has 3 bedrooms?
   (b) What is the probability that the selected house has 2 bedrooms?
   (c) What is the probability that the selected house is either a 2-bedroom or a 3-bedroom house?
   (d) What is the probability that the selected house is neither a 2-bedroom nor a 3-bedroom house?

5-66. The following contingency table describes the marital status of adults in Alberta.

Both Sexes	Single	Married	Widowed	Divorced	Total
Male	721 771	707 131	21 790	63 725	1 514 417
Female	604 777	704 404	93 906	79 732	1 482 819
Total	1 326 548	1 411 535	115 696	143 457	2 997 236

Marital Status of Adults in Alberta

Source: Adapted from Statistics Canada, CANSIM, Matrices 6213-6224 and 6226-6227

(a) Compute the probability that a randomly selected adult is single.

(b) Compute the probability that a randomly selected adult is male.

(c) Compute the probability that a randomly selected adult is single given that the adult is male.

(d) Are the events in (a) and (b) independent?

5-67. A soda water bottling company found that 1 percent of its 1.89-L bottles is not filled according to its specification. If the quality control person randomly selects three bottles from the bottling site,

(a) what is the probability that all three bottles were not filled according to the specification?

(b) what is the probability that all three bottles were filled according to the specification?

5-68. According to a Statistics Canada report on physical activities of Canadians 12 years of age and over, 50.42 percent of the population is male. Of these 50.42 percent, 16.51 percent are engaged in physical activities. What is the probability of selecting a Canadian who is a male and engaged in physical activities? (Source: Adapted from Statistics Canada, CANSIM 11 1040033 and Catalogue no. 82-221-XIE, last modified: March 18, 2001.)

5-69. An insurance company is advertising life insurance for men aged 60 on television. Mortality tables indicate that the probability of a 60-year old man surviving another year is 0.98. If the policy is offered to three men age 60:

(a) What is the probability of all three surviving the year?

(b) What is the probability that all three will not survive?

5-70. Dr. L. Wei is teaching Thermodynamics to first-year students enrolled in the chemical engineering diploma program. The total number of students in the class is large. Based on her experience last year, she estimates that 87 percent of her students will pass the course. If she selects five students randomly:

(a) What is the probability that all five selected students will pass the Thermodynamics course?

(b) What is the probability that none of them will pass the course?

5-71. The marketing research conducted by Customs Signal Alarm revealed that 28 percent of residents in the Lawrence and Brimley area of Scarborough, Ontario, have installed a security system and have asked the security firm to monitor their homes. If three homes are selected at random:

(a) What is the probability that all three of the selected homes have a security system?

(b) What is the probability that at least one of the three selected homes has a security system?

5-72. A juggler has a bag containing ten balls: three green, two yellow, one red, and four blue. The juggler picks a ball at random. Then, without replacing it, he chooses a second ball. What is the probability the juggler first draws a yellow ball followed by a blue ball?

5-73. The board of directors of Saner Automatic Door Company consists of 12 members, 3 of whom are women. A new policy and procedure manual is to be written for the company. A committee of three is randomly selected from the board to do the writing.

(a) What is the probability that all members of the committee are men?

(b) What is the probability that at least one member of the committee is a woman?

5-74. Bank customers at CIBC are asked to select four-digit personal identification numbers (PINs) to pay their Visa Aerogold accounts at ATMs.
(a) What is the sample space of this experiment?
(b) What is the probability that Jineshwar Singh and Nadine Finn select the same PIN?

5-75. The following contingency table groups the students who wrote test number one in Quantitative Methods II, based on the gender and grade of students.

	Grade					
Gender	**A**	**B**	**C**	**D**	**F**	**Total**
Female	9	9	5	4	4	31
Male	7	6	5	2	1	21
Total	16	15	10	6	5	52

One of the students is selected randomly.
(a) What is the probability that the selected student is male?
(b) What is the probability that the selected student is female and received an A?
(c) What is the probability that the selected student received a D?

5-76. Mr. and Mrs. Wilhelms are both retired and living in a retirement community in Victoria, B.C. Suppose the probability that a retired man will live another 10 years is 0.60. The probability that a retired woman will live another 10 years is 0.70.
(a) What is the probability that both Mr. and Mrs. Wilhelms will be alive 10 years from now?
(b) What is the probability that in 10 years Mr. Wilhelms is not living and Mrs. Wilhelms is living?
(c) What is the probability that in 10 years at least one is living?

5-77. A marketing research company provides an assessment of the prospects for women's apparel shops in shopping malls. The company assesses the prospects as good, fair, or poor. Past records show that in 60 percent of the cases the prospects were rated as good, in 30 percent of the cases fair, and in 10 percent of the cases poor. Of those rated good, 80 percent made a profit the same year, of those rated fair, 60 percent made a profit the same year, and of those rated poor, 20 percent made a profit the same year. Joshi's Apparel was rated by the company last year and made profit last year. What is the probability that it was given a rating of poor?

5-78. There are 400 employees at a manufacturing company and 100 of them smoke. There are 250 males working for the company and 75 of them smoke. What is the probability that an employee selected at random:
(a) Is male?
(b) Smokes?
(c) Is male and smokes?
(d) Is male or smokes?

5-79. Dr. Nadine Finn is coordinator for Financial Services Marketing (post-diploma) program in a community college. Her record shows that of 200 students

enrolled in the program, 60 students are taking the Film Studies course, 25 are taking the Remedial Mathematics course, and 15 are taking both courses.
   (a) What is the probability that a student selected randomly for an interview by Dr. Finn is taking the course in Film Studies or Remedial Mathematics?
   (b) What is the probability that a student selected at random by Dr. Finn is taking neither Film Studies nor Remedial Mathematics?

5-80. Lotto Super 7 is played every Friday in Canada. A set of seven numbers is selected, from 1 to 47.
   (a) How many combinations of seven numbers are possible?
   (b) A player is allowed to choose any three sets of seven numbers for a $2.00 ticket. What is the probability of winning if a player plays once using a $2.00 ticket?

5-81. A new job consists of assembling four different parts. All four have different colour codes, and they can be assembled in any order. The production department wants to determine the most efficient way to assemble the four parts. The supervisors are going to conduct some experiments to solve the problem. First, they plan to assemble the parts in this order—green, black, yellow, and blue—and record the time. Then the assembly will be accomplished in a different order. In how many different ways can the four parts be assembled?

5-82. It was found that 60 percent of the tourists to China visited the Forbidden City, the Temple of Heaven, the Great Wall, and other historical sites in or near Beijing. Forty percent visited Xi'an, with its magnificent terracotta soldiers, horses, and chariots that lay buried for more than 2000 years. Thirty percent of tourists went to both Beijing and Xi'an. What is the probability that a randomly selected tourist visited at least one of these places?

5-83. Two identical-looking boxes of men's navy shirts were received from the factory. Box 1 contained 25 polo shirts and 15 dress shirts. Box 2 contained 30 polo shirts and 10 dress shirts. One of the boxes was selected at random, and a shirt was chosen at random from that box to be inspected. The shirt was a polo shirt. Given this information, what is the probability that the polo shirt came from Box 1?

5-84. The operators of Riccardo's Restaurant want to advertise that they have a large selection of meals. They offer four soups, three salads, twelve entrees, six vegetables, and five desserts. How many different meals do they offer? In addition, Riccardo's has an early-bird special: you may omit any one part of the meal except the entrees for a reduced price. How many different meals do they offer for the early bird special?

5-85. Several years ago Wendy's advertised that there are 256 different ways to order a hamburger. You may choose to have, or omit, any combination of the following on your hamburger: mustard, ketchup, onion, pickle, tomato, relish, mayonnaise, and lettuce. Is the advertisement correct? Show how you arrive at your answer.

5-86. Reynolds' Construction Company has agreed not to erect all "look-alike" homes in a new subdivision. Five exterior designs are offered to potential home buyers. The builder has standardized three interior plans that can be incorporated in any of the five exteriors. How many different ways can the exterior and interior plans be offered to potential home buyers?

5-87. A small rug weaver has decided to use seven compatible colours in her new line of rugs. However, in weaving a rug, only five spindles can be used. In her advertisement she wants to indicate the number of different colour groupings for sale. How many colour groupings using the seven colours taken five at a time are there? (This assumes that five different colours will go into each rug—that is, there are no repetitions of colour.)

5-88. To solicit views of staff members on a new teaching technique, "Problem Based Learning," the dean of business in a community college wants to form a group of 3 out of 35 staff members for an in-depth exchange of views. What is the number of combinations?

5-89. A new chewing gum has been developed that is helpful to those who want to stop smoking. If 60 percent of those people chewing the gum are successful in stopping smoking, what is the probability that in a group of four smokers using the gum, at least one will quit smoking?

5-90. Postal codes in Canada consist of three characters and three digits. Each character in the code alternates with a digit, for example M1J 1V3. How many postal codes can be created when all 26 characters and all 10 digits (0 to 9) are used?

5-91. A new sports car model has defective brakes 15 percent of the time and a defective steering mechanism 5 percent of the time. Let's assume (and hope) that these problems occur independently. If exactly one of these problems is present, the car is called a "lemon." If both of these problems are present, the car is a "hazard." Your instructor purchased one of these cars yesterday. What is the probability it is:
(a) A lemon?
(b) A hazard?

5-92. A real estate company bought four tracts of land in Clarington and six tracts of land in Bowmanville in Durham region, east of Toronto. The tracts are all equally desirable and sell for about the same amount.
(a) What is the probability that of these ten tracts, the first two to be sold will be in Bowmanville?
(b) What is the probability that of the first four tracts sold, at least one will be in Clarington?

5-93. Sonia Penuche is teaching Business Mathematics to students in Marketing and Human Resources. These two programs are combined to make the Business Mathematics course cost-effective. Of the 45 students in Marketing, 10 failed, and of the 35 students in Human Resources, 5 failed. Ms. Penuche is required to discuss with each student his or her progress after the test.
(a) What is the probability that a student selected randomly for discussing Business Mathematics is from the Human Resources program? What is the probability that the student has failed?
(b) What is the probability that the selected student is from the Human Resources program, given that the student has failed the course?
(c) Compute the probability that the student selected did not fail the course. What rule of probability did you use to compute the probability?

5-94. A case of 24 cans contains one can that is contaminated. Three cans are to be chosen randomly for testing.

(a) How many different combinations of three cans could be selected?

(b) What is the probability that the contaminated can is selected for testing?

5-95. A community college professor wishes to prepare a test paper on a section of a chapter in a Business Mathematics course. The test includes six questions. She has a test bank of 15 questions on the section. A student who misses the test due to unavoidable circumstances is entitled to write another test on the same section. How many tests can she prepare out of her test bank?

5-96. Horwege Electronics, Inc. purchases TV picture tubes from four different suppliers. Tyson Wholesale supplies 20 percent of the tubes, Fuji Importers 30 percent, Kirkpatricks 25 percent, and Parts, Inc. 25 percent. Tyson Wholesale tends to have the best quality, as only 3 percent of their tubes arrive defective. Fuji Importers' tubes are 4 percent defective, Kirkpatricks' 7 percent defective, and Parts, Inc. 6.5 percent defective.

(a) What is the overall (average) percentage that is defective?

(b) A defective picture tube was discovered in the latest shipment. What is the probability that it came from Tyson Wholesale?

(c) What is the probability that the defective tube came from Fuji Importers? From Kirkpatricks? From Parts, Inc.?

5-97. Visa Gold Centre of a local bank in the Greater Toronto Area has found that 67 percent of cardholders pay their new monthly balance in full on the payment due date. Suppose the credit card centre selects three cardholders randomly.

(a) What is the probability that all three cardholders will pay their new monthly balance in full?

(b) What is the probability that at least one of them will pay his or her new monthly balance in full?

5-98. An investment adviser in an investment management firm has a portfolio of 125 stocks. Of 125 stocks, 70 are blue-chip stocks and the rest are penny stocks. Thirty of the blue-chip stocks have increased in price and 40 of 55 of the penny stocks have decreased in price during the last week.

(a) Cross-classify the stocks based on types of stocks and increase and decrease in their prices.

(b) What is the probability that a stock selected by the investment adviser is blue-chip and has increased in price?

(c) What is the probability that a stock selected by the adviser has decreased in price?

5-99. Tourists from Japan were asked by a tour organizing company to select a group of four tourist attractions from a list of 12 attractions in the Greater Toronto Area.

(a) Count the number of combinations of tourist attractions from which a tourist makes his or her choice.

(b) What is the probability of one such combination being selected by a tourist? Assume that each tourist attraction has equal probability of being selected.

5-100. To reduce theft, the Meredeth Company screens all its employees with a lie detector test that is known to be correct 90 percent of the time (for both guilty and innocent subjects). George Meredeth decides to fire all employees who fail the test. Suppose that 5 percent of the employees are guilty of theft.

(a) Approximately what proportion of the workers are fired?

(b) Of the workers fired, approximately what proportion are actually guilty?

(c) Of the workers not fired, approximately what proportion are guilty?

(d) What do you think of George's policy?

5-101. Peterson's Vitamins, an advertiser in the magazine *Healthy Living*, estimates that 1 percent of the subscribers will buy vitamins from Peterson's. They also estimate that 0.5 percent of non-subscribers will buy the product and that there is one chance in 20 that a person is a subscriber.

(a) Find the probability that a randomly selected person will buy the vitamins.

(b) If a person buys the vitamins, what is the probability he subscribes to *Healthy Living*?

(c) If a person does not buy the vitamins, what is the probability she subscribes to *Healthy Living*?

5-102. ABC Auto Insurance classifies drivers as good, medium, or poor risks. Drivers who apply to them for insurance fall into these three groups in the proportions: 30 percent, 50 percent, and 20 percent, respectively. The probability a good-risk driver will have an accident is 0.01, the probability a medium-risk driver will have an accident is 0.03, and the probability a poor-risk driver will have an accident is 0.10. The company sells Mr. Brophy an insurance policy and he has an accident. What is the probability Mr. Brophy was classified as:

(a) A good-risk driver?

(b) A medium-risk driver?

(c) A poor-risk driver?

www.exercises.ca 5-103

5-103. Go to www.homestore.ca. Click on the menu Million Dollar Homes. Enter Toronto in the city box and select Ontario from the province box. Select single family, approximate price range from $1 million up to $3 million, and type 3 in the minimum number of bedrooms box. Create a table of the type shown below.

Price range ($ millions)	3-bedroom	4-bedroom	More than 4 bedrooms	Total
1 up to 2				
2 up to 3				

Tally the number of houses for each combination of number of bedrooms and the price range ($ millions) 1 up to 2 and 2 up to 3. Using this, complete the table shown above.

Suppose a house is randomly selected from the list.

(a) What is the probability that the selected home has 3 bedrooms?

(b) What is the probability that the selected home has either 3 bedrooms or 4 bedrooms?

(c) What is the probability that the selected home is from the price range $1 million up to $2 million and has 4 bedrooms?

(d) Given that the selected home is a 3-bedroom home, what is the probability that its price is in the price range $2 million up to $3 million?

(e) What is the probability that the selected home has more than 4 bedrooms?

(f) What is the probability that the selected home is priced in the range $1 million up to $2 million?

COMPUTER DATA EXERCISES 5-104 TO 5-106

5-104. The data on life expectancies for different countries are provided in the file Exercise 5-104.xls.

Arrange life expectancy values by three categories: low life expectancy (44.9 up to 60), medium life expectancy (60 up to 70), and high life expectancy (70 up to 80). Use Excel or Minitab to create the frequency distribution. Suppose a country is randomly selected from the above list.
(a) Find the probability that the selected country has low life expectancy.
(b) Find the probability that the selected country has high life expectancy.
(c) Compute the probability of selecting a country with low or high life expectancy. Name the rule of probability used in this question.

5-105. Top_1000Companies.xls includes names of companies, profit or loss, and type of companies. Sort the file using the sorting key "Industry." Select two types of companies, Precious Metals and Financial Services, and create a new file containing the name of companies in one column and profit/loss in the next column. Create a table in which the first column contains the type of companies, the second column includes the number of companies of each type making profit, and the third column contains the number of companies of each type incurring loss. A company is randomly selected from this list.
(a) Find the probability that the selected company made a profit.
(b) Find the probability that the selected company incurred a loss.
(c) Find the probability that the company selected is of the type Financial Services, given that the companies made a profit.
(d) Find the probability that the selected company made a profit of more than $10 000.
(e) Find the probability that the selected company is from the type Precious Metals and made a profit.
(Source: *Report on Business* Magazine, Bell Globemedia Publishing Inc., June 29, 2001.)

5-106. A professor in a community college compiles a list of students containing program names and students' final grades in the Quantitative Methods I course. The listing is saved under the file name Exercise 5-106.xls. Use Pivot Table (Excel) or Minitab to create a contingency table in which programs appear in rows and grades appear in columns.
(a) Compute the probability of selecting at random a student in an Accounting program.
(b) Calculate the probability of selecting at random a student who is from Accounting or Sports and Event Marketing.
(c) Find the probability of selecting at random a Sports and Event Marketing student given the student received a grade B.
(d) Find the probability of selecting at random a student with a grade B given the student is from the Sports and Event Marketing program.
(e) Calculate the probability of selecting at random a student who has received a grade of A+.

CHAPTER 5 — ANSWERS TO SELF-REVIEW

5-1. (a) Yes. The outcome of the experiment is uncertain because we do not know how the stock price will behave on the next trading day, and it is generally accepted that the behaviour of stock prices is random.

(b) The price of the stock will either go up, or go down, or remain the same. Hence, the sample space is {price will go up, price will go down, price will remain the same}.

5-2. (a) See the answer to Self-Review 5-9.

5-3. Let A_1 be the event *the first student passed*, A_2 be the event *the second student passed*, B_1 be the event *the first student failed* and B_2 be the event *the second student failed*.

(a) $\{(A_1 \text{ and } A_2), (A_1 \text{ and } B_2), (B_1 \text{ and } A_2)\}$

(b) $\{(A_1 \text{ and } B_2), (B_1 \text{ and } A_2), (B_1 \text{ and } B_2)\}$

(c) They are *not* mutually exclusive as the outcome $(A_1 \text{ and } B_2)$ belongs to both. They are collectively exhaustive, since every outcome belongs to at least one of them.

5-4. **1.** $\dfrac{4 \text{ queens in deck}}{52 \text{ cards total}} = \dfrac{4}{52} = 0.0769$; classical.

2. $210/500 = 0.420$

3. (a) $\dfrac{\text{Number of times the event occurred}}{\text{Total number of observations}}$

$= \dfrac{156 + 224}{1000} = 0.38$

(b)

Cola	Taste	
	Sweet	**Very sweet**
Cola 1	0.527	0.156
Cola 2	0.093	0.224

(c) Yes. The set of all simple events is mutually exclusive and collectively exhaustive.

5-5. **1.** The marginal probability of the event *very sweet* is $P(\text{very sweet})$
$= P(\text{cola 1 and very sweet}) + P(\text{cola 2 and very sweet})$
$= (0.156 + 0.224)$
$= 0.38$
This is the same as before.

2. Let A be the event *selected company is from financial services or from mining*.
(a) $P(A) = P(\text{financial services}) + P(\text{mining})$
$= 0.33 + 0.1 = 0.43$
(b) $P(\sim A) = 1 - P(A) = 1 - 0.43 = 0.57$

(c)

5-6. Let A = major prescription drugs; B = major dental work.
$P(A) = 0.08$; $P(B) = 0.15$; and $P(A \text{ and } B) = 0.03$.
Hence, $P(A \text{ or } B) = P(A) + P(B) - P(A \text{ and } B) = 0.08 + 0.15 - 0.03 = 0.20$

5-7. **1.** $(0.80)(0.80)(0.80)(0.80) = 0.4096$

2. (a) 0.0000156, found by: $(0.025)(0.025)(0.025)$

(b) The chance of selecting three bags and finding them all underweight is rather remote.

5-8. **1.** (a) $\left(\dfrac{4}{12}\right)\left(\dfrac{3}{11}\right)\left(\dfrac{2}{10}\right)\left(\dfrac{1}{9}\right) = \dfrac{24}{118\,800}$
$= 0.002$

(b) $\left(\dfrac{8}{12}\right)\left(\dfrac{7}{11}\right)\left(\dfrac{6}{10}\right)\left(\dfrac{5}{9}\right) = \dfrac{1680}{118\,800}$
$= 0.1414$

(c) No. There are other possibilities, such as 3 women and 1 man.

2. Let event A_1 = prefers cola 1; and event B_2 = prefers very sweet cola drink.

$$P(A_1 | B_2) = \frac{P(B_2 \text{ and } A_1)}{P(B_2)} = \frac{0.156}{0.38} = 0.41$$

5-9. Let A_1 and B_1 be the events: *the first student selected passed* and *failed*, respectively. Let A_2 and B_2 be the events: *the second student selected passed* and *failed*, respectively.

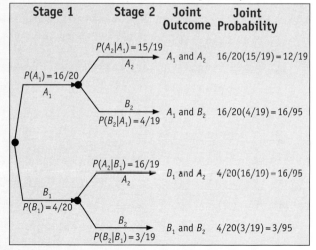

Stage 1	Stage 2	Joint Outcome	Joint Probability
$P(A_1) = 16/20$, A_1	$P(A_2|A_1) = 15/19$, A_2	A_1 and A_2	$16/20(15/19) = 12/19$
	$P(B_2|A_1) = 4/19$, B_2	A_1 and B_2	$16/20(4/19) = 16/95$
$P(B_1) = 4/20$, B_1	$P(A_2|B_1) = 16/19$, A_2	B_1 and A_2	$4/20(16/19) = 16/95$
	$P(B_2|B_1) = 3/19$, B_2	B_1 and B_2	$4/20(3/19) = 3/95$

CHAPTER 5   ANSWERS TO SELF-REVIEW

5-10.

$P(A_3|B_2)$

$$= \frac{P(A_3)P(B_2|A_3)}{P(A_1)P(B_2|A_1) + P(A_2)P(B_2|A_2) + P(A_3)P(B_2|A_3)}$$

$$= \frac{0.50(0.96)}{(0.30)(0.97) + (0.20)(0.95) + (0.50)(0.96)}$$

$$= \frac{0.480}{0.961} = 0.499$$

5-11. **1.** There are 20, found by $(5)(4)$.
      2. There are 72, found by $(3)(2)(4)(3)$.

5-12. **1.** 126, found by: $_9C_4 = \dfrac{9!}{4!(9-4)!} = 126$

      2. 5040, found by:

$$_{10}P_4 = \frac{10!}{(10-4)!} = \frac{(10)(9)(8)(7)(6\!\!\!/)}{6\!\!\!/!} = 5040$$

      3. 30, found by: $_6P_2 = \dfrac{6!}{(6-2)!} = 30$

CHAPTER 6

Discrete Probability Distributions

GOALS

When you have completed this chapter, you will be able to:

- Define the terms *probability distribution* and *random variable*

- Distinguish between discrete and continuous random variables

- Calculate the mean, variance, and standard deviation of a discrete probability distribution

- Describe the characteristics and compute probabilities using the binomial probability distribution

- Describe the characteristics of and compute probabilities using the Poisson probability distribution

 • Describe the characteristics of and compute probabilities using the hypergeometric probability distribution.

JACOB BERNOULLI (1654–1705)

The religious intolerance of the King of Spain forced the illustrious Bernoulli family to leave the Netherlands and settle in Basel, Switzerland. The family played a pivotal role in putting Basel on the world map. From 1622 to 1828, Basel was never without one or two well-known Bernoullis. The city acknowledged the family's contribution and commemorated their academic activities in the Bernoullianum, the building of the University of Basel, dedicated solely to physics, chemistry, and astronomy. Jacob Bernoulli was born into this family on December 27, 1654. On his father's advice, he studied philosophy and theology and received an M.A. in philosophy in 1671 and a degree in theology in 1676 from the University of Basel. While Bernoulli was studying theology, he was also secretly studying mathematics and astronomy against his father's wish. His interest was more in mathematics and astronomy than in theology. After graduating in 1676, he moved to France to study Cartesian philosophy, then to the Netherlands, and England to further his knowledge in mathematics. He came back to Basel and joined the University of Basel in 1683.

In 1681, while theologians were claiming the fall of a comet as a sign of God's anger, Bernoulli believed otherwise and indulged himself in developing the theory of the motion of the comet. Later, he published a pamphlet claiming that his calculation involved the motion of the body of the comet only and not of the tail, in a bid to please the fellow theologians with subtle humour. Bernoulli was appointed professor of mathematics at the University of Basel in 1687 and remained in this position until his death in 1705. He studied Leibniz's publications on calculus, which were not easy for contemporary mathematicians to comprehend, and applied the principles discussed in the publications.

Jacob Bernoulli's work, *Ars Conj* or the *Art of Conjecture,* was published, posthumously in 1713 with a preface by his nephew Nicolas Bernoulli. The first part included works of other mathematicians, the second included the theory of permutations and combinations, the third included solutions of problems related to games of chance, and the fourth was a proposal to apply the theory of probability to economics.

1498
1548
1598
1648
1698
1748
1898
1948
2000

INTRODUCTION

Chapters 2 through 4 are devoted to descriptive statistics. We describe raw data by organizing them into a frequency distribution and portraying the distribution in charts. Also, we compute a measure of central tendency—such as the arithmetic mean, median, or mode—to locate a typical value in the distribution. The range and the standard deviation are used to describe the spread in the data. These chapters focus on summarizing data sets that are explicitly available to us.

From Chapter 5, we begin the study of statistical inference. The objective here is to make inferences about a population based on a set of observations, selected randomly from the population, called a random sample. In Chapter 5, we introduce the concepts of random experiment and probability, and we examine rules of addition and multiplication for calculating probabilities of different events of a random experiment.

In most real world situations, we are interested in certain numerical values associated with the possible outcomes of a random experiment. An assignment of a numerical value to each of the possible outcomes of a random experiment gives us **a random variable**. In this chapter we begin the study of **probability distributions of random variables** which gives information about the distribution of probabilities across the range of possible values of the random variable. It is similar to a frequency distribution, however, instead of describing the past, it describes how likely some future events are.

The mean, variance, and standard deviation of discrete probability distributions as well as two frequently occurring families of discrete probability distributions (the binomial, and Poisson) are also presented in this chapter.

6.1   RANDOM VARIABLES

In many random experiments, our focus of attention lies in the numerical values that we associate with possible outcomes of the experiment. For example, one of the main objectives of the quality control manager is to keep the fraction of manufactured items that do not meet the quality standards (we can call them defective items) within an acceptable limit. This is necessitated by the fact that defective items cost the company in terms of reputation and customer goodwill. Also, defective items are returned for repair during the warranty period, adding to the cost. Hence, when a quality control inspector assesses a manufactured lot, his main focus is on the number of defective items in the lot. This is a random variable and may take values 0, 1, 2, 3, and so on. Now, we can define a random variable.

> i **Random variable**   A random experiment each of whose possible outcomes is a number.

We can associate a random variable with any random experiment by assigning a numerical value to each possible outcome of the experiment. A few examples will illustrate the concept of a random variable.

If we invest $15 000 in a common stock, the possible outcomes of this random experiment are the different possible values of rate of return. The values of the rate of return have been observed to change randomly from day to day. Thus, the rate of return is a random variable.

Another example may be the number of accidents at a busy intersection. On any particular day in the future, the number of accidents at the intersection is random and may be 0, 1, 2, and so on. It is therefore a random variable.

Throughout, we shall denote random variables by upper case letters such as X, Y, or Z, and we shall denote a value taken by a random variable by the corresponding lower case letter such as x, or y, or z. The symbol Z will be reserved throughout the book for a very important random variable, called the *standard normal variable*. We shall discuss it in detail in Chapter 7.

TYPES OF RANDOM VARIABLES

We shall study two main types of random variables: discrete random variables and continuous random variables.

 Discrete Random Variable A random variable which assumes a finite or countably infinite number of possible values.

The number of heads observed when a coin is flipped twice is an example of a discrete random variable. The possible outcomes are HH, TT, HT, and TH. Hence, "the number of heads observed" is a random variable, which can assume any one of the *three* possible values {0, 1, 2}. The total number of values is three, which is finite.

Now, let us toss the coin until we get a run of five heads in a row. The number of tosses we shall require is a random variable. The minimum number of tosses we shall require is five. However, the possible values of the number of tosses are {5, 6, 7, ..., 100 000, ...}. We cannot assign any upper bound to the number of tosses we shall require. It is conceptually possible (though highly, highly unlikely) that the first billion tosses will fail to produce a sequence of five heads in a row. The number of possible values of this random variable (the number of tosses required) is, thus, infinite but still countable.

Other examples of discrete random variables include:

- the number of children in a randomly selected family;
- the number of cars sold by a salesperson in a given day;
- the number of defective items produced in a day.

 Continuous Random Variable A random variable which assumes any value within some interval or a collection of intervals.

A continuous random variable usually results when the desired outcome is the measurement of an attribute such as length, weight, time, or temperature. Some of the examples are listed below:

- height and weight of a randomly selected person;
- length of time a customer waits to receive a credit card authorization in a store;
- the weight of an item bought in a grocery store.

In summary, a discrete random variable usually counts something, whereas a continuous random variable is usually a measure of an attribute such as height.

6.2 WHAT IS A PROBABILITY DISTRIBUTION?

The probability distribution of a random variable shows the distribution of probabilities across the range of possible values of the random variable.

We call the probability distribution of a discrete random variable, **a discrete probability distribution**, and that of a continuous random variable, **a continuous probability distribution**. In this chapter, we will restrict ourselves to discrete probability distributions. In the next chapter, that is, Chapter 7, we will discuss continuous probability distributions.

A discrete probability distribution is a listing of all the possible values of a discrete random variable and their corresponding probabilities. A table, a graph or a formula can represent a discrete probability distribution. A tabular or graphic form of display has more appeal where a visual representation of the distribution is required. However, in the case of a very large number of values of the discrete random variable, a tabular or graphical display becomes cumbersome and loses its shine somewhat. A representation of a discrete probability distribution by a formula is a condensed form of representation and is suitable for discrete random variables with both finite and infinite number of possible values.

> **Discrete Probability Distribution** A listing of all the possible values of a discrete random variable and their corresponding probabilities.

Example 6-1

Suppose we are interested in the number of heads showing face up on three tosses of a coin under identical conditions. This is a discrete random variable. The possible outcomes are: zero heads, one head, two heads, and three heads. What is the discrete probability distribution for the number of heads?

Solution

There are eight possible outcomes. These are illustrated by the tree diagram in Chart 6-1.

Note that the outcome "zero heads" occurred only once, "one head" occurred three times, "two heads" occurred three times, and the outcome "three heads" occurred only once. If the coin is fair, each of the eight possible outcomes will be equally likely, and hence, the probability of each of the eight outcomes will be one eighth. Thus, the probability of zero heads will be one eighth, the probability of one head is three eighths, and so on. The probability distribution is shown in Table 6-1. Note that, since one of these outcomes must happen, the total of the probabilities of all possible outcomes is 1.00. This is always true.

CHART 6-1: Tree Diagram for Tossing a Coin Three Times

Toss 1	Toss 2	Toss 3	Possible Outcomes	Number of Heads
		H	HHH	3
H	H	T	HHT	2
		H	HTH	2
	T	T	HTT	1
		H	THH	2
T	H	T	THT	1
		H	TTH	1
	T	T	TTT	0

TABLE 6-1: Discrete Probability Distribution for the Events of Zero, One, Two, and Three Heads Showing Face Up on Three Tosses of a Coin

Number of Heads x	Probability of Outcome $P(x)$
0	$\dfrac{1}{8} = 0.125$
1	$\dfrac{3}{8} = 0.375$
2	$\dfrac{3}{8} = 0.375$
3	$\dfrac{1}{8} = 0.125$
Total	$\dfrac{8}{8} = 1.000$

MINITAB CHART 6-2: Graphical Presentation of the Probability Distribution of Number of Heads Resulting from Three Tosses of a Fair Coin

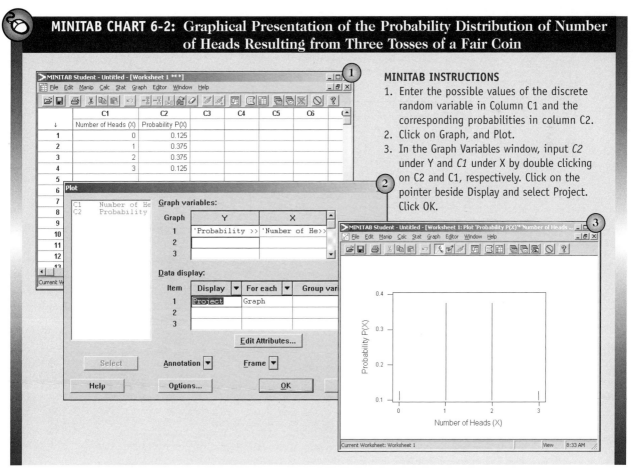

MINITAB INSTRUCTIONS
1. Enter the possible values of the discrete random variable in Column C1 and the corresponding probabilities in column C2.
2. Click on Graph, and Plot.
3. In the Graph Variables window, input *C2* under Y and *C1* under X by double clicking on C2 and C1, respectively. Click on the pointer beside Display and select Project. Click OK.

The same information can be shown using a chart. In Chart 6-2, plotted using Minitab, the locations of the number of heads are shown on the horizontal axis, and the corresponding probabilities by the heights of the lines at these locations.

CHARACTERISTICS OF A DISCRETE PROBABILITY DISTRIBUTION

Before continuing, we should note two important characteristics of a discrete probability distribution.

1. The probability of a particular outcome is between 0 and 1, inclusive. (The probabilities of X, written $P(x)$, in the coin tossing example were 0.125, 0.375, etc.)
2. The sum of the probabilities of all the possible values is 1.00. (Referring to Table 6-1, $0.125 + 0.375 + 0.375 + 0.125 = 1.00$.)

■ SELF-REVIEW 6-1

Based on historic data, the management team of a national park has obtained the following estimate of the probability distribution of the number of persons in a car entering the park.

Number of persons (x)	Probability $P(x)$
1	0.08
2	0.34
3	0.23
4	0.28
5	0.07

(a) Depict the probability distribution graphically.
(b) Find $P(X \geq 2)$.

JOINT DISTRIBUTION AND INDEPENDENCE OF TWO DISCRETE RANDOM VARIABLES

Applications of probability theory in business and economics often involve the study of relationships between two or more random variables. As an example, suppose Bob wants to invest his money in two high-tech stocks—Intec and ICM. An estimate of the joint probability distribution of the percentage rates of return during the next one year on Intec stock (X_1) and ICM stock (X_2) is given in Table 6-2. (It may be noted that in reality, the number of possible values of the rate of return is large. However, to simplify the problem, we assume that each of X_1 and X_2 has three possible values.)

TABLE 6-2: Joint Probability Distribution of Rates of Return on Intec and ICM Stocks

x_1 (%) \ x_2 (%)	−5	5	10	Marginal probabilities of X_1
−10	0.05	0.15	0.0	0.2
8	0.05	0.35	0.1	0.5
20	0.1	0.1	0.1	0.3
Marginal Probabilities of X_2	0.2	0.6	0.2	

Thus, $P(X_1 = -10$ and $X_2 = -5) = 0.05$. (It is the value in the row corresponding to $x_1 = -10$ and column corresponding to $x_2 = -5$.) $P(X_1 = 8$ and $X_2 = 5) = 0.35$, and so on.

From Table 6-2 of joint probability distribution of X_1 and X_2, we can obtain the probability distribution of X_1 (called **the marginal probability distribution of X_1**) as follows: $P(X_1 = -10)$ equals the sum of all the joint probabilities in the row corresponding to $x_1 = -10$. It equals 0.2 and is recorded in the corresponding cell in the last column. Similarly, we obtain $P(X_1 = 8) = 0.5$, and $P(X_1 = 20) = 0.3$.

The marginal probability distribution of X_2 can be similarly obtained as follows: $P(X_2 = -5)$ equals the sum of all the joint probabilities in the column corresponding to $x_2 = -5$. It equals 0.2 and is recorded in the corresponding cell in the last row. Similarly, we get $P(X_2 = 5) = 0.6$, and $P(X_2 = 10) = 0.2$.

Let us now extend the notion of independence of two events, that we introduced in Chapter 5, to the notion of **independence of two random variables**. Intuitively, two random variables are independent if the value of one random variable has no effect on the value that the other random variable will take. In some cases, independence of random variables is easy to verify. For example, let X_1 be the number of heads obtained when a certain coin is tossed, (which can take a value of either 0 or 1) and let X_2 be the number of heads obtained when a second coin is tossed, (which can again take a value of either 0 or 1). Then obviously, the outcome of one coin toss has no effect on the outcome of the other. The two random variables X_1 and X_2 are independent. However, independence of random variables is not always that easy to verify. We need a more formal definition which we give below.

Independence of Two Random Variables   Two random variables X_1 and X_2 are said to be independent if, for any two subsets A and B of possible values that X_1 and X_2 can take, respectively

$P(X_1$ takes a value in A and X_2 takes a value in $B)$
$$= P(X_1 \text{ takes a value in } A)P(X_2 \text{ takes a value in } B). \quad \textbf{6-1}$$

For the joint probability distribution in Table 6-2, $P(X_1 = 8$ and $X_2 = 10) = 0.1$; and $P(X_1 = 8) P(X_2 = 10) = (0.5)(0.2) = 0.1$. The two are equal. However, $P(X_1 = 20$ and $X_2 = 10) = 0.1$, and $P(X_1 = 20) P(X_2 = 10) = (0.3)(0.2) = 0.06$. The two are not equal.

Hence, in this example, the random variables X_1 and X_2 are not independent. (For the random variables to be independent, the equality in Formula 6-1 should hold for every pair of possible values of the two variables.)

■ SELF-REVIEW 6-2

The percentage rates of return, X_1 and X_2, on two stocks have been observed to be independent. From the probability distributions of X_1 and X_2 given below, obtain the joint probability distribution of X_1 and X_2.

x_1 (%)	$P(x_1)$
−5	0.2
6	0.7
15	0.1

x_2 (%)	$P(x_2)$
−15	0.3
10	0.2
30	0.5

FUNCTIONS OF DISCRETE RANDOM VARIABLES

Let us continue with the example in the previous section regarding percentage rates of return for the next one year on the Intec stock (X_1) and the ICM stock (X_2). Suppose Bob has invested $3000 in Intec stock and $2000 in ICM stock. He wants to know the probability distribution of net return on his total investment during the next one year. Let us denote the net return on his total investment by R. Then,

$$R = (3000)\left(\frac{X_1}{100}\right) + (2000)\left(\frac{X_2}{100}\right) = 30X_1 + 20X_2$$

R is a function of random variables X_1 and X_2 and is therefore a random variable. Each combination of possible values of X_1 and X_2 gives us a possible value of R. For example, if $x_1 = -10$ and $x_2 = 5$, then $r = 30(-10) + (20)(5) = -\$200$. The probability distribution of R is given in the columns headed $r = 30x_1 + 20x_2$ and $P(r)$ in Table 6-3.

TABLE 6-3: Probability Distribution of Net Return on Bob's Total Investment in the Two Stocks

x_1	x_2	$r = 30x_1 + 20x_2$	$P(r)$	x_1	x_2	$r = 30x_1 + 20x_2$	$P(r)$
-10	-5	-400	0.05	8	10	440	0.1
-10	5	-200	0.15	20	-5	500	0.1
-10	10	-100	0.0	20	5	700	0.1
8	-5	140	0.05	20	10	800	0.1
8	5	340	0.35				

The functions of random variables that we shall commonly encounter in this book are $(aX_1 + bX_2)$, $(aX_1 + b)^2$.

■ SELF-REVIEW 6-3

For the joint distribution of random variables X_1 and X_2 in Table 6-2, find the probability distribution of each of the following: (a) X_1^2; (b) $2X_1 + 3X_2$.

6.3 THE MEAN, VARIANCE, AND STANDARD DEVIATION OF A PROBABILITY DISTRIBUTION

In Chapters 3 and 4, measures of location and variation are discussed for a frequency distribution. The mean reports the central location of the data, and the standard deviation describes the spread in the data. In a similar fashion, a probability distribution is summarized by its mean and standard deviation. The mean of a probability distribution is denoted by the lower case Greek letter mu (μ) and the standard deviation by the lower case Greek letter sigma (σ).

MEAN OF A DISCRETE RANDOM VARIABLE

The most popular choice of a typical value, for representing a random variable, is its **mean** (also known as its **expected value**). It is denoted by the Greek symbol μ. For a discrete random variable, the mean is defined as the weighted average of the possible values of the random variable, calculated using the probabilities of the values as weights. Thus, it is obtained by multiplying each possible value of the discrete random variable by its probability, and then summing over all the possible values of the variable.

In terms of a formula, it is expressed by:

Mean of a Discrete Probability Distribution $\qquad \mu = E(X) = \sum(xP(x))$	**6-2**
where, the summation is over all the possible values x of X.	

Here,

$E(X)$ is the expected value of X (discrete)

x is the value of X

$P(x)$ is the probability of the possible value (x) of the random variable

In only one trial of a random experiment, a corresponding random variable assumes only one value. If the experiment is repeated many times under identical conditions, the arithmetic mean of all the values of the random variable obtained approaches the mean of the random variable. Thus, the mean of a random variable is the average value of the random variable that we expect in the long run. Hence, it is referred to as the expected value of the random variable.

Example 6-2   Consider again the example in the previous section regarding the percentage rates of return for the next one year on the Intec stock (X_1) and the ICM stock (X_2). The joint probability distribution of X_1 and X_2 is given in Table 6-2. Bob has invested $3000 in Intec stock and $2000 in ICM stock.

(a) What is the expected value of percentage rate of return on Intec stock during the next one year?

(b) What is the expected value of percentage rate of return on ICM stock during the next one year?

(c) What is the expected value of the net return on Bob's total investment in the two stocks during the next one year?

Solution   The marginal probabilities of the percentage rates of return on Intec stock (X_1) and the ICM stock (X_2) are given in Table 6-2.

(a) Using Formula 6-2 with x_1 in place of x, we get:

$E(X_1) = \sum x_1 P(x_1) = (-10)(0.2) + (8)(0.5) + (20)(0.3) = 8\%$

(b) Again, using Formula 6-2, with x_2 in place of x, we get:

$E(X_2) = \sum x_2 P(x_2) = (-5)(0.2) + (5)(0.6) + (10)(0.2) = 4\%$

(c) The net return on Bob's total investment in the two stocks during the next one year is given by:

$$R = 30X_1 + 20X_2$$

A long way to calculate $E(R)$ is to use Formula 6-2 for the probability distribution of R given in Table 6-3. This gives us:

$$E(R) = \sum rP(r)$$
$$= (-400)(0.05) + (-200)(0.15) + (-100)(0.0)$$
$$+ (140)(0.05) + (340)(0.35) + (440)(0.1)$$
$$+ (500)(0.1) + (700)(0.1) + (800)(0.1) = 320.0$$

However, the following formula provides us with a shorter way of calculating the value of $E(R)$.

For any random variables $X_1, X_2, X_3, \ldots, X_n$, and any constants $c_0, c_1, c_2, \ldots, c_n$,
$$E(c_0 + c_1X_1 + c_2X_2 + \cdots + c_nX_n) = c_0 + c_1E(X_1) + c_2E(X_2) + \cdots + c_nE(X_n) \qquad \textbf{6-3}$$

Using Formula 6-3 with $n = 2$, we get:

$$E(R) = E(30X_1 + 20X_2) = 30E(X_1) + 20E(X_2) = 30(8) + 20(4) = 320$$

■ SELF-REVIEW 6-4

A gambler has decided to play roulette according to the following rule. He will play at most twice. In the first game, he will bet \$100 on black. If he wins, he will gain \$100 and he will not play the second time. If he loses, he will play the second game and this time, he will bet \$200 on black. Assuming that the roulette wheel used is a standard one with eighteen black numbers, eighteen red numbers, and a zero that is gray, find the expected value of his gain if he follows this rule.

VARIANCE AND STANDARD DEVIATION

The expected value of a random variable measures the central location of the probability distribution of the variable. However, it does not describe the spread of the values of the random variable. This void is filled by another term known as **standard deviation**. The square of standard deviation is called **variance**. Expected value and standard deviation (or variance) together provide a useful summary of a given probability distribution.

 Variance   For a discrete random variable, the variance is defined as the weighted average of the squares of the deviations of the possible values of the variable from its expected value using probabilities as weights.

Let X be a discrete random variable. Then, as we saw before, $(X - \mu)^2$ is also a discrete random variable. The variance of X is the expected value of the variable $(X - \mu)^2$ and is obtained by multiplying each possible value, $(x - \mu)^2$, of $(X - \mu)^2$ by its probability $P(x)$ and then summing the products. In terms of a formula, we can express it by:

Variance of a Discrete Probability Distribution
$$(\sigma^2) = E[(X - \mu)^2] = \sum ((x - \mu)^2 P(x)) \qquad \textbf{6-4}$$
Where, the summation is over all the possible values x of X.

The computational steps are:

1. Subtract the mean (μ) from each value of the variable, and then square this difference.
2. Multiply each squared difference by its weight (probability).
3. Add the resulting products to find the variance.

> 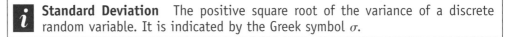 **Standard Deviation** The positive square root of the variance of a discrete random variable. It is indicated by the Greek symbol σ.

We shall sometimes denote variance of a random variable X by $V(X)$ and its standard deviation by $SD(X)$.

Example 6-3

Let us reconsider the problem in Example 6-2 regarding the rates of return for the next one year on the Intec stock (X_1) and the ICM stock (X_2). The joint probability distribution of X_1 and X_2 is given in Table 6-2.

(a) What is the standard deviation of the percentage rate of return on Intec stock during the next one year?
(b) Suppose Bob decides to invest \$3000 in Intec stock and \$2000 in some other stock. The percentage rate of return during the next one year on the third stock (X_3) is independent of X_1 with $E(X_3) = 6\%$ and $SD(X_3) = 8\%$. Find the standard deviation of the net return on his total investment during the next one year.

Solution

(a) We use a table to compute the variance of X_1 using Formula 6-4, with x replaced by x_1.

x_1	$P(x_1)$	$E(X_1)$ (or μ)	$(x_1 - \mu)^2$	$(x_1 - \mu)^2 P(x_1)$
-10	0.2	8	324	64.8
8	0.5	8	0	0
20	0.3	8	144	43.2
Total				108.0

Thus, $V(X_1) = 108$. Recall that standard deviation is the positive square root of variance. So, the standard deviation of X_1 is $\sigma = \sqrt{108} = 10.39$. Now, as the unit of the standard deviation is the same as the unit of the discrete random variable, we can say that, on average, the dispersion of the possible values of the discrete random variable (rate of return of Intec stock) relative to its expected value is 10.39%. To make the interpretation of the standard deviation even clearer, let us say that the rate of return of another stock has an expected value of 8% and a standard deviation of 15%. The expected values of the two rates of return are the same. As 15% is greater than 10.39%, we can say with confidence that there is more spread in the rate of return of the other stock than the Intec stock. In financial investment, standard deviation is often used as a measure of risk. Based on this, we can say that the other stock is a riskier investment than the Intec stock.

Here is an alternative formula for the variance of a discrete probability distribution. The advantage of this formula is that it avoids most of the subtractions.

Variance of a Discrete Probability Distribution	$\sigma^2 = \sum x^2 P(x) - \mu^2$	6-5

For the rate of return on Intec stock we have:

x_1	x_1^2	$P(x_1)$	$x_1^2 P(x_1)$
-10	100	0.2	20
8	64	0.5	32
20	400	0.3	120
Total			172

Using Formula 6-5 with x replaced by x_1 we get

$$V(X_1) = \sigma^2 = \sum x_1^2 P(x_1) - \mu^2 = 172 - (8)^2 = 108$$

This is the same value we found before.

(b) Let R be the net return from the total investment in the two stocks. Then, $R = 30X_1 + 20X_3$.

Since the random variables X_1 and X_3 are independent, the following formula provides us with a shortcut method to compute the variance of R.

For any mutually independent set of random variables $X_1, X_2, X_3, \ldots, X_n$, and any constants $c_0, c_1, c_2, \ldots, c_n$.

$$V(c_0 + c_1 X_1 + c_2 X_2 + \cdots + c_n X_n) = (c_1)^2 V(X_1) + (c_2)^2 V(X_2) + \cdots + (c_n)^2 V(X_n) \quad \textbf{6-6}$$

Using Formula 6-6 with $n = 2$, we get:

$V(R) = V(30X_1 + 20X_3) = (30)^2 V(X_1) + (20)^2 V(X_3) = (900)(108) + (400)(8)^2 = 122\,800.$

So, $SD(R) = \sqrt{122\,800} = 350.43$.

It should be noted that Formula 6-6 applies only when the random variables are mutually independent. If Bob had invested his money in Intec and ICM stocks, then we would not be able to use Formula 6-6 to compute the standard deviation of his total return, since X_1 and X_2 are not independent. In this case, we would have to compute the probability distribution of his total return R and then apply Formula 6-4 or 6-5 to this probability distribution.

■ SELF-REVIEW 6-5

For the data in Example 6-3:

(a) Find the standard deviation of the percentage rate of return of ICM stock.

(b) If Cathy invests $500 in Intec stock and $1000 in the third stock, find the standard deviation of the next one-year return on her total investment.

EXERCISES 6-1 TO 6-8

6-1. Compute the mean and variance of the following discrete probability distribution.

x	P(x)
0	0.20
1	0.40
2	0.30
3	0.10

6-2. An insurance company sells a life insurance policy with a face value of $250 000 to 45-year old males. The annual premium for the life insurance is $543.00. If 0.39 percent of the policyholders are expected to die within a year, what is the company's expected return per policyholder in any year?

6-3. Out of the three pairs of columns listed below only one is a probability distribution.
(a) Which one is it?

x	P(x)	x	P(x)	x	P(x)
5	0.3	5	0.1	0.5	0.5
10	0.3	10	0.3	10	0.3
15	0.2	15	0.2	15	−0.2
20	0.4	20	0.4	20	0.4

(b) For the correct probability distribution, find that the probability that X is:

(1) Exactly 15.   (2) No more than 10.   (3) More than 5.

(c) Find the mean, variance, and standard deviation of the correct probability distribution.

6-4. Which of these random variables are discrete?
(a) The number of new accounts established by a salesperson in a year.
(b) The time between customer arrivals at a bank ATM.
(c) The number of customers in Big Nick's barber shop.
(d) The amount of fuel in your car's gas tank.
(e) The number of stocks bought by an investor.

6-5. A proper dosage for a certain drug is 4 grains. The drug is available in pills with a mean of 4 grains and a standard deviation of 0.2 grains. It is also available in sets of four smaller pills with a mean of 1 grain and a standard deviation of 0.05 grains. Which of the two options is preferable?

6-6. A community college administrator, based on historical enrollment database and an effective advertisement, has obtained the following estimates of the probability distribution of the number of students entering the college next academic year.

Number of Students Entering (x)	Probability P(x)	Number of Students Entering (x)	Probability P(x)
900	0.15	1300	0.15
1100	0.25	1500	0.10
1200	0.35		

(a) What is the expected number of students entering the college next year?
(b) What is the probability that there will be less than or equal to 1300 students entering the college next year?
(c) Compute the standard deviation of the number of students entering the college.

6-7. The following information about the number of persons per family in Canada is provided by Statistics Canada (Census 1996).*

Number of Persons per Family	Percent of Families (%)	Number of Persons per Family	Percent of Families (%)
2 persons	43.51	5 persons	8.38
3 persons	22.61	6 persons	2.02
4 persons	23.07	7 persons	0.41

*The number of families with more than 7 persons is negligible. Their probability is taken to be zero.

(a) Compute the probability of three or fewer persons per family.
(b) Compute the expected number of persons per family.
(c) Compute the standard deviation of the number of persons per family.
(d) Graph the above probability distribution.

6-8. A person intoxicated with alcohol is standing near a signpost on a pavement. Every minute he takes a one foot step either to the left or to the right. The probability is 0.4 that he moves to the right and it is 0.6 that he takes a step to the left. Find the expected value of his distance from the signpost in 4 minutes.

6.4   BINOMIAL PROBABILITY DISTRIBUTION

The binomial probability distribution is a widely occurring discrete probability distribution. The basic concepts required for defining a binomial probability distribution are those of:

(i) *Bernoulli trial* and (ii) *Binomial experiment.*

(i) There are numerous real-world examples of random experiments in which the number of possible outcomes is two. For example, the outcome of a toss of a coin is either "head" or "tail"; a product is classified by the quality control department as either "acceptable" or "not acceptable"; a randomly chosen person may or may not like the taste of a new diet soda. Such a random experiment is called a *Bernoulli trial*; after the eighteenth century Swiss mathematician, Jacob Bernoulli.

 Bernoulli trial   A random experiment in which the number of possible outcomes is two.

Conventionally, we apply terms "success" and "failure" to the two possible outcomes of a Bernoulli trial. However, this classification does not imply that one outcome is good and the other is bad. Out of the two outcomes, the one we are interested in is termed a "success" and the other a "failure." For example, in a coin toss, if you bet that the outcome will be a head, then for you "head" will be a "success" and "tail" will be a "failure."

(ii) Suppose we toss a coin three times. Each toss of the coin is a Bernoulli trial with possible outcomes "head" and "tail." Our random experiment can be expressed as a sequence of three random experiments, (three tosses) each of which is a Bernoulli trial (each coin toss results in one of only two possible outcomes: head or tail). Further, the three trials are *independent* (the outcome of one coin toss has no effect on the outcome of any other coin toss), and they are *identical* (the probability of head is the same in each coin toss, since the same coin is being tossed each time).

A random experiment that can be expressed as a sequence of a fixed number (in the above case, three) of independent and identical Bernoulli trials is called a **Binomial experiment**. (The term "bi" refers to the fact that each individual trial has only two possible outcomes.)

Another good example of a binomial experiment is consumer preference polls. Suppose 250 persons are randomly selected from all over Canada, and each is asked whether he or she likes the taste of a new diet soda. The size of the sample (250) is the number of trials (n). Each trial is a Bernoulli trial. (There are only two possible outcomes per person: either he or she likes the taste of the new diet soda, or does not like the taste.) Let us assume that thirty percent of the population likes the taste of the new diet soda. Then the probability (p) that a randomly selected person likes the taste of the new diet soda is 0.30. For each person in the sample, the probability is the same (0.3) that he or she will like the taste of the drink. Since only 250 persons are chosen randomly from the entire population of Canada, the probability that the response of one person in the sample will affect the responses of others in the sample is almost zero. The 250 Bernoulli trials can be assumed to be independent. Thus, this is a binomial experiment.

> **ℹ Binomial Experiment** A random experiment consisting of a sequence of a fixed number (n) of *independent* and *identical* Bernoulli trials.

The following are the characteristics of a binomial experiment.
1. The experiment consists of a fixed number, n, of Bernoulli trials.
2. The two possible outcomes of each trial are generally denoted as success (S) and failure (F).
3. The outcome of any trial is independent of the outcome of any other trial.
4. The probability of success (p) remains the same from trial to trial.

If the number of possible outcomes of each of the n trials is more than two, and the different trials are independent and identical, then the random experiment is called a *multinomial experiment*.

A binomial random variable is a variable that counts the total number of successes in a binomial experiment. In the case of three tosses of a coin under identical conditions, suppose we are interested in counting the total number of heads. Then, we designate the appearance of "head" as a "success." The total number of heads, X, in three tosses of the coin is then a binomial random variable. The possible values the variable X can take are {0, 1, 2, 3}. (We may end up with a total of 0, or 1, or 2, or 3 heads when the coin is tossed three times.)

In the case of consumer preference polls, suppose the manufacturer of a new diet soda is interested in the number of people, out of the sample of 250 people, who like the taste of the soda. Here, we designate the outcome that "a person likes the taste of soda" as a "success". Then X, the number of people in the sample who like the taste of the soda, is a binomial random variable. The possible values the random variable X can take are {0, 1, 2, 3, … , 250}.

> **ℹ Binomial random variable** A random variable that counts the total number of successes in a *binomial experiment*.

> **ℹ Binomial probability distribution** The probability distribution of a binomial random variable.

To develop a formula for probabilities of a binomial random variable, we will use the example of tossing a coin n times. We will start with $n = 2$. The total number of possible outcomes is 4: *HH, HT, TH,* and *TT.* (Here, we denote *Head* by *H* and *Tail* by *T.*) Let p indicate the probability of *Head* and q the probability of *Tail* in any trial. (Then $p + q = 1$.) As the outcomes of different coin tosses are independent, the probability of outcome. *HH* is $(p)(p) = p^2$, (special rule of multiplication for independent events discussed in Chapter 5). Similarly, the probability of outcome. *HT* is $(p)(q) = pq$, the probability of *TH* is $(q)(p) = qp$, and the probability of *TT* is $(q)(q) = q^2$. The outcome *HH* entails 2 *Heads*, outcome *HT* includes one *Head*, outcome *TH* includes one *Head*, and outcome *TT* entails zero *Heads*. Table 6-4 summarizes the calculations.

The probability of *Heads* in both trials is p^2, the probability of one *Head* is $(pq + pq = 2pq)$, (special rule of addition for mutually exclusive events), and the probability of zero *Heads* is q^2. The sum of probabilities

$$= (p^2 + 2pq + q^2) = (p + q)^2 = 1$$

For $n = 3$, the possible outcomes are displayed in Chart 6-1 on page 234. These outcomes are summarized in Table 6-5.

The probability of *Heads* in all three trials is p^3, the probability of two *Heads* is $(ppq + pqp + qpp = 3p^2q)$, (special rule of addition for mutually exclusive events), similarly, the probability of one *Head* is $(pqq + qpq + qqp = 3pq^2)$, and the probability of zero *Heads* is q^3. The sum of probabilities is:

$$p^3 + 3p^2q + 3pq^2 + q^3 = (p + q)^3 = 1$$

TABLE 6-4: Binomial Experiment for Two Trails, $n = 2$

| Outcomes | | Probability | Binomial Random Variable |
Trial 1	Trial 2		(Number of Heads)
H	*H*	$(p)(p) = p^2$	2
H	*T*	$(p)(q) = pq$	1
T	*H*	$(q)(p) = qp$	1
T	*T*	$(q)(q) = q^2$	0

TABLE 6-5: Binomial Experiment for Three Trials, $n = 3$

| Outcomes | | | Probability | Value of the Binomial Random Variable |
Trial 1	Trial 2	Trial 3		(Total Number of Successes)
H	*H*	*H*	$(p)(p)(p)$	3
H	*H*	*T*	$(p)(p)(q)$	2
H	*T*	*H*	$(p)(q)(p)$	2
H	*T*	*T*	$(p)(q)(q)$	1
T	*H*	*H*	$(q)(p)(p)$	2
T	*H*	*T*	$(q)(p)(q)$	1
T	*T*	*H*	$(q)(q)(p)$	1
T	*T*	*T*	$(q)(q)(q)$	0

Now let us see how we can obtain these probabilities without actually constructing a tree or a table.

In the case of $n = 3$, in every outcome with two heads, the probability is the product of two ps and one q (the number of qs is obtained by $n - 2 = 3 - 2 = 1$), which gives us a probability of $p^2 q$. Also, the number of outcomes with precisely two heads equals the number of ways of allocating heads to two of the three tosses. This is obtained using the Combination Formula 5-16 in Chapter 5 and equals $_3C_2 = \dfrac{3!}{(2!)(3-2)!} = 3$. Thus, the total probability of getting two heads in three tosses of a coin is $(_3C_2)(p^2 q) = 3p^2 q$.

In general, in the case of n tosses of a coin:
the number of ways of obtaining some x heads is calculated from the Combination Formula 5-16 by using x in place of r and equals $_nC_x = \dfrac{n!}{(x!)(n-x)!}$.

The probability of each outcome with precisely x heads equals the product of x ps and $(n - x)$ qs. Hence, it equals $p^x q^{(n-x)}$.

The total probability of obtaining precisely x heads in n tosses of a coin equals $_nC_x p^x q^{(n-x)}$.

For a general binomial random variable, by replacing Head by Success, Tail by Failure, and denoting probability of Success by p, and denoting probability of Failure by $q = (1 - p)$, we get the following formula for probability $P(x)$ of x successes:

Binomial Probability Distribution

$$P(x) = {}_nC_x p^x (1-p)^{(n-x)} = \frac{n!}{x!(n-x)!} p^x (1-p)^{(n-x)}$$

$$x = 0, 1, 2, 3, ..., n$$

6-7

where
n is the number of trials.
x is the number of successes.
p is the probability of success in each trial.

Example 6-4

An employee of Telemarketing Inc., phones six households on any given day to sell merchandise. Based on the employee's past experience, she is successful in selling the merchandise to 15 percent of households she calls. Compute the probability distribution of the number of sales she makes on any given day.

Solution

Let us see if the conditions for the binomial experiment are satisfied. As the employee makes six calls on any given day, the number of trials (n) is six. There are only two outcomes to every trial (call): she sells the merchandise (success) or she does *not* sell the merchandise (failure). The sale of the merchandise to one household does not affect the sale to other households and therefore trials (outcomes of different calls) are independent. The probability of 0.15 is the same for each call. Thus all conditions are satisfied. The total number of sales is indicated by the discrete random variable X. The probability of success in each trial is 0.15.

$$P(X = 0) = \frac{6!}{0!(6-0)!}0.15^0(1-0.15)^{(6-0)} = 0.3771$$

$$P(X = 1) = \frac{6!}{1!(6-1)!}0.15^1(1-0.15)^{(6-1)} = 0.3993$$

$$P(X = 2) = \frac{6!}{2!(6-2)!}0.15^2(1-0.15)^{(6-2)} = 0.1762$$

$$P(X = 3) = \frac{6!}{3!(6-3)!}0.15^3(1-0.15)^{(6-3)} = 0.0415$$

$$P(X = 4) = \frac{6!}{4!(6-4)!}0.15^4(1-0.15)^{(6-4)} = 0.0055$$

$$P(X = 5) = \frac{6!}{5!(6-5)!}0.15^5(1-0.15)^{(6-5)} = 0.0004$$

$$P(X = 6) = \frac{6!}{6!(6-6)!}0.15^6(1-0.15)^{(6-6)} = 0.0000$$

$P(X = 0)$ denotes the probability that no sale is made on a given day. $P(X = 1)$ denotes the probability that the employee makes exactly one sale, and so on. Note that all the probability values in the example are between 0 and 1 and they add up to 1.

CUMULATIVE BINOMIAL PROBABILITY

In the above example of merchandise sales through telephone calls to households, one may be interested in knowing the probability of at most one sale on any given day. In this case we need the cumulative probability distribution. This is similar to the cumulative frequency distributions developed in Chapter 2. The probability of at most one sale on any given day is indicated by $P(X \leq 1)$

$$P(X \leq 1) = P(X = 0) + P(X = 1)$$

$$= 0.3771 + 0.3993$$

$$= 0.7764$$

The rest of the cumulative probabilities are shown in Table 6-6.

TABLE 6-6: Cumulative Distribution of Number of Sales

Values of X (x)	Probability $P(x)$	Cumulative Probability	Found by
0	0.3771	0.3771	
1	0.3993	0.7764	(0.3771 + 0.3993)
2	0.1762	0.9526	(0.3771 + 0.3993 + 0.1762)
3	0.0415	0.9941	
4	0.0055	0.9996	
5	0.0004	1.0000	
6	0.0000	1.0000	

BINOMIAL PROBABILITY TABLES

Binomial table:
A quick way
of determining
a probability.

Binomial probabilities can be computed using Formula 6-7. However, except for problems involving small n (say, $n = 3$ or 4), the calculations are rather tedious. As an aid, an extensive table has been developed that gives the probabilities of 0, 1, 2, 3, … successes for various values of n and p. This table is in Appendix A, and a small portion of the table for the following example is shown in Table 6-7.

TABLE 6-7: Binomial Probabilities for $n = 10$ and Different Values of P

x	0.05	0.1	0.2	0.3	0.4	0.5	0.6	0.7	0.8	0.9	0.95
0	0.599	0.349	0.107	0.028	0.006	0.001	0.000	0.000	0.000	0.000	0.000
1	0.315	0.387	0.268	0.121	0.040	0.010	0.002	0.000	0.000	0.000	0.000
2	0.075	0.194	0.302	0.233	0.121	0.044	0.011	0.001	0.000	0.000	0.000
3	0.010	0.057	0.201	0.267	0.215	0.117	0.042	0.009	0.001	0.000	0.000
4	0.001	0.011	0.088	0.200	0.251	0.205	0.111	0.037	0.006	0.000	0.000
5	0.000	0.001	0.026	0.103	0.201	0.246	0.201	0.103	0.026	0.001	0.000
6	0.000	0.000	0.006	0.037	0.111	0.205	0.251	0.200	0.088	0.011	0.001
7	0.000	0.000	0.001	0.009	0.042	0.117	0.215	0.267	0.201	0.057	0.010
8	0.000	0.000	0.000	0.001	0.011	0.044	0.121	0.233	0.302	0.194	0.075
9	0.000	0.000	0.000	0.000	0.002	0.010	0.040	0.121	0.268	0.387	0.315
10	0.000	0.000	0.000	0.000	0.000	0.001	0.006	0.028	0.107	0.349	0.599

Example 6-5

A poll conducted by Gallup Canada on June 21, 2000, showed that forty percent of investors invested in high-tech stocks. Suppose 10 investors were selected randomly on that day.

(a) What is the probability that exactly two of the selected investors would have invested in high-tech stocks?

(b) What is the probability that at most seven would have invested in high-tech stocks?

Solution

Let us check if the conditions for the binomial distribution are satisfied. The number of selected investors is 10 and thus $n = 10$. There are only two possible outcomes for each investor: the investor invested in high-tech stocks or he did not invest in high-tech stocks. The probability of success (investor invested in high-tech stocks) is 0.40 and is constant. Since only 10 investors are randomly selected from a large number of investors, it is highly unlikely that the decision of one of the ten investors to invest in high-tech stocks will be affected by the decisions of other investors. It is therefore reasonable to assume that the trials are independent.

(a) $n = 10$, $p = 0.40$, and $x = 2$

We search horizontally on the top of the table for the value of p. In this example $p = 0.40$.

We search the value of $x = 2$ in the first column of the table.

The required probability ($P(2)$) is the value in the row corresponding to $x = 2$ and the column corresponding to $p = 0.40$. It is 0.121.

Using Formula 6-7,

$$P(2) = \frac{10!}{2!(10-2)!}0.4^2(1-0.4)^{(10-2)} = 0.121$$

The value of the probability from Table 6-7 is the same as the one calculated from Formula 6-7. This should not surprise us because the binomial distribution table contains pre-solved probabilities for different values of n and p.

(b) $P(X \leq 7) = P(0) + P(1) + P(2) + P(3) + P(4) + P(5) + P(6) + P(7)$

$$= 0.006 + 0.040 + 0.121 + 0.215 + 0.251 + 0.201 + 0.111 + 0.042$$

$$= 0.987$$

This value can also be computed faster using the complement rule.

$$P(X \leq 7) = 1 - P(X > 7)$$

$$= 1 - (P(8) + P(9) + P(10))$$

$$= 1 - (0.011 + 0.002 + 0.000)$$

$$= 0.987$$

USE OF SOFTWARE

The calculation of a binomial probability distribution using tables is easier and faster than Formula 6-7, provided a table is available for the desired values of n and p. Most of the tables provided in textbooks contain only small values of n and limited values of p. In such cases, we can use statistical software, such as Minitab and Excel, to generate probabilities of a specified number of successes for given values of n and p. Below, we have shown how to use Minitab and Excel to calculate the binomial probabilities. To illustrate, we will use the example of merchandise sale through telephone calls.

MINITAB CHART 6-3: Binomial Probability Distribution Using Minitab

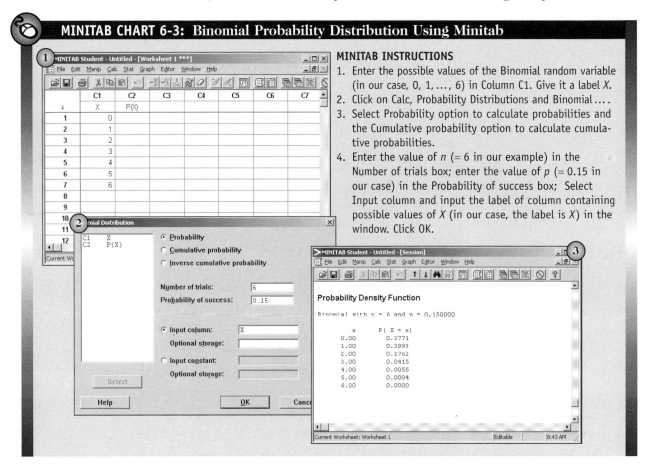

MINITAB INSTRUCTIONS

1. Enter the possible values of the Binomial random variable (in our case, 0, 1, ..., 6) in Column C1. Give it a label X.
2. Click on Calc, Probability Distributions and Binomial ....
3. Select Probability option to calculate probabilities and the Cumulative probability option to calculate cumulative probabilities.
4. Enter the value of n (= 6 in our example) in the Number of trials box; enter the value of p (= 0.15 in our case) in the Probability of success box; Select Input column and input the label of column containing possible values of X (in our case, the label is X) in the window. Click OK.

Probability Density Function

Binomial with n = 6 and p = 0.150000

x	P(X = x)
0.00	0.3771
1.00	0.3993
2.00	0.1762
3.00	0.0415
4.00	0.0055
5.00	0.0004
6.00	0.0000

EXCEL CHART 6-4: Binomial Probability Distribution in Excel

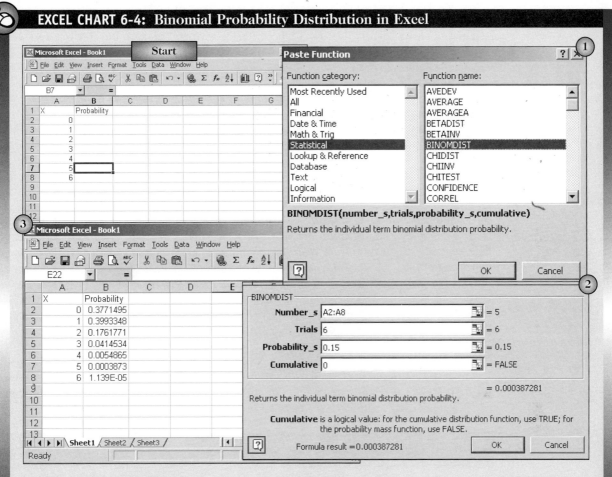

MICROSOFT EXCEL INSTRUCTIONS

1. Enter label X in cell A1, label *Probability* in cell B1 and possible values of the Binomial random variable X (in our example, 0, 1, 2, ..., 6) in column A starting from cell A2. Click on cell B2.
2. Click on f_x (Paste function), select Statistical from the function category menu, and BINOMDIST from the Function name and click OK.
3. Enter Cell locations containing possible values of X in the Number_s box, value of n (= 6 in our case) in the Trials box, and value of p (= 0.15 in our case) in Probability_s box.
4. In the Cumulative box, enter *0* if you desire probabilities, and *1* if you desire cumulative probabilities.
5. The first value appears in cell B2. Drag and fill the remaining cells in column B.

■ SELF-REVIEW 6-6

1. An inspector selects eight faucets randomly from a large batch and conducts a quality control test. The department's directive is that if four or more of the faucets are defective, reject the whole batch. Suppose 4 percent of the faucets in the batch are defective.
   (a) What is the probability that none of the tested faucets will be defective?
   (b) What is the probability that two of the tested faucets will be defective? Use the binomial formula to calculate the probability.

(c) What is the probability that the whole batch will be rejected?

2. Thirty percent of all customers who enter a store will make a purchase. Suppose that six customers enter the store and that these customers make independent purchase decisions.
   (a) What is the probability that no more than two customers will make a purchase?
   (b) What is the probability that at least four customers will make a purchase? (Source: Adapted from *Business Statistics in Practice*, second ed., p.167. Bowerman et al.)

THE SHAPE OF A BINOMIAL DISTRIBUTION

The shape of a binomial probability distribution depends upon the values of n and p. Chart 6-5, below, shows binomial distributions for $n = 10$, and $p = 0.05$, 0.10, 0.20, 0.50, and 0.70. The binomial distribution for p of 0.05 is skewed to the right. As p approaches 0.50, the distribution becomes symmetrical. As p passes 0.50 and moves towards 0.70, the distribution becomes negatively skewed.

We see in Chart 6-6, that for $p = 0.10$, the distribution for $n = 7$ is skewed to the right. But as n gets larger, the distribution becomes more and more symmetrical. In both charts 6-5 and 6-6, we notice that for the probability value of 0.5, the distribution is symmetrical regardless of the value of n.

Thus, the binomial probability distribution is symmetrical when $p = 0.5$, skewed to the right for $p < 0.5$, and skewed to the left for $p > 0.5$. For any value of p other than 0.5, the skewness is reduced as n gets larger.

CHART 6-5: Graphing the Binomial Probability Distribution for a p of 0.05, 0.10, 0.20, 0.50, and 0.70 and an n of 10

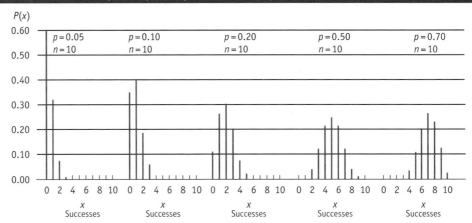

MEAN AND VARIANCE OF A BINOMIAL DISTRIBUTION

Two summary measures (mean and variance) of a binomial distribution, can be determined in terms of n and p. Intuitively, the mean number of successes in the long run in a binomial experiment must equal the product of the number of trials (n) and the probability of success in each trial. In terms of formulae,

CHART 6-6: Chart Representing the Binomial Probability Distribution for a p of 0.10 and an n of 7, 12, 20, and 40

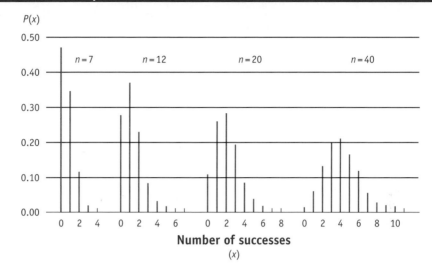

Mean of a Binomial Distribution	$\mu = np$	6-8
Variance of a Binomial Distribution	$\sigma^2 = np(1-p)$	6-9

 We give a detailed derivation of formulae 6-8 and 6-9 in the Chapter 6 Appendix A on the CD-ROM.

Example 6-6

A poll conducted by Gallup Canada on June 21, 2000, showed that 40 percent of investors invested in high-tech stocks. Suppose ten investors were selected randomly on that day.

(a) How many of the selected investors could we expect to have invested in high-tech stocks?

(b) What is the standard deviation of the number of investors (in the sample of 10) who would have invested in high-tech stocks?

Solution

(a) The conditions of the binomial experiment (explained on page 245) are satisfied. Investing in high-tech stocks is chosen as a success. Therefore:

$$p, \text{(probability of success)} = 0.40$$
$$n, \text{(number of trials)} = 10$$
$$\mu = np = (10)(0.40) = 4.0$$

What does $\mu = 4$ tell us?

It tells us that if 40 percent of investors are investing in high-tech and if a random sample of ten investors is selected many times, in the long run, on average, four out of ten investors would have invested in high-tech stocks.

(b) $\sigma^2 = np(1-p) = (10)(0.40)(1-0.40) = 2.40$

$\sigma = \sqrt{(10)(0.40)(1-0.4)} = 1.55$

The standard deviation for the number of investors, out of the ten chosen, who would have invested in high-tech stocks, is 1.55.

The calculations of the mean, and the variance can be verified from formulae 6-2 and 6-4. For the probability distribution from Table 6-7 for $n = 10$ and $p = 0.4$, the detailed calculations are shown below.

Number of investors x	$P(x)$	$xP(x)$	μ	$(x - \mu)^2$	$(x - \mu)^2 P(x)$
0	0.006	0.000	4.0	16	0.096
1	0.040	0.040	4.0	9	0.360
2	0.121	0.242	4.0	4	0.484
3	0.215	0.645	4.0	1	0.215
4	0.251	1.004	4.0	0	0.000
5	0.201	1.005	4.0	1	0.201
6	0.111	0.666	4.0	4	0.444
7	0.042	0.294	4.0	9	0.376
8	0.011	0.088	4.0	16	0.176
9	0.002	0.018	4.0	25	0.050
10	0.000	0.000	4.0	36	0.000
Total		4.002^1			2.402^2

EXERCISES 6-9 TO 6-22

6-9. In a binomial experiment $n = 4$ and $p = 0.25$. Determine the following probabilities using the binomial formula.
(a) $P(X = 2)$
(b) $P(X = 3)$

6-10. In a binomial experiment $n = 5$ and $p = 0.40$. Determine the following probabilities using the binomial formula.
(a) $P(X = 1)$
(b) $P(X = 2)$

6-11. Consider a binomial distribution where $n = 3$ and $p = 0.60$.
(a) Refer to Appendix A and list the probabilities for values of x from 0 to 3.
(b) Determine the mean and standard deviation of the distribution from the general definitions given in formulae 6-2 and 6-4.

6-12. Consider a binomial distribution where $n = 5$ and $p = 0.30$.
(a) Refer to Appendix A and list the probabilities for values of x from 0 to 5.
(b) Determine the mean and standard deviation of the distribution from the general definitions given in formulae 6-2 and 6-4.

6-13. The industry standard suggests that ten percent of new Nissan cars require warranty service within the first year. Suppose Scarborough Nissan in Scarborough, Ontario, sold 12 Nissans yesterday.
(a) What is the probability that none of these vehicles will require warranty service?
(b) What is the probability that exactly one of these vehicles will require warranty service?
(c) Determine the probability that exactly two of these vehicles will require warranty service.
(d) Compute the mean and standard deviation of this probability distribution.

6-14. 2.8 percent of truck drivers in Canada (Statistics Canada, Labour Force Survey, 1998) were women. Suppose the percentage has not changed since then, and twenty truck drivers are selected randomly by a national trucking company to be interviewed about the quality of working conditions.
 (a) What is the probability that two of the drivers selected for the interview will be women?
 (b) What is the probability that none will be women?
 (c) What is the probability that at most two will be women?

6-15. A student randomly guesses at 25 multiple-choice questions in an admission test for skills in mathematics. Each question has five choices. What is the probability that the student gets exactly ten correct?

6-16. A telemarketer makes six phone calls per hour and is able to make a sale to 30 percent of these contacts. During the next two hours, find:
 (a) The probability of making exactly four sales.
 (b) The probability of making no sales.
 (c) The probability of making exactly two sales.
 (d) The mean number of sales in the two-hour period.

6-17. In a binomial distribution, $n = 20$ and $p = 0.10$. Using binomial tables, find
 (a) $P(X \le 5)$
 (b) $P(X \ge 2)$

6-18. Suppose 60 percent of all people prefer Coke to Pepsi. We randomly select 15 people for further study.
 (a) How many would you expect to prefer Coke?
 (b) What is the probability 10 of those surveyed will prefer Coke?
 (c) What is the probability no more than five will prefer Coke?

6-19. A market researcher working for a retail store found that 80 percent of randomly selected customers are repeat customers. Ten customers are randomly selected. What is the probability that:
 (a) Three of the customers selected are repeat customers?
 (b) Between five and seven of the selected customers (including five and seven) are repeat customers?

6-20. In a binomial distribution, $n = 12$ and $p = 0.60$. Using Excel or Minitab software, find
 (a) $P(X \ge 4)$
 (b) $P(X \le 2)$
 (c) Portray the probability distribution graphically. Is the distribution symmetrical or skewed? Explain.

6-21. A local telephone company reports that they can solve customer problems the same day they are reported in 70 percent of the cases. Suppose that 15 cases are randomly selected from those reported this year.
 (a) How many of the problems would you expect to be solved the same day?
 (b) What is the probability that 10 of the problems would be solved the same day?
 (c) What is the probability that 10 or 11 of the problems would be solved the same day?
 (d) What is the probability that more than 10 of the problems would be solved the same day?

6-22. A manufacturer of window frames knows from long experience that 5 percent of the production will have some type of minor defect that will require an adjustment. What is the probability that in a sample of 20 window frames:
(a) None will need adjustment?
(b) At least one will need adjustment?
(c) More than two will need adjustment?

6.5   POISSON PROBABILITY DISTRIBUTION

Another important class of discrete random variables is the Poisson random variable named for the French mathematician Siméon Denis Poisson (1781–1840). Unlike the binomial random variable, the Poisson random variable may assume unlimited values. It usually counts the number of *rare* events (successes) that occur during a specified interval. The interval may be time, distance, specific area or volume. Some typical examples of random variables that approximately follow such a distribution are:

- The number of traffic accidents per month at a busy intersection.
- The number of imperfections in a newly painted car panel.
- The number of death claims received per day by an insurance company.
- The number of customers arriving at a bank during a given time interval.

SIMÉON DENIS POISSON (1781–1840)

1498
1548
1598
1648
1698
1748
1898
1948
2000

Poisson's father had high hopes of his son becoming a medical doctor. But in an early attempt to put a cabbage leaf on blisters, the patient died and this inadvertently also killed his father's wish to see his son as a medical doctor. Fate had something else in store for him. Siméon Denis Poisson was brilliant in mathematics. At the age of seventeen, he came first in the competitive entrance examination at the École Polytechnique. After graduation, he joined École Polytechnique in 1802 as a deputy professor and lectured there from 1802 to 1808. Later, he worked as an astronomer at the Bureau des Longitudes and then as a professor of mechanics at the Faculty of Sciences.

Poisson's work (Poisson's probability distribution) took many years before it was accorded its rightful place in the history of the mathematical theory of probability.

The first person to appreciate the use of Poisson distribution in the statistical analysis of rare events was Von Bortkewitsch (1898). One of his classic examples of application of Poisson distribution was the distribution of the deaths of Prussian soldiers as a result of being kicked by horses.

Near the end of World War II, the Germans developed rocket bombs, which were fired at the city of London. The Allied military command did not know whether these bombs were fired at random or whether they had some type of aiming device. To investigate, the city of London was divided into 576 square regions. The distribution of the number of hits in each square was recorded as follows:

Hits	Regions
0	229
1	211
2	23
3	35
4	1
5	1

To interpret, the above chart indicates that 229 regions were not hit with one of the bombs. One region was hit four times. Using the Poisson distribution, with a mean of 0.93 hits per region, the expected number of hits is as follows:

Hits	Regions
0	227.3
1	211.4
2	98.3
3	30.5
4	7.1
5 or more	1.6

Because the actual number of hits was close to the expected number of hits, the military command concluded that the bombs were falling at random. The Germans had not developed a bomb with an aiming device.

The Poisson distribution has a wide range of applications in the areas such as the study of the number of car arrivals at toll booths on highways per minute, the number of customer arrivals at the checkout counters in retail stores or teller windows in a bank every ten minutes. In order for the Poisson distribution to be a good approximation in these situations, the following criteria should be fulfilled. We refer to these criteria as the characteristics of a Poisson experiment.

1. The random variable counts the number of successes that occur during an interval.
2. The number of successes that occurs in any interval does not depend on the number of successes in other intervals.
3. As the interval gets smaller, the probability that two or more successes will occur in the interval approaches zero. This is also known as the property of a rare event.
4. The probability that a success will occur in an interval is the same for all intervals of equal length; and the average number of successes during an interval is proportional to the length of the interval.

A Poisson distribution can be described mathematically using the formula:

Poisson Distribution	$$P(X = x) = \frac{\mu^x e^{-\mu}}{x!} \quad x = 0, 1, 2, 3, \ldots$$	**6-10**

where,

$P(X = x)$ is the probability of a random variable X achieving the value x.

μ is the arithmetic mean number of occurrences (successes) in a given interval.

e is the constant 2.71828 …. (base of Naperian logarithmic system).

x is a value of the random variable X.

The variance of a Poisson distribution is also equal to its mean. Recall that for a binomial distribution there is a fixed number of trials. For example, for a four-question multiple-choice test there can only be zero, one, two, three, or four successes (correct answers). The random variable, X, for a Poisson distribution, however, can assume a countably *infinite number of values*—that is, 0, 1, 2, 3, 4, 5, …. .

To illustrate the Poisson probability computation, assume baggage is rarely lost by Air Canada. Most flights do not experience any mishandled bags; some have one bag lost; a few have two bags lost; rarely a flight will have three lost bags; and so on. Suppose a random sample of 1000 flights shows a total of 300 bags were lost. Thus, the arithmetic mean number of lost bags per flight is 0.3, found by 300/1000. If the number of lost bags per flight follows a Poisson distribution with $\mu = 0.30$, we can compute the various probabilities by the formula:

$$P(x) = \frac{\mu^x e^{-\mu}}{x!}$$

For example, the probability of not losing any bags is:

$$P(0) = \frac{(0.3)^0 (e^{-0.30})}{0!} = 0.7408$$

In other words, 74 percent of the flights will have no lost baggage. The probability of exactly one lost bag is:

$$P(1) = \frac{(0.3)^1 (e^{-0.30})}{1!} = 0.2222$$

Thus, we would expect to find exactly one lost bag on 22 percent of the flights.

Example 6-7 Consider the previous illustration about the number of bags lost by Air Canada. Suppose the number of bags lost per flight follows a Poisson distribution with a mean of 0.3.

(a) What is the probability that exactly two bags are lost on a particular flight?

(b) What is the probability that at least three bags are lost on a particular flight?

Solution

(a) $P(X = 2) = \dfrac{\mu^x e^{-\mu}}{x!} = \dfrac{0.3^2}{2!} e^{-0.3} = 0.0333$

Thus, we would expect to find exactly two lost bags on about 3 percent of the flights.

(b) $P(X \geq 3) = 1 - P(X \leq 2)$ [(complement rule of probability]

$= 1 - [P(X = 0) + P(X = 1)) + P(X = 2)]$

We have already calculated $P(X = 0)$ and $P(X = 1)$ in our illustration. $P(X = 2)$ is found in (a). Thus,

$$1 - [P(X = 0) + P(X = 1)) + P(X = 2)]$$
$$= 1 - (0.7408 + 0.2222 + 0.0333) = 0.0037$$

Therefore, we would expect to find at least three bags lost on 0.37 percent of the flights.

USE OF THE POISSON DISTRIBUTION TABLE

We can also find the probabilities in (a) and (b) of the above example by using the Poisson Distribution table in Appendix 2 on the CD-ROM accompanying this text. A part of the table is reproduced in Table 6-8 below.

(a) To find $P(X = 2)$ for $\mu = 0.3$, locate the column in Table 6-8, headed "0.3" and read down that column to the row level 2 in the x column. The probability is 0.0333.

(b) To find $P(X \geq 3)$, find $P(X = 0)$, $P(X = 1)$, and $P(X = 2)$ as explained above and then add these values and subtract the sum from one. Thus, $P(X \geq 3)$ $= 1 - (0.7408 + 0.2222 + 0.0333) = 0.0037$.

Computing the cumulative probabilities of a Poisson discrete random variable by using the formula can be cumbersome. The Poisson tables can be faster and easier if the tables include the given value of μ. However, the tables are limited by the amount of space

TABLE 6-8: Poisson Table for Various Values of μ (from Appendix 2)

x	0.1	0.2	0.3	0.4	0.5	0.6	0.7	0.8	0.9
0	0.9048	0.8187	0.7408	0.6703	0.6065	0.5488	0.4966	0.4493	0.4066
1	0.0905	0.1637	0.2222	0.2681	0.3033	0.3293	0.3476	0.3595	0.3659
2	0.0045	0.0164	0.0333	0.0536	0.0758	0.0988	0.1217	0.1438	0.1647
3	0.0002	0.0011	0.0033	0.0072	0.0126	0.0198	0.0284	0.0383	0.0494
4	0.0000	0.0001	0.0003	0.0007	0.0016	0.0030	0.0050	0.0077	0.0111
5	0.0000	0.0000	0.0000	0.0001	0.0002	0.0004	0.0007	0.0012	0.0020
6	0.0000	0.0000	0.0000	0.0000	0.0000	0.0000	0.0001	0.0002	0.0003
7	0.0000	0.0000	0.0000	0.0000	0.0000	0.0000	0.0000	0.0000	0.0000

available in textbooks. To compute the probability distribution of a Poisson random variable with a given value of mean, with more precision, computer software packages become more attractive. We give instructions below, for Minitab and Microsoft Excel.

MINITAB INSTRUCTIONS
1. Enter the desired values of the Poisson random variable X in Column C1. Give it a label X.
2. Click on Calc, Probability Distributions and Poisson ....
3. Select Probability option to calculate probabilities and the Cumulative probability option to calculate cumulative probabilities.
4. Enter the value of the mean in the Mean box; select Input column and input the label of column containing possible values of X (label is X) in the window. Click OK.

MICROSOFT EXCEL INSTRUCTIONS
1. Enter label X in cell A1, label Probability in cell B1 and desired values of the Poisson random variable X in column A starting from cell A2. Click on cell B2.
2. Click on f_x (Paste function), select Statistical from the function category menu, and POISSON from the Function name and click OK.
3. Enter Cell locations containing possible values of X in the X box, the value of the mean in the Mean box.
4. In the Cumulative box, enter 0 if you desire probabilities, and 1 if you desire cumulative probabilities.
5. The first value appears in cell B2. Click on Cell B2 and click Format and Cells. In the Format Cells dialog box, click on the number tab, select Number from the category menu, enter 4 in the decimal places box and click *OK*.
6. Drag and fill the remaining cells in column B.

THE SHAPE OF THE POISSON PROBABILITY DISTRIBUTION

The Poisson probability distribution is always positively skewed. For smaller values of μ it is highly skewed. As μ becomes larger, the distribution becomes more symmetrical. For example, Chart 6-7 shows the distributions of the number of transmission services, muffler replacements, and oil changes per day at Avellino's Auto Shop. They follow Poisson distributions with means of 0.7, 2.0, and 6.0, respectively.

In summary, the Poisson distribution is actually a family of discrete distributions. All that is needed to construct a Poisson probability distribution is the mean number of defects, errors, and so on—designated as μ.

CHART 6-7: Poisson Probability Distributions for Means of 0.7, 2.0, and 6.0

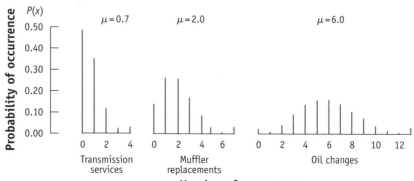

THE POISSON APPROXIMATION TO THE BINOMIAL PROBABILITY DISTRIBUTION

There are many binomial situations where n is very large, and p is very small. In such cases, we may not find a binomial table to look up the probabilities corresponding to random variable. As mentioned earlier, we can use a computer. But if we do not have access to a computer or if it is not convenient to use, we can approximate the binomial distribution by the Poisson distribution without compromising too much accuracy. However, the following three conditions should be simultaneously satisfied.

- The number of trials (n) in the binomial experiment is large.
- The probability (p) is small.
- The product of n and p, that is, np is of moderate magnitude.

In fact, it has been proved by Poisson that if for a given value of n, and a constant, say 8, we define $p = 8/n$, then as the value of n increases, the corresponding binomial distribution becomes closer and closer to a Poisson distribution with $\mu = 8$. How large should the value of n be for a good approximation? As a rule of thumb, the approximation is accepted as good enough when $p \le 0.05$ and $n \ge 20$.

Example 6-8

The business department of a community college is considering buying a photocopy machine with an automatic feeder from a company. The company claims that the probability of a paper jam in the machine is 0.002.
(a) Using a Poisson approximation, find an approximate value of the probability that the machine will not jam any time during the photocopying of a 200-page document.
(b) Using a Poisson approximation, find an approximate value of the probability that the machine will jam exactly once during the photocopying of a 200-page document.
(c) Use the binomial distribution formula for (a). Do the values of probabilities calculated in (a) and (c) agree? Comment on the Poisson approximation to the binomial distribution.

Solution

Let X be the number of times a paper jam will occur during the photocopying of a 200-page document. Then, X has a binomial distribution with $p = 0.002$, $n = 200$.

Since $n > 20$ and $p < 0.05$, we can approximate X by a Poisson random variable with $\mu = (0.002)(200) = 0.4$.
(a) The machine will not jam indicates that the number of jams $= 0$, (that is, $x = 0$).

Therefore, $P(X = 0) \approx \dfrac{\mu^x e^{-\mu}}{x!} = \dfrac{0.4^0 e^{-0.4}}{0!} = 0.6703$.

Thus, the probability of photocopying a document without a paper jam is approximately 0.6703.
(b) The machine will jam exactly once indicates that $x = 1$. Therefore,

$$P(X = 1) \approx \frac{\mu^x e^{-\mu}}{x!} = \frac{0.4^1 e^{-0.4}}{1!} = 0.2681$$

The probability of photocopying a document with exactly one jam is approximately 0.2681.

(c) Using the binomial formula we get:

$$P(X = 0) = \frac{n!}{x!(n-x)!}p^x(1-p)^{(n-x)} = \frac{200!}{0!(200-0)!}(0.002)^0(1-0.002)^{(200-0)}$$
$$= 0.6701$$

The value of $P(X = 0)$ calculated in (a) = 0.6703 and in (c) is 0.6701. The difference is only 0.0002. The two values are very close.

■ SELF-REVIEW 6-7

An insurance company determined the probability that a randomly chosen woman aged 30 will die within the next year is 0.0007. If the company sells 4000 policies to 30 year-old women this year, what is the probability that they will pay on exactly one policy?

EXERCISES 6-23 TO 6-28

6-23. In a Poisson distribution, $\mu = 0.4$.
  (a) Compute $P(X = 0)$.
  (b) Compute $P(X > 0)$.

6-24. In a Poisson distribution, $\mu = 4$.
  (a) Compute $P(X = 2)$.
  (b) Compute $P(X \leq 0)$.
  (c) Compute $P(X > 2)$.

6-25. Pallavi Singh is a loan officer in a local bank. Her past records show that she interviews an average of seven loan applicants per day. Assuming that the number of applicants she interviewed per day follows a Poisson distribution, find the probability that:
  (a) She will interview only three applicants during a certain day.
  (b) She will interview no applicant during a certain day.

6-26. The emergency department at a local hospital receives, on average, five patients per hour. Assuming that the number of patients received per hour follows a Poisson distribution, compute the probability that:
  (a) The emergency department will receive three patients in a given hour.
  (b) The emergency department will receive more than two patients in a given hour.
  (c) The emergency department will receive three patients in a given one half hour.

6-27. It is estimated that 0.5 percent of callers to the finance department of the Greater Toronto Area receive a busy signal. Find the approximate value of the probability that of today's 600 callers, at least four will receive a busy signal.

6-28. Textbook authors and publishers work very hard to minimize the number of errors in a text. However, some errors are unavoidable. Mr. J.A. Carman, statistics editor, reports that the mean number of errors per page is 0.04. Find an approximate value of the probability that there are less than two errors in a particular 50-page chapter.

CHAPTER OUTLINE

I. A random variable is a random experiment, each of whose possible outcomes is a number.
    A. We can associate a random variable with any random experiment by assigning a numerical value to each possible outcome of the experiment.
    B. A discrete random variable is a random variable that assumes a finite or countably infinite number of possible values.
    C. A continuous random variable is a random variable which assumes any value within some interval or a collection of intervals.

II. A discrete probability distribution is a listing of all the possible values of a discrete random variable and their corresponding probabilities. The main features are:
    A. The sum of the probabilities is 1.00.
    B. The probability of a particular outcome is between 0.00 and 1.00.

III. The mean and variance of a discrete probability distribution are computed as follows:

    The mean is equal to:

    $$\mu = \Sigma[xP(x)]$$ 6-2

    The variance is equal to:

    $$\sigma^2 = \Sigma[(x-\mu)^2 P(x)]$$ 6-4

IV. A binomial distribution has the following characteristics.
    A. The outcome of each trial has two possible values: *Success* and *Failure*.
    B. The probability of a *Success* has the same value, p, from trial to trial.
    C. The trials are mutually independent.
    D. The distribution results from a count of the total number of *Successes* in a fixed number of trials.

V. A binomial probability is determined as follows:

    $$P(x) = \frac{n!}{x!(n-x)}p^x(1-p)^{n-x}$$ 6-7

    A. The mean is computed as:

    $$\mu = np$$ 6-8

    B. The variance is

    $$\sigma^2 = np(1-p)$$ 6-9

VI. A Poisson distribution has the following characteristics.
    A. It counts the number of times some event (*Success*) occurs during a specified interval.
    B. The average number of *Successes* during an interval is proportional to the length of the interval.
    C. As the interval gets smaller, the probability that two or more *Successes* will occur in the interval tends to zero.
    D. The number of *Successes* in two non-overlapping intervals are independent.

E. A Poisson probability is determined from the following equation.

$$P(x) = \frac{\mu^x e^{-\mu}}{x!}$$

6-10

F. The mean and the variance of a Poisson distribution are the same.

VII. A binomial distribution with large n and a small p can be approximated by a Poisson distribution with a mean of np.

CHAPTER EXERCISES 6-29 TO 6-59

6-29. What is the difference between a random variable and a probability distribution?

6-30. What is the difference between a discrete and a continuous probability distribution? For each of the following, indicate if the distribution is discrete or continuous.
(a) The length of time to get a haircut.
(b) The number of cars a jogger passes each morning on his or her run.
(c) The number of hits for a team in a high school girl's softball game.
(d) The number of patients treated at Scarborough General Hospital between 6 and 10 p.m. each night.
(e) The number of kilometres your car travelled on the last fill-up.
(f) The number of noticeable surface defects found by quality inspectors on a new car.
(g) The amount of carbonated beverage filled into a 341 mL can.

6-31. What are the characteristics of a binomial experiment?

6-32. Under what conditions will the binomial and the Poisson distributions give roughly the same results.

6-33. Samson Apartments has a large number of units available to rent each month. A concern of management is the number of vacant apartments each month. A recent study revealed the fraction of the time that a given number of apartments are vacant. Compute the mean and standard deviation of the number of vacant apartments.

Number of Vacant Units	Probability
0	0.10
1	0.20
2	0.30
3	0.40

6-34. An investment will be worth $1000, $2000, or $5000 at the end of the year. The probabilities of these values are 0.25, 0.60, and 0.15, respectively. Determine the mean and variance of the worth of the investment.

6-35. The personnel manager of a manufacturing company is studying the number of on-the-job accidents over a period of one month. He developed the following probability distribution. Compute the mean, variance, and standard deviation of the number of accidents in a month.

Number of Accidents	Probability
0	0.40
1	0.20
2	0.20
3	0.10
4	0.10

6-36. Corso Bakery offers special decorated cakes for birthdays, weddings, and other occasions. They also have regular cakes available in their bakery. The following table gives the total number of cakes sold per day and the corresponding probabilities. Compute the mean, variance, and standard deviation of the number of cakes sold per day.

Number of Cakes Sold per Day	Probability
12	0.25
13	0.40
14	0.25
15	0.10

6-37. A Tamiami shearing machine is producing 10 percent defective pieces, which is abnormally high. The quality control engineer has been checking the output by almost continuous sampling since the abnormal condition began. What is the probability that in a sample of 10 pieces:
(a) exactly five will be defective?
(b) five or more will be defective?

6-38. The manager of a nightclub has observed that the number of male customers who visit the club follows a Poisson distribution with a mean of 30 per day, and the number of female customers who visit the club follows a Poisson distribution with a mean of 20 per day. The entrance ticket is $20 per male and $10 per female.
(a) Find the probability that 10 males will visit the club on a randomly selected day.
(b) If the numbers of male and female visitors are mutually independent, find the mean and the standard deviation of the club earnings through entrance tickets.

6-39. A publishing company has estimated the following probability distribution of demand, X, for a certain book.

Demand	Probability
500	0.3
1000	0.5
1500	0.2

They have decided to print 1000 copies of the book. The total cost of printing the 1000 copies will be $20 000; the selling price of the book is $50, and all unsold books can be recycled at $2 per book. How much profit can the company expect from this project?

6-40. Thirty percent of the population in a community is Spanish speaking. A Spanish speaking person is accused of killing a non-Spanish speaking person. Of the first 12 potential jurors selected from the community, only 2 are Spanish speaking and 10 are not. The defendant's lawyer challenges the jury selection, claiming bias against her client. The Crown prosecutor disagrees, saying that the probability of this particular composition is common. What do you think?

6-41. Alex Simpson has been teaching Fluid Mechanics for the last 15 years. He recognized that 15 percent of all the students who took this course received failing grades. A sample of 30 of his past students has been randomly selected.
    (a) What is the probability that at least three of the students would have failed the course?
    (b) What is the probability that exactly three of the students would have failed the course?
    (c) What is the expected value of the number of students who would have failed the course?

6-42. Terry's Tire and Auto Supply, Inc. is considering a 2-for-1 stock split. Before the transaction is finalized at least two-thirds of the 1200 company shareholders must approve the proposal. To evaluate the likelihood the proposal will be approved, the director of finance selected a sample of 18 shareholders. He contacted each and found 14 approved of the proposed split. What is the likelihood of this event, assuming two-thirds of the shareholders approve?

6-43. The *Toronto Star* reported on November 4, 2001, that 15 percent of couples live in a common-law relationship. Suppose nine couples were selected on that day.
    (a) What is the probability that exactly one couple from the selected group of nine would be in a common-law relationship?
    (b) What is the probability that none of the couples selected from the group of nine would be living in a common-law relationship?
    (c) What is the expected value of the number of couples living in a common-law relationship from the selected group of nine?

6-44. *The Daily* (Statistics Canada), in its release on December 8, 1998, reported that 5 percent of college and bachelor degree students default on their loans within two years of graduation. Suppose a random sample of nine college and bachelor degree students is taken.
    (a) What is the probability that exactly two students of the selected group of nine will default on their loans?
    (b) What is the probability that at least three students will default on their loans?
    (c) What is the probability that none of the selected group of nine students will default on the loan?
    (d) What are the average and standard deviation of the number of students from the group of nine who will default on their loans?

6-45. Recent statistics suggest that 15 percent of those who visit a retail site on the World Wide Web make a purchase. A local retailer wished to verify this claim. To do so, she selected a random sample of 16 "hits" to her site. If the claim is correct,
   (a) what is the likelihood that exactly 4 of the 16 would have made a purchase?
   (b) how many purchases should she expect?
   (c) what is the likelihood that four or more "hits" result in a purchase?

6-46. Medical research has shown that the probability of a cure for skin cancer, detected in the early stages, by a certain type of chemotherapy is 72 percent. Several samples, each consisting of seven skin cancer patients who were treated with this type of chemotherapy were randomly selected. The random variable is the number of successfully cured patients in the sample. The probability distribution of the number of successfully cured patients is given below.

x	p(x)
0	0.000
1	0.002
2	0.019
3	0.080
4	0.206
5	0.316
6	0.273
7	0.100

   (a) Find the expected number of cured patients in a sample.
   (b) Calculate the standard deviation of the number of cured patients in a sample.

6-47. Dr. Richmond, a psychologist, is studying the daytime television viewing habits of college students. She believes 45 percent of college students watch soap operas during the afternoon. To further investigate, she selects a random sample of 10 college students. If her belief is correct,
   (a) develop a probability distribution for the number of students in the sample who watch soap operas.
   (b) find the mean and the standard deviation of this distribution.
   (c) what is the probability of finding exactly four who watch soap operas?
   (d) what is the probability less than half of the students selected watch soap operas?

6-48. From the past records of returned electronic pocket calculators, the manufacturer has estimated that 5 percent of pocket calculators are returned for repair while their guarantee is still in effect. If a company buys 30 pocket calculators for its travelling salespeople,
   (a) what is the probability that exactly three pocket calculators will require repair during their guarantee period?
   (b) what is the probability that at least four will require repair during their guarantee period?
   (c) what is the probability that none will require repair during the guarantee period of pocket calculators?

6-49. A manufacturer of computer chips claims that the probability of a defective chip is 0.002. The manufacturer sells chips in batches of size 700 to HBM Computers.
(a) What is the mean number of defective chips per batch?
(b) What is the probability that none of the 700 chips in a batch will be defective?

6-50. An airline company knows that one percent of the people who make flight reservations do not show up. Their policy is therefore to sell 202 tickets for a flight that can hold 200 passengers. Find the approximate value of the probability that there will be a seat for every passenger with a reservation who shows up.

6-51. The sales of Lexus cars in the Greater Toronto Area show a Poisson distribution with a mean of six cars per day.
(a) What is the probability that no Lexus cars will be sold on a particular day?
(b) What is the probability that for five successive days at least one Lexus will be sold each day?

6-52. Suppose 1.5 percent of the plastic spacers produced by a Corson high-speed mould injection machine are defective. For a random sample of 200 spacers, find the probability that:
(a) None of the spacers is defective.
(b) Three or more of the spacers are defective.

6-53. A study of lines at the checkout registers of a retail store located in Scarborough Town Centre revealed that between 4 and 7 p.m. on weekdays there is an average of four customers waiting in line. Assume that the number of customers waiting in line during this period follows a Poisson distribution. What is the probability that you visit the store today during this period and find:
(a) No customers waiting?
(b) Four customers waiting?
(c) Four or fewer customers waiting?
(d) Four or more customers waiting?

6-54. The probability that a baby born will have one of many types of albinism is $\frac{1}{17\,000}$. Of the next 25 000 babies born, what is the probability that:
(a) No baby will have one of the many types of albinism?
(b) More than two will have one of many types of albinism?

6-55. *The Daily* (Statistics Canada) reports that on average, 5.1 motor vehicle thefts take place every fifteen minutes. Assume that the distribution of thefts per fifteen minutes can be approximated by a Poisson probability distribution.
(a) What is the probability that exactly seven motor vehicle thefts will take place during a fifteen-minute period?
(b) What is the probability there will be no motor vehicle thefts during a fifteen-minute period?
(c) What is the probability there will be at least one motor vehicle theft during a fifteen-minute period?
(Source: www.statcan.ca/Daily/English/980127/d980127.htm)

6-56. The New Process, Inc., a large mail order supplier of women's fashions, advertises same-day service on all their orders. Recently the movement of orders has not gone as planned, and there were a large number of complaints. Bud Owens, the supervisor of the Order Handling Department, has completely redone the method of order handling. The goal is fewer than five unfilled orders on hand at the end of 95 percent of the working days. Frequent checks of the unfilled orders at the end of the day revealed that the distribution of the unfilled orders followed a Poisson distribution with a mean of two orders.

(a) Has New Process, Inc. lived up to its integral goal? Cite evidence.
(b) Display graphically, the Poisson probability distribution of unfilled orders.

6-57. A bank in the Greater Toronto area receives, on the average, eight customers between 8:00 a.m. and 9:00 a.m. each day that it is open. Assume that a Poisson process approximates the distribution of customers' arrival.

(a) What is the probability that on a given day that the bank is open between 8:00 a.m. and 9:00 a.m., it will receive exactly three customers?
(b) What is the probability that the bank will receive fewer than three customers in this time period?
(c) What is the probability that the bank will receive more than four customers in this time period?

6-58. According to the "January theory," if the stock market is up for the month of January, it will be up for the year. If it is down in January, it will be down for the year. According to an article in *The Wall Street Journal*, this theory held for 29 out of the last 34 years. Suppose there is no truth to this theory. What is the probability this could occur by chance? (You will probably need a software package such as Excel or Minitab.)

6-59. Fourteen army corps of the German army[3] kept records of the kicking deaths of soldiers from 1875–1894. The number of deaths for 280 army corps-years (14)(20) was 196. Answer the following assuming that the number of deaths follows a Poisson distribution.

(a) Find the expected number of deaths per army corps-year.
(b) Find the probability of exactly three deaths in a randomly selected army corps-year.
(c) Find the probability of at least one death in a randomly selected army corps-year.

COMPUTER DATA EXERCISE 6-60

6-60. Refer to the data in file Exercise 6-60.xls on the CD-ROM. The file contains the listing of 174 randomly selected companies and their employees in the top 1000 companies in the year 2000. Create the frequency distribution of the employees. Convert this frequency distribution into a relative frequency distribution, which is also a probability distribution, by dividing each class frequency by the sum of frequencies. Compute the mean and standard deviation of this probability distribution.

www.exercises.ca 6.61

6-61. Go to www.homestore.ca. Click *homes for sale* menu. Select Ontario in the *province box*. Select Toronto area from *select an area of Ontario box*. Select Durham region from *select an area of Toronto area*. Select Bowmanville, and then select *single-family home*.

The listing of homes appears.

(a) Create a probability distribution for the number of bedrooms in single family homes. Compute the mean and standard deviation of this distribution.

(b) Create the probability distribution for the number of bathrooms in the single-family homes. Compute the mean and standard deviation of this distribution.

(c) Draw a graph depicting the probability distribution in (a) and (b). Comment on the shape of the probability distribution in (a) and (b).

CHAPTER 6   ANSWERS TO SELF-REVIEW

6-1. (a)

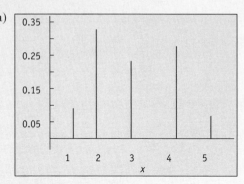

(b) $P(X \geq 2) = P(2) + P(3) + P(4) + P(5)$
$= 0.34 + 0.23 + 0.28 + 0.07 = 0.92$

6-2.

x_1 (%) \ x_2 (%)	−15	10	30
−5	(0.2)(0.3) = 0.06	(0.2)(0.2) = 0.04	(0.2)(0.5) = 0.1
6	(0.7)(0.3) = 0.21	(0.7)(0.2) = 0.14	(0.7)(0.5) = 0.35
15	(0.1)(0.3) = 0.03	(0.1)(0.2) = 0.02	(0.1)(0.5) = 0.05

6-3. Probability distribution of X_1^2

x_1	x_1^2	Probability
−10	100	0.2
8	64	0.5
20	400	0.3

Probability distribution of $R = 2X_1 + 3X_2$

x_1	x_2	$r = 2x_1 + 3x_2$	$P(r)$
−10	−5	−35	0.05
−10	5	−5	0.15
−10	10	10	0.0
8	−5	1	0.05
8	5	31	0.35
8	10	46	0.1
20	−5	25	0.1
20	5	55	0.1
20	10	70	0.1

6-4. Let X_1 be his gain from the first game and let X_2 be his gain from the second game. P(winning in first game) $= 18/37$.

Probability distribution of X_1

x_1	Probability
−100	$19/37 = 0.5135$
+100	$18/37 = 0.4865$

Probability distribution of X_2

x_2	Probability
0	$18/37 = 0.4865$
−200	$(19/37)(19/37) = 0.2637$
200	$(19/37)(18/37) = 0.2498$

$E(X_1) = (-100)(0.5135) + (100)(0.4865) = -2.7$
$E(X_2) = (0)(0.4865) + (-200)(0.2637)$
$\quad\quad + (200)(0.2498) = -2.773$
$E(X_1 + X_2) = E(X_1) + E(X_2) = -2.7 - 2.773 = -5.473$

6-5. (a)

x_2	$P(x_2)$	$E(X_2)$(or μ)	$(x_2 - \mu)^2$	$(x_2 - \mu)^2 P(x_2)$
−5	0.2	4	81	16.2
5	0.6	4	1	0.6
10	0.2	4	36	7.2
Total				24.0

$V(X_2) = 24.0.$ So, $SD(X_2) = \sqrt{24.0} = 4.9\%$

(b) Total return $= R = 5X_1 + 10X_3$
So, $V(R) = V(5X_1 + 10X_3)$
$= (5)^2 V(X_1) + (10)^2 V(X_3)$
$= (25)(108) + (100)(24) = 5100$
So, $SD(R) = \sqrt{5100} = 71.41$

6-6.
1. $n = 8, p = 0.04$
Using binomial formula,

(a) $P(X = 0) = \dfrac{n!}{x!(n-x)!} p^x (1-p)^{(n-x)}$

$= \dfrac{8!}{0!(8-0)!}(0.04)^0 (1-0.04)^{(8-0)}$

$= 0.7214$

(b) $P(X = 2) = \dfrac{n!}{x!(n-x)!} p^x (1-p)^{(n-x)}$

$= \dfrac{8!}{2!(8-2)!}(0.04)^2 (1-0.04)^{(8-2)}$

$= 0.0351$

(c) $P(X \geq 4) = P(4) + P(5) + P(6) + P(7) + P(8)$
≈ 0.00016

2. $n = 6$, $p = 0.30$
Using a binomial table,
(a) $P(X \leq 2) = P(0) + P(1) + P(2)$
$= 0.118 + 0.303 + 0.324$
$= 0.745$

(b) $P(x \geq 4) = P(4) + P(5) + P(6)$
$= 0.060 + 0.010 + 0.001$
$= 0.071$

6-7. $n = 4000$; $p = 0.0007$
So, $\mu = np = (4000)(0.0007) = 2.8$

$$P(X = 1) = \frac{\mu^x e^{-\mu}}{x!} = \frac{(2.8)^1 e^{-2.8}}{1!} = 0.1703$$

The Normal Probability Distribution

GOALS

When you have completed this chapter, you will be able to:

- Explain how probabilities are assigned to a continuous random variable

- Explain the characteristics of a normal probability distribution

- Define and calculate z value corresponding to any observation on a normal distribution

- Determine the probability a random observation is in a given interval on a normal distribution using the standard normal distribution

- Use the normal probability distribution to approximate the binomial probability distribution.

ABRAHAM DE MOIVRE (1667—1754)

Normal distribution is one of the most important concepts in statistics and probability theory. Its significance in the study of statistics and probability theory is due mainly to two results. The first, popularly known as the "normal law of errors," establishes normal distribution as an appropriate distribution of random errors. This result was first published by the American mathematician Robert Adrain in 1808 and was independently obtained by the German scientist Carl Friedrich Gauss one year later. The second result, known as the "central limit theorem," explains the common occurrence of normal distribution in the real world. This result is attributed to Pierre-Simon Laplace.

The honour of being the first person to give the statement of the formula for the normal curve goes to Abraham De Moivre. In particular, he proved that as the value of n increases, the shape of the binomial distribution becomes closer and closer to that of the normal distribution.

Abraham De Moivre (1667–1754) was born a Frenchman, but he emigrated to England at the age of 18 due to political and religious difficulties in his home country. A chance encounter while he was in London with Isaac Newton's *Principia* greatly inspired his interest and diligence in mathematics. His contributions to mathematics have made him a legend among mathematicians, and his contributions to the development of statistics laid a milestone in human understanding of chance events. He dedicated his first book, *The Doctrine of Chances,* to Newton. The aging Newton was reputed to have turned students away with the words, "Go to Mr. De Moivre; he knows these things better than I do." He has been praised in the verse of Alexander Pope for his characteristic accuracy.

Who made the spider's parallel design, Sure as De Moivre, without rule or line?[1]

Despite his worthy achievements and friendships with influential scientists such as Newton, De Moivre led a difficult life due to lack of wealth and the inability to claim an esteemed station. His chief means of living came from tutoring math and publishing his mathematical research works. Tutoring was a particularly difficult occupation, for he often had to travel long distances between the homes of his pupils. In his eighties, he began to suffer from lethargy. It is reported that he discovered he was sleeping an extra 15 minutes each day and from this he calculated the precise date and time of his death—as the point when, he reasoned, he would sleep the whole day through. He was right.

1498
1548
1598
1648
1698
1748
1898
1948
2000

INTRODUCTION

Chapter 6 deals with families of discrete probability distributions. Recall that these distributions are based on discrete random variables, which can assume only a **finite** or **countably infinite** number of possible values. For example, the number of correct answers on an examination with 10 true or false questions can be only $0, 1, 2, \ldots, 10$. Here, the number of possible values is 11 (a finite number). The number of times a coin has to be tossed until we get the first head can only be $1, 2, 3, \ldots$. Here, the number of possible values is countably infinite.

The height of a randomly chosen Canadian adult, however, can be any value in the interval between, say, 80 cm and 250 cm. (We have chosen an extra-large interval to be sure that no possible values are omitted.) The set of all the values in the interval between 80 and 250 is *infinite*. Also, it is not possible to list all these values. Between any two values in the interval, however close they may be to each other, we can always find another value. *The set of all the values in the interval is thus uncountably infinite*. The height of a randomly chosen Canadian adult is a **continuous random variable**. In this chapter, we shall study the class of continuous probability distributions.

> *i* **Continuous Random Variable** One that can assume any value within some interval or a collection of intervals.

A continuous random variable usually results from measuring attributes such as length, weight, time, and temperature. After a brief discussion on the general form of continuous probability distributions, we shall examine in detail a very important member of this class, the *normal probability distribution*, which plays a fundamental role in the theory and application of statistical inference.

7.1 ASSIGNING PROBABILITY TO A CONTINUOUS RANDOM VARIABLE

One of the main distinctions between discrete and continuous random variables is the way the probabilities of events are specified. Recall that the *total sum of probabilities should always be 1*. In the case of a discrete random variable, we can assign a positive probability to each of the values the variable can assume in such a way that the probabilities sum to 1. However, in the case of a continuous random variable, it is not possible to assign a positive probability to each of the (uncountably infinite number of) values in an interval and still have the probabilities sum to 1. Hence, in this case, we assume that the probability that the variable will take on any particular value is zero. Probabilities are instead assigned to intervals of values. This assumption makes sense in practice. For example, the probability that a newborn child will weigh *exactly* 4 kg (not even a fraction of a gram more or less) is zero. But there is a reasonably high probability that the weight of a newborn child will be between 3.9 kg and 4.1 kg.

The probability that a continuous random variable will assume any particular value is zero. Probabilities are instead assigned to intervals of values.

We shall now explain how, for a continuous random variable, probabilities are assigned to intervals of values. Suppose we are interested in the probability distribution of life expectancy at birth of a randomly chosen male human being. This is a continuous random variable. In Chapter 2, we collected sample data on average life expectancy at birth of males in 40 countries and plotted a relative frequency histogram with equal intervals. We saw that *the total area under the relative frequency histogram equals the width of the class intervals*. If we divide the heights of the rectangles (scale) by the width (class interval), then the total area under the scaled relative frequency histogram will equal 1. Also, the area of each rectangle will equal the relative frequency of the class interval (proportion of the data values that fall into that class interval).

Suppose we plot a scaled relative frequency histogram using a very large sample of data (say, data on average life expectancy of males in various regions in different countries during different time periods) and a very small width of the class intervals. Then the area of each rectangle will be a good approximation of the true probability that the life expectancy of a randomly chosen male will be in that class interval. As we make the sample size larger and larger and the width of the class intervals smaller and smaller, the outline of the scaled relative frequency histogram (that is, the shape of the corresponding scaled relative frequency polygon) will converge to a shape that we call the **probability function** (or, simply, *probability curve*) of the random variable. (It is more commonly known as *probability density function since this concept is closely related to the concept of density in physics*.) The probability that the value of the random variable will lie in any specified interval will then equal the area under the probability function within that interval.

To illustrate this concept, we give scaled relative frequency histograms for simulated sample data on the heights of adult Canadian males. Chart 7-1(a) shows

CHART 7-1: Scaled Relative Frequency Histograms on the Heights of Adult Canadian Males (simulated sample data)

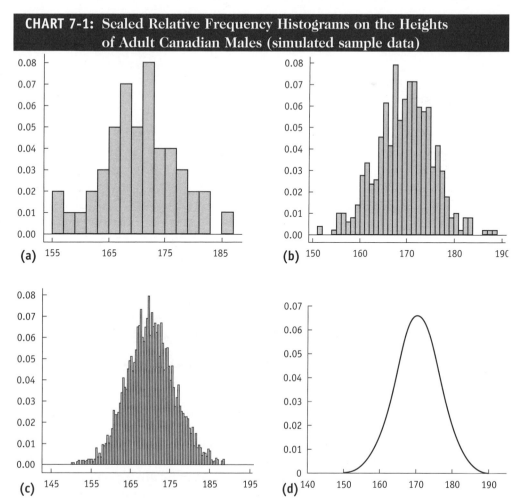

the scaled relative frequency histogram for simulated sample data of size 50 plotted using class intervals of width 2. Similarly, in Charts 7-1(b) and 7-1(c), we have used samples of sizes 500 and 5000 and class intervals of widths 1 and 0.4. Chart 7-1(d) shows the probability function, to which the shapes of scaled relative frequency histograms converge.

A probability function can have any shape, as long as (a) it is non-negative (that is, the curve is above the x-axis), and (b) the total area under the curve is 1.

Example 7-1   A study conducted by a bank has shown that the time (X) taken by its tellers to serve a customer lies in the range of 1 minute to 6 minutes with the probability function:

$$f(x) = 0.2 \text{ for } x \text{ between 1 and 6.}$$

For what fraction of customers is the service time between 2 and 5 minutes?

Solution   The plot of the probability function is shown in Chart 7-2.

CHART 7-2: Probability Function for Bank Customer Service

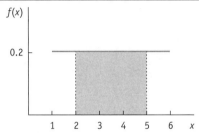

The height of the curve is $f(x) = 0.2$ for each value of x between 1 and 6. Thus, the curve is a horizontal line between $x = 1$ and $x = 6$ at a height of 0.2. The curve is above the x-axis and the total area under the curve is $0.2(6 - 1) = 1$. These are necessary conditions for the curve to be a valid probability function.

We want to find the fraction of customers for whom the service time is between 2 and 5 minutes. This is the area under the curve between 2 and 5 (shown as the shaded area in Chart 7-2) and is equal to $0.2(5 - 2) = 0.6$. Thus, for 60 percent of the customers the service time is between 2 and 5 minutes.

> **i**   Any **probability function** $f(x)$ must satisfy the following properties:
> - $f(x)$ must be non-negative (that is, the curve must be above the x-axis).
> - the total area under the curve must be 1.

■ SELF-REVIEW 7-1

A study has shown that the fuel efficiency (on the highway) of a certain line of compact cars is in the range between 7.2 L/100 km and 8 L/100 km. Suppose its probability function is as follows:

$$f(x) = 1.25 \text{ for } x \text{ between 7.2 and 8.}$$

(a) Plot the curve $f(x)$ and verify that it is a valid probability function.
(b) Find the probability that a randomly selected car of this model will have fuel efficiency (highway driving) in the range between 7.5 L/100 km and 7.8 L/100 km.

In Chapter 6 we saw formulae for calculating expected value and variance of a discrete random variable. The formulae for expected value and variance of a continuous random variable require a knowledge of calculus; we shall not discuss them in this book.

Continuous probability distributions are classified according to the shapes of the probability functions. For example, if the curve is just a horizontal line, as in the example above, then the probability distribution is called a *uniform distribution*. Unfortunately, such a simple case does not occur very often in nature. The distribution that is observed most commonly in nature is *normal distribution*. We shall now study normal distribution in detail.

7.2 NORMAL PROBABILITY DISTRIBUTION

Normal distribution plays a central role in the study of statistical inference. It has tremendous theoretical significance and it serves as a good approximation to an exceptionally large number of random variables that arise in practice, such as hourly wages of employees in a large company, student marks in a large class, percentage daily changes in the TSE 300 index, and errors made in measurement of physical and economic phenomena. In some cases, simple transformations of variables (such as logarithmic transformation) result in normal distribution.

There is not just one normal distribution, but rather a "family" of them. For each combination of values of mean μ and standard deviation σ we get a different normal distribution. Each normal probability function[2] (we shall sometimes call it simply *normal curve*) is defined for all values between $-\infty$ and ∞ and is fully described by its mean μ and standard deviation σ.

Charts 7-3(a, b) portray different normal distributions. There is one normal probability distribution for the lengths of service of the employees of a company's Vancouver plant, where the mean is 20 years and the standard deviation is 3.1 years. There is another normal probability distribution for the lengths of service in the company's Halifax plant, where $\mu = 20$ and $\sigma = 3.9$ years. Chart 7-3(a) portrays three distributions, where the means are the same but the standard deviations are different. Chart 7-3(b) shows the distribution of hourly wages of workers in two different companies. These have different means and standard deviations.

 A random variable that is normally distributed is called a **normal random variable.**

For any random variable X with mean μ and standard deviation σ, the *standardized random variable* is obtained by subtracting μ from it, and dividing by σ. That is,

CHART 7-3(a, b): Normal Probability Distributions with Different Values of Mean and Standard Deviation

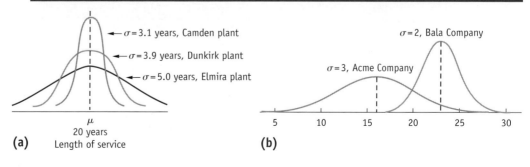

(a) μ 20 years Length of service

(b)

the standardized random variable of X is $\dfrac{(X - \mu)}{\sigma}$. The standardized random variable has mean 0 and standard deviation 1. Such standardization is often helpful when we have to compare two different random variables.

In the case of normal random variables, the process of standardization proves to be very useful. The family of normal random variables has the following properties. If X and Y are normal random variables, then

- Any non-zero multiple of X (such as $3X$ or $-5X$) is a normal random variable.
- If we add any constant to X (such as $X + 3$ or $X - 4$), we get a normal random variable.
- $X + Y$ is a normal random variable.

It follows from the above property that if X is a normal random variable with mean μ and standard deviation σ, then its standardized random variable $\dfrac{(X - \mu)}{\sigma}$ is also a normal random variable and is denoted by the letter Z. We call Z the *standard normal variable*.

 For any normal random variable X with mean μ and standard deviation σ, the standardized random variable $\dfrac{(X - \mu)}{\sigma} = z$ is a normal random variable with mean 0 and standard deviation 1 and is called the **standard normal variable.**

The normal curve corresponding to Z is called *standard normal curve* or *Z-curve* and is given by the equation[3]

Standard Normal Density Function	$f(z) = \dfrac{1}{\sqrt{2\pi}\, e^{z^2/2}}$	7-1

Recall that $\pi = 3.1415\ldots$ and $e = 2.71828\ldots$. Throughout the rest of this book *we shall use the letter Z to denote the standard normal variable.*

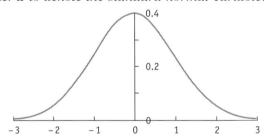

The Z-curve has the following characteristics:
- It has a unique peak at its mean, 0.
- The curve is symmetrical about its mean, 0.
- The curve is bell-shaped. As we move away from the central value 0 in either direction, the curve rapidly approaches but never touches the x-axis.

Since standardization of any normal random variable gives a standard normal variable Z, every normal random variable has the following characteristics.

CHARACTERISTICS OF NORMAL CURVE AND NORMAL RANDOM VARIABLE

- The normal curve is bell-shaped. It has a unique peak at the centre and the curve falls off smoothly in either direction from the central value. It is asymptotic, meaning that the curve gets closer and closer to the x-axis but never actually touches it. That is, the "tails" of the curve extend indefinitely in both directions.

CHART 7-4: Characteristics of a Normal Distribution

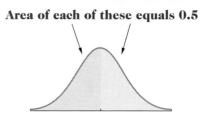

(a)

Normal curve is symmetrical
Two halves identical

Tail   Tail

Theoretically, curve extends to $-\infty$

Mean, median, and mode are equal

Theoretically, curve extends to $+\infty$

(b)

Area of each of these equals 0.5

- The curve is symmetrical about the central value. If we cut the curve vertically at its central value, the two halves are mirror images of each other. The central value is thus the arithmetic mean, μ, and it is also the median and mode of the distribution. The area under the curve to the right of the mean is half, and the area under the curve to the left of the mean is half.
- For any normal random variable X with mean μ and standard deviation σ, the standardized random variable $\dfrac{(X - \mu)}{\sigma}$ is Z (the standard normal variable).

These characteristics of the normal curve are shown in Charts 7-4(a, b).

COMPUTING PROBABILITIES FOR NORMAL PROBABILITY DISTRIBUTION

As we have seen, there is a family of normal distributions. For each combination of values of mean (μ) or standard deviation (σ), we get a different member of this family. The number of normal distributions is therefore unlimited. It would be physically impossible to provide a table of probabilities (such as for the binomial or Poisson) for each combination of values of μ and σ.

Fortunately, as we saw above, the family of normal distributions has the nice property that for any normal random variable X with mean μ and standard deviation σ, the standardized random variable $\dfrac{(X - \mu)}{\sigma}$ is Z, the standard normal variable (normal random variable with mean = 0 and standard deviation = 1). This property makes it possible to use the table of probabilities for Z to compute probabilities for any normal random variable. The table of probabilities for Z is given at the end of the book. We shall call it the Z table.

We shall now see how to use this table to find areas or probabilities under the Z curve. Then we shall see how to find probabilities for any normal random variable by converting it to Z.

COMPUTING PROBABILITIES UNDER THE *Z* CURVE

For any positive number z, the Z table gives the probability or area under the Z curve between its mean value (which is 0) and z. For example, suppose we want the probability that the value of Z lies between 0 and 1.91. Here, $z = 1.91$. In the Z table, go down the column of the table headed by z to 1.9. Then move horizontally to the right and read the probability under the column headed 0.01: it is 0.4719. So, the probability is 0.4719 that the value of Z lies between 0 and 1.91.

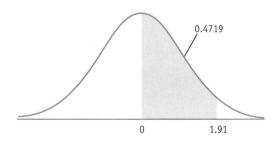

We give below probabilities that the value of Z lies between 0 and z for different z values.

z values	Area under the Z curve between 0 and z
2.84	0.4977
1.0	0.3413
0.49	0.1879
1.325	approx. 0.4074 (midway between 0.4066 and 0.4082)
3.5	approx. 0.5 (for z greater than 3.09, area between 0 and z is almost 0.5)

■ SELF-REVIEW 7-2

Find the probability that the value of Z lies between each of the following pairs of values:

    (a) Between 0 and 1.02.
    (b) Between 0 and 0.16.
    (c) Between 0 and 3.92.

Now let us see how to find probability between a negative z value and 0. Suppose we want to find the area under the Z curve between -2.05 and 0. Since the Z curve is symmetrical about zero, the area between -2.05 and 0 is the same as the area between 0 and 2.05. Using the Z table with $z = 2.05$, we get an area between 0 and 2.05 as 0.4798. Hence, the area between -2.05 and 0 is 0.4798.

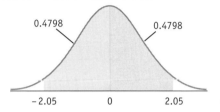

■ SELF-REVIEW 7-3

Find the area under the Z curve within each of the following intervals of values.

    (a) Between -1.37 and 0.
    (b) Between -4.02 and 0.

Suppose we want to find probability that the value of Z is more than 1.36. This is the same as the area under the Z curve to the right of 1.36:

(total area to the right of 0) – (area between 0 and 1.36)
= 0.5 – (value in the Z table corresponding to $z = 1.36$)
= 0.5 – 0.4131 = 0.0869

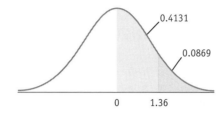

0.4131

0.0869

0   1.36

■ SELF-REVIEW 7-4

Find the area under the Z curve corresponding to each of the following values.
   (a) More than 2.04.
   (b) More than 4.01.
   (c) Less than −2.58.

Let us now see how to find the area under the Z curve between a negative z value and a positive z value. Let us compute the area between −0.98 and 2.12.

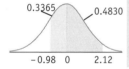

0.3365   0.4830

−0.98 0   2.12

Area between −0.98 and 2.12
   = (area between −0.98 and 0) + (area between 0 and 2.12)
   = (value corresponding to $z = 0.98$) + (value corresponding to $z = 2.12$)
   = 0.3365 + 0.4830 = 0.8195

■ SELF-REVIEW 7-5

Find the probability that the value of Z lies between each of the following pairs of values.
   (a) Between −2.16 and 0.48.
   (b) Between −1.72 and 3.64.
   (c) More than −1.63.

Finally, suppose we want to find the area between two positive values. As an example, suppose we want to find the area between 0.61 and 1.76.
   This is the same as

(area between 0 and 1.76) – (area between 0 and 0.61)
   = (value corresponding to $z = 1.76$) – (value corresponding to $z = 0.61$)
   = 0.4608 – 0.2291 = 0.2317

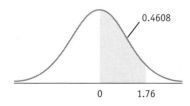

0.4608

0   1.76

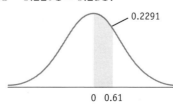

0.2291

0   0.61

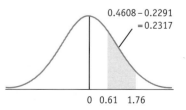

0.4608 − 0.2291
= 0.2317

0   0.61   1.76

■ SELF-REVIEW 7-6

Find the area under the Z curve for each of the following pairs of values.
- (a) Between 1.42 and 2.76.
- (b) Between −2.67 and −0.92.

COMPUTING INVERSE PROBABILITIES UNDER THE *Z* CURVE

Previous examples required finding the area under the Z curve between two given z values or the area to the left or right of a particular z value. In many real-world applications, we are required to find the value of z when a corresponding area under the Z curve is given.

For example, suppose we want to find the value of z such that the area under the Z curve between 0 and z is 0.291.

In the Z table, look for the area of 0.291. From the number 0.291, go horizontally to the left to the column headed by the letter z. This gives us 0.8. Also from the number 0.291, go vertically to the top. This gives us number 0.01. These two together give us a z value of $0.8 + 0.01 = 0.81$.

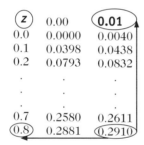
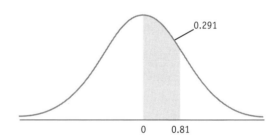

Suppose we want the z value such that the area under the Z curve to the left of it is 0.04.

Since the total area to the left of 0 is 0.5, the required z value must be to the left of 0 (that is, it must be a negative number), and the area between the z value and 0 is $(0.5 - 0.04) = 0.46$. Using the Z table, locate the area of 0.46. Because we do not have this exact number in the table, locate the two areas in the table closest to 0.46. These are 0.4599 and 0.4608. From number 0.4599, go horizontally to the left and vertically to the top to get a z value of $(1.7 + 0.05) = 1.75$. Similarly, the z value corresponding to an area of 0.4608 is 1.76.

Hence, the required z value is between 1.75 and 1.76. Since 0.46 is much closer to 0.4599 than to 0.4608, the z value corresponding to an area of 0.46 must be much closer to 1.75 than to 1.76. Let us approximate it by 1.751. Since the required z value is negative, it must be −1.751.

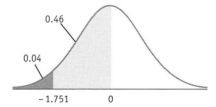

Find the z value such that the area under the Z curve to the right of it is 0.291.

■ SELF-REVIEW 7-7

Find the z value such that the area under the z curve to the right of it is 0.291.

EXERCISES 7-1 TO 7-8

7-1. List the essential properties of a probability function.

7-2. Janet lives in a suburb of Toronto. She has observed that the driving time from her home to her office in downtown Toronto during the morning rush is between 40 minutes and 60 minutes, with probability function $f(x) = 0.05$ for x between 40 and 60. Her office hours are 9:30 a.m. to 5:30 p.m.
   (a) If she starts from her home at 8:45 a.m., what is the probability that she will reach her office on time?
   (b) If she wants to make sure that she reaches her office on time at least 80 percent of the time, when should she start from her home?

7-3. Explain the meaning of the statement, "There is not just one normal probability distribution but a 'family' of them."

7-4. List and discuss the major characteristics of a normal probability distribution. Plot the Z curve. Does it satisfy the required characteristics?

7-5. Using the Z table, find the area under the Z curve corresponding to each of the following values.
   (a) Between -0.36 and 1.82.
   (b) Between 1.47 and 2.71.
   (c) Between 0 and 1.51.
   (d) More than 1.94.
   (e) More than -0.82.

7-6. Using the Z table, find the area under the Z curve corresponding to each of the following values.
   (a) Less than -2.35.
   (b) Equal to 1.82.
   (c) Between -4.03 and -1.35.
   (d) Between -2.37 and 0.
   (e) Between -3.89 and 2.47.
   (f) Between -3.46 and 3.76.

7-7. Using the Z table, find the z value corresponding to each of the following.
   (a) Area to the right of the z value is 0.025.
   (b) Area to the left of the z value is 0.95.
   (c) Area between 0 and the z value is 0.4.

7-8. Using the Z table, find the z value corresponding to each of the following.
   (a) Area between -1.62 and z is 0.3.
   (b) Area between z and 1.46 is 0.46.
   (c) Area between z and 2.06 is 0.2.

COMPUTING PROBABILITIES UNDER AN ARBITRARY NORMAL CURVE

We have seen how to find probabilities for standard normal variable Z using the Z table. Recall that Z is a normal random variable with mean 0 and standard deviation 1.

CHART 7-5: Relationship between *x* values and Corresponding *z* values

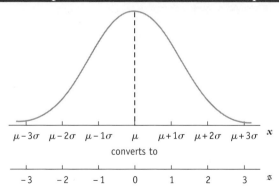

Most of the normal random variables encountered in the real world, however, have a mean other than 0 and a standard deviation other than 1. Luckily, as we saw before, the standardization of any normal random variable X gives us the standard normal variable Z. That is, if X is a normal random variable with mean μ and standard deviation σ, then,

$$\left(\frac{X - \mu}{\sigma}\right) = Z, \text{ and therefore, } \quad X = \mu + Z\sigma \qquad \textbf{7-2}$$

For example, $x = \mu + 1\sigma$ converts to $z = 1.0$. Likewise, $x - \mu - 2\sigma$ converts to $z = -2.0$; $x = \mu \ (= \mu + 0\sigma)$ converts to $z = 0$; $x = \mu - 1.6\sigma$ converts to $z = -1.6$; $z = 2.4$ converts to $x = \mu + 2.4\sigma$.

A value of Z thus indicates how many standard deviations the corresponding value of X is from its mean μ. For $z = 1.0$, the corresponding $x \ (= \mu + 1\sigma)$ is one standard deviation from μ. For $z = -2.0$, the corresponding $x \ (= \mu - 2\sigma)$ is -2.0 standard deviations away from μ.

The relationship between values of X and Z, given by Formula 7-2, implies the following:

> As long as a value of X is k standard deviations away from the value of μ, the corresponding value of Z is k, regardless of the values of μ and σ. The probability corresponding to this value of X can be obtained from the Z table using $z = k$. The probability is therefore the same, no matter what the values of μ and σ are.

This relationship is shown in Chart 7-5 above.

Example 7-2

Analysis of data from January 1980 to December 1999 shows that the percentage monthly change in the TSE 300 index is approximately normally distributed, with a mean of 0.64 percent and a standard deviation of 2.06 percent. What is the z value corresponding to a monthly change of 3 percent? Corresponding to a monthly change of 6 percent?

Solution

Here, $\mu = 0.64$ and $\sigma = 2.06$.

Using Formula 7-2, the z value corresponding to $x = 3$ is $z = \dfrac{(3 - 0.64)}{2.06}$

= approximately 1.145. Thus, $x = 3$ is approximately 1.145 standard deviations away from the value of μ, or $x \approx \mu + (1.145)\sigma$.

The z value corresponding to $x = 6$ is $z = \dfrac{(6 - 0.64)}{2.06}$ = approximately 2.602. That is, $x = 6$ is approximately 2.602 standard deviations away from the value of μ, or $x \approx \mu + (2.602)\sigma$.

■ SELF-REVIEW 7-8

Analysis of data from 1915 to 2000 shows that the percentage annual change in the consumer price index (CPI; all items) in Canada is approximately normally distributed with a mean of 3.36 and a standard deviation of 5.1. What is the z value corresponding to a percentage annual change of 1.0? Corresponding to a percentage annual change of 8.0?

We shall now use the conversion process to calculate the probabilities for any normal random variable using the Z table in Appendix 3 on the CD-ROM.

Example 7-3

In Example 7-2, we reported that the percentage monthly change in the TSE 300 index is approximately normally distributed with a mean of 0.64 percent and a standard deviation of 2.06 percent.

 (a) What is the probability that the percentage change during an arbitrarily selected month will be between 3 and 6 percent?
 (b) What is the probability that the percentage change during an arbitrarily selected month will be between 0 and 4 percent?

Solution

 (a) Here, $\mu = 0.64$ and $\sigma = 2.06$. We have already found in Example 7-2 that the z value corresponding to $x = 3$ is approximately 1.145; the z value corresponding to $x = 6$ is approximately 2.602.

  The probability under the normal curve (with $\mu = 0.64$ and $\sigma = 2.06$) between 3 and 6 equals, approximately, the area under the Z curve between 1.145 and 2.602 = (area between 0 and 2.602) − (area between 0 and 1.145) = 0.4953 − 0.3739 = 0.1214.

  The probability that the percentage change during an arbitrarily selected month will be between 3 and 6 percent is approximately 0.1214.

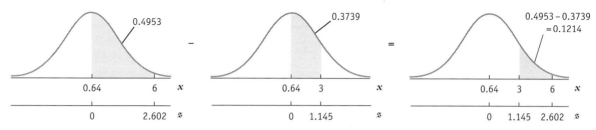

 (b) The z value corresponding to $x = 0$ is $\dfrac{(0 - 0.64)}{2.06} = -0.31$ and the z value corresponding to $x = 4$ is $\dfrac{(4 - 0.64)}{2.06} = 1.63$.

  The probability under the normal curve with ($\mu = 0.64$ and $\sigma = 2.06$) between 0 and 4 equals area under the Z curve between -0.31 and 1.63 = (area between -0.31 and 0) + (area between 0 and 1.63) = (area between 0 and 0.31) + (area between 0 and 1.63) = 0.1217 + 0.4484 = 0.5701.

Hence, the probability that the percentage change during an arbitrarily selected month will be between 0 and 4 percent is approximately 0.5701.

HOW TO FIND NORMAL PROBABILITIES USING COMPUTER SOFTWARE

Below are instructions on how to use Excel and Minitab to find probabilities for an arbitrary normal random variable X with mean, μ, and standard deviation, σ. For any given number x, each of these software packages outputs the entire area under the normal curve of X to the left of the value x (and not just the area between the mean μ and x).

Let us consider Example 7-3 above. Here, $\mu = 0.64$, $\sigma = 2.06$, and we are interested in the area under the normal curve between 3 and 6.

The value obtained from the computer output corresponding to $x = 6$ is 0.995365 and the value corresponding to $x = 3$ is 0.874026. Thus, the area under the normal curve of X to the left of 6 is 0.995365 and the area to the left of 3 is 0.874026.

Hence, the area between 3 and 6 is $(0.995365 - 0.874026) = 0.121339$. Note that this is very close to the number obtained in our hand calculation using the Z table. The small difference is due to rounding error.

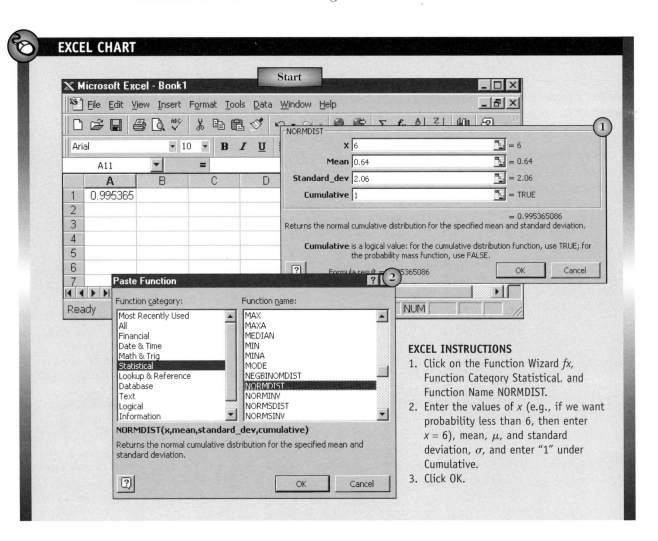

EXCEL CHART

EXCEL INSTRUCTIONS
1. Click on the Function Wizard *fx*, Function Category Statistical, and Function Name NORMDIST.
2. Enter the values of *x* (e.g., if we want probability less than 6, then enter *x* = 6), mean, μ, and standard deviation, σ, and enter "1" under Cumulative.
3. Click OK.

MINITAB CHART

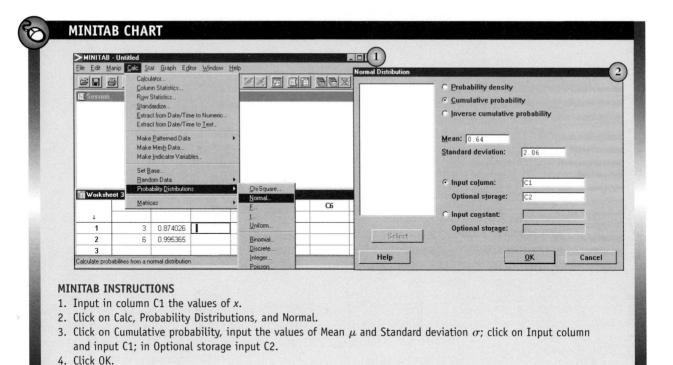

MINITAB INSTRUCTIONS

1. Input in column C1 the values of x.
2. Click on Calc, Probability Distributions, and Normal.
3. Click on Cumulative probability, input the values of Mean μ and Standard deviation σ; click on Input column and input C1; in Optional storage input C2.
4. Click OK.

■ SELF-REVIEW 7-9

Let us continue with the problem in Self-Review 7-7. Thus, the percentage annual change in the consumer price index (CPI; all items) in Canada is approximately normally distributed with a mean of 3.36 and a standard deviation of 5.1. What is the probability that the percentage change during any randomly selected year will be between 1.0 and 8.0?

SOME IMPORTANT AREAS UNDER THE NORMAL CURVE

Below are some areas under the Z curve that will be used extensively in the rest of the book.

- Area between -1 and $+1$ is $0.3413 + 0.3413 = 0.6826$ = approximately 68 percent.
- Area between -1.645 and $+1.645$ is $0.45 + 0.45 = 0.9$, or 90 percent.
- Area between -1.96 and $+1.96$ is $0.475 + 0.475 = 0.95$, or 95 percent.
- Area between -2 and $+2$ is $0.4772 + 0.4772 = 0.9544$ = approximately 95 percent.
- Area between -3 and $+3$ is $0.4987 + 0.4987 = 0.9974$ = practically all of the area.

Using the conversion in Formula 7-2, we get the following areas for an arbitrary normal distribution with mean μ and standard deviation σ.

- Area between $(\mu - 1\sigma)$ and $(\mu + 1\sigma)$ is $0.3413 + 0.3413$ = approximately 68 percent.
- Area between $(\mu - 1.645\sigma)$ and $(\mu + 1.645\sigma)$ is 0.9 or 90 percent.
- Area between $(\mu - 1.96\sigma)$ and $(\mu + 1.96\sigma)$ is 0.95 or 95 percent.
- Area between $(\mu - 2\sigma)$ and $(\mu + 2\sigma)$ is 0.9544 = approximately 95 percent.
- Area between $(\mu - 3\sigma)$ and $(\mu + 3\sigma)$ is 0.9974 = practically all the area.

We show these probabilities diagrammatically below.

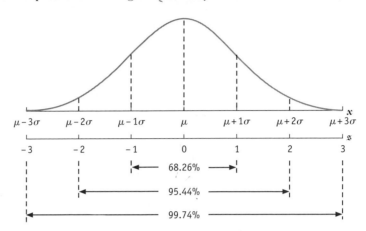

Example 7-4

The bottling machine used by a soft-drink bottling company to put 360 mL of soft drink into bottles has a standard deviation of 2 mL; that is, the volume of the liquid in the filled bottle has a mean of 360 mL and a standard deviation of 2 mL. Assume that the distribution is approximately normal. As per the management policy, bottles containing less than 358 mL are declared underfilled and are discarded; bottles containing more than 362 mL are declared dangerously overfilled and are discarded. What fraction of the bottles are discarded?

Solution

Here, $\mu = 360$ mL, and $\sigma = 2$ mL.

The fraction of bottles that are *not* discarded is the area under the corresponding normal curve between 358 and 362.

The z value corresponding to $x = 358$ is $(358 - 360)/2 = -1$ and the z value corresponding to $x = 362$ is $(362 - 360)/2 = +1$. Hence, $358 = (\mu - 1\sigma)$ and $362 = (\mu + 1\sigma)$. Therefore, the area between 358 and 362 equals the area between $(\mu - 1\sigma)$ and $(\mu + 1\sigma)$, which equals 0.6826.

The fraction of the filled bottles that are not discarded is thus 0.6826. All the remaining filled bottles are discarded. So, the fraction of the filled bottles that are discarded is $1 - 0.6826 = 0.3174$.

EXERCISES 7-9 TO 7-19

7-9.   The mean of a normal distribution is 60; the standard deviation is 5.
   (a) About what fraction of the observations lie between 55 and 65?
   (b) About what fraction of the observations lie between 50 and 70?
   (c) About what fraction of the observations lie between 45 and 75?

7-10. A normal population has a mean of 20.0 and a standard deviation of 4.0.
   (a) Compute the z values associated with 18.0, 20.0, and 25.0.
   (b) What proportion of the population is between 20.0 and 25.0?
   (c) What proportion of the population is less than 18.0?

7-11. A normal population has a mean of 12.2 and a standard deviation of 2.5.
   (a) Compute the z values associated with 10.0 and 14.3.
   (b) What proportion of the population is between 12.2 and 14.3?
   (c) What proportion of the population is less than 10.0?

7-12. A recent study of the hourly wages of maintenance crews for major airlines showed that the distribution of hourly wages is approximately normal with a mean of $22.00 and a standard deviation of $4.00. If we select a crew member at random, what is the probability the crew member earns:
   (a) between $22.00 and $26.00 per hour?
   (b) more than $26.00 per hour?
   (c) less than $20.00 per hour?

7-13. The mean of a normal distribution is 400 kg. The standard deviation is 10 kg.
   (a) What is the area between 415 kg and the mean of 400 kg?
   (b) What is the area between the mean and 395 kg?
   (c) What is the probability that an observation, randomly selected from this distribution, will have a value less than 395 kg?

7-14. A normal distribution has a mean of 50 and a standard deviation of 4.
   (a) Compute the probability of a value between 44.0 and 55.0.
   (b) Compute the probability of a value greater than 55.0.
   (c) Compute the probability of a value between 52.0 and 55.0.

7-15. A normal population has a mean of 80.0 and a standard deviation of 14.0.
   (a) Compute the probability of a value between 75.0 and 90.0.
   (b) Compute the probability of a value 75.0 or less.
   (c) Compute the probability of a value between 55.0 and 70.0.

7-16. CNAE, an all-news AM radio station, finds that the distribution of the lengths of time listeners are tuned to the station follows the normal distribution. The mean of the distribution is 15.0 minutes and the standard deviation is 3.5 minutes. What is the probability that a particular listener will tune in:
   (a) for more than 20 minutes?
   (b) for 20 minutes or less?
   (c) between 10 and 12 minutes?

7-17. According to reports, the mean starting salary for college graduates in the spring of 2003 was $36 280. Assume that the distribution of starting salaries follows the normal distribution with a standard deviation of $3300. What percentage of the graduates has starting salaries:
   (a) between $35 000 and $40 000?
   (b) more than $45 000?
   (c) between $40 000 and $45 000?

7-18. One measure of the quality of customer service is the amount of time a random customer has to wait for service. A bank manager has observed that the amount of time a random customer has to wait to be served at the bank's ATM during peak business hours is approximately normally distributed with a mean of 2.3 minutes and a standard deviation of 0.8 minutes. What is the probability that a randomly chosen customer will have to wait for more than 4 minutes during peak business hours?

7-19. A cola-dispensing machine is set to dispense on average 250 mL of cola per cup. The standard deviation is 4 mL. The distribution of the amounts dispensed follows a normal distribution.

(a) What is the probability that the machine will dispense between 253 mL and 258 mL of cola?

(b) What is the probability that the machine will dispense 260 mL of cola or more?

(c) What is the probability that a machine will dispense between 245 and 255 mL of cola?

COMPUTING INVERSE PROBABILITIES UNDER AN ARBITRARY NORMAL CURVE

The previous examples involved finding the probability corresponding to a given interval of values of a normal random variable. We shall now look at examples that involve finding the value of a normal random variable when the corresponding probability is given.

Let us reconsider Example 7-4. The specification (358, 362) here is often written as (360 − 2, 360 + 2) or (360 ± 2). Suppose the production manager is considering changing this specification to (360 ± a), and she would like to know for what value of a only 5 percent of the filled bottles will be discarded (that is, 95 percent of the bottles *will not* be discarded). We know that the area under the normal curve between $(\mu - 1.96\sigma)$ and $(\mu + 1.96\sigma)$ is 0.95. Hence, a should equal $1.96\sigma = 1.96\,(2) = 3.92$.

As another example, suppose a tire manufacturer wishes to set a minimum mileage guarantee on its new MX100 tire. Tests reveal the mean lifetime of its tires is 108 000 km with a standard deviation of 3280 km. The manufacturer wants to set the minimum lifetime guarantee so that no more than 4 percent of the tires will have to be replaced. What minimum guarantee should the manufacturer announce?

Here, $\mu = 108\,000$ and $\sigma = 3280$, and we want to find a value x such that the fraction of tires with a lifetime less than x is 0.04. That is, we want the area under the normal curve to the left of x to be 0.04. The facts of this problem are shown in the following diagram, where the relationship between x and its corresponding z value is given by

$$z = \frac{(x - \mu)}{\sigma} \quad \text{and} \quad x = (\mu + z\sigma) = 108\,000 + z(3280)$$

We want the area under the Z curve to the left of the z value to be 0.04.

The total area under the Z curve to the left of 0 is 0.5. Hence, the desired z value is to the left of 0 (that is, it is negative) and the area under the Z curve between z and 0 is $(0.5 - 0.04) = 0.46$.

Look in the Z table for an area closest to 0.46. The closest area is 0.4599. Move to the margins from this value to read the z value of 1.75. Because our z value is to the left of 0, we choose − 1.75.

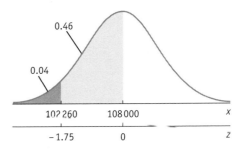

Thus, the desired z value is close to − 1.75. (We cannot find the exact z value from the table because the probability 0.46 does not appear in the table.) We chose an appropriate value of − 1.751.

Hence, the value of x is approximately

$$x = (\mu + z\sigma) = 108\,000 + (-1.751)(3280) = 102\,257$$

So, the manufacturer can advertise free tire replacement for any tire that wears out before it reaches 102 257 km and the company will know that, in the long run, only about 4 percent of the tires will be replaced under the plan.

Both Excel and Minitab can be used to find the value of any normal random variable when the entire probability to the left of this value is specified. The instructions for each package are provided below.

EXCEL INSTRUCTIONS
1. Click on the Function Wizard *fx*, Function Category Statistical, and Function Name NORMINV.
2. Enter the values of probability (e.g., if we want probability to the left of *x* to be 0.2, then enter 0.2), mean, and standard deviation.
3. Click OK.

MINITAB INSTRUCTIONS
1. Input in column C1 the values of *x*.
2. Click on Calc, Probability Distributions, and Normal.
3. Click on Inverse Cumulative Probability, input the values of mean and standard deviation; click on Input Column and input C1; in Optional Storage input C2.
4. Click OK.

■ SELF-REVIEW 7-10

An analysis of the total student marks in the Quantitative Analysis I ADM2623 class at the University of New Brunswick reveals that the marks were approximately normally distributed, with a mean of 59.27 and a standard deviation of 14.34. If only 5 students out of the total of 84 received a grade of A or above, what must have been the cut-off point for a grade of A or above?

EXERCISES 7-20 TO 7-25

7-20. A normal distribution has a mean of 50 and a standard deviation of 4. Determine the value below which 95 percent of the observations will occur.

7-21. A normal distribution has a mean of 80 and a standard deviation of 14. Determine the value above which 80 percent of the values will occur.

7-22. Refer to Exercise 7-19, where the amounts dispensed by a cola machine follow the normal distribution, with a mean of 250 mL and a standard deviation of 4 mL per cup. Find a value such that in only 1 percent of cases the amount of cola dispensed exceeds this value.

7-23. Assume that the mean hourly cost to operate a commercial airplane follows the normal distribution with a mean of $3100 per hour and a standard deviation of $250. What is the operating cost for the lowest 3 percent of the airplanes?

7-24. The monthly sales of Ridus mufflers in Vancouver follows the normal distribution with a mean of 1200 and a standard deviation of 225. The Ridus outlet has decided to replenish the stock at the beginning of every month so that there is only a 5-percent chance of running out of stock. What should be the stock level at the beginning of the month?

7-25. The bottling machine used by a soft-drink bottling company to fill 360 mL of soft drink into bottles has a standard deviation of 3 mL. As per management policy, bottles containing less than 357 mL are declared under-filled and are discarded. Also, bottles containing more than 363 mL are declared dangerously overfilled and are discarded. The machine fills 1000 bottles per day.

(a) Approximately how many bottles are discarded per day?

(b) The management wants to change the lower limit of the acceptance range (357 mL) to reduce the rejection rate to 20 percent. What should be the new lower limit?

(c) The management has decided to replace the bottling machine to bring down the rejection rate of bottles to less than 20 percent while maintaining the current range (357 mL, 363 mL) of acceptance. What should be the standard deviation of the new machine?

7.3   THE NORMAL APPROXIMATION TO THE BINOMIAL

STATISTICS IN ACTION

Normal Distribution and Individual Skill

An individual's skills depend on a combination of many hereditary and environmental factors, each having about the same amount of weight or influence on the skills. Thus, much like a binomial distribution with a large number of trials, many skills and attributes follow the normal distribution. For example, scores on the Scholastic Aptitude Test (SAT) are normally distributed with a mean of 1000 and a standard deviation of 140.

When to use the normal approximation

Chapter 6 describes the binomial probability distribution, which is a discrete distribution. The tables of binomial probabilities in Appendix A go up to $n = 25$. If a real-world problem involved a binomial distribution with $n = 600$, generating the binomial probabilities corresponding to such a large value of n would be very time-consuming. A more efficient approach is to apply the *normal approximation to the binomial.*

Using a normal distribution (a continuous distribution) as a substitute for a binomial distribution (a discrete distribution) with a large value of n seems reasonable because as n increases, the shape of the binomial distribution gets closer and closer to the shape of a normal distribution. Chart 7-6 depicts the change in the shape of a binomial distribution with $p = 0.50$ from $n = 1$, to $n = 3$, to $n = 20$. Notice how the case where $n = 20$ approximates the shape of the normal distribution. That is, compare the case where $n = 20$ to the normal curve in Chart 7-3.

When is the normal distribution a good approximation to the binomial distribution? As per Cochran,[4] for $p = 0.5$, n should be at least 30; for $p = 0.3$, n should be at least 80; for $p = 0.05$, n should be as high as 1400. However, many statisticians agree that the following is adequate for most business and economics applications: "*n should be such that both np and n(1 – p) are at least 5.*"

Before we apply the normal approximation, we must make sure that our distribution of interest is in fact a binomial distribution. Recall from Chapter 6 that four criteria must be met:

- There are only two mutually exclusive outcomes to each trial: a "success" and a "failure."

- The distribution results from counting the number of successes in a fixed number of trials.

- The trials are independent of each other.

- The probability, p, remains the same from trial to trial.

To show the application of the normal approximation to the binomial distribution, let us consider the following example. The questionnaire survey continues to be an important tool for market research and analysis. As we shall see in the next chapter, a factor that significantly affects the statistical quality of the data collected using a questionnaire survey is a non-response error. This occurs when some of the

CHART 7-6: Binomial Distributions for an n of 1, 3, and 20, where $p = 0.50$

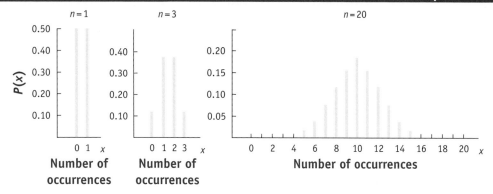

individuals selected to be in the sample refuse to respond to the questionnaire. Suppose it is known that the probability of a non-response is 0.3 (that is, there is a 30-percent chance that a randomly chosen individual will refuse to respond to the questionnaire). If a questionnaire is mailed to 80 randomly chosen individuals, what is the probability that at least 60 of them will respond?

Notice the binomial conditions are met: (1) there are only two possible outcomes—an individual in the sample chosen will either respond (*a success*) or will not respond (*a failure*); (2) we are counting the number of successes—that is, the total number of individuals out of the fixed total number, 80, who will respond; (3) the trials are independent of each other, meaning that if the 34th individual responds, that has no effect on whether the 58th individual will respond; and (4) the probability of an individual responding remains at 0.7 for each of the 80 selected individuals.

Therefore, we could use the binomial Formula 7-3:

$$P(x) = {}_nC_x(p)^x(1-p)^{n-x} \qquad \text{7-3}$$

To find the probability that 60 or more individuals will respond, we need to first find the probabilities $P(X = 60)$, $P(X = 61)$, ... , $P(X = 80)$, using the binomial formula, and add all of these probabilities.

Solving the above problem in this manner is tedious. We can also use a computer software package such as Minitab or Excel to find the various probabilities. Listed below are the binomial probabilities for $n = 80$, $p = 0.70$, and x, the number of individuals who will respond, ranging from 43 to 68. The probability of any number of individuals less than 43 or more than 68 responding is less than 0.001.

Number Responding	Probability	Number Responding	Probability	Number Responding	Probability
43	0.001	52	0.059	61	0.048
44	0.002	53	0.072	62	0.034
45	0.003	54	0.084	63	0.023
46	0.006	55	0.093	64	0.014
47	0.009	56	0.097	65	0.008
48	0.015	57	0.095	66	0.004
49	0.023	58	0.088	67	0.002
50	0.033	59	0.077	68	0.001
51	0.045	60	0.063		

We can find the probability of 60 or more responses by summing $0.063 + 0.048 + \cdots + 0.001$, which is 0.197.

However, in this case, $np = 80(0.7) = 56$ (more than 5) and $n(1 - p) = 80(0.3) = 24$ (more than 5). Hence, the shape of this binomial distribution is close to the shape of the normal distribution. A look at the plot below confirms this. All we need to do is smooth out the discrete probabilities into a continuous distribution. Working with a normal distribution will involve far fewer calculations than working with the binomial.

The trick is to approximate the discrete probability for 56 responses by the area under the continuous curve between 55.5 and 56.5, then approximate the probability for 57 responses by the area between 56.5 and 57.5, and so on. This is just the opposite of rounding off the numbers to a whole number. The probability of 60 or more responses can thus be approximated by the area to the right of 59.5.

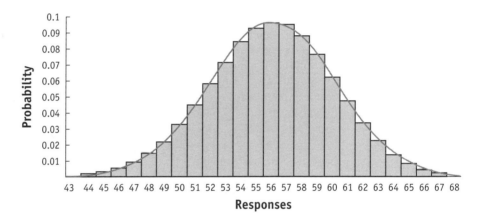

Because we use the normal distribution to determine the binomial probability of 60 or more successes, we must subtract, in this case, 0.5 from 60. The value 0.5 is called the **continuity correction factor**. This small adjustment must be made because a continuous distribution (the normal distribution) is being used to approximate a discrete distribution (the binomial distribution).

> **Continuity Correction Factor**   The value 0.5 subtracted or added, depending on the question, to a selected value when a discrete probability distribution is approximated by a continuous probability distribution.

HOW TO APPLY THE CORRECTION FACTOR

The different cases that may arise are described in this section. For any values x_1 and x_2 between 0 and n, with x_1 less than or equal to x_2, for the probability that number of successes is between x_1 and x_2 (including x_1 and x_2), use the area under the normal curve between $(x_1 - 0.5)$ and $(x_2 + 0.5)$. Except in the following cases:

- If $x_1 = 0$, then use $-\infty$ in the place of $(x_1 - 0.5)$.
- If $x_2 = n$, then use $+\infty$ in the place of $(x_2 + 0.5)$.

We shall illustrate this with examples for $n = 20$.

Set of Successes	x_1	x_2	Area under Normal Curve
Exactly 9 successes	9	9	between 8.5 and 9.5
6 or fewer successes	0	6	to the left of 6.5
Fewer than 6 successes (that is, $\{0, 1, \ldots, 5\}$)	0	5	to the left of 5.5
At least 17 successes (that is, $\{17, 18, 19, 20\}$)	17	20	to the right of 16.5
More than 6 but no more than 9 successes (that is $\{7, 8, 9\}$)	7	9	between 6.5 and 9.5
At least 8 but no more than 10 successes (that is, $\{8, 9, 10\}$)	8	10	between 7.5 and 10.5

To use the normal distribution to approximate the probability that 60 or more individuals in a sample of 80 will respond, follow the procedure shown below.

Step 1 Find the z value corresponding to an x of 59.5 using Formula 7-2, and the mean and the standard deviation of a binomial distribution:

$$\mu = np = 80(0.70) = 56$$

$$\sigma = \sqrt{np(1-p)} = \sqrt{80(0.70)(1-0.70)} = 4.10$$

$$z = \frac{x - \mu}{\sigma} = \frac{59.5 - 56}{4.10} = 0.85$$

Step 2 We want the probability under the normal curve with ($\mu = 56$ and $\sigma = 4.10$) to the right of 59.5. This equals the area under the Z curve to the right of $0.85 = 0.5 -$ (area under the Z curve between 0 and 0.85) $= 0.5 - 0.3023 = 0.1977$.

Thus, 0.1977 is the approximate probability that 60 or more individuals in the sample size of 80 will respond to the questionnaire.

No doubt you will agree that using the normal approximation to the binomial is a more efficient method of obtaining an approximate value of the probability of 60 or more individuals responding. The result compares favourably with that computed on pages 293 and 294 using the exact distribution. The probability using the binomial distribution is 0.197, whereas the probability using the normal approximation is 0.1977.

■ SELF-REVIEW 7-11

A study has revealed that none of the stolen goods are recovered by the homeowners in 80 percent of reported thefts. A sample of 200 theft cases was randomly selected.

  (a) What is the probability that no stolen goods were recovered in 170 or more of the robberies?
  (b) What is the probability that no stolen goods were recovered in 150 or more of the robberies?

EXERCISES 7-26 TO 7-32

7-26. Assume a binomial probability distribution with $n = 50$ and $p = 0.25$. Compute the following:
   (a) The mean and standard deviation of the random variable.
   (b) The probability that X is 15 or more.
   (c) The probability that X is 10 or less.

7-27. Assume a binomial probability distribution with $n = 40$ and $p = 0.55$. Compute the following:
   (a) The mean and standard deviation of the random variable.
   (b) The probability that X is 25 or greater.
   (c) The probability that X is 15 or less.
   (d) The probability that X is between 15 and 25 inclusive.

7-28. Dottie's Tax Service specializes in preparing federal tax returns for professional clients, such as physicians, dentists, accountants, and lawyers. A recent audit by Canada Customs and Revenue Agency of the returns she prepared, indicated that an error was made on 10 percent of the returns she prepared last year. Assuming the same rate continues into this year and she prepares 60 returns, what is the probability that she makes:
   (a) more than six errors?
   (b) at least five errors?
   (c) exactly six errors?

7-29. Express Muffler advertises they can install a new muffler in 30 minutes or less. However, the work standards department at corporate headquarters recently conducted a study and found that 20 percent of the mufflers were not installed in 30 minutes or less. The Montreal branch installed 50 mufflers last month. If the corporate report is correct,
   (a) how many of the installations at the Montreal branch would you expect to take more than 30 minutes?
   (b) what is the likelihood that fewer than 8 installations took more than 30 minutes?
   (c) what is the likelihood that 8 or fewer installations took more than 30 minutes?
   (d) what is the likelihood that exactly 8 of the 50 installations took more than 30 minutes?

7-30. A study conducted by the Holistic Health Club revealed that 30 percent of its new members are significantly overweight. A membership drive in a metropolitan area resulted in 500 new members.
   (a) It has been suggested that the normal approximation to the binomial be used to determine the probability that 175 or more of the new members are significantly overweight. Does this problem qualify as a binomial problem? Explain.
   (b) What is the probability that 175 or more new members are overweight?
   (c) What is the probability that 140 or more new members are significantly overweight?

7-31. Research on first-time young offenders revealed that 38 percent of them went on to commit another crime.
 (a) What is the probability that of the last 100 new young offenders put on probation, 30 or more will commit another crime?
 (b) What is the probability that 40 or fewer of the young offenders will commit another crime?
 (c) What is the probability that between 30 and 40 of the young offenders (including 30 and 40) will commit another crime?

7-32. According to a telephone survey of primary household grocery shoppers conducted by ACNielsen Canada, out of every 10 retail transactions, cash was used in 6, debit cards were used in 3, and credit cards were used in 1. What is the probability that out of 30 randomly selected transactions at a certain grocery store, a debit card will be used in more than 15 of them?

◼▬ CHAPTER OUTLINE

I. A continuous random variable is one that can assume any value within some interval or a collection of intervals.

II. For a continuous random variable,
 A. The probability that the variable will assume any particular value is zero.
 B. Probabilities are defined for intervals of values. For any interval of values, probability equals the corresponding area under a curve, which we call *probability function*. (It is more commonly known as *probability density function*.)

III. Any probability function must satisfy the following properties:
 A. It must be non-negative (that is, the curve must be above the x-axis).
 B. The total area under the curve must be 1.

IV. Normal distribution is a continuous probability distribution.
 A. It is completely described by its mean and standard deviation.
 B. There is a family of normal distributions. Each time the mean or standard deviation changes, a new distribution is created.

V. The normal probability function (normal curve) has the following characteristics:
 A. It is bell-shaped. It has a unique peak at the centre and the curve falls off smoothly in either direction from the central value. It is asymptotic, meaning that the curve gets closer and closer to the x-axis but never actually touches it.
 B. It is symmetrical about the central value, which is the arithmetic mean, median, and mode of the distribution.

VI. The standard normal distribution is a particular normal distribution.
 A. It has a mean of 0.00 and a standard deviation of 1.00.

VII. Any normal distribution can be converted to the standard normal distribution by the following formula.

$$Z = \frac{X - \mu}{\sigma}$$

7-2

VIII. By standardizing a normal distribution, we can report the distance from the mean in units of the standard deviation.

IX. The normal distribution can approximate a binomial distribution under certain conditions:
A. np and $n(1 - p)$ must both be at least 5, where n is the number of trials, and p is the probability of a success.

X. The continuity correction factor of 0.5 is used to extend the continuous value of X one-half unit in either direction. This correction compensates for approximately a discrete distribution by a continuous distribution.

CHAPTER EXERCISES 7-33 TO 7-66

7-33. The net sales and the number of employees for aluminum fabricators with similar characteristics are organized into frequency distributions. Both are normally distributed. For the net sales, the mean is $180 million and the standard deviation is $25 million. For the number of employees, the mean is 1500 and the standard deviation is 120. Interline Inc. had sales of $170 million and 1850 employees.
(a) Convert Interline's sales and number of employees to z values.
(b) Compare Interline's sales and number of employees with those of the other fabricators.

7-34. The accounting department at Barnby Materials Inc., a manufacturer of unattached garages, reports that it takes two construction workers a mean of 32 hours and a standard deviation of 2 hours to erect the Red Barn model. Assume the assembly times follow the normal distribution.
(a) Determine the z values for 29 and 34 hours. What percentage of the garages take between 32 hours and 34 hours to erect?
(b) What percentage of the garages take between 29 hours and 34 hours to erect?
(c) What percentage of the garages take 28.7 hours or less to erect?
(d) Of the garages, 5 percent take how many hours or more to erect?

7-35. A study of long-distance phone calls made from the corporate offices of a large company reveals the duration of calls follows the normal distribution. The mean length of time per call was 4.2 minutes and the standard deviation was 0.60 minutes.
(a) What fraction of the calls last between 4.2 and 5 minutes?
(b) What fraction of the calls last more than 5 minutes?
(c) What fraction of the calls last between 5 and 6 minutes?
(d) What fraction of the calls last between 4 and 6 minutes?
(e) As part of her report to the president, the director of communications would like to report the length of time such that 4 percent of the calls last longer than this time. What is this time?

7-36. Newell Manufacturing Inc. offers dental insurance to its employees. A recent study by the human resources director shows that the annual cost per employee per year followed the normal distribution, with a mean of $1280 and a standard deviation of $420 per year.

(a) What fraction of the employees cost more than $1500 per year for dental expenses?

(b) What fraction of the employees cost between $1500 and $2000 per year?

(c) What fraction of the employees did not have any dental expenses?

(d) What was the 90th percentile of the annual dental costs of the employees (i.e., a dollar amount such that 10 percent of the employees incurred a dental cost that was higher)?

7-37. While soaring health-care costs are becoming a major problem in the United States, excessively long waiting times at emergency rooms in hospitals is becoming a major concern in Canada. The director of emergency medicine at a hospital in Quebec is studying patient waiting times. Waiting time is defined as the time from when a patient enters the facility until he or she is seen by a physician. The study indicates the waiting time follows a normal distribution, with a mean of 100 minutes and a standard deviation of 20 minutes.

(a) For what fraction of the patients is waiting time between 80 and 110 minutes?

(b) What fraction has to wait for less than 90 minutes?

(c) What fraction is seen in more than 90 minutes but less than 130 minutes?

(d) What fraction has a waiting time that is more than 110 minutes but less than 140 minutes?

(e) What is the 5th percentile of the patient waiting times (i.e., duration, in minutes, such that the waiting time of only 5 percent of the patients is less)?

7-38. A study of Furniture Wholesalers regarding the payment of invoices reveals the time from billing until payment is received is approximately normally distributed. The mean time until payment is received is 18 days and the standard deviation is 5 days.

(a) What percentage of the invoices is paid within 14 days?

(b) What percentage of the invoices is paid in more than 25 days?

(c) What percentage of the invoices is paid in more than 14 days but less than 25 days?

(d) The management wants to encourage customers to pay their monthly invoices as soon as possible. Therefore, it announced that a 2-percent reduction in price would be in effect for customers who pay within 7 days of the billing date. A study conducted a few months after the announcement showed that the percentage of customers who paid within 7 days was 4.8 percent. What was the change in the percentage of customers who paid within 7 days?

7-39. The annual commissions earned by sales representatives of Machine Products Inc., a manufacturer of light machinery, follows the normal distribution. The mean yearly amount earned is $50 000 and the standard deviation is $8000.

(a) What percentage of the sales representatives earn more than $55 000 per year?

(b) What percentage of the sales representatives earn between $40 000 and $65 000?

(c) What percentage of the sales representatives earn between $38 000 and $45 000?

(d) The sales manager wants to award the sales representatives who earn large commissions a bonus of $2000. He can award a bonus to 20 percent of the representatives. Based on past data what should be the cut-off point between those who earn a bonus and those who do not?

7-40. The weights of cans of Monarch pears follow approximately the normal distribution with a mean of 1000 g and a standard deviation of 50 g. Calculate the percentage of the cans that weigh:
(a) Less than 860 g.
(b) Between 1055 g and 1100 g.
(c) Between 860 g and 1055 g.

7-41. Management at Koop Electronics is considering adopting a bonus system to increase production. One suggestion is to pay a bonus if the weekly production rate is in the top 5 percent based on past experience. Past records indicate the weekly production rate follows approximately the normal distribution. The mean of this distribution is 4000 units per week and the standard deviation is 60 units per week. If the suggestion is adopted, for what production rates will the bonus be paid?

7-42. V-Haul Truck Lines uses the Ford Super 1310 exclusively. Management made a study of the maintenance costs and determined that the number of kilometres travelled during the year followed the normal distribution. The mean of the distribution was 95 000 km and the standard deviation was 3000 km.
(a) What percentage of the Ford Super 1310s logged 100 000 km or more?
(b) What percentage of the trucks logged more than 91 000 km but less than 94 000 km?
(c) How many of the Fords travelled 98 000 km or less during the year?
(d) Is it reasonable to conclude that any of the trucks were driven more than 108 000 km? Explain.

7-43. The annual income of a large group of supervisors at Telco Industries follows approximately the normal distribution. The mean amount earned yearly is $48 000 and the standard deviation is $1200. The length of service of the same supervisors also follows approximately the normal distribution, with a mean of 20 years and a standard deviation of 5 years. John McMaster earns $50 400 annually and has 10 years of service.
(a) Compare his income with those of the other supervisors.
(b) Compare his length of service with those of the other supervisors.
(c) The president of Telco wants to give a bonus to those supervisors at the lower end of the income distribution. If he gives a raise to the lowest 8 percent, what is the cut-off point between those who receive the bonus and those who do not?

7-44. An executive at Westinghouse Canada drives from his home in the suburbs near Toronto to his office in the centre of the city. His driving times can be approximated by the normal distribution with a mean of 45 minutes and a standard deviation of 8 minutes.
(a) What percentage of days will it take him 40 minutes or less to drive to work?
(b) What percentage of days will it take him 50 minutes or more to drive to work?
(c) Explain to the executive why the probability is 0 that it will take him exactly 40 minutes to get to work.

(d) Some days there will be accidents or other delays, so the trip will take longer than usual. How long will the longest 10 percent of the trips take?

7-45. A large retailer offers a "no-hassle" return policy. The number of items returned per day follows approximately the normal distribution. The mean number of items returned is 10.3 per day, and the standard deviation is 2.25 per day.
(a) What percentage of days are 8 or fewer items returned?
(b) What percentage of days are between 12 and 14 items returned?
(c) Is there any chance of a day with no returns?

7-46. A recent study shows that 20 percent of all employees steal from their company each year. If a company employs 50 people, what is the probability that:
(a) Fewer than 5 employees steal?
(b) More than 5 employees steal?
(c) Exactly 5 employees steal?
(d) More than 5 but fewer than 15 employees steal?

7-47. Two-litre plastic bottles used for bottling cola are shipped in lots of 100. Suppose every bottle has a 5-percent chance of being defective. It may leak, it may be too small, and so forth.
(a) In the sample of 100, how many of the bottles would you expect to be defective? What is the standard deviation?
(b) Explain why this situation meets the binomial assumptions.
(c) What is the probability that a shipment of plastic bottles contains 8 or more defective ones?
(d) What is the probability that between 8 and 10 bottles (including 8 and 10) are defective?
(e) What is the probability that there are exactly 8 defective bottles ?
(f) What is the probability that there are no defective bottles?

7-48. The dean of a school of business in Ontario has observed that 10 percent of the students drop Basic Statistics the first time they enroll. In Dr. Punnen's Statistics class this semester there are 60 students who have enrolled for the first time. Compute the following probabilities.
(a) How many students would you expect to drop the class? What is the standard deviation?
(b) Does this situation meet the binomial assumptions? Justify your answer.
(c) What is the probability that at least 8 students will drop the course?
(d) What is the probability that 8 or fewer drop the course?
(e) What is the probability that exactly 8 drop the course?

7-49. It is estimated that 10 percent of students taking a course in introduction to statistics at a certain university fail. Eighty students are taking the course this term.
(a) How many would you expect to fail? What is the standard deviation?
(b) What is the probability that exactly 10 students will fail?
(c) What is the probability that at least 5 students will fail?

7-50. A study has shown that 40 percent of the high-speed chases involving automobiles result in a minor or major accident. During a month in which 50 high-speed chases occur, what is the probability that 25 or more will result in a minor or major accident?

7-51. A poll conducted by the *National Post* in mid-2001 showed that Canadians, who have 9 percent of the world's fresh water supply at their disposal, are divided almost equally on whether to trust the water regulated by their local governments. Forty-six percent of respondents said they do not believe the water supplied to their homes is safe. Assuming that the opinions have not changed significantly since then, what is the probability that in a random group of 50 Canadians, fewer than 20 will distrust the quality of water supplied to their homes?

7-52. The goal at Canadian airports handling international flights is to clear each of these flights within 45 minutes. Let's interpret this to mean that 95 percent of the flights are cleared in 45 minutes each, so 5 percent of the flights take longer to clear. Let's also assume that the distribution is approximately normal.
   (a) If the standard deviation of the time to clear an international flight is 5 minutes, what is the mean time to clear a flight?
   (b) Suppose the standard deviation is 10 minutes, not the 5 minutes suggested in part (a). What is the new mean?
   (c) A customer has 30 minutes from the time her flight lands to catch her limousine. Assuming a standard deviation of 10 minutes, what is the likelihood that she will be cleared in time?

7-53. The registrar at Maritime University (MU) studied the grade point averages (GPAs) of students over many years. Assume the GPA distribution is approximately normal with a mean of 3.10 and a standard deviation of 0.30.
   (a) What is the probability that a randomly selected MU student has a GPA between 2.00 and 3.00?
   (b) What percentage of the students are on probation (i.e., have a GPA less than 2.00)?
   (c) The student population at MU is 10 000. How many students are on the dean's list (i.e., have a GPA of 3.70 or higher)?
   (d) To qualify for a Bell scholarship, a student must be in the top 10 percent. What GPA must a student attain to qualify for a Bell scholarship?

7-54. Lori will graduate from high school this year. She took the American College Test (ACT) for college admission and received a score of 30. Her high school principal informed her that only 2 percent of the students taking the exam receive a higher score. The mean score for all students taking the exam is 18.3. Lori's friends Karrie and George also took the test but were not given any information by the principal other than their scores. Karrie scored 25 and George 18. Based on this information, what were Karrie's and George's percentile ranks? Assume that the distribution of scores is approximately normal.

7-55. The weights of canned hams processed at the Shediac Ham Company follow the normal distribution with a mean of 4.2 kg and a standard deviation of 0.4 kg. The label weight is given as 4 kg.
   (a) What proportion of the hams actually weigh less than the amount claimed on the label?
   (b) The owner of the company, Glen, is considering two proposals to reduce the proportion of hams below label weight. He can increase the mean weight to 4.3 kg and leave the standard deviation the same, or he can leave the mean weight at 4.2 kg and reduce the standard deviation from 0.4 kg to 0.2 kg. Which change would you recommend?

7-56. Most four-year automobile leases allow up to 80 000 km. If the lessee goes beyond this amount, a penalty of 15 cents per kilometre is added to the lease cost. Suppose the distribution of kilometres driven on four-year leases is approximately normal. The mean is 72 000 km and the standard deviation is 8000 km.
   (a) What percentage of the leases will yield a penalty because of excess mileage?
   (b) If the automobile company wanted to change the terms of the lease so that, as per the past data, 25 percent of the leases went over the limit, where should the new upper limit be set?
   (c) One definition of a low-mileage car is one that is four years old and has been driven less than 60 000 km. What percentage of the cars returned are considered low-mileage?

7-57. The annual sales of romance novels follow approximately normal distribution. However, the mean and the standard deviation are unknown. Forty percent of the time, sales are more than 470 000, and 10 percent of the time, sales are more than 500 000. What are the mean and the standard deviation?

7-58. In establishing warranties on TV sets the manufacturer wants to set the limits so that few will need repair at the manufacturer's expense. On the other hand, the warranty period must be long enough to make the purchase attractive to the buyer. For a new TV the number of months until repairs are needed is approximately normally distributed with a mean of 36.84 and a standard deviation of 3.34 months. Where should the warranty limits be set so that only 10 percent of the TVs need repairs at the manufacturer's expense?

7-59. DeKorte Telemarketing is considering purchasing a machine that randomly selects and automatically dials telephone numbers. DeKorte Telemarketing makes most of its calls during the evening, so calls to business phones are wasted. The manufacturer of the machine claims that its programming reduces the calls to business phones to 15 percent of all calls. To test this claim, the director of purchasing at DeKorte programmed the machine to select a sample of 150 phone numbers. What is the likelihood that 30 or more of the phone numbers selected are business phone numbers, assuming the manufacturer's claim is correct?

7-60. Mensa is an organization whose membership requires an IQ in the top 2 percent of the general population. Five hundred people are chosen randomly.
   (a) What is the probability that no more than 4 of them will qualify for membership to Mensa?
   (b) What is the probability that at least 8 of them will qualify for membership to Mensa?

7-61. According to a report in *The Globe and Mail* dated April 13, 2001, a study from ACNielsen Canada shows that 69 percent of Canadian households owned a personal computer in 2000. If 50 households in Canada were randomly selected in 2000, what is the probability that 40 or more of them would own a personal computer?

7-62. Maintaining an optimal inventory of perishable items is an important problem faced by grocery stores that has great economic significance. Items left unsold after the expiry date have to be disposed of, resulting in losses. On the other hand, if the store does not maintain enough stock, then some demand may go unsatisfied, resulting in loss of business and possible loss of customer goodwill. One solution is to replenish stock often and in small quantities each time. In this case, the replenishing cost becomes high. Cathy, the manager of a grocery store in Vancouver, has observed that the weekly demand for tomatoes is approximately normally distributed with a mean of 800 kg and a standard deviation of 80 kg. She has decided to adopt the policy of ordering a fresh stock of 900 kg of tomatoes every Monday morning and disposing of tomatoes left unsold on Saturday evening.

(a) What is the probability that the store will run out of tomatoes by Saturday evening?

(b) What is the probability that more than 150 kg of tomatoes will be left unsold and will have to be disposed of on Saturday evening?

(c) What is the probability that the store will run out of stock more than 10 times in a period of 50 weeks?

7-63. Based on the analysis of past data that showed an average of 10 percent no-shows on New Year's day, the management of a hotel in Victoria with 100 rooms has decided to accept reservations for 105 rooms on the next New Year's day. What is the probability that all the arriving guests will receive a room?

7-64. The maintenance department in a government building has decided to change the battery in each of the 120 clocks in the building once every year (365 days). It is known that the functional lifetime of the particular brand of battery used is approximately normally distributed with a mean of 430 days and a standard deviation of 40 days.

(a) What is the probability that batteries in at least 10 clocks will be non-functional by the time they are replaced?

(b) What is the probability that all the four clocks in the main hall will be functional when the batteries are replaced?

(c) If it is desired that the probability should be at least 0.9 that all four clocks in the main hall will be functional when the batteries are replaced, after how many days should the batteries be replaced?

7-65. Refer to Exercise 7-62. Suppose the manager wants to change the order quantity from 900 kg to some other number to reduce the probability of stock-out to 4 percent. What should be the new order quantity?

www.exercises.ca 7-66

7-66. Go to the Web site www.statcan.ca/english/Estat/licence.htm. After reading and accepting the licence agreement, click on "search CANSIM II." Click on "series number," input series number "D845650," and click "continue" twice. Retrieve monthly data on housing starts in Canada from 1960 to present in "WK1 (Generic Worksheet File), time as rows." Format *housing starts in Canada* into an Excel or Minitab worksheet.

(a) Find the mean and standard deviation of this data set.

(b) Assuming that the data are normally distributed, calculate the probability that the number of housing starts during a randomly selected month was more than 150 000. Compare this with the actual fraction of months during which the number of housing starts was more than 150 000. Does the normal distribution yield a good approximation of the actual result?

COMPUTER DATA EXERCISES 7-67 TO 7-70

7-67. Refer to the data set in file Exercise 7-67.xls on annual percentage increase in the CPI index (all items) in Canada. Calculate the mean and the standard deviation of the data set. Assuming that the data are normally distributed, calculate, using a software package, the probability that during a randomly selected year, the percentage change in the CPI index will not exceed 2 percent. Compare this with the actual fraction of years during which the percentage change in the CPI index exceeded 2 percent. Does the normal distribution yield a good approximation of the actual result?

7-68. Refer to the data set in file Exercise 7-68.xls on percentage monthly increase in the TSE 300 index. Calculate the mean and standard deviation of the data set. Assuming that the data are normally distributed, calculate, using a software package, the probability that the percentage monthly increase in the TSE 300 index during a randomly selected month will be at least 1.5 percent. Compare this with the actual fraction of months during which the percentage increase in the TSE 300 index was at least 1.5 percent. Does the normal distribution yield a good approximation of the actual result?

7-69. Refer to the data set in file Exercise 7-69.xls on the one-year percentage return on common equity of a randomly chosen sample from globeinvestor.com's list of the top companies in Canada in 2000. Calculate the mean and standard deviation of the data set. Assuming that the data are normally distributed, calculate, using a software package, the probability that the percentage return on common equity of a randomly selected company in the list is more than 2 percent. Compare this with the actual fraction of companies with a percentage return on common equity of more than 2 percent. Does the normal distribution yield a good approximation of the actual result?

7-70. Refer to the data set in file Exercise 7-70.xls on total marks of students in a Quantitative Methods and Analysis class at the University of New Brunswick.
(a) Calculate the mean and standard deviation of the data set.
(b) The passing mark is 45 percent. Assuming that the data are normally distributed, calculate using a software package, what fraction of students failed the course. Compare this with the actual fraction of students who failed.
(c) It is desired that only the top 5 percent of students should receive a grade of A-plus. Assuming that the data are normally distributed, calculate the lower limit for a grade of A-plus. Using the actual data, find out how many students would have actually received a grade of A-plus if this limit were applied.

CHAPTER 7   ANSWERS TO SELF-REVIEW

7-1. (a) The curve is above the x-axis. Also, total area under the curve is $(1.25)(8.0 - 7.2) = 1.0$. Hence this curve is a valid probability density function.

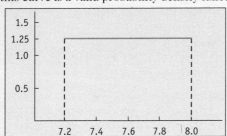

(b) Area under the curve between 7.5 and $7.8 = 1.25(7.8 - 7.5) = 0.375$

7-2. (a) 0.3461
(b) 0.0636
(c) Almost 0.5

7-3. (a) 0.4147
(b) Almost 0.5

7-4. (a) $0.5 - 0.4793 = 0.0207$
(b) Almost $(0.5 - 0.5) =$ almost 0
(c) This equals (area to the left of 0)
$-$ (area between -2.58 and 0)
$= 0.5 - 0.4951 = 0.0049$

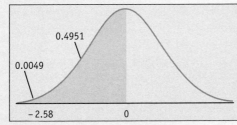

7-5. (a) Equals (area between -2.16 and 0)
$+$ (area between 0 and 0.48)
$= 0.4846 + 0.1844 = 0.6690$
(b) Equals (area between -1.72 and 0)
$+$ (area between 0 and 3.64) $= 0.4573$
$+$ (almost 0.5) $=$ almost 0.9573
(c) Equals (area between -1.63 and 0)
$+$ (area to the right of 0) $= 0.4484 + 0.5 = 0.9484$

7-6. (a) Equals (area between 0 and 2.76)
$-$ (area between 0 and 1.42)
$= 0.4971 - 0.4222 = 0.0749$
(b) Equals (area between -2.67 and 0)
$-$ (area between -0.92 and 0)
$= 0.4962 - 0.3212 = 0.1750$

7-7. Area between 0 and $z = 0.5 - 0.291 = 0.209$
Hence, $z =$ approx. 0.553

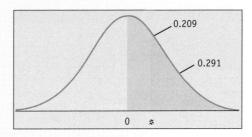

7-8. (a) z value corresponding to 1.0 is
$$\frac{1.0 - 3.36}{5.1} = -0.463$$
(b) z value corresponding to 8.0 is
$$\frac{8.0 - 3.36}{5.1} = 0.91$$

7-9. This equals area between 1.0 and 8.0
$=$ area under z curve between -0.463 and 0.91
$=$ (area between -0.463 and 0)
$+$ (area between 0 and 0.91)
$=$ (approximately) $0.1784 + 0.3186 = 0.497$

7-10. We want a number x such that area to the right of x is $\dfrac{5}{84} = 0.059$
Hence the area between μ and x must be $0.5 - 0.059 = 0.441$. The z value such that area between 0 and z under Z curve is 0.441 equals approximately 1.563.
Hence, the required value of x is $(\mu + 1.563\sigma)$ $= 59.27 + (1.563)(14.34) = 81.68$

7-11. $\mu = np = 200(0.80) = 160$, and $\sigma = \sqrt{np(1 - p)}$
$= \sqrt{200(0.80)(1 - 0.80)} = 5.66$ Then,

(a) $z = \dfrac{169.5 - 160}{5.66} = 1.68$

From the Z table, we find that the area corresponding to $z = 1.68$ is 0.4535. Subtracting from 0.5000 gives the required area $= 0.0465$

(b) $z = \dfrac{149.5 - 160}{5.66} = -1.86$

From the Z table, the area between -1.86 and 0 is 0.4686. Hence, the required area is $0.5 + 0.4686 = 0.9686$.

A REVIEW OF   CHAPTERS 5–7

This section is a review of the major concepts, terms, symbols, and formulae introduced in Chapters 5, 6, and 7. These three chapters are concerned with methods of dealing with uncertainty. As an example of the uncertainty in business, consider the role of the quality assurance department in most mass production firms. Usually, the department has neither the personnel nor the time to check, say, all 200 plug-in modules produced during a two-hour period. Standard procedure may call for selecting a sample of 5 modules and shipping all 200 modules if the 5 operate correctly. However, if 1 or more in the sample is defective, all 200 are checked. Assuming that all 5 function correctly, quality assurance personnel cannot be absolutely certain that their action (allowing shipment of the modules) will prove to be correct. It could be that the 5 selected at random are the only ones out of the 200 that function properly! Probability theory lets us measure the uncertainty involved, in this case, of shipping out defective modules. Also, probability as a measurement of uncertainty comes into play when we buy a Lotto 6/49 ticket and want to know the probability of winning a jackpot.

Chapter 5 notes that a *probability* is a value between 0 and 1 inclusive, which expresses one's belief that a particular event will occur. A weather forecaster might state that the probability of rain tomorrow is 0.20. The project director of a firm bidding on a subway station in Bangkok might assess the firm's chance of being awarded the contract at 0.50. We look at the ways probabilities can be combined using rules of addition and multiplication, some principles of counting, and the importance of Bayes' theorem.

Chapter 6 presents *discrete* probability distributions—the *binomial distribution* and the *Poisson distribution*. Discrete probability distributions are listings of all the possible outcomes of an experiment and the probability associated with each outcome. A probability distribution allows us to evaluate sample results.

As an example, a consumer research firm, such as National Family Opinion (NFO), conducted a survey to find whether grocery shoppers can identify the brand name of a product if the name does not appear on the can, box, or package. For question 1, NFO deleted the name of a soup and gave the shopper five choices: (1) Campbell's, (2) Knorr, (3) Progresso, (4) Chalet Suzanne, and (5) Heinz.

There were six similar questions, and 1000 shoppers participated in the experiment. There is a possibility that shoppers unfamiliar with various labels and brand names would select a name at random—that is, guess the brand name. A binomial probability distribution is generated to see what a random distribution of choices would look like. These probabilities are in column 2 of the following table; the numbers expected are in column 3. Note that we expect only 2 of the 1000 shoppers to *guess* five of the six questions correctly. We expect practically no shoppers to guess six out of six. The actual distribution of responses is in column 4. A comparison of columns 3 and 4 indicates that a large percentage of the shoppers can identify the brand name of the product by looking at the label. NFO would conclude that it is highly unlikely for such a large number of shoppers to select so many correct brand names by chance.

1 Number of Correct Identifications	2 Probability*	3 Expected Number by Chance	4 Actual Number in Survey
0	0.262	262	5
1	0.393	393	16
2	0.246	246	10
3	0.082	82	27
4	0.015	15	81
5	0.002	2	346
6	0.000	0	515
	1.000	1000	1000

* Probabilities from Appendix A

Chapter 7 introduces the class of continuous probability distributions. A very important member of this class, *the normal probability distribution*, is studied in detail. Some phenomena, such as hourly wages of employees in a large company, student marks in a large class, percentage daily changes in TSE 300 index, errors made in measurement of physical and economic information, approximate a normal distribution. In some cases, simple transformations of variables, (such as logarithmic transformations), result in a normal distribution.

Actually, there is a family of normal distributions—each with its own mean and standard deviation. There is a normal distribution, for example, for a mean of $100 and a standard deviation of $5, another for a mean of $149 and a standard deviation of $5.26, and so on. It was noted that a normal probability distribution is bell-shaped and symmetrical about its mean and that the tails of the normal curve extend in either direction infinitely. Since there are an unlimited number of normal distributions, it is difficult to compare two or more distributions directly. Instead, the distributions of interest are *standardized*. The distribution of these standardized values is normal and is called the *standard normal distribution*. The standard normal distribution has a mean of 0 and a standard deviation of 1. It is very useful, for example, for comparing distributions in different units. The distribution of the incomes of middle managers and the distribution of their efficiency ratings is an example of distributions in different units. It is also used to compute the probability that various events will happen.

■ GLOSSARY

Chapter 5

Bayes' theorem   Developed by Reverend Bayes in the 1700s, it is designed to find the probability of one event, A, occurring, given that another event, B, has already occurred.

Classical probability   Probability assigned to outcomes of a random experiment on the assumption that each of the outcomes is equally likely. Using this concept of probability, if there are n possible outcomes, the probability of a particular outcome is $1/n$. Thus, on the toss of a coin, the probability of a head is $1/n = 1/2$.

Combination formula   A formula to count the number of possible ways of choosing r objects from a set of n objects. If the order a, b, c is considered the same as b, a, c, or c, b, a, and so on, the number of choices is found by:

$$_nC_r = \frac{n!}{r!(n-r)!}$$

Conditional probability   The likelihood that an event will occur given that another event has already occurred.

Empirical Probability   Estimate of probability of outcome of a random experiment based on past experience. An insurance company estimates the probability of accidental death for a particular person in a particular city based on accidental death of a proportion of the population of the city. For example, if 100 of every 100 000 persons died of accidental death, the insurance company can estimate the probability of accidental death for a particular person by dividing 100 by 100 000, that is,

$$\frac{100}{100\,000} = 0.001$$

Event   A collection of one or more outcomes of a random experiment. For example, an event may be three defective valves in an incoming shipment of valves for a 351 cu. in. Ford V8 engine.

General rule of addition   Used to find the probability of a complex event made up of A or B.

$$P(A \text{ or } B) = P(A) + P(B) - P(A \text{ and } B)$$

General rule of multiplication   Used to find the probabilities of a complex event made up of A and B. Example: It is known that there are 3 defective radios in a box containing 10 radios. What is the probability of selecting 2 defective radios on the first two selections from the box?

$$P(A \text{ and } B) = P(A)P(B \mid A) = \frac{3}{10} \times \frac{2}{9} = \frac{6}{90} = 0.067$$

where $P(B \mid A)$ means "the probability of B occurring given that A has already occurred."

Independent   The occurrence of one event has no effect on the probability of the occurrence of another event.

Multiplication formula   One of the formulae used to count the number of possible outcomes of an experiment. It states that if there are m ways of doing one thing and n ways of doing another, there are $m \times n$ ways of doing both. Example: A sports shop offers two sport coats and three contrasting pants for $400. How many different outfits can there be? Answer: $m \times n = 2 \times 3 = 6$.

Outcome   A particular result of a random experiment.

Permutation formula   A formula to count the number of possible ways of choosing ordered sets of r objects out of n objects. If a, b, c is one choice, b, a, c another, c, a, b

another, and so on, the total number of choices is determined by

$$_nP_r = \frac{n!}{(n-r)!}$$

Probability   A value between 0 and 1, inclusive, that reports the likelihood that a specific event will occur.

Random experiment   A process (i) that is (at least conceptually) repetitive in nature, (ii) the outcome of any trial which is uncertain and is always one of a well-defined set of possible outcomes, and (iii) that has associated with each of its outcomes, a number called the probability of the outcome, such that if we conduct a large number of trials of the experiment, the fraction of times an outcome will occur will on the average be equal to its probability.

Sample space   A collection or set of all the possible outcomes of a random variable.

Special rule of addition   For this rule to apply, the events must be mutually exclusive. For two mutually exclusive events, the probability of A or B occurring is found by:

$$P(A \text{ or } B) = P(A) + P(B)$$

Example: The probability of a one-spot or a two-spot occurring on the toss of one die is

$$P(A \text{ or } B) = \frac{1}{6} + \frac{1}{6} = \frac{2}{6} = \frac{1}{3}$$

Special rule of multiplication   If two events are not related—that is, they are independent—this rule can be applied to determine the probability of their joint occurrence.

$$P(A \text{ and } B) = P(A)P(B)$$

Example: The probability of two heads on two tosses of a coin is:

$$P(A \text{ and } B) = P(A)P(B) = \frac{1}{2} \times \frac{1}{2} = \frac{1}{4}$$

Subjective probability   Probability assigned to an event based on whatever information is available—hunches, personal opinion, opinions of others, rumors, and so on.

Chapter 6

Binomial random variable   A discrete random variable with the following characteristics:

  1. It counts the total number of successes in a fixed number, n, of Bernoulli trials.

  2. Each Bernoulli trial has only two possible outcomes—*Success* and *Failure*.

  3. Each trial is independent of every other trial, meaning that the outcome of trial 1 (success or failure) in no way affects the outcome of trial 2.

  4. The probability of a success ($=p$) stays the same from trial to trial.

Continuous random variable   A random variable that may assume any value within some interval or collection of intervals.

Discrete probability distribution   A listing of all the possible values of a discrete random variable and their corresponding probabilities.

Discrete random variable   A random variable that can assume any one of only a countable number of possible values.

Poisson distribution   A distribution often used to approximate binomial probabilities when n is large and p is small. What is considered "large" or "small" is not precisely defined, but a general rule is that n should be equal to or greater than 20 and p equal to or less than 0.05.

Random variable   A random experiment each of whose possible outcomes is a number. For example, a count of the number of accidents (a random experiment) on Highway 401 during a week might be 10, or 11, or 12, or some other number.

Chapter 7

Continuity correction factor   Used to improve the accuracy of the approximation of a discrete distribution (binomial) by a continuous distribution (normal).

Normal probability distribution   A continuous distribution that is bell-shaped, with the mean dividing the distribution into two equal parts. Further, the normal curve extends infinitely in either direction; that is, it never touches the x-axis. By converting a normal distribution to a *standard normal distribution*, we can, for example, compare two or more normal distributions having significantly different means or distributions that are in different units (such as incomes and years of service).

z value   The distance between a selected value and the population mean measured in units of the standard deviation.

■ EXERCISES

PART I—FILL IN THE BLANKS

  1. Based on your assessment of the stock market, you state that chances are 50–50 that stock prices will start to go down within two months. This concept of probability based on your belief is called _____.

2. A study of absenteeism from the classroom is being conducted. In our study of probability, this particular activity is called _____.

3. Refer to Exercise 2. It was found that 126 students were absent from Monday morning classes. This number (126) is called _____.

4. To apply this rule of addition:

$$P(A \text{ or } B \text{ or } C) = P(A) + P(B) + P(C)$$

the events must be _____.

5. Management claims that the probability of a defective relay is only 0.001. The name of the rule used for finding the probability of the relay *not* being defective is _____. The formula for that rule is _____. The probability of a particular relay not being defective is _____.

6. For a probability distribution, the sum of the probabilities of all possible outcomes must equal _____.

7. Is the binomial distribution a discrete or continuous probability distribution? _____.

8. The characteristics of a binomial probability distribution are: _____, _____, _____, and _____.

9. The Poisson probability distribution is (discrete or continuous)? _____.

10. To construct a Poisson distribution, you need _____.

11. The characteristics of a normal probability distribution and its accompanying normal curve are: _____, _____, and _____.

12. If we convert values of a normal distribution to a distribution that has a mean of 0 and a standard deviation of 1, this probability distribution is called the _____.

PART II—PROBLEMS

13. A self-study course on management principles was offered to all employees of TMC Electronics. At the end of the time period, the employees were tested, with the following results:

Course Grade	Number of Employees
A	20
B	35
C	90
D	40
F	10
Withdrew	5

What is the probability that an employee selected at random:
a. Earned an A?
b. Earned a C or better?
c. Did not fail or withdraw?

14. It is claimed that Aldradine, a new medicine for acne, is 80 percent effective—that is, when applied to a random person with acne problems, the probability of a significant improvement is 0.8. It is applied to the affected area of a group of 15 people. What is the probability that:
a. all 15 will show significant improvement?
b. fewer than 9 of 15 will show significant improvement?
c. twelve or more people will show significant improvement?

15. Based on historical data of claims against the house insurance policies, an insurance company finds that there is an average of four claims against the policy in an 8-year period.
    a. What is the probability that no claims were submitted against the policy in the 8-year period?
    b. What is the probability of at least one claim submitted against the policy in the 8-year period?

16. A study of the attendance at the Montreal Canadiens NHL games during the 2000–01 season revealed that the distribution of attendance is approximately normal with a mean of 20 105 and a standard deviation of 750.
    a. What is the probability a randomly selected game has an attendance of 21 000 or more?
    b. What percent of the games have an attendance between 19 000 and 21 000?
    c. Find the number such that for twenty percent of the games, attendance was less than this number.

17. The following table presents the major causes of death in Canada per 100 000 persons.

	Men	Women	Total
All cancers	230	149	379
Cardiovascular Diseases	307	188	495
Other	265	258	523
Total	802	595	1397
www.stacan.ca/Daily/English/990513/s990513d.htm			

   a. What is the probability that a randomly chosen Canadian will die from cancer?
   b. What is the probability that a randomly chosen Canadian will be a woman and will die from a cardiovascular disease?
   c. What is the probability that a randomly chosen Canadian man will die of cancer or a cardiovascular disease?

18. Revenue Canada has set aside 2000 tax returns in which the amount of charitable contributions seemed excessive. A sample of six returns is selected from the group. If two or more of this sampled group have "excessive" amounts deducted for charitable contributions, the entire group will be audited. What is the probability that the entire group will be audited, if out of the 2000 returns, 400 have "excessive" deductions? What if 600 have "excessive" deductions?

19. An automobile dealer stocks two models of a certain make of car. Model A costs $21 736 and model B costs $34 000. Of all the customers who expressed an interest in buying a car, 6 percent would buy model A, 15 percent would buy model B, and 79 percent would not buy a car. Find the expected sales per customer.

20. Prior to signing a contract with an author, a publishing company asks its marketing department to analyze the potential market for the book. The following table includes the number of copies sold and estimated corresponding probabilities.

Number of Copies Sold	Probability
12 000	0.4
15 000	0.2
20 000	0.1
30 000	0.3

a. Calculate the expected value and the standard deviation of the number of copies sold for the book.
b. Calculate the expected value and the standard deviation of the revenue earned by the publishing company if each book sells for $89.

■ CASES

A. INTERNET PLAGIARISM

With the Internet providing large sources of information on almost all topics, students are often tempted to cut and paste material from articles available on the Internet and thus plagiarize on their term papers. This has become a serious problem for universities, which are trying to take steps to prevent such tendencies. One professor has developed a software package that, given two articles, randomly selects some five-word phrases from one article and checks if they are in the other. He plans to use this to compare the 2500 word term paper of each of his students with each of a list of 500 articles, available on the Internet, which he believes are popular among students. He needs your help to set up a critical value of common phrases. If a student paper is found to have more phrases in common with any one of the articles on the Internet than the critical value, he plans to question him or her about it. He wants to be careful not to falsely accuse an honest student. He has observed that for any choice of an article and a term paper, written independently of the article, the probability of a randomly chosen five-word phrase in the term paper also appearing in the article is 0.04.

1. Suppose the professor compares twenty randomly chosen five-word phrases from a student term paper with an article on the Internet.
   a. Suppose the student term paper is written totally independently of the article on the Internet. What is the probability that at least 5 of the randomly chosen phrases will be in the article on the Internet? What about 10?
   b. Based on your answer to (1a), would it be fair to suspect a student of plagiarism if at least 5 of the 20 randomly chosen phrases in his term paper are also found in the article on the Internet? What about 10?

2. Suppose the professor compares 200 randomly chosen five-word phrases from a student term paper with an article on the Internet.
   a. Suppose the student term paper is written totally independently of the article on the Internet. What is the probability that more than 5 of the randomly chosen phrases will be in the article on the Internet? What about more than 15?

   b. Based on your answer to (2a), would it be fair to accuse a student of plagiarism if more than five of the randomly chosen phrases in his term paper are also found in the article on the Internet? What about more than 15?

3. Now, suppose the professor compares 200 randomly chosen five-word phrases from a student term paper with an article on the Internet; and he repeats this independently for every one of the 500 articles on the Internet.
   a. If the student's term paper is written totally independently of the articles on the Internet, what is the probability that for at least one of the articles on the Internet, more than 15 of the randomly chosen phrases from the term paper will be in the article?
   b. Based on your answer to (3a), would it be fair to accuse a student of plagiarism if, for at least one of the articles on the Internet, more than 15 of the randomly chosen phrases in his term paper were also found in the article?

Based on your answers to the questions above, what policy would you recommend to the professor?

B. GEOFF "APPLIES" HIS EDUCATION

Geoff Brown is the manager of a small telemarketing firm and is evaluating the sales rate of experienced workers in order to set minimum standards for new hires. During the past few weeks, he has recorded the number of successful calls per hour for the staff. These data appear below along with some summary statistics he worked out with a statistical software package. Geoff has been a student at the local community college and has heard of what seem like many different kinds of probability distributions (binomial, normal, Poisson, etc.). Could you give Geoff some advice on which distribution to use to fit these data as well as possible and how to decide when a probationary employee should be accepted as having reached full production status? This is important because it means a pay raise for the employee, and there have been some probationary employees in the past who have quit because of discouragement that they would never meet the standard.

Successful sales calls per hour during the week of August 14:

4 2 3 1 4 5 5 2 3 2 2 4 5 2 5 3 3 0 1 3 2 8 4 5 2 2 4 1 5 5
4 5 1 2 4

Descriptive statistics:

N	Mean	Median	Trmean	Stdev	Semean
35	3.229	3.000	3.194	1.682	0.284

Min	Max	Q1	Q3
0.0	8.000	2.000	5.000

C. BANK CARD

Before banks issue a credit card, they usually rate or score the customer in terms of his or her projected probability of being a profitable customer. A typical scoring table appears below.

Age	Under 25 (12 pts)	25–29 (5 pts)	30–34 (0 pts)	35+ (18 pts)
Time at same address	<1 yr (9 pts)	1–2 yrs (0 pts)	3–4 yrs (13 pts)	5+ yrs (20 pts)
Auto age	None (18 pts)	0–1 yr (12 pts)	2–4 yrs (13 pts)	5+ yrs (3 pts)
Monthly car payment	None (15 pts)	$1–$99 (6 pts)	$100–$299 (4 pts)	$300+ (0 pts)
Housing costs	$1–$199 (0 pts)	$200–399 (10 pts)	Owns (12 pts)	Lives with relatives (24 pts)
Chequing/ savings accounts	Both (15 pts)	Chequing only (3 pts)	Savings only (2 pts)	Neither (0 pts)

The score is the sum of the points on the six items. For example, Sushi Brown is under 25 years old (12 pts), has lived at the same address for 2 years (0 pts), owns a 4-year-old car (13 pts), with car payments of $75 (6 pts), housing costs of $200 (10 pts), and a chequing account (3 pts). She would score 44.

A second chart is then used to convert scores into the probability of being a profitable customer. A sample chart of this type appears below.

Score	30	40	50	60	70	80	90
Probability	0.70	0.78	0.85	0.90	0.94	0.95	0.96

Sushi's score of 44 would translate into a probability of being profitable of approximately 0.81. In other words 81 percent of customers like Sushi will make money for the bank card operations.

Here are the interview results for three potential independently selected customers.

Name	David Born	Edward Brendan	Ann McLaughlin
Age	42	23	33
Time at same address	9	2	5
Auto age	2	3	7
Monthly car payment	$140	$99	$175
Housing cost	$300	$200	Owns clear
Chequing/savings accounts	Both	Chequing only	Neither

a. Score each of these customers and estimate their probability of being profitable.
b. What is the probability that all three are profitable?
c. What is the probability that none of them are profitable?
d. Find the entire probability distribution for the number of profitable customers among this group of three.

CHAPTER 8

Sampling Methods and the Central Limit Theorem

GOALS

When you have completed this chapter, you will be able to:

- Explain under what conditions sampling is the proper way to learn something about a population

- Describe methods for selecting a sample

- Define and construct a sampling distribution of the sample mean

- Explain the central limit theorem

- Use the central limit theorem to find probabilities of selecting possible sample means from a specified population.

We find the earliest results on sampling theory in the work of Pierre-Simon Laplace (1749–1827). The sampling techniques considered by Laplace were, however, non-probability sampling. Some of the pioneers of the theory and application of probability sampling were A.N. Kiaer (1838–1919), A.L. Bowley (1869–1957), and P.C. Mahalanobis (1893–1972). Significant credit for the tremendous acceptance sampling theory has received world-wide goes to Professor Mahalanobis.

Prasanta Chandra Mahalanobis was born in Calcutta, India. He graduated in physics in 1912 and completed tripos in mathematics and physics from King's College, Cambridge, England in 1915. Just before returning to India after graduation, he accidentally came across a volume of the statistical journal *Biometrica*. It was love at first sight. Statistics became his main area of interest and he developed and applied statistical techniques successfully to problems in such diverse areas as anthropology, epidemiology, demography, meteorology, flood control, estimation of crop yield, and development of national economic plans.

Mahalanobis' greatest contributions to statistics are in the area of large-scale sample surveys. He made fundamental methodological and philosophical contributions to survey sampling and his techniques were applied successfully to various real-world problems, such as estimation of the yield of the jute crop in the province of Bengal. The famous American statistician and economist H. Hotelling commented, "No technique of random sampling has, so far as I can find, been developed in the United States or elsewhere, which can compare in accuracy with that described by Professor Mahalanobis."

From 1947 to 1951, Mahalanobis was chairman of the United Nations Subcommission on Statistical Sampling. His tireless efforts were largely responsible for the final recommendation of this subcommission that sampling methods be extended to all parts of the world.

Mahalanobis founded the Indian Statistical Institute, one of the top institutes of statistical study in the world. He also founded *Sankhya,* a statistical journal that is still rated as one of the best.

Mahalanobis was elected a Fellow of the Royal Society, London, in 1945. He received *Padma Vibhushan,* the highest national honour, from the President of India in 1968.

1498
1548
1598
1648
1698
1748
1898
1948
2000

INTRODUCTION

Chapters 1 through 4 emphasized techniques for describing key characteristics of a given data set. That is, we concentrated on analysis of a data set that is fully available to us. Chapters 5 through 7 laid the foundation for statistical inference with the study of probability theory, discrete random variables, and continuous random variables. Recall that in statistical inference, we deal with situations where we do not have full access to the entire data of interest (the population). In this case, our objective is to infer desired information about the population by appropriately choosing a part of the population, which is called a *sample*, and analyzing the sample data. Often, the desired information about the population is the value of a population parameter such as the *arithmetic mean* (μ) or *standard deviation* (σ). In this case, we calculate from the sample the value of an appropriate sample statistic and use it as an estimate of the population parameter.

Ideally, we would like to choose a sampling technique and a sample statistic in such a way that the value of the sample statistic is guaranteed to be close to the actual value of the desired population parameter. Unfortunately, no such statistical technique exists (unless, of course, we decide to collect the entire population data). However, amazingly, techniques exist that are very likely (with very high probability) to produce a value that is close to the value of the population parameter even when a sample of a size as small as 100 is chosen from a very large population. For example, by interviewing just a few hundred appropriately chosen voters in Canada, we can pretty well know the opinions of all the millions of Canadian voters. We shall discuss such techniques in this book. The two main steps in any such technique are:

(i) **Choice of a proper method for selecting sample data.** It is absolutely essential that the selected sample be a good representative of the population data. As the saying goes, "garbage in, garbage out." If the sample chosen is not a good representative of the entire population then no technique of analyzing the data is known that will produce a value that is likely to be close to the value of the desired population parameter. In this chapter, we shall look at different methods for selecting a sample.

(ii) **Proper analysis of the sample data.** Given sample data that are good representatives of the population, an appropriate sample statistic has to be chosen whose value is likely to be close to the value of the population parameter.

We begin this chapter by discussing methods of selecting a sample from a population. We then construct the probability distribution of the sample mean when the sample is chosen using *simple random sampling with replacement*, the simplest and most basic probability sampling technique. This gives us an understanding of how the sample means tend to cluster around the population mean. Finally, we discuss the *central limit theorem*, one of the most important results in statistics. We infer from it that when the sample is chosen using simple random sampling with replacement, the shape of the distribution of the sample mean tends to follow approximately the normal probability distribution for even a moderate sample size.

8.1 SAMPLING THE POPULATION

In many cases sampling is the only way to determine something about the population. Some of the major reasons for sampling are outlined below.

1. **The destructive nature of certain tests** In the area of industrial production, steel plates, wires, and similar products must have a certain minimum tensile strength. To ensure that the product meets the minimum standard, the quality assurance department selects a sample from the current production. Each piece is stretched until it breaks, and the breaking point (usually measured in megapascals) is recorded. Obviously, if all the wire or all the plates were tested for tensile strength, none would be available for sale or use. For the same reason, only a sample of photographic film is selected and tested by Kodak to determine the quality of all the film produced, and only a few potato seeds are tested for germination by potato farmers prior to the planting season.

2. **The physical impossibility of checking all items in the population** Sometimes, the population of interest is data on all the fish, birds, snakes, or mosquitoes in Canada. In this case, not only is the population large, but also these creatures are constantly moving, being born, and dying. Instead of even attempting to count all the ducks in Canada or weigh all the fish in Lake Erie, we make estimates using various techniques—such as counting all the ducks on some randomly selected ponds, making creel checks, or setting nets at predetermined places in the lake. The only way we can estimate the gold content of the ore in the gold mines in the Hemlo area in Ontario is by analysis of a sample of the area's ore. In the 1997 Bre-X scandal, Canadian mining promoter David Walsh misled investors by billions of dollars by releasing a false report of analysis for sample ore from an Indonesian jungle mine.

3. **The prohibitive cost of studying all the items in a population** Public opinion polls and consumer testing organizations, such as Pollara, usually contact fewer than 2000 of the nearly 8.2 million families in Canada. Some consumer-panel-type organizations charge about $50 000 to mail samples and tabulate responses to test a product (such as breakfast cereal, cat food, or perfume). The same product test using all 8.2 million families would cost about $1 billion.

4. **The adequacy of sample results** Even if funds were available, it is doubtful that the additional accuracy of a 100-percent sample—that is, the entire population—is essential in most problems. For example, the federal government uses the sample data collected from a few grocery stores scattered throughout Canada to determine the monthly index of food prices. The prices of bread, beans, milk, and other major food items are included in the index. It is unlikely that the inclusion of all grocery stores in Canada would significantly affect the index, since the prices of milk, bread, and other staple foods usually do not vary by more than a few cents from one chain store to another.

5. **The time involved in contacting the whole population** A candidate for a national office may wish to determine her chances for election. A sample poll using the regular staff of field interviewers of a professional polling firm would take only one or two days. By using the same staff and interviewers and working seven days a week, it would take nearly 20 years to contact all the voting population! Even if a large staff of interviewers could be assembled, the cost of contacting all of the voters would probably not be worth the expense. As we shall see, for even a moderately sized sample, the sample poll will most likely (with very high probability) yield a small interval containing the actual percentage of popular votes the candidate might receive. In other words, if she is actually going to receive 80 percent of the popular vote, then the sample poll will most likely yield an interval such as (78, 81.2) or (77.8, 82.9). In such a case, the additional expense and time needed to find for certain, the exact percentage of the popular vote she might receive, does not seem justified.

8.2 SAMPLING TECHNIQUES

Sampling techniques can be categorized into two types: (i) sampling without replacement, and (ii) sampling with replacement.

In **sampling without replacement**, each data unit in the population is allowed to appear in the sample no more than once. For example, suppose we want to choose a sample of heights of 20 students from a class of 150 students. If we use sampling without replacement, the height for a student named Rob Li will appear in the sample no more than once.

 Sampling without replacement   Each data unit in the population is allowed to appear in the sample no more than once.

Consider a simple example where there are only four students in the class and their heights (in centimetres) are {180, 160, 190, 175}. The population in this case is small, of size $N = 4$. Suppose we choose a sample of size 2 from this population using sampling without replacement. Then, the set of possible samples is {{180, 160}, {180, 190}, {180, 175}, {160, 190}, {160, 175}, {190, 175}}. The total number of possible samples is 6 (= $_4C_2$). In general, *if the population size is N and we want a sample of size n without replacement, the total number of such samples is* $_NC_n$. Note that if two of the students in the population had the same height and the population was {180, 160, 190, 160}, then the possible samples of size 2 in sampling without replacement would be {{180, 160}, {180, 190}, {180, 160}, {160, 190}, {160, 160}, {190, 160}}. (We choose pairs of data units—not pairs of data values—and we record the values of the selected data units.)

In **sampling with replacement**, each data unit in the population is allowed to appear in the sample more than once. For example, suppose there are three students in the class and their heights, which form our population, are {180, 160, 165}. If we choose a sample of size 2 from this population using sampling with replacement, then the set of possible samples is {{180, 180}, {180, 160}, {180, 165}, {160, 160}, {160, 165}, {165, 165}}.

 Sampling with replacement   Each data unit in the population is allowed to appear in the sample more than once.

Another categorization of sampling techniques is (i) probability sampling and (ii) non-probability sampling.

Probability sampling is a sampling technique in which a probability distribution of the number of times different data units can appear in the sample is pre-assigned. The sample is selected randomly in accordance with this probability distribution. **Non-probability sampling** is a sampling technique that does not involve random selection. Here, inclusion of an item in the sample is based on the convenience or judgment of the person conducting sampling.

 Probability sampling   Data units in the population are pre-assigned a probability distribution of the number of times different data units can appear in the randomly selected sample.

Non-probability sampling   This does not involve random selection; inclusion of an item in the sample is based on the convenience or judgment of the person conducting sampling.

A typical example of non-probability sampling is "person on the street" interview conducted by television news programs to get a feel for public opinion on various issues. Exit polls, as conducted by network television stations on election days, are another example of non-probability sampling.

In both probability and non-probability sampling, the sample selected *may or may not* be a good representative of the population. However, in probability sampling we know the odds (probability) of representing the population well, and we can use probability theory to make powerful statements about the accuracy and precision of results based on such a sample. In the case of non-probability sampling, however, no such statements can be made. We wish to point out that in certain situations, such as choosing a sample of cancer patients to test a new cancer drug, the researchers do not have the option of choosing a probability sample. They have to manage with the patients who volunteer to participate. In this book, we shall study *only probability sampling*.

8.3   PROBABILITY SAMPLING METHODS

There is no one "best" method of selecting a probability sample from a population of interest. A method used to select a sample from data in invoices in a file drawer might not be the most appropriate method for choosing a national sample of votes. However, all probability sampling methods have a similar goal, namely, *to allow chance to determine the data items to be included in the sample*.

SIMPLE RANDOM SAMPLING

This is the simplest and most basic probability sampling technique. Most of the probability sampling techniques used in practice can be considered variations of this technique. We can categorize it into two types: (i) without replacement, and (ii) with replacement.

SIMPLE RANDOM SAMPLING WITHOUT REPLACEMENT (SRN)

Simple random sampling without replacement (SRN) is a technique of sampling without replacement in which each possible sample of the desired size *n* has the same probability of being selected. In SRN, each data unit in the population has the same chance of being selected.

 Simple random sampling without replacement (SRN)   A technique of sampling without replacement in which each possible sample of the desired size *n* has the same probability of being selected.

To illustrate this technique, suppose we want to study the number of years of service of the 5600 employees of Chapters, Inc. Thus, we have one unit of data for each employee (his or her number of years of service), and the population size (the total size of the data set) is 5600. Suppose we want to choose a sample of size 52. Since there is one unit of data per employee, this is equivalent to choosing a sample of 52 employees out of the total of 5600 employees. One way of choosing a simple random sample without replacement is to write the name of each employee on a small slip of paper and deposit all of the slips in a box. After they have been thoroughly mixed, the first selection is made by drawing a slip out of the box without looking at it.

The data value corresponding to the selected employee (his or her years of service) is added to the sample. The drawn slip of paper is discarded. (So, now the box contains one less slip of paper.) This process is repeated until a sample of size 52 is chosen.

An obvious variation of simple random sampling without replacement is simple random sampling with replacement.

SIMPLE RANDOM SAMPLING WITH REPLACEMENT (SRR)

Simple random sampling with replacement (SRR) is a modification of the SRN technique in which after an element is drawn from the population, it is replaced into the population. (For example, if a slip of paper is drawn from a box, the corresponding data is recorded and the slip of paper is returned to the box.)

 Simple random sampling with replacement (SRR)   A modification of the SRN technique; after an element is drawn from the population it is replaced into the population.

SRR is rarely used in real-world applications; there is no sense in choosing the same employee more than once. However, in this chapter, we shall mainly use SRR for sample selection for two reasons:

(i)   This technique is very easy to analyze mathematically.

(ii)   In most real-world applications, the population size is large. In this case, even if we use SRR, the chance of an item being selected twice is very small. Hence, in such cases, SRN and SRR are almost identical and all the results we shall give for SRR will approximately hold for SRN. When the population size is small, however, the results on SRR will not exactly apply to the case of SRN, and you will have to consult a specialized book on sampling theory for correct formulae.

SELECTING A SIMPLE RANDOM SAMPLE USING RANDOM NUMBERS

A table of random numbers is an efficient way to select members of the sample

In practice, actually drawing slips of paper from a box is not very convenient. A more convenient method of selecting a simple random sample is to use the identification number of each employee and a table of random numbers, such as the one in Appendix B. As the name implies, these numbers are generated by a process that has almost all the characteristics of a random process, and the probability that employee number 0351 will be selected is almost the same as for employee number 3722 or 2643. Bias is almost eliminated from the selection process.

Let us see how we can use this table to select the sample data on employees of Chapters Inc. using simple random sampling without replacement (SRN). Since there are 5600 employees, we shall allocate them numbers from 0000 to 5599; we shall use four-digit random numbers. We must first choose a starting point in the table. Any starting point will do. Suppose we start with the number in the third column and fourth row: 37397. We can now proceed from this number either along rows or along columns. We shall move along rows. The random numbers, starting from this number, are:

37397   93379   56454   59818   59827   74164   71666   46977   61545   00835
93251   87203   36759   49197   85967   01704   19634   21898   17147...

Since we shall use four-digit numbers, let us rearrange these numbers in sets of 4:

3739	7933	7956	4545	9818	4582	7741	6471
6664	6977	6154	5008	3593	2518	7203	3675
9491	9785	9670	1704	1963	4218	9817...	

The first four digits are 3739. Thus, 3739 is the number of the first employee and we add the data value (years of service) corresponding to this employee to our sample. The next two sets of four digits are 7933 and 7956. We skip these numbers, since the largest number allocated to an employee is 5599. The next four digits are 4545. The data on this employee forms the second element of our sample. We continue the process, discarding a number if it is more than 5599 or if it has been obtained before, until we get a sample of the desired size.

GENERATING RANDOM NUMBERS USING COMPUTER SOFTWARE

We can also use Excel or Minitab to generate random numbers (or what are more popularly called *pseudo-random numbers*).

Suppose we want 100 random numbers of, say, three digits each (that is, between 000 and 999). Charts 8-1 and 8-2 provide instructions for Minitab and Excel.

Recall that if we are interested in using random numbers to select an SRN sample of size, say, 100, then since the same random number appearing a second time will have to be discarded, we may actually need more than 100 random numbers. It is necessary, therefore, to generate some extra random numbers. (A total of 200 numbers will be safe.)

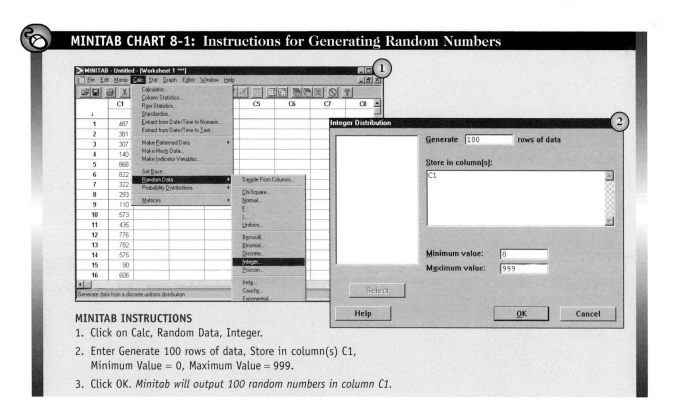

MINITAB CHART 8-1: Instructions for Generating Random Numbers

MINITAB INSTRUCTIONS

1. Click on Calc, Random Data, Integer.

2. Enter Generate 100 rows of data, Store in column(s) C1,
   Minimum Value = 0, Maximum Value = 999.

3. Click OK. *Minitab will output 100 random numbers in column C1.*

EXCEL CHART 8-2: Instructions for Generating Random Numbers

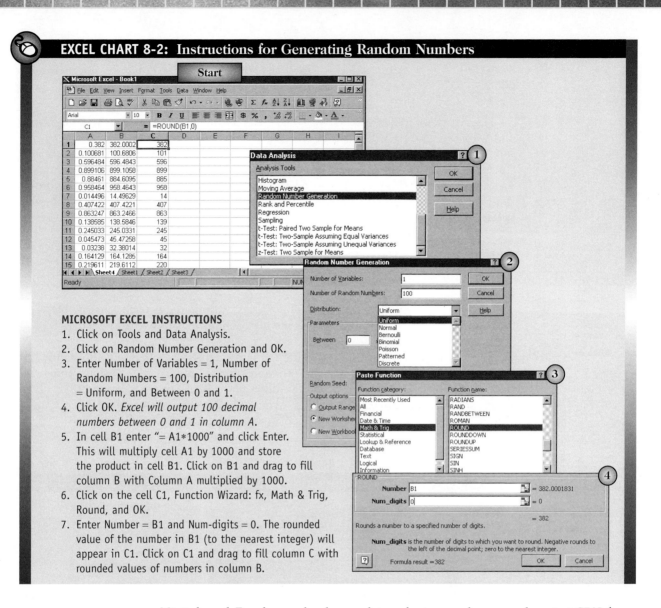

MICROSOFT EXCEL INSTRUCTIONS

1. Click on Tools and Data Analysis.
2. Click on Random Number Generation and OK.
3. Enter Number of Variables = 1, Number of Random Numbers = 100, Distribution = Uniform, and Between 0 and 1.
4. Click OK. *Excel will output 100 decimal numbers between 0 and 1 in column A.*
5. In cell B1 enter "= A1*1000" and click Enter. This will multiply cell A1 by 1000 and store the product in cell B1. Click on B1 and drag to fill column B with Column A multiplied by 1000.
6. Click on the cell C1, Function Wizard: fx, Math & Trig, Round, and OK.
7. Enter Number = B1 and Num-digits = 0. The rounded value of the number in B1 (to the nearest integer) will appear in C1. Click on C1 and drag to fill column C with rounded values of numbers in column B.

Minitab and Excel can also be used to select a random sample using SRN from any given population data set. Below, we give instructions for selecting a sample size of $n = 20$ from a given data set using SRN. It should be noted that Minitab also allows sampling using SRR.

Instructions for Selecting a Random Sample

MINITAB INSTRUCTIONS

1. Input data in Column C1.
2. Click on Calc, Random data, Sample from Columns.
3. Input Sample 20 rows from column C1.
4. Store samples in C2.
5. If you want SRR, select Sample with replacement.
6. Click OK.

EXCEL INSTRUCTIONS

1. Input data in Column A.
2. Click Tools, Data Analysis, Sampling, OK.
3. Fill in Input Range, Range of values in Column A, Random Number of Samples = 20, Output Range = B1.
4. Click OK.

STATISTICS IN ACTION

Finding Random Numbers

With the significant role played by inferential statistics in all branches of science, the availability of large sources of random numbers has become a necessity. The first book of random numbers, containing 41 600 random digits generated by L. Tippett, was published in 1927. In 1938, R.A. Fisher and F. Yates published 15 000 random digits generated using two decks of cards. In 1955, RAND Corporation published a million random digits, generated by the random frequency pulses of an electronic roulette wheel. By 1970, applications of sampling required billions of random numbers. Methods have since been developed for generating, using a computer, digits that are "almost" random and hence are called *pseudo-random*. The question of whether a computer program can be used to generate numbers that are truly random remains a debatable issue.

■ SELF-REVIEW 8-1

The class roster in Table 8-1 lists the students enrolled in Quantitative Methods and Analysis I. Five students are to be randomly selected to provide data on their perception about the course.

(a) Using the random numbers 31, 07, 86, 25, 16, 07, 36, 73, select a sample of size five using SRN.

(b) Using the same random numbers as in (a), select a sample of size five using SRR.

(c) Now use the random numbers starting from the beginning of row 2 of Appendix B and select a sample of size five using SRN.

TABLE 8-1: Class List of Students in BA 2603(1A)
Quantitative Methods and Analysis I Instructor: S. KABADI

ID Number	Name	Gender	ID Number	Name	Gender
00	Allaby, P.	M	20	Mahon, C.	M
01	Ashworth, W.	F	21	Malloy, J.	M
02	Aube, D.	M	22	Matheson, S.	F
03	Avery, L.	F	23	McDougall, D.	M
04	Brittany, S.	M	24	Merriam, R.	M
05	Beswick, B.	F	25	Miller, C.	M
06	Calabrese, A.	M	26	Morin, N.	F
07	Casey, K.	F	27	Morofsky, B.	F
08	Chamberlain, J.	F	28	Nicholson, J.	F
09	Chedore, M.	F	29	Nicolle, D.	M
10	Colbourne, C.	F	30	Paul, C.	F
11	Cowan, S.	M	31	Phillips, C.	M
12	Demers, E.	M	32	Pile, A.	M
13	Devereux, L.	F	33	Putnam, A.	F
14	Gendreau, P.	M	34	Richards, C.	M
15	Goetzen, C.	M	35	Ross, C.	M
16	Goggin, K.	F	36	Sheaves, G.	F
17	Hawker, K.	F	37	Thornton, T.	M
18	Hayden, A.	M	38	Watson, C.	M
19	Lawrence, C.	F	39	Wheeler, C.	F

OTHER PROBABILITY SAMPLING METHODS

Simple random sampling is the simplest and most basic probability sampling technique. We shall briefly discuss in this subsection three of the other popular probability sampling techniques: (i) systematic random sampling, (ii) stratified random sampling, and (iii) cluster sampling.

SYSTEMATIC RANDOM SAMPLING

The simple random sampling procedure may be awkward in certain research situations. For example, suppose the population of interest consists of data in 2000 invoices located in file drawers. Drawing a simple random sample would first require

In a systematic sample the first item is chosen at random

numbering the invoices from 0000 to 1999. Using a table of random numbers, a sample of, say, 100 numbers would then have to be selected. An invoice to match each of these 100 numbers would have to be located in the file drawers. This would be a very time-consuming task—instead, a *systematic random sample* could be selected by going through the file drawers and selecting every 20th invoice for study. The first invoice should be chosen from 1 to 20 using a random process (such as using a table of random numbers). As an example, if the 10th invoice were chosen as the starting point the sample would consist of the 10th, 30th, and 50th ... invoices. Since the first item is chosen at random from 1 to 20, this is a probability sampling technique in which every data item has the same probability of being selected to be in the sample.

In **systematic random sampling**, the data units in the population are arbitrarily numbered from 1 to N. A number between 1 and N is selected. Let us denote this number by k. One data unit is randomly selected to be in the sample. Starting with this data unit, every kth data unit is added to the sample until a sample of desired size n is obtained.

> ⓘ **Systematic random sampling** A sampling technique that involves arbitrarily numbering data units from 1 to N, and selecting a number, k, between 1 and N. Starting with a randomly selected data unit, every kth data unit is added to the sample until a sample of desired size n is obtained.

We shall now give rules for choosing the number k and the starting data unit.

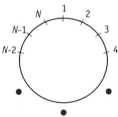

- Suppose N/n is a whole number. Then k is chosen as N/n. A number between 1 and k is chosen randomly as the starting number. As an example, consider the class list of students given in Table 8-1. Here, $N = 40$. Suppose we want to choose a systematic random sample of size $n = 5$. Then $k = 40/5 = 8$. Renumber the students 1 to 40. Suppose the number selected randomly between 1 and 8 happens to be 2. Then our sample will contain the 2nd, 10th, 18th, 26th, and 34th students in the list.

- Suppose N/n is not a whole number. Then, k is chosen as the whole number just below N/n. The data units of the population are arranged clockwise along the circumference of a circle. A number from 1 to N is chosen randomly as the starting number. The data unit corresponding to the starting number is added to the sample; then, moving clockwise along the circumference of the circle, the data unit corresponding to every kth number is added to the sample.

Consider the class list in Table 8-1. Suppose we want a sample of size $n = 7$. Then, $N/n = 40/7 = 5.714$, not a whole number. Hence, we choose $k = 5$. Select a number randomly between 1 and 40; suppose it happens to be 26. Then our sample will contain the 26th, 31st, 36th, 1st, 6th, 11th, and 16th students in the list.

Now let us look at a different application of systematic random sampling. Suppose the management of a Canadian Tire store wants to study the total value of the items purchased by each customer during each visit to the store. In this case, the population is the value of the items purchased by each customer during each trip to the store. There is no obvious way of selecting a sample from this population using simple random sampling. The following variation of the systematic random sampling technique is useful. Choose a suitable number k. Select randomly a number r between 1 and k. Interview the rth customer leaving the store, and then interview every kth customer leaving the store until a sample of desired size is obtained. For example, suppose we choose $k = 20$, and the randomly selected number between 1 and 20 happens to be 11. Then we shall interview the 11th customer, the 31st customer, and so on.

Systematic random sampling has two main advantages over simple random sampling: (i) the sample is easier to collect, and (ii) the sample values are more evenly distributed over the list of population units.

The second point above, however, can be a disadvantage if the listing of the population items exhibits a pattern. For example, suppose we want to study the total daily sales at a Canadian Tire store and we select a systematic random sample with $k = 7$. If we select a number r randomly between 1 and 7 and record the total sales during the days r, $r + 7$, and so on, then each of these days will be the same day of the week (either they will all be Mondays, or they will all be Tuesdays, etc.). The resultant sample will then represent the total sales only on a particular day of the week and not on all days.

STRATIFIED RANDOM SAMPLING

In many real-world situations, the population is fairly heterogeneous. But it is possible to divide it into subgroups that are relatively more homogeneous. For example, suppose we are interested in the average height of adults in a city. Since males tend to be taller than females, dividing the population into males and females gives us two relatively more homogeneous subgroups. As another example, suppose we wish to estimate average income per family in a city. In most cities, the residential areas can be divided into wealthy areas, middle-class areas, and poor areas. Such relatively more homogeneous subgroups in a diverse population are called *strata* (singular *stratum*). In such situations, a sample that better represents the population can be obtained by using **stratified random sampling**, which takes these strata into consideration.

 Stratified random sampling The population is divided into subgroups, called *strata*, and a sample is selected from each stratum using Simple Random Sampling.

Since the objective is to obtain a sample that is a good representative of the population, it is advisable to assign to each stratum a sample size proportional to the size of the stratum. In this case, for every stratum the ratio of the size of sample selected from the stratum to the total size of the stratum is the same, and equals (n/N). This is called *proportional stratified random sampling*.

For instance, the problem might be to study the advertising expenditures of the 500 top companies in Canada. Suppose the objective of the study is to determine whether firms with high returns on equity (a measure of profitability) spent more of each sales dollar on advertising than firms with a low return or a deficit. Assume that the 500 firms were divided into five strata (see Table 8-2). If, say, 50 firms are to be selected

TABLE 8-2: Number Selected for a Proportional Stratified Random Sample

Stratum	Profitability (return on equity)	Number of Firms	Percentage of Total	Number Sampled*
1	30 percent and over	20	4	2
2	20 up to 30 percent	40	8	4
3	10 up to 20 percent	190	38	19
4	0 up to 20 percent	180	36	18
5	Deficit	70	14	7
Total		500	100	50

* 2 percent of 50 = 1: 10 percent of 50 = 5: etc.

for intensive study, then two firms with a level of profitability of 30 percent or more would be included. Four firms in the 20–30 percent stratum would be selected at random, and so on.

In some situations, it is not possible to assign to each stratum a sample size proportional to the size of the stratum. In such a case, we use *non-proportional stratified random sampling*. In some cases, use of non-proportional sampling becomes necessary to ensure that the sample has certain desired properties.

In a non-proportional stratified random sampling, the number of items chosen in each stratum is disproportionate to the respective numbers in the population. We then weight the sample results according to the stratum's proportion of the total population. For example, if non-proportional sampling were used in the preceding case, we would weight the result of stratum 1 (such as its sample mean) by 4/100, stratum 2 by 8/100, stratum 3 by 38/100, and so on. Regardless of whether a proportional or a non-proportional sampling procedure is used, every item or person in the population has a chance of being selected for the sample.

Stratified random sampling has the advantage, in some cases, of more accurately reflecting the characteristics of the population than does simple random or systematic random sampling. Note in Table 8-2 that 4 percent of the firms have a return on equity of 30 percent or more (stratum 1), and 14 percent have a deficit (stratum 5). If a simple random sample of 50 were taken, we might not by chance select any firms in stratum 1 or 5. A proportional stratified random sample, however, would ensure that two firms in stratum 1 and seven firms in stratum 5 are represented in the sample.

CLUSTER SAMPLING

Cluster sampling is often employed to reduce the cost of sampling a population scattered over a large geographic area. In **cluster sampling** a population is divided into groups, called clusters. A sample of clusters of predetermined size is selected using simple random sampling. The collection of all the data units in all the selected clusters forms our final sample.

 Cluster sampling The population is divided into groups, called clusters; a sample of clusters of predetermined size is selected using simple random sampling and the collection of all the data units in all the selected clusters forms the final sample.

To illustrate the use of cluster sampling, suppose we want to study the monthly expenditure on food of families in Halifax. To select a sample of families using simple random sampling or stratified random sampling, we shall need an appropriate list of families in Halifax. Also, the geographical location of the residences of the families in a sample so selected may be scattered all over Halifax, and therefore collecting data on these families may be time-consuming and costly. A more convenient, less costly, and less time-consuming method is to consider each street block as a cluster and to select a sample of blocks using simple random sampling. The data are then collected on each family on each of the selected blocks.

The discussion of sampling methods in the preceding sections did not include all the sampling methods available to a researcher. Should you become involved in a major research project in marketing, finance, accounting, or other areas, you would need to consult books devoted solely to sampling theory and sample design.

■ SELF-REVIEW 8-2

Refer to Self-Review 8-1 and the class list in Table 8-1.
   (a) Suppose we want to select a sample of size 4 using systematic random sampling. What should be the value of k? Suppose the starting random number selected happened to be 7. What will be the corresponding systematic random sample?
   (b) Now, suppose we want to select a sample of size 9 using systematic sampling. What should be the value of k? Suppose the starting random number selected happened to be 17. What will be the corresponding systematic sample?
   (c) Suppose we want to make sure that the sample has an equal number of males and females. Using random numbers 31, 07, 86, 25, 16, 07, 36, 73, 92, 11, 37, 17, 81, 29, 03, 82, 12, 96, and 63, select a sample of size 6 using stratified random sampling.
   (d) Divide the set of 40 students into 10 clusters—00 up to 03, 04 up to 07, ..., 36 up to 39. Use cluster sampling and the random numbers in (c) to select a sample of size 8.

SUMMARY OF ADVANTAGES AND DISADVANTAGES OF DIFFERENT PROBABILITY SAMPLING METHODS

Simple random sampling is the basic probability sampling technique. We shall outline below the merits and drawbacks of other sampling techniques using simple random sampling as a reference point.

- A stratified random sample is generally (in a probabilistic sense) a better representative of the population data since it makes use of relative homogeneity of data within each stratum. However, partitioning data into homogeneous strata is not always feasible.

- Systematic random sampling is one of the easiest methods to implement and is often used just for convenience. However, there are situations (such as selecting a random sample of Canadians crossing the Canada–USA border) in which systematic random sampling is the best available method. A systematic random sample is generally not a very good representative of population. However, if the population data exhibit a pattern, then the quality of such a sample is likely to be very good or very bad, depending on the nature of the pattern.

- Cluster sampling is generally used because of the convenience and cost-effectiveness in collecting such a sample data. However, contrary to the case of stratified random sampling, if data values within each cluster are heterogeneous and all clusters are reasonably similar, then a sample produced using cluster sampling is likely to be a very good representative of the population data.

EXERCISES 8-1 TO 8-2

8-1. Discuss advantages and disadvantages of different probability sampling methods.

8-2. The table below lists the top 20 companies in Canada during 2000, together with their total revenue (in thousands of dollars).

ID Number	Company	Total Revenue
00	BCE Inc.	18 209 000
01	Royal Bank of Canada	22 841 000
02	Cdn. Imp. Bank of Commerce	23 124 000
03	Bank of Nova Scotia	18 996 000
04	Thompson Corp.	6 569 000
05	Bank of Montreal	18 629 000
06	Canadian Pacific	16 152 900
07	Bell Canada	13 185 000
08	Imperial Oil	16 859 000
09	Quebecor Inc.	10 934 800
10	Manulife Financial	14 152 000
11	PanCanadian Petroleum	7 475 900
12	Toronto-Dominion Bank	20 075 000
13	Bombardier Inc.	16 194 000
14	Alberta Energy Co.	6 329 300
15	Alcan Inc.	9 244 000
16	Talisman Energy	4 946 900
17	Petro-Canada	9 521 000
18	Magna International	10 720 000
19	Shell Canada	8 189 000

Suppose we wish to select a sample of companies from this list to study various economic indicators.

(a) Select a sample of size 8 using SRN.

(b) Select a sample of size 8 using SRR.

(c) Select a sample of size 8 using systematic random sampling.

(d) Divide the list of companies into three groups: (i) those with total revenue of more than $16 billion, (ii) those with total revenue in the range of $8 billion to $16 billion, and (iii) those with total revenue of less than $8 billion. Using these as strata, select a sample of size 9, using stratified random sampling.

(e) Select a cluster sample of size 8, using the groups (00 up to 03), (04 up to 07), (08 up to 11), (12 up to 15), and (16 up to 19) as clusters.

(Each time, use random numbers in Appendix B on page 835 of the text starting from the beginning of row 7.)

8.4   SAMPLING AND NON-SAMPLING ERRORS

Our aim in a sampling study is to select an appropriate sample, analyze it, and obtain an estimate of the value of a desired population parameter. The estimate obtained from the sample almost always differs from the true value of the population parameter, and this error is made up of two parts: (i) sampling error and (ii) non-sampling error.

SAMPLING ERROR

This error is inherent in the sampling process and the choice of estimator. It is due to the fact that the sample contains only a part of the population data. The characteristics of this error depend on characteristics of the population data, choice of the sampling technique, and choice of the estimator. As an example, suppose our population, the efficiency ratings of all five production employees working in a company, is {97, 103, 96, 99, and 105}. A statistician who does not have access to these entire population data is interested in estimating the mean value of all the ratings (population mean). Suppose he decides to choose a sample of size 2, using SRN, and use the value of sample mean as an estimator of the population mean. If the selected sample of two ratings happens to be {97, 105}, the value of the sample mean will be $(97 + 105)/2 = 101$. If the selected sample happens to be {103, 96}, the value of sample mean will be $(103 + 96)/2 = 99.5$. The population mean is $(97 + 103 + 96 + 99 + 105)/5 = 100$. Thus, the sampling error of the first sample is $(101 - 100) = 1$, and the sampling error of the second sample is $(99.5 - 100) = -0.5$.

NON-SAMPLING ERROR

This error has no direct relationship to the sampling technique or the estimator used and may occur due to some other reasons. The three main causes of non-sampling errors are errors in data recording, non-response error, and sample selection error.

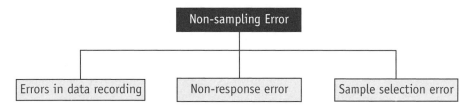

- **Errors in data recording:** such errors occur when the value of a data unit selected to be in the sample is simply wrongly recorded. As an example, suppose we want to collect data on annual incomes of households. Then a household selected to be part of the sample may simply report wrong income. In the U.S. presidential election in 2000, all the polls underestimated the votes received by Buchanan. The reason now widely accepted is that due to the strange design of some ballots, a significant number of voters who intended to vote for Gore ended up voting for Buchanan. Sometimes, when the data values are to be measured using some instrument, error may occur due to faulty equipment.

- **Non-response error:** such an error occurs when a member of the sample refuses to respond. If we fail to obtain values of a significant portion of data units selected to be in the sample and we simply neglect these data units and replace them with others, then the resultant sample is called a *self-selected sample*. The data values corresponding to the members who refuse to respond may have a specific characteristic and not including these values in the sample may create a bias, thereby causing the value of the estimate to be further away from the value of the desired population parameter. Every attempt should therefore be made to collect as many data values as possible corresponding to the selected sample.

- **Sample selection error:** the two basic steps in any probability sampling technique are (i) formation of an appropriate list of population units, and (ii) selection of a sample using this list according to the specified probability distribution. If the selected list does not include some of the population units, then these data values will not be available for inclusion in the sample, thereby adding to the inaccuracy of the estimate obtained. Also, lack of availability of the list in a user-friendly form often makes the task of randomly choosing the sample difficult. For example, if we are required to collect data from a random sample of shoppers at a shopping mall, it is difficult to follow a strictly random process. We often become biased toward a friendly face and are tempted to avoid people with menacing looks.

A classic case of erroneous sampling study is one conducted in the United States in 1936 by *Literary Digest*, a popular magazine of that time, to predict the outcome of the presidential election. The conclusion of the polls conducted by *Literary Digest* was that the Republican candidate, A. Landon, would win by a margin of 3 to 2. But in the election, the Democratic candidate, F. Roosevelt, won 62 percent of the electoral votes. It is interesting to note that an alternative poll conducted by George Gallup at about the same time correctly predicted Roosevelt as the winner. So what went wrong with the poll conducted by *Literary Digest*? Firstly, the sample was chosen from the list of the magazine's subscribers and of those who owned telephones; in 1936, both these groups consisted of dominantly rich people who supported Republicans, while a large part of the population, who were dominantly Roosevelt supporters, had no chance to be part of the sample. Secondly, out of the 10 million ballots mailed, only about 2.3 million were returned, resulting in a self-selected sample.

8.5   SAMPLING DISTRIBUTION OF THE SAMPLE MEAN

As we saw in the previous section, an estimate of the value of a population parameter obtained from sample data differs from the actual value of the population parameter because of sampling and non-sampling errors. For estimation technique to be useful, (i) these errors should be small enough, and (ii) we should have some knowledge of the probability distribution of the errors. We shall now study the probability distribution of the sampling error when:

(i)   the sampling technique used is simple random sampling with or without replacement;

(ii) the population parameter of interest is the population mean; and

(iii) the sample mean is used as the estimator of the population mean.

We shall show that in this case it is possible to keep the probability high that the sampling error will be small enough. This would enable a quality-assurance department in a mass-production firm to release a shipment of microchips based on a sample of only 50 chips, or CBC to make a fairly accurate prediction of results for a federal election based on a sample of votes of only about 1000 registered voters. In particular, we shall study the probability distribution of the sample mean when a sample is obtained using simple random sampling with or without replacement. *Since we shall be studying only the sampling error, we shall assume that the non-sampling error is zero.*

The efficiency rating example, discussed at the top of page 329, showed that the means of samples of a specified size vary from sample to sample. The mean efficiency rating of the first sample of two employees was 101, and the second sample mean was 99.5. A third sample would probably result in a different mean. The population mean was 100. If for a particular sampling technique we organize the means of all the possible samples of two ratings together with the probabilities of their occurrence into a probability distribution, we obtain the **sampling distribution of the sample mean** corresponding to that sampling technique.

> **i** **Sampling distribution of the sample mean** The probability distribution of values of the sample mean when the sample is selected using a specific sampling technique.

The sampling distribution of the sample mean depends on the sampling technique used. For the same population data, we shall get one sampling distribution for SRR, another distribution for SRN, another for stratified random sampling, and so on.

8.6 SAMPLING DISTRIBUTION OF THE SAMPLE MEAN USING SIMPLE RANDOM SAMPLING WITH REPLACEMENT (SRR)

We shall now discuss the sampling distribution of the sample mean for simple random sampling with replacement (SRR). Recall that when the population size is large, this sampling technique is almost the same as simple random sampling without replacement (SRN).

Example 8-1

Hansa Industries has only five production employees. The hourly earnings of the five employees (considered population) are given in Table 8-3.
   (a) What is the population mean?
   (b) What is the sampling distribution of the sample mean when a sample of size 2 is chosen using SRR?
   (c) What is the sampling distribution of the sample mean when a sample of size 3 is chosen using SRR?
   (d) What are the means and standard deviations of the sampling distributions in (b) and (c)?
   (e) What observations can be made about the population distribution and the above two sampling distributions?

TABLE 8-3: Hourly Earnings of the Production Employees of Hansa Industries

Employee	Hourly Earnings ($)
Joe	8
Sue	8
Roy	10
Rupa	12
Lee	10

Solution

   (a) The population mean is
   $$\mu = \frac{(8 + 8 + 10 + 12 + 10)}{5} = \$9.6$$

   (b) To arrive at the sampling distribution of the sample mean, all of the 25 possible samples of size 2 that can result when SRR is used are listed in Table 8-4 together with their means. (Recall that to choose a sample using SRR we write the names of the five employees on five pieces of paper, deposit all five pieces of paper in a box, and choose a piece of paper randomly. We note the name of the employee selected, replace the piece of paper in the box, and again choose a piece of paper randomly. Alternatively, we assign the five data units labels 00, 01, 02, 03, 04, and select two random numbers between 00 and 04 using the random number table. Verify that we may end up with any one of the 25 choices in Table 8-4.) The resulting probability distribution is summarized in Table 8-5.

TABLE 8-4: Sample Means for All Possible Samples of Size 2 for SRR

Sample	Employees	Hourly Earnings ($)	Mean ($\bar{x}$)	Sample	Employees	Hourly Earnings ($)	Mean ($\bar{x}$)
1	Joe, Joe	8, 8	8	14	Roy, Rupa	10, 12	11
2	Joe, Sue	8, 8	8	15	Roy, Lee	10, 10	10
3	Joe, Roy	8, 10	9	16	Rupa, Joe	12, 8	10
4	Joe, Rupa	8, 12	10	17	Rupa, Sue	12, 8	10
5	Joe, Lee	8, 10	9	18	Rupa, Roy	12, 10	11
6	Sue, Joe	8, 8	8	19	Rupa, Rupa	12, 12	12
7	Sue, Sue	8, 8	8	20	Rupa, Lee	12, 10	11
8	Sue, Roy	8, 10	9	21	Lee, Joe	10, 8	9
9	Sue, Rupa	8, 12	10	22	Lee, Sue	10, 8	9
10	Sue, Lee	8, 10	9	23	Lee, Roy	10, 10	10
11	Roy, Joe	10, 8	9	24	Lee, Rupa	10, 12	11
12	Roy, Sue	10, 8	9	25	Lee, Lee	10, 10	10
13	Roy, Roy	10, 10	10				

TABLE 8-5: Sampling Distribution of the Sample Mean for SRR ($n = 2$)

Value of Sample Mean	No. of Occurrences	Probability
8	4	0.16
9	8	0.32
10	8	0.32
11	4	0.16
12	1	0.04

(c) Similar to (b) above, the sampling distribution of the sample mean when a sample of size 3 is chosen using SRR can be obtained by listing all the 125 samples of size 3 that can result when SRR is used and computing their means (see Table 8-6). The resulting probability distribution is summarized in Table 8-7.

TABLE 8-6: Sample Means for All Possible Samples of Size 3 for SRR

Sample	Employee	Hour. Earn. ($)	Mean
1	Joe, Joe, Joe	8, 8, 8	8
2	Joe, Joe, Sue	8, 8, 8	8
3	Joe, Joe, Roy	8, 8, 10	8.67
.			
.			
.			
124	Lee, Lee, Rupa	10, 10, 12	10.67
125	Lee, Lee, Lee	10, 10, 10	10

TABLE 8-7: Sampling Distribution of the Sample Mean for SRR ($n = 3$)

Value of Sample Mean	No. of Occurrences	Probability
8	8	0.064
8.67	24	0.192
9.33	36	0.288
10	32	0.256
10.67	18	0.144
11.33	6	0.048
12	1	0.008

(d) We shall denote the mean of the sampling distribution of the sample mean, $\overline{X}$, by $\mu_{\overline{X}}$ and its standard deviation by $\sigma_{\overline{X}}$. Thus, for $n = 2$ we get

$$\mu_{\overline{X}} = 8(0.16) + 9(0.32) + \cdots + 12(0.04) = 9.6$$

$$\sigma_{\overline{X}} = \sqrt{(8 - 9.6)^2 0.16 + (9 - 9.6)^2 0.32 + \cdots + (12 - 9.6)^2 0.04}$$
$$= 1.058$$

For $n = 3$, we have,

$$\mu_{\overline{X}} = 8(0.064) + 8.67(0.192) + \cdots + 12(0.008) = 9.6$$

$$\sigma_{\overline{X}} = \sqrt{(8 - 9.6)^2 0.064 + (8.67 - 9.6)^2 0.192 + \cdots + (12 - 9.6)^2 0.008} = 0.864$$

(e) Refer to Chart 8-3.

CHART 8-3: Population Distribution and Sampling Distributions of Sample Mean for SRR with $n = 2$ and $n = 3$

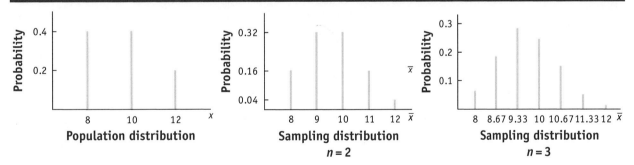

The following observations can be made:

For each of the cases $n = 2$ and $n = 3$, the mean of the sample means is 9.6. This is the same as the value of the population mean μ.

Standard deviation of population values is $\sigma = 1.497$, the standard deviation of values of sample means for $n = 2$ is 1.058 ($= 1.497/\sqrt{2}$), and the standard deviation of values of sample means for $n = 3$ is 0.864 ($= 1.497/\sqrt{3}$). We shall show below that, in general, when a sample of size n is chosen using SRR, the standard deviation of the values of the sample means is $\sigma/\sqrt{n}$.

The shapes of the population distribution and the sampling distributions of the sample mean are different. The shape of the distribution of the sample mean for $n = 3$ is closer to a bell shape than that of the population distribution.

■ SELF-REVIEW 8-3

The lengths of service of all the executives employed by Standard Chemicals are:

Name	Years
Mr. Das	20
Mr. Hu	22
Ms. Mehta	26
Mr. Irwin	24
Ms. Jones	28

Suppose we treat these five numbers (lengths of service) as our population.
(a) What are the values of the population mean and standard deviation?
(b) What is the sampling distribution of the sample mean when a sample of size 2 is chosen from this population using SRR?
(c) What are the mean and standard deviation of the sampling distribution of the sample mean?

We shall now show that observations in part (e) of Example 8-1 can also be justified theoretically using the rules of expected value and variance that we discussed in Chapter 6.

Suppose we use SRR to choose a sample of size n. The first data value that will be chosen can be any one of the data units in the population with equal probability. (That is, it can be the hourly earnings of any one of Joe, Sue, Roy, Rupa, or Lee.) Hence, this first value is a random variable; we shall denote it by X_1. X_1 has the same probability distribution as the population and, hence $\mu_{X_1} = \mu$, and $\sigma_{X_1} = \sigma$. Similarly, the second value, the third value, and so on are all random variables. We shall denote them by X_2, X_3, and so on. Since each data value is replaced before drawing the next one, each of $X_2, X_3, \ldots, X_n$ has the same distribution as the population and they are all mutually independent. Hence, $\mu_{X_1} = \mu_{X_2} = \cdots = \mu_{X_n} = \mu$; $\sigma_{X_1} = \sigma_{X_2} = \cdots = \sigma_{X_n} = \sigma$; and $X_1, X_3, \ldots, X_n$ are mutually independent.

Now, $\bar{X} = \dfrac{(X_1 + X_2 + \cdots + X_n)}{n}$. Hence, using the law of expected value, we get:

$$\mu_{\bar{X}} = \frac{\mu_{X_1} + \mu_{X_2} + \mu_{X_3} + \cdots + \mu_{X_n}}{n} = \frac{\mu + \mu + \mu + \cdots + \mu}{n} = \mu \qquad \text{8-1}$$

and using the law of variance, we get:

$$\sigma_{\bar{X}}^2 = \frac{\sigma_{X_1}^2 + \sigma_{X_2}^2 + \sigma_{X_3}^2 + \cdots + \sigma_{X_n}^2}{n^2} = \frac{\sigma^2 + \sigma^2 + \sigma^2 + \cdots + \sigma^2}{n^2} = \frac{\sigma^2}{n}$$

Hence,

$$\sigma_{\bar{X}} = \sqrt{\frac{\sigma^2}{n}} = \frac{\sigma}{\sqrt{n}}. \qquad \text{8-2}$$

The standard deviation $\sigma_{\bar{X}}$ of the sampling distribution of the sample mean is termed the **standard error of the mean**. Thus, when a sample of size n is selected using SRR, the standard error of the mean is $\sigma_{\bar{X}} = \dfrac{\sigma}{\sqrt{n}}$.

■ SELF-REVIEW 8-4

The data on a one-year percentage return on common equity for the top 1000 Canadian companies in 2000 has a mean of 10.3 percent and a standard deviation of 441.5 percent. What will be the mean and standard deviation of the sampling distribution of the sample mean if a sample of size 40 is drawn from this population using SRR?

EXERCISES 8-3 TO 8-6

8-3. A population consists of the following four values: {12, 12, 14, 16}.
   (a) What are the values of the population mean and standard deviation?
   (b) Count the number of possible samples that may result if a sample of size 3 is chosen from this population using SRR.
   (c) What is the sampling distribution of the sample mean when a sample of size 2 is chosen using SRR?
   (d) What are the mean and standard deviation of the sampling distribution?
   (e) What relationship do you observe between the mean of the sampling distribution and the population mean?
   (f) What relationship do you observe between the standard deviation of the sampling distribution and the population standard deviation?

8-4. A population consists of the following five values: {2, 2, 4, 4, 8}.
   (a) What are the values of the population mean and standard deviation?
   (b) Count the number of possible samples that may result if a sample of size 2 is chosen from this population using SRR.
   (c) What is the sampling distribution of the sample mean when a sample of size 2 is chosen using SRR?
   (d) What are the mean and standard deviation of the sampling distribution?
   (e) What relationship do you observe between the mean of the sampling distribution and the population mean?
   (f) What relationship do you observe between the standard deviation of the sampling distribution and the population standard deviation?

8-5. In the law firm Koop and Associates there are four partners. Listed below are the numbers of cases each associate actually tried in court last month.

Associate	Number of Cases
Hick	2
Storoszczuk	6
Hu	3
Aggarwal	5

   (a) What are the values of the population mean and the standard deviation?
   (b) What is the sampling distribution of the sample mean when a sample of size 2 is chosen using SRR?
   (c) What are the mean and standard deviation of the sampling distribution?
   (d) Compare the mean and standard deviation of the sampling distribution with the corresponding population values.

8-6. There are four sales representatives at a certain Ford dealership. The numbers of cars they sold last week are listed below.

Sales Representative	Cars Sold
1	8
2	6
3	4
4	10

(a) What are the values of the population mean and standard deviation?
(b) What is the sampling distribution of the sample mean when a sample of size 2 is chosen using SRR?
(c) What are the mean and standard deviation of the sampling distribution?
(d) Compare the mean and standard deviation of the sampling distribution with the corresponding population values.

THE SHAPE OF THE SAMPLING DISTRIBUTION OF THE SAMPLE MEAN USING SRR

Let us now investigate the shape of the sampling distribution of the sample mean using SRR.

We saw above that if we denote the random variable corresponding to the first item drawn from the population by X_1, that corresponding to the second item by X_2, and so on, then the probability distribution of each of $X_1, X_2, \ldots, X_n$ is the same as the population distribution. If the population distribution is normal, then the distribution of each of $X_1, X_2, \ldots, X_n$ is normal, and hence $\bar{X} = \dfrac{(X_1 + X_2 + \cdots + X_n)}{n}$ is normally distributed. (The sum of normal random variables is always a normal random variable. Also, dividing a normal random variable by any number—in this case $1/n$—gives us a normal random variable.)

What if the population is not normally distributed? If the sampling distribution of the sample mean were different for different population distributions, then our task of developing a nice theory of estimation would be difficult. Luckily, a very important result in statistics called the central limit theorem shows us that if the sample is drawn using SRR, then for a large sample size the sampling distribution of the sample mean is always approximately normal, regardless of the shape of the population distribution. (We saw some indications of this in Chart 8-5.) Now, we shall discuss the central limit theorem.

8.7   THE CENTRAL LIMIT THEOREM

This very important result in statistics tells us that if a sample of size n is drawn from a given population using SRR, then for larger and larger values of n, the shape of the sampling distribution of the sample mean becomes closer and closer to a normal probability distribution. This is an extremely useful conclusion in statistics. We can reason about the distribution of the sample mean with absolutely no information about the shape of the original distribution from which the sample is taken. In other words, the **central limit theorem** is true for any population distribution.

1498
1548
1598
1648
1698
1748
1898
1948
2000

PIERRE-SIMON LAPLACE (1749–1827)

The central limit theorem, one of the most significant results in statistics, is attributed to Pierre-Simon Laplace (1749–1827), a rather controversial character who is considered by many to be one of the most brilliant scientists of the late eighteenth century. He has a noteworthy place in the annals of mathematical history.

Laplace was a Frenchman with a farm-labourer background. In his early years, he studied for a career in the church according to the intentions of his father. However, at the age of 16, he discovered his talents in mathematics. Thereupon, he abandoned his former studies to pursue his new interest and quickly rose to great heights at a young age, securing a position as a professor of mathematics at the École Militaire and eventually becoming a member of the Academie des Sciences in Paris. The majority of his scientific work involved making advances in mathematics, physics, and especially astronomy.

Aside from his scientific career, Laplace had a noteworthy political career. During the time of Napoleon Bonaparte, Laplace was awarded the Legion of Honour and served briefly as Minister of the Interior. He held this position only briefly (about six weeks) and was removed because, in the words of Napoleon himself, "he brought the spirit of the infinitely small into the government." He was appointed Count of the Empire in 1806 and became a Marquis in 1817 under the order of the Bourbons.

> **i Central limit theorem** If a sample of size n is selected from any population using simple random sampling with replacement (SRR), then for larger and larger values of n, the shape of the sampling distribution of the sample mean becomes closer and closer to the shape of a normal probability distribution.

An important question is *how large should the value of n be for the sampling distribution to be approximated by normal distribution for practical purposes?* The answer to this question depends on the population distribution. For some symmetric population distributions, the sampling distribution becomes close to normal for values of n as small as 10. However, examples of highly skewed distributions can be constructed for which n has to be as large as a few hundred before an approximate normal shape is observed. *In most cases, a shape that can be considered approximately normal for most business and economics applications is observed for n = 30 or more.* In Example 8-1 regarding the hourly earnings of the five production employees of Hansa Industries, we plotted in Chart 8-3 (on page 333) the sampling distribution of the sample mean for $n = 2$ and 3, and we saw a significant change in shape toward normality. If we plot the distribution for $n = 20$ or 30, we shall get a shape very close to normal. This concept is summarized in Chart 8-4 on the next page.

Observe the convergence to a normal distribution regardless of the shape of the population distribution.

CHART 8-4: Results of the Central Limit Theorem for Several Populations

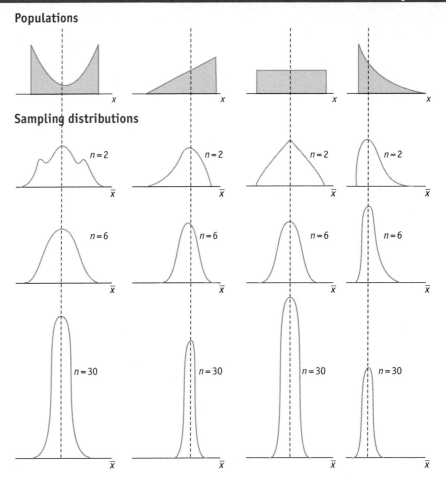

Typically, a sample of size 30 is large enough for the sampling distribution of the sample mean to be approximated by normal probability distribution for most business and economics applications.

VERIFICATION OF THE CENTRAL LIMIT THEOREM

Though a rigorous mathematical proof of the central limit theorem exists, the mathematics involved is far beyond the scope of this book. For a student interested in verifying the theorem, there are three alternatives.

1. **Enumeration** Choose some values of n, say 10, 20, and 30. For each of these values of n, generate the values of sample mean for all the possible samples that can be obtained using simple random sampling with replacement, calculate the probability distribution, and plot it. This will take an enormous amount of time, especially if the population size is large.

2. **Empirical method** Assign a number to each data unit in the population, write each number on a slip of paper, and deposit all these slips of paper in a box. Choose some values of n, say 10, 20, and 30. For each of these values of n, actually draw a sample using simple random sampling with replacement as described before and calculate the sample mean. Repeat this process to get a large enough number

of sample means, calculate the relative frequencies of different values, and plot them. If we choose a large enough number of samples, the shape of the resultant distribution will be a good approximation of the shape of the sampling distribution of the sample mean. Getting a large enough number of values of sample mean will, again, take a lot of time.

3. **Computer simulation** We have already seen in this chapter how to use Excel or Minitab to generate random numbers. The empirical method above can be carried out using Excel or Minitab to generate for each value of *n,* a distribution that is a good approximation of the sampling distribution of the sample mean. This approach is called *computer simulation.*

USING THE SAMPLING DISTRIBUTION OF THE SAMPLE MEAN

Most business decisions are made on the basis of sampling results. Here are some examples.

• The Arm and Hammer Company wants to ensure that its laundry detergent actually contains 5.9 L, as indicated on the label. Historical summaries from the filling process indicate that the mean amount per container is 5.9 L and the standard deviation is 0.15 L. The quality technician in her 10 a.m. check of 40 containers finds the mean amount per container is 5.85 L. Should the technician shut down the filling operation, or is the sampling error reasonable?

• The ACNielsen Company provides information to companies advertising on television. Research indicates that an average adult Canadian watches an average of 21 hours of television per week. Suppose the standard deviation is 1.50 hours per week. If we randomly select a sample of 50 adult Canadians, would it be reasonable to find that they watch an average of 24 hours of television per week?

• Otis Canada Inc. wishes to develop specifications for the number of people who can ride in a new oversized elevator. Suppose the mean weight for an adult Canadian is 75 kg and the standard deviation is 7 kg. However, the distribution of weights does not follow the normal probability distribution; it is positively skewed. What is the likelihood that for a sample of 30 adults their mean weight is 80 kg or more?

In each of these situations, we have a population about which we have some information. We wish to compute the probability of getting a certain range of values of sample mean when a sample is chosen from that population, and understand how to incorporate this information in our decision making.

Using ideas discussed in the previous section, we can compute the probability that a sample mean will fall within a certain range. We know that if the sample is chosen using SRR, the distribution of sample means will follow approximately the normal probability distribution if one of the following two conditions is satisfied:

1. The sample is taken from an approximately normally distributed population. In this case the size of the sample is not a factor.
2. The shape of the population is not known or the shape is known to be non-normal, and the sample size *n* is large. (Typically a sample of size 30 or more is considered large enough for most business and economics applications.)

Under each of the above two conditions, the distribution of $\bar{X}$, the sample mean, will be approximately normal with mean μ (same as the population mean) and standard deviation approximately $\dfrac{\sigma}{\sqrt{n}}$, where σ is the population standard deviation. Hence, the corresponding standardized variable

$$\frac{\bar{X} - \mu}{\sigma/\sqrt{n}} \qquad \text{8-3}$$

is, approximately, the standard normal variable, Z. Thus, any value $\bar{x}$ of sample mean can be standardized to a z value using Formula 8-3 as follows:

$$z = \frac{\bar{x} - \mu}{\sigma/\sqrt{n}} \qquad \text{8-4}$$

Example 8-2

The quality assurance department for Cola, Inc. maintains records regarding the amount of cola in its "jumbo" bottle. The actual amount of cola in each bottle is critical, but varies a small amount from one bottle to the next. Cola Inc. does not wish to under-fill the bottles because it will then have a problem with truth in labelling. On the other hand, it cannot overfill each bottle, because of safety reasons and also because it would be giving product away, hence reducing profits. The mean amount per bottle is 3 L and the population standard deviation is 40 mL. (a) A random sample of 64 bottles is chosen from the filling line using SRR, and the amount of cola in these bottles is recorded. What is the probability that the value of the sample mean will be at least 3.014 L? (b) At 8 a.m. today, the quality technician randomly selected 64 bottles from the filling line using SRN. The mean amount of cola contained in the bottles is 3.014 L. Is this an unlikely result? To put it another way, is the sampling error unusual? Is it likely that the process is putting too much cola in the bottles?

Solution

The sample size ($n = 64$) is large enough (greater than 30). Hence, it follows from the central limit theorem that the sampling distribution of sample mean $\bar{X}$ is approximately normal with mean $\mu_{\bar{X}} = \mu = 3$ and standard deviation $\sigma_{\bar{X}} = \dfrac{\sigma}{\sqrt{n}} = \dfrac{0.04}{\sqrt{64}} = 0.005$.

(a) We want the area under the normal curve to the right of 3.014. The z value corresponding to $\bar{x} = 3.014$ is

$$z = \frac{\bar{x} - 3}{0.005} = \frac{3.014 - 3}{0.005} = 2.8$$

The probability that the sample mean will be at least 3.014 is the area under the Z curve to the right of 2.8.

From the Z table, we find that the area under the Z curve between 0 and 2.8 is 0.4974.

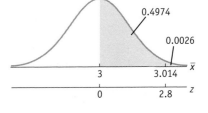

Hence, the area under Z curve to the right of 2.8 is $0.5 - 0.4974 = 0.0026$. So, the probability that the sample mean will be at least 3.014 is 0.0026.

(b) We find from the solution in part (a) that the probability that the sample mean will be at least 3.014 is 0.0026. Thus, the probability of getting a sampling error of $(3.014 - 3.0 =)$ 0.014 or higher is 0.0026 percent

This is, therefore, a very rare and unusual result and can be interpreted as follows. If the mean value of the amount of cola filled in the bottle is 3 L with a standard deviation of 40 mL, then it is very unlikely (probability $= 0.0026$) that the value of the sample mean of a sample of size 64 will be 3.014 L or more. In other words, if the sample mean is 3.014 L or more, then it is highly likely that the mean value of the amount of cola filled by the process into bottles is no longer 3 L. The process most likely needs readjustment and the quality technician should see the production supervisor to further investigate if the amount of cola filled in each bottle should be reduced.

■ SELF-REVIEW 8-5

Refer to the Cola information in Example 8-2. Compute the probability that a sample of 64 jumbo bottles would have a sample mean of 2.995 L or less. If the mean amount of cola in a sample of 64 bottles happens to be 2.995 L, would you call it an unlikely result?

There are many sampling situations in business where we wish to make a statement about the population, but we do not have much knowledge about the population. Here, the power of the central limit theorem helps. We know that irrespective of the shape of the population distribution, if we select a sufficiently large sample using SRR, the sampling distribution of the sample mean will follow approximately the normal distribution.

Often, we do not know the population standard deviation σ. In this case, a logical alternative is to replace σ in Formula 8-3 by its estimator, the sample standard deviation, S.

However, even when the population distribution is normal, the variable $\left(\dfrac{\bar{X} - \mu}{S/\sqrt{n}} \right)$ is not a standard normal variable. The probability distribution of this random variable, when the population distribution is normal, was studied in detail by Gosset, who published his findings under the name "Student." Hence, this distribution is termed Student's t distribution (or, sometimes, just t distribution).

Like the normal distribution, Student's t distribution is a family of distributions. Each member of this family is uniquely given by the value of its parameter called "degrees of freedom," which is denoted by "df". For each value of $df = 1, 2, \ldots$, we get a unique curve. Some key probabilities under different t distributions (i.e., for different values of df) are given in the t-table in Appendix 4 on the CD accompanying this book. We shall discuss Student's t distribution in more detail in Chapter 9. For larger and larger values of df, the shape of the t distribution becomes closer and closer to the shape of the standard normal distribution; as df tends to infinity, it converges to the standard normal distribution.

Gosset showed that if the population distribution is normal, the distribution of $\left(\dfrac{\bar{X} - \mu}{S/\sqrt{n}} \right)$ is Student's t distribution with $df = (n - 1)$. In this case, if $\bar{x}$ is the value of the sample mean $\bar{X}$ obtained from a selected sample and s is the corresponding value of sample standard deviation S, then we call $\dfrac{\bar{x} - \mu}{s/\sqrt{n}}$ the corresponding t value.

That is,

$$ t = \frac{\bar{x} - \mu}{s/\sqrt{n}} \qquad\qquad 8\text{-}5 $$

For large values of n, $df = (n - 1)$ is large and, in this case, we can approximate the t distribution by Z distribution. (Such an approximation is not really necessary. Probabilities under t distribution can be easily obtained using Excel or Minitab, but we shall defer discussion of this to Chapter 9.)

Example 8-3

We wish to verify the claim that the mean value of the market capitalization (in millions) of the top 1000 companies in Canada during 2000 (as listed by globeinvestor.com) was 1173. Suppose the population distribution is normal. A sample of 100 of these companies is selected using SRR and the sample mean of values of market capitalization is 1126. The sample standard deviation is 4350. Based on the sample data, can we say that the assertion that the mean value of market capitalization of the top 1000 companies is 1173 is reasonable?

Solution

Since the sample size $n = 100$ is large, we can assume that the distribution of $\left(\dfrac{\bar{X} - \mu}{S/\sqrt{n}} \right)$

is approximately standard normal. (We shall see in Chapter 9 how to find the probabilities using t distribution.) The value of the sample standard deviation is $s = 4350$.

If the claim is correct, then $\mu = 1173$. In this case, the z value corresponding to

$\bar{x} = 1126$ is $z = \dfrac{1126 - 1173}{4350/\sqrt{100}} = -0.108$.

Referring to the Z table, the area under the Z curve between -0.108 and 0 is approximately 0.043. Hence, the area to the left of -0.108 is approximately $(0.5 - 0.043) = 0.457$. Thus, if the true population mean is 1173, then there is a very high chance (45.7 percent) of

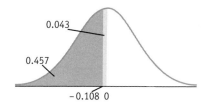

getting a sample mean of 1126 or less. Conversely, since we got a value of the sample mean of 1126, we do not have reason to doubt that the claim is true.

■ SELF-REVIEW 8-6

Suppose a report claims that the average monthly rent of a two-bedroom apartment in Vancouver is $890. To verify the claim, a statistician selected a sample of size 50 apartment buildings using SRR and got the value of the sample mean of $864 and a sample standard deviation of $70. Based on the sample data, what can we say about the claim? (Assume that the population distribution is approximately normal.)

EXERCISES 8-7 TO 8-10

8-7.   It is claimed that the mean of a certain population data is 60. The standard deviation of the population is known to be 12. You select a random sample of size 100. In each of the following cases, what will be your reaction to the claim?
(a) The value of the sample mean obtained is 63.
(b) The value of the sample mean obtained is 59.

8-8. It is claimed that the mean of a certain population of unknown shape is 75. The standard deviation of the population is known to be 5. You select a random sample of size 40. In each of the following cases, what will be your reaction to the claim?
(a) The value of the sample mean obtained is 74.5.
(b) The value of the sample mean obtained is 77.

8-9. The average mark (out of a maximum of 100) of a class of 300 students on a statistics examination is 68.2 with a standard deviation of 9.2. Suppose a random sample of marks of 40 students is selected using SRR. What is the probability that the sample mean will be (a) less than 65? (b) more than 72?

8-10. A tire manufacturer claims that the mean lifetime of its MX100 tires is 108 000 km, with a standard deviation of 3280 km. To test this claim, a random sample of 100 tires is selected using SRR and their lifetimes are calculated.
(a) What is the probability that the value of the sample mean will be more than 109 000 km?
(b) What is the probability that the value of the sample mean will be less than 108 400 km?
(c) If the value of the sample mean happens to be 108 800 km, what does it say about the manufacturer's claim?

8.8 SAMPLING DISTRIBUTION OF THE SAMPLE MEAN USING SIMPLE RANDOM SAMPLING WITHOUT REPLACEMENT (SRN)

The central limit theorem states that if a sample of size n is selected from any population using simple random sampling with replacement (SRR), then for larger and larger values of n, the shape of the sampling distribution of the sample mean becomes closer and closer to the shape of a normal probability distribution.

Unfortunately, this result does not hold in general when we use SRN. In the problem with the hourly earnings of the five production employees as population, for example, the population size, N, is 5. In this case if we use SRN, then, since no data unit can appear in the sample more than once, the sample size can be no more than 5. For $n = 5$, the sample contains all the values in the population, and we get the precise value of population mean. For $n = 4$, the sampling distribution is highly non-normal.

Fortunately, however, in most practical applications, the population size is fairly large. As pointed out before, in this case SRR is almost identical to SRN. (Even if we allow the same data unit in the population to be chosen more than once, for a large population size the probability of any data unit actually appearing more than once in the sample will be negligible.) Hence, in this case, all the results for the case of SRR will apply approximately to the case of SRN. We summarize this below.

If the population size N is large, the ratio n/N is smaller than 0.05, and a sample of size n is chosen using simple random sampling without replacement (SRN), then:

- The mean $\mu_{\bar{X}}$ of the sampling distribution of the sample mean is exactly equal to the population mean.

- The standard error of the mean, $\sigma_{\bar{X}}$, is approximately equal to $\dfrac{\sigma}{\sqrt{n}}$.

- If the population distribution is normal, then the shape of the sampling distribution of the sample mean is almost normal. If the population distribution is not normal, then as the sample size n becomes larger and larger, the shape of the sampling distribution of the sample mean becomes closer and closer to a normal probability distribution.

When the population size N is small, the analysis of sampling distribution of sample mean becomes more complex. It can be shown that, in general, when a sample of size n is chosen using simple random sampling without replacement (SRN), and the population size is N, the standard deviation $\sigma_{\bar{X}}$ of values of sample means is

$$\sigma_{\bar{X}} = \frac{\sigma}{\sqrt{n}} \sqrt{\left(\frac{N-n}{N-1} \right)} \qquad \text{8-6}$$

 We illustrate this with an example in the Chapter 8 Appendix A on the CD accompanying the book.

The term $\sqrt{\left(\dfrac{N-n}{N-1} \right)}$ is called the **finite correction factor**. Note that $\sqrt{\left(\dfrac{N-n}{N-1} \right)}$ is less than 1. Hence, SRN gives us a smaller standard deviation of $\bar{X}$ then SRR.

When the population size N is large compared to n, the term $\sqrt{\left(\dfrac{N-n}{N-1} \right)}$ almost equals 1. In this case, $\sigma_{\bar{X}}$ approximately equals $\dfrac{\sigma}{\sqrt{n}}$. Thus, in this case, we get the same formulae as in the case of SRR.

Example 8-4

Let us reconsider the problem in Example 8-3. We wish to verify the claim that the mean value of the market capitalization (in millions) of the top 1000 companies in Canada during 2000 (as listed by globeinvestor.com) was 1173. Suppose the standard deviation of the data is known to be 3500. A sample of 100 of these companies is selected using SRN and the sample mean of values of market capitalization is 1200. Assuming that the sampling distribution of $\bar{X}$ is approximately normal, can we say that the assertion that the mean value of market capitalization of the top 1000 companies is 1173 is reasonable?

Solution

Since $n/N = 100/1000$ is greater than 0.05, we shall use the *finite correction factor*.

Thus, $\sigma_{\bar{X}} = \dfrac{\sigma}{\sqrt{n}} \sqrt{\left(\dfrac{N-n}{N-1} \right)} = \dfrac{3500}{\sqrt{100}} \sqrt{\left(\dfrac{900}{999} \right)} = 332.205.$

If the claim is correct, then $\bar{X}$ is approximately normally distributed with a mean of 1173 and a standard deviation of 332.205.

In this case, the z value corresponding to $\bar{x} = 1200$ is $z = \dfrac{1200 - 1173}{332.205} = 0.081.$

From the Z table, we find that the area under the Z curve to the right of 0.081 is approximately $(0.5 - 0.0323) = 0.4677$.

Thus, if the true population mean is 1173, then there is a very high chance (46.77 percent) of getting a sample mean of 1200 or more. Conversely, since we got a value of the sample mean of 1200, there is no reason to doubt that the claim is true.

■ SELF-REVIEW 8-7

Let us consider once again the example in Self-Review 8-4 concerning the data on one-year percentage return on common equity of the top 1000 Canadian companies in 2000. The mean of this data set is 10.3 percent, and the standard deviation is 441.5 percent. Suppose we select a sample of size 200 from this population using SRN. Assuming that the sampling distribution of $\bar{X}$ is approximately normal, find the probability that the value of the sample mean will be (a) less than 2 percent; (b) more than 40 percent.

EXERCISES 8-11 TO 8-14

8-11. It is claimed that the mean value of rent for a one-bedroom apartment in Victoria is $580 per month. To test the claim, a random sample of the monthly rents of 50 one-bedroom apartments was selected using SRN, and the values of the sample mean and the sample standard deviation obtained were $565 and $150, respectively. Based on the sample information, what can we say about the claim?

8-12. It is claimed that it takes an average of 330 minutes for taxpayers to prepare, copy, and mail an income tax return form. A consumer watchdog agency selected a random sample of 40 taxpayers using SRN. In each of the following cases, what will be your reaction to the claim?
   (a) The values of the sample mean and the sample standard deviation obtained are 320 minutes and 80 minutes, respectively.
   (b) The values of the sample mean and the sample standard deviation obtained are 350 minutes and 80 minutes, respectively.
   (c) State the assumptions made in arriving at your answers to parts (a), and (b).

8-13. A manager of a video store claims that the average sale amount per invoice at his store last month was $450 with a standard deviation of $60. The store records show that a total of 400 invoices were issued last month. An independent auditor selected a sample of 50 of these invoices using SRN and obtained a value of the sample mean of 470. Assuming that the sampling distribution of $\bar{X}$ is approximately normal, what is your reaction to the manager's claim based on the sample information?

8-14. The director of student placement services at a university announced that the average monthly income of their 200 business students who graduated last winter was $3000, with a standard deviation of $600. To verify this claim, a group of second year business students selected a sample of 36 of the business graduates from last winter using SRN. The mean monthly income of the students in the sample was $2900. Assuming that the sampling distribution of $\bar{X}$ is approximately normal, what is your reaction to the director's claim based on the sample information?

8.9 SAMPLING DISTRIBUTION OF PROPORTION

In some applications, the data units in the population have only two values, say, 1 and 0, and we are interested in estimating the proportion p of data units with a value of 1. Let us consider some examples:

- Suppose a politician conducts polls to estimate her popularity among voters. In this case, each data unit (that is, each vote) will be either "in favour of" or "against" our candidate. We can represent this by 1 for in favour and 0 for against. The politician is interested in estimating the fraction of voters favouring her. This is the same as the proportion p of population data units, which have a value of 1.

- Suppose we are interested in estimating the fraction of homes in Vancouver that have a finished basement. Again, every home either has a finished basement (which can be recorded as 1), or it does not (which can be recorded as 0).

In this case, the population distribution is:

Data Value	Probability
1	p
0	$(1-p)$

As we saw in Chapter 6, this is a binomial distribution with $n = 1$; the value of the population mean $\mu = p$, and the population standard deviation $\sigma = \sqrt{p(1-p)}$.

If we select a sample of size n from this population using SRR, then each data unit in the sample will have a value of 0 or 1. In this case, the sample mean $\bar{X}$ is

$$\bar{X} = \frac{\text{number of "1"s in the sample}}{n} = \text{fraction of data values in the sample with a}$$

value of "1".

Since in this case, the sample mean actually denotes the proportion of sample units with a value of 1, we shall denote $\bar{X}$ by $\hat{p}$. Using the central limit theorem (or the normal approximation of a binomial distribution, discussed in Chapter 7), we get that for a large sample size, $\hat{p}$ is approximately normally distributed with mean

p and standard deviation $\dfrac{\sigma}{\sqrt{n}} = \sqrt{\dfrac{p(1-p)}{n}}$.

How large should the value of n be for the normal approximation to be acceptable? As per Cochran,[1] for $p = 0.5$, n should be at least 30; for $p = 0.3$, n should be at least 80; for $p = 0.05$, n should be as high as 1400. However, many statisticians agree that the following general rule is adequate for most business and economics applications: "n should be such that both np and $n(1 - p)$ are at least 5."

Example 8-5

A multinational company claims that 45 percent of its employees are female. To verify the claim, a statistician selected a sample of 40 employees of the company using SRN and found out that 30 percent were female. Based on this, what can we say about the company's claim?

Solution

Let us denote a data value of 1 if the employee selected is female and a data value of 0 if the employee selected is male. The population size (total number of employees in the multinational company) is large. Hence, SRN is almost the same as SRR. If the company's claim is correct, then population mean = proportion of females in the population = $p = 0.45$ and the population standard deviation is $\sigma = \sqrt{0.45(1-0.45)} = 0.5$.

Now, $np = 40(0.45) = 18 > 5$, and $n(1-p) = 40(0.55) = 22 > 5$. Thus, we can assume that the sample size n is large enough for normal approximation and, hence, $\hat{p}$ is approximately normally distributed with a mean $= 0.45$ and a standard deviation

$$= \frac{0.5}{\sqrt{40}} \approx 0.08.$$

The z value corresponding to $\hat{p} = 0.3$ is $z = \dfrac{0.3 - 0.45}{0.08} \approx -1.88$.

From the Z table, we get the probability of getting a z value of -1.88 or smaller $= 0.5 - 0.4699 = 0.0301$.

This is a fairly small number. Hence, the evidence collected from the sample is not in favour of the company's claim. It seems likely that the company's claim may not be true.

EXERCISES 8-15 TO 8-16

8-15. Statistics Canada reported in August 2001 that the unemployment rate in Canada was 7.2 percent. Suppose that, to verify this claim soon after its release, a statistician selected a sample of size 200 from the Canadian workforce using SRN.
   (a) If the Statistics Canada report is correct, what is the probability that more than 8 percent of people in her sample will be unemployed?
   (b) If 8 percent of the sampled workers were unemployed, what would be your reaction to the Statistics Canada report?

8-16. A study conducted by the *National Post* in mid-2001 indicates that 46 percent of Canadians do not believe the water supplied to their homes is safe. To verify this statement, a researcher selected a sample of 1000 Canadians using SRN.
   (a) If the findings of the *National Post* are correct and the views of the people have not changed since then, what is the probability that more than 55 percent of the Canadians sampled will distrust the quality of water supplied to their homes?
   (b) If 55 percent of the people sampled say that they distrust the quality of water supplied to their homes, what can you say about the statement made by the *National Post*?

CHAPTER OUTLINE

I. There are many reasons for sampling a population:
   A. Often, testing destroys the item being tested and it cannot be returned to the population.

   B. It may be impossible to check or locate all the members of the population.

   C. The cost of studying all the items in the population may be prohibitive.

   D. The results of a sampling study may adequately estimate the value of the population parameter, thus saving time and money.

   E. It may be too time-consuming to contact all members of the population.

II. A. Sampling may be done with replacement or without replacement. In sampling with replacement, each data unit in the population is allowed to appear in the sample more than once.

B. In sampling without replacement, each data unit can appear in the sample at the most once.

III. Probability and non-probability are the two types of sampling techniques.

A. In a probability sampling, all members of the population have a preassigned probability of being selected for the sample. There are several probability sampling methods.

1. In simple random sampling without replacement (SRN), all samples of size n have the same chance of being selected.

2. Simple random sampling with replacement (SRR) is a modification of the SRN technique in which each data unit is allowed to appear more than once.

3. In systematic sampling, a random starting point is selected, and then every kth item thereafter is selected to be in the sample.

4. In stratified sampling, the population is divided into several groups, called *strata*, and then a sample is selected from each stratum using simple random sampling.

5. In cluster sampling, the population is divided into units, called *clusters*. A sample of clusters is drawn using simple random sampling. The collection of all the data items in all the selected clusters forms our final sample.

B. In non-probability sampling, inclusion in the sample is based on the judgment or convenience of the person conducting the sample.

IV. The sampling error is the difference between the population parameter and the sample statistic that can be solely attributed to the sampling technique used and the sample statistic selected.

V. The sampling distribution of the sample mean is a probability distribution of all the possible values of the sample mean.

VI. In the case of SRR, for any given sample size n,

A. the mean of the sample means is equal to the population mean;

B. the standard deviation of values of sample means, which is called *standard error of the mean*, is equal to $\sigma/\sqrt{n}$, where σ is the population standard deviation.

C. If the population follows the normal distribution, then the sampling distribution of the sample mean will also follow the normal distribution for samples of any size.

D. If the population is not known to follow the normal distribution, but the sample size is large, then the central limit theorem tells us that the sampling distribution of the sample mean will follow the approximately normal distribution. Typically, a value of n larger than 30 is large enough for most applications in business and economics.

E. When the population standard deviation σ is unknown, we substitute the sample standard deviation, S, for σ. In this case, if the population distribution is normal, then $\left(\dfrac{\bar{X} - \mu}{S/\sqrt{n}}\right)$ follows "Student t distribution with $(n - 1)$ degrees of freedom." For large values of n, this distribution has almost the same shape as that of the standard normal distribution.

VII. In the case of SRN,

(a) The mean of the sample means is equal to the population mean.

(b) The standard error of the mean is $\sigma_{\bar{X}} = \dfrac{\sigma}{\sqrt{n}}\sqrt{\left(\dfrac{N - n}{N - 1}\right)}$, where N is the population size and σ is the population standard deviation.

(c) If the population size N is large, then SRN is almost the same as SRR. Hence, in this case, the standard error of the mean is approximately equal to $\dfrac{\sigma}{\sqrt{n}}$.

CHAPTER EXERCISES 8-17 TO 8-38

8-17. A statistician wants to choose a sample of annual family income of ten families in your city using SRR. Describe a scheme that would be suitable for the purpose.

8-18. What are sampling and non-sampling errors? Could the value of the sampling error be zero? If it were zero, what would this mean?

8-19. List the reasons for conducting a sampling study. Give an example of each reason for sampling.

8-20. The financial institutions in Alberta providing banking services (including credit unions and trust companies) are to be surveyed. Some of them are very large, with assets of more than $500 million; others are medium-sized, with assets between $100 million and $500 million; and the remaining have assets of less than $100 million. Explain how you would select a sample of these institutions.

8-21. Plastic Products is concerned about the inside diameter of the plastic PVC pipe it produces. A machine extrudes the pipe, which is then cut into three-metre lengths. About 720 pipes are produced per machine during a two-hour period. How would you go about taking a sample from the two-hour production on a particular machine?

8-22. A study of motel facilities in a metropolitan area showed there were 25 facilities. The city's convention and visitors' bureau is studying the number of rooms at each location. The results are as follows:

90, 72, 75, 60, 75, 72, 84, 72, 88, 74, 105, 115, 68, 74, 80, 64, 104, 82, 48, 58, 60, 80, 48, 58, 100.

(a) Using random numbers from the first row of the table in Appendix B, select a random sample of the number of rooms in five motels from this population, using (i) SRR; (ii) SRN.

(b) Obtain a systematic sample of size 5 using 03 as the starting number.

(c) Obtain a systematic sample of size 8 using 09 as the starting number.

(d) Suppose the last 10 motels are "cut-rate" motels. Use stratified sampling to select a random sample of three regular motels and two cut-rate motels. (Use random numbers in the 8th row of Appendix B.)

8-23. As a part of its customer-service program, Air Canada has decided to select 10 passengers from today's first Toronto–Halifax flight to be interviewed in depth regarding airport facilities, service, food, and so on. To identify the sample, each passenger was given a number when boarding the aircraft. The numbers started with 001 and ended with 250.

(a) Select a sample of size 10 using SRN. (Use random numbers in row 10 of Appendix B.)

(b) Select a systematic sample of size 10 using 17 as the starting random number.

(c) Evaluate the two methods by giving the advantages and possible disadvantages.

(d) In what other way could a random sample be selected from the 250 passengers?

8-24. The quality control department employs four technicians during the day shift. Listed below is the number of times each technician instructed the production supervisor to shut down the manufacturing process last week.

Technician	Shutdowns
Rahim	4
Cox	5
Lee	3
Telatko	2

(a) If a sample of size 2 is chosen using SRR, how many samples are possible?

(b) Find the sampling distribution of the sample mean if a sample of size 2 is chosen using SRR.

(c) Compare the mean and standard deviation of the sample means with the population mean and standard deviation.

8-25. At the downtown office of a bank there are five tellers. Last week the tellers made the following number of errors each; 2, 3, 5, 3, and 5. An auditor who does not have access to this population data wants to randomly select a sample of size 2.

(a) If the auditor decides to use SRR, how many samples of size 2 are possible?

(b) Find the sampling distribution of the sample mean when a sample of size 2 is chosen using SRR.

(c) Compute the mean and standard deviation of the sample mean and compare them to the population.

8-26. The Sony Corporation produces an AM/FM Walkman that requires two AA batteries. Suppose the mean life of these batteries in this product is 35.0 hours. The distribution of battery lives closely follows the normal probability distribution, with a standard deviation of 5.5 hours. As a part of its testing program, Sony tests samples of 25 batteries, selected using SRN.

(a) What can you say about the shape of the distribution of the sample mean?

(b) What is the standard error of the mean?

(c) What fraction of the sample will have a mean useful life of greater than 36 hours?

(d) What fraction of the samples will have a mean useful life greater than 34.5 hours?

(e) What fraction of the samples will have a mean useful life between 34.5 and 36.0 hours?

8-27. A refrigerator manufacturer has six sales representatives at its Saint John outlet. Listed below is the number of refrigerators sold by each representative last month.

Sales Representative	Number Sold
Cunningham	54
Shah	50
Van Dal	52
Lin	48
Camp	50
Myak	52

(a) If a sample of size 4 is chosen using SRR, how many samples are possible?

(b) Find the sampling distribution of the sample mean if a sample of size 2 is selected using SRR.

(c) What are the mean and standard deviation of the population? What are the mean and standard deviation of the sample mean in part (b)?

8-28. Recent studies indicate that the typical 50-year old woman spends $350 per year for personal care products. The distribution of the amounts spent is positively skewed. We select a sample of 40 women using SRN. The mean amount spent for those sampled is $335 and the standard deviation of the sample is $45. What conclusion can we draw from this about the report that the population mean is $350 per year?

8-29. CRA CDs has set the mean lengths of the "cuts" on a CD to 135 seconds (2 minutes and 15 seconds). This will allow the disc jockeys to have plenty of time for commercials within each 10-minute segment. Assume the distribution of the length of the cuts follows approximately the normal distribution with a standard deviation of eight seconds. Suppose we select a sample of 40 cuts from various CDs sold by CRA CDs using SRN.

(a) What can we say about the shape of the distribution of the sample mean?

(b) What is the standard error of the mean?

(c) What percentage of the sample means will be greater than 138 minutes?

(d) What percentage of the sample means will be greater than 133 minutes?

(e) What percentage of the sample means will be greater than 133 but less than 138 minutes?

8-30. The TransCanada Trucking Company claims that the mean weight of its delivery trucks when they are fully loaded is 2500 kg and the standard deviation is 70 kg. Assume that the population follows the normal distribution. It has decided to select and weigh 40 trucks using SRN. Find a number, a, such that approximately 95 percent of the sample means will be in the interval $(2500 \pm a)$.

8-31. In the March 23, 2001 issue of *BC Stats Infoline*, it is reported that in 1998 the mean age at marriage for British Columbians was 28.8 years. The shape and the standard deviation of the population are both unknown. If a random sample of 60 B.C. men married in 1998 is selected using SRN, what is the likelihood that their mean age at marriage will be less than 28 years? Assume that the standard deviation of the sample is 2.5 years.

8-32. Suppose we roll a fair die two times.
(a) How many different samples are there?
(b) List each of the possible samples and compute the mean.
(c) On a chart similar to Chart 8-3, compare the distribution of sample means with the distribution of the population.
(d) Compute the mean and the standard deviation of each distribution and compare them.

8-33. The manager of Churchill's Grocery store claims that the mean amount purchased by each customer at the store is $23.50. The population is positively skewed. Answer the following questions for a sample of 50 customers selected using SRN:
(a) If the sample mean and the sample standard deviation are $25.00 and $5.00, respectively, what would be your reaction to the manager's claim?
(b) Suppose the claim is correct and the population standard deviation is known to be $6.00. Find a number, u, such that approximately 90 percent of the sample means will be in the interval $(23.5 \pm u)$.

8-34. In the June 1, 2001 issue of *BC Stats Infoline*, it is reported that a typical B.C. worker earned $666.14 per week in March 2001. Suppose a sample of 40 B.C. workers is selected using SRN, and their weekly earnings during March 2001 are recorded. In each of the following cases, what would be your reaction to the published report?
(a) The values of the sample mean and the sample standard deviation are $655 and $26.80, respectively.
(b) The values of the sample mean and the sample standard deviation are $670 and $25, respectively.

8-35. The mean SAT score for Division I student athletes is 947, with a standard deviation of 205. If you select a sample of 60 of these students using SRR, what is the probability the mean is below 900?

8-36. A politician claims that his popularity in his province is 60 percent. A sample of 100 voters from the province is selected using SRN.
(a) If the politician's claim is correct, what is the probability that at least 70 percent of the voters in the sample will support him?
(b) Suppose that only 48 percent of the voters in the sample supported our politician. What can you say about his claim?

8-37. As per the report published by the Canadian Federation of Agriculture, the number of farms in Canada has declined by about 18.3 percent since 1976. However, the total amount of land farmed has stayed relatively stable. This is because the average farm size has increased significantly. The 1996 census reported that there were 276 548 farms in Canada, and the average farm size was 608 acres. Suppose you wish to verify the claim that the average farm size has not changed since 1996 by selecting and analyzing sample data on 100 farms.

(a) What sampling method would you use to select a sample? Why?

(b) Suppose you selected a sample of 100 farms using SRN and obtained values of $\bar{x} = 560$ acres and $s = 180$ acres. Based on this information, what can you say about the claim?

8-38. A study conducted by Gallup in February 2000 indicated that 48 percent of Canadians above the age of 18 oppose same-sex marriage. Suppose we select a sample of 500 Canadians above the age of 18 using SRN.

(a) Assuming that opinions have not changed much since then, what is the probability that less than 40 percent of people in the sample will oppose same-sex marriage?

(b) If 40 percent of the sampled people say that they oppose same-sex marriage, what can you say about the findings of the Gallup study?

www.exercises.ca 8-39 TO 8-40

8-39. You need to find the typical earnings per share for an airline. You decide to sample six airlines from information available on the Internet using SRN. In its industry profile section, Yahoo! lists the following airline companies.

AMR Corporation	Deutsche Lufthansa AG	Ryanair Holdings Inc.
Air Canada, Inc.	Frontier Airlines, Inc.	SkyWest, Inc.
AirTran Holdings, Inc.	Great Lakes	
	Aviation, Ltd.	Southwest Airlines Co.
Alaska Air Group, Inc.	Hawaiian Airlines, Inc.	Tower Air, Inc.
America West		Trans World Airlines,
Holdings	Japan Airlines Co., Ltd.	Inc.
Amtran, Inc.	KLM Royal Dutch	
	Airlines	UAL Corporation
Atlantic Coast		
Airl Hldgs	Lan Chile S. A.	US Airways Group, Inc.
British Airways plc	Mesa Air Group, Inc.	Vanguard Airlines
China Eastern Airlines	Mesaba Holdings, Inc.	Virgin Express Holdings
China Southern Airlines	Midway Airlines Corp.	Western Pacific Airlines
Continental Airlines, Inc.	Midwest Express Holdings	
Delta Air Lines, Inc.	Northwest Airlines Corp.	

Number the above airlines from 00 to 33.

(a) Which airlines would be included in the sample if the random numbers are 13, 07, 41, 24, 05, 43, 01, 21?

(b) Find the current earnings per share of each of the companies in the sample as follows: Go to http://finance.yahoo.com. Click on Canadian data, Global Symbol Lookup. Type name of the company. Click on Symbol.

(c) Find the sample mean of earnings per share.

(d) Which airlines would be included in the sample if you use systematic sampling and random digits 04 is the starting point?

8-40. The Web site www.statcan.ca/english/Estat/licence.htm is a warehouse of statistical data on Canada. Go to this Web site; after accepting the licence agreement, click on Search CANSIM II. Click on Series number, input series number D845650, and click Continue twice. Retrieve monthly data from 1960

onwards in WK1 (Generic Worksheet File), time as rows format of housing starts in Canada into an Excel or Minitab worksheet.
(a) Find the mean and standard deviation of this data set.
(b) Select a sample of size 30 from this data using SRR. (Minitab will give you the sample directly. Follow instructions given in the chapter. If you use Excel, then generate random numbers and use them to get the desired sample.) Find the sample mean. Compare this value with the value of the population mean and comment, using the central limit theorem.

■■■ COMPUTER DATA EXERCISES 8-41 TO 8-43

8-41. Refer to the annual snowfall data in Halifax in file Exercise 8-41.xls on the CD.
(a) Find the population mean and standard deviation.
(b) Each of these data values is the sum of the amounts of snowfall during all the winter days in the year. Comment, using the central limit theorem, on the shape of the population distribution that you would expect.
(c) Plot a histogram of the population data. Is the shape of the histogram consistent with your expectation in (b)?
(d) What would be the mean and standard deviation of the sampling distribution of the sample mean if a sample of size 30 were selected from this data using SRR? What is the probability of getting a sample mean larger than 2030?
(e) Select a sample of size 30 using SRN. (Use Minitab or Excel.) Find the value of the sample mean.

8-42. One measure of the annual inflation rate is percentage change in the annual CPI index. Refer to the data on percentage increase in the CPI index (all items) in Canada from 1914 to 2000 given in file Exercise 8-42.xls on the CD.
(a) Find the population mean and standard deviation.
(b) What would be the mean and standard deviation of the sampling distribution of the sample mean if a sample of size 30 were selected from this data using SRR? What is the probability of getting a sample mean larger than 3 percent?
(c) Select a sample of size 30 using SRR. (Generate random numbers using Excel or Minitab.) Find the value of the sample mean and compare it with the value of the population mean, using the central limit theorem.

8-43. Suppose we are interested in standard deviation of annual inflation rates in Canada. Refer to the data on percentage increase in the CPI index (all items) in Canada from 1915 to 2000 in the file Exercise 8-43.xls on the CD.
(a) Find the population standard deviation.
(b) Sample standard deviation is a good estimator of population standard deviation. Select 50 samples each of size 30 using SRN. Find values of sample standard deviations. Plot a histogram of the values of sample standard deviations. The shape of the histogram is likely to be a good approximation of the sampling distribution of the sample standard deviation. Comment on the shape of the histogram.

CHAPTER 8   ANSWERS TO SELF-REVIEW

8-1. (a) {Phillips, C., Casey, K., Miller, C., Goggin, K., Sheaves, G.}

(b) {Phillips, C., Casey, K., Miller, C., Goggin, K., Casey, K.}

(c) {Wheeler, C., Chedore, M., Ross, C., Phillips, C., Putnam, A.}

8-2. (a) Here, $N = 40$, $n = 4$. So, $k = \dfrac{N}{n} = \dfrac{40}{4} = 10$.

The systematic sample will include the 7th, 17th, 27th, and 37th students (that is, students numbered 6, 16, 26, and 36). The sample will be {Calabrese A., Goggin K., Morin, N., Sheaves, G.}.

(b) Here, $N = 40$, $n = 9$. So, $\dfrac{N}{n} = \dfrac{40}{9} = 4.44$.

Hence, $k = 4$. The systematic sample will include students numbered 16, 20, 24, 28, 32, 36, 00, 04, 08.

(c) To choose a sample of 3 male students using SRN, renumber the 21 male students 00–20, in the order in which they appear. Using the given random numbers we get the sample {Goetzen, C., Pile, A., McDougall, D.}.

To choose a sample of 3 female students, using SRN, renumber the 19 female students 00–18 in the order in which they appear. Continuing from the last random number used, we get the sample {Sheaves, G., Casey, K., Morin, N.}.

(d) The sample of clusters we get is the 7th and 3rd clusters. So the final sample is students numbered {08, 09, 10, 11, 24, 25, 26, 27}.

8-3. (a) $\mu = \dfrac{20 + 22 + 26 + 24 + 28}{5} = 24$;

$$\sigma = \sqrt{\dfrac{(20 - 24)^2 + \cdots + (28 - 24)^2}{5}} = \sqrt{8}$$

$$= 2.828$$

(b) Sampling Distribution of the Sample Mean for SRR ($n = 2$)

Value of Sample Mean	No. of Occurrences	Probability
20	1	0.04
21	2	0.08
22	3	0.12
23	4	0.16
24	5	0.20
25	4	0.16
26	3	0.12
27	2	0.08
28	1	0.04

(c) $\mu_{\bar{X}} = 20(0.04) + \cdots + 28(0.04) = 24$;

$$\sigma_{\bar{X}} = \sqrt{(20 - 24)^2 0.04 + \cdots + (28 - 24)^2 0.04}$$

$$= 2$$

8-4. The mean of the sample means $= \mu_{\bar{X}} =$ population mean $= 10.3\%$

The standard error $=$ standard deviation of values of sample mean $= \dfrac{\sigma}{\sqrt{n}} = \dfrac{441.5}{\sqrt{40}} = 69.81\%$.

8-5. $\bar{X}$ is approximately normally distributed with

$\mu_{\bar{X}} = 3\,\text{L}$ and $\sigma_{\bar{X}} \approx \dfrac{\sigma}{\sqrt{n}} = \dfrac{0.04}{\sqrt{64}} = 0.005$. z value

corresponding to $\bar{x} = 2.995$ is $z = \dfrac{2.995 - 3}{0.005} = -1$

Area to the left of -1 under the Z curve is $0.5 - 0.3413 = 0.1587$

The probability of obtaining a value of the sample mean of 2.995 L or less is fairly high (probability $= 0.1587$). Hence, it would *not* be proper to call a sample value of 2.995 L an unlikely result.

8-6. Since the population distribution is approximately normal, $\bar{X}$ is approximately normally distributed. Suppose the claim is true. Then, $\mu_{\bar{X}} = \mu = 890$

and $\sigma_{\bar{X}} \approx \dfrac{\sigma}{\sqrt{n}}$

If we substitute $s = 70$ for σ, we get

$$t = \dfrac{\bar{x} - \mu}{s/\sqrt{n}} = \dfrac{864 - 890}{70/\sqrt{50}} = -2.626$$

Since the sample size ($n = 50$) is large enough, we can approximate "t" by "z." Area under the Z curve to the left of -2.626 is approximately $(0.5 - 0.4956) = 0.0044$. If the claim is true, the chance of getting a value of the sample mean of 864 or smaller is approximately 0.44 percent. This is very small. Hence, it is reasonable to conclude that the claim is untrue.

8-7. Since $n/N = 200/1000$ is greater than 0.05, we shall use the *finite correction factor*. Thus,

$$\sigma_{\bar{X}} = \dfrac{\sigma}{\sqrt{n}} \sqrt{\left(\dfrac{N - n}{N - 1}\right)} = \dfrac{441.5}{\sqrt{200}} \sqrt{\left(\dfrac{800}{999}\right)} = 27.937$$

$\bar{X}$ is approximately normally distributed with a mean of 10.3 and a standard deviation of 27.937.

(a) z value corresponding to $\bar{x} = 2$ is
$z = \dfrac{2 - 10.3}{27.937} = -0.297$. The area under
the Z curve to the left of -0.297 is
approximately $(0.5 - 0.1167) = 0.3833$

(b) z value corresponding to $\bar{x} = 40$ is
$z = \dfrac{40 - 10.3}{27.937} = 1.063$. The area under
the Z curve to the right of 1.063 is approximately $(0.5 - 0.3561) = 0.1439$

CHAPTER 9

Estimation and Confidence Intervals

GOALS

When you have completed this chapter, you will be able to:

- Define a point estimator, a point estimate, and desirable properties of a point estimator such as unbiasedness, efficiency, and consistency

- Define an interval estimator and an interval estimate

- Define a confidence interval, confidence level, margin of error, and a confidence interval estimate

- Construct a confidence interval for the population mean when the population standard deviation is known

- Construct a confidence interval for the population mean when the population is normally distributed and the population standard deviation is unknown

- Construct a confidence interval for a population proportion

- Determine the sample size for attribute and variable sampling

- Construct a confidence interval for the population variance when the population is normally distributed.

JERZY NEYMAN (1894–1981)

The history of the statistical theory of inference can be traced back to the works of Jacob Bernoulli, and significant contributions were made by Pierre-Simon Laplace. But the credit for putting the theory on a sound foundation goes to Jerzy Neyman (1894–1981).

Jerzy Neyman was born to Polish parents in Bendery, Russia. Neyman's first love was physics. But because of his clumsiness in the laboratory, he chose instead his second love, mathematics. During the war between Russia and Poland soon after the First World War, Neyman was jailed in Russia as an enemy alien. On his release in 1921, in an exchange of prisoners, he went to Poland. Here, he undertook a research career in statistics and lectured in statistics at various universities in Poland such as the University of Warsaw and the University of Krakow. In 1925 he went to London on a one-year Rockefeller research fellowship to work with Karl Pearson; however, he apparently found Pearson surprisingly ignorant of modern mathematics. It is said that he was bothered by Pearson's ignorance of the difference between independence and lack of correlation. However, his collaboration with Egon Pearson, son of Karl Pearson, over the next decade led to path-breaking research in statistics. Neyman and Pearson put the theory of hypothesis testing on a firm foundation. Neyman developed a sound theory of confidence interval estimators and, with his students, vastly extended the theories. This is supposed to have prompted David Kendall to remark, "We have all learned to speak Statistics with a Polish accent."

Due to financial difficulties in Poland, Neyman joined the Egon Pearson lab in London in 1934, and from there moved to Berkeley, California in 1938. Here, he set up a department of statistics that gained popularity as one of the best in the world.

Jerzy Neyman's achievements have received wide recognition. He was awarded the Guy Medal in Gold from the Royal Statistical Society (London) and the U.S. National Medal of Sciences. For a more detailed biography of Jerzy Neyman, see *The Statistical Pioneers*, by James W. Tankard Jr., Schenkman Publishing Co., 1984.

1498
1548
1598
1648
1698
1748
1898
1948
2000

INTRODUCTION

The previous chapter introduced sampling. We stressed that frequently it is not feasible to inspect an entire population: it may be too time-consuming to examine the entire population, testing may destroy the product, the cost to examine the entire population may be too great, or the results of a sample may be inadequate. We introduced several sampling techniques. We studied in detail the sampling distribution of the sample mean when the sample is chosen using simple random sampling.

Chapter 8 assumed that information about certain population parameters, such as the mean and the standard deviation, is available. In most business situations, however, such information is *not* available. In fact, an important application of sampling is in estimation of values of population parameters. For example, in many situations we need to know the value of the population mean, but it is either not possible or not feasible to collect the entire population data. In such a case, we select a random sample of observations from the population and compute from it a value that is likely to be close to the value of the population mean. We call such a value an *estimate of the population mean*. The mean of the selected sample is commonly used as an estimate of the population mean. The formula for the sample mean is then called an *estimator of the population mean*. Sometimes, we are interested in estimating the value of population variance. In this case, the sample variance of a selected sample is commonly used as an estimate of the population variance. In this chapter, we introduce basic ideas of statistical theory of estimation and inference.

 An **estimator** of a population parameter is the outcome of a procedure that involves two steps:

(i) selection of a sample of a particular size from the population using a certain sampling technique, and

(ii) application of a certain computational procedure to the selected sample data.

An outcome of an estimator of a population parameter obtained is used as an estimate of the population parameter.

In this book, in most of the results on estimation, we assume that *the sample is selected using simple random sampling*. This makes the outcome of step (i) random. For step (ii) we generally use a formula. The resultant estimator is thus a random variable.

In this chapter, we discuss two main types of estimators of population parameters: (i) *point estimators* and (ii) *interval estimators*. We begin by studying point estimators. A point estimator is an estimator such that each of its possible outcomes is a single number (such as 3.6 or 5 or −2.1). A more informative estimator is an interval estimator. Each estimate based on an interval estimator is an interval or range of values and is called an *interval estimate*.

As we shall see, an interval estimate may or may not contain the value of the population parameter being estimated. The two important criteria for evaluating an interval estimator are:

(i) accuracy: this is defined as the probability that an interval estimate obtained will contain the value of the population parameter. It is generally called the confidence level of the estimator; and

(ii) precision: this is generally measured by the width of the interval estimates. The width is generally determined by the confidence level and the standard error of the estimator.

We desire interval estimators with *high accuracy* (*high confidence level*) and *high precision* (*narrow interval estimates*). However, precision and accuracy are generally inversely related. The higher the accuracy (confidence level), the lower the precision (i.e., the larger the width of the interval estimates). We discuss how to design an interval estimator to keep the confidence level sufficiently high and the width of the interval estimates sufficiently small.

We assume in most of this chapter that the sample is selected using simple random sampling with replacement (SRR). In a few cases, where we consider simple random sampling without replacement (SRN), we state this explicitly. Recall that when the population size is large, SRN is almost the same as SRR.

9.1 POINT ESTIMATOR

> *i* If each of the possible outcomes of an estimator is a single number (such as 4.1 or −3.2), the estimator is called a **point estimator**.

For example, suppose we wish to estimate the average number of hours the executives at Nortel worked last week. Here, the population of interest is the number of hours each of the executives at Nortel worked last week, and we wish to estimate the population mean. The following could be used as a point estimator. Select a random sample of 50 executives, record the number of hours each one of them worked last week, and compute the sample mean. This point estimator can take different values depending on the selected sample. It is thus a random variable. If the mean of a selected sample happens to be 56.2 hours, then 56.2 is an estimate of the population mean. We give below some more business situations involving the use of point estimators.

- A politician may wish to estimate the fraction of voters who favour her. The fraction of voters favouring the politician in a random sample of 1000 voters serves as a good point estimator of the fraction of all the voters who favour her.

- One way to measure the health of the economy of a nation is to calculate the mean and variance of annual incomes of households. While the mean measures the average strength of the economy, a low value of variance implies a fairly even distribution of wealth. Statistics Canada uses the sample mean and the sample variance of annual household incomes of a randomly selected sample of 38 000 households to estimate the population mean and variance.

- Recent medical studies indicate that exercise is an important part of a person's overall health. The director of human resources at OCF, a large glass manufacturer, wants an estimate of the number of hours per week employees spend exercising. A sample of 70 employees reveals that the mean number of hours of exercise last week is 3.3. The sample mean of 3.3 hours is an estimate of the unknown population mean, the mean hours of exercise for all employees.

The choice of a point estimator should depend on whether a point estimate obtained would be close enough to the actual value of the population parameter. Obviously, an ideal point estimator is one that always takes the value of the population parameter being estimated. However, this is impossible to achieve unless our sample is the entire population itself. In fact, in some situations a point estimator may never take the value of the population parameter being estimated.

As an example, suppose the population of interest is heights (in cm) of all students in a class of four students and the population data are {162, 172, 158, 180}. Then, the population mean is 168 cm. Suppose a researcher who does not have access to this entire population and wants to estimate the population mean decides to use, as a point estimator, the sample mean of a sample of size two. For this point estimator, none of the 10 possible values of estimates equals the value of the population mean. (You may verify this by calculating the values of the sample mean for each of the 10 possible samples of size two.) Therefore, there is zero chance that the estimate obtained by the researcher will equal the value of the population mean.

We accept a point estimator of a population parameter as good if its possible values are concentrated close to the value of the parameter and they are distributed evenly on both sides of it. Accordingly, the properties of unbiasedness and efficiency are accepted as desirable properties of a point estimator.

UNBIASEDNESS

CHART 9-1: Distribution of an Estimator of a Population Parameter θ

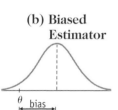

(a) Unbiased Estimator

(b) Biased Estimator

A point estimator of a population parameter is said to be an **unbiased estimator** if its expected value equals the value of the population parameter. This implies that if we select a large number of samples and obtain the corresponding large number of estimates using this point estimator, then these estimates will be distributed on either side of the value of the population parameter and their average value will almost certainly be very close to the value of the population parameter. A point estimator that is not unbiased is said to be a **biased estimator**.

> i An **unbiased estimator** of a population parameter is a point estimator of the parameter such that its expected value equals the value of the parameter.

The difference between the expected value of the point estimator and the value of the population parameter being estimated is called the size of the bias (see Charts 9-1a and 9-1b).

We saw in Chapter 8 that the sample mean $\bar{X}$ has $E(\bar{X}) = \mu$. Thus, $\bar{X}$ is an unbiased point estimator of the population mean μ. However, the sample median is not always an unbiased estimator of μ. It can similarly be shown that the sample variance S^2 is an unbiased point estimator of the population variance, σ^2.

■ SELF-REVIEW 9-1

Suppose the population of interest is heights (in cm) of all students in a class of four students and the population data are {160, 170, 165, 173}. Find the expected values of sample variance and sample standard deviation when a sample of size 2 is chosen. Verify that the sample variance is an unbiased estimator of the population variance, while the sample standard deviation is not an unbiased estimator of the population standard deviation.

Unbiasedness is a very important property and will be crucial to the results discussed in Sections 9.3 through 9.7. However, an unbiased estimator gives the true value of the population parameter *only on the average*. It does not guarantee that the individual values of estimates will be close to the value of the population parameter. For example, suppose the value of a population parameter is 200. Consider a point estimator of the population parameter, which can take a value of 20 or 380, each with a probability of half. (That is, if we repeatedly obtain estimates using this estimator, half the time the value obtained is 20 and half the time it is 380.) Then, this is an unbiased estimator ($\frac{1}{2}(20) + \frac{1}{2}(380) = 200$ = value of the population parameter). However, in this case, neither of the two possible values of the estimator is close to the value of the population parameter.

Therefore, not every unbiased estimator is necessarily a good estimator. We require, in addition, that the possible values of estimates be concentrated close to the value of the population parameter.

RELATIVE EFFICIENCY AND EFFICIENCY

The basic idea behind the term **efficiency** is that the probability should be high that the value of an estimate obtained will be close to the value of the population parameter. Unfortunately, statisticians have not agreed upon a precise, simple definition of this term. In the context of unbiased estimators, however, efficiency can be easily defined in terms of variance of the estimators.

An unbiased estimator of a population parameter is said to be **relatively more efficient** than another unbiased estimator of the parameter if its variance is smaller than that of the other estimator.

Chart 9-2 below, shows distributions of two unbiased estimators, A and B, of a population parameter θ. Estimator A has a smaller variance. Hence, it is relatively more efficient than estimator B.

Needless to say, if we have two unbiased estimators, then we shall choose one that is relatively more efficient, provided the costs of obtaining estimates based on these two estimators are more or less the same.

> i An unbiased estimator of a population parameter is said to be **efficient** if it has minimum variance in the class of unbiased estimators of the parameter.

The choice of sample mean as an estimator of population mean should be intuitively obvious. However, a mathematical justification for it also exists. We have already seen that the sample mean is an unbiased estimator of μ. It can be shown that if the population distribution is normal, then for any fixed sample size n, the sample mean has the smallest variance among all the unbiased estimators of μ. Thus, in this case, *sample mean is an efficient estimator of μ.*

Another desirable property of a point estimator is *consistency*. We shall discuss it in Section 9.6.

CHART 9-2: Distribution of Two Unbiased Estimators of a Population Parameter θ

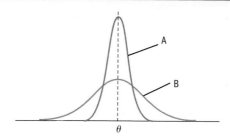

EXERCISES 9-1 TO 9-4

9-1. Define an unbiased estimator.

9-2. Suppose we are interested in estimating the largest value in a certain population data set. (For example, we may be interested in estimating the size of the largest fish in a lake or the maximum drop in a single day in the value of the TSE 300 index in the last 30 years.) Consider the following point estimator: select a random sample of size n from the population. Find the largest value in the sample.
   (a) Do you think this is an unbiased estimator of the "largest value in the population"? Why?
   (b) Suppose the population data set is the marks of all the students in an advanced-level statistics class of four students and is {85, 60, 92, 78}. Find all the possible estimates for this point estimator when sample size is 2, and check if this is an unbiased estimator of the "largest value in the population."

9-3. Define relative efficiency of an unbiased estimator.

9-4. The sample median is not always an unbiased estimator of the population mean μ. However, it can be shown that if the population is normally distributed then the sample median $\hat{X}$ has $E(\hat{X}) = \mu$ and $\sigma_{\hat{X}} = 1.25 \dfrac{\sigma}{\sqrt{n}}$. For a given sample size, compare the sample mean and the sample median and identify which is a relatively more efficient estimator of the mean of a normally distributed population.

9.2 INTERVAL ESTIMATOR AND CONFIDENCE INTERVAL

We saw in the previous section that the value of a point estimate will hardly ever be exactly equal to the value of the population parameter being estimated. A point estimate by itself, therefore, does not give us sufficient information about the value of the population parameter. It has to be supplemented by additional information about how close the estimated value is likely to be to the actual value of the population parameter. A more useful estimator, in this sense, is an interval estimator. An estimator such that each of the possible estimates obtained from it is an interval or range of numbers—such as all the numbers between 5 and 8; we denote it by (5, 8), where 8 is the upper limit and 5 is the lower limit—is called an *interval estimator*.

Out of all the interval estimates, which are outcomes of an interval estimator, some will contain the true value of the population parameter being estimated and some will not. Suppose that the probability is 0.9 that an interval estimate obtained will contain the value of the population parameter. (That is, if we obtain a large number of interval estimates using this estimator, then 90 percent of these intervals will contain the population parameter.) Then we call the interval estimator a *90 percent or 0.9 confidence interval* and we call 90 percent, or 0.9, its *confidence level*. This measures the accuracy of the estimator. The confidence level is commonly denoted by $(1 - \alpha)$. Thus, for a 90-percent confidence level, $(1 - \alpha) = 0.9$ or $\alpha = 1 - 0.9 = 0.1$. For a 99-percent confidence level, $\alpha = 1 - 0.99 = 0.01$. We call the upper and lower limits of a confidence interval the *upper and lower confidence limits*, respectively. The upper and lower confidence limits are random variables. (Their values may vary from interval estimate to interval estimate.)

> i An **interval estimator** of a population parameter is an estimator of the parameter such that each of its possible outcomes is an interval or range of numbers. An outcome of an interval estimator is called an **interval estimate**. It is an interval in which we expect the value of the population parameter to lie. If the probability is $(1 - \alpha)$ that an interval estimate obtained will contain the value of the population parameter, then we call the interval estimator a **$(1 - \alpha)$ confidence interval** and we call $(1 - \alpha)$ its **confidence level**. The upper and lower limits of a confidence interval are called **upper** and **lower confidence limits**, respectively.

For example, suppose the Canadian Management Association decides to use a 95-percent confidence interval to estimate the mean income of middle managers in the retail industry. If this interval estimator is used repeatedly to obtain several confidence interval estimates, then some of these intervals will contain the true value of the mean income while others will not.

Chart 9-3, below, shows some of the possible values of interval estimates. Note that not all of the intervals include the population mean. Both of the endpoints of the fifth interval are less than the population mean. Since the estimator used is a 95-percent confidence interval, if we use it to obtain several hundred interval estimates, then about 95 percent of those intervals will contain the true value of the mean income while about 5 percent will not.

Suppose a government agency wishes to estimate the mean yearly income of construction workers in Ontario and use this information for some important policy decision. Suppose we use a 90-percent confidence interval and obtain an interval estimate of ($53 000, $59 000$). The fact that we used a 90-percent confidence interval merely implies that an interval estimate obtained may or may not contain the value of the population mean and the probability is 0.9 of obtaining an interval containing the value of the population mean. The specific interval estimate obtained, such as ($53 000, $59 000$), may or may not contain the true value of the population mean. Should the agency therefore assume that this particular interval contains the population mean and incorporate this in its policy decision? This is a decision the management will have to make and it will depend on (i) the value of the confidence level of the estimator and (ii) the cost of making a decision based on wrong information, if in reality the interval does not contain the value of the population mean. In certain applications, a confidence level of 90 percent is considered high enough, while in certain sensitive cases we require higher values of confidence levels.

CHART 9-3: Some Confidence Interval Estimates of μ

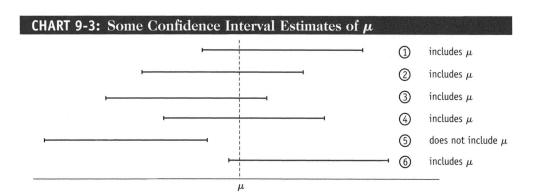

One convenient method of designing a confidence interval estimator for a population parameter is to take an unbiased point estimator of the parameter and define an interval of reasonable width around it. We shall now see how to design such estimators for population mean and population variance.

9.3 CONFIDENCE INTERVALS FOR POPULATION MEAN (WHEN σ IS KNOWN)

We saw in Chapter 7 how to calculate probabilities corresponding to the standard normal variable Z. For convenience, let us introduce a new notation.

Let us call the region under the Z curve to the right of a given z value, the *right tail* and the region under the curve to the left of a given z value, the *left tail*.

For any value a between 0 and 1, let us denote by z_a the z value with area (probability) of the corresponding right tail equal to a. If a is between 0 and 0.5 then the area between 0 and z_a is $(0.5 - a)$. The value of z_a is therefore the z value in the Z table corresponding to a probability of $(0.5 - a)$.

For example, $z_{0.05}$ is the z value in the Z table (Appendix 3 on the CD-ROM) corresponding to probability of $(0.5 - 0.05) = 0.45$ and equals 1.645; $z_{0.025}$ is the z value in the Z table corresponding to a probability of $(0.5 - 0.025) = 0.475$ and it equals 1.96.

By symmetry of the Z curve, the area of the left tail corresponding to $-z_a$ is also a.

Now, for any value α between 0 and 1, let $a = \alpha/2$. Then, the left tail probability corresponding to $-z_{\alpha/2}$ and the right tail probability corresponding to $z_{\alpha/2}$ are each $\alpha/2$.

Therefore, the area between $-z_{\alpha/2}$ and $z_{\alpha/2}$ is $(1 - \alpha)$.

We thus have,

$$P(-z_{\alpha/2} \leq Z \leq z_{\alpha/2}) = (1 - \alpha) \qquad \text{9-1}$$

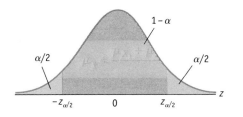
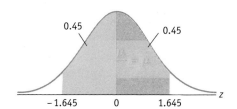

For example, for $\alpha = 0.1$, we have $\alpha/2 = 0.05$, $z_{0.05} = 1.645$, and $(1 - \alpha) = 0.9$. Hence, $P(-1.645 \leq Z \leq 1.645) = 0.9$.

Similarly, we get,

$$P(-1.96 \leq Z \leq 1.96) = 0.95$$
$$P(-2.58 \leq Z \leq 2.58) = 0.99$$

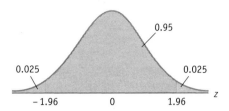
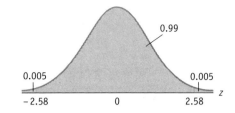

We saw in Chapter 8 that the sample mean $\bar{X}$ has $E(\bar{X}) = \mu$ (the population mean) and its standard deviation (also called standard error of the mean) is $\sigma_{\bar{X}} = \dfrac{\sigma}{\sqrt{n}}$, where σ is the population standard deviation. Furthermore, if the population is approximately normally distributed or the sample size is large, then $\bar{X}$ is approximately normally distributed, and therefore $Z = \dfrac{(\bar{X} - \mu)}{\sigma/\sqrt{n}}$ is approximately standard normal. Making this substitution for Z in Formula 9-1, we get:

$$P\left(-z_{\alpha/2} \leq \frac{\bar{X} - \mu}{\sigma/\sqrt{n}} \leq z_{\alpha/2}\right) = (1 - \alpha) \qquad \text{9-2}$$

Simple algebraic manipulation of Formula 9-2 yields the following.[1]

$$P(\bar{X} - z_{\alpha/2}\,\sigma/\sqrt{n} \leq \mu \leq \bar{X} + z_{\alpha/2}\sigma/\sqrt{n}) = (1 - \alpha) \qquad \text{9-3}$$

For example,

$$P(\bar{X} - 1.645\sigma/\sqrt{n} \leq \mu \leq \bar{X} + 1.645\sigma/\sqrt{n}) = 0.90$$
$$P(\bar{X} - 1.96\sigma/\sqrt{n} \leq \mu \leq \bar{X} + 1.96\sigma/\sqrt{n}) = 0.95$$
$$P(\bar{X} - 2.58\sigma/\sqrt{n} \leq \mu \leq \bar{X} + 2.58\sigma/\sqrt{n}) = 0.99$$

■ SELF-REVIEW 9-2

Find the appropriate value of z in each of the following cases:

(a) $P(\bar{X} - z\sigma/\sqrt{n} \leq \mu \leq \bar{X} + z\sigma/\sqrt{n}) = 0.8$

(b) $P(\bar{X} - z\sigma/\sqrt{n} \leq \mu \leq \bar{X} + z\sigma/\sqrt{n}) = 0.94$

(c) $P(\bar{X} - z\sigma/\sqrt{n} \leq \mu \leq \bar{X} + z\sigma/\sqrt{n}) = 0.98$

The above expressions have the following interpretation:

Suppose the population is normally distributed or the sample size n is large. If we select a sample of size n and compute the interval $(\bar{X} - 1.645\sigma/\sqrt{n}, \bar{X} + 1.645\sigma/\sqrt{n})$, then the probability is 0.9 that the interval obtained will contain the value of the population mean μ. Thus, $(\bar{X} - 1.645\sigma/\sqrt{n}, \bar{X} + 1.645\sigma/\sqrt{n})$ is a 90-percent confidence interval.

We often write it as $(\bar{X} \pm 1.645\sigma/\sqrt{n})$.

It follows similarly that, $(\bar{X} - 1.96\sigma/\sqrt{n}, \bar{X} + 1.96\sigma/\sqrt{n})$(or $(\bar{X} \pm 1.96\sigma/\sqrt{n})$) is a 95-percent confidence interval and

$(\bar{X} - 2.58\sigma/\sqrt{n}, \bar{X} + 2.58\sigma/\sqrt{n})$ (or $(\bar{X} \pm 2.58\sigma/\sqrt{n})$) is a 99-percent confidence interval.

 In general,

$$(\bar{X} - z_{\alpha/2}\sigma/\sqrt{n}, \bar{X} + z_{\alpha/2}\sigma/\sqrt{n}) \text{ or } (\bar{X} \pm z_{\alpha/2}\sigma/\sqrt{n}) \qquad \text{9-4}$$

is a $(1 - \alpha)$ confidence interval of the population mean, μ.

$(1 - \alpha)$ is called the confidence level.

$\bar{X} - z_{\alpha/2}\sigma/\sqrt{n}$ is called the lower confidence limit (LCL).

$\bar{X} + z_{\alpha/2}\sigma/\sqrt{n}$ is called the upper confidence limit (UCL).

■ SELF-REVIEW 9-3

If a sample of size n is chosen from a population that is approximately normally distributed, find expressions for each of the following:

(a) An 80-percent confidence interval for the population mean.
(b) A 98-percent confidence interval for the population mean.
(c) An 85-percent confidence interval for the population mean.

A COMPUTER SIMULATION

With the aid of a computer, we can randomly select samples from a population, quickly compute the confidence interval, and show how confidence intervals usually, but not always, include the population parameter. Example 9-1 will help to explain.

Example 9-1

From many years in the automobile leasing business, Town Bank knows the distance driven, (in thousands of km), on a four-year lease is normally distributed with a mean of 80 and a standard deviation of 8. Suppose we want to find what proportion of the 95-percent confidence interval estimates will include the population mean of 80. Select 60 random samples, of size 30 each, from a normal distribution with a mean of 80 and a standard deviation of 8. Calculate, for each sample, the 95-percent confidence interval estimate.

Solution

We start with Minitab instructions for (i) generating 60 random samples, each of size 30, from a normal distribution with mean 80 and standard deviation 8; and (ii) calculating the corresponding 60 interval estimates.

MINITAB INSTRUCTIONS FOR GENERATING RANDOM DATA
1. Click on Calc, Random Data, and Normal.
2. Enter Generate 30 rows of data, Store in column(s): C1–C60, Mean: 80, Standard deviation: 8.
3. Click OK.

MINITAB CHART: 9–4

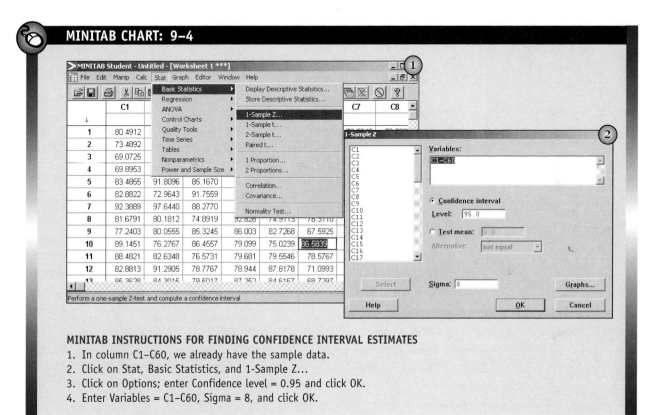

MINITAB INSTRUCTIONS FOR FINDING CONFIDENCE INTERVAL ESTIMATES
1. In column C1–C60, we already have the sample data.
2. Click on Stat, Basic Statistics, and 1-Sample Z...
3. Click on Options; enter Confidence level = 0.95 and click OK.
4. Enter Variables = C1–C60, Sigma = 8, and click OK.

The results of 60 random samples of size 30 each are in the table below. Of 60 confidence interval estimates with a 95-percent confidence level produced, 2—or 3.33 percent—did not include the population mean of 80. The intervals that do *not* include the population mean are highlighted. Another set of 60 confidence intervals would have a different result. The 3.33 percent is close to the estimate that 5 percent of the intervals will not include the population mean and the 58 of 60, or 96.67 percent, is close to 95 percent.

Variable	Mean	95.0% CI	Variable	Mean	95.0% CI
C1	81.81	(78.95, 84.67)	C8	79.18	(76.32, 82.04)
C2	79.92	(77.06, 82.78)	C9	**76.95**	**(74.09, 79.81)**
C3	80.33	(77.47, 83.19)	C10	78.79	(75.92, 81.65)
C4	81.02	(78.15, 83.88)	C11	78.86	(76.00, 81.73)
C5	78.98	(76.12, 81.84)	C12	81.93	(79.06, 84.79)
C6	79.13	(76.27, 82.00)	C13	82.45	(79.59, 85.32)
C7	80.90	(78.04, 83.77)	C14	79.92	(77.06, 82.78)

Variable	Mean	95.0% CI	Variable	Mean	95.0% CI
C15	79.60	(76.74, 82.47)	C38	78.13	(75.27, 81.00)
C16	78.50	(75.64, 81.36)	C39	81.40	(78.54, 84.26)
C17	79.95	(77.08, 82.81)	C40	81.09	(78.23, 83.95)
C18	79.79	(76.93, 82.65)	C41	79.04	(76.17, 81.90)
C19	80.67	(77.81, 83.54)	C42	77.37	(74.50, 80.23)
C20	78.98	(76.11, 81.84)	C43	78.98	(76.12, 81.84)
C21	81.01	(78.14, 83.87)	C44	80.50	(77.63, 83.36)
C22	80.24	(77.38, 83.10)	**C45**	**83.43**	**(80.57, 86.29)**
C23	77.95	(75.09, 80.81)	C46	79.42	(76.56, 82.28)
C24	79.39	(76.52, 82.25)	C47	78.07	(75.21, 80.93)
C25	79.53	(76.67, 82.40)	C48	81.95	(79.09, 84.81)
C26	78.94	(76.07, 81.80)	C49	81.63	(78.77, 84.49)
C27	78.01	(75.15, 80.87)	C50	77.99	(75.13, 80.85)
C28	81.16	(78.30, 84.03)	C51	80.09	(77.23, 82.96)
C29	81.18	(78.32, 84.04)	C52	81.46	(78.60, 84.32)
C30	79.54	(76.68, 82.40)	C53	78.05	(75.19, 80.92)
C31	81.67	(78.81, 84.53)	C54	79.72	(76.86, 82.58)
C32	82.09	(79.23, 84.96)	C55	79.46	(76.60, 82.32)
C33	78.91	(76.04, 81.77)	C56	79.53	(76.67, 82.39)
C34	79.90	(77.03, 82.76)	C57	79.46	(76.60, 82.32)
C35	82.16	(79.30, 85.03)	C58	79.84	(76.97, 82.70)
C36	79.16	(76.30, 82.03)	C59	78.31	(75.44, 81.17)
C37	80.10	(77.23, 82.96)	C60	79.73	(76.87, 82.59)

To explain the calculation in more detail: Minitab began by selecting a random sample of 30 observations from a population with a mean of 80 and a standard deviation of 8. The mean of these 30 observations is 81.81. The endpoints of the confidence interval are 78.95 and 84.67. These endpoints are determined by substituting in Formula 9–4 the sample value $\bar{x}$ of $\bar{X}$.

$$\bar{x} \pm z_{0.025}\frac{\sigma}{\sqrt{n}} = 81.81 \pm 1.96\frac{8}{\sqrt{30}} = 81.81 \pm 1.96(1.46) = (78.95, 84.67)$$

We could also use Excel to generate the required output; see instructions below.

EXCEL INSTRUCTIONS: GENERATING RANDOM DATA
1. Click on Tools, Data Analysis, Random Number Generation.
2. Input Number of Variables = 60, Number of Random Numbers = 30, Distribution = Normal, Mean = 80, Standard Deviation = 8. Choose New Worksheet Ply under Output options and click OK.

EXCEL INSTRUCTIONS: FINDING CONFIDENCE INTERVAL ESTIMATES
1. Find the mean of each of the 60 columns A to BH. (See instructions in Chapter 3.)
2. Copy the columns of means and paste it as new column BJ. (This can be done by right clicking on BJ1 and selecting Paste Special, Values, and Transpose.)
3. In new column BK, input 60 values of $z_{\alpha/2}\,\sigma/\sqrt{n}$ (in this case, 1.96 $8/\sqrt{30}$ = 2.86).
4. Let BL1 = BK1, and BM1 = BJ1 + BK1. Drag BL1 and BM1 to fill 60 cells. The entries in BL and BM give lower and upper limits of confidence level estimates, respectively.

Example 9-2

An economics professor wishes to estimate the mean value of earnings per share of the list of the top 1000 companies in Canada during 2000 as published by Globe Interactive. He selected a random sample of 30 of the companies and recorded their earnings per share. The sample data are given below.

0.30	1.39	0.51	1.24	−0.24	0.68	1.61	8.21	−3.04	0.07
−0.14	0.17	6.61	−12.21	1.12	−0.98	0.69	0.2	0.42	−3.04
2.94	−0.44	−0.56	−0.26	1.61	1.23	0.04	1.2	0.13	−0.52

The population is known to be approximately normally distributed. Suppose the population standard deviation is 3.04.

    (a) Obtain a point estimate of the mean value of earnings per share of the 1000 companies.

    (b) Find a 95-percent confidence interval estimate of the mean value of earnings per share of the 1000 companies.

    (c) Interpret the results.

Solution

Since the population is approximately normally distributed, and the value of n is also reasonably large, $\bar{X}$ is approximately normally distributed.

    (a) The best point estimate we can get of the unknown value of the population mean is the value of the sample mean $\bar{x} = \dfrac{(0.3 + 1.39 + \cdots + 0.13 - 0.52)}{30}$

         $= 0.298$.

    (b) Using Formula 9-4, we get the following 95-percent confidence interval estimate for the population mean: $(\bar{x} \pm z_{0.025}\sigma/\sqrt{n}) = (0.298 \pm (1.96)$ $(3.04)/\sqrt{30}) = (0.298 \pm 1.088)$, or $(-0.79, 1.386)$.

Solutions to (a) and (b) above could also be obtained using Excel or Minitab. If we use Excel, we shall have to separately compute $\bar{x}$ and the margin of error and then add and subtract the margin of error from $\bar{x}$ to get the interval estimate. The printout of the Minitab output is provided below.

MINITAB OUTPUT
One-Sample Z: C1
The assumed sigma = 3.04

Variable	N	Mean	StDev	SEMean	95.0% CI
C1	30	0.298	3.221	0.555	(−0.790, 1.386)

    (c) The above 95-percent confidence interval estimate has the following interpretation. Suppose we select a large number of samples of 30 companies each, and for each sample we compute the sample mean and a 95-percent confidence interval estimate, such as we did above. Then about 95 percent of these intervals will contain the value of population mean μ. About 5 percent of the intervals will not contain the value of μ. We do not know if the interval $(-0.790, 1.386)$ obtained above contains the value of μ. However given the high confidence level of the estimator, it will not be unreasonable to expect this interval to contain the value of μ.

■ SELF-REVIEW 9-4

Suppose the monthly percentage changes in the TSE 300 index from 1980 to 2000 are approximately normally distributed with a standard deviation of 2.05 percent. To estimate the mean value of monthly percentage changes during this period, a sample of size 20 was selected and is given below. (Source: CANSIM D100050.)

| 3.92 | 1.69 | 1.79 | −1.00 | −2.05 | 1.41 | 2.65 | −1.09 | 3.92 | 1.48 |
| 2.00 | 0.85 | 0.31 | 1.46 | 3.92 | 0.94 | 0.46 | 2.91 | 0.23 | 0.71 |

Find a 90-percent confidence interval estimate of the population mean.

MARGIN OF ERROR

 In the expression $(\bar{X} \pm z_{\alpha/2}\sigma/\sqrt{n})$ for $(1 - \alpha)$ confidence interval of the population mean μ, the term $\pm z_{\alpha/2}\sigma/\sqrt{n}$ is called the **margin of error**.

Thus, the margin of error for a 90-percent confidence interval of μ is $\pm 1.645\sigma/\sqrt{n}$, and for a 95-percent confidence interval of μ is $\pm 1.96\sigma/\sqrt{n}$. The margin of error decides the width (precision) of the confidence interval. Its value depends on σ, n, and α. As we discussed before, the confidence level $(1 - \alpha)$ measures the accuracy of the interval estimator. For given values of σ, and n, if we increase the confidence level $(1 - \alpha)$ then α decreases and therefore, $z_{\alpha/2}$ increases. This causes the margin of error, and therefore the width of the interval, to increase (and its precision to decrease). Please note that for a given value of $(1 - \alpha)$, if we increase the sample size n, the margin of error decreases. (For example, calculate margins of error for $(\sigma = 2, (1 - \alpha) = 0.95, n = 10)$ and for $(\sigma = 2, (1 - \alpha) = 0.95, n = 50)$.) We shall come back to this point in Section 9.6.

EXERCISES 9-5 TO 9-8

9-5. Give expressions for the standard error of the mean, margin of error, and confidence interval for population mean μ in each of the following cases.
   (a) Population is approximately normally distributed, a sample of size 8 is chosen, and we want $\alpha = 0.1$.
   (b) A sample of size 50 is chosen, and we want $\alpha = 0.025$.
   (c) A sample of size 60 is chosen, and we want $\alpha = 0.01$.

9-6. Find expressions for margin of error and confidence interval for population mean μ in each of the following cases.
   (a) A sample of size 64 is chosen and we want $\alpha = 0.025$.
   (b) Population is approximately normally distributed, a sample of size 15 is chosen, and we want $\alpha = 0.01$.
   (c) A sample of size 100 is chosen, and we want $\alpha = 0.05$.
   (d) Population is approximately normally distributed, a sample of size 9 is chosen, and we want $\alpha = 0.1$.

9-7. The Canadian Sugar Producers' Association wants to estimate the mean yearly sugar consumption by adult Canadians. A sample of yearly sugar consumption by 16 Canadian adults was selected and the value of the sample mean obtained was 26 kg. Assuming the population is approximately normally distributed with a standard deviation of 6 kg, develop a 90-percent confidence interval estimate for the population mean.

9-8. The Greater Toronto Area Chamber of Commerce wants to estimate the mean time workers employed in the downtown area spend getting to work. A sample of 15 workers revealed the following numbers of minutes travelled:

29	38	38	33	37	21	42	34	29	35
40	38	34	42	30					

Assuming that the population distribution is approximately normal with a standard deviation of 5.2, develop a 98-percent confidence interval estimate for the population mean. Interpret the result.

9.4 CONFIDENCE INTERVALS FOR POPULATION MEAN WHEN THE POPULATION STANDARD DEVIATION (σ) IS UNKNOWN

In Section 9-3, we obtained an expression for the confidence interval for the population mean using the sample mean as a point estimator when (i) either the population is approximately normally distributed or the sample size is large enough, and (ii) the value of the population standard deviation σ is known. Though situations where μ is unknown but σ is known occur sometimes in manufacturing environments, such cases are uncommon in business and economics. We shall now deal with the situations where both μ and σ are unknown. In Chapter 9 Appendix A on the CD-Rom, we develop confidence intervals for unknown population variance σ^2. In this section, we shall develop confidence intervals for population mean μ when σ is unknown.

We shall now obtain expressions for the confidence interval for μ when

(i) the population is normally distributed; and

(ii) the population standard deviation is unknown.

We have seen that under condition (i) $\bar{X}$ is normally distributed with mean μ and standard deviation $\dfrac{\sigma}{\sqrt{n}}$. Thus, $\dfrac{\bar{X} - \mu}{\sigma/\sqrt{n}} = Z$ (the standard normal variable). This allows us to obtain an expression for a $(1 - \alpha)$ confidence interval for μ as $(\bar{X} \pm z_{\alpha/2}\, \sigma/\sqrt{n})$.

Now, if the value of the population standard deviation σ is unknown, the logical alternative is to replace σ by its estimator S, obtained from the sample. But the random variable $\dfrac{\bar{X} - \mu}{S/\sqrt{n}}$ is not normally distributed.

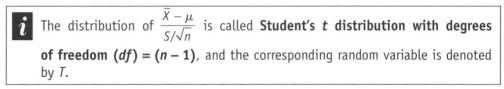

> **𝑖** The distribution of $\dfrac{\bar{X} - \mu}{S/\sqrt{n}}$ is called **Student's t distribution with degrees of freedom (df) = ($n - 1$)**, and the corresponding random variable is denoted by T.

(For a precise definition of Student's t distribution, refer to Chapter 9 Appendix B on the CD-ROM.)

WILLIAM SEALY GOSSETT (1876–1937)

William Sealy Gossett (1876–1937) was born in Canterbury, England. He obtained a first in mathematical moderations in 1897 and a first-class degree in chemistry in 1899, both from New College, Oxford. Soon after graduation, he joined Arthur Guinness and Sons, the brewers in Dublin, and remained with Guinness for the rest of his life. At Guinness, William was involved in statistical work concerning the effect of different factors on the quality of beer. This work mainly involved small-sample data sets. Since most of the statistical results available at that time dealt with large samples, a significant part of his research involved original, path-breaking work on small-sample theories. In this, he benefitted immensely from his association with Karl and Egon Pearson, R. Fisher, and J. Neyman. Due to the obsession with secrecy in industrial circles in the United Kingdom at that time, Guinness permitted him to publish his work provided a pseudonym was used. Hence, he published all his work under the name "Student." His most well-known work is his 1908 paper, "The Probable Error of a Mean," in which he gave a characterization of and the table of probabilities for the distribution of $\dfrac{(\bar{X} - \mu)}{S/\sqrt{n}}$ when a random sample of size n is chosen from a normal distribution. This distribution is now known as "Student's t distribution."

Gossett was a modest, kind, and tolerant man who disliked controversy. He was a good carpenter and was very fond of operas. For a more detailed biography of William Gossett, see *"Student": A Statistical Biography of William Sealy Gosset—Based on writings by E.S. Pearson*, edited by R.L. Plackett and G.A. Barnard, Oxford University Press, 1990.

STUDENT'S *t* DISTRIBUTION

Student's t distributions have the following characteristics:

- Like the Z (standard normal) distribution, Student's t distribution is a continuous distribution, and it takes values between $-\infty$ and $+\infty$.
- Like the Z distribution, it is bell-shaped and symmetrical about zero.
- We have different t distributions for different values $v = 1, 2, \ldots$ of degrees of freedom.
- The t distribution is more spread out and flatter at the centre than the Z distribution. For larger and larger values of df, the t distribution becomes closer and closer to standard normal distribution.

The t distributions for different values of df and the standard normal distribution are shown graphically in Chart 9-5.

PROBABILITIES UNDER A *t* DISTRIBUTION

Gosset developed a table of probabilities under t distributions. Some key probabilities are given in the table of "Student's t distribution" at the end of the book. We shall refer to it as the **t table**.

For example, suppose we want a value t such that the area (probability) under the t curve with $df = 12$ to the right of this t value is 0.025. We call the region under the curve

CHART 9-5: t Distributions for $df = 2$ and $df = 10$ and the Standard Normal Distribution

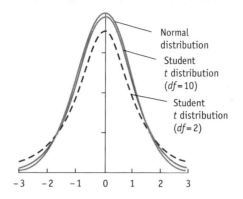

to the right of the t value the *right tail* and the region under the curve to the left of the t value the *left tail*. We denote the number, with corresponding right-tail probability equal to 0.025, by $t_{0.025}$. This number is given in the t table in the row corresponding to $df = 12$ and the column corresponding to "level of significance for one-tailed test" = 0.025. Thus, $t_{0.025} = 2.179$.

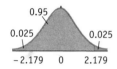

Note that a t distribution is symmetrical about zero. Hence, the left-tail probability corresponding to $-t_{0.025}$ ($= -2.179$) also equals 0.025. This gives us the area between -2.179 and $+2.179$ equal to $(1 - 0.025 - 0.025) = 0.95$.

In general, for any α between 0 and 1, the number $t_{\alpha/2}$ is such that the right-tail probability corresponding to it equals $\alpha/2$; the left-tail probability corresponding to $-t_{\alpha/2}$ also equals $\alpha/2$. The sum of the areas of the two tails equals α. The area under the t curve between $-t_{\alpha/2}$ and $t_{\alpha/2}$ is thus $(1 - \alpha)$; that is,

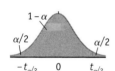

$$P(-t_{\alpha/2} \leq T \leq t_{\alpha/2}) = (1 - \alpha) \qquad \text{9-5}$$

The value of $t_{\alpha/2}$ is given in the t table in the row corresponding to the given value of df and the column corresponding to "level of significance for one-tailed test" = $\alpha/2$.

Example 9-3

(a) For a t curve corresponding to $df = 12$, find $t_{0.1}$.
(b) For a t curve corresponding to $df = 20$, find the value of t such that the area under the curve to the left of t is 0.01.
(c) For a t curve corresponding to $df = 15$, find the value of t such that the area under the curve to the right of t is 0.95.
(d) For a t curve corresponding to $df = 40$, find the value of t such that the area under the curve between $-t$ and t is 0.9.

Solution

(a) We want the value of $t_{0.1}$. This is given in the t table in the row corresponding to $df = 12$ and the column corresponding to "level of significance for one-tailed test" = 0.1 and equals 1.356.
(b) The right-tail probability corresponding to $t_{0.01}$ is 0.01. Hence, the left-tail probability corresponding to $-t_{0.01}$ is also 0.01. The required value of t is thus $-t_{0.01}$. The value $t_{0.01}$ is given in the t table in the row corresponding to $df = 20$ and the column corresponding to "level of significance for one-tailed test" = 0.01. It equals 2.528. Thus, the desired value of t is -2.528.

(c) Since the area to the right of t is required to be 0.95, the area to the left of t is $(1 - 0.95) = 0.05$. Thus, $t = -t_{0.05}$. The value $t_{0.05}$ is given in the t table in the row corresponding to $df = 15$ and the column corresponding to "level of significance for one-tailed test" = 0.05 and equals 1.753. Thus, $t = -1.753$.

(d) $(1 - \alpha) = 0.9$. Hence, $\alpha = 0.1$ and $P(-t_{0.05} \leq T \leq t_{0.05}) = 0.9$. The value of $t = t_{0.05}$ is given in the t table in the row corresponding to $df = 40$ and the column corresponding to "level of significance for one-tailed test" = 0.05 and equals 1.684.

■ SELF-REVIEW 9-5

(a) For a t distribution with $df = 20$, find the value of t such that the area under the curve between $-t$ and $+t$ is 0.9.

(b) For a t distribution with $df = 15$, find $t_{0.1}$.

(c) For a t distribution with $df = 10$, find the value of t such that the left tail area is 0.01.

The t table gives only the important probabilities under the t curves. General areas under the t curves can be obtained using computer software. Instructions for this using Excel and Minitab are provided in Charts 9-6 and 9-7.

Suppose we want an area between -2.4 and $+2.4$ under the t curve with $df = 10$. MegaStat in Excel gives the area to the right of $+2.4$, which is denoted by $p(\text{upper})$, and the area to the right of -2.4, which is denoted by $p(\text{lower})$. We see from the computer output that $p(\text{upper}) = 0.0187$ and $p(\text{lower}) = 0.9813$. Thus, the area between -2.4 and $+2.4$ is $p(\text{lower}) - p(\text{upper}) = 0.9813 - 0.0187 = 0.9626$.

Minitab, on the other hand, gives the cumulative probability (the total area to the left of $+2.4$) to be 0.981342. Hence, the right-tail area $= \alpha/2 = (1 - 0.981342)$

EXCEL CHART 9-6

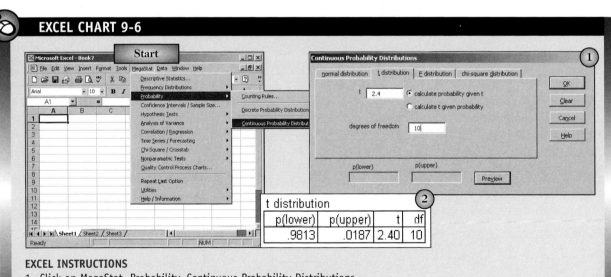

EXCEL INSTRUCTIONS

1. Click on MegaStat, Probability, Continuous Probability Distributions.

2. Select t distribution.

3. Select Calculate probability given t, enter value of t ($= 2.4$ in our case), degrees of freedom ($= 10$ in our example) and click OK. The output will appear on Excel worksheet.

(For finding inverse probability, select Calculate t given probability.)

MINITAB CHART 9-7

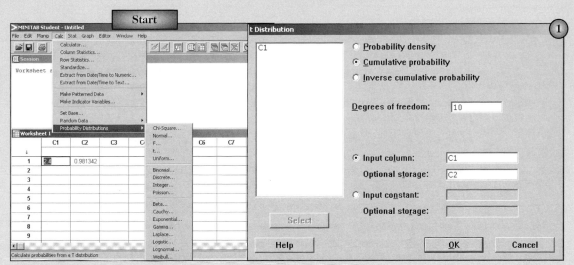

MINITAB INSTRUCTIONS

1. In column C1, input the value of t (in our example $t = 2.4$).

2. Click on Calc, Probability Distributions, and t.

3. Select Cumulative probability. Enter Degrees of freedom (in our example it is 10), Input column C1 and Optional storage = C2. Click OK. The output will appear in column C2.

(For finding inverse probability, select Inverse cumulative probability instead of Cumulative probability.)

= 0.0186584. So, $\alpha = 2(0.018658) = 0.037316$ and the area between -2.4 and $+2.4$ is $(1 - \alpha) = (1 - 0.037316) = 0.962684$.

For both MegaStat and Minitab, instructions for finding inverse probability (that is, finding the value of t corresponding to given values of df and probability) are similar. In MegaStat, we have to choose "calculate t given probability" instead of "calculate probability given t." In Minitab, choose "Inverse cumulative probability" instead of "Cumulative probability."

COMPUTING CONFIDENCE INTERVALS FOR POPULATION MEAN WHEN σ IS UNKNOWN

We saw on page 373 that if a population is normally distributed, then for a sample of size n, $T = \dfrac{\bar{X} - \mu}{S/\sqrt{n}}$ follows a Student's t distribution with $df = (n - 1)$. In this case, a $(1 - \alpha)$ confidence interval for population mean μ can be obtained by using the t curve rather than the Z curve.

For example, if $n = 20$, then under the above conditions $T = \dfrac{\bar{X} - \mu}{S/\sqrt{n}} = \dfrac{\bar{X} - \mu}{S/\sqrt{20}}$ has t distribution with $df = 19$.

Suppose we want to obtain a 95-percent confidence interval. Then, $(1 - \alpha) = 0.95$ and hence, $\alpha = 1 - 0.95 = 0.05$.

From the t table, we get $t_{\alpha/2} = t_{0.025} =$ the t value corresponding to $df = 19$ and one-tail probability = 0.025 as 2.093.

Hence, for $df = 19$,

$$P\left(-2.093 \leq \frac{\bar{X} - \mu}{S/\sqrt{20}} \leq 2.093\right) = 0.95.$$

This gives us:

$$P(\bar{X} - 2.093S/\sqrt{20} \leq \mu \leq \bar{X} + 2.093S/\sqrt{20}) = 0.95.$$

Thus, a 95-percent confidence interval for μ is

$$(\bar{X} - 2.093S/\sqrt{20}, \ \bar{X} + 2.093S/\sqrt{20}) \text{ (or } \bar{X} \pm 2.093S/\sqrt{20}).$$

> **i**   In general, if a sample of size n is selected from a normally distributed popula-
> tion, then a $(1 - \alpha)$ confidence interval for the population mean μ is given by
>
> $$(\bar{X} - t_{\alpha/2}S/\sqrt{n}, \ \bar{X} + t_{\alpha/2}S/\sqrt{n}) \text{ or } (\bar{X} \pm t_{\alpha/2}S/\sqrt{n}) \qquad \textbf{9-6}$$

Recall that when the value of σ is known, the 95-percent confidence interval is $(\bar{X} \pm 1.96\sigma/\sqrt{n})$. When we replace σ with S, the number 1.96 has to be replaced by 2.093. We shall give an intuitive justification for this. If we repeatedly select samples of a given size n and calculate $\bar{x}$ and the interval $(\bar{x} \pm 1.96\sigma/\sqrt{n})$, about 95 percent of these intervals will contain the value of μ. Now, if instead we calculate $\bar{x}$, s, and the interval $(\bar{x} \pm 1.96s/\sqrt{20})$, then many of the values of s are likely to be smaller than σ, resulting in narrower intervals that are less likely to contain μ. Hence, to make up for this, the number 1.96 needs to be replaced by a bigger number, 2.093.

We give below confidence intervals for μ for different values of n and confidence levels. Find the intervals using the t table and check your answers with those given below.

n	Confidence Level	α	df	$t_{\alpha/2}$ value	Confidence Interval
8	98%	0.02	7	2.998	$(\bar{X} \pm 2.998S/\sqrt{8})$
20	90%	0.1	19	1.729	$(\bar{X} \pm 1.729S/\sqrt{20})$
30	95%	0.05	29	2.045	$(\bar{X} \pm 2.045S/\sqrt{30})$

Note in the t table that t values corresponding to $df = \infty$ are the same as z values.

Example 9-4

In Example 9-2, we considered the problem of estimating the mean value of earnings per share of the top 1000 companies in Canada during 2000. We assumed that the population standard deviation was known. Now, suppose the population standard deviation is unknown but we know that the population distribution is approximately normal. The following sample of size 10 was selected:

6.42   0.53   0   0.01 -0.55 0.94   0.06 -0.45 0.48   0.34

    (a) Using this sample data, obtain a 95-percent confidence interval estimate for the mean value of earnings per share of the 1000 companies.
    (b) Interpret the result.

Solution

(a) Since the population is approximately normally distributed, $T = \dfrac{\bar{X} - \mu}{S/\sqrt{10}}$ has, approximately, t distribution with $df = (n - 1) = 9$. Thus, a 95-percent confidence interval is $(\bar{X} \pm t_{0.025}S/\sqrt{10})$.

The value of $t_{0.025}$ corresponding to $df = n - 1 = 9$ is given in the t table in the row corresponding to $df = 9$ and the column corresponding to "level of significance for one-tailed test" = 0.025 and equals 2.262.

$$\bar{x} = \frac{6.42 + 0.53 + \cdots + 0.48 + 0.34}{10} = 0.778$$

$$s = \sqrt{\frac{(6.42 - 0.778)^2 + (0.53 - 0.778)^2 + \cdots + (0.34 - 0.778)^2}{9}}$$

$$= 2.033$$

Hence, a 95-percent confidence interval estimate is $(0.778 \pm 2.262(2.033)/\sqrt{10})$ or $(-0.676, 2.232)$.

(b) For obtaining the above interval, we have used an estimator that is not guaranteed to produce an interval containing the population mean. However, if it is used repeatedly, a large number of times, the population mean will lie in about 95 percent of the intervals produced. In the current attempt, we obtained an interval of $(-0.676, 2.232)$. We do not know if this interval contains μ. However, the fact that 95 percent of the intervals produced contain μ gives us reason enough to be optimistic that this interval will contain μ.

Solution Using Computer Software

We give below instructions for obtaining a confidence interval using Excel (see Chart 9-8) and Minitab (see Chart 9-9).

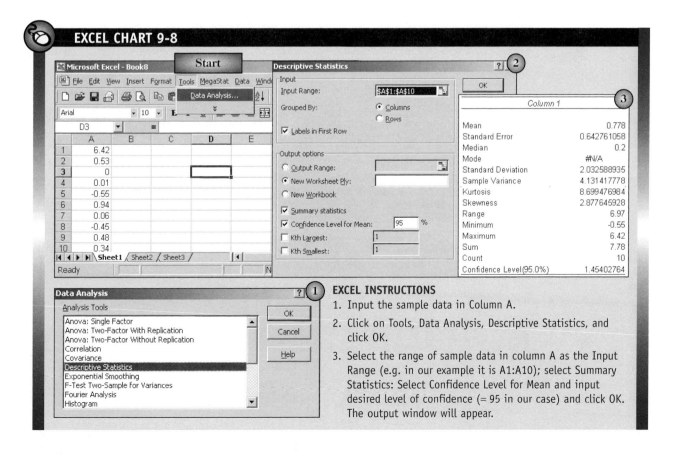

EXCEL CHART 9-8

EXCEL INSTRUCTIONS

1. Input the sample data in Column A.

2. Click on Tools, Data Analysis, Descriptive Statistics, and click OK.

3. Select the range of sample data in column A as the Input Range (e.g. in our example it is A1:A10); select Summary Statistics: Select Confidence Level for Mean and input desired level of confidence (= 95 in our case) and click OK. The output window will appear.

MINITAB CHART 9-9

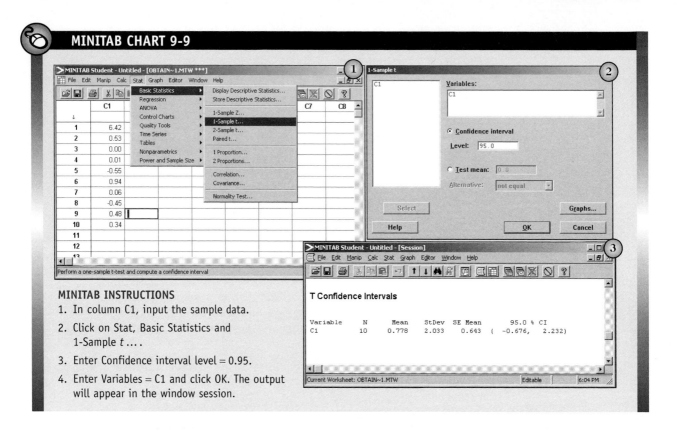

MINITAB INSTRUCTIONS

1. In column C1, input the sample data.

2. Click on Stat, Basic Statistics and 1-Sample t ....

3. Enter Confidence interval level = 0.95.

4. Enter Variables = C1 and click OK. The output will appear in the window session.

■ SELF-REVIEW 9-6

In Self-Review 9-4, we considered the problem of estimating the mean value of monthly percentage changes in the TSE 300 index from 1980 to 2000. We assumed that the population standard deviation was known. Now, suppose that the population standard deviation is unknown but we know that the population is normally distributed. The following sample of size 20 was selected.

| 3.92 | 1.69 | 1.79 | −1.00 | −2.05 | 1.41 | 2.65 | −1.09 | 3.92 | 1.48 |
| 2.00 | 0.85 | 0.31 | 1.46 | 3.92 | 0.94 | 0.46 | 2.91 | 0.23 | 0.71 |

Using this sample data, obtain a 95-percent confidence interval estimate for the average monthly percentage changes in the TSE 300 index.

We wish to point out that the confidence interval given by Formula 9-6 is correct only when the population is normally distributed. However, statisticians have observed that the estimator (9-6) is a fairly robust interval estimator. That is, even when the population is quite non-normal, it serves as a good approximation.

EXERCISES 9-9 TO 9-15

9-9. Answer each of the following:
   (a) For t distribution with $df = 30$, find the value of t such that the area under the curve between $−t$ and $+t$ is 0.8.

(b) For t distribution with $df = 6$, find $t_{0.005}$.

(c) For t distribution with $df = 24$, find the value of t such that the left-tail area is 0.1.

(d) For t distribution with $df = 12$, find the value of t such that the left-tail area is 0.9.

(e) For t distribution with $df = 14$, find $t_{0.995}$.

9-10. Answer each of the following:

(a) For t distribution with $df = 7$, find the value of t such that the area under the curve between $-t$ and $+t$ is 0.99.

(b) For t distribution with $df = 18$, find the value of t such that the left-tail area is 0.025.

(c) For t distribution with $df = 8$, find $t_{0.025}$.

(d) For t distribution with $df = 8$, find the value of t such that the left-tail area is 0.99.

(e) For t distribution with $df = 10$, find $t_{0.99}$.

In each of the Exercises 9-11 to 9-15, assume that the population distribution is approximately normal.

9-11. Answer each of the following:

(a) A sample of size 12 is selected from a population data. Explain how you will obtain from it a 95-percent confidence interval estimate for the population mean.

(b) A sample of size 20 is selected from a population. Explain how you will obtain from it a 90-percent confidence interval estimate for the population mean.

(c) A sample of size 8 is selected from a population. Explain how you will obtain from it a 99-percent confidence interval estimate for the population mean.

9-12. Answer each of the following:

(a) A sample of size 15 is selected from a population. Explain how you will obtain from it a 95-percent confidence interval estimate for the population mean.

(b) A sample of size 24 is selected from a population. Explain how you will obtain from it a 98-percent confidence interval estimate for the population mean.

(c) A sample of size 12 is selected from a population. Explain how you will obtain from it a 99-percent confidence interval estimate for the population mean.

9-13. The manager of the Inlet Square Mall wants to estimate the mean amount spent per shopping visit by customers. A sample of size 20 customers selected revealed the following amounts spent:

$48.16	$42.22	$46.82	$51.54	$23.78	$41.86	$51.35	$58.84
$54.86	$37.92	$52.64	$48.59	$50.82	$46.94	$52.68	$43.88
$61.83	$61.69	$49.17	$61.46				

Obtain a 99-percent confidence interval estimate for the population mean. Would it be reasonable to assume that the population mean is $50.00? What about $60.00? Justify your answers.

9-14. Nortel Networks and Air Canada are two large employers in Toronto. As a part of a feasibility study to estimate the mean cost of offering child care for the employees of these companies, a sample of 10 employees who use child care was selected from the two companies. The amounts spent by these employees on child care last week are recorded below.

$382 $286 $208 $428 $189 $160 $416 $262 $226 $191

Develop a 98-percent confidence interval estimate for the population mean. Interpret the result. Would it be reasonable to assume that the population mean is $320?

9-15. The owner of Britten's Egg Farm wants to estimate the mean number of eggs per chicken. A sample of 20 chickens was selected and the data on eggs laid by these chickens in a certain month was recorded. The values of the sample mean and sample standard deviation obtained were 21.9 eggs per month and 2.1 eggs per month, respectively.
   (a) What is the best point estimate of the value of the population mean?
   (b) Develop a 98-percent confidence interval estimate for the population mean.
   (c) Explain why we need to use the t distribution in (b).
   (d) Would it be reasonable to conclude that the population mean is 22 eggs? What about 24 eggs?

9.5   CONFIDENCE INTERVAL FOR PROPORTION

As we saw in Chapter 8, in some applications the data units in the population have only two values, say 1 and 0, and we are interested in estimating the proportion p of population data items with a value of 1. For example, suppose a politician conducts polls to estimate her popularity among voters. In this case, each data unit (that is, each vote) will be either *in favour of* our candidate (we shall denote this by a 1) or *against* (we shall denote this by a 0). Hence, the population distribution is:

Data value	Probability
1	p
0	$(1-p)$

The value of the population mean μ is p and that of population standard deviation σ is $\sqrt{p(1-p)}$.

If we select a sample of size n from this population, then each data unit in the sample will have a value of 0 or 1 and the sample mean $\bar{X}$ is

$$\bar{X} = \frac{\text{number of "1"s in the sample}}{n} = \text{fraction of data units in the sample with value "1".}$$

Since here $\bar{X}$ stands for fraction or proportion of data units in the sample with value 1, we shall denote it by $\hat{p}$.

Again, it follows by the central limit theorem discussed in Chapter 8 (or the normal approximations of binomial distributions discussed in Chapter 7) that if the sample size n is large, $\hat{p}$ is approximately normally distributed with mean p and standard error

standard deviation of $\hat{p}$ equal to $\dfrac{\sigma}{\sqrt{n}} = \sqrt{\dfrac{p(1-p)}{n}}$.

It is generally accepted that the following guideline is adequate for most business and economics applications for using the normal approximation: "n should be such that each np and $n(1-p)$ is at least 5." Thus,

 For large enough n, the following is a $(1-\alpha)$ confidence interval for population proportion p:

$$(\hat{p} \pm z_{\alpha/2}\sigma/\sqrt{n}) = (\hat{p} \pm z_{\alpha/2}\sqrt{p(1-p)/n}) \qquad 9\text{-}7$$

The above formula for confidence interval is not useful, because it requires knowing the value of p, and we do not know the value of p because this is precisely what we are trying to estimate! However, it can be shown that $\hat{p}(1-\hat{p})/(n-1)$ is an unbiased estimator of the variance, $p(1-p)/n$, of $\hat{p}$.

For a large enough value of n, $\dfrac{\hat{p}-p}{\sqrt{\hat{p}(1-\hat{p})/n}}$ is approximately a standard normal variable. Thus,

 For large n, the following is an *approximate* $(1-\alpha)$ confidence interval for p:

$$(\hat{p} \pm z_{\alpha/2}\sqrt{\hat{p}(1-\hat{p})/n}). \qquad 9\text{-}8$$

Example 9-5

Lead is found in jewellery, and incidents of elevated blood lead levels in children caused by sucking or chewing on jewellery have recently been reported. In a study conducted by Health Canada in late 2000, from a sample of 95 inexpensive jewellery items (costing less than $20 each) 65 were found to a have lead content ranging from 50 to 100 percent. Obtain an approximate 90-percent confidence interval estimate for the fraction of inexpensive jewellery items that have 50 percent or more lead content.

Solution

The value of the sample proportion $\hat{p}$ is $65/95 = 0.68$. Considering this value of $\hat{p}$ to be close to p, we have $np \approx n\hat{p} = 65 > 5$ and $n(1-p) \approx n(1-\hat{p}) = 30 > 5$. So, we can assume that $\hat{p}$ is approximately normally distributed. Hence, using Formula 9-8, we get the following approximate 90-percent confidence interval estimate of p:

$$(0.68 \pm (1.645)\sqrt{0.68(1-0.68)/95}) = 0.68 \pm 0.079 \text{ or } (0.601, 0.759).$$

A more involved formula for exact $(1-\alpha)$ confidence interval estimator is given by M.S. Bartlett. (For details, see Chapter 9 Appendix B on the CD-ROM accompanying the book.)

■ SELF-REVIEW 9-7

A market survey was conducted to estimate the proportion of homemakers in Ontario who would recognize the brand name of a cleanser based on the shape and the colour of the container. Of the 1400 homemakers sampled, 420 were able to identify the brand by name.

    (a) Obtain a point estimate of the value of population proportion.
    (b) Develop an approximate 99-percent confidence interval estimate for the population proportion.

SOLUTION USING COMPUTER SOFTWARE

We shall now provide instructions for computing confidence interval estimates for the population proportion using computer software. Let us consider an example.

Example 9-6

To study what fraction of houses on sale in Victoria, B.C., have a finished basement, a researcher selected a random sample of 20 houses on sale. The data are recorded below. (Here, 1 indicates that the house had a finished basement, while 0 indicates that the house did not have a finished basement.)

1	0	0	1	0	0	1	1	1	0
1	0	0	1	1	0	1	1	0	1

Obtain a 95-percent confidence interval for the fraction of houses on sale in Victoria that have a finished basement.

Solution

The Excel and Minitab instructions and outputs are given in Charts 9-10 and 9-11.

It should be noted that this computer solution is based on Formula 9-8, which uses the normal approximation. In this problem, $\hat{p} = 0.55$. Thus, $n\hat{p} > 5$ and $n(1 - \hat{p}) > 5$. Thus, normal approximation is valid and an approximate 95-percent confidence interval estimate of population proportion is $(0.332, 0.7687)$. It should be noted that this interval estimate is too wide to be of much practical use. In the next section, we shall see how to design a confidence interval of required accuracy and precision.

EXCEL CHART 9-10

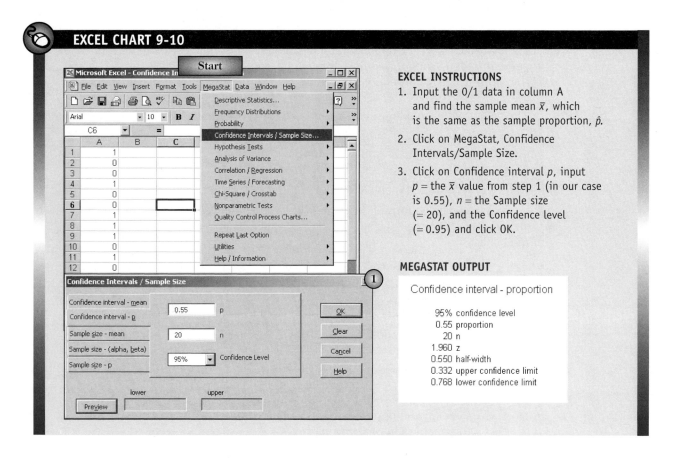

EXCEL INSTRUCTIONS

1. Input the 0/1 data in column A and find the sample mean $\bar{x}$, which is the same as the sample proportion, $\hat{p}$.

2. Click on MegaStat, Confidence Intervals/Sample Size.

3. Click on Confidence interval p, input p = the $\bar{x}$ value from step 1 (in our case is 0.55), n = the Sample size (= 20), and the Confidence level (= 0.95) and click OK.

MEGASTAT OUTPUT

Confidence interval - proportion

```
95%    confidence level
0.55   proportion
20     n
1.960  z
0.550  half-width
0.332  upper confidence limit
0.768  lower confidence limit
```

MINITAB CHART 9-11

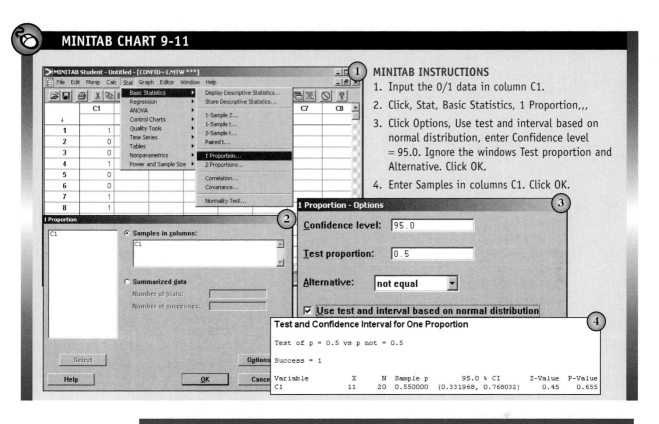

MINITAB INSTRUCTIONS

1. Input the 0/1 data in column C1.

2. Click, Stat, Basic Statistics, 1 Proportion,,,

3. Click Options, Use test and interval based on normal distribution, enter Confidence level = 95.0. Ignore the windows Test proportion and Alternative. Click OK.

4. Enter Samples in columns C1. Click OK.

Test and Confidence Interval for One Proportion

Test of p = 0.5 vs p not = 0.5

Success = 1

Variable	X	N	Sample p	95.0 % CI	Z-Value	P-Value
C1	11	20	0.550000	(0.331968, 0.768032)	0.45	0.655

EXERCISES 9-16 TO 9-19

9-16. The owner of the West End Kwick Fill Gas Station wished to determine the proportion of customers that use his new "pay at the pump" feature. This feature allows customers to use a credit card at the pump and never enter the station. He surveyed 100 customers and found that 80 paid at the pump.
  (a) Obtain a point estimate of the value of the population proportion.
  (b) Estimate the value of the standard error of the population proportion.
  (c) Develop a 95-percent confidence interval estimate for the population proportion.
  (d) Interpret your findings.

9-17. Maria Wilson is considering running for mayor of the town of Sudbury. Before completing the petitions, she decides to conduct a survey of voters in Sudbury. A sample of 400 voters revealed that 300 would support her in the election.
  (a) Obtain a point estimate of the value of the population proportion.
  (b) Estimate the value of the standard error of the population proportion.
  (c) Develop a 99-percent confidence interval estimate for the population proportion.
  (d) Interpret your findings.

9-18. The CBC network is considering replacing one of its prime-time crime investigation shows with a new family-oriented comedy show. Before a final decision is made, network executives commission a random sample of 400 viewers. After viewing the comedy, 250 indicated they would watch the new show and suggested it replace the crime investigation show.

(a) Obtain a point estimate of the value of the proportion of all Canadian viewers who would prefer replacing the crime investigation show with a comedy show.
(b) Obtain an estimate of the standard error of the proportion.
(c) Develop a 99-percent confidence interval estimate for the population proportion.
(d) Interpret your findings.

9-19. Gateway Printing purchases plastic cups on which to print logos for sporting events, proms, birthdays, and other special occasions. Ashok Mehta, the owner, received a large shipment this morning. To ensure the quality of the shipment he selected a random sample of 300 cups. He found 15 to be defective.
(a) Obtain a point estimate of the proportion of defectives in the population?
(b) Develop a 95-percent confidence interval estimate for the proportion of defectives in the population.
(c) Mehta has an agreement with his supplier that he is to return lots in which 10 percent or more are defective. Should he return this lot? Explain your decision.

9.6　CHOOSING AN APPROPRIATE SAMPLE SIZE

An interval estimator with a too-low confidence level (*too-low accuracy*) and/or too-wide interval estimates (*too-low precision*) is not very useful. If we want to know the average marks (out of a maximum of 100) of students in a class, a 99-percent confidence interval estimate of (0, 100) will be too wide an interval to be useful. Also, a 10-percent confidence interval estimate of (74.5, 74.6) will be useless, since in this case there is a 90-percent chance that an interval estimate obtained will not contain the value of the population mean. A 95-percent confidence interval estimate of, say, (74, 78) will, however, provide useful information to students. We are interested in confidence intervals with a high confidence level (high accuracy) and narrow interval estimates (high precision). For a given population and size of the sample, if we try to keep the width of interval estimates small, then the likelihood becomes less that an interval estimate obtained will contain the value of the population mean and, thus, the confidence level of the estimator becomes low. In practice, management fixes the values of the confidence level and the width of interval estimates and it is the job of a statistician to design an interval estimator that meets these requirements. Fortunately, many of the point estimators commonly used in practice have an important property called *consistency*, which makes it possible to design an interval estimator that meets the requirements by choosing a large enough sample size.

CONSISTENCY OF A POINT ESTIMATOR

This property refers to a change in the probability distribution of the estimator as the sample size n is increased to infinity. (Such a property is called an *asymptotic* property.)

 A consistent estimator of a population parameter is a point estimator of the parameter, the probability distribution of which tends to become increasingly concentrated on the value of the parameter as the sample size n tends to infinity.[2]

Chart 9-12 illustrates the essential behaviour of a consistent estimator. Here, for $n = 10$, the estimator is a biased estimator of the population parameter θ and it has a large variance. But as n increases, both the bias and the variance of the estimator decrease. As n tends to infinity, both the bias and the variance tend to zero. In the case of unbiased estimators, we have the following simpler result.[3]

> *i* An unbiased estimator of a population parameter is a *consistent* estimator if its variance tends to zero as the sample size n tends to infinity.

CHART 9-12: Distribution of a Consistent Estimator of a Population Parameter θ for Different Sample Sizes

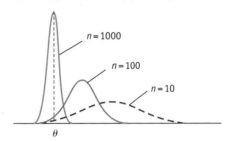

We saw in Chapter 8 that $\bar{X}$ is an unbiased estimator of μ, and the standard deviation of $\bar{X}$ (also called the standard error of the mean) is $\sigma_{\bar{X}} = \dfrac{\sigma}{\sqrt{n}}$. For any small positive number ϵ, we can make $\dfrac{\sigma}{\sqrt{n}}$ less than ϵ by choosing n greater than $\left(\dfrac{\sigma}{\epsilon}\right)^2$. Thus, $\bar{X}$ is a consistent estimator of μ.

Example 9-7

Suppose we use the sample mean, $\bar{X}$, as a point estimator of the mean μ of a certain population. If the population standard deviation is known to be 8, how large a sample should we choose to keep the value of the standard error of the mean less than 0.4?

Solution

We are given that $\sigma = 8$. To keep the standard error of the mean less than $\epsilon = 0.4$, we should choose $n > \left(\dfrac{\sigma}{\epsilon}\right)^2 = \left(\dfrac{8}{0.4}\right)^2 = 400$.

We shall now use the consistency property of the sample mean to design an interval estimator for μ of required accuracy and precision.

CASE 1: THE POPULATION VARIANCE IS KNOWN

Suppose we wish to obtain a 95-percent confidence interval estimate of the population mean μ. We saw that $\bar{X}$ is an unbiased and consistent estimator of μ and the standard deviation of $\bar{X}$, also called the standard error of the mean, is $\sigma_{\bar{X}} = \dfrac{\sigma}{\sqrt{n}}$. We also saw that if the population distribution is normal or the sample size is large, then $\bar{X}$ can be assumed to be normally distributed and, in this case, $(\bar{X} \pm 1.96\sigma/\sqrt{n})$ is a 95-percent confidence interval of μ.

If we want the width of the interval estimate to be ± 0.1, then we should have a margin of error $(1.96\sigma/\sqrt{n}) = 0.1$.

This implies that $\sqrt{n} = \dfrac{1.96\sigma}{0.1}$ or, $n = \left(\dfrac{1.96\sigma}{0.1}\right)^2$.

Thus, if we know the value of σ, we can calculate the appropriate sample size.

In general, suppose we are interested in $(1 - \alpha)$ confidence interval $(\bar{X} \pm z_{\alpha/2}\sigma/\sqrt{n})$ for some α. If we want the margin of error to be no more than $\pm E$, for some number E, then we should have

$$z_{\alpha/2}\sigma/\sqrt{n} \le E \tag{9-9}$$

This implies that $\sqrt{n} \ge \dfrac{z_{\alpha/2}\sigma}{E}$

or,

$$n \ge \left(\dfrac{z_{\alpha/2}\sigma}{E}\right)^2 \tag{9-10}$$

This value of n may not be a whole number. If it is a fraction, it is rounded up to its next higher number.

Example 9-8

The quality control manager of a soft drink bottling company has decided to set up the following daily procedure for obtaining a 95-percent confidence interval estimate for the mean amount of soft drink dispensed in the bottles labelled 350 mL. Select a sample, and use the sample mean as a point estimator of the population mean to obtain an appropriate 95-percent confidence interval estimate. The standard deviation of the amount of drink dispensed per bottle is known to be 16 mL. If she wants the margin of error to be at the most ± 2 mL, what should be the sample size?

Solution

Let us hope that the sample size will be large enough (at least 30) for $\bar{X}$ to be approximately normally distributed. For the margin of error to be no more than $\pm E = \pm 2$,

we must choose a sample size n at least $\left(\dfrac{z_{0.025}\sigma}{E}\right)^2 = \left(\dfrac{(1.96)(16)}{2}\right)^2 = 245.86$.

This is larger than 30, as we had hoped. So, for the margin of error to be ± 2 or smaller, the sample size n should be at least 246.

■ SELF-REVIEW 9-8

Reconsider Self-Review 9-4. The monthly percentage changes in the TSE 300 index from 1980 to 2000 are known to be approximately normally distributed, with a standard deviation of 2.05 percent. It is desired to obtain a 95-percent confidence interval estimate of the mean percentage monthly change during this period. The width of the interval estimate should be no more than ± 0.5 percent. What should be the sample size?

CASE 2: THE POPULATION VARIANCE IS UNKNOWN

We saw above that if the population distribution is normal and the population standard deviation σ is unknown, then for any value of α, a $(1 - \alpha)$ confidence interval for μ is given by $(\bar{X} \pm t_{\alpha/2}S/\sqrt{n})$, where the value of $t_{\alpha/2}$ is obtained from Student's t distribution with $df = (n - 1)$. Now, suppose we want the margin of error to be at the most $\pm E$, for some number E. Then we should have

$$\frac{t_{\alpha/2}S}{\sqrt{n}} \leq E \qquad \textbf{9-11}$$

This implies that $\sqrt{n} \geq \dfrac{t_{\alpha/2}S}{E}$

or,

$$n \geq \left(\frac{t_{\alpha/2}S}{E} \right)^2 \qquad \textbf{9-12}$$

Thus, we can calculate the value of n if we know the values of $t_{\alpha/2}$ and S. But the value of $t_{\alpha/2}$ depends on the value of df (which equals $(n - 1)$) and S, the sample standard deviation, is a random variable whose distribution depends on n.

In fact, it can be shown that in this case, no finite value of n exists that is guaranteed to produce a $(1 - \alpha)$ confidence interval with a margin of error no more than $\pm E$.

Statisticians have developed alternative schemes to produce an interval estimator that meets the given requirements. These schemes are based on a technique called *sequential sampling*. We shall not discuss them here.

A value of n, for which the corresponding interval estimator approximately meets the requirements, can be obtained as follows: select a pilot sample, the size of which is decided based on judgment. Calculate the standard deviation s of this pilot sample. Use Formula 9-12 with the standard deviation s of the pilot sample as an estimate of the population standard deviation, and replace the t value by the z value corresponding to the given confidence level to get

$$n \geq \left(\frac{z_{\alpha/2}s}{E} \right)^2 \qquad \textbf{9-13}$$

Example 9-9

A student in public administration wants to determine the mean earnings per month of members of city councils in large cities. In particular, he wants to obtain a 95-percent confidence level estimate for the mean with margin of error no more than $100. The student found a report by the Ministry of Labour that estimated the standard deviation to be $1000. If the population is known to be approximately normally distributed, find an approximate value of the sample size.

Solution

An approximate lower bound on the required value of the sample size n is

$$\left(\frac{z_{\alpha/2}s}{E} \right)^2 = \left(\frac{z_{0.025}(1000)}{100} \right)^2 = \left(\frac{1.96(1000)}{100} \right)^2 = 384.16.$$

So, if a sample of size 385 is selected, there is a fairly high chance that the 95-percent confidence interval estimate obtained will have a margin of error less than or equal to $100. But this is not guaranteed. The margin of error may turn out to be larger than $100.

■ SELF-REVIEW 9-9

The university registrar needs assistance in determining how many transcripts to study. The registrar wants to estimate the arithmetic mean grade point average of all graduating seniors during the past 10 years. The mean grade point average is to be estimated within plus or minus 0.05 of the population mean. The standard deviation is estimated to be 0.279. Use a 99-percent level of confidence.

CASE 3: THE CASE OF PROPORTION

As we saw before, in this case population data consist of only two types of values, say 0 and 1, and we are interested in estimating p, the fraction of population items with a value of 1. Here, p is also the population mean μ, and the population standard deviation σ is $\sqrt{p(1-p)}$. Thus, when $\mu = p$ is unknown, σ is also unknown.

If an approximate value $\bar{p}$ of p is known presumptively, then we can use it to find an approximate value $\bar{\sigma} = \sqrt{\bar{p}(1-\bar{p})}$ of σ. By substituting $\bar{\sigma}$ for σ in Formula 9-10, we get for any given value of a margin of error E, the following approximate lower bound on the required value of n:

CHART 9-13: Values of $\sqrt{p(1-p)}$ for values of p Between 0 and 1

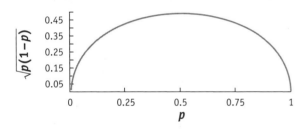

$$n \geq \left(\frac{z_{\alpha/2}\bar{\sigma}}{E} \right)^2 \qquad \textbf{9-14}$$

For any sample of this size, there is a high chance that the margin of error will be no more than $\pm E$, provided this value of n is large enough for both np and $n(1-p)$ to be larger than 5. (Otherwise, we cannot assume a normal approximation and, therefore, Formula 9-14 is not valid.) However, this is only an approximate lower bound. For this value of n, the margin of error is not guaranteed to be $\pm E$ or less and may sometimes be much larger.

Luckily in the case of proportion, we can find a value of n that definitely meets the requirement. It can be shown that for any value of p,

$$\sigma = \sqrt{p(1-p)} \leq 0.5 \qquad \textbf{9-15}$$

This should be clear from Chart 9-13 above, which shows values of $\sqrt{p(1-p)}$ for values of p between 0 and 1.

Hence, substituting σ by 0.5 in Formula 9-10, we get the following relationship.

$$\left(\frac{0.5z_{\alpha/2}}{E} \right)^2 \geq \left(\frac{z_{\alpha/2}\sigma}{E} \right)^2$$

Thus, for sample size

$$n \geq \left(\frac{0.5z_{\alpha/2}}{E} \right)^2 \qquad \textbf{9-16}$$

the margin of error is guaranteed to be no more than $\pm E$, provided this value of n is large enough for a normal approximation to be valid.

Example 9-10

A researcher wants to estimate the proportion of cities in Canada that have private refuse collectors. In particular, she wants to obtain a 90-percent confidence level estimate of the population proportion and she wants the margin of error to be no more than ± 0.05. In a study conducted three years back, the value of the population proportion was estimated to be 0.3; our researcher does not expect the population proportion to be much different now. What should be the sample size?

Solution

Using Formula 9-16, we get

$$\left(\frac{0.5z_{\alpha/2}}{E}\right)^2 = \left(\frac{0.5(1.645)}{0.05}\right)^2 = 270.6$$

This value is large enough for normal approximation. (Since the value of p is expected to be close to 0.3, we have $271(0.3) > 5$ and $271(0.7) > 5$.) So, a value of $n = 271$ is sufficient.

By using Formula 9-14, we get an approximate value of n as:

$$n \geq \left(\frac{z_{\alpha/2}\bar{\sigma}}{E}\right)^2 = \left(\frac{1.645\sqrt{0.3(1-0.3)}}{0.05}\right)^2 = 227.31$$

The value of n should be chosen somewhere between 228 and 271, depending on the cost of choosing a sample.

■ SELF-REVIEW 9-10

As a part of her project in a finance course, a student wants to obtain a 95-percent confidence interval estimate of the fraction of New Brunswickers in the age group 20 up to 40 who invest in the stock market. If she wants the margin of error to be no more than ± 0.04, how large a sample should she select?

EXERCISES 9-20 TO 9-28

9-20. Suppose we want to estimate the mean value of earnings per share of the top 1000 companies in Canada during 2000, and we use the sample mean as the point estimator. If the population standard deviation is 3.04, how large a sample should we choose to keep the value of the standard error of the mean less than 0.3?

9-21. We want to estimate the population mean within 5, with a 99-percent level of confidence. The population standard deviation is known to be 15. How large a sample is required?

9-22. A population standard deviation is known to be 10. We want to estimate the population mean within 2, with a 95-percent level of confidence. How large a sample is required?

9-23. The best previously known estimate of the population proportion is to be within plus or minus 0.10, with a 99-percent level of confidence. The best estimate of the population proportion is 0.45. How large a sample is required?

9-24. The best previously known estimate of the population proportion is to be within plus or minus 0.05, with a 95-percent level of confidence. The best known estimate of the population proportion is 0.15. How large a sample is required?

9-25. A processor of carrots cuts the green top off each carrot, washes the carrots, and inserts six to a package; 20 packages are inserted in a box for shipment. To test the weight of the boxes, a few were checked. The sample mean weight was 9.1 kg with sample standard deviation 0.2 kg. How many boxes must the processor sample to be 95 percent confident that the sample mean does not differ from the population mean by more than 0.05 kg?

9-26. A survey is being planned to determine the mean amount of time corporate executives watch television. A pilot survey indicated that the sample mean time per week is 12 hours, with a sample standard deviation of 3 hours. Estimate the mean viewing time within one-quarter hour. The 98-percent level of confidence is to be used. How many executives should be surveyed?

9-27. Past surveys revealed that 30 percent of tourists going to Windsor, Ontario, to gamble during a weekend, spend more than $1000. Casino management wants to update this percentage.
   (a) The new study is to use the 90-percent confidence level. The estimate is to be within 1 percent of the population proportion. What is the necessary sample size?
   (b) Management said that the sample size determined above is too large. What can be done to reduce the sample? Based on your suggestion, recalculate the sample size.

9-28. Suppose the Prime Minister's office wants an estimate of the proportion of the population who support his current policy on gun control. The Prime Minister wants the estimate to be within 0.04 of the true proportion. Assume a 95-percent level of confidence. A preliminary estimate of the proportion supporting current policy obtained by the Prime Minister's advisers is 0.60.
   (a) How large a sample is required?
   (b) How large a sample would be necessary if no estimate is available for the proportion who support current policy?

9.7 FINITE POPULATION CORRECTION FACTOR (OPTIONAL)

So far, in this chapter, we have assumed that the sample is chosen using simple random sampling with replacement (SRR). We pointed out that when the population size N is very large, SRN is approximately the same as SRR. Now let us consider the case in which SRN is used and the population size is not very large.

We saw in Chapter 8 that when the population size N is finite and a sample of size n is chosen using SRN, the sample mean $\bar{X}$ has $\mu_{\bar{X}} = \mu$ and

$$\sigma_{\bar{X}} = \frac{\sigma}{\sqrt{n}}\sqrt{\frac{N-n}{N-1}} \qquad\qquad 9\text{-}17$$

where μ is the population mean, and σ is the population standard deviation. We pointed out that when N is very large as compared to n, the term $\sqrt{\dfrac{N-n}{N-1}}$, (called the **finite correction factor**), almost equals 1 and hence we can approximate $\sigma_{\bar{X}}$ by $\dfrac{\sigma}{\sqrt{n}}$.

However, when the ratio (n/N) is reasonably large, this approximation may not be suitable and it is better to use the exact Formula 9-17.

As a rule, we use the finite correction factor when (n/N) is 0.05 or more. In this case, it has been observed that when the population size is moderately large, the population distribution is approximately normal, and the ratio n/N is not too large, the confidence interval

$$\bar{X} \pm t_{\alpha/2}\frac{S}{\sqrt{n}}\left(\sqrt{\frac{N-n}{N-1}}\right) \qquad\qquad 9\text{-}18$$

is a good approximation for a $(1-\alpha)$ confidence interval for μ. Here, $t_{\alpha/2}$ is chosen from the Student's t distribution table corresponding to $df = (n-1)$.

Example 9-11

There are 250 families in a village in Nova Scotia. A poll of 40 families reveals the sample mean of annual church contributions is $450 with a sample standard deviation of $75. Assuming that the population distribution is approximately normal, construct a 90-percent confidence interval estimate for the mean annual contribution.

Solution

First note that the population is moderately large and $n/N = 40/250 = 0.16$ is greater than 0.05, but not too large. Hence, substituting the sample value $\bar{x}$ of $\bar{X}$ in Formula 9-18, we get the following approximate 90-percent confidence interval estimate:

$$\bar{x} \pm t_{0.05}\frac{s}{\sqrt{n}}\left(\sqrt{\frac{N-n}{N-1}}\right) = 450 \pm 1.684\frac{75}{\sqrt{40}}\left(\sqrt{\frac{250-40}{250-1}}\right)$$

$$= 450 \pm 18.34 = (431.66,\ 468.34).$$

EXERCISES 9-29 TO 9-32

In each of exercises 9-29, 9-30, and 9-32, assume that the population distribution is approximately normal and the sample is chosen using SRN.

9-29. Forty-nine items are randomly selected from a population of 500 items. The sample mean is 40 and the sample standard deviation is 9. Develop an approximate 99-percent confidence interval estimate for the population mean.

9-30. Thirty-six items are randomly selected from a population of 300 items. The sample mean is 35 and the sample standard deviation is 5. Develop an approximate 95-percent confidence interval estimate for the population mean.

9-31. There are 300 welders employed in the shipbuilding industry in Halifax.
A study of 30 welders, selected using SRN, revealed that 18 graduated from
a registered welding course. Construct an approximate 95-percent confidence
interval estimate for the proportion of all welders who graduated from
a registered welding course.

9-32. The attendance at the Montreal Canadiens game last night was 20 760.
A random sample of 2000 of those in attendance revealed that the mean
number of soft drinks consumed per person was 1.86 with a standard deviation
of 0.50. Develop an approximate 99-percent confidence interval estimate for
the mean number of soft drinks consumed per person.

CHAPTER OUTLINE

I. An *estimator of a population parameter* is the outcome of a procedure
that involves two steps: (i) selection of a sample of a particular size from
the population using a certain sampling technique, and (ii) application of
a certain computational procedure to the selected sample data. An outcome
of an estimator of a population parameter is used as an estimate of the population parameter.
   A. We assume that the sample is selected using *simple random sampling with
   replacement (SRR)* and for step (ii) we use a formula.

II. We discuss two main types of estimators of population parameters:
(i) *point estimators* and (ii) *interval estimators*.

III. If each of the possible outcomes of an estimator is a single number, the
estimator is called a *point estimator*.
   A. Some of the desirable properties of a point estimator are (i) unbiasedness,
   (ii) efficiency, and (iii) consistency.

   B. A point estimator of a population parameter is said to be an unbiased
   estimator if its expected value equals the value of the population parameter.
   The sample mean and the sample variance are unbiased estimators of
   the population mean and the population variance respectively.

   C. An unbiased estimator of a population parameter is said to be *relatively more
   efficient* than another unbiased estimator of the parameter if its variance is
   smaller than that of the other estimator. An unbiased estimator is said to
   be *efficient* if it has minimum variance in the class of all the unbiased
   estimators.

   D. A point estimator of a population parameter is said to be *consistent* if its
   distribution tends to become increasingly concentrated on the value of
   the population parameter as the sample size n tends to infinity.

   E. An *unbiased estimator* of a population parameter is a *consistent* estimator
   if its variance tends to zero as the sample size n tends to infinity. The sample
   mean is a consistent estimator of the population mean.

IV. If each possible outcome of an estimator is an interval or range of numbers,
the estimator is called an *interval estimator*. Any outcome of an interval
estimator is called an interval estimate. It is an interval in which we expect the
value of the population parameter to lie.

A. If the probability is $(1 - \alpha)$ that an interval estimate obtained will contain the value of the population parameter, then we call the interval estimator a $(1 - \alpha)$ confidence interval, and we call $(1 - \alpha)$ its confidence level.

B. If the population distribution is normal or the sample size is large, then

$$(\bar{X} - z_{\alpha/2}\,\sigma/\sqrt{n},\ \bar{X} + z_{\alpha/2}\,\sigma/\sqrt{n})\ \text{or}\ (\bar{X} \pm z_{\alpha/2}\,\sigma/\sqrt{n}) \qquad \textbf{9-4}$$

is a $(1 - \alpha)$ *confidence interval* of the population mean, μ.

$\pm z_{\alpha/2}\,\sigma/\sqrt{n}$ is called the *margin of error*.

$\bar{X} - z_{\alpha/2}\sigma/\sqrt{n}$ is called the *lower confidence limit (LCL)*.

$\bar{X} + z_{\alpha/2}\sigma/\sqrt{n}$ is called the *upper confidence limit (UCL)*.

C. If a sample of size n is drawn from a normally distributed population with a standard deviation σ, $\dfrac{(n-1)s^2}{\sigma^2}$ follows χ^2 distribution with $df = (n - 1)$.

D. If the population is normally distributed, then for a sample of size n,

$T = \dfrac{\bar{X} - \mu}{S/\sqrt{n}}$ follows Student's t distribution with $df = (n - 1)$. In this case, a $(1 - \alpha)$ confidence interval for the population mean μ is given by

$$(\bar{X} - t_{\alpha/2}S/\sqrt{n},\ \bar{X} + t_{\alpha/2}S/\sqrt{n})\ \text{or}\ (\bar{X} \pm t_{\alpha/2}S/\sqrt{n}) \qquad \textbf{9-6}$$

where $t_{\alpha/2}$ is such that the corresponding right-tail area under the t curve with $df = (n - 1)$ is $\alpha/2$.

V. In some applications, we are interested in estimating the proportion p of population data items with a specific characteristic. In this case, if the sample size n is large enough, the following is an approximate $(1 - \alpha)$ confidence interval for p:

$$(\hat{p} \pm z_{\alpha/2}\sqrt{\hat{p}(1 - \hat{p})/n}) \qquad \textbf{9-8}$$

where, $\hat{p}$ is the sample proportion (fraction of sample units that have the characteristic).

VI. If we are interested in a $(1 - \alpha)$ confidence interval $(\bar{X} \pm z_{\alpha/2}\sigma/\sqrt{n})$ and we want the margin of error to be no more than $\pm E$, then we should choose

$$n \geq \left(\frac{z_{\alpha/2}\sigma}{E}\right)^2 \qquad \textbf{9-10}$$

VII. If the population distribution is normal, the population standard deviation σ is unknown, and we want a $(1 - \alpha)$ confidence interval for μ, then if a value s of sample standard deviation is available from a previous sample, a value of n for which the margin of error is approximately $\pm E$ is given by:

$$n \approx \left(\frac{z_{\alpha/2}s}{E}\right)^2 \qquad \textbf{9-13}$$

VIII. In the case of proportion, an approximate value of n for which the margin of error is $\pm E$ is given by:

$$n \approx \left(\frac{z_{\alpha/2}\bar{\sigma}}{E} \right)^2 \qquad \text{9-14}$$

where $\bar{p}$ is an approximate value of p that is known *a priori* and $\bar{\sigma} = \sqrt{\bar{p}(1 - \bar{p})}$.

A. A value of n that is guaranteed to meet the requirement is:

$$n \geq \left(\frac{0.5z_{\alpha/2}}{E} \right)^2 \qquad \text{9-16}$$

IX. When the population is finite and a sample of size n is chosen using SRN,

$\sigma_{\bar{X}} = \dfrac{\sigma}{\sqrt{n}} \sqrt{\dfrac{N-n}{N-1}}$, where σ is the population standard deviation.

A. When the population size is moderately large and the population distribution is approximately normal,

$$\bar{X} \pm t_{\alpha/2} \frac{S}{\sqrt{n}} \left(\sqrt{\frac{N-n}{N-1}} \right) \qquad \text{9-18}$$

is a good approximation for $(1 - \alpha)$ confidence interval for μ, where the Student's t distribution has $df = (n - 1)$.

CHAPTER EXERCISES 9-33 TO 9-62

9-33. The N.B. Tourism Department plans to sample information centre visitors entering the province to learn the fraction of visitors who plan to camp in the province. Current estimates are that 35 percent of visitors are campers. How large a sample would you take to estimate at a 95-percent confidence level the population proportion with a margin of error of ± 2 percent?

9-34. A sample of 352 subscribers to *Maclean's* magazine shows the mean time spent using the Internet is 13.4 hours per week with a sample standard deviation of 6.8 hours. Find the 95-percent confidence interval estimate for the mean time *Maclean's* subscribers spend on the Internet.

9-35. A research firm conducted a survey to determine the mean amount steady smokers spend on cigarettes during a week. A sample of 49 steady smokers revealed that $\bar{x} = \$54$ and $s = \$10$.
   (a) What is the point estimate? Explain what it indicates.
   (b) Using the 95-percent level of confidence, determine the confidence interval estimate for μ. Explain what it indicates.

9-36. Refer to the previous exercise. Suppose that 64 smokers (instead of 49) were sampled. Assume the sample mean and the sample standard deviation remain the same ($\$54$ and $\$10$, respectively).
   (a) What is the 95-percent confidence interval estimate of μ?
   (b) Explain why this interval is narrower than the one determined in the previous exercise.

9-37. A sample survey is to be conducted to determine the mean family income in a rural area of Saskatchewan. The question is, how many families should be sampled? In a pilot sample of 10 families, the sample standard deviation was $500. The sponsor of the survey wants you to use the 95-percent confidence level. The estimate is to be within $100. How many families should be interviewed?

9-38. Bob Nale is the owner of Nale's Shell GasTown. Bob would like to estimate the mean number of litres of gasoline sold to his customers. From his records he selects a random sample of 60 sales and finds that the mean number of litres sold per customer is 21.2 and the sample standard deviation is 4.1 litres.
(a) What is the point estimate of the population mean?
(b) Develop a 99-percent confidence interval estimate for the population mean.
(c) Interpret the meaning of (b).

9-39. A meat inspector in Calgary has been given the assignment of estimating the mean net weight of packages of ground chuck labelled 1 kg. Of course, he realizes that the weights cannot be precisely 1 kg. A sample of 36 packages revealed the mean weight to be 1.01 kg, with a sample standard deviation of 0.02 kg.
(a) Obtain a point estimate of the population mean.
(b) Determine a 95-percent confidence interval estimate for the population mean.

9-40. A random sample of 85 group leaders, supervisors, and similar personnel at a multinational company revealed that, on the average, they spent 6.5 years on the job before being promoted. The standard deviation of the sample was 1.7 years. Construct a 95-percent confidence interval estimate for the average number of years on the job of all such personnel.

9-41. A recent study of 50 self-service gasoline stations in the Greater Toronto Area revealed that the mean price of unleaded gas is $0.64 per litre. The sample standard deviation is $0.01 per litre.
(a) Determine a 99-percent confidence interval estimate for the population mean price.
(b) Would it be reasonable to conclude that the population mean is $0.63? Why or why not?

9-42. The mean daily sales at a fast-food restaurant for a random sample of 50 days are $3000. The sample standard deviation is $300.
(a) What is the estimated mean daily sales of the population?
(b) Find a 99-percent confidence interval estimate for the population mean.
(c) The management claims that the population mean is $3500. What is your reaction based on the sample results?

9-43. In a survey conducted by Ipsos-Reid in August 2001, 63 percent of the 1000 Canadian adults surveyed said that they are less likely to buy genetically modified (GM) food products.
(a) Construct a 95-percent confidence interval estimate for the proportion of Canadians who are less likely to buy GM food products.
(b) Based on the survey research, what would be your reaction to the claim that less than 60 percent of Canadians are opposed to GM food products?

9-44. Dottie Kleman is the "Cookie Lady." She bakes and sells cookies at 50 different locations in Canada. Ms. Kleman is concerned about absenteeism among her workers. The information below reports the number of days absent for a sample of 10 workers during the last two-week pay period.

4   1   0   2   1   1   2   1   0   2

Assuming that the population distribution is approximately normal, answer the following.
(a) Determine the sample mean and standard deviation.
(b) Develop a 99-percent confidence interval estimate for the population mean. (Provide justification for your approach.)
(c) Is it reasonable to conclude that the typical worker did not miss more than one day during a pay period?

9-45. As part of an annual review of its accounts, a discount brokerage selects a random sample of 36 customers. Their accounts are reviewed for total account valuation, which showed a mean of $32 000 and a sample standard deviation of $8200. What is a 90-percent confidence interval estimate for the mean account valuation of the population of customers?

9-46. Canadians seem to be divided on the issue of whether legal benefits and obligations of married couples should be extended to common-law couples, regardless of sexual orientation. In February 2000, Gallup conducted a poll to study the views of Canadians on this issue. They selected a random sample of 1003 adults aged 18 or more; 48 percent of the individuals in the sample opposed same-sex marriage. Assuming that opinions have not changed much since then, calculate a 95-percent confidence interval estimate for the fraction of Canadian adults who oppose same-sex marriage. Based on this, what would be your reaction to the statement that "less than half of Canadian adults oppose same-sex marriage"?

9-47. The proportion of public accountants who had changed companies within the last three years is to be estimated. The 95-percent level of confidence is to be used and the margin of error should be no more than ±3 percent. A study conducted several years ago revealed that the percent of public accountants changing companies within three years was 21.
(a) To update this study, the files of how many public accountants should be studied?
(b) How many public accountants should be contacted if no previous estimates of the population proportion are available?

9-48. A recent survey of 50 unemployed male executives showed that it took an average of 26 weeks for them to find another position. The standard deviation of the sample was 6.2 weeks. Construct a 95-percent confidence interval estimate for the population mean. Based on your findings, would it be reasonable to accept the claim that the population mean is 28 weeks? Justify your answer.

9-49. You plan to conduct a survey to find what proportion of the workforce has two or more jobs. You decide on the 95-percent confidence level and the margin of error of ±2 percent. A pilot survey reveals that 5 of the 50 sampled hold two or more jobs. How many in the workforce should be interviewed to meet your requirements?

9-50. With the conviction of Robert Latimer in 1997 for the mercy killing of his disabled daughter, the issue of doctor-assisted suicide became a popular topic in Canada. A poll was conducted by the Gallup Organization in November 1998 that involved a sample of 1004 adults aged 18 or above. 77 percent of the individuals in the sample favoured mercy killing by doctors. (That is, they were of the opinion that doctors should be allowed to end the life of a patient whose life is immediately threatened by a disease that causes the patient to experience great suffering.) Calculate a 95-percent confidence interval estimate for the fraction of Canadian adults who favoured mercy killing in November 1998.

9-51. Dr. Susan Benner is an industrial psychologist. She is currently studying stress among executives of Internet companies. She has developed a questionnaire that she believes measures stress. A score above 80 indicates stress at a dangerous level. A random sample of 15 executives revealed the following stress level scores.

94	78	83	90	78	99	97	90	97	90
93	94	100	75	84					

Assume that the population distribution is approximately normal.
(a) Find the mean stress level for this sample and obtain a point estimate of the population mean.
(b) Construct a 95-percent confidence level estimate for the population mean.
(c) Is it reasonable to conclude that Internet executives have a mean stress level in the dangerous level, according to Dr. Benner's test?

9-52. The Badik Construction Company limits its business to constructing decks. The mean time to construct one of their standard decks is eight hours for a two-person construction crew. The information is based on a sample of 40 decks recently constructed. The standard deviation of the sample was three hours.
(a) Determine a 90-percent confidence interval estimate for the population mean.
(b) Would it be reasonable to conclude that the population mean is actually nine hours? Justify your answer.

9-53. The Canadian Restaurant Association collected information on the number of meals eaten outside the home per week by young married couples. A survey of 60 couples showed the sample mean number of meals eaten outside the home was 2.76 meals per week, with a standard deviation of 0.75 meals per week. Construct a 98-percent confidence interval estimate for the population mean.

9-54. Low wages paid by Canadian businesses are being blamed for causing a brain drain in Canada. In a poll conducted in mid-2000 by Stornoway Communications in partnership with Canoe, a sample of 522 Canadian adults was selected. Nine out of ten in the sample stated that they have considered moving to the U.S. 81 percent said higher pay was the big lure. High taxes were of particular concern to respondents over the age of 35. Calculate a 99-percent confidence interval estimate for the fraction of Canadian adults who had considered moving to the U.S. in mid-2000.

9-55. The manufacturer of a new line of ink-jet printers would like to include as a part of its advertising the number of pages a user can expect from a print cartridge. A sample of 10 cartridges revealed the following number of pages printed.

2698 2028 2474 2395 2372 2475 1927 3006 2334 2379

Assume that the population distribution is approximately normal.
(a) Obtain a point estimate of the population mean.
(b) Develop a 95-percent confidence interval estimate for the population mean.

9-56. The Human Relations Department of Electronics, Inc. would like to include a dental plan as part of the benefits package. The question is: how much does a typical employee and his family spend per year on dental expenses? A sample of 45 employees revealed the mean amount spent last year was $1820, with a standard deviation of $660.
(a) Construct a 95-percent confidence interval estimate for the population mean.
(b) The information from (a) was given to the president of Electronics, Inc. He indicated he could afford $1700 per employee for dental expenses. Is it possible that the population mean could be $1700? Justify your answer.

9-57. The Warren County Telephone Company claims in its annual report that "the typical customer spends $60 per month on local and long-distance service." A sample of 12 subscribers revealed the following amounts spent last month (in $).

64 66 64 66 59 62 67 61 64 58 54 66

Assume that the population distribution is approximately normal.
(a) What is the point estimate of the population mean?
(b) Develop a 90-percent confidence interval estimate for the population mean.
(c) Is the company's claim that the "typical customer" spends $60 per month reasonable? Justify your answer.

9-58. A student conducted a study and reported that the 95-percent confidence interval estimate for the population mean ranged from 46.08 to 53.92. She was sure that the mean of the sample was 50, the population standard deviation was 16 and that the sample size was at least 30, but cannot remember the exact number. Can you help her out?

9-59. In a poll conducted by Ipsos-Reid in August 2001 to study the opinions of Ontarians on the Walkerton water tragedy, 22 percent of the 1001 Ontarians surveyed blamed the provincial government for the tragedy. Assuming that the population distribution is approximately normal, construct a 95-percent confidence interval estimate for the proportion of Ontarians who blame the provincial government in this case.

9-60. An important factor in selling a residential property is the number of people who look through the home. A sample of 15 homes recently sold in Vancouver revealed the mean number looking through the home was 24 and the standard deviation of the sample was 5 people. Assuming that the population distribution is approximately normal, develop a 98-percent confidence interval estimate for the population mean.

9-61. In a survey conducted by *Maclean's* in January 2001 to study public opinion about the Canadian health-care system, 54 percent of the 1400 Canadians surveyed voted in favour of moderate user fees and charges.
(a) Construct a 95-percent confidence interval estimate for the proportion of Canadians who favour moderate user fees and charges.
(b) Based on your answer to (a), is it reasonable to conclude that a majority of Canadians favour moderate user fees and charges?

9-62. Police chief Aaron Ard of River City reports that 500 traffic citations were issued last month. A sample of 35 of these citations showed the mean amount of the fine was $54, with a standard deviation of $4.50. Assuming that the population distribution is approximately normal, construct a 95-percent confidence interval estimate for the mean amount of a citation in River City.

www.exercises.ca 9-63 TO 9-64

9-63. An excellent site for information on houses for sale in Canada is www.homestore.ca. Suppose you want to obtain a 95-percent confidence interval estimate for the average sale price of *single family houses* currently on sale in Burnaby, B.C. Go to this site, and click on Province: British Columbia, Area: Vancouver, Burnaby. Select a random sample of sale prices of 10 houses using SRR. (Use the random number table in Appendix B to select the numbers.) Assuming that the population distribution is approximately normal, obtain a 95-percent confidence interval for the population mean.

9-64. An excellent site for information on Canadian business is www.stategis.gc.ca. Suppose we are interested in obtaining a 95-percent confidence interval estimate for the mean monthly business bankruptcy rate in Canada during the last 6 years. Randomly select a sample 10 of these months using SRR. (Number these months from 1 to 72. Randomly select a sample of 10 numbers from 1 to 72 using a random number table.) Now, go to the page strategis.ic.gc.ca/engdoc/alpha.html#A. Find the number of business bankruptcies during each of the months in the sample. Assuming that the data are approximately normally distributed, find a 95-percent confidence interval estimate of the population mean.

COMPUTER DATA EXERCISES 9-65 TO 9-67

9-65. Refer to Real Estate Data.xls on the CD, which reports sample information on the homes sold in Victoria, B.C., in 2001.
(a) Develop a 95-percent confidence interval estimate for the mean selling price of the homes.
(b) Develop a 90-percent confidence interval estimate for the fraction of homes that were sold for more than $240 000.
(c) Develop a 98-percent confidence interval estimate for the population mean of the number of bedrooms.

(d) Develop a 90-percent confidence interval estimate for the proportion of homes sold that have a garage.

(e) Develop a 95-percent confidence interval estimate for the proportion of homes sold that have two or more bathrooms.
(Note: In each of (b), (d), and (e), you will have to first convert the data manually to 0/1 data before using the instructions given for Excel or Minitab.)

9-66. Refer to the file 100 of Top 1000 Companies.xls on the CD, which provides information on earnings per share of 100 of the top 1000 companies in Canada in 2000 (published by *Globe Interactive*). Treat this as the population data.

(a) Find the population mean.

(b) Select 60 samples each of size 30, using SRN. (See instructions in Chapter 8.) For each sample, calculate the sample mean and sample standard deviation and 98-percent confidence interval estimate for the population mean.

(c) Check what fraction of the confidence intervals contains the value of population mean. Comment on your findings.

9-67. Refer to the data in file Exercise 9-67.xls on the CD, which provides values of the TSE 300 index BCE and Air Canada stock prices at the end of 20 randomly selected weeks in the year 2000.

(a) Develop a 92-percent confidence interval estimate for the mean value of the TSX index during the year 2000.

(b) Develop a 95-percent confidence interval estimate for the mean value of BCE stock during 2000.

(c) Develop a 90-percent confidence interval estimate for the mean value of Air Canada stock during 2000.

CHAPTER 9   ANSWERS TO SELF-REVIEW

9-1. $\mu = \dfrac{160 + 170 + 165 + 173}{4} = 167$

$\sigma^2 = \dfrac{(160 - 167)^2 + \cdots + (163 - 167)^2}{4} = 24.5$

$\sigma = \sqrt{24.5} \approx 4.95$

Sample No.	Samples	Probability	s^2	s
1	160, 160	1/16	0	0
2	160, 170	1/16	50	7.071
3	160, 165	1/16	12.5	3.536
4	160, 173	1/16	84.5	9.192
5	170, 160	1/16	50	7.071
6	170, 170	1/16	0	0
7	170, 165	1/16	12.5	3.536
8	170, 173	1/16	4.5	2.121
9	165, 160	1/16	12.5	3.536
10	165, 170	1/16	12.5	3.536
11	165, 165	1/16	0	0
12	165, 173	1/16	32	5.657
13	173, 160	1/16	84.5	9.192
14	173, 170	1/16	4.5	2.121
15	173, 165	1/16	32	5.657
16	173, 173	1/16	0	0

$E(S^2) = 0\left(\dfrac{1}{16}\right) + 50\left(\dfrac{1}{16}\right) + \cdots + 32\left(\dfrac{1}{16}\right) + 0\left(\dfrac{1}{16}\right)$

$\qquad = 24.5$

$E(S) = 0\left(\dfrac{1}{16}\right) + 7.071\left(\dfrac{1}{16}\right) + \cdots + 5.657\left(\dfrac{1}{16}\right)$

$\qquad + 0\left(\dfrac{1}{16}\right) = 3.889$

Thus, $E(S^2) = \sigma^2$. But, $E(S) \neq \sigma$

9-2. (a) $(1 - \alpha) = 0.8$; So, $\alpha = 1 - 0.8 = 0.2$; $\alpha/2 = 0.1$; area between 0 and $z_{0.1}$ is $(0.5 - 0.1) = 0.4$. From the Z table, $z = z_{0.1} \approx 1.282$

   (b) $(1 - \alpha) = 0.94$; So, $\alpha/2 = 0.03$; area between 0 and $z_{0.03}$ is $(0.5 - 0.03) = 0.47$. From the Z table, $z = z_{0.03} \approx 1.88$

   (c) $(1 - \alpha) = 0.98$; So, $\alpha/2 = 0.01$; area between 0 and $z_{0.01}$ is $(0.5 - 0.01) = 0.49$. From the Z table, $z = z_{0.01} \approx 2.327$

9-3. (a) $(\bar{X} \pm 1.282\sigma/\sqrt{n})$;   (b) $(\bar{X} \pm 2.327\sigma/\sqrt{n})$;

   (c) $(\bar{X} \pm 1.44\sigma/\sqrt{n})$

9-4. $(1.326 \pm (1.645)(2.05)/\sqrt{20}) = (1.326 \pm 0.754)$ or $(0.572, \ 0.80)$

9-5. (a) $\alpha = (1 - 0.9) = 0.1$. $t = t_{\alpha/2} = t_{0.05}$ (for $df = 20$) $= 1.725$ (from the t table).

   (b) From the t table, we get $t_{0.1}$ (for $df = 15) = 1.341$

   (c) $t = -t_{0.01}$ (for $df = 10) = -2.764$ (from the t table).

9-6. $\bar{x} = 1.326$; $s = 1.649$; $\alpha = (1 - 0.95) = 0.05$. From the t table, we find that for $df = (n - 1) = 19$, $t_{\alpha/2} = t_{0.025} = 2.093$. Hence, a 95-percent confidence interval estimate for population mean is:

$(1.326 \pm (2.093)(1.649)/\sqrt{20}) = (1.326 \pm 0.772)$
$= (0.554, \ 2.098)$

Excel (MegaStat) Output	
Descriptive Statistics	**# 1**
count	20
mean	1.3260
sample variance	2.7205
sample standard deviation	1.6494
standard error of the mean	0.3688
confidence interval, 95% lower	0.5541
confidence interval, 95% upper	2.0979
confidence interval, 99% lower	0.2708
confidence interval, 99% upper	2.3812

Minitab Output	
One-Sample T: C1	
Variable	C1
N	20
Mean	1.326
StDev	1.649
SE Mean	0.369
95.0% CI	(0.554, 2.098)

9-7. (a) The best point estimate of the value of the population proportion is,

$\hat{p}$ is $\dfrac{420}{1400} = 0.3$.

(b) An approximate 99-percent confidence interval estimate is

$$\hat{p} \pm z_{0.005}\sqrt{\hat{p}(1-\hat{p})/n}$$
$$= 0.3 \pm (2.575)\sqrt{0.3(0.7)/1400}$$
$$= (0.2685,\ 0.3315).$$

9-8. $\left(\dfrac{1.96\,(2.05)}{0.5}\right)^2 = 64.58$

So, n should be at least 65.

9-9. $\left(\dfrac{z_{\alpha/2}s}{E}\right)^2 = \left(\dfrac{z_{0.005} \times 0.279}{0.05}\right)^2 = \left(\dfrac{2.575 \times 0.279}{0.05}\right)^2$

$= 206.45$. Hence, he should choose a sample size of 207.

9-10. $\left(\dfrac{0.5z_{\alpha/2}}{E}\right)^2 = \left(\dfrac{0.5 \times z_{0.025}}{0.04}\right)^2 = \left(\dfrac{0.5 \times 1.96}{0.04}\right)^2$

$= 600.25$. So, a value of $n = 601$ would be large enough.

A REVIEW OF   CHAPTERS 8 AND 9

Chapter 8 began by describing the reasons sampling is necessary. We sample because it is often impossible to study every item, or individual, in some populations. It would be too expensive and time-consuming, for example, to contact and record the annual incomes of all the families in Canada. Also sampling often destroys the product. A drug manufacturer cannot test the properties of each tablet manufactured because there would be none left to sell. To estimate a population parameter, therefore, we sample the population. A sample is a part of the population. To obtain a good estimate, care must be taken to ensure that every member of our population has a chance of being selected. A number of probability-type sampling methods can be used, including *simple random sampling*, *stratified random sampling*, *systematic sampling*, and *cluster sampling*.

Regardless of the sampling method selected, the value of a sample statistic obtained is seldom equal to the value of the corresponding population parameter. For example, the mean of a sample is seldom exactly the same as the mean of the population. The difference between the values of a sample statistic and the corresponding population parameter is due to two types of errors: (i) sampling error and (ii) non-sampling error.

In Chapter 8 we demonstrated that if we selected a sample using simple random sampling with replacement (SRR), then the mean of the sample means of all possible samples would be exactly equal to the population mean. We also showed that the standard deviation of the distribution of the sample means was equal to the population standard deviation divided by the square root of the sample size. Hence, we conclude that there was less dispersion in the distribution of the sample means than in the population. Also, as we increased the number of observations in each sample, we decreased the variation in the sampling distribution. When the population size is large, simple random sampling without replacement is almost the same as simple random sampling with replacement.

The Central Limit Theorem is the foundation of statistical inference. If the population, from which we select the samples, follows a normal probability distribution, and the sample is selected using *SRR*, the distribution of the sample means will also follow a normal distribution. The Central Limit Theorem states that even if the population distribution is not normal, the distribution of the sample means will approach a normal distribution as we increase the size of the sample. From a practical standpoint, when the sample contains at least 30 observations we conclude that the distribution of the sample means will approximately follow a normal distribution.

Our focus in Chapter 9 was on point estimators and interval estimators. An estimator of a population parameter is the outcome of a procedure which involves (i) selection of a sample and (ii) application of a computational formula to the selected sample data. Each outcome of a point estimator is a single number, which is used to estimate the population parameter. Each outcome of an interval estimator is a range of numbers within which we expect the value of the population parameter to lie. An interval estimator is called a $(1 - \alpha)$ confidence interval if the probability is $(1 - \alpha)$ that an interval estimate obtained will contain the value of the population parameter. $(1 - \alpha)$ is called the confidence level of the estimator. The width of the interval estimates measures the precision of the estimator. For example, based on a sample, we estimate that the mean annual income of all the accountants in Montreal (the population) is $85 200; that estimate is called a *point estimate*. If we state that the population mean is probably in the interval between $78 600 and $91 400, that estimate is called an *interval estimate*. The two endpoints ($78 600 and $91 400) are the *confidence limits* for the population mean. We described the procedure for establishing a confidence interval for the population mean as well as for the population proportion. In this chapter we also provided a means to determine the necessary sample size, based on the dispersion in the population, the level of confidence desired, and desired precision of the estimate.

■ GLOSSARY

Central limit theorem If a sample is selected using *SRR*, the sampling distribution of the sample means approaches a normal distribution as the sample size increases, regardless of the shape of the population distribution.

Cluster sampling A method often used to lower the cost of sampling if the population is dispersed over a wide geographic area. The area is divided into groups which are called clusters. A sample of clusters of predetermined size is selected using simple random sampling. The collection of all the data units in the selected clusters forms our final sample.

Confidence level of an interval estimator Probability that an interval estimate obtained will contain the value of the population parameter.

Consistent estimator of a population parameter A point estimator of the parameter such that its distribution tends to become increasingly concentrated on the value of the population parameter as the sample size n tends to infinity.

Efficient estimator of a population parameter An unbiased estimator of the parameter, which has minimum variance in the class of unbiased estimators of the parameter.

Estimator of a population parameter Outcome of a procedure which involves two steps: (i) selection of a sample of a particular size from the population using a certain sampling technique and (ii) application of a certain computational procedure to the selected sample data.

Interval estimator An estimator of a population parameter such that each of its possible outcomes is an interval or range of numbers (such as (5, 8)).

Non-probability sampling A sampling technique that does not involve random selection. Here, inclusion of an item in the sample is based on convenience or judgment of the person conducting the sampling.

Non-sampling error The difference between values of point estimate and population parameter, which has no direct relationship to the sampling technique or the estimator used and may occur due to some other reasons.

Point estimator An estimator of a population parameter such that each of its possible outcomes is a single number (such as 4.1 or −3.2).

Probability sampling A sampling technique in which a probability distribution of the number of times different data units can appear in the sample is pre-assigned. The sample is selected randomly in accordance with this probability distribution.

Sampling distribution of the sample mean The probability distribution of values of the sample mean when the sample is selected using a specific sampling technique.

Sampling error The difference between values of point estimate and population parameter, the cause of which can be attributed entirely to the sampling process and the choice of estimator.

Sampling without replacement Sampling technique in which each data unit in the population is allowed to appear in the sample *no more* than once.

Sampling with replacement Sampling technique in which data units in the population are allowed to appear in the sample more than once.

Simple random sampling without replacement (*SRN*) A technique of sampling without replacement in which each possible sample of the desired size n has the same probability of being selected.

Simple random sampling with replacement (*SRR*) A modification of the SRN technique in which data units in the population are allowed to appear in the sample more than once.

Stratified random sampling A population is divided into subgroups, called strata, and a sample is selected from each stratum using *simple random sampling*.

Systematic random sampling The data units in the population are arbitrarily numbered from 1 to N. A number between 1 and N is selected. Let us denote this number by k. One data unit is randomly selected to be in the sample. Starting with this data unit, every kth data unit is added to the sample, until a sample of desired size n is obtained.

Unbiased estimator of a population parameter A point estimator of the parameter such that its expected value equals the value of the parameter.

■ EXERCISES

PART I—MULTIPLE CHOICE

1. The 6200 employees are given identification numbers from 0001 to 6200. A number between 0001 and 0200 is selected randomly and happens to be 0153. Data is collected on employees numbered 0153, 0353, 0553, and so on. This type of sampling is called:
   a. simple random sampling.
   b. systematic sampling.
   c. stratified random sampling.
   d. cluster sampling.

2. You divide a precinct into blocks. Then you select a set of 12 blocks randomly and record all the data on each of the selected blocks. The total of all this data is our sample. This type of sampling is called:
   a. simple random sampling.
   b. systematic sampling.
   c. stratified random sampling.
   d. cluster sampling.

3. In the absence of non-sampling error, the sampling error is:
   a. equal to the population mean.
   b. a population parameter.
   c. the difference between the sample statistic and the population parameter.
   d. always positive.

4. Which of the following are correct statements about confidence intervals?
   a. a confidence interval estimate cannot contain negative numbers.
   b. they are always based on the Z distribution.
   c. every confidence interval estimate must include the population parameter.
   d. none of the above is always correct.

5. The endpoints of a confidence interval are called:
   a. confidence levels.
   b. the test statistics.
   c. the degrees of confidence.
   d. the confidence limits.

6. We compute the mean and the standard deviation of a sample of 50 observations from a population that is positively skewed and has a standard deviation of 4. We wish to develop a confidence interval for the mean. Which of the following statements is correct?
   a. We cannot develop a confidence interval because the population is not normal.
   b. We can use a t distribution.
   c. We can use z because the Central Limit Theorem shows that the distribution of the sample means will approximate the normal distribution.
   d. None of the above statements are correct.

7. Which of the following is *not* a correct statement about a t distribution?
   a. It is positively skewed.
   b. It a continuous distribution.
   c. It has a mean of 0.
   d. There is a family of t distributions.

8. As the number of degrees of freedom increases in a t distribution
   a. it approaches the standard normal distribution.
   b. it becomes more and more skewed.
   c. it becomes a continuous distribution.
   d. it becomes flatter.

9. Which of the following are correct statements about the sample mean when a sample is chosen using *SRR*?
   a. it is an unbiased estimator of the population mean.
   b. it is a consistent estimator of the population mean.
   c. it is an efficient estimator of the population mean.
   d. none of the above.

10. We select a sample of 15 observations from a normal population and wish to develop a 98 percent confidence interval for the mean. The appropriate value of t is:
    a. 2.947.
    b. 2.977.
    c. 2.624.
    d. None of the above.

PART II—PROBLEMS

11. A recent study indicated that women took an average of 8.6 weeks of unpaid leave from the job after the birth of a child. Assume that this distribution follows, approximately, a normal probability distribution with a standard deviation of 2.0 weeks. We select a sample of 35 women who recently returned to work after the birth of a child. What is the likelihood that the mean of this sample is at least 8.8 weeks?

12. The manager of the Tee Shirt Emporium reports that the mean number of shirts sold per week is 1210 with a standard deviation of 325. The distribution of sales follows a normal distribution. What is the likelihood of selecting a sample of 25 weeks and finding the sample mean to be 1100 or less?

In Exercises 13–19, assume that the population distribution is approximately normal.

13. The owner of the North-Pacific Café wished to estimate the mean number of lunch customers per day. A sample of 60 days revealed a mean of 160 per day, the sample standard deviation was 20 per day. Develop a 98 percent confidence interval estimate for the mean number of customers per day.

14. The manager of the local Hamburg Express wishes to estimate the mean time customers spend at the drive-thru window. A sample of 80 customers experienced a mean waiting time of 2.65 minutes, the sample standard deviation was 0.45 minutes. Develop a 90 percent confidence interval estimate for the mean waiting time.

15. The office manager for a large company is studying the usage of its copy machines. A random sample of six copy machines revealed the following number of copies (reported in 000s) made yesterday.

    826   931   1126   918   1011   1101

    Develop a 95-percent confidence interval for the mean number of copies per machine.

16. John Kleman is the host of a radio news program in Saskatchewan. During his morning program, John asks listeners to call in and discuss current local and national news. This morning John was concerned with the number of hours children under 12 years of age watch TV per day. The last 5 callers reported that their children watched the following number of hours of TV last night.

    3.0   3.5   4.0   4.5   3.0

    Would it be reasonable to develop a confidence interval from these data to show the mean number of hours children under 12 years of age watch TV? If yes, construct an appropriate confidence interval estimate and interpret the result. If no, why would a confidence interval not be appropriate?

17. Historically, Widgets' Manufacturing produces 250 widgets per day. Recently the new owner bought a new machine to produce more widgets per day. A sample of 16 days production revealed a mean of 240 units; the sample standard deviation was 35. Construct a confidence interval for the mean number of widgets produced per day. Does it seem reasonable to conclude that the mean daily widget production has increased? Justify your conclusion.

18. The manufacturer of a power tube used in expensive stereo equipment wishes to estimate the useful life of the tube (in thousands of hours). The estimate is to be within 0.10 (100) hours. Assume a 95 percent level of confidence and that the standard deviation of the useful life of the tube is 0.90 (900 hours).

19. The manager of a home improvement store wishes to estimate the mean amount of money spent in the store. The estimate is to be within $4.00 with a 95 percent level of confidence. The manager does not know the standard deviation of the amounts spent, but expects it to be around $25.00. How large of a sample is needed?

20. In a survey conducted by Ipsos-Reid Group and GPC Communications in May 2001, 4704 adults across Canada were asked which issue facing Canada, the Government of Canada should focus on most. Twenty-six percent of the respondents cited health care as their top priority. Develop a 95-percent confidence interval estimate for the proportion of Canadian adults who feel that government should give top priority to health care.

21. In recent times the percentage of buyers purchasing a new vehicle via the Internet has been large enough that local automobile dealers are concerned about its impact on their business. The information needed is an estimate of the proportion of purchases via the Internet. How large a sample of purchasers is necessary for the estimate to be within 2 percentage points with a 98 percent level of confidence? Current thinking is that about 8 percent of vehicles are purchased via the Internet.

22. Historically, the proportion of adults over the age of 24 who smoke has been 0.30. In recent years much information has been published and aired on radio and TV that smoking is not good for one's health. A sample of 500 adults revealed only 25 percent of those sampled smoked. Develop a 98-percent confidence interval estimate for the proportion of adults who currently smoke. Would you agree that the proportion is less than 30?

23. With the Quebec separatist movement and the Western alienation issue, national unity continues to be an important issue in Canada. In a survey of Canadian adults conducted by Ipsos-Reid Group and GPC Communications in May 2001, 4704 adults across Canada were asked what priority the government of Canada should place on the issue of Canadian unity. Of those in the sample, 62 percent responded that the priority should be high.
    a. Obtain a 95 percent confidence interval estimate for the fraction of Canadian adults who believe that the government of Canada should give high priority to the issue of Canadian unity.
    b. What would be your reaction, based on the answer to part (a) to the statement that less than 60 percent of Canadian adults believe that this issue should be given high priority by the Canadian government?

■ CASE STUDY

CENTURY NATIONAL BANK

Oil is one of the major exports of Canada and forms a significant part of Canadian economy. With the uncertain situation in the oil and gas sector resulting in significant fluctuations in oil prices, the Canadian Minister of Industry wants to review the state of the Canadian oil and gas industry and government policy towards the industry. In case the industry growth is not significant, the government may consider giving extra incentives to the industry. One indicator of the state of the industry is the average price earnings ratio. Since the price earnings ratio reflects expected growth of a company or a sector in the future, a trend in the average price earnings ratio will be used as a policy criterion by the minister. The statistical advisers to the minister have randomly selected a set of 18 Canadian companies in oil and gas industry that are listed on the Toronto Stock Exchange. The data on price earnings ratios of these companies published in July 2001, December 2000, and July 2000 issues of *TSE Review* are tabulated below.

a. Based on this sample data, obtain a 95 percent confidence interval estimate for the average price earnings ratios of the Canadian oil and gas industry during each of July 2001, December 2000, and July 2000.

b. Based on the interval estimates, what can we say about the trend in the oil and gas industry? Do you think the industry is growing? What would be your recommendation to the Canadian Minister of Industry?

Jul '01	Dec '00	Jul '00
12.8	12.2	11.7
6.3	5.1	7.1
5.4	8.3	11.5
5.1	19.7	16.3
11.2	18.8	16.8
5.6	11.8	13.4
2.3	2.6	7.6
13.8	8.6	81.5
13.5	14.1	38.9
51.9	40.9	43.8
4.3	7.1	8.3
4.3	21.5	112.5
4.9	7	10.6
9.6	17.5	17.9
2.8	8.5	7.7
9.6	32	15.8
6.5	8.6	11.9
6.5	8.6	11.9

CHAPTER 10

One Sample Tests of Hypothesis

GOALS

When you have completed this chapter, you will be able to:

- Define null and alternative hypotheses and hypothesis testing

- Define Type I and Type II errors

- Describe the five-step hypothesis testing procedure

- Distinguish between a one-tailed and a two-tailed test of hypothesis

- Conduct a test of hypothesis about a population mean

- Conduct a test of hypothesis about a population proportion

- Explain the relationship between hypothesis testing and confidence interval estimation

- Compute the probability of a Type II error and power of a test.

EGON S. PEARSON (1895–1980)

It is generally accepted that John Arbuthnott (1710) was the first to publish a result regarding a statistical test of hypothesis. Arbuthnott developed a test to demonstrate that, *"This equality of (number of) males and females is not the effect of Chance but a Divine Providence"*.[1] In 1812, Pierre-Simon Laplace developed and implemented a statistical scheme to test the hypothesis that *comets are not regular members of the solar system*. However, it was R.A. Fisher (1925) who laid the foundation of the modern theory of hypothesis testing. The theory, in its currently accepted form, was developed by J. Neyman and E. Pearson (1933).

Egon S. Pearson (1895–1980) was the only son of Karl Pearson, one of the founders of the twentieth-century science of statistics. He grew up under the loving protection of his father and remained under his protection until fairly late in his life. He was, from a very early age, exposed to his father's work on statistics and the statistical journal, *Biometrika*, that he was editing. One of his favourite games, as a five year old, was creating his own journal, which as he later recalled, "... was all scrawls with chalk". He held his father in very high esteem and at times referred to him as his paternal "god."

After receiving his B.A., he joined his father's Department of Applied Statistics at University College, London, as a lecturer in 1921. Here, he attended his father's lectures and began his research career in statistics. However, his most significant research work began in 1925 when he met Jerzy Neyman. The two together developed the *Neyman-Pearson theory of testing statistical hypotheses*, which has become one of the most fundamental theories in statistics.

After his father's death, Egon assumed the role of Managing Editor of *Biometrika* and also undertook the task of revising his father's two volume work on *Tables for Statisticians and Biometricians*, which appeared in 1954 and 1972.

During World War II, Egon undertook war work. He was a key member of the Operations Research group in the Ordnance Board, Ministry of Defence, and worked on projects such as analysis of the fragmentation of shells hitting aircraft. He found this work "undeniably personally rather enjoyable" ... "despite bombings, V1 flying bombs, and V2 rockets".[2] He was awarded a C.B.E. for his war service. In spite of his great accomplishments, Egon Pearson was an unassuming man, reputed for his modesty and warmth, fairness and promptness.

For a more detailed biography of Egon Pearson, see *The Statistical Pioneers*, by James W. Tankard Jr., Schenkman Publishing Co., 1984.

1498
1548
1598
1648
1698
1748
1898
1948
2000

INTRODUCTION

Chapter 5 began our study of statistical inference. Recall that in statistical inference, we deal with situations where we do not have full access to the entire data of interest (the population). In this case, our objective is to infer desired information about the population by appropriately choosing a part of the population, which is called a sample, and analyzing the sample data. In classical statistics, the problems of statistical inference are mainly of two types: (i) estimation, and (ii) hypothesis testing.

Chapters 5 through 7 laid the foundation for statistical inference with the study of probability theory, discrete random variables and continuous random variables. Chapter 8 introduced different sampling techniques and the concept of sampling distribution of a sample statistic. In particular, we discussed in reasonable depth, the properties of sampling distribution of the sample mean. Chapter 9 discussed the statistical theory of estimation. Here, we are interested in estimating the value of a particular population parameter. We considered two types of estimators: (i) point estimators, and (ii) confidence intervals.

In this chapter, we begin our study of the *statistical theory of hypothesis testing*. Here, *we mean by* **hypothesis**, *a statement about a population distribution such that: (i) it is either true or false, but never both, and (ii) with full knowledge of the population data, it is possible to identify, with certainty, whether it is true or false.* Some examples of hypotheses we might want to test are:

- The mean number of kilometres driven by those leasing a Chevy Blazer for three years is 52 000 km.
- The mean time Canadian families live in a particular single-family dwelling is 11.8 years.
- The mean starting salary for graduates of four-year business schools is $2800 per month.
- Eighty percent of those who play Lotto 6/49 regularly never win more than $100 in any one play.

We deal with situations where we are given a *pair of complementary hypotheses* about a population distribution. Thus, precisely one of these two hypotheses is true. One of the hypotheses is usually based on a theory or is a claim made by some organization. Our objective is to select sample data from the population and, based on analysis of this sample data and additional information about the population that is available to us, decide which of the two hypotheses is true.

As we saw in Chapter 9, when a decision is based on analysis of sample data and not the entire population data, it is not possible to make a correct decision all the time. Our objective then is to keep the probability of making a wrong decision reasonably small.

10.1   BASIC FRAMEWORK OF STATISTICAL THEORY OF HYPOTHESIS TESTING

To make the basic ideas of statistical theory of hypothesis testing clear, let us use an analogy from the Canadian legal system. Suppose a person is accused of murder and is being tried in a court of law. The judge (or the jury) considers the following *complementary pair of hypotheses*: (i) *the person is innocent*, or (ii) *the person is guilty*. These two hypotheses cover the entire range of possibilities. The judge (or the jury) listens to the arguments and counter-arguments of the Crown prosecutor and the defence (sample data) and makes one of two decisions: (i) *the person is guilty*, or (ii) *the person is not guilty*. It may be noted that the system does not guarantee that a correct decision will be made all the time. Once in a while, a guilty person may be set free and once in a while, an innocent person may be declared guilty. The different possibilities are given in the table below.

Reality \ Court Decision	The person is declared "not guilty"	The person is declared "guilty"
The person is "innocent"	Correct decision	*Error*
The person is "guilty"	*Error*	Correct decision

It should be intuitively clear that, for a pre-specified limit on the amount sample information that can be collected, an attempt by the judge (or jury) to reduce the probability of one of the two types of errors will result in an increase in the probability of the other type of error. It is therefore important to decide which of these two types of errors is more serious and concentrate more on reducing it.

In this society, it is agreed that declaring an innocent person guilty is a much more serious error than setting a guilty person free. That is, if in doubt, the judge should declare the person "not guilty". A person should be declared "guilty" only if the judge is convinced so *"beyond a reasonable doubt."*

The hypothesis *"the person is innocent"* is thus, the **default hypothesis**. We denote it by the symbol H_0. We call its complementary hypothesis, *"the person is guilty,"* the **alternative hypothesis** and denote it by H_1. Falsely rejecting the default hypothesis (H_0), which is the more serious error, is called a **Type I error**. We call the other type of error a **Type II error**.

The court trial is an attempt by the Crown prosecutor to prove the alternative hypothesis, *"the person is guilty."* The default hypothesis, *"the person is innocent,"* is not rejected unless there is overwhelming evidence against it.

It may be noted that the judge does not declare the accused "innocent." The person is declared "guilty" or "not guilty." In the second case, the judge states that, "There is insufficient evidence to declare the person guilty." Hence, by default, the person will be accepted as innocent.

The above analogy describes the framework used in the statistical theory of hypothesis testing.

We are interested in proving a certain *hypothesis* **about a population distribution**. We accept its complementary hypothesis as the **default hypothesis** and denote it by H_0. The hypothesis being proved is called the **alternative hypothesis** and is denoted by H_1.

Our task is to collect sample data, analyze it and draw one of the following two conclusions: (i) we have sufficient evidence to reject H_0 in favour of H_1, or (ii) we do not have sufficient evidence to reject H_0 in favour of H_1.

Since our objective is to check if there is sufficient evidence to reject or nullify H_0, the default hypothesis H_0 is called the **null hypothesis**.

The possible outcomes are summarized in the table below.

Test Result / Reality	Do not reject H_0	Reject H_0 in favour of H_1
H_0 is true	No error	Type I error
H_1 is true	Type II error	No error

While both types of errors should be avoided, the Type I error (falsely rejecting the null hypothesis) is considered a more serious type of error. *The probability of a Type I error is called the* **level of significance of the test** *and is denoted by the Greek letter* α (pronounced alpha). *The probability of a Type II error is denoted by the Greek letter* β (pronounced beta). The test is designed to *restrict its level of significance,* α, *to a pre-specified value, and, in addition, minimize the probability of a Type II error,* β.

> **Hypothesis testing**   Given a pair of complementary hypotheses about a population distribution, called null and alternative hypotheses, hypothesis testing is a statistical technique of analyzing sample data selected randomly from the population and making one of the following two decisions: (i) "we have sufficient evidence to reject the null hypothesis in favour of the alternative hypothesis," or (ii) "we do not have sufficient evidence to reject the null hypothesis." The test is designed to keep the probability of a Type I error equal to a pre-specified value, α, and minimize the probability of a Type II error.

10.2   FIVE-STEP PROCEDURE FOR TESTING A HYPOTHESIS

We shall present a five-step procedure that systematizes hypothesis testing. The steps are shown in the following diagram. We will discuss in detail each of the steps.

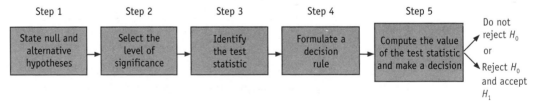

Step 1 — State null and alternative hypotheses → Step 2 — Select the level of significance → Step 3 — Identify the test statistic → Step 4 — Formulate a decision rule → Step 5 — Compute the value of the test statistic and make a decision → Do not reject H_0 or Reject H_0 and accept H_1

STEP 1: STATE THE NULL HYPOTHESIS (H_0) AND THE ALTERNATIVE HYPOTHESIS (H_1)

The first step is to state *the null hypothesis* (H_0) and *the alternative hypothesis* (H_1). The hypotheses considered are always about the **population distribution**.

We generally start with the alternative hypothesis. This is the hypothesis we are interested in proving. Usually, it is a *research hypothesis*, that is, it is based on a theory or is a claim made by some organization, based on some research.

> **Alternative hypothesis**   The hypothesis, about the population distribution, that we are interested in proving. We denote it by H_1. This is usually a research hypothesis.

The null hypothesis is the complement of the alternative hypothesis. We accept it as the default hypothesis. If the sample data provides strong evidence against the null hypothesis (and therefore in favour of the alternative hypothesis), we reject the null hypothesis in favour of the alternative hypothesis. In the absence of any strong evidence in favour of the alternative hypothesis, we do not reject the null hypothesis. A null hypothesis generally represents status quo.

> **i** **Null hypothesis** The complement of the alternative hypothesis. We denote it by H_0. We accept the null hypothesis as the default hypothesis. It is not rejected unless there is convincing sample evidence against it, (that is, in favour of H_1). It generally represents status quo.

It should be emphasized that if the null hypothesis is not rejected based on the sample data, we cannot say that the null hypothesis is true. To put it another way, failing to reject H_0 does not prove that H_0 is true. It means that the sample data has failed to provide convincing evidence against H_0, (that is, in favour of H_1).

We give below some examples of null and alternative hypotheses.

- A pharmaceutical company claims that their new medicine for a certain disease is more effective than existing medicines for the disease. Suppose the best medicine, currently available on the market, has an effectiveness of 60 percent. (That is, the probability of a random patient, who tries the medicine, recovering from the disease is 0.6.) Before approving the company's claim, Health Canada will conduct a test of hypothesis to check if the new medicine is really more effective. To protect Canadians from ineffective drugs, Health Canada will *not* accept the company's claim unless there is substantial evidence in its favour. The two hypotheses are thus:

  H_0: The new medicine is not more effective than existing medicines.
  H_1: The new medicine is more effective than existing medicines.

  If the effectiveness of the new medicine (probability that a random patient, trying the medicine, will recover from the disease) is p, then the two hypotheses can be written as:

  H_0: $p \leq 0.6$
  H_1: $p > 0.6$

- Suppose the result of the statistical test conducted by Health Canada is in favour of the new medicine. The pharmaceutical company now wants it to be officially recorded that the effectiveness of the new medicine is $p = 0.70$ and they provide statistical evidence in support of the claim. Suppose Health Canada studies the statistical evidence and finds it sound. In this case, they are still supposed to conduct their own statistical study before approving the claim. However this time, they will accept the company's claim, unless their study provides significant evidence that the effectiveness is less than 0.7. In other words, the null and alternative hypotheses are now:

  H_0: $p \geq 0.7$
  H_1: $p < 0.7$

- The quality engineer at the packaging department of Kraft General Foods Canada Inc. has observed that the machine setting has a tendency to shift upwards, resulting in an increase in the mean weight of its boxes of Grape Nuts cereal above the required amount of 453 grams indicated on the label. She has observed that it is not possible for the setting to shift downwards. The management wants to periodically conduct a statistical test of significance, based on weights of a random sample of recently packaged boxes, to check if the setting has shifted. Recall that any statistical test of hypothesis involves two types of errors—Type I error and Type II error. In the case where the mean weight is more than 453 grams, and the problem is not rectified, the company will lose money due to the extra cereal in the boxes. On the other hand, rectification of the problem will require the packaging operation to be shut down for some time, resulting in a greater loss. The loss due to shutdown will be all the more significant if the plant is shut down when in reality the setting has not shifted. Shutting down the plant falsely is therefore a more significant error. Hence, unless there is overwhelming evidence against it, it will be assumed that the setting has not shifted and the mean weight is 453 grams. Thus, if we denote the mean weight of the boxes by μ, the null and alternative hypotheses are:

H_0: $\mu = 453$
H_1: $\mu > 453$

Since it is not possible for the setting to shift downward, these are complementary hypotheses, (that is, exactly one of them is true).

- One way to test an axiomatic theory in physics or economics is to test hypotheses based on the theory. The theory is not rejected unless there is significant evidence against some hypothesis based on it. A certain axiomatic theory in economics implies that the mean annual inflation rate (measured as percentage change in the Consumer Price Index (CPI) of all the items) in Canada during the last century was at least 3.6%. A group of students wants to test this hypothesis to see if it provides significant evidence against the theory. If we denote the mean annual inflation rate by μ, the null and alternative hypotheses are:

H_0: $\mu \geq 3.6$
H_1: $\mu < 3.6$

- A social scientist claims that the time use pattern of Canadian youths has changed since 1998. We wish to test this claim. In particular, we wish to test if the number of hours Canadian youths sleep at night has changed since 1998. Suppose we decide not to accept the scientist's claim unless we get significant sample evidence in its favour. As per a report published by Statistics Canada, in 1998 an average Canadian male in the age group 15 to 24 slept 8.5 hours per night. Thus, null and alternative hypotheses are:

H_0: $\mu = 8.5$
H_1: $\mu \neq 8.5$

- A company manufactures two types of light bulbs. The first type of light bulbs have a mean life of 2400 hours, while the second type have a mean life of 2000 hours. The two types of bulbs are identical in exterior appearance and can be distinguished only by the specifications stamped on each bulb. A batch of 5000 bulbs got mixed up, before they were stamped and the supervising engineer is not sure whether they are of superior or inferior type. He therefore decides to select a random sample of bulbs from the batch and test them. The whole batch of bulbs will be sold as inferior type, unless there is significant evidence based on the test that the bulbs are of the superior type. In this case, the null and alternative hypotheses are:

H_0: $\mu = 2000$
H_1: $\mu = 2400$

- In finance literature, a commonly used measure of risk of a stock is the standard deviation of the return. The larger the standard deviation, the more risky the stock.

An investor is considering moving her investment from one stock to another, provided she can get sufficient evidence that the second stock is less risky. If we denote the standard deviations of the returns on the two stocks by σ_1 and σ_2, then, the null and alternative hypotheses are:

$$H_0: \sigma_1 \leq \sigma_2$$
$$H_1: \sigma_1 > \sigma_2$$

- The top management of an airline company has observed that there seem to be more no-shows for flights out of Toronto, than for flights out of Montreal. If this is true, then it is likely to have a non-trivial effect on the airline policies regarding flight scheduling and the sale of tickets. The management has therefore decided to conduct a test of hypothesis to check if there is significant evidence that the number of no-shows for flights out of Toronto is more. The null and alternative hypotheses in this case are:

H_0: The distribution of no-shows for flights out of Toronto is no larger than for flights out of Montreal.

H_1: The distribution of no-shows for flights out of Toronto is larger than for flights out of Montreal.

In the first seven examples above, the hypotheses are about the value(s) of population parameter(s). In the last example, the hypotheses are about relative shapes of two population distributions. In general, the hypotheses considered in a test of hypothesis may be about the value of a single parameter of a population, about relative values of parameters of different populations, or about relative shapes of two or more population distributions.

In this chapter, we only consider hypotheses about the value of a single parameter of a population, such as the population mean or the population proportion. Our hypotheses will be of the form $\mu = 5$ or $\mu \leq 4$ or $\mu > 9$ or $\mu \neq 3$ or $p < 0.6$. For convenience, we shall only consider the cases where the null hypothesis contains the equality sign. (For example: $\mu = 5$ or $\mu \leq 4$ or $\mu \geq 9$ or $p = 0.4$) This is merely to avoid mathematical complexities so that we can highlight the basic ideas in hypothesis testing.

■ SELF-REVIEW 10-1

(a) An axiomatic theory of the stock market, developed by a group of economists, implies that the mean value of monthly percentage changes in the TSE 300 index during the last forty-five years is no more than 0.2. A group of students, who do not have access to the entire data on the TSE 300 index, want to collect sample data and conduct a test of hypothesis to check if it provides significant evidence against the theory. What should be the null and alternative hypotheses?

(b) An economist claims that she has analyzed the data released by Globe Interactive on the performance of the top 1000 companies in Canada during the year 2000. She claims that the mean value of earnings per share of the top 1000 Canadian companies during the year is 0.604. A group of students wants to verify the claim before using it in their research paper. They do not have access to the full data on the top 1000 companies, but can collect the data on a sample of the companies. They will accept the claim, unless their test provides strong evidence against it. What should be the null and alternative hypotheses?

STATISTICS IN ACTION

STEP 2: SELECT THE LEVEL OF SIGNIFICANCE

After setting up the null hypothesis and the alternative hypothesis, the next step is to state the level of significance.

>
> **Significance level of a test**   The probability of a Type I error. That is, the probability of rejecting the null hypothesis (H_0) when it is true. It is designated by the Greek letter α (pronounced alpha).

The level of significance is also sometimes called the level of risk. This may be a more appropriate term because it is the risk you take of rejecting the null hypothesis when it is true.

There is no one level of significance that is applied to all tests. You, the researcher, must decide on the level of significance before formulating a decision rule and collecting data. The most commonly used value of α is 0.05.

To illustrate how it is possible to reject a true hypothesis, suppose the contract, signed by a computer manufacturer with a supplier of printed circuit boards (PCBs), specifies that any shipment of PCBs containing more than 6 percent substandard boards will be rejected.

A shipment of 4000 boards was received on November 21. Since it is very time consuming to inspect all 4000 boards, the company decided to use the following test of hypothesis: the null hypothesis is that the shipment contains 6 percent or less substandard boards. (Rejecting a good shipment is definitely a more serious type of error). The alternative hypothesis is that more than 6 percent of the boards are substandard. Select a sample of 50 boards and inspect them. If the sample contains more than 6 percent, (that is, more than 3), substandard boards, reject the shipment. We call the number 3, **the critical value of the test**.

A sample of 50 PCBs revealed that 4 boards were substandard. Hence, the shipment was rejected.

If the shipment was actually substandard, then the decision to return the shipment to the supplier was correct. However, suppose these 4 substandard boards were the only substandard boards in the entire shipment of 4000 boards. Then only 0.1 percent of the boards ($4/4000 = 0.001$) were substandard. In that case, less than 6 percent of the entire shipment was substandard and rejecting the shipment was an error. In terms of hypothesis testing, we rejected the null hypothesis that the shipment was not substandard when we should not have rejected it. By rejecting a true null hypothesis, we committed a Type I error. The probability of committing a Type I error is α.

We can reduce the value of α by increasing the critical value of the test from 3 to say, 10. However, this will increase the probability of a Type II error.

>
> **Type II Error**   The error committed when we do not reject a null hypothesis when it is false. The probability of committing a Type II error is designated by the Greek letter, β (pronounced beta).

The computer manufacturer would commit a Type II error if, unknown to the manufacturer, an incoming shipment of PCBs contained 15 percent substandard boards and yet the shipment was accepted. How could this happen? Suppose, by chance, only 2 of the 50, (that is, 4 percent), boards in the sample tested were substandard, and 48 of the 50 were good boards. According to the stated procedure, because the sample contained less than 6 percent substandard boards, the shipment was accepted.

The test is designed to restrict α, the probability of a Type I error, to a pre-specified value and, at the same time, minimize the probability of Type II error, β.

STEP 3: IDENTIFY THE TEST STATISTIC

We now select an appropriate sample statistic and base our decision on the value of the statistic obtained from the selected sample data. Such a statistic is called the **test statistic**. Since the value of the test statistic depends on the randomly selected sample data, it is a random variable.

 Test Statistic A suitably chosen sample statistic. It is a random variable, whose value is determined from the sample data. We make our decision based on the value of the test statistic obtained from the selected sample data.

Let us consider the problem mentioned before regarding the average weight of the boxes of Grape Nuts cereal produced by the Kraft General Foods, Canada. The null and alternative hypotheses in this case are:

H_0: $\mu = 453$
H_1: $\mu > 453$

We saw in chapters 8 and 9 that the sample mean, $\bar{X}$, is the best point estimator of the population mean. (It is an unbiased and consistent estimator of the population mean. It is also an efficient estimator under fairly general conditions.) Hence, it would be reasonable to base our decision on the value of $\bar{X}$ calculated from weights of a sample of Grape Nuts cereal boxes.

If the null hypothesis is correct, (that is, the value of μ is 453), then the probability is small that the value of $\bar{X}$ will be much different from 453. Since the value of μ can only be 453 or larger, a value of $\bar{X}$ much smaller than 453 will only strengthen the hypothesis that the value of μ is 453. A value of $\bar{X}$ much larger than 453 will, however, suggest that the value of μ might be more than 453.

A logical decision rule is, thus, to *select a critical value x_U and if the value $\bar{x}$ of sample mean calculated from the sample data is greater than x_U, declare that "most likely H_0 is false and hence, we should reject H_0 in favour of H_1." If the computed value $\bar{x}$ is less than or equal to x_U, "do not reject H_0." x_U is thus the dividing point between the region where H_0 will be rejected and the region where H_0 will not be rejected.

Suppose the population standard deviation σ is known. Then, we can standardize $\bar{X}$ to get the following equivalent decision rule: calculate the value $\dfrac{\bar{x} - 453}{\sigma/\sqrt{n}}$ from the sample data. If it is greater than $a_U = \dfrac{x_U - 453}{\sigma/\sqrt{n}}$, then declare that "most likely H_0 is false and hence, we should reject H_0 in favour of H_1." Otherwise, "do not reject H_0."

Thus, $\dfrac{\overline{X} - 453}{\sigma/\sqrt{n}}$ is **a standardized test statistic** and we call a_U **the critical value** of the standardized test statistic.

How large should the value $\dfrac{\overline{x} - 453}{\sigma/\sqrt{n}}$ be for us to decide to reject H_0 in favour of H_1? In other words, what should be the critical value, a_U? As we shall see later, the answer to this depends on the value of the significance level of the test.

Suppose the population distribution is normal. If the value of the population standard deviation is known, then when H_0 is true, (that is, $\mu = 453$), $\dfrac{\overline{X} - 453}{\sigma/\sqrt{n}} = Z$, the standard normal variable. We call it the **Z statistic** and we call the corresponding test a **Z test**.

Suppose the population distribution is not normal. If it is approximately normal, or the sample size is large, then when H_0 is true, (that is, $\mu = 453$), we saw in Chapter 8 that $\dfrac{\overline{X} - 453}{\sigma/\sqrt{n}} \approx Z$. We shall therefore treat it as a **Z statistic** and we shall apply the rules of a **Z test**.

Now, suppose the population distribution is normal and the population standard deviation is unknown. In this case, when H_0 is true (that is, $\mu = 453$), we saw in Chapter 9 that $\dfrac{\overline{X} - 453}{S/\sqrt{n}} = T$ has Student's t distribution. We shall use T as our test statistic. We call it a **t statistic** and we call the corresponding test a **t test**.

In this chapter, we shall use only Z statistics and t statistics. In later chapters we shall use other test statistics such as F, χ^2 (pronounced as, and sometimes written as *chi-square*), and so on.

STEP 4: FORMULATE A DECISION RULE

A decision rule is a rule for deciding for which values of the test statistic we should reject H_0 in favour of H_1, and for which values of the test statistic we should not reject H_0. The set of values of the test statistic for which we decide to reject the null hypothesis is called the **rejection region**.

For illustration, let us continue with the problem regarding the average weight of the boxes of Grape Nuts cereal produced by Kraft General Foods, Canada. In this case, the null and alternative hypotheses are:

H_0: $\mu = 453$
H_1: $\mu > 453$

Suppose the population standard deviation σ is known. Then, as we saw before, a good choice of test statistic is $\dfrac{\overline{X} - 453}{\sigma/\sqrt{n}}$. We also saw that a logical decision rule is to choose a positive number a_U as a critical value and reject H_0 if the value of the test statistic obtained from sample data is greater than a_U.

The probability of a Type I error will then be the probability that the value of the test statistic will be greater than a_U, when H_0 is correct, (that is when $\mu = 453$). We should choose the number a_U such that when $\mu = 453$, this probability does not exceed the selected value of level of significance α. Since we simultaneously want to keep the probability of a Type II error low, we should not unnecessarily resist rejecting H_0 for too large values of the test statistic. (This will increase the probability of a Type II error.) Hence, the critical value a_U should be such that when $\mu = 453$, the probability that

CHART 10-1: Rejection Region and Significance Level for a Right-Tailed Test

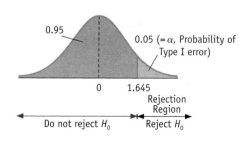

$\dfrac{\bar{X} - 453}{\sigma/\sqrt{n}}$ will be greater than a_U equals the selected value of the level of significance α.

Suppose the population is approximately normally distributed or the sample size is large, and $\mu = 453$. Then, $\dfrac{\bar{X} - 453}{\sigma/\sqrt{n}} \approx Z$, a standard normal variable. We shall treat it is a standard normal variable. Thus, in this case, we shall choose the value a_U such that the area (probability) under the Z curve to the right of a_U is α. In chapters 8 and 9, we denoted this by z_α. Suppose we choose the level of significance $\alpha = 0.05$. Then, $a_U = z_{0.05} = 1.645$. (This is the z value in the Z table corresponding to the probability of $(0.5 - 0.05) = 0.45$.) The **rejection region** is thus to the right of 1.645. We portray this in Chart 10-1. Note in the chart that,

- The test statistic is assumed to be a Z statistic. Its sampling distribution is a standard normal distribution.
- The rejection region is the region greater than 1.645. The value 1.645 is the critical value.
- The region where the null hypothesis is not rejected is to the left of, and including, 1.645.
- The area under the curve corresponding to the rejection region is 0.05, which is precisely the level of significance chosen.
- The rejection region includes only the right tail of the distribution. Such a test is therefore called **a right-tailed** or **upper-tailed test**.

> i **Rejection Region** The set of possible values of the test statistic for which, as per our decision rule, the null hypothesis H_0 will be rejected.

> i **Critical Values** The dividing points between the rejection region and the region where H_0 is not rejected.

Another equivalent, and more popular way of stating the decision rule is in terms of what is called the **P-value**. We shall discuss this in Section 10.5.

STEP 5: COMPUTE THE VALUE OF THE TEST STATISTIC AND MAKE A DECISION

The fifth and final step in hypothesis testing is making a decision to reject or not to reject the null hypothesis. The decision is based on the value of the test statistic, computed from the sample, and the decision rule selected in Step 4.

Let us continue with the problem regarding the average weight of the boxes of Grape Nuts cereal. Refer to Chart 10-1. If, the value $\dfrac{\bar{x} - 453}{\sigma/\sqrt{n}}$, computed from the selected sample data, is 2.34, the null hypothesis will be rejected at the 0.05 significance level. This decision is based on the fact that 2.34 lies in the rejection region, that is, it lies beyond 1.645. We would reject the null hypothesis, reasoning that if the null hypothesis is correct, then it is highly improbable (probability < 0.05) that the computed value of Z would be that large.

Had the computed value of Z been say 0.71, the null hypothesis would not be rejected. (The value 0.71 does not lie in the rejection region.) It would be reasoned that the probability of obtaining a value of Z equal to 0.71 or higher, when the null hypothesis is correct, is fairly high. Hence, obtaining such a value of Z is not inconsistent with the statement of the null hypothesis.

Only one of the two decisions is possible in hypothesis testing—either *reject H_0 in favour of H_1 or do not reject H_0.* We wish to re-emphasize that there is always a possibility that the null hypothesis will be rejected when it should not be rejected (Type I error). Also, there is a definable chance that the null hypothesis will not be rejected when it should be rejected (Type II error).

10.3 ONE-TAILED AND TWO-TAILED TESTS OF SIGNIFICANCE

We discussed above the different steps of a statistical test of significance and applied them to the case of the weights of the boxes of Grape Nuts cereal. We saw that if the value of the population standard deviation, σ, is known, then a good choice of a test statistic is $\dfrac{\bar{X} - 453}{\sigma/\sqrt{n}}$. If the value of σ is not known, then we would use $\dfrac{\bar{X} - 453}{S/\sqrt{n}}$ as a test statistic. In either case, our decision rule is to choose a critical value a_U and reject the null hypothesis if the value of the test statistic calculated from the sample is greater than a_U. In this case, the rejection region contains only the right tail of the distribution of the test statistic. This is therefore called **a right-tailed or an upper-tailed test**. The value a_U should be such that when $\mu = 453$, the probability of rejecting H_0, (that is, the probability that the value of the test statistic will be greater than a_U), should equal the selected value of the level of significance, α.

Now let us consider the problem we introduced in the previous section, regarding the claim made by a social scientist about the change in sleeping patterns of Canadian youths. We wish to test if the average number of hours Canadian youths sleep at night has changed from the 1998 value of 8.5 hours per night, reported by Statistics Canada. In this case, the null and alternative hypotheses are:

H_0: $\mu = 8.5$
H_1: $\mu \neq 8.5$

Again, we shall base our decision on the value of $\bar{X}$. If H_0 is true, the probability is high that the value of $\bar{X}$ will be close to 8.5; the probability is low that the value of $\bar{X}$ will be far away from 8.5, in either direction. Hence, a logical decision rule will be to choose a lower bound x_L (smaller than 8.5) and an upper bound x_U (larger than 8.5) and reject H_0 if the calculated value of the test statistic is smaller than x_L or if it is greater than x_U.

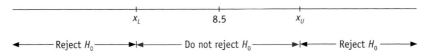

If the population standard deviation, σ, is known, then we can standardize $\bar{X}$ to get the following equivalent decision rule: calculate the value $\dfrac{\bar{x} - 8.5}{\sigma/\sqrt{n}}$ from the sample

CHART 10-2: Rejection Region and Significance Level of a Two-Tailed Test

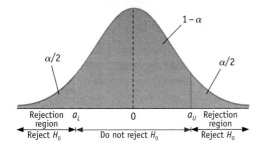

data. If it is smaller than $a_L = \dfrac{x_L - 8.5}{\sigma/\sqrt{n}}$ or if it is greater than $a_U = \dfrac{x_U - 8.5}{\sigma/\sqrt{n}}$, then reject H_0 in favour of H_1. Otherwise, do not reject H_0.

This is portrayed in Chart 10-2.

The rejection region is made up of two parts: the part greater than a_U and the part less than a_L. It contains both tails of the distribution of the test statistic. Hence, this is called a **two-tailed test**.

The values a_U and a_L are the **critical values**. They should be chosen such that the probability of a Type I error (that is, when H_0 is true, the probability of the value of the test statistic lying in the rejection region) equals the given value of the level of significance, α.

Since the rejection region is made up of two parts, the probability of the value of the test statistic lying in each part of the rejection region, when H_0 is true, should be $\alpha/2$. (Due to symmetry, we divide the probability, α, equally between the two parts.)

If the population standard deviation is unknown, we use $\dfrac{\bar{X} - 8.5}{S/\sqrt{n}}$ as the test statistic.

As one more example, let us consider the problem introduced in Section 10.2 regarding the mean annual inflation rate (measured as percentage changes in the consumer price index (CPI) of all the items) in Canada during the last century. A certain axiomatic theory in economics implies that the mean annual inflation rate in Canada during the last century was at least 3.6 percent. A group of students wants to test this hypothesis, to see if it provides significant evidence against the theory. In this case, the null and alternative hypotheses are:

H_0: $\mu \geq 3.6$
H_1: $\mu < 3.6$

Again, we shall base our decision on the value of $\bar{X}$.

If H_0 is true (that is, the value of μ is 3.6 or more), the probability is high that the value of $\bar{X}$ will be close to or larger than 3.6, while it is unlikely that the value of $\bar{X}$ will be much smaller than 3.6. Hence, a logical decision rule is to choose a suitable lower bound number x_L as the critical value and reject H_0 if the value $\bar{x}$, calculated from the sample, is smaller than x_L.

CHART 10-3: Probabilities of Type I Error for Different Values of μ Satisfying H_0

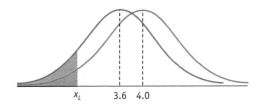

The probability of a Type I error will then be the probability of the value of $\bar{X}$ being smaller than x_L, when H_0 is correct. We should choose the number x_L such that for any value of μ satisfying H_0, (that is, for any $\mu \geq 3.6$), this probability does not exceed the selected value of level of significance α.

Of all the possible values of $\mu \geq 3.6$, the probability of $\bar{X}$ being less than x_L will be maximum when $\mu = 3.6$. (The smaller the value of μ, the higher will be the probability of $\bar{X}$ being smaller than x_L.) We illustrate this in Chart 10-3

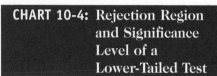

CHART 10-4: Rejection Region and Significance Level of a Lower-Tailed Test

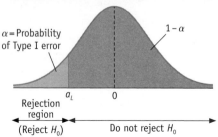

α = Probability of Type I error

$1 - \alpha$

a_L 0

Rejection region (Reject H_0)

Do not reject H_0

when $\bar{X}$ is normally distributed. Note that the area to the left of x_L under the curve with $\mu = 3.6$ is larger than that under the curve with $\mu = 4.0$.

Hence, x_L should be such that when $\mu = 3.6$, the probability of $\bar{X}$ being smaller than x_L equals α, the significance level of the test.

If the population standard deviation, σ, is known, then we can standardize $\bar{X}$ to get the following equivalent decision rule: calculate the value $\dfrac{\bar{x} - 3.6}{\sigma/\sqrt{n}}$ using the sample data. If it is smaller than $a_L = \dfrac{x_L - 3.6}{\sigma/\sqrt{n}}$, then reject H_0 in favour of H_1. Otherwise, do not reject H_0. This is portrayed in Chart 10-4.

The rejection region is thus the region to the left of the critical value a_L. This is a **left-tailed** or **lower-tailed test** since the rejection region contains just the left tail of the distribution of the test statistic. The value a_L should be chosen such that when $\mu = 3.6$, the probability of $\dfrac{\bar{X} - 3.6}{\sigma/\sqrt{n}}$ being smaller than a_L equals the selected value of the level of significance, α.

In summary,

CHOICE OF TEST STATISTIC

If the null hypothesis is of the form $\mu = \mu_0$, $\mu \le \mu_0$, or $\mu \ge \mu_0$, for some value μ_0, then we use as test statistic:

$\dfrac{\bar{X} - \mu_0}{\sigma/\sqrt{n}}$ if the value of the population standard deviation, σ, is known;

$\dfrac{\bar{X} - \mu_0}{S/\sqrt{n}}$ if the value of the population standard deviation, σ, is *not* known.

We call μ_0 the **test value** of μ.

TYPES OF TESTS
CASE 1

Every value of the population parameter corresponding to H_1 is to the right of every value of the population parameter corresponding to H_0, (e.g., H_0: $\mu \le 453$, H_1: $\mu > 453$; or H_0: $\mu = 100$, H_1: $\mu > 100$; or H_0: $\mu = 20$, H_1: $\mu = 80$). Our decision rule will be to choose an upper critical value a_U and reject the null hypothesis if the value of the test statistic computed from the selected sample is greater than a_U. The rejection region contains only the right tail of the distribution of the test statistic. Thus, this is a **right-tailed** or **upper-tailed test**.

CASE 2

Every value of the population parameter corresponding to H_1 is to the left of every value of the population parameter corresponding to H_0, (e.g., H_0: $\mu \ge 80\,000$, H_1: $\mu < 80\,000$; or H_0: $\mu = 100$, H_1: $\mu < 100$; or H_0: $\mu = 80$, H_1: $\mu = 20$). Our decision rule will be to choose a lower critical value a_L and reject the null hypothesis if the value of the test statistic computed from the selected sample is less than a_L. The rejection region contains only the left tail of the distribution of the test statistic. Hence, this is a **left-tailed** or **lower-tailed test**.

CASE 3

Values of the population parameter corresponding to H_1 lie on either side of the values of the population parameter corresponding to H_0, (e.g., H_0: $\mu = 8.5$; H_1: $\mu \neq 8.5$): Our decision rule will be to choose lower and upper critical values a_L and a_U and reject the null hypothesis if the value of the test statistic computed from the selected sample is greater than a_U or if it is less than a_L. The rejection region contains both tails of the distribution of the test statistic. Thus, this is a **two-tailed test**.

■ SELF-REVIEW 10-2

For each of the problems (a) and (b) in Self-Review 10-1, identify the test statistic, the nature of the decision rule, and the type of the test.

10.4 TESTING FOR POPULATION MEAN WHEN POPULATION STANDARD DEVIATION, σ, IS KNOWN

In Section 10.2, we illustrated the five steps of the hypothesis testing procedure for the problem of average weight of boxes of Grape Nuts cereal. We assumed that the population standard deviation is known and either the population distribution is approximately normal or the sample size is large. In this case, when H_0 is true, our test statistic is approximately a standard normal variable. We treated it as a standard normal variable. Thus, the test we used was an upper-tailed Z test. Let us now illustrate the procedure for a two-tailed Z test and a lower-tailed Z test, assuming that the population standard deviation is known.

Example 10-1 | Reconsider the problem regarding the claim made by a social scientist about the sleeping pattern of Canadian youths. Assume that the population distribution is approximately normal with a standard deviation of 0.9. Design a test of significance with a level of significance, $\alpha = 0.05$.

Solution | Let us use the five-step procedure discussed previously in this chapter.

Step 1 | As we saw before, in this case the null and alternative hypotheses are:
H_0: $\mu = 8.5$
H_1: $\mu \neq 8.5$

Step 2 | We have selected the level of significance $\alpha = 0.05$.

Step 3 We shall use $\dfrac{\bar{X} - 8.5}{\sigma/\sqrt{n}} = \dfrac{\bar{X} - 8.5}{0.9/\sqrt{n}}$ as our test statistic. The population is approximately

normally distributed. Hence, if H_0 is true, $\dfrac{\bar{X} - 8.5}{0.9/\sqrt{n}} \approx Z$, a standard normal variable.

We shall treat it as a Z statistic.

Step 4 This is a two-tailed test. Our decision rule is to choose lower and upper critical values a_L and a_U and reject H_0 if the calculated value of the Z statistic is larger than a_U or smaller than a_L.

The values a_L and a_U should be chosen such that the probability of a Type I error (that is, when H_0 is true, the probability of the value of the test statistic lying in the rejection region) equals the given value of level of significance $= 0.05$. This implies that when $\mu = 8.5$, the probability of the value of a test statistic greater than a_U should be $0.05/2 = 0.025$ and the probability of the value of a test statistic smaller than a_L should also be 0.025. Hence, $a_U = z_{0.025} = 1.96$ and $a_L = -z_{0.025} = -1.96$ (Recall that $z_{0.025}$ is the number such that the area to the right of it under the Z curve is 0.025. It is the z value in the Z table corresponding to the probability of $(0.5 - 0.025) = 0.475$.)

The decision rule is: reject H_0 in favour of H_1 if the computed value of the test statistic is smaller than -1.96 or if it is larger than 1.96. Do not reject H_0 if the computed value of the test statistic falls in the region between -1.96 and 1.96, (including -1.96 and 1.96).

Step 5 To implement the test, we shall take a random sample from the population, compute the value of the test statistic, $z = \dfrac{\bar{x} - 8.5}{0.9/\sqrt{n}}$, and based on this value and the decision rule, arrive at a decision to reject H_0 in favour of H_1 or not to reject H_0.

As an example, suppose the following sample data is collected on the average number of sleeping hours at night of 25 randomly selected Canadians in the age group 15–24.

7.8	9.1	9.5	10.2	9.9	9.7	9.2	8.7	7.9
9.6	8.9	9.1	8.1	9.8	8.8	8.3	9.2	9.4
9.0	8.9	7.8	8.4	8.6	7.9	8.7		

Then, $\bar{x} = \dfrac{(7.8 + 9.1 + \cdots + 7.9 + 8.7)}{25} = 8.9$

The value of the test statistic is $z = \dfrac{(\bar{x} - 8.5)}{0.9/\sqrt{25}} = \dfrac{(8.9 - 8.5)}{0.9/5} = 2.22$.

The value 2.22 is greater than 1.96. It lies in the rejection region. Hence, we shall reject H_0 in favour of H_1. There is sufficient evidence, at significance level $\alpha = 0.05$, to reject H_0 and accept the claim that the average number of hours Canadian youths sleep at night is different from 8.5 hours.

COMPUTER SOLUTION

Minitab Chart 10-5 opposite illustrates the solution; we also give instructions for obtaining the above solution using Excel.

We read from the Minitab output that the z value is 2.22. The Minitab output does not give us the rejection region. Instead, it gives **95 percent confidence interval estimate** $(= (8.547, 9.253))$ and **P-value** $(= 0.026)$. We shall discuss these in the following sections.

MINITAB CHART 10-5

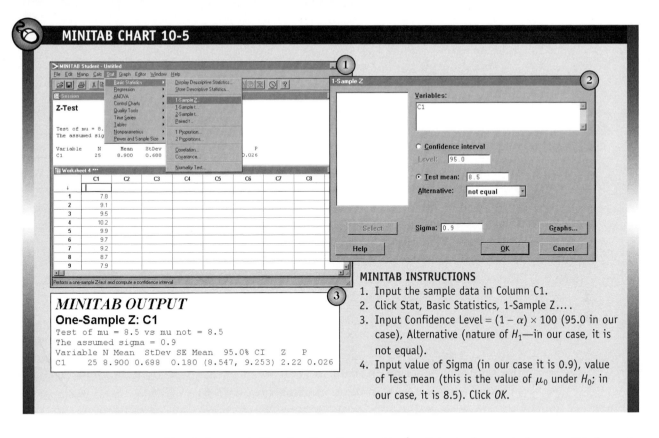

MINITAB INSTRUCTIONS

1. Input the sample data in Column C1.
2. Click Stat, Basic Statistics, 1-Sample Z....
3. Input Confidence Level = $(1 - \alpha) \times 100$ (95.0 in our case), Alternative (nature of H_1—in our case, it is not equal).
4. Input value of Sigma (in our case it is 0.9), value of Test mean (this is the value of μ_0 under H_0; in our case, it is 8.5). Click OK.

MINITAB OUTPUT

One-Sample Z: C1

```
Test of mu = 8.5 vs mu not = 8.5
The assumed sigma = 0.9
Variable N Mean  StDev SE Mean  95.0% CI    Z    P
C1   25 8.900 0.688  0.180 (8.547, 9.253) 2.22 0.026
```

Excel does not directly give the result of a Z test when σ is known. We have to input the sample data in column A and go to Tools: Data Analysis: Descriptive Analysis, enter input range, click Summary Statistics check box and click OK. We give the output below.

Column 1	
Mean	8.9
Standard Error	0.137598
Median	8.9
Mode	7.8
Standard Deviation	0.687992
Sample Variance	0.473333
Kurtosis	−0.80747
Skewness	−0.0509
Range	2.4
Minimum	7.8
Maximum	10.2
Sum	222.5
Count	25

The output includes, among other things, the value of the sample mean $\bar{x} = 8.9$.

The value of the sample statistic can then be computed, using Excel or a calculator as $z = \dfrac{(\bar{x} - 8.5)}{0.9/\sqrt{25}} = \dfrac{(8.9 - 8.5)}{0.9/5} = 2.22.$

Example 10-2

Let us consider the problem introduced in Section 10.2 regarding the mean annual inflation rate (measured as percentage changes in the CPI Index of all the items) in Canada during the last century. A certain axiomatic theory in economics implies that the mean annual inflation rate in Canada during the last century was 3.6 percent or higher. A group of students wants to test this hypothesis, to see if it provides significant evidence against the theory. Suppose the percentage changes in the annual CPI index (all the items) in Canada during the last century are normally distributed with a standard deviation of 5.1. Design a test of hypothesis with a level of significance, $\alpha = 0.01$.

Solution

Let us use the five-step procedure discussed in Section 10.2.

Step 1

As we saw in Section 10.2, the null and alternative hypotheses are:

H_0: $\mu \geq 3.6$

H_1: $\mu < 3.6$

Step 2

We have selected the level of significance $\alpha = 0.01$.

Step 3

We shall use $\dfrac{\bar{X} - 3.6}{\sigma/\sqrt{n}} = \dfrac{\bar{X} - 3.6}{5.1/\sqrt{n}}$ as the test statistic.

Step 4

This is a lower-tailed test. Our decision rule is to choose a lower critical value a_L and reject H_0 if the calculated value of the test statistic is smaller than a_L. As we saw before, the value a_L should be chosen such that when $\mu = 3.6$, the probability of the value of the test statistic lying in the rejection region, $\alpha = 0.01$.

The population is normally distributed. Hence, when $\mu = 3.6$, $\dfrac{\bar{X} - 3.6}{5.1/\sqrt{n}} = Z$. This is a Z statistic.

We want to choose the value a_L such that the area under the Z curve to the left of a_L is 0.01. That is, we want $a_L = -z_{0.01} \approx -2.326$. So, the rejection region is the region less than -2.326.

The decision rule is: reject H_0 in favour of H_1 if the computed value of the test statistic is smaller than -2.326. Do not reject H_0 if the computed value of the test statistic is larger than or equal to -2.326.

Step 5

To implement the test, we shall take a random sample from the population, compute the value of the test statistic $z = \dfrac{\bar{x} - 3.6}{5.1/\sqrt{n}}$, and based on this value and the decision rule, arrive at a decision to reject H_0 in favour of H_1 or not to reject H_0.

As an example, the following sample of annual percentage changes in the CPI index during ten randomly selected years in the last century was collected (Source: *CANSIM* data):

3.0	8.2	1.1	-4.5	4.0
3.0	1.2	-8.4	0.0	9.8

Then, $\bar{x} = \dfrac{(3.0 + 8.2 + \cdots + 0.0 + 9.8)}{10} = 1.74$.

The value of the test statistic is $z = \dfrac{(\bar{x} - 3.6)}{5.1/\sqrt{10}} = \dfrac{(1.74 - 3.6)}{5.1/\sqrt{10}} = -1.15$.

Since the value -1.15 is greater than -2.326, we shall *not* reject H_0. We do *not* have sufficient evidence, at significance level $\alpha = 0.01$, to reject H_0, that is, to reject the hypothesis based on the theory.

We can use Minitab or Excel to obtain a solution for the above example. In the case of Minitab, the only difference from the instructions for the previous example is: under Alternatives, input "less than," since this is a lower-tailed test.

In general, in the case of an upper-tailed test, input "greater than," in the case of a lower-tailed test, input "less than," and in the case of a two-tailed test, input "not equal to."

We give the Minitab output below.

MINITAB OUTPUT
One-Sample Z: C1
Test of mu = 3.6 vs mu < 3.6
The assumed sigma = 5.1

Variable	N	Mean	StDev	SE Mean	99.0% Upper Bound	z	P
C1	10	1.74	5.38	1.61	5.49	−1.15	0.124

The computed z value obtained from the Minitab output is -1.15, which is the same as the one we obtained before. In addition, the Minitab output gives a **99 percent Upper Bound = 5.49**, and **P-value = 0.124**. We shall discuss these in the following sections. Instructions for Excel are similar to the previous case.

Example 10-3

Now, consider the problem introduced in Section 10.2 about the light bulbs. A batch of 5000 light bulbs either belongs to the superior type, with a mean life of 2400 hours, or to the inferior type, with a mean life of 2000 hours. By default, the bulbs will be sold as the inferior type. Suppose the lifetimes of both types of bulbs are approximately normally distributed with a standard deviation of 300 hours. Design a test of hypothesis with a level of significance, $\alpha = 0.025$.

Solution

Let us use the five-step procedure discussed in Section 10.2.

Step 1

As we saw in Section 10.2, the null and alternative hypotheses are:
$$H_0: \mu = 2000$$
$$H_1: \mu = 2400$$

Step 2

We have selected the level of significance $\alpha = 0.025$.

Step 3

We shall use $\dfrac{\bar{X} - 2000}{\sigma/\sqrt{n}} = \dfrac{\bar{X} - 2000}{300/\sqrt{n}}$ as our test statistic.

Step 4

Since the value of μ corresponding to the alternative hypothesis $(=2400)$ is larger than that corresponding to the null hypothesis $(=2000)$, this is an upper-tailed test. Our decision rule is to choose an upper critical value a_U and reject H_0 if the calculated value of the test statistic is greater than a_U.

The population distribution is approximately normal. Hence, when H_0 is true, $\dfrac{\bar{X} - 2000}{300/\sqrt{n}} \approx Z$, a standard normal variable. We shall treat it as a Z statistic.

The value a_U should be such that the area under the Z curve to the right of it equals 0.025. That is, $a_U = z_{0.025} = 1.96$. The rejection region is the region greater than 1.96. The decision rule is: reject H_0 in favour of H_1 if the computed value of the test statistic is greater than 1.96. Do not reject H_0 if the computed value of the test statistic is smaller than or equal to 1.96.

Step 5 To implement the test, we shall take a random sample from the population, compute the value of the test statistic $z = \dfrac{\bar{x} - 2000}{300/\sqrt{n}}$, and based on this value and the decision rule, arrive at a decision to reject H_0 in favour of H_1 or not to reject H_0.

REJECTION REGION FOR Z TEST WITH LEVEL OF SIGNIFICANCE, α

Upper-tailed Z test:	The upper critical value is z_α. Rejection region: the region to the right of z_α. Reject H_0 if the computed z value is greater than z_α.
Lower-tailed Z test:	The lower critical value is $-z_\alpha$. Rejection region: the region to the left of $-z_\alpha$. Reject H_0 if the computed z value is less than $-z_\alpha$.
Two-tailed Z test:	The lower and upper critical values are $-z_{\alpha/2}$, and $z_{\alpha/2}$. Rejection region: the region to the left of $-z_{\alpha/2}$, and also the region to the right of $z_{\alpha/2}$. Reject H_0 if the computed z value is less than $-z_{\alpha/2}$, or if it is greater than $z_{\alpha/2}$.

■ SELF-REVIEW 10-3

(a) Consider problem (a) in Self-Review 10-1, regarding the mean value of monthly percentage changes in the TSE 300 index during the last 45 years. Suppose the population is normally distributed and the population standard deviation is 6.24.

   (i) Identify the rejection region and the decision rule, for $\alpha = 0.04$.

   (ii) Consider the following sample data on percentage changes in the TSE 300 index during 12 months, randomly selected from the last 45 years (Source: *CANSIM* data).

4.8	3.4	4.7	0.8	0.9	1.9
-2.8	-1.7	0.3	2.0	3.0	1.6

   Compute the value of the test statistic. What should be our decision?

(b) Consider problem (b) in Self-Review 10-1, regarding the mean value of earnings per share of the top 1000 Canadian companies during the year 2000. Suppose the population is approximately normally distributed and the population standard deviation is 3.04.

   (i) Identify the rejection region and the decision rule, for $\alpha = 0.08$.

   (ii) Consider the following sample data on earnings per share of 15 companies, selected randomly from the list of top 1000 companies in Canada during the year 2000, (Source: Top 1000 data published by *Globe Interactive*).

1.7	0	0.3	0	-13.8	1.9	0.3	0.8
0.2	-0.8	0.6	0.7	2.8	3.8	1.4	

   Compute the value of the test statistic. What should be our decision?

10.5 *P*-VALUE IN HYPOTHESIS TESTING

Let us reconsider Example 10-1, regarding the claim made by a social scientist about the sleeping pattern of Canadian youths. Here, the null and alternative hypotheses are:

H_0: $\mu = 8.5$

H_1: $\mu \neq 8.5$

We saw that this is a two-tailed test. If the population distribution is approximately normal, or the sample size is large, our test statistic, $\dfrac{\bar{X} - 8.5}{\sigma / \sqrt{n}}$, is approximately a Z statistic and we treat it as a Z statistic. Our decision rule is then: reject H_0 if the computed z value (the value of the test statistic calculated from the sample data) is larger than $a_U = z_{\alpha/2}$ or if it is smaller than $a_L = -z_{\alpha/2}$.

In our example, we selected $\alpha = 0.05$. Hence, $z_{0.025} = 1.96$, and $-z_{0.025} = -1.96$. The value of the test statistic obtained from the sample was $z = 2.22$. Since this was in the rejection region (larger than 1.96), we rejected H_0. Thus, the result of our test was: we have sufficient evidence, at $\alpha = 0.05$, to reject H_0 in favour of H_1.

If, instead, we had chosen $\alpha = 0.01$, then our rejection region would be the region above $z_{0.005} = 2.575$ and the region below -2.575. In this case, since the computed z value ($= 2.22$) is between -2.575 and 2.575, the result of our test would be: we do *not* have sufficient evidence, at $\alpha = 0.01$, to reject H_0 in favour of H_1. Do *not* reject H_0.

Thus, for a given value of α,

if $a_U = z_{\alpha/2} < z = 2.22$, our decision would be to reject H_0; and

if $a_U = z_{\alpha/2} \geq z = 2.22$, our decision would be do *not* reject H_0.

The critical value α^*, for which the change in decision takes place, is such that $z = 2.22 = a_U = z_{\alpha^*/2}$.

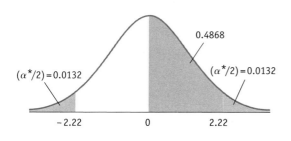

0.4868

$(\alpha^*/2) = 0.0132$

$(\alpha^*/2) = 0.0132$

-2.22 0 2.22

From the Z table, we get $\alpha^* = 2(0.5 - 0.4868) = 0.0264$. (See the chart to the left. From the Z table, we get the area under the Z curve between 0 and 2.22 equal to 0.4868. Hence, $\alpha^*/2 = $ area to the right of $2.22 = (0.5 - 0.4868) = 0.0132$. So, $\alpha^* = 2(0.0132) = 0.0264$.) We call this the **P-value of the instance of the test**. It is the value of α for which the computed z value is a critical value. Hence, it can also be interpreted as the **observed level of significance**.

For $\alpha \leq \alpha^* = 0.0264$, the value of $a_U = z_{\alpha/2}$ would be greater than or equal to 2.22 and our decision would be: do *not* reject H_0.

For $\alpha > 0.0264$, the value of a_U would be less than 2.22. In this case, the computed z value ($= 2.22$) would lie in the rejection region and our decision would be to reject H_0.

> **ⓘ** The **P-value of an instance of a test of hypothesis** is the value of the level of significance, α^*, for which a critical value of the test statistic (either a_L or a_U) equals the computed value of the test statistic. It can be interpreted as the observed level of significance.
>
> For a choice of value of α, larger than the P-value, the result of the test instance would be "reject H_0 in favour of H_1."
> For a choice of value of α, smaller than or equal to the P-value, the result of the test instance would be "do *not* reject H_0."

Now, reconsider the problem we discussed in Example 10-2, regarding the mean annual inflation rate (measured as percentage changes in the CPI Index of all the items) in Canada during the last century. In this case, the null and alternative hypotheses are:

H_0: $\mu \geq 3.6$

H_1: $\mu < 3.6$

This is a lower-tailed test. The value of the population standard deviation is known to be 5.1. Hence, we used $\dfrac{\bar{X} - 3.6}{5.1/\sqrt{n}}$ as the test statistic. Since the population distribution is assumed to be normal, this is a lower-tailed Z test. The critical value of the test statistic is $a_L = -z_\alpha$ and the rejection region is the region below $-z_\alpha$.

The value of the test statistic, computed from the sample data, was $z = -1.15$.

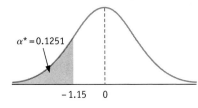

Hence, the P-value of this instance of the test is the value α^* of the significance level of the test such that $a_L = -z_{\alpha^*} = z = -1.15$, or $z_{\alpha^*} = 1.15$.

From the Z table on the inside back cover of this text, we get $\alpha^* = 0.1251$. (From the Z table, we get the area under the Z curve between 0 and 1.15 equal to 0.3749. So, $\alpha^* = (0.5 - 0.3749) = 0.1251$.) Note that this is almost the same as the P-value in the Minitab output on page 429. (The slight difference is due to rounding error in the computation of the z value.)

For any value of α, smaller than or equal to the P-value, the critical value $a_L = -z_\alpha$ of the test statistic would be smaller than or equal to -1.15 and our decision would be "do not reject H_0." For any value of α, larger than the P-value, the critical value of the test statistic would be greater than -1.15 and our decision would be "reject H_0."

In general, the P-value for an instance of a test of hypothesis is defined as follows:

Type of Test	P-Value (= α^*)	
	For general test statistic	**For Z statistic**
Upper-tailed test	α^* is such that the value of the test statistic obtained from sample $= a_U$	α^* is such that $z = z_{\alpha^*}$
Lower-tailed test	α^* is such that the value of the test statistic obtained from sample $= a_L$	α^* is such that $z = -z_{\alpha^*}$
Two-tailed test	α^* is such that the value of the test statistic obtained from sample $=$ either a_U or a_L	α^* is such that $|z| = z_{\alpha^*/2}$

■ SELF-REVIEW 10-4

(a) Consider the problem (a) in Self-Review 10-3.

   (i) Compute the P-value using the Z table. Compare this value with the P-value in the Minitab output.

   (ii) What would be your decision for the significance level $\alpha = 0.3$? For $\alpha = 0.01$?

(b) Consider the problem (b) in Self-Review 10-3.

   (i) Compute the P-value using the Z table. Compare this value with the P-value in the Minitab output.

   (ii) What would be your decision for the significance level $\alpha = 0.1$? For $\alpha = 0.48$?

10.6 RELATIONSHIP BETWEEN THE HYPOTHESIS TESTING PROCEDURE AND THE CONFIDENCE INTERVAL ESTIMATION (OPTIONAL)

You may have observed similarities between the hypothesis testing procedure, discussed in the previous sections, and the confidence interval estimator we discussed in Chapter 9. For example, both are based on the properties of the sampling distribution of the sample mean that we discussed in Chapter 8. In fact, J. Neyman developed the theory of confidence interval as almost a parallel theory to his joint work with E. Pearson on the theory of hypothesis testing. We shall now make the relationship between the two theories clear.

CASE 1: TWO-TAILED TEST

Let us consider the following two-tailed test:

H_0: $\mu = \mu_0$

H_1: $\mu \neq \mu_0$

Suppose the population is normally distributed and the population standard deviation, σ, is known. Then, for a given value of the significance level, α, our decision rule is:

Do not reject H_0 if $-z_{\alpha/2} \leq \dfrac{\bar{x} - \mu_0}{\sigma/\sqrt{n}} \leq z_{\alpha/2}$.

It follows from the discussion in Chapter 9, that the expression $-z_{\alpha/2} \leq \dfrac{\bar{x} - \mu_0}{\sigma/\sqrt{n}} \leq z_{\alpha/2}$ is equivalent to the expression $\bar{x} - z_{\alpha/2}\sigma/\sqrt{n} \leq \mu_0 \leq \bar{x} + z_{\alpha/2}\sigma/\sqrt{n}$. Hence, the above decision rule can be equivalently stated as:

Do not reject H_0 if $\bar{x} - z_{\alpha/2}\sigma/\sqrt{n} \leq \mu_0 \leq \bar{x} + z_{\alpha/2}\sigma/\sqrt{n}$, that is, if μ_0 lies in the interval $(\bar{x} - z_{\alpha/2}\sigma/\sqrt{n},\ \bar{x} + z_{\alpha/2}\sigma/\sqrt{n})$.

The interval $(\bar{x} - z_{\alpha/2}\sigma/\sqrt{n},\ \bar{x} + z_{\alpha/2}\sigma/\sqrt{n})$ is the $(1 - \alpha)$ confidence interval estimate of the population mean, μ. (See Formula 9-4 on page 368.)

Hence, our decision rule can be equivalently stated as:

> Do not reject H_0 if μ_0 lies in the $(1 - \alpha)$ confidence interval estimate of the population mean, computed from the sample data.

The following simple argument will show that the probability of Type I error corresponding to this decision rule is α. By definition of confidence interval, the probability is $(1 - \alpha)$ that the value of the population mean will lie in a computed interval estimate. If the true value of the population mean is μ_0, then the probability that H_0 will be rejected equals the probability that μ_0 will not lie in the computed confidence interval estimate, which equals $1 - (1 - \alpha) = \alpha$.

We reproduce below the Minitab output from page 427 for the problem regarding the claim made by a social scientist regarding the sleeping patterns of Canadian youths.

Here, we selected $\alpha = 0.05$. The Minitab output gives us a $((1 - \alpha) \times 100 =)$ 95 percent confidence interval estimate of $(8.547, 9.253)$. Since 8.5, the test value of μ, does not lie in the interval, we reject H_0 in favour of H_1.

MINITAB OUTPUT
One-Sample Z: C1
Test of mu = 8.5 vs mu not = 8.5
The assumed sigma = 0.9

Variable	N	Mean	StDev	SE Mean	95.0% CI	z	P
C1	25	8.900	0.688	0.180	(8.547, 9.253)	2.22	0.026

CASE 2: LOWER-TAILED TEST

Let us consider the lower-tailed test:

H_0: $\mu \geq \mu_0$

H_1: $\mu < \mu_0$

Again, let us assume that the population is normally distributed and the population standard deviation, σ, is known. Then, for a given value of the significance level, α, our decision rule is:

Do not reject H_0 if $\dfrac{\bar{x} - \mu_0}{\sigma/\sqrt{n}} \geq -z_\alpha$.

Using algebraic manipulations, as in the previous case, it can be shown that this expression is equivalent to the expression $\mu_0 \leq \bar{x} + z_\alpha \sigma/\sqrt{n}$. Hence, the above decision rule can be equivalently stated as:

Do *not* reject H_0 if $\mu_0 \leq \bar{x} + z_\alpha \sigma/\sqrt{n}$, that is, if μ_0 is less than or equal to $\bar{x} + z_\alpha \sigma/\sqrt{n}$.

> *The region below and including $\bar{X} + z_\alpha \sigma/\sqrt{n}$ is called a **$(1 - \alpha)$ upper confidence interval** and the value $\bar{X} + z_\alpha \sigma/\sqrt{n}$ is called a **$(1 - \alpha)$ upper confidence bound** for μ.*

Hence, our decision rule can be equivalently stated as:

> *Do not reject H_0 if μ_0 is less than or equal to the value of the $(1 - \alpha)$ upper confidence bound for μ, computed from the sample data.*

Let us consider the Minitab output for the problem of regarding the mean annual inflation rate (measured as percentage changes in the CPI Index of all the items) in Canada during the last century. Here, we selected $\alpha = 0.01$.

MINITAB OUTPUT
One-Sample Z: C1
Test of mu = 3.6 vs mu < 3.6
The assumed sigma = 5.1

Variable	N	Mean	StDev	SE Mean	99.0% Upper Bound	z	P
C1	10	1.74	5.38	1.61	5.49	-1.15	0.124

The Minitab output gives us a $((1 - \alpha) \times 100 =)$ 99 percent upper confidence bound of 5.49. Since 3.6, the test value of μ, is less than this upper bound, we do *not* reject H_0.

CASE 3: UPPER-TAILED TEST

It can be similarly shown that in the case of an upper-tailed Z test for μ, our decision rule can be equivalently stated as:

Do not reject H_0 if μ_0 is greater than or equal to $\bar{x} - z_\alpha \sigma/\sqrt{n}$.

The interval above and including $\bar{X} - z_\alpha \sigma/\sqrt{n}$ is called a **$(1-\alpha)$ lower confidence interval** and the value $\bar{X} - z_\alpha \sigma/\sqrt{n}$ is called a **$(1-\alpha)$ lower confidence bound** for μ. Hence, our decision rule can be equivalently stated as:

> Do not reject H_0 if μ_0 is greater than or equal to the value of the $(1 - \alpha)$ lower confidence bound for μ, computed from the sample data.

■ SELF-REVIEW 10-5

(a) Consider the problem (a) in Self-Review 10-3.
   (i) Compute the $(1 - \alpha)$ confidence interval estimate or upper confidence bound or lower confidence bound, whichever is appropriate.
   (ii) What would be your decision based on the value(s) calculated in (i)? Is this consistent with the decision based on the P-value?
(b) Consider the problem (b) in Self-Review 10-3.
   (i) Compute the $(1 - \alpha)$ confidence interval estimate or upper confidence bound or lower confidence bound, whichever is appropriate.
   (ii) What would be your decision based on the value(s) calculated in (i)? Is this consistent with the decision based on the P-value?

10.7 TYPE II ERROR

Recall that the level of significance, denoted by the symbol α, is the probability of a Type I error. That is, it is the probability that the null hypothesis is rejected when it is true.

In a hypothesis testing situation, there is also the possibility that a null hypothesis is not rejected when it is actually false, (that is, when H_1 is true). Such an error is called a Type II error. We denote the probability of a Type II error by the Greek letter β (beta).

Since a Type I error is a more serious type of error, in designing tests of hypothesis, we pre-select the value of the level of significance, α, and design the test such that the probability of a Type I error is no more than α and, subject to this, the probability of a Type II error, β, is minimum. All the tests we have considered so far are of this type. (The proof of optimality of the tests follows from the famous result of Neyman and Pearson on the test of hypothesis. It is too mathematical and beyond the scope of this book.)

To illustrate the computation of the value of β corresponding to a given test, let us consider the problem, discussed in Example 10-3, regarding lifetimes of light bulbs. A batch of 5000 light bulbs either belongs to a superior type, with a mean life of 2400 hours, or to an inferior type, with a mean life of 2000 hours. By default, the bulbs will be sold as the inferior type.

The null and alternative hypotheses are:

H_0: $\mu = 2000$
H_1: $\mu = 2400$

This is an upper-tailed test. We designed the following (approximate) Z test for it when the lifetimes of both types of bulbs are approximately normally distributed with a standard deviation of 300 hours. We used the level of significance, $\alpha = 0.025$.

CHART 10-6(a): Probability of a Type II error

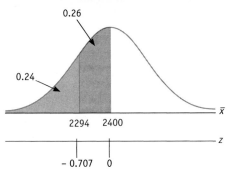

CHART 10-6(b): Relationship between α and β

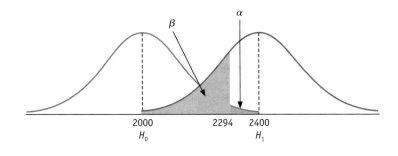

Using the selected sample data, compute the value $z = \dfrac{\bar{x} - 2000}{\sigma/\sqrt{n}} = \dfrac{\bar{x} - 2000}{300/\sqrt{n}}$. If the computed z value is greater than 1.96, reject H_0 in favour of H_1. If the computed z value is smaller than or equal to 1.96, do not reject H_0.

The above decision rule can be equivalently stated as: if the computed value, $\bar{x}$, is greater than $x_U = (2000 + 1.96(300/\sqrt{n})$, reject H_0 in favour of H_1. If the computed value, $\bar{x}$, is smaller than or equal to x_U, do not reject H_0.

The test was designed to keep the value of α at approximately 0.025. Let us now compute the corresponding value of β, the probability of a Type II error.

Suppose H_0 is false and H_1 is true (that is, the true value of μ is 2400). Then $\bar{X}$ is approximately normally distributed with a mean of 2400 and a standard deviation $\sigma/\sqrt{n} = 300/\sqrt{n}$. The probability of a Type II error is the probability of not rejecting H_0. By our decision rule, this is the probability that the value of $\bar{X}$ obtained will be less than or equal to x_U.

Suppose we select a sample of 4 bulbs. Then $\bar{X}$ has a mean of 2400 and a standard deviation of $300/\sqrt{4} = 150$; and $x_U = (2000 + 1.96(300/\sqrt{4}) = 2294$. The probability that the value of $\bar{X}$ obtained will be less than or equal to $x_U = 2294$ is approximately $0.5 - 0.26 = 0.24$. (See Chart 10-6(a). Note that the z value corresponding to 2294 is $\dfrac{2294 - 2400}{150} = -0.707$).

In Chart 10-6(b) above, the shaded areas show the probabilities of Type I and Type II errors, when $n = 4$.

- If we decrease the value of α, the value z_α increases and the critical value x_U moves to the right; therefore, the value of β increases. Conversely, if we increase the value of α, x_U moves to the left, thereby decreasing the value of β.

- Suppose we increase the sample size, n, from 4 to 9. Then, the standard deviation of $\bar{X}$ is $300/\sqrt{9} = 100$, and $x_U = (2000 + 1.96(300/\sqrt{9}) = 2196$. If H_1 is true, then $\bar{X}$ has a mean of 2400 and a standard deviation of $300/\sqrt{9} = 100$. The probability that the value of $\bar{X}$ obtained will be less than, or equal to, $x_U = 2196$ equals (approximately) $(0.5 - 0.4793) = 0.0207$.

If we choose a sample of size $n = 25$, then $x_U = (2000 + 1.96(60) = 2117.6$, the standard deviation of $\bar{X}$ is $300/\sqrt{25} = 60$, and the probability of a Type II error, (that is, the probability that the value of $\bar{X}$ obtained will be less than or equal to 2117.6) is almost 0. (We leave this as an exercise.)

Thus, as n increases from 4 to 25, (i) the standard deviation of $\bar{X}$ decreases, and (ii) the value of x_U moves to the left. Each of these contributes to a reduction in the value of β, which decreases from 0.24 to almost 0.

In summary,

> *For a fixed sample size, decreasing the value of α increases the value of β, and increasing the value of α decreases the value of β. For a given value of α, the value of β can be decreased by increasing the sample size.*

In the previous example regarding the lifetimes of light bulbs, we designed the test for $\alpha = 0.025$. We then calculated the corresponding values of β, and the probabilities of a Type II error for various values of the sample size. The value $(1 - \beta)$ is called the **power of the test**. For example, when the sample size $n = 4$, we obtained $\beta = 0.24$. The corresponding power of the test is $(1 - 0.24) = 0.76$.

 Power of a test The probability of rejecting H_0 when H_0 is false. In other words, it is the probability of correctly identifying a true alternative hypothesis. It is equal to $(1 - \beta)$.

 We provide further details and an illustrative example on the power of a test in Chapter 10 Appendix A on the CD-ROM.

■ SELF-REVIEW 10-6

(a) For problem (a) in Self-Review 10-3, find the value of β, the probability of Type II error, when the true value of μ is 3.0.
(b) For problem (b) in Self-Review 10-3, find the value of the power of the test when the true value of μ is 1.6.

EXERCISES 10-1 TO 10-8

For each of Exercises 10-1– 10-4 answer the following questions: a) Is this a one- or two-tailed test? b) What is the decision rule? c) What is the value of the test statistic? d) What is your conclusion regarding H_0? e) What is the P-value? Interpret it.

10-1. The following information is available.

H_0: $\mu = 50$
H_1: $\mu \neq 50$

The sample mean is 49, and the sample size is 36. The population standard deviation is 5. Use $\alpha = 0.05$.

10-2. The following information is available.

H_0: $\mu \leq 10$
H_1: $\mu > 10$

The sample mean is 12 for a sample size of 36. The population standard deviation is 3. Use $\alpha = 0.02$.

10-3. A sample of 49 observations is selected from a population. The sample mean is 21. The population standard deviation is 6. Conduct the following test of hypothesis using the 0.05 significance level.

H_0: $\mu \leq 20$
H_1: $\mu > 20$

10-4. A sample of 64 observations is selected from a population. The sample mean is 215. The population standard deviation is 15. Conduct the following test of hypothesis using the 0.03 significance level.

H_0: $\mu \geq 220$
H_1: $\mu < 220$

For exercises 10-5 and 10-6, answer the following: a) State the null hypothesis and the alternative hypothesis. b) State the decision rule. c) Compute the value of the test statistic. d) What is your conclusion? e) What is the P-value? Interpret it.

10-5. The manufacturer of the X-15 steel-belted radial truck tire claims that the mean mileage the tire can be driven before the tread wears out is 80 000 km. The standard deviation of the mileage is 8000 km. The Crosset Truck Company bought 48 tires and found that the mean mileage for their trucks is 79 200 km. From Crosset's experience, can we conclude, at $\alpha = 0.05$, that the manufacturer's claim is wrong?

10-6. The MacBurger restaurant chain claims that the waiting time of customers for service has a mean of 3 minutes. The standard deviation is known to be 1 minute. The quality-assurance department found, in a sample of 50 customers at the Warren Road MacBurger, that the mean waiting time was 2.75 minutes. At the 0.05 significance level, can we conclude that the mean waiting time is less than 3 minutes?

10-7. The mean annual turnover rate of the 200-count bottle of Bayer Aspirin has in the past been 6.0 with a standard deviation of 0.50. (This indicates that the stock of Bayer Aspirin turns over on the pharmacy shelves an average of 6 times per year.) It is suspected that the mean turnover rate has changed and is not 6.0. We wish to test if there is sufficient evidence, at $\alpha = 0.05$, to conclude that the mean turnover rate has changed. Assume that the population distribution is approximately normal and that the standard deviation has not changed.
(a) State the null hypothesis and the alternative hypothesis.
(b) What is the probability of a Type I error?
(c) Give the formula for the test statistic.
(d) State the decision rule.
(e) A random sample of 64 bottles of the 200-count size Bayer Aspirin showed a mean turnover rate of 5.84 times per year.
    (i)   Shall we reject the null hypothesis?
    (ii) What is the P-value? Interpret it.
    (iii) What is the probability of a Type II error if the actual value of the population mean is 5.9? Find the corresponding value of power of the test.

10-8. Refer to the problem in the text regarding the mean annual inflation rate in Canada during the last century. Assume that the population is approximately normally distributed with a standard deviation = 5.1.
(a) Design a test for $\alpha = 0.05$.
(b) Compute the corresponding probability of a Type II error for $n = 16$, and $\mu = 0.32$. Find the corresponding value of power of the test.

10.8 TESTING FOR POPULATION MEAN WHEN POPULATION STANDARD DEVIATION, σ, IS UNKNOWN

STATISTICS IN ACTION

A central focus of modern financial theory is the development and testing of general equilibrium models for pricing of capital assets. *F* tests and *t* tests are commonly used to validate or obtain evidence against suitability of different models.

For example, one of the earliest statistical tests of hypothesis for a popular type of model called the Mean-Variance model was developed by Black, Jensen, and Scholes (1972). They developed and applied *t* tests for a set of ten stock portfolios, with two of the ten providing significant evidence against the model at 0.05 level of significance.

In sections 10.4 to 10.7, we assumed that the population standard deviation is known. In most real-world cases, however, the population standard deviation is unknown. In this case, as in Chapter 9, we substitute it by its estimate, s, obtained from the sample data. Thus, if the null hypothesis is of the form $\mu = \mu_0$, $\mu \le \mu_0$, or $\mu \ge \mu_0$, for some value μ_0, then we use $\dfrac{\bar{X} - \mu_0}{S/\sqrt{n}}$ as a test statistic.

In chapters 8 and 9, we discussed in reasonable detail, the sampling distribution of the statistic $\dfrac{\bar{X} - \mu}{S/\sqrt{n}}$, when the population is normally distributed. In particular, we saw that, when the population is normally distributed, the distribution of $\dfrac{\bar{X} - \mu}{S/\sqrt{n}}$ is Student's t distribution with $(n - 1)$ degrees of freedom. This statistic is fairly robust in the sense that, even when the population distribution is fairly non-normal, Student's t distribution with $(n - 1)$ degrees of freedom serves as a good approximation to the distribution of $\dfrac{\bar{X} - \mu}{S/\sqrt{n}}$, even for moderately large values of n. Thus,

---

When the population is normally distributed and the population mean is μ_0, the distribution of our test statistic $T = \dfrac{\bar{X} - \mu_0}{S/\sqrt{n}}$ is Student's t distribution with $(n - 1)$ degrees of freedom. We call it a **t statistic** and the corresponding test a **t test**. Our decision rules for a t test are as follows:

Decision Rules for a t Test with Level of Significance, α

Upper-tailed t test	The upper critical value is t_α (degrees of freedom, $df = (n - 1)$). Rejection region: the region to the right of t_α. Reject H_0 if the computed t value is greater than t_α.
Lower-tailed t test	The lower critical value is $-t_\alpha$ (degrees of freedom, $df = (n - 1)$). Rejection region: the region to the left of $-t_\alpha$. Reject H_0 if the computed t value is less than $-t_\alpha$.
Two-tailed t test	The lower and upper critical values are $-t_{\alpha/2}$, and $t_{\alpha/2}$. Rejection region: the region to the left of $-t_{\alpha/2}$, and also the region to the right of $t_{\alpha/2}$. Reject H_0 if the computed t value is less than $-t_{\alpha/2}$, or if it is greater than $t_{\alpha/2}$.

We shall illustrate the decision rule with an example.

Example 10-4

Let us reconsider the problem regarding the mean annual inflation rate (measured as percentage annual change in the CPI Index of all the items) in Canada during the last century. A group of students want to conduct a test of hypothesis to seek evidence that the mean annual inflation rate in Canada during the last century was less than 3.6 percent. They have collected the following sample data of annual percentage changes in the CPI index during ten randomly selected years in the last century (Source: *CANSIM* data):

3.0   8.2   1.1   −4.5   4.0   3.0   1.2   −8.4   0.0   9.8

Suppose the population distribution is normal. Design a test of significance with a level of significance, $\alpha = 0.01$, assuming that the value of the population standard deviation is unknown.

Solution

Let us use the five-step procedure discussed in Section 10.2.

Steps 1 and 2

These first two steps are the same as in the case when σ is known, which we discussed in Section 10.4. Thus, the null and alternative hypotheses are:

H_0: $\mu \geq 3.6$
H_1: $\mu < 3.6$

The level of significance $\alpha = 0.01$.

Step 3

We shall use $T = \dfrac{\bar{X} - 3.6}{S/\sqrt{n}}$ as our test statistic.

Step 4

This is a lower-tailed test. Since the population is normally distributed, this is a t test. Our decision rule is:

Reject H_0 in favour of H_1 if the computed t value, (that is, the value of the t statistic) is less than $-t_{0.01}$ (degrees of freedom, $df = n - 1 = 9$). Do not reject H_0 if the computed t value is greater than or equal to $-t_{0.01}$.

The value $-t_{0.01}$ ($df = 9$) is obtained from the t table corresponding to $df = 9$ and level of significance for one-tailed test $= 0.01$. It equals -2.821.

Step 5

From the given sample data we get,

$$\bar{x} = \frac{(3.0 + 8.2 + \cdots + 0.0 + 9.8)}{10} = 1.74.$$

$$s = \sqrt{\frac{(3.0 - 1.74)^2 + \cdots + (9.8 - 1.74)^2}{9}} = 5.38.$$

The value of the test statistic is $t = \dfrac{(\bar{x} - 3.6)}{s/\sqrt{10}} = \dfrac{(1.74 - 3.6)}{5.38/\sqrt{10}} = -1.09.$

Since the t value -1.09 is greater than -2.821, we shall *not* reject H_0. We do *not* have sufficient evidence, at significance level $\alpha = 0.01$, to reject H_0.

In Charts 10-7 and 10-8 we give solutions to the problem using Minitab and Excel.

The t value obtained from the Minitab output is -1.09, which is the same as the one we obtained manually. In addition, the Minitab output gives a P-value $= 0.151$. We saw in Section 10.5 that the P-value of an instance of a test is the observed level of significance. It is the value, α^*, of the level of significance for which the computed t value ($= -1.09$) equals a critical value of the test (in this case, $-t_\alpha$). In our example, this value, which we can also obtain independently using Minitab or Excel (see Charts 9-6 and 9-7 in Chapter 9), equals 0.151.

Type of Test	P-Value $(-\alpha^*)$
Upper-tailed t test	α^* is such that $t = t_{\alpha^*}$ ($df = n - 1$)
Lower-tailed t test	α^* is such that $t = -t_{\alpha^*}$ ($df = n - 1$)
Two-tailed t test	α^* is such that $|t| = t_{\alpha^*/2}$ ($df = n - 1$)

We saw in Section 10.5 that we can state our decision rule in terms of the P-value. Since the selected value of α ($= 0.01$) is smaller than the P-value ($= 0.151$), our decision

MINITAB CHART 10-7

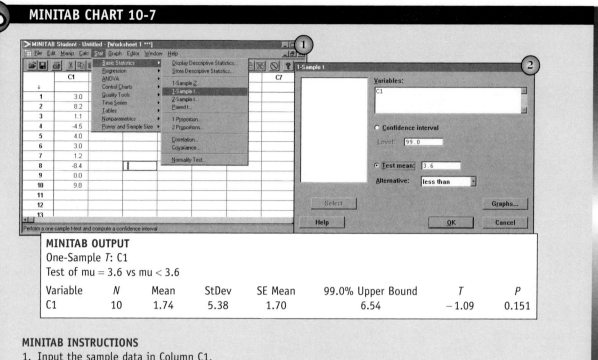

MINITAB OUTPUT
One-Sample T: C1
Test of mu = 3.6 vs mu < 3.6

Variable	N	Mean	StDev	SE Mean	99.0% Upper Bound	T	P
C1	10	1.74	5.38	1.70	6.54	-1.09	0.151

MINITAB INSTRUCTIONS
1. Input the sample data in Column C1.
2. Click Stat, Basic Statistics, 1-Sample t ....
3. Input Confidence interval = $(1 - \alpha) \times 100$ (99.0 in our case), Alternative (nature of H_1—in our case, it is *less than*)
4. Input Variables: C1, the Value of Test mean (this is the value of μ under H_0—in our case, it is 3.6). Click OK.

"do *not* reject H_0" follows. If the selected value of α was greater than the P-value, our decision would have been "reject H_0."

We discussed in Section 10.6, the equivalence between the hypothesis testing procedure and the confidence interval estimator in the case of a Z test. A similar equivalence can be shown in the case of a t test, using the same logic. We give the equivalent decision rules for a t test below, in terms of confidence intervals:

> For a two-tailed t test:
> Do *not* reject H_0 if the test value of the population mean, μ_0, lies in the **$(1 - \alpha)$ confidence interval estimate of the population mean**, $(\bar{x} - t_{\alpha/2}s/\sqrt{n},\ \bar{x} + t_{\alpha/2}s/\sqrt{n})$, computed from the sample data.
>
> For an upper-tailed t test:
> Do *not* reject H_0 if the test value of the population mean, μ_0, is greater than or equal to the **$(1 - \alpha)$ lower confidence bound**, $\bar{x} - t_{\alpha}s/\sqrt{n}$.
>
> For a lower-tailed t test:
> Do *not* reject H_0 if μ_0 is less than or equal to the **$(1 - \alpha)$ upper confidence bound** $\bar{x} + t_{\alpha}s/\sqrt{n}$.
>
> Here, the degrees of freedom of the t distribution are $df = (n - 1)$.

The Minitab output gives a $((1 - 0.01) \times 100 =)$ 99 percent upper confidence bound = 6.54. Our decision, "do *not* reject H_0" follows from the fact that the test value of the population mean (= 3.06) is less than the 99 percent upper confidence bound.

EXCEL CHART 10-8

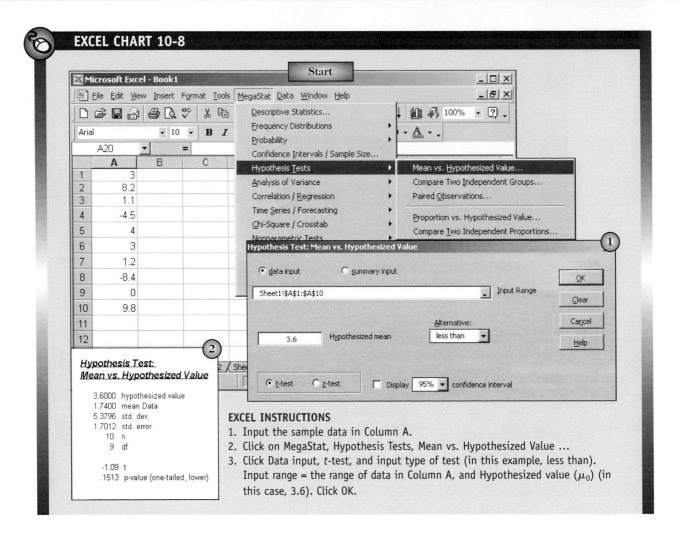

EXCEL INSTRUCTIONS
1. Input the sample data in Column A.
2. Click on MegaStat, Hypothesis Tests, Mean vs. Hypothesized Value ...
3. Click Data input, *t*-test, and input type of test (in this example, less than).
   Input range = the range of data in Column A, and Hypothesized value (μ_0) (in this case, 3.6). Click OK.

In Excel, Data Analysis under the Tools menu does not have a macro for *t*-test. A macro for this is, however, available in MegaStat. The screen shots and output for MegaStat are given in Chart 10-8. We see that the *t*-value (= −1.09) and the *P*-value (= 0.1513) in the MegaStat output are almost the same as those in the Minitab output. The minor differences are due to rounding error. MegaStat also computes a 90%, 95%, or 99% confidence interval. (For this, click on Display in screen 2 and choose the appropriate level of confidence interval.)

It may be noted that, even in the case of a one-tail test, the lower and upper limits of confidence interval given in MegaStat output are $\bar{x} - t_{\alpha/2} \dfrac{s}{\sqrt{n}}$ and $\bar{x} + t_{\alpha/2} \dfrac{s}{\sqrt{n}}$, respectively. So, these are not the $(1 - \alpha)$ lower and upper confidence bounds in the decision rule stated in terms of confidence intervals, as given on the previous page.

Also, it may be noted that if instead of the entire sample data, we only have information about the values of $\bar{x}$, s, and n, then in MegaStat, we input the values of $\bar{x}$, s, and n, in rows 2, 3, and 4, respectively of column A (we leave row 1 blank), we choose *summary input*, instead of *data input*, and input as *Input Range*, the first 4 rows of Column A.

■ SELF-REVIEW 10-7

Reconsider the problems (a) and (b) in Self-Review 10-3. This time assume that the values of the population standard deviation are not known. In each case, compute the value of the test statistic. What should be our decision at the level of significance, $\alpha = 0.05$?

EXERCISES 10-9 TO 10-22

For each of the exercises 10-9 through 10-22, assume that the population distribution is approximately normal.

For each of exercises 10-9 and 10-10, answer the following: a) State the decision rule. b) Compute the value of the test statistic. c) What is your conclusion?

10-9.   Consider the following hypotheses:

H_0: $\mu \leq 10$
H_1: $\mu > 10$

For a random sample of 10 observations the sample mean was 12 and the sample standard deviation 3. Use the 0.05 significance level.

10-10. Consider the following hypotheses:

H_0: $\mu = 400$
H_1: $\mu \neq 400$

For a random sample of 12 observations the sample mean was 407 and the sample standard deviation 6. Use the 0.01 significance level.

For each of the exercises 10-11 and 10-12 answer the following: a) State the null and alternative hypotheses. b) State the decision rule. c) Compute the value of the test statistic. d) What is your conclusion?

10-11. A recent national survey found that high school students watched an average (mean) of 6.8 videos per month. A random sample of 36 college students revealed that the mean number of videos watched last month was 6.2, with a sample standard deviation of 0.5. At the 0.05 significance level, can we conclude that college students watched on average, less than 6.8 videos last month?

10-12. At the time she was hired as a server at the Grumney Family Restaurant, Beth Brigden was told. "You can average more than $20 a day in tips." Over the first 35 days she was employed at the restaurant, the mean daily amount of her tips was $24.85, with a sample standard deviation of $3.24. At the 0.01 significance level, can Ms. Brigden conclude that she is earning an average of more than $20 in tips per day?

10-13. From past records it is known that the mean life of a certain brand of battery used in a digital clock is 305 days. The battery was recently modified to last longer. A sample of 20 of the modified batteries had a mean life of 311 days with a sample standard deviation of 12 days. Did the modification increase the mean life of the battery?

10-14. The Rocky Mountain district sales manager of Rath Publishing, a college book publishing company, claims that the sales representatives make an average of 40 sales calls per week on professors. Several reps said that this estimate is too low. To investigate, a random sample of 35 sales representatives revealed that the mean number of calls made last week was 42. The sample standard deviation was 2.1 calls. Using the 0.05 significance level, can we conclude that the mean number of calls per sales representative for all sales representatives last week was more than 40?

10-15. The management of White Industries is considering a new method of assembling its golf carts. The present method requires 42.3 minutes, on the average, to assemble a cart. The mean assembly time for a random sample of 24 carts using the new method is 40.6 minutes and the standard deviation of the sample is 2.7 minutes. Using the 0.10 level of significance, can we conclude that the new method is faster?

10-16. The records of Yellowstone Trucks revealed that the mean life of spark plugs it currently uses is 34 200 km. A spark plug manufacturer claimed that its plugs have a mean life in excess of 34 200 km. The fleet owner purchased a large number of sets of this new brand of plugs. A sample of 18 sets revealed that the sample mean life was 35 600 km and the sample standard deviation was 2400 km. Is there sufficient evidence to substantiate the manufacturer's claim at the 0.05 significance level?

10-17. Fast Service, a chain of automotive tune-up shops, advertises that its personnel can change the oil, replace the oil filter, and lubricate any standard automobile in no more than 15 minutes, on average. The National Business Bureau received complaints from customers that service takes considerably longer. To check the Fast Service claim, the bureau had service done on 21 unmarked cars. The mean service time was 18 minutes, and the sample standard deviation was 1 minute. Use the 0.05 significance level to check if there is sufficient evidence against Fast Service's claim.

10-18. A machine is set to fill a small bottle with 9.0 g of medicine. A sample of eight bottles revealed the following amounts (in grams) in each bottle.

9.2　8.7　8.9　8.6　8.8　8.5　8.7　9.0

At the 0.01 significance level, can we conclude that the mean weight per bottle is less than 9.0 g?

10-19. A Manitoba chicken farm has observed that the mean weight of the chickens at five months is 1.9 kg. In an effort to increase their weight, a special additive is included in the chicken feed. The subsequent weights of a random sample of five-month-old chickens were (in kilograms):

2.01　1.92　1.89　1.9　1.85　1.94　1.92　1.93　2.0　1.98

At the 0.01 level, has the special additive increased the mean weight of the chickens? Compute the P-value.

10-20. The liquid chlorine added to swimming pools to combats algae has a relatively short shelf life before it loses its effectiveness. Records indicate that the mean shelf life of a 15-litre jug of chlorine is 2160 hours (90 days). As an experiment, Holdlonger was added to the chlorine to find whether it would increase the shelf life. A random sample of nine jugs of chlorine had these shelf lives (in hours):

2159   2170   2180   2179   2160   2167   2171   2181   2185

At the 0.025 level of significance, has Holdlonger increased the mean shelf life of the chlorine? Compute the P-value.

10-21. N.B.'s Trout Farmers' Association contends that the mean number of cut-throat trout caught during a full day of fly-fishing in its lakes and rivers is 4.0. To make their yearly update, the fishery personnel asked a sample of fly-fishermen to keep a count of the number caught during the day. The numbers were: 4, 4, 3, 2, 6, 8, 7, 1, 9, 3, 1, and 6. At the 0.05 level, can we conclude that the mean number caught is greater than 4.0? Determine the P-value.

10-22. Hugger polls contend that agents conduct a mean of 53 in-depth home surveys per agent every week. A streamlined survey form has been introduced, and Hugger wants to evaluate its effectiveness. The number of in-depth surveys conducted during a week by a random sample of agents is:

53   57   50   55   58   54   60   52   59   62   60   60   51   59   5

At the 0.05 level of significance, can we conclude that the mean number of interviews conducted by the agents is more than 53 per week? Compute the P-value.

■ 10.9   TESTS CONCERNING PROPORTIONS

In Chapter 9, we discussed confidence intervals for population proportion. In such a case, each data unit in the population has one of only two possible values, which we denoted "1" and "0." We are interested in the *proportion of p of the population data items*, which have a value of "1."

Let us consider, as an example, the problem mentioned in Section 10.2 regarding the effectiveness of a new drug. In this case, a patient, to whom the drug is administered, will either recover from the disease or will not. We are interested in the effectiveness of the drug, which is the probability that a randomly chosen patient, when treated with this drug, will recover from the disease. This could also be defined as the fraction, p, of all the potential patients who would recover from the disease if all of them were treated with this drug. Thus, each potential patient would either recover, (which we denote by "1"), or would not recover, (which we denote by "0"). We are interested in the fraction, p, of data items with a value of "1" in this conceptual, infinite population.

We shall now discuss how to conduct a test of hypothesis regarding the value of a population proportion.

Suppose we select a sample of size n from this population, (that is, we randomly select n persons suffering from the disease, administer the drug to them and collect the 0/1 sample data). We saw in Chapters 8 and 9, that the sample mean, $\hat{p}$, which is also the sample proportion, has $E(\hat{p}) = p$, and $\sigma_{\hat{p}} = \sqrt{\dfrac{p(1-p)}{n}}$.

Hence, the following is a good choice of a test statistic.

If the null hypothesis is of the form $p = p_0, p \le p_0$, or $p \ge p_0$, for some value p_0, then we shall use $\dfrac{\hat{p} - p_0}{\sqrt{p_0(1 - p_0)/n}}$ as our test statistic.

We saw in Chapter 8 that for a large value of the sample size, n, the distribution of $\hat{p}$ is approximately normal. If the value n is such that $np \ge 5$ and $n(1 - p) \ge 5$, the normal approximation is good enough for most business and economics applications. It follows from this that,

> *If the value of the population proportion is p_0, and the value of n is large enough, (that is, $n(p_0) \ge 5$ and $n(1 - p_0) \ge 5$), the distribution of the test statistic*
>
> $$\dfrac{\hat{p} - p_0}{\sqrt{p_0(1 - p_0)/n}}$$ *is approximately standard normal. That is, our test statistic is*
>
> *approximately a Z statistic. We shall treat it as a Z statistic and our decision rule will be the same as that in the case of the Z test that we gave in Section 10.4.*

Example 10-5

Let us reconsider the problem regarding the effectiveness of a new drug developed by a pharmaceutical company for a certain disease. The company claims that the new drug is more effective than the best currently available on the market, which has an effectiveness of 60 percent. Health Canada wants to conduct a test of significance before approving the drug. A sample of thirty patients suffering from the disease was randomly selected and each of them was treated with the new drug. The results are recorded below. (Here, "1" implies that the patient recovered and "0" implies that the patient did not recover.)

```
0 1 1 1 0 1 1 1 0 1 0 0 1 1 0 0 1 0 1 1 1 1
0 1 1 1 1 0 1 1
```

Design a test of hypothesis with a level of significance, $\alpha = 0.05$.

Solution

We shall use our five-step procedure, discussed in Section 10.2.

Step 1

As we saw in Section 10.2, the null and alternative hypotheses are:
H_0: $p \le 0.6$
H_1: $p > 0.6$

Step 2

We have selected a level of significance, $\alpha = 0.05$.

Step 3

We shall use $\dfrac{\hat{p} - 0.6}{\sqrt{0.6(1 - 0.6)/n}}$ as our test statistic.

Step 4

This is an upper-tailed test, since the values of the parameter p satisfying H_1 are all larger than the values of p which satisfy H_0.

$n = 30$. So, $n(p_0) = 30(0.6) = 18 > 5$ and $n(1 - p_0) = 30(1 - 0.6) = 12 > 5$. Hence, the test statistic is approximately a Z statistic. We shall treat it as a Z statistic. Our decision rule is: reject H_0 in favour of H_1 if the computed z value is greater than $z_\alpha = z_{0.05} - 1.645$. Do *not* reject H_0 if the computed value of the test statistic is less than or equal to 1.645.

Step 5

From the given sample data, we get, $\hat{p} = \dfrac{20}{30} = 0.6667$.

Hence, the computed z value (value of the test statistic) is $z = \dfrac{0.6667 - 0.6}{\sqrt{0.6(1 - 0.6)/30}}$

$= 0.7457$

The value 0.7457 is less than the critical value, 1.645. It does not lie in the rejection region. Hence, our decision is: do *not* reject H_0. We do *not* have sufficient evidence, at significance level $\alpha = 0.05$, to reject H_0. In other words, there is *insufficient* evidence in support of the hypothesis that the new drug is more effective.

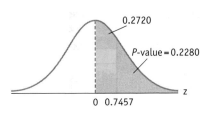

The P-value is the observed level of significance. It is the value α^* of the level of significance such that $z_{\alpha^*} = 0.7457$. Hence, $\alpha^* \approx (5 - 0.2720) = 0.2280$. (From the Z table, we get the area under the Z curve between 0 and 0.7457 to be approximately 0.2720. Hence, the area to the right of 0.7457 is $(0.5 - 0.2720) = 0.2280$.)

We arrive at the same decision as above by observing that the selected value of α ($= 0.05$) is less than the P-value ($= 0.2280$).

We now give instructions for solving the above problem using Minitab and Excel.

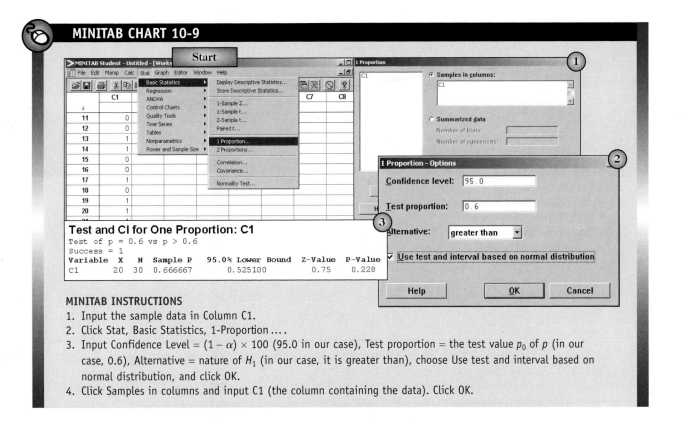

MINITAB CHART 10-9

Test and CI for One Proportion: C1

```
Test of p = 0.6 vs p > 0.6
Success = 1
Variable   X    N   Sample P   95.0% Lower Bound   Z-Value   P-Value
C1        20   30   0.666667       0.525100         0.75      0.228
```

MINITAB INSTRUCTIONS

1. Input the sample data in Column C1.
2. Click Stat, Basic Statistics, 1-Proportion ....
3. Input Confidence Level = $(1 - \alpha) \times 100$ (95.0 in our case), Test proportion = the test value p_0 of p (in our case, 0.6), Alternative = nature of H_1 (in our case, it is greater than), choose Use test and interval based on normal distribution, and click OK.
4. Click Samples in columns and input C1 (the column containing the data). Click OK.

We see from the Minitab output that the computed value of the test statistic is $z = 0.75$. (The value has been rounded to two decimal places.) The P-value is 0.228. These are the same as the values we obtained manually. Besides, the Minitab output also gives us a 95 percent lower bound of 0.5251. Since $p_0 = 0.6$ is above this lower bound, our decision should be to *not* reject H_0 and this decision is consistent with the decision based on the rejection region and the P-value.

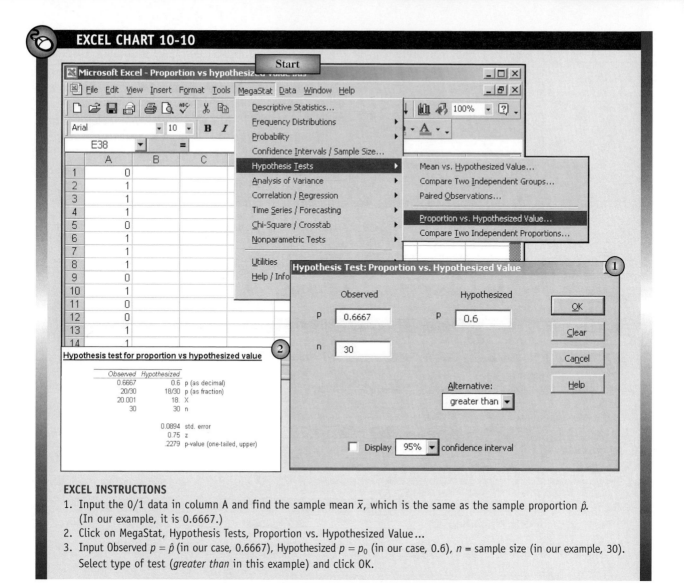

EXCEL CHART 10-10

EXCEL INSTRUCTIONS

1. Input the 0/1 data in column A and find the sample mean $\bar{x}$, which is the same as the sample proportion $\hat{p}$. (In our example, it is 0.6667.)
2. Click on MegaStat, Hypothesis Tests, Proportion vs. Hypothesized Value...
3. Input Observed $p = \hat{p}$ (in our case, 0.6667), Hypothesized $p = p_0$ (in our case, 0.6), n = sample size (in our example, 30). Select type of test (*greater than* in this example) and click OK.

If instead of the entire sample data, we only have information about the sample size (number of trials) and the number of 1s (number of successes) in the sample data, then in the Minitab instructions, we choose *Summarized data* instead of *Samples in columns* and input the data summary.

The screen shots and output for Excel (MegaStat) are given in Chart 10-10. We see that the z-value (-0.75) and the P-value ($= 0.2269$) in the MegaStat output are almost the same as those in the Minitab output. The minor differences are due to rounding error.

MegaStat also computes a 90%, 95%, or 99% confidence interval. (For this, click on Display in screen 2 and choose the appropriate level of confidence interval.) It may be noted that, even in case of a one-tail test, the lower and upper limits of confidence interval given in MegaStat output are limits for $(1 - \alpha)$ confidence interval, and these are not the $(1 - \alpha)$ lower and upper confidence bounds in the decision rule stated in terms of confidence intervals as given on page 441.

■ SELF-REVIEW 10-8

A recent insurance industry report indicated that at least 40 percent of those persons involved in minor traffic accidents this year have been involved in at least one other traffic accident in the last five years. An advisory group, believing that this was too large, decided to investigate if there is significant evidence against the report. A sample of 200 traffic accidents this year showed 74 persons were also involved in another accident within the last five years. Use the 0.01 level of significance.

    (a) State the null and alternative hypotheses.
    (b) Can we use Z as the test statistic? Explain why or why not.
    (c) What should be our decision rule?
    (d) Compute the value of the test statistic and state your decision.
    (e) Determine and interpret the P-value.

EXERCISES 10-23 TO 10-28

10-23. The following hypotheses are given.

H_0: $p \leq 0.70$
H_1: $p > 0.70$

A sample of 100 observations revealed $\hat{p} = 0.75$. At the 0.05 significance level, can the null hypothesis be rejected?

10-24. The following hypotheses are given.

H_0: $p = 0.40$
H_1: $p \neq 0.40$

A sample of 120 observations revealed that $\hat{p} = 0.30$. At the 0.05 significance level, can the null hypothesis be rejected?

10-25. The National Safety Council reported that 52 percent of Canadian Highway drivers are men. A sample of 300 cars travelling eastbound on Highway 401 yesterday revealed that 170 were driven by men. At the 0.01 significance level, can we conclude that a larger proportion of men were driving on Highway 401 yesterday than the national statistics indicate?

10-26. A recent article reported that a job awaits only one in three new college graduates. The major reasons given were an overabundance of college graduates and a weak economy. A survey of 200 recent graduates from your school revealed that 80 of them had jobs. At the 0.03 significance level, can we conclude the larger proportion of recent graduates of your school who have jobs is greater than one in three?

10-27. Chicken Delight claims that 90 percent of its orders are delivered within 10 minutes of the time the order is placed. A sample of 100 orders revealed that 82 were delivered within the promised time. At the 0.10 significance level, can we conclude that less than 90 percent of the orders are delivered in less than 10 minutes?

10-28. Past records show that 50 percent of the students at Canadian universities change their major area of study after their first year in a program. A random sample of 100 students revealed that 48 had changed their major area of study after their first year of the program. Has there been a significant decrease in the proportion of students who change their major after the first year of the program? Test at the 0.05 level of significance.

CHAPTER OUTLINE

I. Given a pair of complementary hypotheses about a population distribution, called null hypothesis (H_0) and alternative hypothesis (H_1), the objective of hypothesis testing is to make one of the following two decisions: (i) reject H_0 and accept H_1 as correct or (ii) do *not* reject H_0.

II. There are two types of errors that can occur in a test of hypothesis.

   A. A Type I error occurs when a true null hypothesis is rejected.

   1. The probability of a Type I error is called the level of significance of the test and it is denoted by α.

   B. A Type II error occurs when a false null hypothesis is *not* rejected.

   1. The probability of a Type II error is denoted by β.

   2. The value $(1 - \beta)$ is called the power of the test.

III. The steps in conducting a test of hypothesis are:

   A. State the null hypothesis (H_0) and the alternative hypothesis (H_1).

   B. Select the level of significance of the test.

   1. The most frequently used significance levels are 0.01, 0.05, and 0.10, but any value between 0 and 1.00 is possible.

   C. Select the test statistic.

   1. A test statistic is a value calculated from the sample information used to determine whether to reject the null hypothesis.

   2. Two test statistics are considered in this chapter.

   (a) When the population standard deviation, σ, is known, we use $\dfrac{\bar{X} - \mu_0}{\sigma/\sqrt{n}}$ as the test statistic, where μ_0 is the test value of μ. If the population distribution is normal, and the population mean $\mu = \mu_0$, $\dfrac{\bar{X} - \mu_0}{\sigma/\sqrt{n}} = Z$, the standard normal variable. We call it a Z statistic and the corresponding test a Z test. If the population distribution is approximately normal or the sample size is large, and the population mean $\mu = \mu_0$, $\dfrac{\bar{X} - \mu_0}{\sigma/\sqrt{n}} \approx Z$. We treat it as a Z statistic and use the Z test.

   (b) When the population standard deviation, σ, is unknown, we use $\dfrac{\bar{X} - \mu_0}{S/\sqrt{n}}$ as the test statistic. If the population distribution is normal, and the population mean $\mu = \mu_0$, the distribution of $\dfrac{\bar{X} - \mu_0}{S/\sqrt{n}} = T$, is Student's t distribution with $(n - 1)$ degrees of freedom. We call the corresponding test a t test.

(c) For a large value of degrees of freedom, t distribution is almost the same as the standard normal distribution.

3. For testing the value of a population proportion, we use as test statistic

$$\frac{\hat{p} - p_0}{\sqrt{\dfrac{p_0(1 - p_0)}{n}}}.$$ When $np_0 \geq 5$ and $n(1 - p_0) \geq 5$, the test statistic has

approximately standard normal distribution. Hence, this is approximately a Z test.

D. State the decision rule.

1. The decision rule indicates the condition or conditions when the null hypothesis is rejected.

2. In a two-tailed test, the rejection region is evenly split between the upper and lower tails.

3. In a one-tailed test, all of the rejection region is in either the upper or the lower tail.

4. Critical values of a test are the dividing points between the rejection region and the region where H_0 is not rejected.

E. Select a sample, compute the value of the test statistic, make a decision regarding the null hypothesis, and interpret the results.

IV. The P-value of an instance of a test of hypothesis is the observed level of significance of the test. It is the value of the level of significance, α^*, for which a critical value of the test statistic (either a_L or a_U) equals the computed value of the test statistic.

■— CHAPTER EXERCISES 10-29 TO 10-56

For each of the exercises 10-29 to 10-56, assume that the population distribution is approximately normal.

10-29. A new weight-watching company, Weight Reducers International, advertises that those who join will lose, on average, 5 kg in the first two weeks. A random sample of 50 people who joined the new weight reduction program revealed the mean loss during the first two weeks to be 4.6 kg with a sample standard deviation of 1.3 kg. At the 0.05 level of significance, can we conclude that those joining Weight Reducers, on average, will lose less than 5 kg during the first two weeks? Determine the P-value.

10-30. Dole Pineapple Inc. is concerned that their 250 g cans of sliced pineapple are being overfilled. The quality-control department took a random sample of 50 cans and found that the arithmetic mean weight was 252 g, with a sample standard deviation of 6 g. At the 5 percent level of significance, can we conclude that the mean weight is greater than 250 g? Determine the P-value.

10-31. A real estate sales agency, Farm Associates, specializes in selling farm property in Nova Scotia. Their past records indicate that the mean selling time for farm property is 90 days. Because of current economic conditions, they believe that the mean selling time is now greater than 90 days. A province-wide survey of a random sample of 100 farms sold recently revealed that the mean selling time was 94 days, with a sample standard deviation of 22 days. At the 0.10 significance level, can we conclude that there has been an increase in the selling time?

10-32. According to the local union president, the mean gross income of plumbers in a city, is normally distributed, with a mean of $50 000 and a standard deviation of $3000. A recent CBC investigative reporter found, for a sample of 120 plumbers, the mean gross income was $50 500. At the 0.10 significance level, is it reasonable to conclude that the mean income is not equal to $50 000? Determine the P-value.

10-33. A Statistics Canada study shows that the mean amount of time per day Canadian men above the age of 15 spend on paid work is 3.1 hours. You believe this figure is too high and decide to conduct your own test. In a random sample of 60 Canadian men above the age of 15, you find that the mean is 2.95 hours of paid work per day and that the sample standard deviation is 1.2 hours. Can you conclude that the population mean is less than 3.1 hours? Use the 0.05 significance level. Determine the P-value and explain its meaning.

10-34. In a TV news segment on the price of gasoline, it was reported last evening that the mean price nationwide is $0.69 per litre for self-serve regular unleaded. A random sample of 35 stations in the Montreal area revealed that the mean price was $0.70 per litre and that the sample standard deviation was $0.02 per litre. At the 0.05 significance level, can we conclude that the price of gasoline was higher in the Montreal area yesterday than the national average? Determine the P-value.

10-35. The Rutter Nursery Company packages their pine bark mulch in 25-kg bags. From a long history, the production department reports that the standard deviation of the bag weight is 1.2 kg. At the end of the each day, Jeff Rutter, the production manager, weighs 10 bags and computes the mean weight of the sample. The weights of 10 bags from today's production are given below:

24.2   24.1   25.3   23.8   23.9   24.6   24.8   25.6   24.8   24.5

(a) Can Mr. Rutter conclude that the population mean of weights of bags today is less than 25 kg? Use the 0.01 significance level.
(b) In a brief report, explain why Mr. Rutter can use the Z statistic as the test statistic.
(c) Compute the P-value.

10-36. In a recent national survey the mean weekly allowance for a nine-year-old child from his or her parents was reported to be $3.65. A random sample of 45 nine-year-olds in Edmonton revealed the mean allowance to be $3.69 with a sample standard deviation of $0.24. At the 0.05 significance level, is the mean allowance in Edmonton for nine-year-olds different from the reported national mean of $3.65?

10-37. The manufacturer of the Ososki motorcycles advertises that the cycle will average 2.6 litres per 100 km. A sample of eight bikes revealed the following fuel consumption ratio (litres/100 km):

2.5   2.4   2.8   2.4   2.5   2.3   2.6   2.4

At the 0.05 level, is the mean gasoline consumption ratio less than the advertised 2.6 litres per 100 km?

10-38. The Myers' Summer Casual Furniture Store tells customers that a special order will take six weeks (42 days). During recent months, the owner has received several complaints that the special orders are taking longer than 42 days. A random sample of 12 special orders delivered in the last month showed that the mean waiting time was 51 days with a sample standard deviation of 8 days. At the 0.05 significance level, can we conclude that customers are waiting an average of more than 42 days? Compute the P-value.

10-39. A typical Canadian college student drinks an average of 4.8 litres of coffee per month. A sample of 12 students at the University of Windsor revealed the following amounts of coffee consumed last month.

4.75   4.96   4.57   4.82   4.85   5.82   5.43   4.65
4.60   5.14   4.89   5.26

At the 0.05 significance level, is there a significant difference between the average amount consumed at the University of Windsor and the national average of 4.8 litres?

10-40. The post-anesthesia care area (recovery room) at a hospital in Montreal was recently enlarged. The hope was that with the enlargement the mean number of patients per day would be more than 25. A random sample of 15 days revealed the following numbers of patients:

25   27   25   26   25   28   28   27   24
26   25   29   25   27   24

At the 0.01 significance level, can we conclude that the mean number of patients per day is more than 25? Compute the P-value and interpret it.

10-41. The Web site www.egolf.com claims that they receive an average of 6.5 returns per day from online shoppers. For a sample of 12 days, they received the following number of returns:

0   4   3   4   9   4   5   9   1   6   7   10

At the 0.01 significance level, can we conclude that the population mean of the number of returns is less than 6.5?

10-42. During recent seasons, Major League Baseball has been criticized for the length of the games. A report indicated that the average game lasts 3 hours and 30 minutes. A sample of 17 games revealed the following times for completion. (Note that the minutes have been changed to fractions of hours, so that a game that lasted 2 hours and 24 minutes is reported at 2.40 hours.)

2.98   3.40   2.70   2.25   3.23   3.17   2.93
3.18   3.80   2.38   3.75   3.20   3.27   2.52
2.58   4.45   2.45

Can we conclude that the mean time for a game is less than 3.50 hours? Use the 0.05 significance level.

10-43. The Watch Corporation of Switzerland claims that their watches on average, will neither gain nor lose time during a week. A sample of 18 watches provided the following gains (+) or losses (−) in seconds per week.

Is it reasonable to conclude that the mean gain or loss in time for the watches is not 0?

+0.38	−0.20	−0.38	−0.32	+0.32	−0.23	+0.30	+0.25
−0.10	−0.37	−0.61	−0.48	−0.47	−0.64	−0.04	+0.20
−0.68	+0.05						

Use the 0.05 significance level. Determine the *P*-value.

10-44. Listed below are the rates of return for one year (reported in percent) for a sample of 12 mutual funds that are classified as taxable money market funds.

4.63	4.15	4.76	4.70	4.65	4.52	4.70	5.06
4.42	4.51	4.24	4.52				

Using the 0.05 significance level, can we conclude that the mean rate of return of all such mutual funds is more than 4.50 percent?

10-45. A cola-dispensing machine is set to dispense 250 ml of cola per cup, with a standard deviation of 10 ml. The manufacturer of the machine would like to set the control limits in such a way that if a large number of samples of size 36 are collected, approximately 5 percent of the sample means will be greater than the upper control limit, and approximately 5 percent of the sample means will be less than the lower control limit.
(a) At what values should the control limits be set?
(b) What is the probability that if the population mean shifts to 245 ml, this change will not be detected?
(c) What is the probability that if the population mean shifts to 253 ml, this change will not be detected?

10-46. One of the major automakers wishes to review its warranty. The warranty covers the engine, transmission, and drive train of all new cars for up to two years or 30 000 km, whichever comes first. The manufacturer's quality-assurance department claims that the mean number of kilometres driven by owners in the first two years is more than 30 000. A sample of 35 cars revealed that the mean number of kilometres was 30 850 with a standard deviation of 3200 km. Can we conclude at the 0.05 significance level, that the quality-assurance department's claim is correct?

10-47. The following null and alternative hypotheses are given.
H_0: $\mu \le 50$
H_1: $\mu > 50$

Suppose the population standard deviation is 10. The probability of a Type I error is set at 0.01. We want the probability of a Type II error to be 0.30, if the population mean happens to be 55. How large a sample is necessary to meet these requirements?

10-48. The owners of the Franklin Park Mall wish to study customer shopping habits. From earlier studies, the owners are under the impression that a typical shopper spends 0.75 hours at the mall, with a standard deviation of 0.10 hours. Recently the mall owners added some specialty restaurants designed to keep shoppers in the mall longer. This is expected to have no effect on the standard deviation of the times spent. The consulting firm, Brunner and Swanson Marketing Enterprises, has been hired to evaluate the effects of the restaurants on the mean time spent. A sample of 45 shoppers by Brunner and Swanson, revealed that the sample mean of times spent in the mall was 0.80 hours.

(a) Develop a test of hypothesis to determine whether there is sufficient evidence to conclude that the mean time spent in the mall is more than 0.75 hours. Use the 0.05 significance level.

(b) Suppose the mean shopping time has actually increased from 0.75 hours to 0.77 hours. What is the probability this increase would not be detected?

(c) When Brunner and Swanson reported the information in part (b) to the mall owners, the owners were upset with the statement that a survey may not be able to detect a change from 0.75 to 0.77 hours of shopping time. How could this probability be reduced?

10-49. A national grocer's magazine reports the typical shopper spends eight minutes in line waiting to check out. A sample of 24 shoppers at the local Farmer Jack's showed a mean of 7.5 minutes with a standard deviation of 3.2 minutes. Can we conclude, at $\alpha = 0.05$, that the mean waiting time at Farmer Jack's is less than that reported in the national magazine?

10-50. An insurance company, based on past experience, estimates the mean damage for a natural disaster in its area is $5000. After introducing several plans to prevent loss, they randomly sampled 200 policyholders and found the mean amount per claim was $4800 with a standard deviation of $1300. Can we conclude, at $\alpha = 0.05$, that after the introduction of the prevention plans, the mean amount of a claim is less than $5000?

10-51. In 2000 the mean fare to fly from Halifax to Toronto, on a discount round trip ticket was $367. A random sample of round trip discount fares on this route last month gives:

421   336   390   430   410   350   370   380   399   365
391   375   381

At the 0.01 significance level, can we conclude that the mean fare has increased? What is the P-value?

10-52. The policy of the Suburban Transit Authority is to add a bus route if more than 55 percent of potential commuters indicate they would use that particular route. A sample of 70 potential commuters revealed that 42 would use a proposed route from Bowman Park to the downtown area. Can we conclude that the Bowman-to-downtown route meets the STA criterion? Use the 0.05 significance level.

10-53. Tina Dennis is the comptroller for Meek Industries. She believes that the current cash flow problem at Meek is due to the slow collection of accounts receivable. She believes that more than 60 percent of the accounts are in arrears more than three months. A random sample of 200 accounts showed that 140 were more than three months old. At the 0.01 significance level, can she conclude that more than 60 percent of the accounts are in arrears for more than three months?

10-54. From past experience a television manufacturer found that 10 percent or less of its sets needed any type of repair in the first two years of operation. In a random sample of 80 sets manufactured two years ago, 14 needed repair.

At the 0.05 significance level, has the percent of sets needing repair increased? Determine the *P*-value.

10-55. Past experience at the Crowder Travel Agency indicated that 44 percent of those persons who wanted the agency to plan a vacation for them wanted to go to Europe. During the most recent busy season, a sample of 1000 plans was selected at random from the files. It was found that 480 persons wanted to go to Europe on vacation. Has there been a significant upward shift in the percentage of persons who want to go to Europe? Test at the 0.05 significance level.

10-56. An urban planner claims that, nationally, 20 percent of all families renting condominiums at the beginning of a year, move during that year. A random sample of 200 families renting condominiums in Toronto at the beginning of a year revealed that 56 moved during that year. At the 0.01 significance level, does this evidence suggest that a larger proportion of people renting condominiums moved in the Toronto area, than the national average of 20 percent? Determine the *P*-value.

www.exercises.ca 10-57 TO 10-58

10-57. It was reported in the Pro Ice Hockey home page, http://proicehockey.about.com, in December 2001 that the average salary of NHL players during the year 2000–01 was $1 483 949. The same Web site also has links to sites that report the salaries of players. You believe that the average salary has increased since than. Select a random sample of 20 current players and record their salaries during the current year. Conduct a statistical test of hypothesis to check if there is significant evidence that the current average salary is more than $1 483 949. Use $\alpha = 0.05$. What is the *P*-value? Interpret it. (Assume that the population is approximately normally distributed.)

10-58. A real estate agent claims that house prices in Oshawa, Ontario have increased by 20 percent since the spring of 1988. The Spring 1988 issue of *The Land Economist* indicates that the average price of single family houses in Oshawa during that period was $190 000. Suppose you do not believe that prices have increased so much and you want to conduct a test of hypothesis to check if there is significant evidence, at $\alpha = 0.05$, that the real estate agent's claim is wrong. Go to the Web site *www.homestore.ca*. Click on province: *Ontario*, area: *Durham, Oshawa*. Select a random sample of sale prices of 15 houses using *SRR*. (Use the random number table to select the random numbers). What is the *P*-value? Interpret it. (Assume that the sale prices of homes are approximately normally distributed.)

► COMPUTER DATA EXERCISES 10-59 TO 10-60

10-59. Refer to the data in file Exercise 10-59.xls on the CD for the end of the week prices for BCE stock during 20 randomly selected weeks in the year 2000. Conduct a test of hypothesis to check if there is significant evidence, at

$\alpha = 0.05$, that the mean value of the end of the week prices of the BCE stock during the year 2000 was different from 18.6. What is the P-value? Intrepret it. (Assume that the stock price is approximately normally distributed.)

10-60. Refer to the real estate data in file Exercise 10-60.xls on the CD, which reports sample information on the houses sold in Victoria, B.C. during the year 2001.

(i) According to a RBC financial group report, the average house price in Victoria during the year 2001 was $210 200. Conduct a test of hypothesis to check if there is significant evidence, at $\alpha = 0.05$, that the average price of houses sold in Victoria during the year 2001 was more than $210 200. What is the P-value? Interpret it.

(ii) A real estate agent claims that the median value of house prices in Victoria during 2001 was $221 000. Using significance level $\alpha = 0.05$, conduct a test of hypothesis to check if there is significant evidence that the median price of the houses sold in Victoria during the year 2001 was less than $221 000. What is the P-value? Interpret it. (Assume that the sale prices of homes are approximately normally distributed.)

CHAPTER 10   ANSWERS TO SELF-REVIEW

10-1. (a) $H_0: \mu \le 0.2$; $H_1: \mu > 0.2$
(b) $H_0: \mu = 0.604$; $H_1: \mu \ne 0.604$

10-2. (a) We shall choose as test statistic:

$\dfrac{\bar{X} - 0.2}{\sigma/\sqrt{n}}$ if the value of σ is known.

$\dfrac{\bar{X} - 0.2}{S/\sqrt{n}}$ if the value of σ is unknown.

This is an upper-tailed test. Our decision rule will be to choose an upper critical value, a_U, and reject H_0 if the computed value of the test statistic is greater than a_U.

(b) We shall choose as a test statistic:

$\dfrac{\bar{X} - 0.604}{\sigma/\sqrt{n}}$ if the value of σ is known.

$\dfrac{\bar{X} - 0.604}{S/\sqrt{n}}$ if the value of σ is unknown.

This is a two-tailed test. Our decision rule will be to choose an upper critical value, a_U, and a lower critical value, a_L, and reject H_0 if the computed value of the test statistic is greater than a_U, or if it is less than a_L.

10-3. (a) (i) This is an upper-tailed Z test. The upper critical value is $a_U = z_{0.04}$ ≈ 1.751. Our decision rule is: reject H_0 if the computed z value is greater than 1.751.

(ii) $\bar{x} = \dfrac{4.8 + 3.4 + \cdots + 1.6}{12} = 1.58$;

$z = \dfrac{(1.58 - 0.2)}{6.24/\sqrt{12}} = 0.76$

Since, 0.76 is less than 1.751, our decision is: we do *not* have sufficient evidence, at $\alpha = 0.04$ to reject H_0.

(b) (i) This is (approximately) a two-tailed Z test. The upper critical value is $a_U = z_{\alpha/2} = z_{0.04}$ ≈ 1.751, and the lower critical value is $a_L = -z_{0.04} \approx -1.751$. Our decision rule is: reject H_0 if the computed z value is greater than 1.751, or if it is less than 1.751.

(ii) $\bar{x} = \dfrac{1.7 + 0 + \cdots + 1.4}{15} = -0.007$;

$z = \dfrac{(-0.007 - 0.604)}{3.04/\sqrt{15}} = -0.78$

Since, -0.78 is between -1.751 and $+1.751$, our decision is: we do *not* have sufficient evidence, at $\alpha = 0.08$, to reject H_0.

10-4. (a) (i) The computed z value is 0.76. The P-value, α^* is such that $z_{\alpha^*} = 0.76$. This equals $(0.5 - 0.2764)$ $= 0.2236$

(ii) $\alpha = 0.3$ is more than 0.2236. Our decision is: reject H_0.

$\alpha = 0.01$ is less than 0.2236. Our decision is: do *not* reject H_0.

(b) (i) The computed z value is -0.78. The P-value, α^* is such that $z_{\alpha^*/2} = 0.78$. This equals $2(0.5 - 0.2823)$ $= 0.4354$.

(ii) $\alpha = 0.1$ is less than 0.4354. Our decision is: do *not* reject H_0.

$\alpha = 0.48$ is more than 0.4354. Our decision is: reject H_0.

10-5. (a) (i) This is an upper tailed Z test. $\alpha = 0.04$ Hence, the value of 96 percent lower confidence bound is

$\bar{x} - z_{0.04}\ \sigma/\sqrt{n}$

$= 1.58 - 1.751\left(\dfrac{6.24}{\sqrt{12}}\right) = -1.574$

(ii) Since the test value $\mu_0 = 0.2$ is greater than -1.574, our decision is: do *not* reject H_0. $\alpha = 0.04$ is less than the P-value $(= 0.2236)$ computed in Self-Review 10-4(a). Hence, the decision based on the P-value is the same.

(b) (i) This is two upper-tailed Z test. $\alpha = 0.08$ Hence, a 92 percent confidence interval estimate is

$(\bar{x} - z_{0.04}\sigma/\sqrt{n},\ \bar{x} + z_{0.04}\sigma/\sqrt{n})$

$= \left(\begin{array}{c} -0.007 - 1.751\dfrac{3.04}{\sqrt{15}}, \\[2mm] -0.007 + 1.751\dfrac{3.04}{\sqrt{15}} \end{array}\right)$

$= (-1.381, 1.367)$

(ii) Since the test value $\mu_0 = 0.604$ is in the 92 percent confidence interval estimate, our decision is: do *not* reject H_0. $\alpha = 0.08$ is less than the P-value $(= 0.4354)$ computed in Self-Review 10-4(b). Hence, the decision based on the P-value is the same.

10-6. (a) (i) The critical value of

$$\bar{X} \text{ is } \mu_0 + z_{0.04}\ \sigma/\sqrt{n}$$

$$= 0.2 + 1.751 \frac{6.24}{\sqrt{12}} = 3.354$$

If true value of μ is 3.0, then $\bar{X} \sim Normal$

$$\left(3, \frac{6.24}{\sqrt{12}}\right) = Normal\ (3, 1.801)$$

$$\beta = P(\bar{X} < 3.354) = P(Z < 0.1966) = 0.578$$

(ii) The critical values of $\bar{X}$ are

$$\mu_0 - z_{0.04}\sigma/\sqrt{n} = 0.604 - 1.751\frac{3.04}{\sqrt{15}}$$

$$= -0.77,$$

and

$$\mu_0 + z_{0.04}\sigma/\sqrt{n} = 0.604 + 1.751\frac{3.04}{\sqrt{15}}$$

1.978

If true value of μ is 1.6, then $\bar{X} \sim Normal$
(1.6, 0.785)

$$\beta = P(-0.77 \le \bar{X} \le 1.978)$$

$$= P(-3.019 \le Z \le 0.482)$$

$$= 0.4987 + 0.1851 = 0.6838.$$

10-7. In the case of problem (a), Self-Review 10-3,

our test statistics is $T = \dfrac{\bar{X} - 0.2}{S/\sqrt{12}}$. This is an

upper-tailed t test.
   The critical value is $a_U = t_{0.05}, (df = 11) = 1.796$.
So, our decision rule is: reject H_0 if the computed
t value is greater than 1.796
$\bar{x} = 1.58$;

$$s = \sqrt{\frac{(4.8 - 1.58)^2 + \cdots + (1.6 - 1.58)^2}{11}} = 2.303$$

$$t = \frac{\bar{x} - 0.2}{s/\sqrt{n}} = \frac{1.58 - 0.2}{2.303/\sqrt{12}} = 2.076$$

Since the computed t value is greater than 1.796,
we shall reject H_0.
   In the case of problem (b), Self-Review 10-3,

our test statistics is $T = \dfrac{\bar{X} - 0.604}{S/\sqrt{15}}$. This is

a two-tailed t test.

The critical values are $a_U = t_{0.025}, (df = 14)$
$= 2.145$, and $a_L = -t_{0.025}, (df = 14) = -2.145$.
So, our decision rule is: reject H_0 if the computed
t value is greater than 2.145 or if it is less
than -2.145.
$\bar{x} = -0.007$;

$$s = \sqrt{\frac{(1.7 + 0.007)^2 + \cdots + (1.4 + 0.007)^2}{14}}$$

$$= 3.9958$$

$$t = \frac{\bar{x} - 0.604}{s/\sqrt{n}} = \frac{-0.007 - 0.604}{3.9958/\sqrt{15}} = -0.59$$

Since the computed t value is between -2.145 and
$+2.145$, we do *not* have sufficient evidence, at
$\alpha = 0.05$, to reject H_0 in favour of H_1.

10-8. (a) $H_0\text{: } p \ge 0.4;\ H_1\text{: } p < 0.4$

(b) The test statistic is $\left(\dfrac{\hat{p} - 0.4}{\sqrt{(0.4)(0.6)/200}}\right)$.

$np_0 = 200(0.4) = 80 > 5;\ n(1 - p_0) = 200(1 - 0.4)$
$= 120 > 5$. Hence, the test statistic is approximately a Z statistic. This is an approximate
Z test.

(c) This is a lower-tailed Z test. The critical value
is $a_L = -z_\alpha = -z_{0.01} = -2.326$. The decision
rule is: reject H_0, if the computed z value is
less than -2.326.

(d) $\hat{p} = 74/200 = 0.37;\ z = \dfrac{0.37 - 0.4}{\sqrt{(0.4)(0.6)/200}}$

$= -0.866$. Since the computed z value,
-0.866, is more than -2.326, we do *not* have
sufficient evidence to reject H_0.

(e) P-value is the value α^* such that
$-z_{\alpha^*} = -0.866$. It equals approximately
$(0.5 - 0.3065) = 0.1935$

For the value of the level of significance less
than, or equal to, 0.1935, our decision rule is: do
not reject H_0. For the value of the level of significance greater than 0.1935, our decision will be:
reject H_0.

CHAPTER 11

Statistical Inference: Two Populations

GOALS

When you have completed this chapter, you will be able to:

- Explain the difference between dependent and independent samples

- Conduct a test of hypothesis and obtain a confidence interval estimate for the difference between two population means using independent samples

- Conduct a test of hypothesis and obtain a confidence interval estimate for the difference between two population means using a matched pair sample

- Conduct a test of hypothesis and obtain a confidence interval estimate for the difference between two population proportions.

FRANCIS YSIDRO EDGEWORTH (1845–1926)

Some of the most significant contributions to statistical inference, about the difference between two population means, were made by R.A. Fisher and W.S. Gosset. But the credit for being one of the first to undertake a systematic study of the subject goes to Professor F.Y. Edgeworth.

Francis Ysidro Edgeworth (1845–1926) was born in Edgeworthstown, Ireland. His father died when he was two years old, and he was brought up by tutors until he went to Trinity College, Dublin, at the age of seventeen. Here he studied modern languages, and he graduated from Oxford University in 1869 with first class in *literae humaniores*. Very little is known about his life from 1870 until he was called to the bar in 1877.

He obtained the position of lecturer in logic at King's College, London, in 1880. He was appointed Professor of Economics at the College in 1888, and the Tooke Chair of Economic Science in 1890. In 1891, he was appointed the Drummond Professor of Political Economy at Oxford, and remained there for the rest of his life.

Existing records show no indication of Edgeworth having received any formal training in mathematics, beyond elementary algebra. Considering that he was a self-trained mathematician, the depth of knowledge of mathematics demonstrated in his first book, *Mathematical Psychics*, published in 1881, is astounding. Here, Edgeworth developed *Calculus of Feeling, of Pleasure and Pain*. Marshall, one of the all-time top economists, in his review of the book bluntly says, "This book shows clear signs of genius, and a promise of great things to come".[1]

By the year 1883, Edgeworth developed a strong interest in statistics and probability theory, which was intensified by contact with his distant cousin Galton. He maintained this interest till the end of his life. His enthusiasm for the subject is illustrated by the following charming anecdote by Bowley.[2] As a party of economists was cycling out of Cambridge, in 1904, and Edgeworth began to talk statistics, Cannan dew alongside Bowley and said, "Put on the pace, Bowley, he cannot talk mathematics at more than 12 miles an hour." Edgeworth's key work on the topic of statistical inference involving difference in two population means was published in a series of four papers in 1885.

His three volumes on index numbers, published in 1887, have been referred to by Pigou as, "of a kind to which the term *classical* may properly be applied."[3]

Edgeworth was a kind and affectionate man with a sharp and candid eye for human nature. He was also reserved, complicated, proud and touchy. He never married; but it was not for want of susceptibility. His difficult nature cut him off from full intimacy. Marshall, remembering his mixed parentage, used to say: "Francis is a charming fellow, but you must be careful with Ysidro."[4]

1498
1548
1598
1648
1698
1748
1898
1948
2000

INTRODUCTION

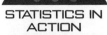

STATISTICS IN ACTION

Trading Is Hazardous to Your Wealth

Barber and Odean[5] study the investment performance of common stocks held directly by households. They consider the investment record of 66 465 households at a large discount brokerage firm from January 1991 to December 1996. The sample of house-holds is partitioned into quintiles according to the mean monthly turnovers. The study shows that those that trade most (the fifth quintile) earn an average 11.4 percent, while those that trade the least (the first quintile) earn an average of 18.5 percent. The difference is significant at $\alpha = 0.01$. Their central message is that "trading is hazardous to your wealth."

Chapter 5 began our study of inferential statistics. Chapters 5 through 7 laid the foundation with the study of probability theory, discrete random variables, and continuous random variables. Chapter 8 introduced different sampling techniques and the concept of sampling distribution of a sample statistic. Chapter 9 discussed the statistical theory of estimation. We discussed in detail, some point and interval estimators of population mean and population proportion. Chapter 10 began our study of hypothesis testing. We described the nature of hypothesis testing and developed procedures for conducting tests of hypothesis about values of the population mean and the population proportion. Our procedures involved: (i) selecting a single random sample from the population, (ii) choosing a suitable test statistic and a decision rule, (iii) computing the value of the test statistic from the selected sample, and (iv) making a decision based on the value of the test statistic and the decision rule.

In this chapter, we shall expand the ideas in chapters 9 and 10 to develop confidence interval estimators of, and procedures for, testing hypotheses about the difference in values of means or proportions of two populations. Some examples of parameters we might want to study are:

- Difference between the mean amount of residential real estate sold by male agents and female agents in Calgary.

- Difference in the mean number of defective items produced on the day and the afternoon shifts at Kimble products.

- Difference in the mean number of days absent between young workers (under 21 years of age) and older workers (more than 60 years of age) in the fast-food industry.

- Difference between the proportions of University of New Brunswick graduates and University of Windsor graduates who pass the Certified Accountancy Examination on their first attempt.

We shall develop procedures based on the difference in values of the sample means, or proportions, of two samples selected randomly from the two populations. The sampling distribution of the difference in values of the two sample means, or proportions, depends on whether the two samples are selected independently or whether they are dependent. We discuss these two cases separately. In the next section, we consider the case of population means when the two samples are selected independently. In Section 11.2, we deal with the case of population means when the two samples are dependent. In Section 11.4, we deal with the case of population proportions.

11.1   DIFFERENCE BETWEEN TWO POPULATION MEANS: INDEPENDENT SAMPLES

Let us start with an example. The employees at the East Vancouver plant of a multinational company are demanding higher salaries than those offered at the company plant located in Oshawa, Ontario. Their justification for this demand for pay differential is that the difference between the average price of single-family houses in East Vancouver and that in Oshawa is more than $60 000. Before making a decision on this issue, the company management wants to study the difference in the prices of single-family houses for sale at the two locations. In particular, let μ_1 and μ_2 be the mean values of prices of single-family houses for sale in East Vancouver and Oshawa. Then the management wants to study the difference $(\mu_1 - \mu_2)$.

HYPOTHESIS TESTING FOR DIFFERENCE BETWEEN TWO POPULATION MEANS

The first logical step would be to test if the employees' claim, about the difference between average prices of single-family houses in the two locations, is correct.

Example 11-1

The company wants to conduct a test of hypothesis to check if there is sufficient evidence that the difference between the mean values of prices of single-family houses on sale in East Vancouver and in Oshawa, is greater than $60 000. Accordingly, they collect, *independently*, samples of prices of single-family houses on sale at the two locations. These are recorded below (in thousands of dollars, rounded to the nearest thousand.) (Source: *www.homestore.ca*)

| East Vancouver | 345 290 279 259 410 174 252 455 228 369 |
| Oshawa | 219 122 200 134 179 204 129 132 174 142 136 159 168 170 227 |

Assuming that the population distributions are approximately normal, can we conclude at the 0.05 significance level that the difference between the two population means is greater than $60 000?

Solution

We shall use the five-step procedure introduced in Chapter 10.

Step 1

Let μ_1 and μ_2 be the mean values of prices of single-family houses for sale in East Vancouver and Oshawa respectively. Then, the null and alternative hypotheses are:

$$H_0: (\mu_1 - \mu_2) \le 60$$

$$H_1: (\mu_1 - \mu_2) > 60$$

Step 2

The level of significance, α, has been chosen as 0.05.

Step 3

A logical approach would be to compute the values of the sample means, $\bar{X}_1$ and $\bar{X}_2$, of the independent random samples and base our conclusion on the analysis of the value of the difference $(\bar{X}_1 - \bar{X}_2)$.

We know from Chapter 8 that,

$$E(\bar{X}_1) = \mu_1, \quad E(\bar{X}_2) = \mu_2, \quad V(\bar{X}_1) = \frac{\sigma_1^2}{n_1}, \quad \text{and} \quad V(\bar{X}_2) = \frac{\sigma_2^2}{n_2}$$

Here, σ_1 and σ_2 are the standard deviations of the two populations.

Using Formula 6-3 on page 240, discussed in Chapter 6, we get[6]:

$$E(\bar{X}_1 - \bar{X}_2) = \mu_1 - \mu_2 \qquad \text{11-1}$$

So, $(\bar{X}_1 - \bar{X}_2)$ *is an unbiased estimator of* $(\mu_1 - \mu_2)$.

Variance of $(\bar{X}_1 - \bar{X}_2)$ $\qquad V(\bar{X}_1 - \bar{X}_2) = \frac{\sigma_1^2}{n_1} + \frac{\sigma_2^2}{n_2}$ $\qquad$ **11-2**

Hence, the standard deviation of $(\bar{X}_1 - \bar{X}_2)$ is

| The standard deviation of $(\bar{X}_1 - \bar{X}_2)$ | $\sigma_{(\bar{X}_1 - \bar{X}_2)} = \sqrt{\dfrac{\sigma_1^2}{n_1} + \dfrac{\sigma_2^2}{n_2}}$ | 11-3 |

We saw in Chapter 8 that if the population distributions are normal, then each of $\bar{X}_1$ and $\bar{X}_2$ is normally distributed, and hence, $(\bar{X}_1 - \bar{X}_2)$ is normally distributed. (The sum or difference of two normal random variables is a normal random variable.)

This implies that

$$\left(\frac{(\bar{X}_1 - \bar{X}_2) - (\mu_1 - \mu_2)}{\sqrt{\dfrac{\sigma_1^2}{n_1} + \dfrac{\sigma_2^2}{n_2}}} \right) \qquad \text{11-4}$$

is a standard normal variable.

If the values of the population standard deviations are unknown, we substitute in Formula 11-4, σ_1^2 and σ_2^2 by their unbiased estimators, S_1^2 and S_2^2 to get the random variable:

$$\left(\frac{(\bar{X}_1 - \bar{X}_2) - (\mu_1 - \mu_2)}{\sqrt{\dfrac{S_1^2}{n_1} + \dfrac{S_2^2}{n_2}}} \right) \qquad \text{11-5}$$

It can be shown[7] that when the population distributions are normal, a *reasonable approximation* to the distribution of the random variable 11-5 is *Student's t distribution*, with degrees of freedom.

| Degrees of Freedom | $df = \dfrac{(S_1^2/n_1 + S_2^2/n_2)^2}{\left(\dfrac{(S_1^2/n_1)^2}{n_1 - 1} + \dfrac{(S_2^2/n_2)^2}{n_2 - 1} \right)}$ | 11-6 |

The approximation is better for larger values of sample sizes.

Since the null hypothesis is $H_0: (\mu_1 - \mu_2) \le 60$, we shall use as the test statistic:

$$\left(\frac{(\bar{X}_1 - \bar{X}_2) - 60}{\sqrt{\dfrac{S_1^2}{n_1} + \dfrac{S_2^2}{n_2}}} \right)$$

Step 4 In our problem, the population distributions are approximately normal. Hence, when H_0 is true, our test statistic has approximately a Student's t distribution. This is an upper-tailed (right-tailed) t test. The critical value is $t_\alpha = t_{0.05}$. Our decision rule is: reject H_0 if the computed t value, (value of the test statistic) is greater than $t_{0.05}$. The degrees of freedom of the t distribution are given by Formula 11-6.

Step 5 From the sample data, we get

$$\bar{x}_1 = \frac{345 + \cdots + 369}{10} = 306.1, \; \bar{x}_2 = \frac{219 + \cdots + 227}{15} = 166.3$$

$$s_1 = \sqrt{\frac{(345 - 306.1)^2 + \cdots + (369 - 306.1)^2}{9}} = 87.0$$

$$s_2 = \sqrt{\frac{(219 - 166.3)^2 + \cdots + (227 - 166.3)^2}{14}} = 34.2$$

$$t = \left| \frac{(\bar{x}_1 - \bar{x}_2) - 60}{\sqrt{\dfrac{s_1^2}{n_1} + \dfrac{s_2^2}{n_2}}} \right| = \left| \frac{(306.1 - 166.3) - 60}{\sqrt{\dfrac{(87.0)^2}{10} + \dfrac{(34.2)^2}{15}}} \right| = 2.76$$

The degrees of freedom = df =

$$\frac{(s_1^2/n_1 + s_2^2/n_2)^2}{\left(\dfrac{(s_1^2/n_1)^2}{n_1 - 1} + \dfrac{(s_2^2/n_2)^2}{n_2 - 1} \right)} = \frac{((87.0)^2/10 + (34.2)^2/15)^2}{\left(\dfrac{((87.0)^2/10)^2}{9} + \dfrac{((34.2)^2/15)^2}{14} \right)} \approx 10$$

From the t table on the inside back cover of this text, we find that for $df = 10$, $t_{0.05} = 1.812$. Hence, the rejection region is the region greater than 1.812.

Since the computed t value ($= 2.76$) is greater than 1.812, our decision is: we have sufficient evidence, at $\alpha = 0.05$, to reject H_0 and accept the employees' claim that the mean value of prices of single-family houses for sale in East Vancouver is more than $60\,000 higher than the mean value of prices in Oshawa.

We give below Minitab and Excel instructions for solving the problem.

MINITAB CHART 11-1

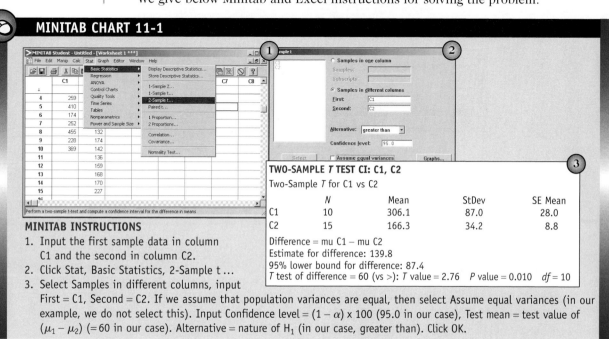

MINITAB INSTRUCTIONS

1. Input the first sample data in column C1 and the second in column C2.
2. Click Stat, Basic Statistics, 2-Sample t ...
3. Select Samples in different columns, input First = C1, Second = C2. If we assume that population variances are equal, then select Assume equal variances (in our example, we do not select this). Input Confidence level = $(1 - \alpha) \times 100$ (95.0 in our case), Test mean = test value of $(\mu_1 - \mu_2)$ (= 60 in our case). Alternative = nature of H_1 (in our case, greater than). Click OK.

TWO-SAMPLE *T* TEST CI: C1, C2

Two-Sample T for C1 vs C2

	N	Mean	StDev	SE Mean
C1	10	306.1	87.0	28.0
C2	15	166.3	34.2	8.8

Difference = mu C1 − mu C2
Estimate for difference: 139.8
95% lower bound for difference: 87.4
T test of difference = 60 (vs >): T value = 2.76 P value = 0.010 df = 10

The Minitab output in Chart 11-1 gives us computed t value = 2.76, and the P-value = 0.01. The P-value is smaller than the selected value of α (= 0.05). Hence, based on the P-value, we arrive at the same decision as before, (that is, we have sufficient evidence, at $\alpha = 0.05$, to reject H_0 and accept the employees' claim). (Recall that the decision rule can be stated in terms of P-value as: reject H_0 in favour of H_1 if the P-value is less than the selected level of significance, α. For details, you may refer to Sections 10.5 and 10.8.)

The computed t value in the Excel output in Chart 11-2 (this is called t *Stat* in the output) is the same as the one in the Minitab output and the one computed by hand.

Excel does not give separate outputs for one-tailed and two-tailed tests. In the same output, it gives the values of t_α (termed t *critical one-tail*) and $t_{\alpha/2}$ (called t *critical two-tail*). The critical value for an upper-tailed (right-tailed) t test is t_α, the critical value for a lower-tailed (left-tailed) t test is $-t_\alpha$, and the critical values for a two-tailed test are $-t_{\alpha/2}$ and $t_{\alpha/2}$.

Also, in the same output Excel gives the P-values for one-tailed and two-tailed tests. The P-value of a two-tailed test is termed $P(T <= t)$ *two-tail* in the output. The P-values of upper- and lower-tailed tests can be obtained from the output as follows.

> *In the case of an upper-tailed test:*
> *If the t value is positive, then the P-value is the same as the value in the output termed $P(T <= t)$ one-tail.*
> *If the t value is negative, then the P-value equals $(1 - $ the value $P(T <= t)$ one-tail).*
>
> *In the case of a lower-tailed test, the rules are just the opposite.*

EXCEL CHART 11-2

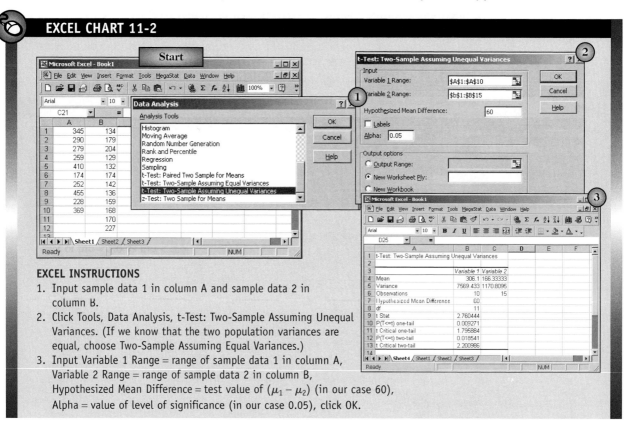

EXCEL INSTRUCTIONS

1. Input sample data 1 in column A and sample data 2 in column B.
2. Click Tools, Data Analysis, t-Test: Two-Sample Assuming Unequal Variances. (If we know that the two population variances are equal, choose Two-Sample Assuming Equal Variances.)
3. Input Variable 1 Range = range of sample data 1 in column A, Variable 2 Range = range of sample data 2 in column B, Hypothesized Mean Difference = test value of $(\mu_1 - \mu_2)$ (in our case 60), Alpha = value of level of significance (in our case 0.05), click OK.

In our example, the t value is positive (2.76). Since this is an upper-tailed (right-tailed) test, the *P*-value equals the value $P(T <= t)$ *one-tail in the output, which equals approximately* 0.0093. This is the same, (up to rounding) as the *P*-value in the Minitab output (= 0.01).

We could also obtain a solution by using MegaStat in Excel, by choosing *Hypothesis Tests* and *Compare Two Independent Groups....*

THE CASE WHEN $\sigma_1^2 = \sigma_2^2 = \sigma^2$

In certain situations, the two populations under consideration are known to have the same variance (that is, $\sigma_1^2 = \sigma_2^2 = \sigma^2$). In this case, Formula 11-3 for the standard deviation of $(\bar{X}_1 - \bar{X}_2)$ reduces to:

$$\sigma_{(\bar{X}_1 - \bar{X}_2)} = \sqrt{\sigma^2 \left(\frac{1}{n_1} + \frac{1}{n_2} \right)} \qquad \text{11-7}$$

If the value of σ^2 is unknown, then we replace it by, what is called its **pooled estimator**, S_p^2, defined as:

| **Pooled Estimator of Variance** | $S_p^2 = \dfrac{(n_1 - 1)S_1^2 + (n_2 - 1)S_2^2}{(n_1 + n_2 - 2)}$ | **11-8** |

If each of the two populations is normally distributed, then,

$$T = \left(\frac{(\bar{X}_1 - \bar{X}_2) - (\mu_1 - \mu_2)}{\sqrt{S_p^2 \left(\frac{1}{n_1} + \frac{1}{n_2} \right)}} \right) \qquad \text{11-9}$$

follows Student's t distribution[10] with degrees of freedom $df = (n_1 + n_2 - 2)$.

Hence, in this case, a good choice of a test statistic is

$$\left(\frac{(\bar{X}_1 - \bar{X}_2) - d_0}{\sqrt{S_p^2 \left(\frac{1}{n_1} + \frac{1}{n_2} \right)}} \right) \qquad \text{11-10}$$

Here, we assume that the null hypothesis is of the form

$$H_0: \mu_1 - \mu_2 = d_0; \quad \text{or} \quad H_0: \mu_1 - \mu_2 \leq d_0; \quad \text{or} \quad H_0: \mu_1 - \mu_2 \geq d_0.$$

For example, in the housing problem considered above, the value of d_0 is 60.

We summarize below the different choices of a test statistic and the corresponding type of test. (Again, we assume that the null hypothesis is of one of the three forms mentioned above.)

Case	Test statistic	Type of Test	Decision rule
(i) The population standard deviations are known	$\left(\dfrac{(\bar{X}_1 - \bar{X}_2) - d_0}{\sqrt{\dfrac{\sigma_1^2}{n_1} + \dfrac{\sigma_2^2}{n_2}}} \right)$	If the population distributions are normal, then the test statistic is a Z statistic, and the test is a Z test. Suppose the population distributions are approximately normal or the sample sizes are large. Then the above test statistic is approximately a Z statistic and we treat the test as a Z test.	*Upper-tailed Z test:* Reject H_0 if the computed z value is greater than z_α. *Lower-tailed Z test:* Reject H_0 if the computed z value is less than $-z_\alpha$. *Two-tailed Z test:* Reject H_0 if the computed z value is less than $-z_{\alpha/2}$ or if it is greater than $z_{\alpha/2}$.
(ii) We know that $\sigma_1^2 = \sigma_2^2 = \sigma^2$. But value of σ^2 is unknown	$\left(\dfrac{(\bar{X}_1 - \bar{X}_2) - d_0}{\sqrt{S_p^2 \left(\dfrac{1}{n_1} + \dfrac{1}{n_2} \right)}} \right)$	If the population distributions are normal, then when H_0 is true, the test statistic has a t distribution with $df = (n_1 + n_2 - 2)$. Hence, this is a t statistic and the test is a t test.	*Upper-tailed t test:* Reject H_0 if the computed t value is greater than t_α. *Lower-tailed t test:* Reject H_0 if the computed t value is less than $-t_\alpha$.
(iii) $\sigma_1^2 \neq \sigma_2^2$; and their values are unknown	$\left(\dfrac{(\bar{X}_1 - \bar{X}_2) - d_0}{\sqrt{\dfrac{S_1^2}{n_1} + \dfrac{S_2^2}{n_2}}} \right)$	If the population distributions are normal then, under H_0, this test statistic has *approximately* t distribution with degrees of freedom given by Formula 11-6. Hence, this is approximately a t statistic and we treat the test as a t test.	*Two-tailed t test:* Reject H_0 if the computed t value is less than $-t_{\alpha/2}$ or if it is greater than $t_{\alpha/2}$. (In case (ii) $df = (n_1 + n_2 - 2)$. In case (iii), the value of df is given by Formula 11-6.)

As we pointed out in Chapter 9, the Student's t distribution is fairly robust. That is, it serves as a good approximation to the distribution of the test statistic in cases (ii) and (iii), even if the population distributions are non-normal (provided, of course, they are not too non-normal).

It should be noted that for a very large value of degrees of freedom, t distribution is almost the same as the Z distribution.

■ SELF-REVIEW 11-1

Owens' Lawn Care manufactures and assembles lawn mowers, which are shipped to dealers all over the country. Dr. Nair has developed a new procedure for mounting the engine on the frame of the lawn mower. He claims that the mean time to mount the engine on the frame using the new procedure is less than that using the existing procedure. The variances of the mounting times, using the two procedures are approximately the same. To test whether the new procedure is faster, it was decided to conduct a time and motion study. A sample of five employees was timed using the existing procedure, and an independent sample of six employees was timed using the new procedure. The results, in minutes, are shown below.

Existing Procedure   5   4   9   7   5

New Procedure   3   7   4   8   5   4

Can we conclude, at the 0.10 significance level, that Dr. Nair's claim is correct? Assume that the populations are approximately normally distributed.

CONFIDENCE INTERVALS FOR THE DIFFERENCE BETWEEN TWO POPULATION MEANS

Let us continue with the problem regarding demand by the employees of the East Vancouver plant of a multinational company for an income differential. Based on the result of the test of hypothesis, management of the company has decided to accept the employees' claim, and offer an income differential to employees in their East Vancouver plant. To decide on the value of the income differential, however, they need a confidence interval estimate of the difference between the mean values of prices of single-family houses for sale at the two locations.

Case (i): Values of σ_1 and σ_2 are known.	if the two populations are normally distributed or the sample sizes are large, then a $(1 - \alpha)$ confidence interval for $(\mu_1 - \mu_2)$ is given by $$(\bar{X}_1 - \bar{X}_2) \pm z_{\alpha/2}\sqrt{\frac{\sigma_1^2}{n_1} + \frac{\sigma_2^2}{n_2}}.$$
Case (ii): $\sigma_1^2 = \sigma_2^2 = \sigma^2$. But the value of σ is unknown	if the populations are normally distributed, then a $(1 - \alpha)$ confidence interval for $(\mu_1 - \mu_2)$ is given by $$(\bar{X}_1 - \bar{X}_2) \pm t_{\alpha/2}\sqrt{S_p^2\left(\frac{1}{n_1} + \frac{1}{n_2}\right)}.$$ The t distribution has $(n_1 + n_2 - 2)$ degrees of freedom.
Case (iii): $\sigma_1^2 \neq \sigma_2^2$; and their values are unknown	if the populations are normally distributed, then an *approximate* $(1 - \alpha)$ confidence interval for $(\mu_1 - \mu_2)$ is given by $$(\bar{X}_1 - \bar{X}_2) \pm t_{\alpha/2}\sqrt{\left(\frac{S_1^2}{n_1} + \frac{S_2^2}{n_2}\right)}.$$ The degrees of freedom of the t distribution are given by Formula 11-6.

Using the results discussed above, regarding the sampling distribution of the difference between the two sample means, and proceeding the same way as in Sections 9.4 and 9.6, we get the expressions for confidence intervals for $(\mu_1 - \mu_2)$, the difference between the two population means. These are given in the table at the bottom of page 469. Here, S_1 and S_2 are the sample standard deviations of the two samples, and S_p is as given in Formula 11-8.

Example 11-2

Reconsider the previous example about the difference between the mean values of prices of houses on sale in East Vancouver and Oshawa, Ontario. The management of the company wants to obtain a 95 percent confidence interval estimate for the difference in mean values of prices of single-family houses for sale at the two locations. Using the sample data in the previous example, obtain a 95 percent confidence interval for the difference in population means. Interpret the result.

Solution

Since the population distributions are approximately normal, and no information is available about the values of the population standard deviations, we shall use the confidence interval in case (iii) in the above table.

In the previous example, we have already calculated:

$$\bar{x}_1 = 306.1; \; \bar{x}_2 = 166.3; \; s_1 = 87.0; \; s_2 = 34.2; \; df = 10.$$
$$\alpha = (1 - 0.95) = 0.05. \text{ For } df = 10, \; t_{\alpha/2} = t_{0.025} = 2.228.$$

Hence, a 95 percent confidence interval estimate for $(\mu_1 - \mu_2)$ is:

$$(\bar{x}_1 - \bar{x}_2) \pm t_{\alpha/2} \sqrt{\left(\frac{s_1^2}{n_1} + \frac{s_2^2}{n_2} \right)} = (306.1 - 166.3)$$

$$\pm 2.228 \sqrt{\left(\frac{(87.0)^2}{10} + \frac{(34.2)^2}{15} \right)} = (75.4, \, 204.2)$$

This interval estimate has the following interpretation. The technique we have used, has a probability of approximately 0.95 of producing an interval containing the true value of the difference in population means, $(\mu_1 - \mu_2)$. The interval (75.4, 204.2), we obtained, may or may not contain the value of $(\mu_1 - \mu_2)$. However, given the high confidence level (approx. 0.95), it is reasonable to assume that $(\mu_1 - \mu_2)$ lies in the interval.

We see that the interval estimate (75.4, 204.2) is very wide. If a narrower confidence interval is desired, we shall have to choose larger samples.

COMPUTER SOLUTION

We can obtain the required confidence interval estimate using Minitab and Excel.

For Minitab, the instructions are the same as those for a 2-sample t test, given in Chart 11-1, except that under "Alternative," input "not equal." The Minitab output follows.

Two-Sample T-Test and CI: C1, C2
Two-sample T for C1 vs C2

	N	Mean	StDev	SE Mean
C1	10	306.1	87.0	28.0
C2	15	166.3	34.2	8.8

Difference = **mu C1 – mu C2**
Estimate for difference: 139.8
95% CI for difference: (75.4, 204.2)
T-Test of difference = 60 (vs not =): T-Value = 2.76, P-Value = 0.020 df = 10

It may be noted that the 95 percent confidence interval estimate in the Minitab output is the same as the one we computed manually.

Data Analysis, under *Tools* in Excel does not have a macro for directly computing the confidence interval estimate for the difference in values of two population means. However, using MegaStat, we can obtain a 90%, 95%, or 99% confidence interval estimate by choosing *Hypothesis Tests*, *Compare Two Independent Groups ...*, inputting data, and choosing type of test, *Display*, and desired confidence level.

■ SELF-REVIEW 11-2

Consider the problem in Self-Review 11-1. Obtain a 90 percent confidence interval for the difference between the population means of times to mount the engines on the frames, using the existing procedure and using Dr. Nair's procedure.

EXERCISES 11-1 TO 11-10

In each of the exercises 11-1 to 11-10, assume that the population distributions are approximately normal.

11-1. A sample of 40 observations is selected from one population. The sample mean is 102 and the sample standard deviation is 5. A sample of 50 observations is selected independently from a second population. The sample mean is 99 and the sample standard deviation is 6. Can we conclude at the 0.01 significance level, that the two population means are different?

11-2. A sample of 65 observations is selected from one population. The sample mean is 2.67 and the sample standard deviation is 0.75. A sample of 50 observations is selected independently from a second population. The sample mean is 2.59 and the sample standard deviation is 0.66. Can we conclude, at the 0.05 significance level, that the mean of the first population is greater?

For exercises 11-3 and 11-4, assume that the population variances are equal.

11-3. A random sample of 10 observations from a population revealed a sample mean of 23 and a sample standard deviation of 4. An independent random sample of 8 observations from a second population revealed a sample mean of 26 and a sample standard deviation of 5. Can we conclude at the 0.05 significance level, that there is a difference in the population means?

11-4. A random sample of 15 observations from a population revealed a sample mean of 350 and a sample standard deviation of 12. An independent random sample of 17 observations from a second population revealed a sample mean of 342 and a sample standard deviation of 15. Can we conclude at the 0.1 significance level, that there is a difference in the population means?

11-5. The Gibbs' Baby Food Company wishes to compare the weight gain of infants using their brand versus their competitor's brands. A random sample of 30 babies using the Gibbs' products revealed a mean weight gain of 3.5 kg in the first three months after birth. The sample standard deviation was 1.01 kg. A random sample of 20 babies using the competitor's brand revealed a mean increase in weight of 3.7 kg, with a sample standard deviation of 1.3 kg. At the 0.05 significance level, can we conclude that babies using the Gibbs' brand gained less weight? Compute a 99 percent confidence interval estimate for the population mean additional weight gained by babies using the Gibbs' brand.

11-6. As a part of a study of corporate employees, the Director of Human Resources for PNC wants to compare the distance travelled to work by employees at their office in downtown Edmonton with those in downtown Montreal. A random sample of 35 Edmonton employees showed they travelled a mean of 590 km per month, with a sample standard deviation of 50 km per month. A sample of 40 Montreal employees showed they travelled a mean of 610 km per month, with a sample standard deviation of 40 km per month. At the 0.05 significance level, is there a difference between the mean number of kilometres travelled per month by Edmonton and Montreal employees? Compute a 90 percent confidence interval estimate for the difference between the two population means.

11-7. A financial analyst wants to compare the turnover rates, in percent, for shares of oil-related stocks versus other stocks, such as GE and IBM. She randomly selected 32 oil-related stocks and 49 other stocks. The mean turnover rate of the sample of oil-related stocks was 31.4 percent with a sample standard deviation of 5.1 percent. For the sample of other stocks, the mean rate was computed to be 34.9 percent and the sample standard deviation was 6.7 percent. Is there a significant difference in the turnover rates of the two types of stocks? Use the 0.01 significance level.

11-8. A recent study compared the time spent together by single- and dual-earner couples. Random samples of 15 single-earner and 12 dual-earner couples were selected. According to the records kept by the wives during the study, the mean amount of time spent together watching television among the single-earner couples was 61 minutes per day, with a sample standard deviation of 15.5 minutes. For the dual-earner couples the mean number of minutes spent watching television together was 48.4 minutes, with a sample standard deviation of 18.1 minutes. At the 0.01 significance level, can we conclude that the single-earner couples, on average, spend more time watching television together?

11-9. Random samples of scores on an examination given in Statistics 201 are:

Men	72	69	98	66	85	76	79	80	77
Women	81	67	90	78	81	80	76		

At the 0.01 significance level, is the population mean of grades of the women higher than that of the men? Assume that the population variances are equal.

11-10. Ms. Lisa Monnin is the budget director for the New Process Company. She would like to compare the daily travel expenses for the sales staff and the audit staff. She collected the following sample information.

Sales ($)	131	135	146	165	136	142	
Audit ($)	130	102	129	143	149	120	139

Can she conclude at the 0.1 significance level, that the population mean of daily expenses is greater for the sales staff than the audit staff? Assume that the population variances are equal.

11.2 DIFFERENCE BETWEEN TWO POPULATION MEANS: DEPENDENT SAMPLES

In the previous section, we developed a test for the difference between the means of two populations, based on random samples selected *independently* from the two populations. That is, the sample data collected from one population is in no way related to the sample data collected from the other population.

There are situations in which the data units in the two populations can be matched or paired. That is, every data unit in one population can be paired with a unique data unit in the other population. In such a case, we draw a random sample of pairs of data units. We give some examples below.

- **A "before-and after study"**: We shall illustrate this case with two examples. Suppose we want to show that, by placing speakers in the production area and playing soothing music, we can increase productivity of workers. In this case, the two populations of interest are: the productivity of workers without the music, and the productivity of workers with music. We begin by selecting a random sample of workers and measuring their output without the music. The speakers are then installed in the production area, and we measure the output of the *same* workers again. There is a pair of measurements on each randomly selected worker—before placing the speakers in the production area and after. The measurements are taken, one before and one after, *on the same set of workers*. As a second example, suppose we want to study the effectiveness of a weight-loss program. The two populations of interest are: weights of individuals before starting the program, and weights of individuals after the program. A sample of participants in the study is randomly selected. The weight of each individual in the sample is recorded before starting the program. Each of the participants is then asked to follow the program for a specified duration of time, after which the weight of each individual in the *same* sample is again recorded. The final data contains a paired sample on the two populations: weights before and weights after on the *same set of people*.

- **Matching according to a common characteristic**: Suppose we are interested in comparing the mean one-year percentage return and the mean five-year percentage return on Canadian mutual funds. We can select two independent random samples of Canadian mutual funds, and record one-year percentage return on the first sample, and a five-year percentage return on the second sample. In this case, it is possible that, entirely by chance, one sample may consist of more successful mutual funds than the other sample. Therefore, the corresponding sample data may indicate that the mean percentage return is higher than what it actually is. The problem can be remedied by choosing, randomly, just one sample of mutual funds, and recording for each of these funds, the one-year percentage return, and the five-year percentage return.

Let us denote the pairs in the sample by $(X_{1,1}, X_{2,1})$, $(X_{1,2}, X_{2,2})$, ... , $(X_{1,n}, X_{2,n})$. Here, $\{X_{1,1}, X_{1,2}, ... , X_{1,n}\}$ is the sample data on population 1 and $\{X_{2,1}, X_{2,2}, ... , X_{2,n}\}$ is the sample data on population 2. The two data values in each pair usually have a common characteristic. The two samples are then no longer independent. They are **dependent**, or related.

As another example, suppose a professor at St. Thomas University, Fredericton, believes that the average grade in the course *Introduction to Statistics* received by graduates in Economics is lower than the average grade received by these students in *Introduction to Economics*. The same scale is used in both courses to convert the grade out of 100 to a letter grade. Hence, he has decided to study the difference between μ_1, the mean value of grades (out of 100) in the Statistics course and μ_2, the mean value of grades in the Economics course, of the graduates in Economics. He chose a random sample of n graduates in Economics, and recorded for each student in the sample, his or her grades in both the Statistics and Economics courses. His data thus consists of a pair of grades, one in the Statistics course and one in the Economics course, for each student in the sample. The two values in each pair have a common characteristic: they are the grades of the same student.

Let (X_1, X_2) be a randomly selected pair of data values, where X_1 belongs to population 1 and its pair, X_2, belongs to population 2. Let $D = X_1 - X_2$, the difference between the two values in the pair. Then,

$$E(X_1) = \mu_1; \quad E(X_2) = \mu_2; \quad \text{and} \quad E(D) = \mu_D = \mu_1 - \mu_2 \qquad \textbf{11-11}$$

Hence, instead of studying the difference in mean values of the two populations, we can study the mean value, μ_D, of D. The problem of studying the difference in means of two populations thus reduces to the problem of studying the mean of a single population (D = the difference between the pairs of data values in the two populations). We can use for this, the methods discussed in Chapters 9 and 10.

For the pairs, $(X_{1,1}, X_{2,1})$, $(X_{1,2}, X_{2,2})$, ... , $(X_{1,n}, X_{2,n})$ in the paired sample, let us compute the sample of differences,

$$D_1 = X_{1,1} - X_{2,1}; \; D_2 = X_{1,2} - X_{2,2}; \; ... \; ; \; D_n = X_{1,n} - X_{2,n}$$

Let

$$\bar{D} = \frac{D_1 + \cdots + D_n}{n} \qquad \textbf{11-12}$$

Then,

$$E(\bar{D}) = \mu_D = \mu_1 - \mu_2 \qquad \textbf{11-13}$$

That is, $\bar{D}$ is an unbiased estimator of $\mu_1 - \mu_2$.

Let S_D be the sample standard deviation of the sample $D_1, ... , D_n$.

If the two populations are normally distributed,

The distribution of	$T = \dfrac{\bar{D} - \mu_D}{S_D/\sqrt{n}}$	is Student's t distribution with degrees of freedom, $df = n - 1$.	11-14

HYPOTHESIS TESTING FOR THE DIFFERENCE BETWEEN TWO POPULATION MEANS

Let us continue with the problem regarding the difference between the mean values of grades of students at St. Thomas University in Statistics and Economics courses.

Example 11-3

A professor at St. Thomas University wants to conduct a test of hypothesis to check if there is sufficient evidence that the mean value, μ_1, of grades (out of 100) in *Introduction to Statistics* received by their Economics graduates is lower than the mean value, μ_2, of their grades in *Introduction to Economics*. He randomly selected eleven Economics graduates. Their grades in both courses are recorded below.

Name	Stats	Econ	Name	Stats	Econ
Meena Ahsan	80	75	Rob Penney	70	65
Chun Cheng	75	70	Melody Sexton	83	85
Jan Harvey	75	80	Mary Tan	83	87
Jim Lim	85	90	Cathy Williams	90	95
Sarita Sen	70	75	Darren Young	80	85
Meera Patel	87	90			

Can we conclude, at the 0.05 significance level, that the population mean of the student grades in *Introduction to Statistics* is lower than the population mean of student grades in *Introduction to Economics*? Assume that the populations are approximately normally distributed.

Solution

We shall use the five-step procedure from Chapter 10.

Step 1

Let $D = X_1 - X_2$, represent the difference between grades in Statistics and Economics courses of a randomly selected student. Using Formula 11-13, the null and alternative hypotheses can be written as:

$$H_0: \mu_D \geq 0$$
$$H_1: \mu_D < 0$$

Step 2

We have selected $\alpha = 0.05$.

Step 3

We shall use $\dfrac{\bar{D} - 0}{S_D/\sqrt{n}} = \dfrac{\bar{D}}{S_D/\sqrt{11}}$ as the test statistic.

Step 4

The two populations are approximately normally distributed. Hence, when $\mu_D = 0$, the test statistic has approximately Student's t distribution with degrees of freedom $df = (n - 1) = 10$. Hence, this is approximately a t statistic and our test is approximately a lower-tailed t test involving the mean of a single population, D. This is the same as the t test for the mean of a single population discussed in Section 10.9.) Our decision rule is: *reject H_0 if the computed t value is less than* $-t_\alpha = -t_{0.05} = -1.812$.

Step 5   Let us first compute the sample values of $D = X_1 - X_2$.

Statistics	80	75	75	85	70	87	70	83	83	90	80
Economics	75	70	80	90	75	90	65	85	87	95	85
Difference (d)	5	5	-5	-5	-5	-3	5	-2	-4	-5	-5

$$\bar{d} = \frac{5 + \cdots - 5}{11} = -1.73; \quad s_D = \sqrt{\frac{(5+1.73)^2 + \cdots + (-5+1.73)^2}{10}} = 4.43$$

$$t = \frac{\bar{d}}{s_D/\sqrt{11}} = \frac{-1.73}{4.43/\sqrt{11}} = -1.29.$$

The computed t value is greater than the critical value, -1.812. Hence, we do *not* have sufficient evidence, at $\alpha = 0.05$, to reject H_0. There is *insufficient* evidence, at $\alpha = 0.05$, to accept the statement that the mean grade of the Economics graduates in *Introduction to Statistics* is less than their mean grade in *Introduction to Economics*.

We give in Charts 11-3 and 11-4 Minitab and Excel instructions and output for the above problem.

The Minitab output gives t value $= -1.29$, which is the same as the one we computed by hand. In addition, the Minitab output gives P-value $= 0.112$. Since the P-value is greater than $\alpha = 0.05$, our decision based on P-value would be: do *not* reject H_0. This is the same as the decision based on the rejection region.

The computed value of the t statistic in the Excel output is -1.29. This is the same (rounding up) as the one obtained manually and also using Minitab.

Also, the P-value in the MegaStat output is 0.1125, which is almost the same as the one in Minitab output. The small difference is due to rounding.

MINITAB CHART 11-3

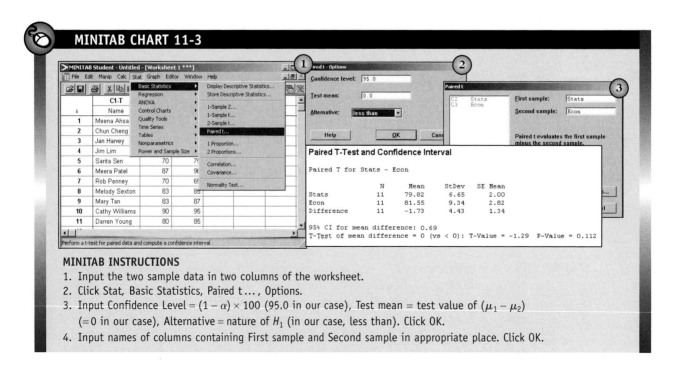

MINITAB INSTRUCTIONS
1. Input the two sample data in two columns of the worksheet.
2. Click Stat, Basic Statistics, Paired t..., Options.
3. Input Confidence Level $= (1 - \alpha) \times 100$ (95.0 in our case), Test mean $=$ test value of $(\mu_1 - \mu_2)$
   ($= 0$ in our case), Alternative $=$ nature of H_1 (in our case, less than). Click OK.
4. Input names of columns containing First sample and Second sample in appropriate place. Click OK.

EXCEL CHART 11-4

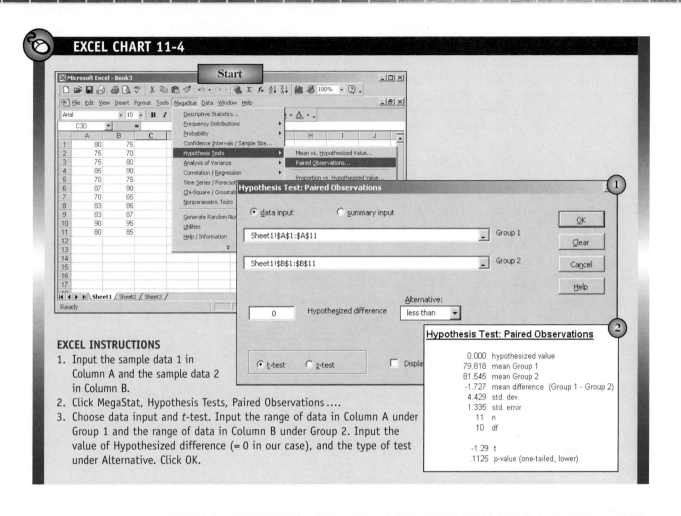

EXCEL INSTRUCTIONS
1. Input the sample data 1 in Column A and the sample data 2 in Column B.
2. Click MegaStat, Hypothesis Tests, Paired Observations....
3. Choose data input and t-test. Input the range of data in Column A under Group 1 and the range of data in Column B under Group 2. Input the value of Hypothesized difference (= 0 in our case), and the type of test under Alternative. Click OK.

■ SELF-REVIEW 11-3

An economist believes that the mean value of weekly percentage increase in BCE stock price in the year 2000 was higher than the weekly percentage increase in TSE 300 index. To check if there is significant evidence in support of his belief, he randomly selected eight weeks in the year 2000 and recorded percentage increases in the TSE 300 index and BCE stock price during these weeks. The data is recorded below.

| TSE 300 | −3.8 | −7.5 | −1.5 | −3.1 | −0.9 | −1.4 | 2.9 | 1.7 |
| BCE | 8.3 | −6.5 | −1.3 | 1.8 | 12.9 | 4.0 | 5.1 | 7.2 |

Can we conclude at $\alpha = 0.05$ that the economist's belief is correct? Assume that the population distributions are approximately normal.

CONFIDENCE INTERVALS FOR THE DIFFERENCE BETWEEN TWO POPULATION MEANS

We have already seen in the previous subsection that matching of the data values in the two populations allows us to reduce the study of $(\mu_1 - \mu_2)$, (that is, the difference in values of the means of two populations) to the study of the mean $\mu_D (= \mu_1 - \mu_2)$

of only one population, D. Recall that values of D are differences between the matched values of the two populations. A $(1 - \alpha)$ confidence interval for $(\mu_1 - \mu_2) = \mu_D$ is therefore obtained from Formula 9-16 by replacing $\bar{X}$ and S by $\bar{D}$ and S_D. Thus,

> *if a matched pair sample of size n is selected from two normally distributed populations, and $\bar{D}$ is the mean value of differences between matched pairs in the sample, then a $(1 - \alpha)$ confidence interval for $(\mu_1 - \mu_2) = \mu_D$ is given by*

$(1 - \alpha)$ Confidence Interval for $\mu_{\hat{D}}$	$\bar{D} \pm t_{\alpha/2}\, S_D / \sqrt{n}$	**11-15**

Example 11-4

Let us continue with the previous example regarding the difference between the mean values of grades in the Statistics course and in the Economics course received by Economics graduates at St. Thomas University. The professor wants to estimate the value of difference between the two population means. Using the sample data in the previous example, obtain a 99 percent confidence interval estimate for the difference in the two means.

Solution

We have already calculated in the previous example, $\bar{d} = -1.73$, $s_D = 4.43$. $\alpha = (1 - 0.99) = 0.01$. For $df = (n - 1) = 10$, we have $t_{\alpha/2} = t_{0.005} = 3.169$. Hence, using Formula 11-15, we get a 99 percent confidence interval estimate of

$$-1.73 \pm (3.169)(4.43)/\sqrt{11} = (-5.9628, 2.5028).$$

The confidence interval estimate can be obtained using Excel or Minitab by finding the sample values of differences, D, and using the instructions in Charts 9-8 and 9-9.

■ SELF-REVIEW 11-4

Consider the problem in Self-Review 11-3. Using the matched pair data provided, obtain a 95 percent confidence interval estimate for the difference between the average percentage weekly changes in TSE 300 index and the BCE stock prices during the year 2000.

11.3 ADVANTAGES AND DISADVANTAGES OF USING A MATCHED PAIR SAMPLE

In certain cases, such as the study of effectiveness of a weight-loss program, the matched pair sample is obviously more suitable and easier to collect. In some cases, however, we have a choice. (For example, in the case of the study of the effect of music on productivity, we could choose different, independent random samples of workers before and after the speakers are installed.) In such cases, by choosing a proper matching criterion, the power of the test (that is, the probability of accepting a true alternative hypothesis) can be increased, for the same value of α (significance level of the test).

To see this, let us go back to the problem of comparing the mean values of grades of Economics graduates in Statistics and Economics courses at St. Thomas University.

The null and alternative hypotheses are:

H_0: $\mu_1 - \mu_2 \geq 0$
H_1: $\mu_1 - \mu_2 < 0$

Suppose we select a random sample of 11 Economics graduates, and record their grades only in Statistics; and we *independently*, choose another sample of 11 Economics graduates, and record their grades in Economics. The two independent samples are recorded below.

| Statistics | 83 | 71 | 78 | 86 | 81 | 71 | 88 | 82 | 85 | 90 | 78 |
| Economics | 85 | 73 | 72 | 86 | 91 | 92 | 63 | 93 | 87 | 85 | 89 |

The Excel output of the test of hypothesis is given below.

t TEST: TWO-SAMPLE ASSUMING UNEQUAL VARIANCES		
	Variable 1	Variable 2
Mean	81.18182	83.27273
Variance	39.36364	93.41818
Observations	11	11
Hypothesized Mean Difference	0	
df	17	
t Stat	-0.60181	
$P(T <= t)$ One-Tail	0.27762	
t Critical One-Tail	1.739606	
$P(T <= t)$ Two-Tail	0.55524	
t Critical Two-Tail	2.109819	

We observe the following:

- The value of the t statistic in the case of independent samples ($= -0.6018$) is significantly closer to zero than in the case of the matched pair sample ($= -1.29$).

  This is usually the case when the pairing criterion leads to a high positive correlation between the paired samples. (If the grade of a student is high in the Statistics course, then most likely the student is good and therefore his or her grade in the Economics course is likely to be high. On the other hand, if a student received a low grade in the Statistics course, then it is quite likely that he or she will receive a low grade in the Economics course. We say in this case that the paired samples are positively correlated. We shall study the concept of correlation between two variables in detail in Chapter 13.) In general, in the case of a positive correlation between the matched samples, the standard deviation of $\bar{D}$ is smaller than the standard deviation in Formula 11-3 of the random variable $(\bar{X}_1 - \bar{X}_2)$ when independent samples are used. The value of the t statistic in the case of a matched-pair sample thus tends to be further away from zero than that in the case of independent samples. As a result, when H_1 is true, the probability of the computed t value lying in the rejection region tends to be higher in the case of a matched pair sample.

- The critical value in the case of an independent sample ($= -1.739$) is closer to zero than that in the case of matched pair samples ($= -1.81$). This is because the degrees of freedom of the t statistic in the case of a matched pair sample is $(n - 1) = 10$, while that in the case of independent samples is much larger ($= 17$). This contributes towards a decrease in the probability of rejection of H_0, when H_1 is true.

- In our example, the positive correlation is high enough to dominate the effect of the decrease in degrees of freedom. Hence, the resultant probability of rejection of H_0, when H_1 is true, is higher in the case of a matched pair sample.

We conclude the following from this:

> It is advantageous to use a matched pair sample only when the pairing is done in such a way that the corresponding paired samples have high positive correlation. (That is, large values have a higher chance of being paired with large values, and small values have a higher chance of having small partners.)
>
> If the paired samples do not have sufficiently large positive correlation, then the resultant test is likely to be weaker than the one with independent samples, due to a smaller value (= $(n-1)$) of degrees of freedom of the test statistic.

EXERCISES 11-11 TO 11-16

In each of the following, assume that the population distributions are approximately normal.

11-11. The following sample information shows the number of defective units produced on the day shift and the afternoon shift for a sample of four days last month.

	Day			
	1	2	3	4
Day Shift	10	12	15	19
Afternoon Shift	8	9	12	15

At the 0.05 significance level, can we conclude that, last month, the population mean of the number of defective units produced on the afternoon shift was less than that of the day shift?

11-12. The following paired observations show the number of traffic citations given for speeding by RCMP officers Dhondt and Meredith for the last five months.

	Month				
	May	June	July	August	September
Officer Dhondt	30	22	25	19	26
Officer Meredith	26	19	20	15	19

At the 0.05 significance level, can we conclude that there is a difference in the population means of the number of citations given by the two officers?

11-13. A survey is conducted at North Atlantic University to measure the effect of the change in environment on international students. One of the facets of the study is a comparison of student weights upon arrival on campus with weights one year later. A random sample of 11 international students is chosen for the study.

Name	Weight (in kg)		Name	Weight (in kg)	
	On Arrival	One Year Later		On Arrival	One Year Later
Nassar	56	65	Farouk	68	69
Hu	71	71	Thatcher	80	84
Obie	45	44	Sambul	91	95
Silverman	86	96	Onassis	82	82
Mehta	47	53	Pierre	116	122
Joshi	62	61			

Can we conclude, at the 0.01 significance level, that there is, on average, an increase in weight during the first year? Using the same sample data, obtain a 95 percent confidence interval estimate for the mean increase in weight during the first year.

11-14. The management of Discount Furniture, a chain of discount furniture stores, designed an incentive plan for salespeople. To evaluate this innovative plan, 12 salespeople were selected at random, and their weekly incomes before and after the plan were recorded.

Salesperson	Before	After	Salesperson	Before	After
Sid Mahone	$320	$340	Peg Mancuso	$625	$631
Carol Quick	290	285	Anita Loma	560	560
Ashok Varde	421	475	John Cuso	360	365
Andy Jones	510	510	Carl Utz	431	431
Jean Sloan	210	210	A.S. Kushner	506	525
Fan Tseng	402	500	Fern Lawton	505	619

Can we conclude that there was a significant increase in the typical salesperson's weekly income due to the innovative incentive plan? Use the 0.05 significance level. Using the same sample data, obtain a 90 percent confidence interval estimate for the increase in the typical salesperson's weekly income due to the plan.

11-15. Harry Hutchings is the owner of Hutchings' Weight Lifting Clinic. He claims that by taking a special vitamin, a weight lifter can increase his strength. Ten student athletes are randomly selected and given a test of strength using the standard bench press. After two weeks of regular training, supplemented with the vitamin, they are tested again. The results are shown below.

Name	Amount Pressed	
	Before	After
Evie Gorky	86	89
Bob Mack	115	114
Lou Brandon	156	156
Karl Unger	96	97
Sue Koontz	52	51
Pat O'Leary	57	58
Kim Dennis	85	87
Connie Kaye	53	54
Tom Dama	89	88
Maxine Sims	57	56

Can we conclude, at the 0.01 significance level, that the special vitamin increased the strength of the student athletes?

11-16. The federal government recently granted funds for a special program designed to reduce crime in high-crime areas. A study of the results of the program in eight high-crime areas of Toronto, Ontario, yielded the following data.

				Number of Crimes by Area				
	A	B	C	D	E	F	G	H
Before	14	7	4	5	17	12	8	9
After	2	7	3	6	8	13	3	5

Has there been a decrease in the number of crimes since the inauguration of the program? Use the 0.01 significance level.

11.4 DIFFERENCE BETWEEN TWO POPULATION PROPORTIONS

In the previous three sections, we discussed problems of statistical inference about the difference in values of two population means. In a significant number of real-world problems, the population data is qualitative. In such a case, we are interested in estimating or testing hypothesis about the fraction of population data units that have a specific value. We can replace each data value in the population by a "1" if the current value is the one we desire, and by "0" if the value is not the one we desire. We are then interested in estimating, or testing, the hypothesis about the fraction of data units that have a value "1." (We call this the *population proportion*.) In Chapters 9 and 10, we discussed procedures for estimation and hypothesis testing of the value of a single population proportion. In this section, we shall develop procedures for the interval estimation of, and testing hypotheses about the difference in values of two population proportions. Here are some examples:

- General Motors is considering a new design for the Pontiac Grand Am. The management wishes to know if there is a difference in the proportion of potential buyers under 30 years of age, who like the new design, and those over 60 years of age, who like the design.
- Air Canada is investigating the fear of flying among adults after the World Trade Center attack on September 11, 2001. Specifically, they want to know if there is a difference in the proportions of men and women who are fearful of flying.

In each of the above cases, every population item can be classified as a "1" or a "0." For example, in the Grand Am case, each potential buyer is assigned a value of "1" if he or she "likes the new design" and a "0" if the buyer "does not like the new design."

We wish to compare the proportion, p_1, of "1"s in the first population, with the proportion, p_2, of "1"s in the second population. We collect independent samples from the two populations, and compute the sample proportions, $\hat{p}_1 = \dfrac{X_1}{n_1}$ and $\hat{p}_2 = \dfrac{X_2}{n_2}$. Here, X_1 and X_2 are the number of data units in the respective samples with a value of "1." Based on these, we estimate, and test hypotheses about, the difference in values of the two population proportions.

HYPOTHESIS TESTING FOR THE DIFFERENCE BETWEEN TWO POPULATION PROPORTIONS

The following example will illustrate the two-independent-sample test for difference in population proportions.

Example 11-5

The Manelli Perfume Company recently developed a new fragrance that they plan to market under the name Heavenly. The sales department at Manelli is particularly interested in the difference between the proportion of younger women and the proportion of older women who would like the new fragrance *well enough to purchase it*. They have decided to select, *independently*, random samples from the population of young women, and the population of older women. Each woman in the selected sample will be asked to smell Heavenly and indicate whether she likes the fragrance well enough to purchase the bottle. Design a test of hypothesis to test whether there is significant evidence that the two population proportions are different. Use a 0.05 level of significance.

Solution

We will use the usual five-step hypothesis testing procedure.

Step 1

We designate by p_1, the *population* proportion of younger women who would purchase Heavenly, and by p_2, the *population* proportion of older women who would purchase it. The null and alternative hypotheses are:

$$H_0: p_1 - p_2 = 0$$
$$H_1: p_1 - p_2 \neq 0$$

Step 2

We have selected the 0.05 level of significance.

Step 3

For the independent samples selected from the two populations, let us define the sample proportions, $\hat{p}_1 = \dfrac{X_1}{n_1}$ and $\hat{p}_2 = \dfrac{X_2}{n_2}$. Here, X_1 and X_2 are the number of data units in the respective samples with a value of "1". Using the same argument as the one used in deriving formulae 11-1 to 11-4, we get the following[11]:

$$E(\hat{p}_1 - \hat{p}_2) = p_1 - p_2 \qquad \textbf{11-16}$$

Thus, $(\hat{p}_1 - \hat{p}_2)$ **is an unbiased estimator of** $(p_1 - p_2)$.

| **Variance of $(\hat{p}_1 - \hat{p}_2)$** | $V(\hat{p}_1 - \hat{p}_2) = \dfrac{p_1(1 - p_1)}{n_1} + \dfrac{p_2(1 - p_2)}{n_2}$ | **11-17** |

The values p_1 and p_2 are unknown. However, under the null hypothesis, we have $p_1 = p_2 =$ say p. Substituting this in 11-17, we get:

$$V(\hat{p}_1 - \hat{p}_2) = p(1 - p)\left(\frac{1}{n_1} + \frac{1}{n_2}\right) \qquad \textbf{11-18}$$

Since the value of p is unknown, we substitute it by the following unbiased estimator, $\hat{p}$, called the **pooled estimator**.

| **Pooled estimator of p** | $\hat{p} = \dfrac{X_1 + X_2}{n_1 + n_2}$ | **11-19** |

This gives us the standardized random variable:

$$\frac{(\hat{p}_1 - \hat{p}_2)}{\sqrt{\hat{p}(1-\hat{p})\left(\dfrac{1}{n_1} + \dfrac{1}{n_2}\right)}}$$

11-20

We shall use Formula 11-20 as our test statistic.

Step 4 This is a two-tailed test. We assume that the sample sizes are large enough so that the distribution of the test statistic can be approximated by the standard normal distribution. Hence, this is approximately a two-tailed Z test. The critical values are $-z_{\alpha/2} = -z_{0.025} = -1.96$, and $z_{\alpha/2} = z_{0.025} = 1.96$. We shall reject the null hypothesis if the computed z value is less than -1.96 or if it is greater than 1.96.

Step 5 We now select two independent samples and make a decision. Suppose a random sample of 100 younger women revealed that 20 liked the Heavenly fragrance well enough to purchase it. Similarly, a sample of 200 older women revealed that 100 liked the fragrance well enough to make a purchase. Then,

$$\hat{p}_1 = \frac{x_1}{n_1} = \frac{20}{100} = 0.20 \qquad \hat{p}_2 = \frac{x_2}{n_2} = \frac{100}{200} = 0.50$$

$n_1 p_1 = 20$, $n_1(1 - p_1) = 80$, $n_2 p_2 = 100$, and $n_2(1 - p_2) = 100$.

Each one of these is greater than 5. Hence n_1 and n_2 are large enough to assume the normality of the test statistic under H_0.

We combine or pool the sample proportions, using Formula 11-19.

$$\hat{p} = \frac{x_1 + x_2}{n_1 + n_2} = \frac{20 + 100}{100 + 200} = 0.40$$

The value of the test statistic is:

$$z = \frac{\hat{p}_1 - \hat{p}_2}{\sqrt{\hat{p}(1-\hat{p})\left(\dfrac{1}{n_1} + \dfrac{1}{n_2}\right)}} = \frac{0.2 - 0.5}{\sqrt{0.4(1 - 0.4)\left(\dfrac{1}{100} + \dfrac{1}{200}\right)}} = -5.00$$

The computed z value of -5.00 is in the area of rejection. That is, it is to the left of -1.96. Therefore, there is sufficient evidence, at the 0.05 significance level, to reject the null hypothesis, that is, to conclude that the two population proportions are different.

To find the P-value, we go to the Z table and look for α such that $z_{\alpha} = 5.00$. That is, we look for $P(Z > 5)$. The largest value of z reported is 3.09 with a corresponding probability of 0.4990. So the probability of finding a z value greater than 5.00 is virtually zero. So we report that the P-value is almost 0.

In the above example, the null hypothesis was H_0: $p_1 - p_2 = 0$. In general, the null hypothesis may be of the form H_0: $p_1 - p_2 = p_d$; or H_0: $p_1 - p_2 \leq p_d$; or H_0: $p_1 - p_2 \geq p_d$, for some given constant p_d.

We summarize the different cases and the corresponding choice of a test statistic in the table below:

Case (i): $p_d \neq 0$	Test statistic $= \dfrac{(\hat{p}_1 - \hat{p}_2) - p_d}{\sqrt{\dfrac{\hat{p}_1(1 - \hat{p}_1)}{n_1} + \dfrac{\hat{p}_2(1 - \hat{p}_2)}{n_2}}}$
Case (ii): $p_d = 0$	Test statistic $= \dfrac{(\hat{p}_1 - \hat{p}_2)}{\sqrt{\hat{p}(1 - \hat{p})\left(\dfrac{1}{n_1} + \dfrac{1}{n_2}\right)}}$

We assume that the sample size is large enough, so that when $(p_1 - p_2) = p_d$, the test statistic can be approximated by the standard normal variable, Z. Our test can then be approximated by the Z test. The decision rule is the same as that for the Z test given in Chapter 10 on page 430.

■ SELF-REVIEW 11-5

Of the 150 adults who tried a new peach-flavoured peppermint patty, 87 rated it excellent. Of the 200 children sampled, 123 rated it excellent. Using a 0.10 level of significance, can we conclude that there is a difference in the proportion of adults and of children who rate the new flavour excellent?

CONFIDENCE INTERVALS FOR THE DIFFERENCE BETWEEN TWO POPULATION PROPORTIONS

Again, we assume that the sample sizes are large enough for the random variable $(\hat{P}_1 - \hat{P}_2)$ to be approximately normally distributed. Substituting p_1 by $\hat{p}_1$, and p_2 by $\hat{p}_2$ in Formula 11-17 for the variance of $(\hat{P}_1 - \hat{P}_2)$, we get the following *approximate* $(1 - \alpha)$ *confidence interval for* $(p_1 - p_2)$.

$(1 - \alpha)$ Confidence Interval for $(p_1 - p_2)$	$(\hat{p}_1 - \hat{p}_2) \pm z_{\alpha/2}\sqrt{\dfrac{\hat{p}_1(1 - \hat{p}_1)}{n_1} + \dfrac{\hat{p}_2(1 - \hat{p}_2)}{n_2}}$	**11-21**

Example 11-6

Consider the previous example regarding the new perfume, Heavenly, developed by the Manelli Perfume Company. Out of a random sample of 100 younger women, 20 liked the Heavenly fragrance, and out of an independently selected random sample of 200 older women, 100 liked the fragrance. Compute a 90 percent confidence interval estimate for the difference in the population proportions of younger and older women who like the fragrance.

Solution

From the sample data,

$$\hat{p}_1 = \frac{x_1}{n_1} = \frac{20}{100} = 0.2; \quad \hat{p}_2 = \frac{100}{200} = 0.5$$

As we verified in the previous example, the values of n_1 and n_2 are large enough to assume normality.

Using Formula 11-21, we get the following 90 percent confidence interval estimate for $p_1 - p_2$:

$$(\hat{p}_1 - \hat{p}_2) \pm z_{\alpha/2} \sqrt{\frac{\hat{p}_1(1 - \hat{p}_2)}{n_1} + \frac{\hat{p}_2(1 - \hat{p}_2)}{n_2}}$$

$$= (0.2 - 0.5) \pm 1.645 \sqrt{\frac{0.2(0.8)}{100} + \frac{0.5(0.5)}{200}} = (-0.3878, -0.2122)$$

■ SELF-REVIEW 11-6

Consider the problem in Self-Review 11-5. Find a 95 percent confidence interval estimate for the difference in population proportions of adults and children who rate the new flavour of the peppermint patty as excellent.

EXERCISES 11-17 TO 11-21

11-17. In a random sample of 100 observations drawn from a population, the number of "1"s $(= x_1)$ is 70. In an independent random sample of 150 observations drawn from a second population, the number of "1"s $(= x_2)$ is 90. Can we conclude, at the 0.05 significance level, that the proportion, p_1, of "1"s in the first population is larger than the proportion, p_2, in the second population? Obtain a 98 percent confidence interval estimate for $(p_1 - p_2)$.

11-18. In a random sample of 200 observations drawn from a population, the number of "1"s $(= x_1)$ is 170. In an independent random sample of 150 observations from the second population, the number of "1"s $(= x_2)$ is 110. Can we conclude, at the 0.05 significance level, that the values of p_1 and p_2, the proportions of "1"s in the first and second population, respectively, are not equal? Obtain a 92 percent confidence interval estimate for $(p_1 - p_2)$.

11-19. The Damon family owns a large grape vineyard in southwestern Ontario. The grapevines must be sprayed at the beginning of the growing season to protect against various insects and diseases. Two new insecticides have just been marketed: Pernod 5 and Action. To test their effectiveness, three long rows were selected and sprayed with Pernod 5, and three others were sprayed with Action. When the grapes ripened, 400 of the vines treated with Pernod 5 were checked for infestation and 24 were found to be infested. Likewise, an independent sample of 400 vines sprayed with Action was checked and 40 were found to be infested. At the 0.05 significance level, can we conclude that the difference in the proportions of infested vines among those treated with Action as opposed to Pernod 5, is more than 0.02?

11-20. The Roper Organization conducted identical surveys in 1990 and 2000. One question asked of women was, "Are most men basically kind, gentle, and thoughtful?" The 1990 survey revealed that, of the 3000 women surveyed, 2010 said that they were. In 2000, 1530 of the independent sample of 3000 women surveyed thought that men were kind, gentle, and thoughtful.

At the 0.05 level, can we conclude that a smaller proportion of women thought men were kind, gentle, and thoughtful in 2000 compared with 1990?

11-21. The research department at the home office of Cambridge Insurance conducts ongoing research on the causes of automobile accidents, the characteristics of the drivers, and so on. A random sample of 400 policies written on single persons revealed 120 had at least one accident in the previous three-year period. Similarly, a sample of 600 policies written on married persons revealed that 150 had been in at least one accident. At the 0.05 significance level, is there a significant difference in the proportions of single and married persons insured by Cambridge Insurance, who had an accident during the three-year period? Using the same sample data, obtain a 95 percent confidence interval estimate for the difference in the two population proportions.

CHAPTER OUTLINE

I.   In this chapter, we develop confidence intervals, and hypothesis-testing procedures for the difference in values of means or proportions of two populations.

II. In the case of population means, we consider the null hypothesis of the form $H_0: \mu_1 - \mu_2 = d_0$; or $H_0: \mu_1 - \mu_2 \leq d_0$; or $H_0: \mu_1 - \mu_2 \geq d_0$.

III. The two samples selected from the two populations may be *independent samples* or *matched pair samples*.

IV. In the case of independent samples:
   A. Case: $\sigma_1^2 = \sigma_2^2 = \sigma^2$. The value of σ is unknown.

   In this case, we use as a test statistic:
   $$\left(\frac{(\bar{X}_1 - \bar{X}_2) - d_0}{\sqrt{S_p^2 \left(\frac{1}{n_1} + \frac{1}{n_2} \right)}} \right).$$

   If the population distributions are normal, this is a t statistic with degrees of freedom $(n_1 + n_2 - 2)$. Here, S_p^2, **the pooled estimator of σ^2 equals**

   $$S_p^2 = \frac{(n_1 - 1)S_1^2 + (n_2 - 1)S_2^2}{(n_1 + n_2 - 2)} \qquad \text{11-8}$$

   The $(1 - \alpha)$ confidence interval for $(\mu_1 - \mu_2)$ is

   $$(\bar{X}_1 - \bar{X}_2) \pm t_{\alpha/2} \sqrt{S_p^2 \left(\frac{1}{n_1} + \frac{1}{n_2} \right)}$$

   B. Case: $\sigma_1^2 \neq \sigma_2^2$; and their values are unknown.

   In this case the test statistic is
   $$\left(\frac{(\bar{X}_1 - \bar{X}_2) - d_0}{\sqrt{\frac{S_1^2}{n_1} + \frac{S_2^2}{n_2}}} \right)$$

If the population distributions are normal, this test statistic is approximately a t statistic with degrees of freedom

$$df = \frac{(S_1^2/n_1 + S_2^2/n_2)^2}{\left(\dfrac{(S_1^2/n_1)^2}{n_1 - 1} + \dfrac{(S_2^2/n_2)^2}{n_2 - 1}\right)} \qquad \text{11-6}$$

An approximate $(1 - \alpha)$ confidence interval for $(\mu_1 - \mu_2)$ is

$$(\bar{X}_1 - \bar{X}_2) \pm t_{\alpha/2}\sqrt{\left(\frac{S_1^2}{n_1} + \frac{S_2^2}{n_2}\right)}$$

V. In the case of matched pair samples:
  A. The two samples are paired such as: $(X_{1,1}, X_{2,1}), (X_{1,2}, X_{2,2}), \ldots, (X_{1,n}, X_{2,n})$. Let D be the difference between two values in a random pair.
  B. In this case the test statistic is $\dfrac{\bar{D} - d_0}{S_D/\sqrt{n}}$.

  If the two populations are normally distributed, this is a t statistic with degrees of freedom, $df = n - 1$.
  C. The $(1 - \alpha)$ confidence interval for $(\mu_1 - \mu_2)$ is

$$\bar{D} \pm t_{\alpha/2}\, S_D/\sqrt{n} \qquad \text{11-15}$$

  D. Matched pair samples give a more powerful test if the paired samples have high positive correlation.

VI. In the case of population proportions, we consider the null hypothesis of the form:
$$H_0: p_1 - p_2 = p_d, \quad \text{or} \quad H_0: p_1 - p_2 \leq p_d, \quad H_0: p_1 - p_2 \geq p_d$$
  A. Case (i): $p_d \neq 0$: In this case, the test statistic is:

$$\frac{(\hat{p}_1 - \hat{p}_2) - p_d}{\sqrt{\dfrac{\hat{p}_1(1 - \hat{p}_1)}{n_1} + \dfrac{\hat{p}_1(1 - \hat{p}_2)}{n_2}}}$$

  B. Case (ii): $p_d = 0$: In this case, our choice of test statistic is:

$$\frac{(\hat{p}_1 - \hat{p}_2)}{\sqrt{\hat{p}(1 - \hat{p})\left(\dfrac{1}{n_1} + \dfrac{1}{n_2}\right)}}$$

  Here, $\hat{p}_1 = \dfrac{X_1}{n_1}$ and $\hat{p}_2 = \dfrac{X_2}{n_2}$, $\hat{p}$ is the **pooled estimator** and equals

$$\hat{p} = \frac{X_1 + X_2}{n_1 + n_2} \qquad \text{11-19}$$

  C. We assume that the sample sizes are large, so that the test statistics are approximate Z statistics.
  D. An *approximate $(1 - \alpha)$ confidence interval for $(\hat{p}_1 - \hat{p}_2)$ is given by*:

$$(\hat{p}_1 - \hat{p}_2) \pm z_{\alpha/2}\sqrt{\frac{\hat{p}_1(1 - \hat{p}_1)}{n_1} + \frac{\hat{p}_2(1 - \hat{p}_2)}{n_2}} \qquad \text{11-21}$$

CHAPTER EXERCISES 11-22 TO 11-42

For each of the exercises 11-22 through 11-42, assume that the populations are approximately normally distributed.

11-22. Clark Heter is an industrial engineer at Lyons' Products. He would like to determine whether there are more units produced on the afternoon shift than on the day shift. A sample of 54 day shift workers showed that the mean number of units produced was 345, with a standard deviation of 21. A sample of 60 afternoon shift workers showed that the mean number of units produced was 351, with a standard deviation of 28 units. Can we conclude at the 0.05 significance level, that the population mean of the number of units produced on the afternoon shift is larger? Obtain a 99 percent confidence interval estimate for the difference in the population means of the number of units produced in the two shifts.

11-23. An official of the Department of Transportation wants to compare the useful life, in months, of two brands of paint used for striping roads. She reviewed 35 road stripes painted using Cooper paint. The mean number of months the paint lasted was 36.2, with a sample standard deviation of 1.14 months. The official then reviewed 40 road stripes painted using King Paint. The mean number of months was 37.0, with a sample standard deviation of 1.3 months. At the 0.01 significance level can we conclude that there is a difference in the mean useful life of the two paints? Compute a 95 percent confidence interval estimate for the difference in the mean useful life of the two paints.

11-24. The *fog index* is used to measure the reading difficulty of written text. It is a rough measure of the number of years of schooling it would take to understand the text. The fog index for a sample of 36 articles from a scientific journal showed a sample mean of 11.0 and a sample standard deviation of 2.65. A sample of 40 articles from trade publications showed a sample mean of 8.9 and a sample standard deviation of 1.64. At the 0.01 significance level, can we conclude that the mean fog index in the scientific journal is higher? Compute a 90 percent confidence interval estimate for the difference in the mean fog index in the scientific journal and trade publications.

11-25. A study of the health benefits packages for employees of large and small firms was recently completed by Pohlman Associates, a management consulting firm. Among the random sample of 15 large firms studied, the mean cost of the benefits package was 17.6 percent of salary, with a sample standard deviation of 2.6 percent. Among the random sample of 12 small firms studied, the mean cost of the benefits package was 16.2 percent of salary, with a sample standard deviation of 3.3 percent. Is there a difference at the 0.05 significance level, between the population means of percent of the employees' salaries spent by large firms and by small firms on health benefits?

11-26. The manager of a package courier service believes that packages shipped at the end of the month are heavier than those shipped earlier in the month. As an experiment, he weighed a random sample of 20 packages at the beginning of the month. He found that the mean weight was 9.1 kg and that the sample standard deviation was 2.6 kg. Ten packages randomly selected at the end of the month had a mean weight of 10.7 kg with a sample standard deviation of 2.5 kg. At the 0.05 significance level, can we conclude that the packages shipped at the end of the month weigh more? Compute a 95 percent confidence interval estimate for the difference in mean weights of packages at the beginning and end of the month.

11-27. The owner of Bun "N" Run Hamburger wishes to compare the sales per day at two locations. The mean number of hamburgers sold for 10 randomly selected days at the North side site was 83.55, and the sample standard deviation was 10.50. For a random sample of 12 days at the South side location, the mean number sold was 78.80 and the sample standard deviation was 14.25. At the 0.05 significance level, can we conclude that there is a difference in the population means of number of hamburgers sold per day at the two locations?

11-28. The Engineering Department at Sims' Software recently developed two chemical solutions designed to increase the usable life of computer disks. A sample of 10 disks treated with the first solution lasted 86, 78, 66, 83, 84, 81, 84, 109, 65, and 102 hours. An independent sample of 14 disks treated with the second solution lasted 91, 71, 75, 76, 87, 79, 73, 76, 79, 78, 87, 90, 76, and 72 hours. At the 0.10 significance level, can we conclude that there is a difference in the population means of lifetimes of disks when exposed to the two types of treatment?

11-29. The Willow Run Outlet Mall has two Haggar Outlet Stores, one located on Peach Street and the other on Plum Street. The two stores are laid out differently, but both store managers claim their layout maximizes the amounts customers will purchase on impulse. A random sample of 10 customers at the Peach Street store revealed they spent the following amounts more than planned: $17.58, $19.73, $12.61, $17.79, $16.22, $15.82, $15.40, $15.86, $11.82, $15.85. A random sample of 14 customers at the Plum Street store revealed they spent the following amounts more than they planned: $18.19, $20.22, $17.38, $17.96, $23.92, $15.87, $16.47, $15.96, $16.79, $16.74, $21.40, $20.57, $19.79, $14.83. At the 0.01 significance level, can we conclude that there is a difference in the mean amounts purchased on an impulse at the two stores? Assume that the population variances are equal.

11-30. Two boats, the *Sea Hawk* and the *Sea Queen*, are competing for a spot in the upcoming *America's Cup* race. To decide which one will represent Canada, they race over a part of the course several times. Below are the sample times in minutes. At the 0.05 significance level, can we conclude that there is a difference in their mean times? Assume that the two populations have the same variance.

Boat	Times (minutes)										
Sea Hawk	12.9	12.5	11.0	13.3	11.2	11.4	11.6	12.3	14.2	11.3	
Sea Queen	14.1	14.1	14.2	17.4	15.8	16.7	16.1	13.3	13.4	13.6	10.8	19.0

11-31. The manufacturer of a compact disc player wanted to know whether a 10 percent reduction in price is enough to increase the sales of their product. To investigate, the owner randomly selected eight outlets and sold the disc player at the reduced price. At some other seven randomly selected outlets, in a different same-sized city, the disc player was sold at the regular price. Reported below is the number of units sold last month at the sampled outlets. At the 0.01 significance level, can the manufacturer conclude that the price reduction resulted in an increase in sales? Assume that the population variances are equal.

Regular price	138	121	88	115	141	125	96	
Reduced price	128	134	152	135	114	106	112	120

11-32. Scott Seggity, owner of Seggity Software, recently purchased a special math coprocessor chip advertised to "drastically reduce processing time." To test the chip, he selected a sample of 12 programs. The selected programs were run on two identical computers, one with the chip and the other without it. The processing times (in seconds) are reported below. At the 0.05 significance level, can Mr. Seggity conclude that the new coprocessor will reduce the mean processing time?

Program	Without	With	Program	Without	With
1	1.23	0.60	7	1.30	0.60
2	0.69	0.93	8	1.37	1.35
3	1.28	0.95	9	1.29	0.67
4	1.19	1.37	10	1.17	0.89
5	0.78	0.62	11	1.14	1.29
6	1.02	0.99	12	1.09	1.00

11-33. Dr. Storoszczuk, Dean of a College of Business, wants to study the effect on student grade point averages (GPAs) of moving from the quarter system to the semester system. (Under the quarter system, the academic year is divided into three ten-week sessions, whereas under the semester system there are two fifteen-week sessions.) Her University recently switched from the quarter to the semester system. To investigate, Dean Storoszczuk selected a sample of 10 students enrolled in the fall quarter last year and the fall semester this year. Listed below are the grades. At the 0.05 significance level, is there evidence that the population means of the student grades declined after the conversion?

Student	Last Fall	This Fall	Student	Last Fall	This Fall
Asad	2.98	3.17	Volmer	2.09	2.08
Becha	2.34	2.04	Anderson	2.45	2.88
Bowerman	3.68	3.62	Bolger	2.96	3.15
Sweede	3.13	3.19	Palmer	2.80	2.49
Davis	3.34	2.90	Weis	4.00	3.98

11-34. The Insurance Institute of Canada wants to compare the yearly costs of auto insurance offered by two leading companies. They select a sample of 15 families, some with only a single insured driver, and others with several teenage drivers, and pay each family a stipend to contact the two companies and ask for a price quote. To make the data comparable, certain features, such as the amount deductible and limits of liability are standardized. The sample information is reported below. At the 0.10 significance level, can we conclude that there is a difference in the population means of amounts quoted?

Family	Maritime Insurance	Ridus Insurance	Family	Maritime Insurance	Ridus Insurance
Becker	$2090	$1610	King	1018	1956
Berry	1683	1247	Kucic	1881	1772
Murty	1402	2327	Joshi	1571	1375
Debuck	1830	1367	Obeid	874	1527
DuBrul	930	1461	Price	1579	1767
Eckroate	697	1789	Kurz	1577	1636
German	1741	1621	Tresize	860	1188
Hu	1129	1914			

11-35. Fairfield Homes is developing two parcels near Winnipeg. In order to test different advertising approaches, they use different media to reach potential buyers. The mean annual family income for a random sample of 75 potential buyers at the first development is $150 000 with a sample standard deviation of $40 000. An independent random sample of 120 potential buyers at the second development had a mean of $180 000 with a sample standard deviation of $30 000. At the 0.05 significance level, can Fairfield conclude that the two population means are different?

11-36. The following data on annual rates of return were collected from five stocks listed on the New York Stock Exchange ("the big board") and five stocks listed on NASDAQ. At the 0.10 significance level, can we conclude that the population mean of annual rates of return is higher on the big board?

NYSE	17.16	17.08	15.51	8.43	25.15
NASDAQ	15.80	16.28	16.21	17.97	7.77

11-37. An investigation of the effectiveness of an anti-bacterial soap in reducing operating room contamination resulted in the accompanying table. The new soap was tested in a sample of eight operating rooms in Ontario during the last year.

Operating Room	A	B	C	D	E	F	G	H
Before	6.6	6.5	9.0	10.3	11.2	8.1	6.3	11.6
After	6.8	2.4	7.4	8.5	8.1	6.1	3.4	2.0

At the 0.05 significance level, can we conclude that the population mean of the contamination measurement is lower after use of the new soap?

11-38. Each month the National Association of Purchasing Managers publishes the NAPM index. One of the questions asked on the survey of purchasing agents is: Do you think the economy is expanding? Last month, of the 300 responses, 160 answered "yes" to the question. This month 170 of the 290 responses indicated they felt the economy was expanding. At the 0.05 significance can we conclude that a larger proportion of the agents believe the economy is expanding this month? What is the P-value? Compute a 95 percent confidence interval estimate for the change in proportion of agents who believe the economy is expanding.

11-39. The manufacturer of Advil, a common headache remedy, recently developed a new formulation of the drug that is claimed to be more effective. To evaluate the new drug, a random sample of 200 current Advil users is asked to try it. After a one-month trial, 180 indicated the new drug was more effective in relieving headaches. At the same time, an independent, random sample of 300 current Advil users is given the current drug but told it is the new formulation. From this group, 261 said it was an improvement. At the 0.05 significance level, can we conclude that the new drug is more effective?

11-40. As part of the recent survey among dual-wage earner couples, an industrial psychologist found that 990 men out of the 1500 surveyed, believed the division of household duties was fair. Out of a sample of 1600 women, 970 believed the division of household duties was fair. At the 0.01 significance level, can we conclude that a larger proportion of men believe the division of household duties is fair? What is the P-value? Obtain a 90 percent confidence interval estimate for the difference in the proportions of men and women who believe that the division of household duties is fair.

11-41. Is there a difference in the proportions of college men versus college women who smoke at least a pack of cigarettes a day? A random sample of 400 college women revealed 72 smoked at least one pack per day. An independent, random sample of 500 college men revealed that 70 smoked at least a pack of cigarettes a day. At the 0.05 significance level, is there a difference between the proportions of college men and women who smoke at least a pack of cigarettes a day, or can the difference in the proportions be attributed to sampling error?

11-42. There are two major Internet providers in a city, one called HTC and the other Mountain. We want to investigate if there is a difference in the proportions of times a customer is able to access the Internet. During a one-week period, 500 calls were placed at random times throughout the day and night to HTC. A connection was made to the Internet on 450 occasions. A similar one-week study of Mountain showed the Internet to be available on 352 of 400 trials. At the 0.01 significance level, can we conclude that there is a difference in the proportions of times the access to the Internet is successful? What is the P-value? Compute a 95 percent confidence interval estimate for the difference in proportions of time the Internet can be accessed successfully using the two service providers.

www.exercises.ca 11-43 TO 11-44

11-43. We wish to test if the mean value of stock prices of the top 1000 companies in Canada in the year 2000, published by _www.globeinvestor.com_, has changed since November 2001. The following is a list of 10 companies, selected randomly from the list of the top 1000 companies, together with their symbols and the prices on November 8, 2001. Go to the Web site _http://www.tse.com_. Click on "symbol," enter the symbol of each company and click "Go" to find the current stock price of the company. Using this data, test if we can conclude, at the 0.05 significance level, that the mean value of stock prices of the list of top 1000 companies, during the year 2000, has changed since November 8, 2001.

Company	Code	Last Price ($)
Bank of Nova Scotia	BNS	47.53
Thomson Corporation	TOC	46.00
Quebecor Inc.	QBR.A	15.25
PanCanadian Petroleum Limited	PCB.DB	101.15
Magna International	MG.A	89.72
Power Corporation of Canada	POW	34.98
National Bank of Canada	NA	25.15
Hollinger Inc.	HLG.C	12.00
Onex Corp.	OCX	21.95
Pengrowth Energy Trust	PGF.UN	15.05

11-44. Go to the Web site *www.homestore.ca*. Randomly select prices of 10 single-family houses for sale in Calgary, Alberta using SRR. (For this, Click on *province: Alberta, area: Calgary*.) Similarly, randomly select prices of 10 single-family houses for sale in Durham, Ontario. (Use the random number table to select the random numbers). Test, if there is significant evidence, at the 0.05 significance level, to conclude that the mean price of houses for sale in Durham is higher than that in Calgary. What is the *P*-value? Interpret it. Also, using the same sample data, obtain a 95 percent confidence interval estimate of the difference in mean value of prices of houses on sale in Calgary, and the mean value of the prices in Durham.

COMPUTER DATA EXERCISES 11-45 TO 11-47

11-45. Refer to the information in the file Real Estate Data.xls, which reports information on the homes sold in Victoria, B.C., last year.
(a) At the 0.05 significance level, can we conclude that there is a difference in the population means of selling prices of homes with a pool and homes without a pool?
(b) At the 0.05 significance level, can we conclude that there is a difference in the population means of selling prices of homes with an attached garage and homes without a garage?
(c) At the 0.05 significance level, can we conclude that there is a difference in the population means of selling prices of homes in Townships 1 and 2.

11-46. Refer to the data in file BASEBALL-2000.xls, which reports information on the 30 major league baseball teams for the 2000 season.
(a) At the 0.05 significance level, can we conclude there is a difference in the population means of home attendance of teams in the American League versus that of teams in the National League?
(b) At the 0.05 significance level, can we conclude there is a difference in the population means of number of home runs for teams that have artificial turf home fields versus teams that have grass home fields?

11-47. In the file 100 of Top 1000 companies.xls, consider the data on year 2000 earnings per share and previous year (1999) earnings per share of these companies, (published by *Globe Investor*). From this sample data, can we conclude, at the 0.05 significance level, that the mean value of the earnings per share of the top 1000 companies was higher during the year 2000 than during the year 1999?

CHAPTER 11   ANSWERS TO SELF-REVIEW

11-1. $H_0: \mu_1 - \mu_2 \leq 0$

$H_1: \mu_1 - \mu_2 > 0$

This is an upper-tailed (right-tailed) t test.

$df = n_1 + n_2 - 2 = 5 + 6 - 2 = 9$;

for $df = 9$, $t_\alpha = t_{0.1} = 1.383$

Decision rule: reject H_0 if the computed t value is greater than 1.383.

$\bar{x}_1 = 6.0$; $\bar{x}_2 = 5.17$; $s_1 = 2.0$; $s_2 = 1.94$;

$$s_p^2 = \frac{4(2.0)^2 + 5(1.94)^2}{9} = 3.881$$

The computed t value $= \dfrac{(6.0 - 5.17) - 0}{\sqrt{(3.881)(1/5 + 1/6)}}$

$= 0.70$.

Since the computed t value is less than 1.383, we do *not* have sufficient evidence, at $\alpha = 0.1$, to reject the null hypothesis and accept Dr. Nair's claim.

11-2. A 90 percent confidence interval estimate is

$(6.0 - 5.17) \pm 1.833\sqrt{(3.881)(1/5 + 1/6)}$

$= (-1.35, 3.02)$

11-3. $H_0: \mu_D \geq 0$

$H_1: \mu_D < 0$

This is a lower tailed t test.

$df = n - 1 = 7$.

Critical value $= -t_\alpha = -t_{0.05} = -1.895$

$\bar{d} = -5.64$; $s_D = 4.96$

The computed t value $= \dfrac{(-5.64 - 0)}{4.96/\sqrt{8}} = -3.22$

Since the computed t value is less than the critical value (-1.895), we reject the null hypothesis. There is sufficient evidence, at 0.05 significance level, that in the year 2000, the mean value of weekly percentage increase in BCE stock prices was higher than the mean value of weekly percentage increase in TSE 300 index.

11-4. A 95 percent confidence interval estimate of difference between the average percentage weekly changes in TSE 300 index and the BCE stock prices during the year 2000 is

$(-5.64 \pm 2.365 \,(4.96)/\sqrt{8}) = (-9.78, -1.49)$

11-5. $H_0: p_1 - p_2 = 0$

$H_1: p_1 - p_2 \neq 0$

This is a two-tailed Z test.

Decision rule: reject H_0 in favour of H_1 if the computed z value is less than $-z_{0.05} = -1.645$ or if it is greater than 1.645.

$\hat{p}_1 = 87/150 = 0.58$; $\hat{p}_2 = 123/200 = 0.615$;

the pooled estimate

$\hat{p} = (87 + 123)/(150 + 200) = 0.6$;

The computed z value

$= \dfrac{(0.58 - 0.615)}{\sqrt{(0.6)(0.4)(1/150 + 1/200)}} = -0.66$

Since the computed z value lies between -1.645 and $+1.645$, we do *not* have sufficient evidence, at the 0.1 significance level, the proportions of adults and children who rate the new flavour excellent are different.

11-6. The 95 percent confidence interval estimate of difference between the two population proportions is $(0.58 - 0.615)$

$\pm 1.96\sqrt{\dfrac{(0.58)(0.42)}{150} + \dfrac{(0.615)(0.385)}{200}}$

$= (-0.139, 0.069)$

Analysis of Variance

GOALS

When you have completed this chapter, you will be able to:

- Explain the general idea of analysis of variance

- List the characteristics of the F distribution

- Organize data into a one-way and a two-way ANOVA table

- Define the terms *treatments* and *blocks*

- Conduct a test of hypothesis to determine whether three or more treatment means are equal

- Develop multiple tests for difference between each pair of treatment means

 - Conduct a test of hypothesis to determine whether the variances of two populations are equal.

SIR RONALD A. FISHER (1890–1962)

-- 1498
1548
-- 1598
1648
-- 1698
1748
-- 1898
1948
2000

The theory of experimental design and the ANOVA technique for analysis of experimental data were developed, almost single-handedly, by Sir Roland A. Fisher.

Ronald Fisher, the youngest of seven children of George Fisher, was born in the northern London suburb of East Finchley on February 17, 1890. He showed glimpses of profound intelligence and mathematical precocity even as a child.

Since childhood, Fisher suffered from chronic myopia. He had to wear lenses so thick that they resembled pebbles and without them he was practically blind. This limited his private reading throughout his life. Most of his learning was through listening while others read aloud to him, and he solved mathematical problems mentally. As a result, he developed a powerful sense of conceptualization and intuitiveness and could visualize complex mathematical relationships geometrically in his mind. This geometric sense is the hallmark of most of his profound results.

In 1912, Fisher graduated from Cambridge University in mathematics and theoretical physics. In his final year of undergraduate study, he published his first research paper, in which he introduced the basic idea of *method of maximum likelihood*, one of his profound contributions to statistics.

For six years after graduation, Fisher tried various jobs such as working for an investment house, doing farm chores in Canada, and teaching high school. However, during this period he continued his research on statistics. He transformed various problems about the distribution of sample statistics into problems in n-dimensional geometry. This led him to develop the Concept of *degrees of freedom*. He also obtained a theoretical characterization of Student's t distribution, and sampling distribution of the correlation coefficient.

In 1919, his growing reputation as a mathematician brought him two offers, one from Karl Pearson's Galton Laboratory in London's University College, and the other from the Rothamsted Experimental Station. Due to what he considered as Pearson's high-handedness and lack of understanding, Fisher decided to reject his offer and joined Rothamsted. As a part of his work there, Fisher developed his well-known theory of experimental design, the ANOVA procedure for analyzing experimental data, and the characterization of an important class of distribution, which is called F distribution after Fisher himself. His 1925 textbook *Statistical Methods for Research Workers* is considered a landmark work in this field. It is fairly difficult to read as M.G. Kendall, a well-known statistician and his friend wrote, "Somebody once said that no student should attempt to read it unless he had read it before."

Besides statistics, his other area of interest was genetics. His profound work in this area earned him the Galton Chair of Eugenics at University College in 1933 and he held this position until 1943. In 1943, Fisher developed a theory based on the new Rh blood groups and predicted the discovery of two new antibodies and an eighth allele. All these were identified soon after. He joined Cambridge University in 1943 as Balfour Professor of Genetics.

His other profound contributions to statistics include: (i) the introduction of the concepts of the null hypothesis and significance level; (ii) distributions of numerous statistical functions, such as the partial and multiple correlation coefficients, and the regression coefficients in the analysis of covariance; and (iii) linear discriminate analysis.

Sir Fisher received numerous prestigious awards and honours during his lifetime and was knighted by Queen Elizabeth in 1952.

INTRODUCTION

In this chapter we continue our discussion of hypothesis testing. Recall that in Chapter 10 we examined the basic framework of statistical theory of hypothesis testing. We developed a five-step procedure to test a hypothesis about the value of the mean of a given population. When the population distribution is normal and the value of the population variance is known, distribution of the test statistic used is standard normal. We called the corresponding test a Z test. When the population distribution is normal but the value of the population variance is unknown, the distribution of the test statistic used is Student's t distribution. We called the corresponding test a t test. In Chapter 11, we extended the techniques developed in Chapter 10 to the case of two populations. In particular we developed tests for difference in values of means and proportions of two given populations.

In this chapter, we expand further on the ideas of hypothesis testing developed in Chapters 10 and 11. We describe a technique, called **analysis of variance (ANOVA)**, for simultaneously testing if several populations have the same value of mean. Here, we assume that all the population distributions are normal and they have equal variance. Since the technique requires that all the populations have the same value of variance, there is a need for a procedure to test the hypothesis that two given populations have equal variance. We discuss such a procedure for two normally distributed populations in Chapter 12 Appendix A on the CD-ROM. All the test statistics studied in this chapter follow what is called an F *distribution*. Hence, we start with a discussion on F distribution.

12.1 THE F DISTRIBUTION

This distribution is named to honour Sir Ronald Fisher, one of the founders of modern-day statistics. The following are the characteristics of the F distribution.[1]

- F distribution is based on the idea of ratios of variances.
- **There is a "family" of F distributions.** A particular member of the family is determined by two parameters, (v_1, v_2), where v_1 is the degrees of freedom in the numerator, and v_2 is the degrees of freedom in the denominator. The shape of the distribution is illustrated by the following graph. There is one F distribution for the degrees of freedom (df) = (29, 28), that is, 29 degrees of freedom in the numerator and 28 degrees of freedom in the denominator. There is another F distribution for df = (19, 6). Note that the shape of the curves changes as the degrees of freedom change.

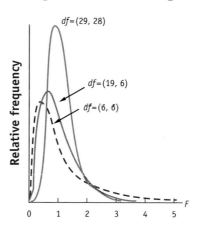

- **The F distribution is continuous.** It can assume any value in the interval between 0 and plus infinity.

- **The F distribution cannot be negative.** The smallest value F can assume is 0.

- **It is positively skewed.** The long tail of the distribution is to the right-hand side. As the number of degrees of freedom increases, the distribution approaches a normal distribution.

- **It is asymptotic to the horizontal axis.** This means, as the value of F increases, the curve approaches the horizontal axis but never touches it. This is similar to the tails of a normal distribution, described in Chapter 7.

Appendix D gives the values of $F_{0.05}$ (a value f such that $P (F \geq f) = 0.05$) and $F_{0.01}$ (a value f such that $P (F \geq f) = 0.01$) for different values of degrees of freedom, $df = (v_1, v_2)$. For example, for $df = (6, 7)$, the value of $F_{0.05}$ is obtained from the table in Appendix D corresponding to the 5 percent level of significance, under the column labelled "6" and the row labelled "7". This value is 3.87.

TABLE 12-1: Critical Values of the F Distribution, $\alpha = 0.05$

Degrees of Freedom for Denominator	Degrees of Freedom for Numerator			
	5	6	7	8
1	230	234	237	239
2	19.30	19.30	19.40	19.40
3	9.01	8.94	8.89	8.85
4	6.26	6.16	6.09	6.04
5	5.05	4.95	4.88	4.82
6	4.39	4.28	4.21	4.15
7	3.97	3.87	3.79	3.73
8	3.69	3.58	3.50	3.44
9	3.48	3.37	3.29	3.23
10	3.33	3.22	3.14	3.07

- The value $F_{0.95}$ for any degrees of freedom (v_1, v_2), equals[2] the value $(1/F_{0.05})$ for $df = (v_2, v_1)$. (Note the reversal of degrees of freedom for the numerator and denominator.) For example, to find the value of $F_{0.95}$ for $df = (8, 6)$, we look at the value of $F_{0.05}$ for $df = (6, 8)$. This equals 3.58. Hence, for $df = (8, 6)$, $F_{0.95}$ equals $(1/3.58)$. In general, for any degrees of freedom (v_1, v_2), and any value α between 0 and 1,

$$F_{(1-\alpha)}(df = (v_1, v_2)) = \frac{1}{F_\alpha}(df = (v_2, v_1)) \qquad \text{12-1}$$

12.2 EXPERIMENTAL AND OBSERVED DATA

In Chapters 9 and 10, we introduced the fundamental concepts of the statistical theories of estimation and hypothesis testing. We applied the concepts to relatively simple problems regarding value of the mean or proportion of a single population.

In most real-world problems, however, we are interested in drawing inference about the relationship between two or more variables. We started discussion on such problems in Chapter 11. In the rest of this Chapter and in Chapters 13 and 14, we shall consider them in further detail. One of the important issues in such cases is the method of selecting the data.

As an example, Bruce Kuhlman, the owner of Kuhlman Farms, wants to study the effects of three different brands of fertilizers, Wolfe, White, and Korosa, on the yield of wheat. Suppose he conducts the following experiment. He chooses three plots of land of equal size, and assigns the Wolfe brand of fertilizer to one of the plots, the White brand to another plot, and the Korosa brand to the third plot. Wheat is planted in these plots at the same time in the same manner. At the end of the growing season, the number of bushels of wheat produced on each plot is recorded. Will the difference in yields in the three plots reflect the difference in effects of the three fertilizers on the yield? The answer is "no," because the above experiment has several shortcomings.

The crop yield does not depend only on the type of fertilizer. It also depends on a large number of other factors. The major ones among these include the amount of sunlight, water supply, type of soil, etc. The difference in yields may therefore be, at least partly, due to difference in these other factors, influencing the crop yield, of the three plots. There are two ways of filtering out the effects of the other factors.

- **Perform a controlled experiment:** Ensure that the levels of all the other factors are the same in the three plots of land. For example, make sure that the three plots of land have the same type of soil, and get the same amount of sunlight and water, and so on.

- **Use complete randomization:** If we cannot control all the other factors, then use randomization in allocating the plots to the three types of fertilizers. That is, randomly select a plot out of the three, and allocate it to Wolfe brand of fertilizer. Then, randomly select a plot out of the remaining two, and allocate it to White brand, and allocate the third plot to Korosa brand. The randomization will ensure that the effects of other factors will become random and will occur as random errors. The yields, X_1, X_2, and X_3, of the three plots assigned to fertilizers Wolfe, White, and Korosa, can then be expressed as

$$X_1 = a + \tau_1 + \epsilon_1.$$
$$X_2 = a + \tau_2 + \epsilon_2.$$
$$X_3 = a + \tau_3 + \epsilon_3.$$

Here, τ_1, τ_2, and τ_3 are the values of yields attributable to the effects of the three types of fertilizers, a is the mean effect of all the other factors, and ϵ_1, ϵ_2, and ϵ_3 are the random effects of the other factors. The random errors, ϵ_1, ϵ_2, and ϵ_3 will have a mean $= 0$ and they will have the same distribution. Due to the presence of random errors, ϵ_1, ϵ_2, and ϵ_3, the values of the yields, X_1, X_2, and X_3, will be different from the mean values ($\mu_i = a + \tau_i$). To estimate the values of μ_1, μ_2, and μ_3, therefore, we shall need larger samples. For example, we may select a larger number of plots, say 12, and allocate randomly 4 plots to each of the three fertilizers.

Most experiments performed in the real world are neither completely controlled experiments (it is impossible to control all the factors), nor are they completely randomized. They are partially controlled experiments. For example, in the Kuhlman Farms problem, efforts should be made to control the more significant factors, (that is, those factors having a large effect on the yield). Otherwise, randomization of the effects of these significant factors will make the variance of the random error large, and in that case, the precision and reliability of the estimators of the μ's obtained will be low. In case we cannot control the values of the significant factors, experiments are designed to minimize the variable effects of these factors. This beautiful branch of statistics, called *experimental design*, has attracted the attention of a large number of scholars and a vast body of literature exists on it. For example, in one such design, we divide the selected plots into groups of three, such that all three plots in a group have (more or less) the same values of the significant factors. Such a group of plots is called a **block**. We then allocate the three plots in each block randomly to the three treatments. Such a design is called a **randomized block design**.

Though controlled experiments are commonly used in branches of science such as physics and chemistry, it is rarely possible to design such experiments in social sciences. Although models used in social sciences reflect an experimental design, the primary source of data in this case is from the observation of real-world outcomes. For example, if we want to study the effect of interest rates on investment, we cannot ask the Bank of Canada to fix values of interest rates to suite our experiment. We therefore observe the values of interest rates and investment during different years. One way to interpret this is to assume that nature is carrying out the experiment, and nature is controlling the values of factors appropriately and/or performing randomization. Large volumes of observed data are now available to researchers. We have already pointed out important sources of data in Chapter 1.

12.3   ONE-WAY ANALYSIS OF VARIANCE

In this section, we discuss the analysis of variance (ANOVA) technique for testing the effect of a single factor on the value of the population mean, when the data is selected using complete randomization. In particular, we consider different levels of the factor. (ANOVA was developed for applications in agriculture and many of the terms related to that context remain. In particular the term *treatments* is used for the different levels of the factor. For example, in the Kuhlman Farms problem, the factor is fertilizer and the treatments are the three types of fertilizers.) Corresponding to each treatment, we have a population, which is the response to the treatment. (For example, for each fertilizer type, the corresponding population is the crop yield.) We shall develop a procedure to test whether the values of population means, corresponding to different treatments are different, when the sample data is obtained using complete randomization. For convenience, we sometimes use the word treatment for the population corresponding to a treatment.

ANOVA ASSUMPTIONS

To use ANOVA, we assume the following:

- The population of the response variable for each treatment is normally distributed.
- The populations have equal variance (σ^2).
- The samples are selected independently.

Let us continue with the Kuhlman Farms problem. Suppose Mr. Kuhlman divides his field into 12 plots of equal size, and randomly assigns the Wolfe brand of fertilizer to four plots, the White brand to four plots, and the Korosa brand to four plots. The wheat is then planted at the same time in the same manner. At the end of the growing season, the number of bushels of wheat produced on each plot is recorded. In this illustration there are three treatments. That is, the three different brands of fertilizer are the three different treatments. Suppose the results, in bushels at the end of the growing season are:

CHART 12-1: Case Where Treatment Means Are Different

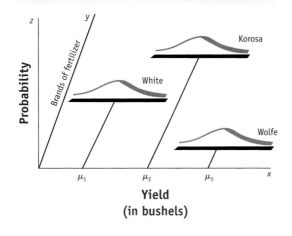

CHART 12-2: Case Where Treatment Means Are the Same

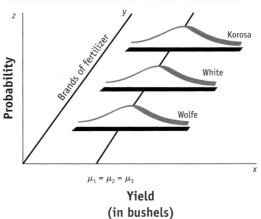

Wolfe	White	Korosa
55	60	50
54	70	54
59	61	49
56	65	51

Is there a difference in the population means of number of bushels of wheat produced under different treatments?

Chart 12-1 illustrates how the populations would appear if there was a difference in the population (treatment) means. Note that we assume that the population distributions are normal and they have equal variance.

Suppose the population means are the same. This is shown in Chart 12-2.

THE ANOVA TEST

How does the ANOVA test work? Recall that we want to determine whether the various samples came from populations with the same value of mean or with different values of means. If all the population means, $(\mu_1, \mu_2, \ldots, \mu_k)$ are equal, then any difference in values of sample means would be due to chance factors $(\epsilon_1, \epsilon_2, \ldots, \epsilon_k)$. If the population means are not all equal, then the difference in values of sample means would be due to difference between values of the population means, in addition to the chance factor.

ANOVA is based on the idea of (i) decomposing the total variation in the entire sample data (sample data on all the populations) into the variation due to treatment effect (this includes variation due to the difference between values of the population means, plus the chance variation), and the random variation (due to sampling error); and (ii) comparing the two variations. In case the population means are not all equal, we expect the variation due to the treatment effect to be larger. A decision rule then decides how much larger the variation due to the treatment effect should be before it provides us with significant evidence that the population means are not all equal. For designing such a decision rule *we need the additional assumption that all the populations have the same variance, σ^2.* Under this assumption, when the population means are all the same, we expect the two variations (variation due to the treatment effect, and the random variation) to be more or less equal. A large value of the ratio of the variation due to the treatment effect to the random variation serves as evidence that the population means are not all the same. How large should the value of this ratio be for us to conclude that we have sufficient evidence to reject H_0? We shall show that when the population distributions are normal and the samples are independent, a scaled version of this ratio (which we use as our test statistic) is an *F statistic*. A critical value will then be obtained using the *F* distribution and the selected value of the level of significance, α.

Refer to the Kuhlman Farms example in the previous section. The owner of the farm wants to determine whether there is a difference in the mean yields of wheat for the various fertilizers. He has 12 plots of land, which he randomly assigned to the three fertilizers. Let us number 1, 2, and 3 the three brands of fertilizers, the Wolfe brand, the White brand, and the Korosa brand. Let $n_1, n_2, \ldots, n_k$ be the sample sizes corresponding to the k treatments. In this example, $k = 3$ (corresponding to fertilizers 1, 2, and 3), and $n_1 = n_2 = n_3 = 4$. Let us denote the sample observations corresponding to treatment 1, $X_{1,1}, \ldots, X_{n_1,1}$, those corresponding to treatment 2, $X_{1,2}, \ldots, X_{n_2,2}$, and so on. In our example, $x_{1,1} = 55, x_{2,1} = 54, \ldots, x_{4,3} = 51$. (Refer to the data given on the previous page.)

To begin, we find the value of $\bar{\bar{X}}$, the overall mean of all the observations. In the fertilizer example, we find the overall mean value of yield of wheat (in bushels) of the 12 plots of land. It is 57 bushels, found by $\dfrac{(55 + 54 + \cdots + 51)}{12}$.

Next, for each observation, we find the difference between the observation and the overall mean. Each of these differences is squared and these squares summed. This term is called the **total variation**, or **Sum of Squares Total (SS Total)**.

> ℹ️ **Sum of Squares Total (SS Total)**   The sum of the squared differences between each observation and the overall mean.

$$\text{SS Total} = \sum_{i,j}(X_{i,j} - \bar{\bar{X}})^2 \qquad \text{12-2}$$

The symbol $\sum_{i,j}$ implies that the quantity $(X_{i,j} - \bar{\bar{X}})^2$ is calculated for all values of $X_{i,j}$, and they are all added together.

In our example, **SS Total** = 434, found by $(55 - 57)^2 + (54 - 57)^2 + \cdots + (51 - 57)^2$.

Let us denote the sample means corresponding to treatments $1, 2, \ldots, k$, by $\bar{X}_{.1}, \bar{X}_{.2}, \ldots, \bar{X}_{.k}$.

For our data, $\bar{x}_{.1} = \dfrac{55 + 54 + 59 + 56}{4} = 56$, $\bar{x}_{.2} = \dfrac{60 + 70 + 61 + 65}{4} = 64$, and

$\bar{x}_{.3} = \dfrac{50 + 54 + 49 + 51}{4} = 51$.

Simple algebraic manipulation shows that total variation can be broken into two components:

$$\text{SS Total} = \sum_{i,j}(X_{i,j} - \bar{\bar{X}})^2 = \sum_{i,j}(X_{i,j} - \bar{X}_{.j} + \bar{X}_{.j} - \bar{\bar{X}})^2 = \text{SST} + \text{SSE} \qquad \text{12-3}$$

Here,

 Sum of Squares due to Treatments (SST) is the weighted sum of squared differences of sample means from the overall mean.

$$\text{SST} = n_1(\bar{X}_{.1} - \bar{\bar{X}})^2 + n_2(\bar{X}_{.2} - \bar{\bar{X}})^2 + \cdots + n_k(\bar{X}_{.k} - \bar{\bar{X}})^2 \qquad \textbf{12-4}$$

 Sum of Squares due to Random Error (SSE) is the sum of squared differences between each observation and the corresponding sample mean.

$$\text{SSE} = \sum_i (X_{i,1} - \bar{X}_{.1})^2 + \sum_i (X_{i,2} - \bar{X}_{.2})^2 + \cdots + \sum_i (X_{i,k} - \bar{X}_{.k})^2 \qquad \textbf{12-5}$$

The symbol $\sum_i$ implies that the quantity is calculated for each value of i and they are all added together.

For example, in our problem,

$$\sum_i (X_{i,1} - \bar{X}_1)^2 = (X_{1,1} - \bar{X}_1)^2 + (X_{2,1} - \bar{X}_1)^2 + (X_{3,1} - \bar{X}_1)^2 + (X_{4,1} - \bar{X}_1)^2$$

*Thus, the total variation in the sample data (**SS Total**) can be divided into two components: (i) a variation between the treatments, (we call this **SST**), and (ii) a variation within the treatments, or the random variation, (we call this **SSE**). The source of the variation **SSE** is the random variation in each of the populations (treatments). The source of the variation **SST** is the random variations in the populations plus the difference in the population means (mean values corresponding to the treatments).*

The decomposition of the total variation in the sample data into (i) variation between the treatments (SST), and (ii) variation within the treatments (SSE), (we call this *random variation*), is the fundamental idea behind all ANOVA tests.

In the fertilizer example,

$$\text{SST} = 4(56 - 57)^2 + 4(64 - 57)^2 + 4(51 - 57)^2 = 344$$

The random variation is,

$$\text{SSE} = (55 - 56)^2 + (54 - 56)^2 + \cdots + (49 - 51)^2 + (51 - 51)^2 = 90$$

It can be shown that SSE can be written as:

$$\text{SSE} = (n_1 - 1)S_1^2 + (n_2 - 1)S_2^2 + \cdots + (n_k - 1)S_k^2 \qquad \textbf{12-6}$$

Here, $S_1^2, S_2^2, \ldots, S_k^2$ are the sample variances of the samples corresponding to the different treatments (populations).

We standardize SSE, to obtain a statistic, called **mean square error (MSE)**, which is an unbiased estimator of σ^2 (the common variance of all the populations). We also standardize SST to obtain a statistic, called **mean square due to treatment (MST)**. When all the population means are equal, the statistic MST is also an unbiased estimator of σ^2. Hence, in this case, the ratio of MST to MSE is close to 1. On the other hand, if the population means are not all equal, then the difference in population means causes the value of SST, and therefore of MST, to be larger. A significantly high value of the ratio of MST to MSE then provides evidence that the population means are not all equal.

Thus, we define,

Mean Squares Error	$MSE = SSE/(n - k)$	**12-7**

Mean Squares for Treatment	$MST = SST/(k - 1)$	**12-8**

Here, $n = n_1 + \cdots + n_k$ is the total number of observations, and k is the total number of treatments.

It can be shown[3] that

- *MSE is an unbiased estimator of σ^2.* In fact, MSE is a generalization of the pooled estimator, S_p^2 of σ^2 that we considered in Chapter 11. (See Formula 11-8.) When $k = 2$, (that is, we have only two populations), $MSE = S_p^2$.

- *When H_0 is true, (that is, all the population means are the same), MST is also an unbiased estimator of σ^2.* However, if the population means are not all the same, for at least one sample, the difference between the sample mean and the overall mean will contain a systematic component. As a result, the expected value of MST will be greater than σ^2.

This suggests the following as a good choice for test statistic,

Test Statistic	$F = \dfrac{MST}{MSE}$	**12-9**

When H_0 is true, both the numerator and the denominator are unbiased estimators of σ^2. Hence, in this case, we expect the value of F to be around 1. If H_0 is false, then the denominator is still an unbiased estimator of σ^2. However, in this case, the value of MST is likely to be greater than σ^2, making the value of F larger than 1. Hence, our decision rule will be to choose an upper critical value, a_U and reject H_0 if the computed F value is larger than the critical value. Thus, this is an upper-tailed test.

When H_0 is true, the test statistic has an F distribution with degrees of freedom $(k - 1, n - k)$. Hence, we shall choose a critical value $a_U = F_{0.05}$ (degrees of freedom, $df = (k - 1, n - k)$.

In our example,

$$MST = SST/k = 344/2 = 172$$
$$MSE = SSE/(n - k) = 90/(12 - 3) = 10$$

Hence,

$$F = \frac{172}{10} = 17.2$$

This value is larger than 1. However, is it large enough for us to reject H_0? That will depend on the choice of the critical value.

Suppose we use $\alpha = 0.05$. Then the critical value is $F_{0.05}$ ($df = (3 - 1, 12 - 3) = (2, 9)$. From Appendix D, we get $F_{0.05} = 4.26$. (This is the number in the column labelled "2" and the row labelled "9".)

Since the computed F value (= 17.2) is greater than the critical value (= 4.26), there is sufficient evidence, at $\alpha = 0.05$, to reject H_0 and conclude that the population means are not all equal. There is a difference in the population mean yields corresponding to the three fertilizers.

Let us consider another example.

Example 12-1 Professor Ram Aneja had students in his marketing class rate his performance as excellent, good, fair, or poor. A graduate student collected the ratings and assured the students that the professor would not receive them until after course grades had been sent to the records' office. The rating (i.e., the treatment) a student gave the professor was matched with his or her course grade, which could range from 0 to 100. The sample information is reported below. Assuming that the population distributions are normal, and the variances of the grades of students in the four rating categories are the same, can we conclude, at the 0.01 significance level, that there is a difference in the mean grades of the students in each of the four rating categories?

Course Grades			
Excellent	**Good**	**Fair**	**Poor**
94	75	70	68
90	68	73	70
85	77	76	72
80	83	78	65
	88	80	74
		68	65
		65	

Solution We will follow the usual five-step hypothesis-testing procedure.

Step 1 State the null hypothesis and the alternative hypotheses. The null hypothesis is that the mean scores are the same for the four ratings. Thus,

H_0: $\mu_1 = \mu_2 = \mu_3 = \mu_4$
H_1: The mean scores are not all equal.

If the null hypothesis is rejected, we conclude that there is a difference in at least one pair of mean ratings, but at this point we do not know which pair or how many pairs differ.

Step 2 Select the level of significance. We selected the 0.01 significance level.

Step 3 Determine the test statistic. We shall use as a test statistic $F = \dfrac{\text{MST}}{\text{MSE}}$, as defined in Formula 12-9.

Step 4 Determine the decision rule. This is an upper-tailed F test. The upper critical value is $F_{0.01}$ $(df = (k - 1, n - k))$.

Here, k = total number of treatments = 4; n = the total number of observations = 22. Hence, the $df = (3, 18)$.

The critical value is obtained from Appendix D and the 0.01 significance level, at the intersection of the column labelled "3" and the row labelled "18". It equals 5.09. So the decision rule is to reject H_0 if the computed F value exceeds 5.09.

Step 5 Select the sample, perform the calculations, and make a decision. It is convenient to summarize the calculations of the F statistic in an ANOVA table. The format for an

ANOVA table is as follows:

ANOVA Table

Source of Variation	Sum of Squares	Degrees of Freedom	Mean Square	F
Treatments	SST	$k-1$	$SST/(k-1) = MST$	MST/MSE
Error	SSE	$n-k$	$SSE/(n-k) = MSE$	
Total	SS Total	$n-1$		

The overall mean $= \bar{\bar{x}} = \dfrac{94 + 90 + \cdots + 74 + 65}{22} = 75.64$

The sample means are:

$$\bar{x}_1 = \frac{94 + 90 + 85 + 80}{4} = 87.25 \qquad \bar{x}_2 = \frac{75 + 68 + 77 + 83 + 88}{5} = 78.20$$

$$\bar{x}_3 = \frac{70 + 73 + \cdots + 65}{7} = 72.86 \qquad \bar{x}_4 = \frac{68 + 70 + \cdots + 65}{6} = 69.0$$

SS Total $= (94 - 75.64)^2 + (90 - 75.64)^2 + \cdots + (74 - 75.64)^2 + (65 - 75.64)^2 = 1485.09$

SST $= 4(87.25 - 75.64)^2 + 5(78.20 - 75.64)^2 + 7(72.86 - 75.64)^2 + 6(69.0 - 75.64)^2$
$= 890.68$

SSE $=$ SS Total $-$ SST $= 1485.1 - 890.7 = 594.4$

Inserting these values into an ANOVA table and computing the value of F, we get:

ANOVA Table

Source of Variation	Sum of Squares	Degrees of Freedom	Mean Square	F
Treatments	890.68	3	296.89	8.99
Error	594.41	18	33.02	
Total	1485.09	21		

The computed F value is 8.99, which is greater than the critical value of 5.09. So, the null hypothesis is rejected. We conclude that the population means are not all equal. The mean scores are not the same in each of the four rating groups. At this point we can only conclude there is a difference in the treatment means. We cannot determine which treatment groups differ or how many treatment groups differ.

In Charts 12-3 and 12-4, we give instructions and outputs for Excel and Minitab for the above problem.

It may be noted that in the Minitab output the term *Factor* is used instead of *Treatment*, while Microsoft Excel output uses the term *Groups*. Thus, Minitab terms SST as *SS corresponding to Source = Factor*, and SSE as *SS corresponding to Source = Error*. Excel terms them, respectively, *SS Between Groups* and *SS Within Groups*.

Excel gives the P-value $= 0.0007428$, while the Minitab output gives the rounded P-value of 0.001. Since the P-value is less than the selected value of level of significance ($= 0.01$), our decision, based on the P-value is the same as above, (that is, reject H_0 in favour of H_1). Excel output also gives us the critical value, F-crit $= 5.0919$. This is the same (rounding up) as the value we obtained using Appendix D.

The Minitab output also gives 95 percent confidence intervals for each population mean.

EXCEL CHART 12-3

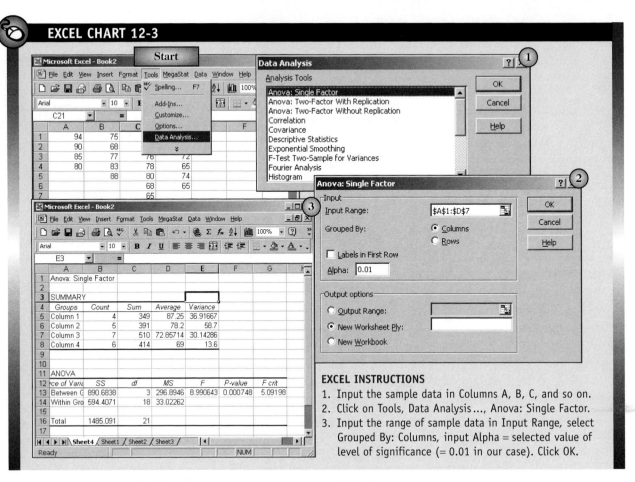

EXCEL INSTRUCTIONS

1. Input the sample data in Columns A, B, C, and so on.
2. Click on Tools, Data Analysis..., Anova: Single Factor.
3. Input the range of sample data in Input Range, select Grouped By: Columns, input Alpha = selected value of level of significance (= 0.01 in our case). Click OK.

MINITAB CHART 12-4

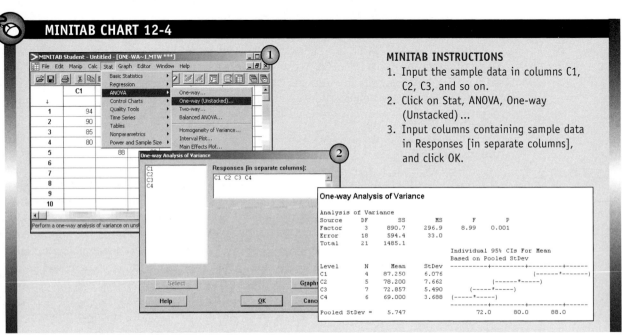

MINITAB INSTRUCTIONS

1. Input the sample data in columns C1, C2, C3, and so on.
2. Click on Stat, ANOVA, One-way (Unstacked) ...
3. Input columns containing sample data in Responses [in separate columns], and click OK.

■ SELF-REVIEW 12-1

Clean-All is a new all-purpose cleaner being test marketed by placing sales displays in three different locations within various supermarkets. The number of 350 mL bottles sold from each location in different supermarkets is reported below.

Near the Bread	20	15	24	18
Near the Beer	12	18	10	15
With Other Cleaners	25	28	30	32

Test if there is sufficient evidence, at the 0.05 significance level, that the population means of number of bottles sold at the three locations are not all the same. Assume that the population distributions are approximately normal with equal variance.

EXERCISES 12-1 TO 12-4

In each of the following, assume that the population distributions are approximately normal with equal variance.

12-1. The following is sample information. Test the hypothesis that the population means corresponding to the treatments are all equal. Use the 0.05 significance level.

Treatment 1	Treatment 2	Treatment 3
8	3	3
6	2	4
10	4	5
9	3	4

12-2. The following is sample information. Test the hypothesis at the 0.05 significance level that the population means corresponding to the treatments are all equal.

Treatment 1	Treatment 2	Treatment 3
9	13	10
7	20	9
11	14	15
9	13	14
12	15	
10		

12-3. A real estate developer is considering investing in a shopping mall on the outskirts of Edmonton, Alberta. Three parcels of land are being evaluated. Of particular importance is the income in the area surrounding the proposed mall. A random sample of four families is selected near each proposed site; following are the sample results. At the 0.05 significance level, can the developer conclude there is a difference in the population means of income in the three areas?

Area #1 ($000)	Area #2 ($000)	Area #3 ($000)
64	74	75
68	71	80
70	69	76
60	70	78

12-4. The manager of a computer software company is studying the number of hours top executives spend at their computer terminals by type of industry. A random sample of five executives from each of the three industries is obtained. At the 0.05 significance level, can the manager conclude there is a difference in the population means of number of hours spent at a terminal per week by executives in the three industries?

Banking	Retail	Insurance
12	8	10
10	8	8
10	6	6
12	8	8
10	10	10

ONE-WAY ANALYSIS OF VARIANCE AND THE t TEST

Why do we need the ANOVA test developed in the previous section? Why can't we just use the t test, discussed in Chapter 11, to compare the means of populations, two at a time?

First of all, let us consider the case of two populations. The t statistic Formula 11-10, used in Chapter 11, when population variances are equal but unknown, is

$$t = \left(\frac{(\bar{X}_1 - \bar{X}_2) - d_0}{\sqrt{S_p^2 \left(\frac{1}{n_1} + \frac{1}{n_2} \right)}} \right)$$

When $d_0 = 0$, (that is, we test for equality of the two means), $(t)^2$ is precisely the F statistic in Formula 12-9, used in the ANOVA test. *Hence, in this case, the two-tailed t test for equality of two population means (assuming equal but unknown population variances), developed in Chapter 11, is identical to the ANOVA test discussed in this section.* However, the t test can be used to test for any non-zero value (d_0) of difference in two population means and also to test if one population mean is greater than another (a one-tail test). The ANOVA test cannot be used for these cases.

In the case of more than two populations, one major problem with the multiple use of the t test is the undesirable build-up of Type I error.

To explain further, let us refer to the Kuhlman Farms example in the previous section. The owner of the farm wants to determine whether there is a difference in the mean yields of wheat for the three fertilizers, the Wolfe brand, the White brand, and the Korosa brand. Let us denote these by A, B, and C.

Suppose we use the t test to compare the three population means, two at a time. Then, we would have to run three different t tests. That is, we would need to compare the mean yields for pairs of fertilizers as follows: A versus B, A versus C, and B versus C. Suppose all the population means are equal. If we set the significance level in each of the three tests at 0.05, the probability of not rejecting H_0 in each test is 0.95 ($= 1 - 0.05$). Suppose we conduct three separate (independent) tests. That is, for each of the three pairs, we conduct a separate experiment, and collect data. Then, the probability of making a correct decision of not rejecting H_0 in every one of the three tests is:

$$P(\text{All correct decisions}) = (0.95)\,(0.95)\,(0.95) = 0.857$$

To find the probability of at least one error (one wrong decision), due to sampling, we subtract this result from 1. So, the probability of at least one incorrect decision, due to sampling, is $1 - 0.857 = 0.143$. To summarize, *if all the population means are equal, and we conduct three independent t tests, the likelihood of at least one wrong decision, due to sampling error, is increased from 0.05 to an undesirable level of 0.143.*

Suppose we conduct only one experiment, as in the previous section, and obtain one sample data on each of A, B, and C. Now, suppose we use the same sample data sets to conduct all three tests, A versus B, A versus C, and B versus C. Then the tests will not be independent. However, in this case too, the likelihood of at least one wrong decision, due to sampling error, will be much greater than 0.05, (though it will not be as high as 0.143). ANOVA allows us to compare the treatment means simultaneously and avoid the build-up of Type I error.

INFERENCES ABOUT TREATMENT MEANS: MULTIPLE COMPARISONS

Suppose we carry out the ANOVA procedure and conclude that the null hypothesis should be rejected, (that is, the treatment means are not all the same). In some instances, we may want to know which treatment means differ and by how much. That is, we may be interested in obtaining confidence interval estimates for the difference between means of each of the $_kC_2 = \dfrac{k(k-1)}{2}$ pairs of populations. We give below two methods of obtaining this information.

We can obtain a $(1 - \alpha)$ confidence interval estimate, separately, for each pair (i, j) of populations, using the following estimator given in case (ii) in the table on page 469, by replacing $\bar{X}_1$ and $\bar{X}_2$ by $\bar{X}_{.i}$ and $\bar{X}_{.j}$ and n_1 and n_2 by n_i and n_j.

$$(\bar{X}_i - \bar{X}_j) \pm t_{\alpha/2} \sqrt{S_p^2 \left(\frac{1}{n_1} + \frac{1}{n_2} \right)} \qquad \text{12-10}$$

(Here, S_p is the pooled estimate of the population standard deviation, calculated using samples i and j.)

If the confidence interval does not contain zero, then we can conclude there is sufficient evidence, at significance level α, that the corresponding two population means are unequal. (For more information on the relationship between hypothesis testing and confidence intervals, an interested student may refer to the optional Section 10-6.

As we saw before, this procedure results in an undesirable build-up of error. We shall discuss below modifications that will improve the performance of this approach.

FISHER'S LSD INTERVAL

If the total number of treatments is k, then the total number of pairs is $_kC_2 = \dfrac{k(k-1)}{2}$.

Let us denote this number by c. (For example, if $k = 4$, then $c = 6$.) If the confidence level used for each pair is $(1 - \alpha)$, then the overall confidence level (probability that each of the c confidence intervals will contain the value of the difference between corresponding population means), will then be somewhere between $(1 - \alpha)$ and $(1 - \alpha)^c$. (This is an unconditional probability. It does not take into account the fact that the test for comparison is made *after* the overall F test rejected the null hypothesis that all population means are equal.) The value $(1 - \alpha)^c$ is greater than or equal to $(1 - c\alpha)$. Hence, one method to keep the overall confidence level greater than $(1 - \alpha)$ that was proposed by Fisher is to use the confidence level $(1 - \alpha/c)$ for the confidence interval for each pair. The factor $(1/c)$ is called the *Bonferroni correction factor*. This, however, leads to extra wide confidence intervals. (In terms of a test of hypothesis, it increases the overall probability of a Type II error, thereby decreasing the power of the test.)

We saw in the previous section that the **mean square error (MSE)** is an unbiased estimator of σ^2. We also saw that when $k = 2$, MSE is the same as the pooled estimator, S_p^2, of σ^2. When $k > 2$, MSE calculated using the sample data on all the treatments, is a more efficient estimator of σ^2 than the pooled estimator S_p^2, calculated using only the samples on the two treatments being compared. Thus, if we replace S_p^2 by MSE in Formula 12-10, we get more precise confidence intervals, and the corresponding tests are more powerful. In this case, the corresponding Student's t distribution has degrees of freedom $(n - k)$.

Thus, for each pair, (i, j) of the populations, we use the confidence interval:

$(1 - \alpha)$ Confidence Interval for $(\mu_1 - \mu_2)$	$(\bar{X}_{.i} - \bar{X}_{.j}) \pm t_{\alpha/2c} \sqrt{\text{MSE}\left(\dfrac{1}{n_i} + \dfrac{1}{n_j}\right)}$	12-11

For the student opinion example (Example 12-1), suppose we want an overall level of significance $\alpha = 0.05$. The total number of t tests is $_4C_2 = \dfrac{(4)(3)}{2} = 6$. Then, applying Bonferroni correction, we shall use for each pair of population means, a confidence level of $(1 - 0.05/6) = 0.9917$. The values of $-t_{\alpha/2c} = -t_{0.0041}$ and $t_{0.0041}$ $(df = (n - k) = (22 - 4) = 18)$ are -2.9646, and 2.9646. (The t table at the end of book will not give us the desired value. We have to use Minitab or Excel for it.) The desired confidence interval is then

$$(\bar{X}_{.i} - \bar{X}_{.j}) \pm 2.9646 \sqrt{\text{MSE}\left(\frac{1}{n_i} + \frac{1}{n_j}\right)}$$

For categories "Excellent" and "Poor," we get the interval estimate:

$$(87.25 - 69.0) \pm 2.9646 \sqrt{33.02\left(\frac{1}{4} + \frac{1}{6}\right)} = (7.25,\ 29.25)$$

Since the interval does not contain zero, we shall conclude that the corresponding population means are unequal.

TUKEY'S STUDENTIZED RANGE TEST

The Fisher LSD test is too conservative. It uses a too large a value, $(= 1 - \alpha/c)$, of the confidence level for individual confidence intervals. This guarantees that the overall confidence level is at least $(1 - \alpha)$. However, in some cases, the resultant overall confidence level turns out to be much larger than $(1 - \alpha)$, and the confidence intervals are unnecessarily too wide. More precise confidence interval estimators have been developed by several statisticians. Popular among these are the ones by Tukey, Dunnett, and Scheffe.

We shall discuss here Tukey's confidence interval. It is based on the following fact. Suppose all the sample sizes are equal. If $\bar{X}_{min}$, and $\bar{X}_{max}$ are the smallest and the largest values of the sample means then it is sufficient to check if there is evidence that the means of populations corresponding to $\bar{X}_{min}$, and $\bar{X}_{max}$ are unequal. Tukey's confidence interval is based on the distribution of the range $(\bar{X}_{max} - \bar{X}_{min})$ when all the population means are equal.

For any pair i, and j of populations, Tukey's confidence interval for $(\mu_i - \mu_j)$ is:

Tukey's Confidence Interval for $(\mu_i - \mu_j)$	$(\bar{X}_{.i} - \bar{X}_{.j}) \pm \dfrac{q_\alpha}{\sqrt{2}} \sqrt{\text{MSE}\left(\dfrac{1}{n_i} + \dfrac{1}{n_j}\right)}$	12-12

Here, the value q_α is obtained from the distribution q, called the studentized range, when all the population means are equal. The parameters of this distribution are (k, v), where k is the number of populations (treatments) and v is the degrees of freedom of MSE $(= n - k)$. As usual, q_α is defined such that $P(q > q_\alpha) = \alpha$. The values of $q_{0.05}$ for different values of parameters of q are given in Appendix C. If for any pair of populations, the corresponding confidence interval does not contain zero, then we can conclude, at significance level α, that the corresponding population means are unequal.

When all the sample sizes are equal, Tukey's approach gives an overall confidence level exactly equal to $(1 - \alpha)$.

For example, let us consider the student opinion problem. For categories "Excellent" and "Poor," $q_{0.05} = 4.00$ (for parameters $(k, n - k) = (4, 18)$). Hence, we get a Tukey interval of:

$$(87.25 - 69.0) \pm \frac{4.0}{\sqrt{2}} \sqrt{33.02\left(\frac{1}{4} + \frac{1}{6}\right)} = (7.75873, 28.74127)$$

It may be noted that this interval is narrower then the one obtained using Fisher's LSD.

■ SELF-REVIEW 12-2

Consider the problem in Self-Review 12-1. Using Tukey's method, test if we can conclude, at the 0.05 significance level, that the population means corresponding to treatments 1 and 3 are unequal.

EXERCISES 12-5 TO 12-8

In each of the following, assume that the population distributions are normal with equal variance.

12-5. Given the following sample information, test the hypothesis that the treatment means corresponding to the three treatments are all equal at the 0.05 significance level.

Treatment 1	Treatment 2	Treatment 3
8	3	3
11	2	4
10	1	5
	3	4
	2	

If H_0 is rejected, can we conclude that the population means corresponding to treatments 1 and 2 differ? Use Fisher's LSD test and an overall confidence level of 0.95.

12-6. Given the following sample information, test the hypothesis that the treatment means are equal at the 0.05 significance level.

Treatment 1	Treatment 2	Treatment 3
3	9	6
2	6	3
5	5	5
1	6	5
3	8	5
1	5	4
	3	1
	7	5
	6	
	4	

If H_0 is rejected, can we conclude that the population means corresponding to treatments 2 and 3 differ? Use Fisher's LSD test and the overall confidence level of 0.95.

12-7. A senior accounting major at the University of New Brunswick has job offers from four CPA firms. To explore the offers further, she asked a random sample of recent trainees how many months each worked for the firm before receiving a raise in salary. The sample information is:

CPA	AB Intl.	Acct	Pfisters
12	14	18	12
10	12	12	14
14	10	16	16
12	10		

(a) At the 0.05 level of significance, is there a difference in the population means of the number of months before a raise was granted among the four CPA firms?

(b) If H_0 is rejected, can we conclude that there is a difference between the mean number of months before a raise at CPA and Acct? Use Tukey's test and the overall confidence level of 0.95.

12-8. A stock analyst wants to determine whether there is a difference in the mean rates of return for three types of stock: utility, retail, and banking stocks. The following sample information is collected.

Rates of Return		
Utility	Retail	Banking
14.3	11.5	15.5
18.1	12.0	12.7
17.8	11.1	18.2
17.3	11.9	14.7
19.5	11.6	18.1
		13.2

(a) Using the 0.05 level of significance, is there a difference in the population means of the rates of return among the three types of stocks?
(b) If H_0 is rejected, can the analyst conclude there is a difference between the mean rates of return for the utility and the retail stocks? Use Tukey's test and the overall confidence level of 0.95.

12.4   TWO-WAY ANALYSIS OF VARIANCE

In Section 12-2, we developed a one-way ANOVA test for equality of means of two or more populations. In this case, the different populations are response variables corresponding to different levels (treatments) of a single factor. We shall now extend this idea to the case of two factors. That is, in this case, different populations are response variables corresponding to different levels (treatments) of two different factors.

RANDOMIZED BLOCK DESIGN

In Section 12-3, we developed an ANOVA test for equality of means of two or more populations, with equal variance, when the samples are drawn independently from the populations. This extended the t test developed in Chapter 11 for the case of two populations. In Chapter 11, we saw that, in the case of two populations, by appropriately matching the data units in the two populations and randomly choosing a matched pair sample, we can develop a more powerful test for the difference between the two population means. This idea can be extended, in the case of more than two populations, to **randomized block design**.

As an example, let us refer to the Kuhlman Farms problem considered in the previous section. The owner of the farm wants to determine whether there is a difference in the mean yields of wheat for three different fertilizers. Here, the *factor* under investigation is *fertilizer*, and the *three different types of fertilizers* are the *three levels of the factor*, or *the three treatments*. We have one population per treatment and we want to test if the population means are all equal. We conducted an ANOVA test for this problem, in which, out of twelve plots of land, four were assigned randomly to each of the three fertilizers.

We know that there are other factors than fertilizer that affect the crop yield. To develop a strong test for *only* the effect of fertilizers, ideally all other significant factors should be held constant. The other alternative, which we followed above, is to use randomization, due to which the other systematic effects get subsumed in the random variation term. However, this increases the value of error variance, σ^2, and our test procedure actually tests if the effect of fertilizer is more significant than the effects of all these other factors that have been randomized. For example, the amount of sunlight is another major factor affecting the yield, and suppose all twelve plots of land considered do not get equal sunlight. Then, the variation due to the difference in amount of sunlight, which we have randomized, will get added to the random variation term, SSE. As a result, the value of the computed F statistic will be smaller, resulting in a weaker test. In this case, effects of other significant factors should be filtered out to increase the power of the test. One way of achieving this is by implementing a **randomized block design**, which we explain next.

Suppose the twelve plots can be grouped into four triplets such that each triplet gets the same amount of sunlight. We shall call each such triplet a **block**. We shall then randomly allocate the three plots in each block to the three different fertilizers. This will give us three observations (yield) corresponding to each block (a fixed value of amount of sunlight) and four observations corresponding to each treatment (fertilizer). We assume that the value $X_{i,j}$ (total yield in the plot corresponding to block i and treatment j) can be expressed as

$$X_{i,j} = a + b_i + \mu_j + \epsilon_{i,j}$$

where, b_i is the mean effect of the ith block on the yield, μ_j is the mean effect of the jth fertilizer, and $\epsilon_{i,j}$ is the random effect. (That is, we assume that the total effect of fertilizer and sunlight equals the effect of fertilizer plus the effect of sunlight.)

In this case, the total variation can be divided into: (i) the variation between the treatments; (ii) the variation between the blocks; and (iii) the random variation.

The following example will further clarify the concept and the test procedure.

Example 12-2 | In Chapter 11, we considered an example where a professor at St. Thomas University wants to conduct a test of hypothesis to compare the mean values of grades (out of 100) in *Introduction to Statistics*, and *Introduction to Economics*, received by their Economics graduates. Now suppose he wants to compare the mean values of grades of their Economics graduates in three courses: *Introduction to Statistics, Introduction to Economics*, and *Mathematics 201*. The grade of a randomly selected student in a course is likely to depend not only on the course but also on the abilities of the student. Since the nature of the three courses is not too different, a student who gets a good grade in one of the courses is likely to get good grades in the other two. Hence, the professor randomly chose four Economics graduates, and recorded for each, his or her grades in the three courses. The sample data is tabulated below:

Course / Student	Intro-Economics (1)	Intro-Statistics (2)	Math 201 (3)
1	76	76	79
2	91	85	88
3	88	83	84
4	85	80	81

Can he conclude, at the 0.05 significance level, that the population means of the values of grades in the three courses are not all equal?

Solution

Here, each student serves as a block. This is a randomized block design. We shall use the five-step procedure.

Step 1

We have numbered the students 1, 2, 3, 4, and the courses 1, 2, 3.
We assume that

- the grade of a student i in course j can be expressed as:

$$X_{i,j} = a + b_i + \mu_j + \epsilon_{i,j}$$

Here, b_i is the mean effect of the aptitude of the student i on his/her grade, μ_j is the mean effect of the course j, and $\epsilon_{i,j}$ is the random effect. We call such a model an additive model. (The effects of the two factors are cummulative.)

- the random terms $\epsilon_{1,1}, \epsilon_{2,1}, \ldots, \epsilon_{4,3}$ are normally distributed with equal variance.

The null and the alternative hypotheses are:
H_0: $\mu_1 = \mu_2 = \mu_3$
H_1: At least one of the μs is different

Step 2

We have selected a significance level of 0.05.

Step 3

As before, let us denote the overall mean of all the observations by $\bar{\bar{X}}$. Suppose the total number of treatments $= k$, and the total, number of blocks $= r$. Then, the total number of observations is $n = (r)(k)$. (In our example, treatments are the courses and hence, $k = 3$. Also, blocks are the students. So, $r = 4$. The total number of observations is $n = (4)(3) = 12$.) Let us denote the sample means corresponding to treatments 1, 2, ..., k, by $\bar{X}_{.1}, \bar{X}_{.2}, \ldots, \bar{X}_{.k}$; and the sample means corresponding to the blocks 1, 2, ..., r by $\bar{X}_{1.}, \bar{X}_{2.}, \ldots, \bar{X}_{r.}$.

In this case, the total variation, SS Total, can be broken into three components:

Total Variation	$\text{SS Total} = \sum_{i,j}(X_{i,j} - \bar{\bar{X}})^2 = \text{SST} + \text{SSB} + \text{SSE}$	**12-13**

where, SST, the sum of squares due to treatments, is defined as:

Sum of Squares Due to Treatment	$\text{SST} = r[(\bar{X}_{.1} - \bar{\bar{X}})^2 + (\bar{X}_{.2} - \bar{\bar{X}})^2 + \cdots + (\bar{X}_{.k} - \bar{\bar{X}})^2]$	**12-14**

The new term, SSB, is the sum of squares due to blocks, and is defined as:

 Sum of Squares Due to Blocks (SSB) The weighted sum of squared differences of the block means from the overall mean.

$$\text{SSB} = k[(\bar{X}_{1.} - \bar{\bar{X}})^2 + (\bar{X}_{2.} - \bar{\bar{X}})^2 + \cdots + (\bar{X}_{r.} - \bar{\bar{X}})^2] \qquad \textbf{12-15}$$

and SSE, the sum of squares due to random error, is given by:

Sum of Squares Due to Random Error	$\text{SSE} = \text{SS Total} - \text{SST} - \text{SSB}$	**12-16**

The number of degrees of freedom of SS Total ($= n - 1$) gets divided into ($k - 1$) degrees of freedom of SST, ($r - 1$) degrees of freedom of SSB, and the remaining ($n - k - r + 1$) degrees of freedom of SSE. Hence, we define mean square error (MSE) as

Mean Square Error	$$MSE = \frac{SSE}{(n - k - r + 1)}$$	**12-17**

Our test statistic is:

$$F = \frac{MST}{MSE}$$

Step 4 We have assumed that the error terms $\epsilon_{i,j}$ are all normally distributed with equal variance. As in the case of one-way ANOVA test, MSE is an unbiased estimator of σ^2. When H_0 is true, all the treatment means are equal and MST is also an unbiased estimator of σ^2. In this case, the test statistic has F distribution with $df = (k - 1, n - k - r + 1)$ (=, in our example, (2, 6)). When H_0 is not true, the difference in the treatment means will tend to make the value of MST larger. This will increase the probability of the computed F value being large. Hence, this is an upper-tailed F test. Our decision rule is: reject H_0 if the computed F value is greater than $F_\alpha = F_{0.05}$ ($df = (k - 1, n - k - r + 1)$). In our example, we get from Appendix D, $F_{0.05}$ ($df = (2, 6)$) = 5.14.

Step 5 For our sample data,

$$\bar{\bar{x}} = \frac{76 + 91 + \cdots + 84 + 81}{12} = 83;$$

$$\bar{x}_{1.} = \frac{76 + 76 + 79}{3} = 77; \text{ similarly, } \bar{x}_{2.} = 88; \ \bar{x}_{3.} = 85; \ \bar{x}_{4.} = 82$$

$$\bar{x}_{.1} = \frac{76 + 91 + 88 + 85}{4} = 85; \text{ similarly, } \bar{x}_{.2} = 81; \ \bar{x}_{.3} = 83.$$

SS Total $= (76 - 83)^2 + (91 - 83)^2 + \cdots + (84 - 83)^2 + (81 - 83)^2 = 250$
SST $= 4[(85 - 83)^2 + (81 - 83)^2 + (83 - 83)^2] = 32$
SSB $= 3[(77 - 83)^2 + (88 - 83)^2 + (85 - 83)^2 + (82 - 83)^2] = 198$
SSE $=$ SS Total $-$ SST $-$ SSB $= 250 - 32 - 198 = 20$

We therefore get,

MSE $=$ SSE/$(n - k - r + 1) = 20/6 = 3.33$
MST $=$ SST/$(k - 1) = 32/2 = 16$

Hence,

$$F = \frac{16}{3.33} = 4.80$$

Since the computed F value ($= 4.80$) is smaller than the critical value ($= 5.14$), we conclude that there is insufficient evidence, at $\alpha = 0.05$, to reject H_0. We do not have sufficient evidence, at the 0.05 level of significance, to conclude that the population means of the values of grades, received by Economics graduates at St. Thomas University in the three courses, are different.

It should be noted that the critical F value in a one-way ANOVA test is F_α ($df = (k - 1, n - k)$), while the critical value in the case of randomized block design is F_α ($df = (k - 1, n - k - r + 1)$). Thus, there is a significant loss of degrees of freedom, which makes the critical value larger. This tends to decrease the power of the test. For randomized block design to provide a more powerful test, the block effect should be substantial enough to significantly reduce the mean square error (MSE) and thus neutralize the effect of loss of degrees of freedom. It is therefore worthwhile to test if the block effect is significant. For this, the null and alternative hypotheses are:

H_0: $b_1 = b_2 = \cdots = b_r$ (that is, there is no block effect)
H_1: $b_1, b_2, \ldots, b_r$ are not all equal.

We use as test statistic:

$$\text{Test Statistic } F_B = \frac{\text{MSB}}{\text{MSE}}$$

Here,

Mean Squares for Blocks	$$\text{MSB} = \frac{\text{SSB}}{(r-1)}$$	**12-18**

The decision rule is: reject H_0 if the computed value of F_B is greater than F_α $(df = (r-1, n-k-r+1))$.

In our example, MSB = 198/3 = 66; the computed value of F_B is 66/3.33 = 19.80. If we use the 0.05 level of significance, then $F_{0.05}$ $(df = (3, 6)) = 4.76$.

Since the computed value of F_B (= 19.80) is greater than the critical value, (= 4.76), we conclude that there is sufficient evidence, at 0.05 significance level, that the block effect is significant.

COMPUTER SOLUTION

We give in Charts 12-5 and 12-6, Excel and Minitab instructions for the above problem.

EXCEL CHART 12-5

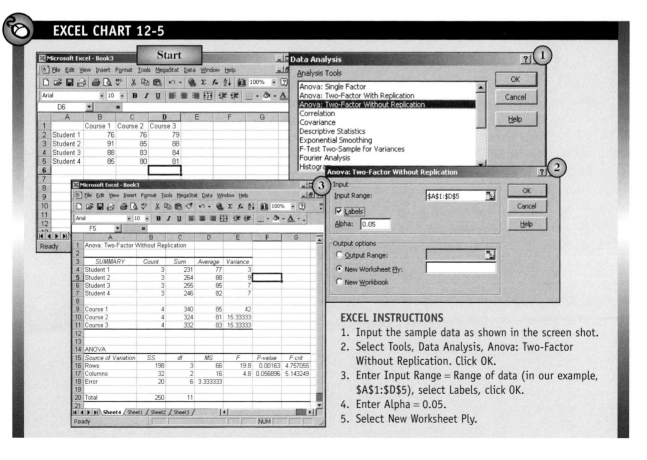

EXCEL INSTRUCTIONS

1. Input the sample data as shown in the screen shot.
2. Select Tools, Data Analysis, Anova: Two-Factor Without Replication. Click OK.
3. Enter Input Range = Range of data (in our example, $A$1:$D$5), select Labels, click OK.
4. Enter Alpha = 0.05.
5. Select New Worksheet Ply.

MINITAB CHART 12-6

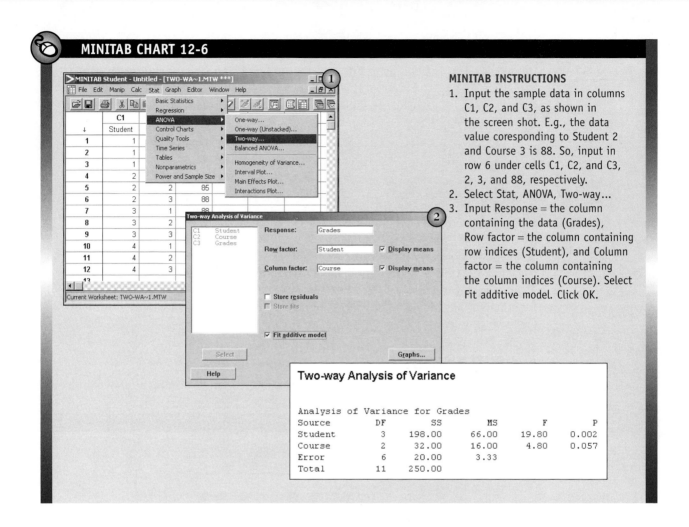

MINITAB INSTRUCTIONS

1. Input the sample data in columns C1, C2, and C3, as shown in the screen shot. E.g., the data value coresponding to Student 2 and Course 3 is 88. So, input in row 6 under cells C1, C2, and C3, 2, 3, and 88, respectively.
2. Select Stat, ANOVA, Two-way...
3. Input Response = the column containing the data (Grades), Row factor = the column containing row indices (Student), and Column factor = the column containing the column indices (Course). Select Fit additive model. Click OK.

In our example, students are the Blocks and correspond to rows, while courses form our Factor, and they correspond to columns. Hence, in the Minitab output, the mean squares (MS) value corresponding to student is MSB, and the MS value corresponding to courses is MST. In the Excel output, MS values corresponding to rows and columns are, respectively, MSB and MST. Both Excel and Minitab give P-values. The P-value corresponding to treatments (courses or columns) is 0.057. Since this is greater than 0.05, we can also conclude from this that there is insufficient evidence to reject the null hypothesis.

■ SELF-REVIEW 12-3

Rudduck Shampoo sells three types of shampoo, one each for dry, normal, and oily hair. Sales, in millions of dollars, for the three types of shampoo for five randomly selected months are given in the following table. Using the 0.05 significance level, test whether the mean sales differ for the three types of shampoo or for the month. Assume that the population distributions are normal with equal variance, and that there is no interactive effect between the different months and the different types of shampoo.

	Sales ($ million)		
Month	Dry	Normal	Oily
June	7	9	12
July	11	12	14
August	13	11	8
September	8	9	7
October	9	10	13

EXERCISES 12-9 TO 12-12

In each of Exercises 12-9 to 12-12, assume that the population distributions are approximately normal with equal variance and that there is no interactive effect between treatments and blocks. For Exercises 12-9 and 12-10, conduct tests of hypotheses to determine whether block and treatment means differ. Use the 0.05 significance level.

12-9.   The following data are given for a randomized block design.

Block	Treatment	
	1	2
A	46	31
B	37	26
C	44	35

12-10.   The following data are given for a randomized block design.

Block	Treatment		
	1	2	3
A	12	14	8
B	9	11	9
C	7	8	8

12-11.   The Chapin Manufacturing Company operates 24 hours a day, five days a week. The workers rotate shifts each week. Management is interested in whether there is a difference in the number of units produced when the employees work on various shifts. A sample of five workers is selected and their output recorded for each shift. At the 0.05 significance level, can we conclude there is a difference in the mean production rate by shift or by employee?

Employee	Day	Afternoon	Night
Mehta	31	25	35
Lum	33	26	33
Clark	28	24	30
Kurz	30	29	28
Morgan	28	26	27

12-12.   The following data shows the number of outpatient surgeries performed last week at three of the hospitals in Toronto. At the 0.05 significance level, can we conclude that there is a difference in the population means of the number of surgeries performed at the three hospitals and on different days of the week?

Day	St. Michael's	West Park	Riverdale
Monday	14	18	24
Tuesday	20	24	14
Wednesday	16	22	14
Thursday	18	20	22
Friday	20	28	24

TWO-FACTOR ANALYSIS OF VARIANCE

In Section 12.3 and the current section, we designed ANOVA tests for equality of mean values of populations corresponding to different levels (treatments) of a single factor. In some situations, we need to study, simultaneously, the effects of two or more factors. For example, we may be interested in studying, simultaneously, the effects of fertilizer, and water, on the crop yield. Such an effect may not be additive. That is, the total effect of fertilizer and water may not equal the effect of fertilizer plus the effect of water. There may be an interactive influence of one factor on the effect of the other factor. In this case, if factors A and B are fixed at treatment levels i and j, and the other factors are randomized, then the corresponding output, $X_{i,j}$ will be:

$$X_{i,j} = a + \mu_i + \lambda_j + \theta_{i,j} + \epsilon_{i,j}$$

Here, μ_i is the mean effect of factor 1 (fixed at treatment level i), λ_j is the mean effect of factor 2 (fixed at treatment level j), $\theta_{i,j}$ is the interactive effect of factors A and B, (fixed at levels i and j, respectively), a is the mean effect of all other factors, and $\epsilon_{i,j}$ is the error term.

We are then interested in testing if there is significant evidence that

(i)   the values of μ_i are not all the same for different levels (treatments) of factor A;

(ii) the values of λ_j are not all the same for different levels (treatments) of factor B;

(iii) a non-zero interactive effect $\theta_{i,j}$ exists for some pairs (i, j).

If there is no interactive effect, then we can use exactly the same approach as in the case of randomized block design, with the second factor replacing the blocks.

If there is an interactive effect, then the ANOVA approach can be directly extended by observing that in this case, the total sum of squares, SS Total, can be decomposed as:

$$\text{SS Total} = \text{SSA} + \text{SSB} + \text{SSAB} + \text{SSE}$$

Here, SSA, SSB, and SSAB are sums of squares due to factor A, factor B, and the interaction between A and B, respectively, and SSE is the sum of squares due to the random error term.

In this case, we need more then one observation for each pair of levels (treatments) of factors A and B. For further details, the reader should refer to an advanced book on statistics.

CHAPTER OUTLINE

I.   The characteristics of an F distribution are:

A. It is continuous.

B. Its values cannot be negative.

C. It is positively skewed.

D. There is a family of F distributions. Each time the degrees of freedom in either the numerator or the denominator changes, a new distribution is created.

II. F distribution is used to test hypotheses above the relative values of the variances of two populations.

A. The sampled populations must be normal.

B. The value of F is computed using the following equation:

$$F = \frac{S_1^2}{S_2^2}$$

12A-1

C. The ratio, F, of the two sample variances is compared to the critical value(s) of F.

III. A one-way ANOVA is used to test whether population means corresponding to several treatments have the same value.

A. The assumptions underlying one-way ANOVA are:

1. The samples are from normally distributed populations.

2. The populations have equal variances.

3. The samples are independent.

B. The essential idea in the ANOVA technique is to decompose the total variation in the data, SS Total, into:

1. SS Total = SST + SSE

2. The formula for SS Total, the sum of squares total is:

$$\text{SS Total} = \sum_{i,j}(X_{i,j} - \bar{\bar{X}})^2$$

12-3

3. The formula for SST, the sum of squares treatment is:

$$\text{SST} = n_1(\bar{X}_{.1} - \bar{\bar{X}})^2 + n_2(\bar{X}_{.2} - \bar{\bar{X}})^2 + \cdots + n_k(\bar{X}_{.k} - \bar{\bar{X}})^2$$

12-4

4. The formula for SSE, the sum of squares error, is:

$$\text{SSE} = \sum_{i}(X_{i,1} - \bar{X}_{.1})^2 + \sum_{i}(X_{i,2} - \bar{X}_{.2})^2 + \cdots + \sum_{i}(X_{i,k} - \bar{X}_{.k})^2$$

12-5

5. This information is summarized in the following table and the value of F determined.

Source of Variation	Sum of Squares	Degrees of Freedom	Mean Square	F
Treatments	SST	$k - 1$	SST/$(k - 1)$ = MST	MST/MSE
Error	SSE	$n - k$	SSE/$(n - k)$ = MSE	
Total	SS total	$n - 1$		

IV. If a null hypothesis of equal treatment means is rejected, we can obtain confidence intervals for the difference in means for each pair of populations, so as to obtain an overall confidence level of at least $(1 - \alpha)$ using two approaches:

A. Fisher's LSD approach gives us the confidence interval:

$$(\bar{X}_{.i} - \bar{X}_{.j}) \pm t_{\alpha/2c}\sqrt{\text{MSE}\left(\frac{1}{n_i} + \frac{1}{n_j}\right)}$$

12-11

B. Tukey's Studentized Range gives us the confidence interval:

$$(\bar{X}_{.i} - \bar{X}_{.j}) \pm \frac{q_\alpha}{\sqrt{2}} \sqrt{MSE\left(\frac{1}{n_i} + \frac{1}{n_j}\right)} \qquad \textbf{12-12}$$

V. In a randomized block design, we consider a second factor variable called the **blocking variable**.

A. In this case, the total variation in the data, SS Total, can be decomposed as:

$$SS\ Total = \sum_{i,j}(X_{i,j} - \bar{\bar{X}})^2 = SST + SSB + SSE$$

B. The formulae for SS Total and SST are the same as in the one-way ANOVA.

C. The formula for SSB, the sum of squares due to blocks, is

$$SSB = k[(\bar{X}_{1.} - \bar{\bar{X}})^2 + (\bar{X}_{2.} - \bar{\bar{X}})^2 + \cdots + (\bar{X}_{r.} - \bar{\bar{X}})^2] \qquad \textbf{12-15}$$

D. The SSE term or sum of squares error is found from the following equation:

$$SSE = SS\ Total - SST - SSB \qquad \textbf{12-16}$$

E. The F statistics for the treatment variable and the blocking variable are determined in the following table.

Source of Variation	Sum of Squares	Degrees of Freedom	Mean Square	F
Treatments	SST	$k - 1$	$SST/(k - 1) = MST$	MST/MSE
Blocks	SSB	$r - 1$	$SSB/(r - 1) = MSB$	MSB/MSE
Error	SSE	$(k - 1)(r - 1)$	$SSE/(k - 1)(r - 1)$	
Total	SS Total	$n - 1$	$= MSE$	

CHAPTER EXERCISES 12-13 TO 12-26

In each of the following, assume that the population distributions are approximately normal with equal variance.

12-13. Random samples of size six were independently selected from each of four populations. The sum of squares total was 250, and the value of MSE was equal to 10. Complete the ANOVA table and test if there is significant evidence, at $\alpha = 0.05$, to infer that the population means are not all equal.

12-14. The following is a partial one-way ANOVA table.

Source	Sum of Squares	df	Mean Square	F
Treatment		2		
Error			20	
Total	500	11		

Complete the table, and test if there is sufficient evidence, at $\alpha = 0.05$, that the population means corresponding to the treatments are not all equal.

12-15. A consumer organization wants to know whether there is a difference in the price of a particular toy at three different types of stores. The price of the toy was checked in a sample of five discount stores, five variety stores, and five department stores. The results are shown below. Use the 0.05 significance level.

Discount	$12	$13	$14	$12	$15
Variety	$15	$17	$14	$18	$17
Department	$19	$17	$16	$20	$19

12-16. A physician who specializes in weight control has three different diets she recommends. As an experiment, she randomly selected 15 patients and then assigned five to each diet. After three weeks, the following weight losses, in kilograms, were noted. At the 0.05 significance level, can she conclude that the population means of the amount of weight loss for the three diets are not all equal?

Plan A	2	3	2	3	2
Plan B	3	4	3	2	3
Plan C	3	4	5	4	5

12-17. The City of Maumee comprises four districts. Police Chief Andy North wants to determine whether there is a difference in the mean number of crimes committed among the four districts. He recorded the number of crimes reported in each district during independently and randomly selected samples of six days each. At the 0.05 significance level, can the Police Chief conclude that the population means of numbers of crimes per day in the four districts are not all the same?

Rec Centre	Key Street	Monclova	Whitehouse
13	21	12	16
15	13	14	17
14	18	15	18
15	19	13	15
14	18	12	20
15	19	15	18

12-18. The personnel director of Cander Machine Products is investigating "perfectionism" on the job. A test designed to measure perfectionism was administered to a random sample of 18 employees. The scores ranged from 20 to about 40. One of the facets of the study involved the early background of each employee. Did the employee come from a rural background, a small city, or a large city?
The scores are:

Rural Area	35	30	36	38	29	34	31
Small Urban Area	28	24	25	30	32	28	
Large Urban Area	24	28	26	30	34		

(a) At the 0.05 level, can we conclude that the population means of scores of employees corresponding to the three backgrounds are not all equal?
(b) If the null hypothesis is rejected, can you state that the mean score of those with a rural background is different from the score of those with a large-city background? (Use Tukey's test.)

12-19. We pointed out in Section 12.3 that, when only two treatments are involved, ANOVA and the Student's t test (Chapter 11) result in the same conclusions. Also, $t^2 = F$. As an example, suppose that 14 randomly selected students were divided into two groups, one consisting of 6 students and the other of 8. One group was taught using a combination of lecture and programmed instruction, the other using a combination of lecture and television. At the end of the course, each group was given a 50-item test. The following is a list of the number of correct answers obtained by each student.

Lecture and Programmed Instruction	19	17	23	22	17	16		
Lecture and Television	32	28	31	26	23	24	27	25

(a) Using analysis of variance techniques, test H_0 that the population means of the two test scores are equal; $\alpha = 0.05$.
(b) Using the t test from Chapter 11, compute t.
(c) Interpret the results.

12-20. One reads that a business school graduate with an undergraduate degree earns more than a high school graduate with no additional education, and a person with a master's degree or a doctorate earns even more. To test this, a random sample of 25 executives from companies with assets over $1 million was selected. Their incomes, classified by highest level of education, follow.

Income ($ thousands)		
High School or Less	Undergraduate Degree	Master's Degree or More
65	69	71
67	77	93
73	105	102
72	93	79
59	101	114
63	104	109
74	109	109
	112	115
	62	93

Test if there is evidence, at the 0.05 level of significance, that the population means of incomes of the three groups are not all equal. If the null hypothesis is rejected, conduct further tests to determine which groups differ. (Use Tukey's method).

12-21. Shank's, Inc., a national advertising firm, wants to know whether the size of an advertisement and the colour of the advertisement make a difference in the response of magazine readers. A random sample of readers is shown ads in four different colours and three different sizes. Each reader is asked to give the particular combination of size and colour a rating between 1 and 10. The rating for each combination is shown in the following table.

Size of Ad	Colour of Ad			
	Red	Blue	Orange	Green
Small	2	3	3	8
Medium	3	5	6	7
Large	6	7	8	8

Is there a difference in the effectiveness of an ad by colour and by size? Use the 0.05 level of significance. Assume there is no interactive effect between the colour and size.

12-22. There are four McBurger restaurants in the Winnipeg area. The numbers of burgers sold at the respective restaurants for each of a randomly selected sample of six weeks are shown below. At the 0.05 significance level, can we conclude that the population means of the number of burgers sold at the four restaurants are not all the same? Assume there is no interactive effect between restaurants and weeks.

Week	Restaurant			
	Metro	Market Plaza	University	River
1	124	160	320	190
2	234	220	340	230
3	430	290	290	240
4	105	245	310	170
5	240	205	280	180
6	310	260	270	205

12-23. The city of Saskatoon employs people to assess the value of homes for the purpose of establishing real estate tax. The city manager routinely sends each assessor to the same set of five randomly selected homes and then compares the results. The information is given below, in thousands of dollars. Can we conclude that there is a difference in the assessors, at $\alpha = 0.05$? Assume there is no interactive effect between assessors and homes.

Home	Assessor			
	Zawodny	Norman	Cingle	Holiday
A	$153.00	$155.00	$149.00	$145.00
B	$150.00	$151.00	$152.00	$153.00
C	$148.00	$152.00	$147.00	$153.00
D	$170.00	$168.00	$165.00	$164.00
E	$184.00	$189.00	$192.00	$186.00

12-24.

Item	Supermarkets		
	A	B	C
1	$1.12	$1.02	$1.07
2	$1.14	$1.10	$1.21
3	$1.72	$1.97	$2.08
4	$2.22	$2.09	$2.32
5	$2.40	$2.10	$2.30
6	$4.04	$4.32	$4.15
7	$5.05	$4.95	$5.05
8	$4.68	$4.13	$4.67
9	$5.52	$5.46	$5.86

Three supermarket chains in the Toronto area (let us label them A, B, and C) each claim to have the lowest overall prices. As part of an investigative study on supermarket advertising, *The Toronto Sun* conducted a study. First, a random sample of nine grocery items was selected. Next, the price of each selected item was checked at each of the three chains on the same day. At the 0.05 significance level, is there a difference in the population means of prices at the supermarkets and for the items? Assume there is no interactive effect between items and supermarkets.

12-25. A research firm wants to compare the effect of different grades of gasoline: unleaded regular, mid-grade, and super premium, on automobile fuel efficiency. Because of differences in the performance of different automobiles, seven different automobiles were randomly selected and treated as blocks. Therefore, each grade of gasoline was tested (on the highway) with each type of automobile. The results of the trials, in litres per 100 km, are shown in the following table. At the 0.05 significance level, is there a difference in the effects of different types of gasolines and automobiles on fuel efficiency? Assume that there is no interactive effect between different types of gasoline and automobiles.

Automobile	Unleaded Regular	Mid-grade	Super Premium
1	7.8	8.0	8.3
2	8.0	7.9	8.2
3	8.1	8.2	8.5
4	8.1	8.1	8.3
5	8.3	8.4	8.7
6	8.4	8.2	8.4
7	8.3	8.5	9.0

12-26. The weights (in grams) of a sample of M&Ms Plain candies, classified according to colour are given in the file Exercise 12-26.xls on the CD. Use a statistical software system to determine whether there is a difference in the mean weights of candies of different colours. Use the 0.05 significance level.

www.exercises.ca 12-27 TO 12-33

12-27. The Web site www.globefund.com has a wealth of information on Canadian mutual funds. Go to this Web site, click on "Fund Filter" (under Tools), select an asset class, and click on "Go" and "Five star ratings." Randomly choose data on one-year percentage returns on one company for each pair of (one- to five-star rating) and (Canadian Balanced Funds and Health care). Using this data, perform a two-way ANOVA to test if there is significant evidence, at the 0.05 significance level, that there is a difference between population means for one-year percentage returns for Canadian Balanced funds and Health Care funds. Assume there is no interactive effect between the type of fund and the star ratings. Also, assume the population distributions are normal with equal variance.

12-28. The percentage of quarterly changes in the gross domestic product for 20 countries can be obtained from www.oecd.org by clicking on "statistics" and "quarterly growth rates in GDP...". Copy the data for Canada, Japan, and the United States into three columns into Minitab or Excel. Perform an ANOVA to test if the three population means are equal. Use the 0.05 level of significance, and assume the population distributions are approximately normal with equal variance.

COMPUTER DATA EXERCISES 12-29 TO 12-31

12-29. Refer to the data in file BASEBALL-2000.xls, which reports information on the 30 Major League Baseball teams for the 2000 season. Assume that in each of the following the population distributions are approximately normal.

   (a) At the 0.10 significance level, is there a difference in the variances of the number of stolen bases among the teams who play their home games on natural grass versus artificial turf?

   (b) Create a variable that classifies a team's total attendance into three groups: less than 2.0 (million), 2.0 up to 3.0, and 3.0 or more. At the 0.05 significance level, can we conclude that the population means of the number of games won for the three groups are not all equal? (Assume that the population variances are equal.)

   (c) Using the same attendance variable developed in part (b), can we conclude that the population means of team batting averages in the three groups are not all equal? Use $\alpha = 0.1$ (Assume that the population variances are equal.)

12-30. Refer to the data in file OECD.xls, which reports information on census, economic, and business data for 29 countries. Assume that in each of the following population distributions are approximately normal with equal variance.

   (a) Categorize the 29 countries indicating whether they are in Europe, North America, or the Far East. Can we conclude, at the 0.05 significance level, that there is a difference in the mean percent of the population over 65 years of age?

   (b) Use the same three categories developed in part (a). Divide the Gross Domestic Product by the population to create a new variable. This variable shows the per capita GDP. Can we conclude, at the 0.05 significance level, that there is a difference in the mean of this variable by geographic region?

12-31. Refer to the data in file Real Estate Data.xls, which reports information on the homes sold in Victoria, B.C. area last year. Check if we can conclude, at the 0.02 significance level, each of the following. Assume that in each case the population distributions are approximately normal.

   (a) There is a difference in the population variances of the selling prices of the homes that have a pool versus those that do not have a pool.

   (b) The population means of the selling prices of the homes among the five townships are not all the same. (Assume here that the population variances are equal.)

CHAPTER 12   ANSWERS TO SELF-REVIEW

12-1. H_0: $\mu_1 = \mu_2 = \mu_3$
H_1: At least one treatment mean is different.
Decision rule is: reject H_0 if $F > 4.26$
SS Total $= (20 - 20.58)^2 + (15 - 20.58)^2 + \cdots +$
$(30 - 20.58)^2 + (32 - 20.58)^2 = 566.92$
SST $= 4(19.25 - 20.58)^2 + 4(13.75 - 20.58)^2$
$+ 4(28.75 - 20.58)^2 = 460.67$
SSE $= 566.92 - 460.67 = 106.25$

Source	Sum of Squares	Degrees of Freedom	Mean Square	F
Treatment	460.67	2	230.335	19.510
Error	106.25	9	11.806	
Total	566.92	11		

Since the computed F value is greater than 4.26, there is sufficient evidence, at $\alpha = 0.05$, to conclude that the population means are not all the same.

12-2. The value $q_{0.05}$ ($df = (3, 9)$) is 3.95.
Hence, Tukey's 95 percent confidence interval estimate, for the difference in population means corresponding to treatments 1 and 3, is

$$(19.25 - 28.75) \pm \frac{3.95}{\sqrt{2}}\sqrt{11.806\left(\frac{1}{4} + \frac{1}{4}\right)}$$

$$= (-16.286, -2.714)$$

Since the interval estimate does not contain zero, we can conclude, at the 0.05 significance level, that the corresponding population means are unequal.

12-3. For types: let the different treatment means be μ_1, μ_2, and μ_3.
H_0: $\mu_1 = \mu_2 = \mu_3$
H_1: The treatment means are not all equal.
$F_{0.05}$ ($df = (2, 8)$) $= 4.46$. Hence, we shall reject H_0 if $F > 4.46$.

For months: let the different block means be b_1, b_2, b_3, b_4, and b_5.
H_0: $b_1 = b_2 = b_3 = b_4 = b_5$
H_1: The block means are not all equal.
$F_{0.05}$ ($df = (4, 8)$) $= 3.84$. Hence, we shall reject H_0 if $F > 3.84$.

The analysis of variance table is as follows:

Source	df	SS	MS	F
Types	2	3.60	1.80	0.39
Months	4	31.73	7.93	1.71
Error	8	37.07	4.63	
Total	14	72.40		

The null hypothesis *cannot* be rejected for either types or months. There is *insufficient* evidence, at the 0.05 significance level, to conclude that there is a difference in the mean sales among types or months.

A REVIEW OF CHAPTERS 10–12

This section is a review of the major concepts and terms introduced in Chapters 10, 11, and 12.

Chapter 10 began our study of hypothesis testing. In statistical hypothesis testing, we are interested in proving a certain hypothesis about a population distribution. We accept its complementary hypothesis as the **default hypothesis**. It is called the *null hypothesis* and is denoted by H_0. The hypothesis being proved is called the **alternative hypothesis** and is denoted by H_1. When we complete the test, our conclusion is one of the following: (i) *We have sufficient evidence to reject H_0 and accept H_1*; (ii) *we do not have sufficient evidence to reject H_0*. The test is designed to restrict the probability of falsely rejecting H_0 to a predetermined value α.

In Chapter 10, we considered only hypotheses about the value of the mean of a single population and those about the value of a single population proportion. We assumed that the population distribution is normal or the sample size is large. In this case, when the population variance is known, the test for population mean is a z test. When the population variance is unknown and the population distribution is normal, the test is a t test. For large values of the sample size, t distribution is almost the same as the z distribution, and hence, the two tests are almost identical. In the case of a population proportion, the value of population variance depends on the value of the population proportion. We assumed that the sample size is large. The test developed is then a z test.

In Chapter 11, we extended the ideas of Chapter 10 to develop tests for hypotheses about relative values of means of two populations. We considered two types of tests.

(i) Tests involving samples drawn independently from the two populations. In this case, we assumed that the population distributions are normal. We developed a t test for the case of equal population variances, and an approximate t test for the case for unequal population variances.

(ii) Tests involving a matched pair sample. In this case, by considering only the difference between the pairs of values in the sample, we reduced the test to the case of a test of mean of a simple population.

We also considered hypotheses about relative values of two population proportions, and developed a z test for the case of independent samples.

Chapter 11 dealt with hypothesis concerning relative values of means of two populations. Chapter 12 presented a procedure called the *analysis of variance*, or *ANOVA* to simultaneously test whether several populations have identical means. As an example of the analysis of variance, a test could be conducted to find whether there is any difference in effectiveness among five fertilizers on the wheat yield. This type of analysis is referred to as *one-factor ANOVA* because it enables us to draw conclusions about the difference between the effects of different levels (treatments) of a single factor (such as fertilizer) on the population mean (such as yield).

The test is based on the assumption that population distributions are normal with equal variance. The procedure involves collecting random sample data independently from the populations and decomposing the total variation in the total sample data (on all populations) into variation within samples (called *random variation* or *sum of squares due to error* (SSE)) and variation between samples (called *treatment variation*, or *sum of squares due to treatments* (SST)). The test statistic used is the ratio of normalized values of SST and SSE. When all population means are equal, this follows a probability distribution called the *F distribution*. The test statistic is called an *F statistic* and the test is called an *F test*. We set up an ANOVA table to organize the calculation of the *F* value into a convenient form.

If we want to draw conclusions about the simultaneous effects of two factors or variables, the *two-factor ANOVA* technique is applied. In this case too, the test statistic used follows *F* distribution under the null hypothesis and is called an *F statistic*. An *F* statistic is also used when we want to test a hypothesis about relative values of variances of two populations.

GLOSSARY

Chapter 10

Alternative hypothesis The hypothesis, about a population distribution, that we are interested in proving. We denote it by H_1. This is usually a research hypothesis.

Critical Values The dividing points between the rejection region and the region where H_0 is not rejected.

Hypothesis Testing Given a pair of complementary hypotheses about a population distribution, called *null and alternative hypotheses*, hypothesis testing is a statistical technique of analyzing a sample data selected randomly from the population and making one of the following two decisions: (i) we have sufficient evidence to reject the null hypothesis in favour of the alternative hypothesis; or (ii) we do *not* have sufficient evidence to reject the null hypothesis. The test is designed to keep the probability of Type I error less than a prescribed value, α, and minimize the probability of Type II error.

Null Hypothesis The complement of the alternative hypothesis. We denote it by H_0. We accept the null hypothesis as the default hypothesis.

One-Tailed Test Test in which the rejection region is only in one tail of the distribution of the test statistic.

P-value of an Instance of a Test of Hypothesis The value of the level of significance, α^*, for which a critical value of the test statistic equals the computed value of the test statistic. It can be interpreted as the observed level of significance.

Power Function of a Test The function which, for given values of α and n, assigns to every possible value of the population parameter corresponding to H_1, a value equal to the corresponding power of the test.

Power of a Test The probability of rejecting H_0 when H_0 is false. In other words, it is the probability of correctly identifying a true alternative hypothesis.

Rejection Region The set of possible values of the test statistic for which, as per our decision rule, the null hypothesis H_0 will be rejected.

Significance Level of a Test The probability of Type I error. That is, the probability of rejecting the null hypothesis (H_0) when it is true. It is designated by the Greek letter α (pronounced *alpha*).

Test Statistic A suitably chosen sample statistic. We make our decision based on the value of the test statistic obtained from the selected sample data.

Two-Tailed Test Test in which there is a rejection region in each of the two tails of the distribution of the test statistic.

Type I Error The error committed when we reject a true null hypothesis.

Type II Error The error committed when we do not reject a null hypothesis when it is false. The probability of committing a Type II error is designated by the Greek letter, β (pronounced *beta*).

Chapter 11

Matched Pair Sample Sample chosen by matching or pairing elements in two populations and choosing a random sample of matched pairs.

Independent Samples Random samples chosen independently from two populations that are in no way related to each other.

Pooled Estimator of the Population Variance A weighted average of S_1^2 and S_2^2 used as an estimator of the common variance, σ^2, of the two populations.

Chapter 12

Analysis of Variance (ANOVA) A technique used to test simultaneously whether the means of several populations are equal. It uses the F distribution as the distribution of the test statistic.

Block A second source of variation, in addition to the factor under consideration.

Factor A cause or specific source of variation in data.

Treatment A particular level of the factor under consideration.

EXERCISES

PART I—MULTIPLE CHOICE

1. In a one-tailed z test using the 0.01 significance level, the critical value is either
   a. -1.96 or $+1.96$.
   b. -1.65 or $+1.65$.
   c. -2.58 or $+2.58$.
   d. 0 or 1.
   e. None of these is correct.

2. A Type II error is committed if we:
   a. Reject a true null hypothesis.
   b. Accept a true alternative hypothesis.
   c. Do not accept a true alternative hypothesis.
   d. Accept both the null and alternative hypotheses at the same time.
   e. None of these is correct.

3. The hypotheses are H_0: $\mu = 78$ kg and H_1: $\mu \neq 78$ kg
   a. A one-tailed test is being applied.
   b. A two-tailed test is being applied.
   c. A three-tailed test is being applied.
   d. The wrong test is being applied.
   e. None of these is correct.

4. The 0.01 significance level is used in an experiment, and a lower-tailed z test is applied. Computed z is -1.8. This indicates:
   a. H_0 should not be rejected.
   b. We should reject H_0 and accept H_1.
   c. We should take a larger sample.
   d. We should have used the 0.05 level of significance.
   e. None of these is correct.

5. The test statistic for testing a hypothesis about a population mean when the population distribution is normal and the population standard deviation is not known is:
   a. z b. t c. F d. χ^2

6. We want to test a hypothesis for the difference between two population means. The null and alternative hypotheses are stated as
   H_0: $\mu_1 = \mu_2$
   H_1: $\mu_1 \neq \mu_2$
   a. A left-tailed test should be applied.
   b. A two-tailed test should be applied.
   c. A right-tailed test should be applied.
   d. We cannot determine whether a left-, right-, or a two-tailed test should be applied based on the information given.
   e. None of these is correct.

7. The F distribution:
   a. Is defined over only non-negative values of F.
   b. Is defined over only negative values of F.
   c. Is the same as the t distribution.
   d. Is the same as the z distribution.
   e. None of these is correct.

8. For a normally distributed population, as the sample size increases, the distribution of $\left(\dfrac{\bar{X} - \mu}{s/\sqrt{n}} \right)$ approaches
   a. ANOVA.
   b. The standard normal or z distribution.
   c. The Poisson distribution.
   d. Zero.
   e. None of these is correct.

9. An ANOVA test was conducted for comparison of population means. The null hypothesis was rejected. This indicates
   a. There was too many degrees of freedom.
   b. There is no difference between the population means.

c. There is a difference between at least two population means.
d. A larger sample should be selected.
e. None of these is correct.

PART II—PROBLEMS

10. Research by the Bank of Montreal revealed that only 8 percent of their customers wait more than five minutes to do their banking. Management considers this reasonable, and will not add more tellers unless the proportion becomes larger than 8 percent. The branch manager at a Toronto branch believes the wait is longer than the standard at her branch and requests additional part-time tellers. To support her request, the branch manager reports that in a sample of 100 customers, 10 waited more than five minutes. At the 0.01 significance, is it reasonable to conclude that more than 8 percent of the customers wait more than five minutes at this branch?

For each of the problems 11–15, assume that the populations are approximately normally distributed.

11. A machine is set to produce tennis balls so the mean bounce is 90 cm when the ball is dropped from a platform of a certain height. The supervisor suspects that the mean bounce of the balls produced is less than 90 cm. As an experiment, 42 balls were dropped from the platform and the mean height of the bounce was 88.75 cm, with a sample standard deviation of 2.25 cm. At the 0.05 significance level can the supervisor conclude that the mean bounce height is less than 90 cm?

12. It was hypothesized that university clerical employees did not engage in productive work 20 minutes on the average out of every hour. Some claimed the time lost was greater than 20 minutes. An actual study was conducted at a University in Ontario using a stopwatch and other ways of checking the work habits of the clerical employees. A random check of the employees revealed the following unproductive times, in minutes, during a one-hour period (exclusive of regularly scheduled breaks):
    10   25   17   20   28   30   18   23   18

    Using the 0.05 significance level, is it reasonable to conclude the mean unproductive time is greater than 20 minutes per hour?

13. A test was conducted involving the mean holding power of two glues designed for plastic. First, a small plastic hook was coated at one end with Epox glue and fastened to a sheet of plastic. After it dried, weight was added to the hook until it separated from the sheet of plastic. The weight was then recorded. This was repeated until 12 hooks were tested. The same procedure was followed for Holdtite glue, but only 10 hooks were used. The sample results, in kilograms, were:

	Epox	Holdtite
Sample mean	114	115
Sample standard deviation	2.3	3.6

    At the 0.01 significance level, is there a difference between the population mean of holding power of Epox and that of Holdtite?

14. An additive, formulated to add to the life of paints, is to be tested. The top half of a piece of wood was painted using the regular paint. The bottom half was painted with the paint including the additive. The same procedure was followed for a total of 10 pieces of wood. Then each piece was subjected to high-pressure water and brilliant light. The data,

number of hours each piece lasted before it faded beyond a certain point, follow:

	Number of Hours by Sample									
	A	B	C	D	E	F	G	H	I	J
Without additive	325	313	320	340	318	312	319	330	333	319
With additive	323	313	326	343	310	320	313	340	330	315

Using the 0.05 significance level, determine whether the additive is effective in prolonging the life of the paint.

15. A Montreal cola distributor is featuring a super-special sale on 12-packs. She wonders where in the grocery store to place the cola for maximum attention. Should it be near the front door of the grocery store, in the cola section, at the checkout registers, or near the milk and other dairy products? Four stores with similar total sales were randomly selected for an experiment. In one store the 12-packs were stacked near the front door, in another they were placed near the checkout registers, and so on. Sales were checked at specified times in each store for exactly four minutes. The results were:

Cola at the Door	In Soft Drink Section	Near Registers	Dairy Section
$6	$5	$7	$10
8	10	10	9
3	12	9	6
7	4	4	11
	9	5	
		7	

The distributor wants to find out whether there is sufficient evidence at the 0.05 significance level to infer that the mean sales for cola stacked at the four locations in the store are not all the same. What should be her conclusion? Assume that the population variances are equal.

■ CASE STUDY A

The ministry of labour wants to study the trends and patterns in youth unemployment rates in Canada. Consider the sample data in file Youth Unemployment in Canada.xls on the accompanying CD-ROM.

Divide the time period 1976–2000 into three groups: 1976–1984, 1985–1992, and 1993–2000. Test if there is significant evidence that the mean youth unemployment rates during these three periods are not all the same. In case the null hypothesis is rejected, test which of the three means differ.

Using the entire sample data, test if there is significant evidence that the mean unemployment rates during the four quarters are not all the same. If the null hypothesis is rejected, test which of the population means differ.

■ CASE STUDY B

Ms. Gene Dempsey manages the emergency care centre at the Bell Grove Medical Centre. One of her responsibilities is to have enough nurses so that incoming patients needing service can be handled promptly. It is stressful for patients to wait a long time for emergency care even when their care needs are not life threatening. Ms. Dempsey gathered information regarding the number of patients who came in to emergency over the last several weeks. This data is given in file Case Study B.xls on the CD accompanying the text. The centre is not open on weekends. Does it appear that there are any differences in the number of patients served by the day of the week? If there are differences, which days seem to be the busiest?

CHAPTER 13

Correlation and Simple Regression Analysis

GOALS

When you have completed this chapter, you will be able to:

- Identify a relationship between variables on a *scatter diagram*

- Measure and interpret a degree of relationship by a *coefficient of correlation*

- Conduct a *test of hypothesis* about the coefficient of correlation in a population

- Identify the roles of *dependent* and *independent* variables, the concept of regression, and its distinction from the concept of correlation

- Measure and interpret the strength of relationship between two variables through a *regression line* and the *technique of least squares*

- Conduct *analysis of variance* and calculate *coefficient of determination*

- Conduct a *test of hypothesis* for a regression model and each coefficient of regression

 • Estimate *confidence* and *prediction intervals*.

SIR FRANCIS GALTON (1822–1911)

Along with Francis Ysidro Edgeworth and Karl Pearson, Sir Francis Galton helped create a statistical revolution. His major contributions to the field of statistics were the concepts of correlation and simple regression. Galton dedicated the majority of his efforts and great works to the study of heredity, and the science of eugenics that he founded. However, it was his study of the seeds of both parent and second-generation sweet peas that provided Galton with some important insights, which eventually led to the formal discovery of regression analysis. It was Galton's work on the relationship between the stature of parents and their offspring that formed the basis for further developments in correlation and regression analysis.

Francis Galton's father was a medical practitioner and wanted Francis to follow his profession. He therefore first studied medicine at Cambridge despite his lack of interest. After his father's death, he inherited a large amount of wealth and gave up the pursuit of a medical career to focus on the things that interested him most. One of his first endeavours was to travel to South West Africa where he explored and mapped the region, one of the first to do so. In 1853 he received the gold medal from the Royal Geographical Society in recognition of his achievements. His cousin's book, *Origin of Species* (1859), had a major impact on the future of Galton's work. Galton wrote to Darwin and said that reading his book "formed a real crisis in my life; your book drove away the constraint of my old superstition as if it had been a nightmare and was the first to give me freedom of thought".[1]

Galton seems to have always been interested in numbers and could often be observed simply counting the number of related events he happened to see in a day. Twice he had his portrait painted and after counting the number of brush strokes it took he guessed that it was approximately 20 000 strokes per portrait. Oddly enough, Galton had very little confidence in his own mathematical ability and often employed the help of experts to aid him. After explaining the relationship he had found between average height of sons and height of parents to Hamilton Dickson, a mathematician from Cambridge, Dickson easily provided a mathematical proof that formed the basis of what is now known as the correlation coefficient. Since, in his experiment, Galton had observed the son's heights (Y), on average, *regress* towards the average height of all parents (X), he used the word *regression* for this relationship. Thus, if a parent's height were above X by ten centimetres, then the son's height, on average, would be above Y by less than ten centimetres. This *regression effect* occurs in situations where the variables have joint normal distribution with almost equal variances, and it is therefore termed a *regression fallacy* by statisticians. In statistics, the word *regression* is now popularly used for regression analysis without any implication of the regression effect.

Due to Galton's many achievements, he was knighted in 1909. Telling his friend Pearson the news, he wrote, "A precious bad knight I should make now, with all my infirmities. Even seven years ago it required some engineering to get me on the back of an Egyptian donkey, and I have worsened steadily since."[2]

INTRODUCTION

Chapters 2 through 4 dealt with *descriptive statistics*. We organized raw data into a frequency distribution, and computed several measures of central tendency and dispersion to describe the major characteristics of the data. Chapters 5 to 7 introduced the theoretical concepts of probability and probability distributions. Chapter 8 introduced various sampling techniques and the concept of sampling distribution of a statistic. These were used in chapters 9 to 12 to draw inferences about a population parameter, such as the population mean, based on the information contained in a sample. We constructed confidence intervals and tested hypotheses about mean or proportion of one population and the difference between means of two or more populations. All of these tests involved just *one* interval, or ratio level variable, such as the quality of life in Ontario, the price of Bell Canada shares, or the popularity of Liberals (a proportion) in Newfoundland.

We shift our emphasis in this chapter. We shall now study the relationship between *two* variables, such as investment and profit, or inflation and unemployment. We first study the direction and degree of relationship between two variables through the technique of correlation analysis. We then develop a more powerful technique called regression analysis. How closely are productivity and wages of Canadian workers related? Is there a relationship between the amount IBM spends on advertising and its sales? Can we estimate the cost to heat a home in Winnipeg during the winter months based on the number of square feet in the home?

We begin this chapter by examining the meaning and purpose of correlation analysis. Then we look at a chart designed to portray the relationship between two variables: a scatter diagram. We continue our study of correlation through a formula that will allow us to estimate the degree of relationship by a single value (on an interval scale), and conduct a test of hypothesis about the correlation in the population.

We then study the relationship between two variables through an equation of a line. This is called simple regression analysis. This would allow us to measure the strength of relationship between two variables in terms of the slope of a line (on a ratio scale). Our discussion on regression analysis includes: (1) origin, the nature of data and the nature of relationship; (2) the regression model; (3) derivation of point estimators of the regression line based on the method of least squares; (4) analysis of variance, derivation of the standard error of the estimate and the coefficient of determination; (5) tests of hypotheses for the regression parameters and the model; and (6) confidence intervals and prediction intervals. The last topic is covered in the file Chapter 13 Appendix A on the CD-ROM. We discuss the model diagnostics in detail in the next chapter.

13.1   CORRELATION

THE NATURE OF CORRELATION ANALYSIS

Correlation refers to the possibility of togetherness in the variation of two variables. We may observe movements in two qualitative variables such as thoughts or feelings of two individuals. For example, we usually observe movements in thoughts of two friends in the same direction; movements in thoughts of two adversaries in the opposite direction; and movements in thoughts of two strangers showing very little or no direction. However, we should always remember that the concept of correlation does not imply a cause and effect relationship between two variables.

Correlation analysis, in statistics, is the study of the *linear relationship between two or more random variables, which are measurable on an interval or ratio scale.* We shall limit our discussion in this chapter to bivariate distributions, a record of simultaneous (paired) observations on two variables. For example, we observe movements in pairs of random variables, such as the height and weight of many individuals, rates of inflation and unemployment over a number of years or a number of countries, closing prices of two stocks on the last fifty Fridays, assets and net income of several corporations, or grades of thirty students in Statistics and Accounting. In correlation analysis, we are interested in both the direction of the relationship and the degree or closeness of the relationship.

For example, we may wish to study how the income per capita and the quality of life are related. Data showing the index of per capita income (in the form of an index, value in year 1971 = 100 represents GDP per capita in 1971 at 1992 prices = $17 053) and the quality of life or well-being index (based on a number of factors such as consumption of goods and services, stock of wealth, poverty and inequality, and economic security including personal security from crime and ill health, unemployment, family break-up, poverty in old age, etc.). A tabular representation of data, see Table 13-1, gives us a rough idea of the relationship. As evident from the numbers, both income per capita index and the well-being index have gone up during the sample period, 1971–97. However, a closer look at the table reveals that the income in 1977 (120.24) is 20 percent higher than the income in 1971, while the well-being index remained almost unchanged (an increase from 100 to 100.67). A similar argument can be made for the years 1973 and 1996. We could do similar analyses for samples of other years. However, we can get a better idea of what is happening behind these numbers by plotting all observations on a chart, called a **scatter diagram**.

THE SCATTER DIAGRAM

 A **scatter diagram** portrays the paired observations on any two variables on a chart.

A scatter diagram displays each pair of observations as one point on a chart, observations on one variable on the *x*-axis (the horizontal axis) and on another variable on the *y*-axis (the vertical axis). Let us draw a scatter diagram (Chart 13-1) corresponding to the data in Table 13-1. To plot the chart, we first mark each axis starting from numbers close to the minimum values through numbers close to the maximum values of each variable. There is no rule as to which axis should be used for which variable. We then take a pair of observations, one at a time, find the points corresponding to the values of the two variables on the *x* and *y* axes, and draw perpendicular from each point corresponding to the values on each axis. The point of intersection of the two perpendiculars gives us one point on the chart for one pair of observations.

 Please note that in this chapter and onwards, we use uppercase letters (X, Y symbols) for both random and non-random variables; we use lowercase letters (x, y) for corresponding implied values of those variables.

For example, the first pair of observations on income (100) and well-being (100) is right on the point of origin "O," the intersection of the two axes. The point "A" refers to the pair of observations ($x = 103.11$, $y = 106.28$) for the year 1972. Similarly, point "B" corresponds to the pair of observations for the year 1997 ($x = 155.00$, $y = 112.53$). By repeating this exercise for all pairs of observations, we obtain the scatter diagram for the

TABLE 13-1: Income Per Capita (Index) and Well-Being (Index) of Canadians (1971–97)

CHART 13-1: Scatter Diagram

Year	Income	Well-Being
1971	100.00	100.00
1972	103.11	106.28
1973	109.21	109.99
1974	112.15	108.85
1975	113.00	105.15
1976	117.62	102.15
1977	120.24	100.67
1978	123.87	102.18
1979	127.82	102.60
1980	127.99	105.56
1981	130.21	106.46
1982	124.87	109.24
1983	127.00	107.97
1984	132.92	107.69
1985	138.80	110.33
1986	141.05	109.23
1987	145.00	108.04
1988	150.05	113.69
1989	151.25	116.53
1990	149.39	114.36
1991	144.75	112.68
1992	144.04	112.49
1993	145.73	112.62
1994	149.58	111.81
1995	150.98	110.63
1996	151.09	110.70
1997	155.00	112.53

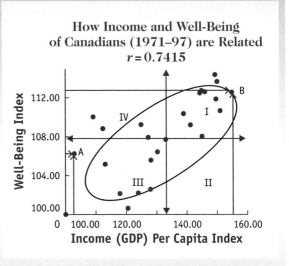

How Income and Well-Being of Canadians (1971–97) are Related
$r = 0.7415$

Source: An Index of Economic Well-Being for the Canadian Provinces, November 2000, Centre for the Study of Living Standards, Appendix: Table P10-9

entire data set. As shown below, we can draw scatter diagrams easily with computer software. The direction of movements in the two variables is now more visible. Most of the observations on income and well-being are seen moving together from the southwest to the northeast direction in the shape of an upward sloping "band," called an **ellipse**.

We can identify the observations that contribute to positive versus negative linear association by dividing the scatter diagram into four quadrants through the means of the two variables. We have drawn two lines (the blue arrowhead lines) in the scatter diagram through the means of the two variables (132.84, 108.54). Observations in quadrant I (Northeast) are above their mean values and observations in quadrant III (Southwest) are below their mean values.

Thus, the values of the two variables in quadrants I and III move together in the same direction (a positive association). In quadrant II (Southeast), on the other hand, the values of the variable X are above the mean, while the values of the variable Y are below the mean. The converse is true for quadrant IV (Northwest). Thus, the variables move in opposite directions in quadrants II and IV, implying a negative association. However, overall, the forces of positive association are much stronger than the forces of negative association giving us an indication of an overall positive association (even friends disagree on some points!). In passing, we should note that it is not only the number of points in quadrants I and III against the number of points in quadrants II and IV that is important, but also how far the points are from their mean values.

USING EXCEL AND MINITAB TO DRAW A SCATTER DIAGRAM

In Excel Chart 13-2 and Minitab Chart 13-3, we show how to use Excel and Minitab to chart observations for pairs of values of two variables on a scatter diagram. In Excel Chart 13-2, we chart GDP on the horizontal axis (mean = 212.05) and Unemployment (mean = 8.28) on the vertical axis. Here, we witness a negative association. If you were to divide the scatter diagram in four quadrants through the mean values, you would see that most of the points lie in quadrants II and IV. There are very few points that lie in quadrants I and III. Overall, the forces of negative association are much stronger than the forces of positive association giving us an indication of an overall negative association (even enemies agree on some points!).

EXCEL CHART 13-2: Using Excel to Draw Scatter Diagram

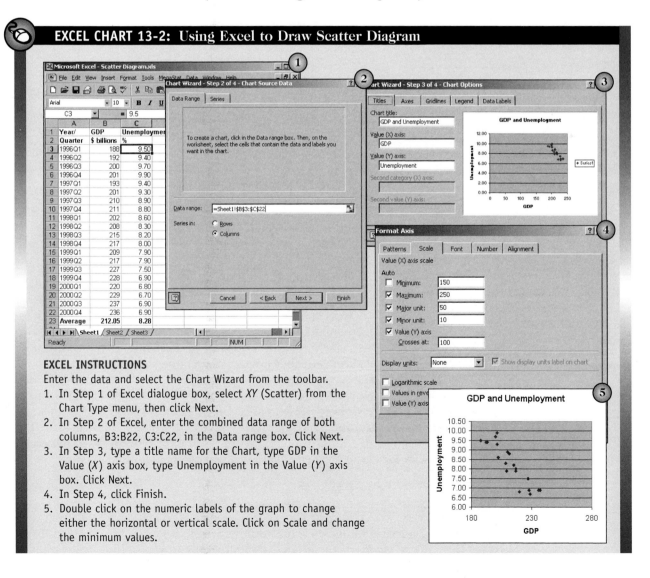

EXCEL INSTRUCTIONS
Enter the data and select the Chart Wizard from the toolbar.
1. In Step 1 of Excel dialogue box, select *XY* (Scatter) from the Chart Type menu, then click Next.
2. In Step 2 of Excel, enter the combined data range of both columns, B3:B22, C3:C22, in the Data range box. Click Next.
3. In Step 3, type a title name for the Chart, type GDP in the Value (*X*) axis box, type Unemployment in the Value (*Y*) axis box. Click Next.
4. In Step 4, click Finish.
5. Double click on the numeric labels of the graph to change either the horizontal or vertical scale. Click on Scale and change the minimum values.

MINITAB CHART 13-3: Minitab for Scatter Diagram (Inflation and Interest Rate)

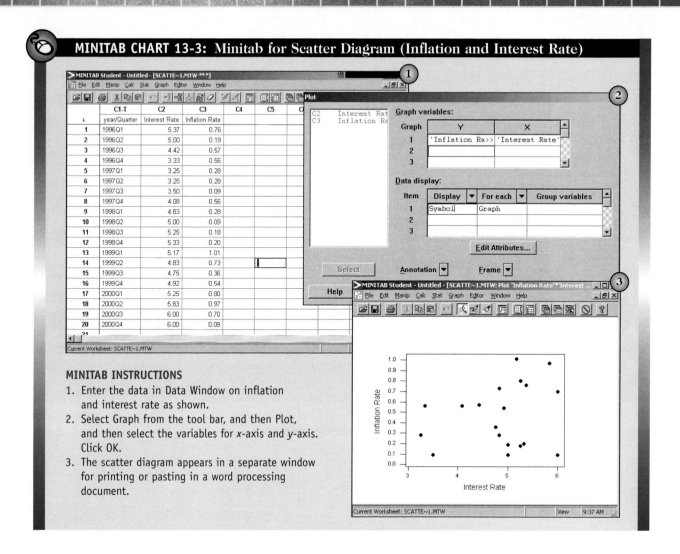

MINITAB INSTRUCTIONS

1. Enter the data in Data Window on inflation and interest rate as shown.
2. Select Graph from the tool bar, and then Plot, and then select the variables for *x*-axis and *y*-axis. Click OK.
3. The scatter diagram appears in a separate window for printing or pasting in a word processing document.

In Minitab Chart 13-3, we use Minitab to chart observations on a scatter diagram to show the relationship between inflation rate and interest rate (1996–2000, quarterly) in Canada. Theoretically, we expect a strong positive association between these variables. In general, a higher inflation rate increases the demand for money and therefore the interest rate—the price of money. A higher interest rate increases business costs, which in turn filter through higher prices. The scatter diagram does not show a good pattern thus implying a very weak relationship, if any. Part of the problem may be due to a seemingly non-linear pattern and some extreme values in the data set (see some unusual observations in the left part of the scatter). However, this is the most the scatter diagram can tell us. It cannot give us any idea about the degree or the strength of association in the form of a numerical value. There are two numerical measures of linear association, called **covariance** and **coefficient of correlation**.

COVARIANCE

Covariance is a measure of linear association between variables. It is defined as an average (arithmetic mean) of the products of variations in each of the two variables from their mean values. The formula for covariance for a population is:

$$\sigma_{xy} = \frac{\sum (x - \mu_x)(y - \mu_y)}{N} \qquad \text{13-1}$$

where σ_{xy} (called *sigma sub xy*) is a Greek letter used as a symbol for the covariance between X and Y for the population. The term in the numerator $((x - \mu_x)(y - \mu_y))$ is the product of variations in x and y values from their means. $\sum$ sums up all such products, and then dividing the sum of all products by N (the number of paired observations in the population) gives an average (the arithmetic mean) of the products of variations in the variables. Hence, it is called *covariance*.

For sample data (n pairs of observations), we replace the population symbols by sample symbols: symbols σ_{xy} by S_{xy}; μ_x and μ_y by $\bar{x}$ and $\bar{y}$; and N by $n - 1$.

In relation to a scatter diagram (see Chart 13-1), points for which x is greater than $\bar{x}$ and y is greater than $\bar{y}$ (quadrant I) make the product $(x - \bar{x})(y - \bar{y})$ positive. Points for which x is less than $\bar{x}$ and y is less than $\bar{y}$ (quadrant III) also make the product $(x - \bar{x})(y - \bar{y})$ positive. Why? In quadrant II $(x - \bar{x})$ is positive but $(y - \bar{y})$ is negative, and in quadrant IV $(x - \bar{x})$ is negative but $(y - \bar{y})$ is positive, thus making the product $(x - \bar{x})(y - \bar{y})$ negative in both quadrants II and IV. Thus, points in quadrants I and III would pull the covariance in the positive direction and points in quadrants II and IV would pull the covariance in the negative direction. The overall direction of the covariance depends on whether the positive or the negative forces are stronger. If points in quadrants I and III have a stronger effect compared to the points in quadrants II and IV, as is true in the case of income and well-being, covariance will be positive. If points in quadrants II and IV have a stronger effect compared to the points in quadrants I and III, as is true in the case of GDP and unemployment (Excel Chart 13-2), the covariance will be negative. If the positive and negative forces are equal, the value of covariance will be zero. Note that the value of covariance would be different for different data sets.

Example 13-1 | Let us find the value of sample covariance for income and well-being. Three columns of Table 13-2 repeat the information in Table 13-1 for the period 1987–97 (a smaller sample of observations is used to keep our calculations and presentation manageable). Note, $\sum(x - \bar{x})$ and $\sum(y - \bar{y})$ should equal zero except for rounding error.

TABLE 13-2

Year (1)	Income (X) (2)	Well-Being (Y) (3)	$(x - \bar{x})$ (4)	$(y - \bar{y})$ (5)	$(x - \bar{x})(y - \bar{y})$ (6)
1987	145.00	108.04	−3.81	−4.33	16.4973
1988	150.05	113.69	1.24	1.32	1.6368
1989	151.25	116.53	2.44	4.16	10.1504
1990	149.39	114.36	0.58	1.99	1.1542
1991	144.75	112.68	−4.06	0.31	−1.2586
1992	144.04	112.49	−4.77	0.12	−0.5724
1993	145.73	112.62	−3.08	0.25	−0.77
1994	149.58	111.81	0.77	−0.56	−0.4312
1995	150.98	110.63	2.17	−1.74	−3.7758
1996	151.09	110.70	2.28	−1.67	−3.8076
1997	155.00	112.53	6.19	0.16	0.9904
Totals	1636.86	1236.08	−0.05	0.01	19.8135
					$= \sum(x - \bar{x})(y - \bar{y})$
Mean	148.81	112.37			

First, we calculate the mean of x and y values as shown in the last row of columns 2 and 3; second, we find $(x - \bar{x})$ and $(y - \bar{y})$ as in columns 4 and 5; and third, we find the product of $(x - \bar{x})$ and $(y - \bar{y})$ as given in column 6. Lastly, we sum all these products, which equal 19.8135. Dividing this by 10 (= n – 1), we obtain the value of covariance equal to 19.8135/10 = 1.98135. The covariance has a positive sign indicating that income and well-being, during 1987–97, are positively associated. We can compare the values of covariance for different samples or populations so long as the variables are measured in the same units and scale.

Why is covariance positive, or negative, or zero?
If you look closely at the numbers in columns 4 and 5 for the years 1988–90 and 97, you will find both x and y are above their mean values (both $(x - \bar{x})$ and $(y - \bar{y})$ are positive), giving us positive cross-products in column 6. We also have a positive cross-product in column 6 for the year 1987 since both x and y are below their mean values, (both $(x - \bar{x})$ and $(y - \bar{y})$ are negative, giving us their cross-product as a positive number). For all these years, the two variables move in the same direction, which contributes to a positive association between X and Y. However, for each of the years 1991–93, x is below the mean $((x - \bar{x})$ is negative) and y is above the mean $((y - \bar{y})$ is positive), thus giving us a negative cross-product in column 6. Similarly, for each of the years 1994–96, x is above the mean and y is below the mean, and hence the cross-product is negative. For all these years (1991–96), income and well-being are negatively related. However, the sum of negative cross-products (– 10.6156) is smaller than the sum of the positive cross products (+ 30.4291). Therefore, the sum of all cross-products is positive (19.8135). In other words, overall we have a positive value for the covariance because the positive forces in the relationship between income and well-being are stronger than the negative forces.

In the case of GDP and unemployment, (see Excel Chart 13-2) the negative forces are stronger than the positive forces, resulting in a negative relationship. If the positive and negative forces were to be equal in magnitude, the value of the covariance would be zero. Here is a small challenge for you! Compare the degree of association in data sets of two different sets of variables in Charts 13-2 and 13-3. Can you make a valid comparison in terms of values of covariance of these two different data sets?

However, covariance is not a popular measure of association due to its heavy dependence on the units in which each variable is measured. If we measured the indices of income per head and well-being with 1971 equal to 1000 instead of 100, there would be a 10-fold increase in each $(x - \bar{x})$ and $(y - \bar{y})$, resulting in a 100-fold increase in the value of covariance, thus implying a 100-fold increase in the strength of relationship! Likewise, if a researcher were measuring covariance between height and weight of all students in a class, but used centimetres and kilograms instead of inches and pounds, the covariance would simultaneously increase approximately by a multiple of 2.54 and decrease approximately by a multiple of 2.2. Why? Would the covariance increase or decrease? By how much?

THE COEFFICIENT OF CORRELATION

Obviously, we cannot rely on the numerical value of covariance—a fickle measure of the strength of relationship that changes with a change in units/scale. Statisticians have solved this problem by standardizing X and Y variables. As you learned in Chapter 7, we standardize a variable by first taking the difference in actual values from the mean value of the variable, and then dividing each of the differences by the standard deviation of the variable. Thus, we standardize variable X through $(x - \mu_x)/\sigma_x$ and variable Y through $(y - \mu_y)/\sigma_y$. The covariance between (or an average of the product of) the values of two standardized variables $(x - \mu_x)/\sigma_x$ and $(y - \mu_y)/\sigma_y$ is then called the *coefficient of correlation*. Of course, as is true with many other things in life, there is a price tag attached with it. The coefficient of correlation, unlike the covariance of the original variables X and Y, is measured only on an interval scale. We can therefore compare two values of correlation coefficient as being only higher or lower (just like temperature) but not attribute any meaning to their differences.

> **ⅈ** **Coefficient of correlation** is a measure of the degree of linear relationship between two random variables. It is defined as the covariance between (or an average of the product of) two standardized random variables.

Although Francis Galton's work on heredity involved the concept of correlation, Karl Pearson (see Chapter 15), one of Galton's great admirers, is credited with formalizing the concept. Formally, we define the coefficient of correlation, ρ_{xy} (ρ is a Greek letter pronounced as *rho*) for the population, and r_{xy} for the sample, in *three equivalent ways*:

$$\textbf{Population}\quad \rho_{xy} = \frac{\sigma_{xy}}{\sigma_x \sigma_y} = Cov\left(\frac{(x - \mu_x)}{\sigma_x}\right)\left(\frac{(y - \mu_y)}{\sigma_y}\right) = \sum \frac{(x - \mu_x)(y - \mu_y)}{N\sigma_x \sigma_y} \qquad \text{13-2}$$

$$\textbf{Sample}\quad r_{xy} = \frac{S_{xy}}{S_x S_y} = Cov\left(\frac{(x - \bar{x})}{S_x}\right)\left(\frac{(y - \bar{y})}{S_y}\right) = \sum \frac{(x - \bar{x})(y - \bar{y})}{(n - 1) S_x S_y} \qquad \text{13-3a}$$

Often we drop the subscripts x and y from ρ, r, and σ for simplicity unless it presents ambiguity in a particular context. Inserting the formulae for S_x and S_y (as you learned in Chapter 4), we get the following formulation for the coefficient of correlation for sample data. (What happened to $(n - 1)$?).

$$r = \frac{\sum (x - \bar{x})(y - \bar{y})}{\sqrt{\sum (x - \bar{x})^2} \sqrt{\sum (y - \bar{y})^2}} \qquad \text{13-3b}$$

Computing the coefficient of correlation from the above equation requires calculating $(x - \bar{x})$ and $(y - \bar{y})$, for each pair of observations, which can both be tedious and, in general, result in a somewhat inaccurate value of r due to rounding. We used this method for covariance in Example 13-1 to illustrate the concept. These problems are overcome by rewriting the formula for r as:

$$\textbf{The Computational Formula}\quad r = \frac{n\sum xy - (\sum x)(\sum y)}{\sqrt{n\sum x^2 - (\sum x)^2} \sqrt{n\sum y^2 - (\sum y)^2}} \qquad \text{13-3c}$$

To find the coefficient of correlation for any data, we need only find the values for $\sum x$ and $\sum y$, $\sum xy$, and $\sum x^2$ and $\sum y^2$. Let us try this in the following example.

Example 13-2 | An instructor at St. Thomas University in Fredericton is interested in finding the coefficient of correlation between grades (out of 100) obtained by students in Statistics (X) and Economics (Y) courses.

Solution

To begin, the instructor selects a random sample of 11 students from all those who have taken both courses and records their grades in Table 13-3.

TABLE 13-3: Correlation between Grades in Statistics and Economics

Name	Stats x	Econ y	xy	x^2	y^2
Meena Ahsan	80	75	6000	6400	5625
Chun Cheng	75	70	5250	5625	4900
Jan Harvey	75	80	6000	5625	6400
Jim Lim	85	90	7650	7225	8100
Sarita Sen	70	75	5250	4900	5625
Meera Patel	87	90	7830	7569	8100
Rob Penney	70	65	4550	4900	4225
Melody Sexton	83	85	7055	6889	7225
Mary Tan	83	87	7221	6889	7569
Cathy Williams	90	95	8550	8100	9025
Darren Young	80	85	6800	6400	7225
Totals (Σ)	878	897	72 156	70 522	74 019

As the formula suggests, the instructor computes the sums of x and y (Σx and Σy), the sums of products of x and y (Σxy), and the sums of squares of x and y (Σx^2 and Σy^2). The last row of the Table 13-3 gives all the sums needed by the formula. Thus,

$$\sum x = 878; \quad \sum y = 897; \quad \sum xy = 72\,156; \quad \sum x^2 = 70\,522 \quad \sum y^2 = 74\,019$$

He then puts these numbers in the formula as follows:

$$r = \frac{(11)(72\,516) - (878)(897)}{\sqrt{(11)(70\,522) - (878)^2}\,\sqrt{(11)(74\,019) - (897)^2}}$$

The result is the value of the correlation coefficient: $r = 0.901$.

What does the value of r indicate?

As we noted earlier, the coefficient of correlation is an index. By algebraically manipulating the formula for the coefficient of correlation, it can be shown that the value r can reach a maximum of $+1$ and a minimum of -1. The sign of r depends on the term in the numerator, the covariance between X and Y (Why?). The values of r equal to ± 1 indicate perfect correlation. That is, each value of the variable X is linearly associated with only one value of the variable Y, and vice versa. In other words, all pairs of observations (x, y) lie on a straight line. If $r = 1$, the line is upwardly sloping, and when $r = -1$ the line is downwardly sloping. Both are examples of perfect correlation between two random variables. See Charts 13-5a and 13-5b. Likewise, sample data may yield the value of $r = 0$. The value of $r = 0$ signifies an absence of linear association between variables. We may obtain the value of $r = 0$, because (i) the underlying relationship is non-linear (shown in Chart 13-6a), or (ii) the variables are statistically independent, or (iii) by chance, our sample was not a good representation of the population. See Chart 13-6b.

Note, theoretically, *if two variables are statistically independent, the coefficient of correlation must be zero.* In practice, however, we may find a high correlation between the price of coffee and the price of sugar, though we expect the two prices to be fairly independent. Such correlations are called spurious or absurd correlations. *However, zero or an extremely low value of the coefficient of correlation does not imply that the two variables are independent.* For example, we may find zero or practically zero correlation between exchange rate and inflation, though theoretically we expect a high correlation between these variables.

Often, values of r lie somewhere between 0 and ±1. A value closer to ±1 indicates a strong association, and a value closer to zero indicates a weak association. The following chart (Chart 13-4) displays the strength of association for various values of r. You should, however, note that the values associated with the words "strong" and "weak" are only suggestive. Others may like to associate these words with slightly different values. Note that *the strength of association does not depend on the sign of the coefficient of correlation* (see Charts 13-5 and 13-6c and d) and the sign is an indicator of only the direction of association. Furthermore, we should remember that a value of r that is twice as large (say 0.8 as compared to 0.4) does not mean that the relationship is twice as strong.

CHART 13-4: The Strength of Association

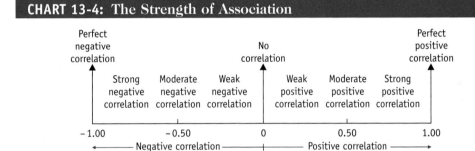

CHART 13-5: Scatter Diagrams Showing Perfect Negative Correlation and Perfect Positive Correlation

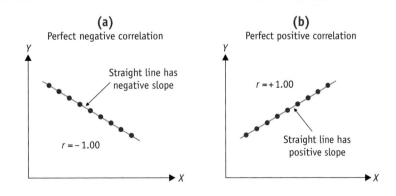

Examples of degrees of correlation

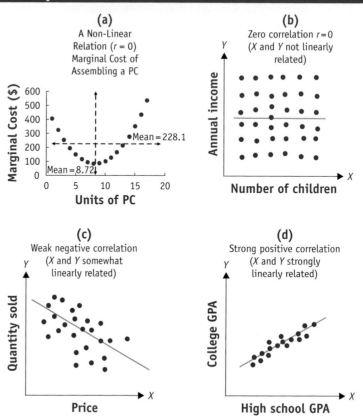

CHART 13-6: Imperfect Association

(a) A Non-Linear Relation ($r = 0$) Marginal Cost of Assembling a PC — Marginal Cost ($) vs Units of PC — Mean = 228.1, Mean = 8.72

(b) Zero correlation $r = 0$ (X and Y not linearly related) — Annual income vs Number of children

(c) Weak negative correlation (X and Y somewhat linearly related) — Quantity sold vs Price

(d) Strong positive correlation (X and Y strongly linearly related) — College GPA vs High school GPA

SOME CAVEATS

How good is the value of r?

While the value of the correlation coefficient can be very useful in analyzing the underlying relationship between variables, we must, however, use extreme caution when drawing conclusions from a value of the coefficient of correlation obtained from a particular sample data set. As we have noted earlier, a different sample data set may yield a different value of the coefficient of correlation. If the sample data is not fully representative of the underlying population, our conclusions may be erroneous. We shall learn how to test the correlation coefficient in the population based on sample values in the following section. However, even if the sample is representative of the population, a value of the correlation coefficient may lead us to make erroneous conclusions in the following circumstances.

OUTLIERS AND AVERAGING

The coefficient of correlation is the arithmetic mean of the product of two "standardized" variables. Note, we do not imply normality in every case when we standardize a variable. We saw in Chapter 3, how conclusions based on arithmetic means can be misleading in the presence of some extremely large or small observations in a data set. The value of the coefficient of correlation is also influenced by unduly large or small observations. We should therefore carefully check for the presence of such observations before drawing any conclusions from the value of r.

STATISTICS IN ACTION

Does Smoking Cause Cancer?

The last fifty years have witnessed a reduction in smoking by more than 50 percent. How did it all happen? In 1955, Richard Doll published a report showing a strong positive relationship between the annual rate of cigarette consumption (per person, 1930) and the annual death rate (per million men in 1950) from lung cancer in eleven countries. He found the correlation coefficient to be approximately 0.73, indicating a fairly strong degree of association. Some researchers questioned Doll's analysis, since it seemed to imply that the countries smoked! As we know, studies based on rates and averages can give misleading results. Later studies based on individuals, however, confirmed Doll's conclusions. These studies led epidemiologists to conclude that smoking causes lung cancer! Some researchers, including Sir R.A. Fisher, questioned the "causality" hypothesis. These researchers explained the association between smoking and cancer due to genetic confounding: the genes (a confounder variable) of smokers carry the information on both cancer and a temptation for smoking based on the hereditary factors. Some later studies conducted on twins tend to refute Fisher's hypothesis.

A second problem, often ignored by practitioners, occurs when we conclude the strength of association between individual entities based on the coefficient of correlation between aggregates or averages of those entities. For example, a conclusion about the strength of relationship between individual stocks and bonds based on the coefficient of correlation between an overall bond index (an average) and an overall stock index (an average) can be very misleading. Individual stocks and bonds would tend to have much larger variations compared to the variations in aggregates or averages. A correlation between S&P/TSX Index and a Bond Index should not be used to infer that all stocks and bond prices have the same correlation.

LINEAR VERSUS NON-LINEAR RELATIONSHIPS

The concept of the correlation coefficient covered in this chapter is applicable only to linear or approximately linear relationships. While there are several relationships in business and economics that can be approximated by a linear relationship, many business and economic relationships, such as the one between costs and production, are inherently non-linear. For the non-linear relationships, our concept of correlation will often give us misleading results. For example, some of you may have encountered a U-shaped marginal cost curve, a relationship between the cost of producing each additional unit of output (Y) and the units of output produced (X). In this case, although the variables are highly related, the value of the correlation coefficient would practically be zero. See Chart 13-6a.

SPURIOUS (OR ABSURD) RELATIONSHIPS

The value of the correlation coefficient is based on a mathematical formulation. Thus, one may collect data and find a high correlation between the occurrence of sunspots and business cycles, or birth rate and crime rate in a country, or population of mice and production of rice in a country, or professors' salaries and consumption of liquor, etc. Such correlations are called *spurious* or *absurd*.

CORRELATION AND CAUSALITY

When we see a high degree of correlation between variables, we may be tempted to conclude a dependence of one variable on another variable, that is, a cause and effect relationship between the variables. Correlation, as defined in statistics, does not imply *causality* between variables. *Causality (a cause and effect relationship between variables) is the subject to be determined by the underlying theory of relationship between variables.*

For example, we may find a high negative correlation (say, $r = -0.85$) between grade point average of a student (Y) and the amount of outside work (X). This strong negative relationship may be attributable to any or all of the following reasons: (a) longer hours of outside work does not leave enough time for study (X causes Y); (b) a student with a lower grade point average does not receive scholarships and therefore needs to work longer hours at a paid job (Y causes X); (c) a higher interest in practical work compared to academic work (both X and Y affected by a third set of factors such as *interest*); or (d) the sample is not a good representation of the population and therefore the relationship is purely due to chance factors. Likewise, a higher inflation rate may cause lower unemployment, or lower unemployment may cause higher inflation, or the negative relation between unemployment and inflation could be due to a "third" factor (e.g., a big increase in energy prices), or by chance. When we find a high degree of correlation due to a set of common or third factors, such common factors are usually called *confounding variables. Thus, the coefficient of correlation is neutral with respect to causality.*

■ SELF-REVIEW 13-1

It is widely speculated that there is some relationship between unemployment and crime. To find the exact nature of the relationship between these variables in Canada, we have collected the following data on Unemployment Rate (UR, in %) and the total number of crimes (Crime, in thousands) committed in Canada for the years 1986–1999. (Source: Statistics Canada, series labels: D980404 and D9500.)

     (a) Draw a scatter diagram for the data and comment on the nature of the relationship between Unemployment Rate and the total number of crimes.

     (b) Find the coefficient of correlation between UR and Crime. Interpret.

Year	UR (X)	Crime (Y)	Year	UR (X)	Crime (Y)
1986	9.7	2374	1993	11.4	2841
1987	8.8	2471	1994	10.4	2747
1988	7.8	2486	1995	9.4	2737
1989	7.6	2533	1996	9.7	2745
1990	8.1	2720	1997	9.1	2637
1991	10.3	2993	1998	8.3	2568
1992	11.2	2952	1999	7.6	2476

EXERCISES 13-1 TO 13-6

13-1. The following pairs of observations represent the tips (in dollars) received by Mary and Will at Pizza Delight (at lunch time) in St. John's on a sample of five randomly selected days:

Mary (X):   4   5   3   6   10
Will (Y):   4   6   5   7   9

Determine the covariance between X and Y. How can this result be interpreted? What might change your interpretation?

13-2. The following pairs of observations represent the price ($000) of a sample of eight randomly selected houses and the building area for each house (sq. metres) in Quebec City:

Price (X):	120	130	150	130	140	170	160	150
Area (Y):	100	120	140	130	140	160	150	130

Determine the coefficient of correlation. Interpret your results.

13-3. It seems plausible to assume that there should exist a positive correlation between the profit levels and the accumulated assets for a majority of Canadian firms. The following sample observations were randomly selected from a list of the top 1000 firms in Canada. (Source: *Globe & Mail Interactive Services*)

Company Name	Profits ($ million)	Assets ($ million)
Aliant Inc.	148.2	2875
Cominco Ltd.	159.0	2964
Domtar Inc.	163.0	4019
Empire Co.	135.0	4023
Nova Scotia Power	114.5	2812
Petro Canada	233.0	8661
Sears Canada	199.6	3456
Talisman Energy	176.8	7819

(a) Draw a scatter diagram.
(b) Compute the coefficient of correlation.
(c) Are the results you obtained in parts (a) and (b) consistent with the assumed direction of this relationship?
(d) Why may certain discrepancies arise in this type of exercise?

13-4. The debate over the relationship between Unemployment Rate (UR) and Inflation Rate (IR) has been highly contested within the economics community for some time. An officer (your supervisor?) at the Bank of Canada has asked you to estimate a quantitative measure of this relationship. Given below are the quarterly observations for Unemployment Rate and Inflation Rate for 1996–2000. (Source: Statistics Canada, adapted).

Year/Q	UR (%)	IR (%)	Year/Q	UR (%)	IR (%)
1996Q1	9.50	0.76	1998Q3	8.20	0.18
1996Q2	9.40	0.19	1998Q4	8.00	0.20
1996Q3	9.70	0.57	1999Q1	7.90	1.01
1996Q4	9.90	0.56	1999Q2	7.90	0.73
1997Q1	9.40	0.28	1999Q3	7.50	0.36
1997Q2	9.30	0.28	1999Q4	6.90	0.54
1997Q3	8.90	-0.09	2000Q1	6.80	0.80
1997Q4	8.80	0.56	2000Q2	6.70	0.97
1998Q1	8.60	0.28	2000Q3	6.90	0.70
1998Q2	8.30	0.09	2000Q4	6.90	0.09
			Average	8.28	0.453

(a) Find the covariance between UR and IR.
(b) Determine the coefficient of correlation. Interpret your results.
(c) What would you tell the officer at the Bank of Canada?

13-5. The owner of Wood Motors in Edmonton wants to study the relationship between the age of a car and its selling price (in $000). Listed below is a random sample of 12 used cars sold at Wood Motors during the last week.

Car	Age (years)	Selling Price ($000)	Car	Age (years)	Selling Price ($000)
1	9	8.0	7	8	7.0
2	7	6.0	8	11	8.0
3	11	3.6	9	10	8.0
4	12	4.0	10	12	6.0
5	8	5.0	11	6	8.0
6	7	10.0	12	6	8.0

(a) Draw a scatter diagram. Find the covariance.
(b) Determine the coefficient of correlation. Interpret the results.
(c) Is the relationship in accordance with your expectations?

13-6. Refer to Table 13-2 and calculate the correlation coefficient between income (x) and well-being (y). Be sure to use all eleven years of data provided in the table under columns 2 and 3.

13.2 TESTING THE SIGNIFICANCE OF THE CORRELATION COEFFICIENT

Recall, in Example 13-2, the instructor found a very high correlation (0.9) between grades in Economics and Statistics. However, only 11 students were sampled. Could it be that the correlation in the population is actually less than or equal to 0? This would mean that the correlation of 0.9 was due to chance. The population in this example consists of all students who took both courses.

Resolving this dilemma requires a test to answer the obvious question: could there be zero correlation in the population from which the sample was selected? To put it another way, did the computed r come from a population of paired observations with zero correlation? The null and alternative hypotheses are:

H_0: $\rho \leq 0$ (The value of the correlation coefficient in the population is less than or equal to zero.)
H_1: $\rho > 0$ (There is a positive correlation.)

From the way H_1 is stated, we know that the test is one-tailed.

Assuming that the two variables (grades in Statistics and Economics) have a bivariate (joint) normal distribution, the formula for testing the null hypothesis is given as,

Test Statistic for the Coefficient of Correlation $t = \dfrac{r\sqrt{n-2}}{\sqrt{1-r^2}}$ with ($n - 2$) degrees of freedom   13-4

The value of the t statistic for our example is: $t = \dfrac{0.9\sqrt{11-2}}{\sqrt{1-(0.9)^2}} = \dfrac{0.9(3)}{\sqrt{1-0.81}} = 6.19$

CHART 13-7: Decision Rule for the Test of Hypothesis for ρ at 1 Percent Level of Significance and 9 Degrees of Freedom

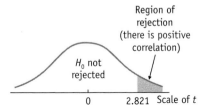

Using the 0.01 level of significance, the critical value of the t statistic for 9 degrees of freedom (= 11 − 2) is 2.821. The decision rule states that if the computed value of t falls below the critical value of t, the null hypothesis is *not* rejected. Obviously, 6.19 is much larger than the critical value of 2.821. We therefore conclude that there is sufficient evidence in favour of the alternative hypothesis. To locate the critical value of 2.821, refer to the t table at the back of the book for $df = n − 2 = 11 − 2 = 9$. Also see Chart 13-7.

The computed value of t is in the rejection region. Thus, H_0 is rejected at 0.01 (or 1 percent) significance level. This means the correlation in the population is greater than zero. From a practical standpoint, it tells the instructor that there is a positive correlation in the population of student grades for Economics and Statistics.

We can also interpret the test of hypothesis in terms of P-values. A P-value is the likelihood of finding a value of the test statistic larger than the one computed, when H_0 is true. To determine the P-value, go to the t distribution in the t table and find the row for 9 degrees of freedom. Since the computed value of the test statistic is 6.19, find the value closest to 6.19 in that row. For a one-tailed test at the 0.0005 significance level, the critical value of t is 4.781. Because 6.19 is still larger than the highest critical value in the table for 9 degrees of freedom, we conclude that the p-value for rejecting the null hypothesis is less than 0.0005.

However, as noted above, the test of hypothesis is based on a very stringent assumption of bivariate normal distribution. When this assumption is violated, or we are unsure about the probability distribution underlying the population, we can use an alternative method, a non-parametric technique, developed by C. Spearman in 1904. In addition, **Spearman's rank correlation coefficient** is useful for finding correlation among variables that are measurable only on an ordinal scale. We shall discuss Spearman's rank correlation in Chapter 15 along with other non-parametric test statistics.

Both Minitab and Excel MegaStat will output the value of the correlation coefficient between two variables. In addition to the value of the coefficient of correlation, Minitab reports the P-value for the test of hypothesis that the correlation in the population between the two variables is 0. The Excel and Minitab output are given below. The results are the same as those calculated earlier. However, the P-value given in the Minitab output is for a two-tailed test. For a one-tailed test, the relevant P-value can be obtained by dividing the Minitab P-value by 2. MegaStat output (not shown) gives the two-tailed critical values of r at 0.05 and 0.01 levels of significance. When the computed value of r > critical value, we reject the two-tailed null hypothesis of $r = 0$. MegaStat output can be obtained by choosing MegaStat → Correlation → Correlation Matrix → Input Range → OK.

EXCEL CHART 13-8: Finding Covariance and the Coefficient of Correlation (for data in Table 13-3)

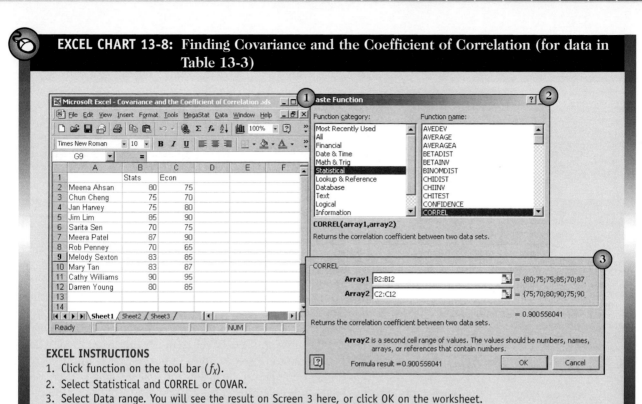

EXCEL INSTRUCTIONS

1. Click function on the tool bar (f_X).
2. Select Statistical and CORREL or COVAR.
3. Select Data range. You will see the result on Screen 3 here, or click OK on the worksheet. You can use the same steps to find the value of covariance.

MINITAB CHART 13-9: Covariance and the Coefficient of Correlation (for the Data in Table 13-3)

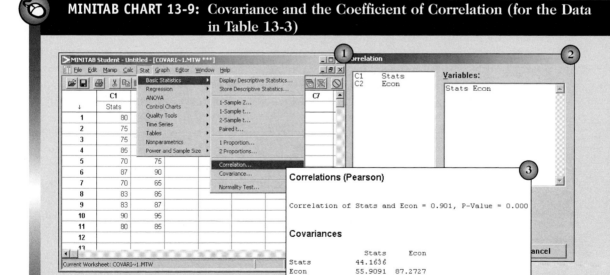

MINITAB INSTRUCTIONS

Input the data as in Table 13-3 for X and Y using Stats and Econ as headings.

1. Click Stat, Basic Statistics, Correlation.
2. Double click the variables to enter them into the variable box. Then click OK. Repeat with Stat, Basic Statistics, Covariance.
3. The output will be generated in the Session window.

■ SELF-REVIEW 13-2

Refer to Self-Review 13-1. Test the null hypothesis that the coefficient of correlation between the unemployment rate and crime rate is less than or equal to zero (H_0: $\rho \leq 0$), against the alternative hypothesis that it is positive (H_1: $\rho > 0$).

EXERCISES 13-7 TO 13-10

13-7. The following hypotheses are given:

H_0: $\rho \leq 0$
H_1: $\rho > 0$

A random sample of 12 paired observations for Research & Development expenditures for 12 companies indicated a correlation of 0.32. Can we conclude that the correlation in the population is greater than zero? Use the 0.05 significance level.

13-8. The following hypotheses are given:

H_0: $\rho \geq 0$
H_1: $\rho < 0$

A random sample of 15 paired observations on investment and interest rates have a correlation of -0.46. Can we conclude that the correlation in the population is less than zero? Use the 0.05 significance level.

13-9. The Alberta Refining Company is studying the relationship between the pump price of gasoline and the number of litres sold at a particular gasoline station. For a sample of 20 stations last Tuesday, the correlation was 0.78. At the 0.01 significance level, is the correlation in the population greater than zero?

13-10. A study of 20 worldwide financial institutions showed the correlation between their assets and pre-tax profit to be 0.86. At the 0.05 significance level, can we conclude that there is a positive correlation in the population?

■ 13.3 REGRESSION ANALYSIS

THE NATURE OF DATA

In the previous section, we developed measures of association between two random variables. The underlying population of the random variables was assumed to have a joint bivariate distribution. In a bivariate distribution, we have a sub-population of values of the variable Y for each value of the variable X. Likewise, for each value of the variable Y, we have a sub-population of values of the variable X. Since both variables are random, *a priori* (without a theory), we cannot say what makes the two variables move in a particular direction. The variable X may depend on Y; Y may depend on X; both X and Y may depend on each other; or both variables may move in a particular direction due to an influence of some other variables. For example, well-being may depend on income, income may depend on well-being, both income and well-being may depend on each other, or both income and well-being may be influenced by an overall development in a country. Similar arguments can be made about a relationship between variables such as student grades in two courses, relationship between smoking and drinking coffee, and economic development in two countries. We measured the degree of association between such pairs of random variables by the coefficient of correlation, *without implying causation* in any direction.

However, causation is a fact of life. Human behaviour in general is driven by some causal rather than altruistic motives. Whether we are professors, students, doctors or politicians, we are driven by some expectations in our daily pursuits. Even in natural phenomena, as Einstein once said, "God does not play dice with the world." Nature is also interwoven by some pattern of cause and effect relationships. Theorists can establish causality between a set of variables by assuming an absence of the influence of variables outside their focus of interest. A counterpart of this in empirical studies requires conducting controlled experiments that you are familiar with from the last chapter. In a controlled experiment, we can isolate the effect of other variables by either completely randomizing the subjects as in medical experiments, or physically disallowing the influence of other variables from the relationship under investigation as in experiments with garden peas in genetics. In fact, the classical regression analysis, called *biometry* earlier, owes its development to controlled experiments.

As we have noted earlier, data in social sciences is observational rather than the result of controlled experiments. Both income and interest rates vary simultaneously to influence investment. Could we control income at a particular level, while we study the influence of interest rates on investment? This is like asking Canadians to wait for an increase in income for the next 10 years, and allow us to randomly choose five of the next 10 years when the Governor of the Bank of Canada would be requested to increase the interest rate for the sake of a scientific experiment. A tall order indeed! Would a researcher be able to randomly assign some individuals to study at university and others to sit home while she conducts a study of the influence of education on income? There is no perfect substitute for a controlled experiment. However, the multiple regression analysis, discussed in the next chapter, does allow us to isolate, to a large extent, the influence of other variables in observational data, if the data satisfies certain assumptions.

WHY REGRESSION ANALYSIS?

In classical regression analysis, we assume one variable (say X) to be fixed at some predetermined levels by the investigator (thus, it is a non-random variable) and another variable (say Y) as the random variable. For example, we may collect data on household income by family size in Vancouver. Here family size (say, 1 to 10) is a non-random variable. For each family size, we have thousands of values of income (a random variable).

In the classical regression analysis, the random variable is called the dependent (the response or explained) variable. Likewise, the non-random variable is called the independent (the predetermined or explanatory) variable. The random variable has a sub-population of values for each predetermined value of the non-random variable.

In simple regression analysis, where both variables are random, we randomly select a sub-population of observations on one variable (say Y) for each predetermined value of the other variable (say X). Often, a theory (or theories) from the particular discipline may provide guidance as to which variable should be kept at predetermined levels. For example, in the analysis of demand for a commodity, we normally assume "price" as the independent variable and "quantity demanded" as the dependent

Who is responsible for lower math scores in Ontario? Schools or the economy?

Recent studies have shown that mathematics performance of Ontario students has consistently fallen behind the performance of students in three other provinces and many countries. Findings of a 1999 study commissioned by the Government of Ontario revealed that math performance of Grade 3 children from lower income families generally lag behind the average performance for the province. The same study also shows a relation between lower socio-economic status and lower birth weight of children (*quoted in* Canadian Initiative on Social Statistics: A Prospectus. *SSHRC and Statistics Canada, 1999*).

variable. When there is no theory, or the theory cannot provide proper guidance, we should conduct two regression analyses. For example, in the case of student grades in Economics and Statistics, we can conduct one regression analysis assuming grades in Economics as the dependent variable with grades in Statistics as the independent variable, and another regression analysis assuming grades in Statistics as the dependent variable and grades in Economics as the independent variable.

Regression analysis is general, not only in terms of its ability to deal with more versatile populations, but also in terms of explaining the nature of relationships. While the correlation analysis could give us only the direction of the relationship and the strength of the relationship on an interval scale, the regression analysis can give us the direction of the relationship as well as the strength of the relationship on a ratio scale. Thus, regression analysis also enables us to measure the amount of change in the dependent variable in response to a unit change in the independent variable. Furthermore, the regression analysis allows us to make predictions about the possible values (unobserved) of the dependent variable for given values of the independent variable. For these reasons, regression analysis is considered the heart of multi-variate statistical analysis. The phrase **simple** or **basic regression analysis** is used for the relationship between two variables and the phrase **multiple regression analysis** for cases involving more than two variables. In this chapter, we shall deal with simple regression analysis. We study multiple regression analysis in the next chapter.

> *i* **Regression Analysis**   Enables us to find the direction of relationship, the strength of relationship, as well as to predict yet unobserved values of the dependent variable.

THE NATURE OF RELATIONSHIP

In order to estimate the strength of relationship between any two variables through regression analysis, we would first need to know the nature of the functional relationship, i.e., how a change in one variable affects another variable. Sometimes, guidance may be available from a theory underlying the relationship between the variables. For example, as income increases, the proportion of income spent on food first increases and then declines. Given the capital stock, under certain assumptions, marginal cost of production first declines and then increases. These relationships are **non-linear**. However, in most cases, theories give us only an indication of the possible direction of the relationship. Quantity demanded is negatively related to price, or the quantity supplied is positively related to price. Furthermore, in some cases, we may not have even a precise indication of the direction of the relationship from any theory. Is growth in income positively or negatively associated with income inequalities? In the case of correlation analysis, you may recall, we assumed a **linear relationship**, the simplest form of relationship between two variables. In simple regression analysis, we continue with the assumption of linear relationship. A linear relationship is mathematically easy to handle. Further, a variety of non-linear relationships can also be easily handled (by transforming them into linear relationships) by linear regression techniques.

DETERMINISTIC VERSUS STATISTICAL RELATIONSHIPS

Generally, theories give us guidance in determining the form of a functional (e.g., linear, quadratic, cubic, exponential, etc.) relationship. In a functional relationship, the values of the dependent variable are determined uniquely by the given values of the parameters and the independent variable(s). Such relations are therefore also called *deterministic*. For example, a linear relationship between the quantity of oranges (in dozens, per week) demanded (Q) by a typical family (two adults and two children) and the price of oranges (P) can be expressed as $Q = \alpha + \beta P$. Here α represents the dozens of oranges demanded at zero price (the maximum number of oranges per week a family could consume) and β represents the amount of decrease in oranges demanded ($\beta < 0$) for a unit increase in price. Given the values of α and β (the parameters), we get a unique value of quantity demanded for each value of price. Thus, if $\alpha = 5$, $\beta = -0.6$ and $P = 3$ dollars per dozen, the quantity demanded is uniquely *determined* as $Q = 5.0 - 0.6(3.0) = 3.2$ dozens per week.

However, if we were to collect data on 20 families, we would find differences in their consumption patterns for a variety of reasons, including family income, family size, taste, etc. Some families consume less than 3.2 dozen and others more than 3.2 dozen at the same price. These differences in observations on the consumption of oranges by each family (of the same size) can be captured by the deviations from the typical family's consumption. These deviations in the population of observations are called "errors" in statistics. Statisticians use a Greek letter such as ϵ (pronounced as *epsilon*), as a symbol for the error term in the population. A statistical relationship can therefore be written as $Q = \alpha + \beta P + \epsilon$. Since statisticians deal with observations, they use statistical relationships to estimate the mathematical relation.

> ***i*** A functional (mathematical) relationship such as $y = \alpha + \beta x$ is a deterministic relationship with one value of Y for each value of X. In statistics, we use a stochastic (statistical) relationship such as $y = \alpha + \beta x + \epsilon$, where ϵ is a random error with a probability distribution for each value of the variable X. Thus, we have a sub-population of the values of the variable Y with a mean: $\mu_{y|x} = \alpha + \beta x$ (the deterministic part of the stochastic relationship) for each value of the variable X.

Example 13-3

For example, let us take the case of the Northside Ford dealer who operates a dealership with 10 salespeople. There is a widespread belief amongst auto dealers that a followup call to customers who visit showrooms is an effective way to increase sales. Before deciding to hire a skilled secretary for this purpose, he asks his salespeople to make some follow-up calls to their customers for six weeks and report the results to the dealership. Salespeople are given the freedom to determine the number of calls per week they wish to make.

Solution

The results of the experiment are given below in Table 13-4. The table contains a population of 60 pairs of observations (six observations for each of the ten values of X). Each row contains the number of calls made by a salesperson and the sales per week for six weeks. Thus, each salesperson has a sub-population of sales (six values) corresponding to the number of calls made by the salesperson. Jeff makes 40 calls ($x = 40$) with a sub-population of sales as 55, 75, 60, 80, 70, 50. Jeff thus has six pairs of observations (40 calls and 55 sales, 40 calls and 75 sales, etc.). The averages of the sub-populations of sales for each salesperson ($\mu_{y|x}$) are listed in the last column. The symbol $\mu_{y|x}$ indicates the population average of the y values for a given value of x. The average of y values for Brian is 45.

Is there any relationship between the number of calls and sales? Chart 13-10 depicts a scatter diagram of all 60 observations (the entire population) in Table 13-4. You probably see only 24 points (excluding the points joining the line) on the scatter diagram! Why? As the number of calls increases, the scatter of points for each sub-population, together with the average of each sub-population, is seen moving upwards.

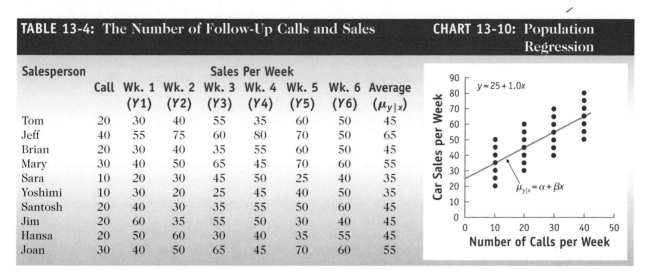

TABLE 13-4: The Number of Follow-Up Calls and Sales

Salesperson	Call	Wk. 1 (Y1)	Wk. 2 (Y2)	Wk. 3 (Y3)	Wk. 4 (Y4)	Wk. 5 (Y5)	Wk. 6 (Y6)	Average ($\mu_{y|x}$)
Tom	20	30	40	55	35	60	50	45
Jeff	40	55	75	60	80	70	50	65
Brian	20	30	40	35	55	60	50	45
Mary	30	40	50	65	45	70	60	55
Sara	10	20	30	45	50	25	40	35
Yoshimi	10	30	20	25	45	40	50	35
Santosh	20	40	30	35	55	50	60	45
Jim	20	60	35	55	50	30	40	45
Hansa	20	50	60	30	40	35	55	45
Joan	30	40	50	65	45	70	60	55

CHART 13-10: Population Regression

The line joining the average values of all sub-populations (average sales) is upwardly sloping. This is called the *population regression line*. A positive slope of the line indicates a positive relation between the number of calls and the average number of sales. The value of the slope gives us a measure of the strength of the relationship.

THE BASIC POPULATION REGRESSION MODEL (PRM)

A model is a set of assumptions about the forces and relationships underlying a hypothesis. In our case, a relationship between the follow-up calls and sales is a hypothesis. The basic regression model for a population is based on the following assumptions. The first assumption has already been explained above.

Assumption #1

The independent variable (X) is non-random (non-stochastic); its values are fixed (predetermined) in repeated sampling; and for any sample size "n," the variance of X-values is non-zero and a finite number. The non-random nature of the independent variable allows us to maintain statistical independence between the independent variable and the error term. Fixing the values of the independent variable in repeated sampling allows us to derive probability distribution of Y for each value of X. If there is no variation in the values of X, we cannot estimate the regression line. Recent advances in statistics enable us to deal with cases where the independent variable(s) are also random. In this case, however, we still require (a weaker assumption) statistical independence between the independent variable and the error term.

Assumption #2

The dependent and the independent variables are linearly related. The model can also be used for several non-linear relationships that are easily transformable into linear relationships.

POPULATION REGRESSION LINE (PRL)

A population regression line is a line joining the average values of the *dependent* variable for each of the predetermined values of the *independent* variable. We can write this in symbols as:

$$E(y\,|\,x) = \mu_{y|x} = \alpha + \beta x \qquad \qquad \text{13-5}$$

Where α is the intercept of the line and β is the slope of the line, and $E(y|x)$ is the expected value of the variable Y (an average of Y-values) for each value of the variable X.

The intercept of a line is the point on the vertical axis where the line intersects the axis. Thus, the intercept is the value of the variable Y, when the value of the variable X equals zero. In our example, the value of the intercept is $\alpha = 25$. It implies that the average sales without any follow-up calls ($x = 0$) equal 25. *We should, however, note at the outset that the intercept of a line is a mathematical construct; it may have no meaningful value in real-world circumstances*, particularly when the point corresponding to $x = 0$ lies farther away from the observable range of data. The slope of the line is defined as an average change in the values of the dependent variable for a unit change in the values of the independent variable, or the *rise over run* between any two points on the PRL. Thus, in our example, an increase in the number of calls from 20 to 30 (run) increases average value of sales from 45 to 55 (rise). The slope of the population regression line is thus, $\beta = \dfrac{\text{rise}}{\text{run}} = \dfrac{55 - 45}{30 - 20} = \dfrac{10}{10} = 1.0$. The value of the

slope in our case implies that, *on average*, each call is a success! That is, an increase of one follow-up call (x) results in an increase of average sales ($\mu_{y|x}$) by one unit. Note, as a line has the same slope at all points on the line, the value of β is the same at every point on the line.

Thus in our example of calls and sales, the population regression line is $\mu_{y|x} = 25 + 1.00x$.

POPULATION REGRESSION EQUATION

The population regression line gives us an average value of the variable Y (sales) for each value of the variable X (the number of calls). Thus, it represents the deterministic part of the statistical relationship. While some actual values of Y may equal the average value (by coincidence), most of the actual values would be different from the average value. For example, Mary makes 30 calls per week with average sales per week equal to 55. However, all six values of her actual sales are different from the average. Some actual values are above the average and others are below the average as shown in the Table 13-5 below.

TABLE 13-5

	Week 1	Week 2	Week 3	Week 4	Week 5	Week 6
Calls (X)	30	30	30	30	30	30
Actual sales (Y)	40	50	65	45	70	60
Average sales ($\mu_{y|x}$)	55	55	55	55	55	55
Error (ϵ)	-15	-5	10	-10	15	5

The difference between the actual values and the average values for each subpopulation is called an error. Thus, actual values of Y for each of the given X-values equal:

$$y = \mu_{y|x} + \epsilon \qquad \text{13-6a}$$

ADRIEN-MARIE LEGENDRE (1752–1833)

The method of least squares first circulated in 1805. It is generally credited to Adrien-Marie Legendre. He developed the statistical procedure to determine the paths of orbiting comets. There is some dispute as to whether the procedure had one or two or more discoverers.

Little is known about the early years of Legendre's life. He was born to a wealthy family from Paris. He had finished his studies at the Collége Mazarin, in Paris, by the time he was 18. He focussed intensively on the study of mathematics and physics. His other well-known mathematical achievements came in the areas of elliptic integrals, number theory, and geometry. His discovery of the method of least squares, fitting a curve to observed data, was most influenced by his contributions to the theory of gravitational attraction.

In 1809, four years after Legendre published his work using the method of least squares, Carl Friedrich Gauss published his version of the least squares method. Gauss went on to claim that he had been using the method since 1795 and tried to sway the general credit for the discovery in his favour. The dispute was never settled. However, Legendre's realization of the potential benefit of this discovery is worth noting.

> Of all the principles that can be proposed for this purpose, I think there is none more general, more exact, or easier to apply, than that which we have used in this work; it consists of making the sum of the squares of the errors a minimum. By this method, a kind of equilibrium is established among the errors which, since it prevents the extremes from dominating, is appropriate for revealing the state of the system which most nearly approaches the truth.[3]

Legendre's method, popularly known as **ordinary least squares**, consists of finding a line that will minimize the sum of the squared errors, thus avoiding the problem of positive and negative errors cancelling each other out. As well, the method has good mathematical and statistical properties, particularly under the assumptions for the population regression made above; the estimated line has many of the desirable properties for an estimator discussed in Chapter 9.

Recall, $y = a + bx + e$ and $\hat{y} = a + bx$; and therefore, $e = (y - \hat{y})$.
By squaring and then summing all errors, we get

$$\sum (e)^2 = \sum (y - \hat{y})^2 \qquad \text{13-9}$$

Thus, the OLS estimates are based on the principle of

$$\text{Min} \sum (e)^2 = \text{Min} \sum (y - \hat{y})^2 = \text{Min} \sum [y - (a + bx)]^2 \qquad \text{13-10}$$

Minimization of $\sum [y - (a + bx)]^2$ with respect to a and b by methods of calculus requires

$$\sum e = \sum [y - (a + bx)] = 0 \qquad \text{13-11}$$

$$\sum xe = \sum x[y - (a + bx)] = 0 \qquad \text{13-12}$$

These two equations are called the *normal equations* of the OLS. Through simple manipulation these normal equations yield the following formulae for a and b:

Slope of the Regression Line	$b = \dfrac{n(\sum xy) - (\sum x)(\sum y)}{n(\sum x^2) - (\sum x)^2}$	**13-13**
Y-intercept	$a = \dfrac{\sum y}{n} - b\dfrac{\sum x}{n}$	**13-14**

Where,
x is a value of the independent variable
y is a value of the dependent variable
n is the number of the pairs of observations in a sample.

This is the most common method to obtain the estimated line of regression: $\hat{y} = a + bx$ as an estimator of the population line of regression: $\mu_{y|x} = \alpha + \beta x$

Where,
$\hat{y}$ is an estimator of $\mu_{y|x}$,
a is an estimator of α; the intercept of the line, the value of $\hat{y}$ when $x = 0$, and
b is an estimator of β; the slope of the line, the change in $\hat{y}$ for a unit change in x.

PROPERTIES OF THE ORDINARY LEAST SQUARES ESTIMATORS (OLSE)

How accurate is the sample regression line as an estimator of the population regression line? Recall the sample regression line is defined by the estimators a and b and the population regression line is defined by the parameters α and β. We can therefore ask the same question: how accurate are the ordinary least squares estimators (OLSE) a and b as estimators of α and β?

Note the difference between the concepts of an estimator and an estimate. *An estimator is a formula, whereas an estimate is a particular value obtained from a sample based on the formula for the estimator.* Thus the formulae for estimating a and b are the estimators. A particular value (such as $a = 200$, $b = 1.5$) obtained by applying the formula to a sample data, is an estimate.

We discussed some desirable properties for an estimator in Chapter 9. We are pleased to say that, given our population regression model, the ordinary least squares estimators have the following properties (we omit the tedious proofs here):

1. They can be expressed as a *linear* function of the dependent variable Y.
2. They are *unbiased.* That is, given the values of x, if we repeated our sample many times and obtained the values of a and b for each sample, then the average value of these estimates from all samples will approximate the true values of the parameters α and β.
3. In the class of all linear and unbiased estimators, the OLSE are the *best* in the sense that OLSE have the *least variance* compared to all other linear and unbiased estimators. This is called the **Gauss-Markov Theorem**.

Given the assumptions of our regression model,

> *i*   The Ordinary Least Squares Estimators (OLSE) a and b are the Best Linear Unbiased Estimators (BLUE) of α and β. In brief, *OLSE are BLUE.*

Example 13-4

Recall the sample of 10 paired observations from the experiment conducted by the Northside Ford dealership (Table 13-6). To make a decision whether to hire a secretary to help with follow-up calls, the auto dealer would like us to provide specific information about the relationship between the number of sales and follow-up calls. Use the method of least squares to determine a linear relationship between the two variables. What is the expected number of sales by a salesperson who makes 40 follow-up calls?

TABLE 13-7

Salesperson Col. 1	x 2	y 3	x^2 4	y^2 5	xy 6	$\hat{y}$ 7
Tom	20	30	400	900	600	42.63
Jeff	40	60	1600	3600	2400	66.32
Brian	20	40	400	1600	800	42.63
Mary	30	60	900	3600	1800	54.47
Sara	10	30	100	900	300	30.79
Yoshimi	10	40	100	1600	400	30.79
Santosh	20	40	400	1600	800	42.63
Jin	20	50	400	2500	1000	42.63
Hansa	20	30	400	900	600	42.63
Joan	30	70	900	4900	2100	54.47
Average	22	45				45
Totals	220	450	5600	22100	10800	449.99

Solution

Table 13-7 repeats the sample information from Table 13-6. It also includes sums needed to calculate the estimates a and b and the estimated sales. The necessary calculations to determine the estimated relation are as follows:

$$b = \frac{n(\sum xy) - (\sum x)(\sum y)}{n(\sum x^2) - (\sum x)^2} = \frac{10(10\,800) - (220)(450)}{10(5600) - (220)^2} = 1.1842$$

$$a = \frac{\sum y}{n} - b\frac{\sum x}{n} = \frac{450}{10} - 1.1842\frac{220}{10} = 18.9476$$

As a result, the estimated regression equation is $\hat{y} = 18.9476 + 1.1842x$.

Thus, if a salesperson makes 40 calls, she or he can expect to sell 66.32 cars (you can round to 66!) per week. This is found by replacing the x by its value 40 in the regression equation. Thus, expected sales for $x = 40$ equals $\hat{y} = 18.9476 + 1.1842(40) = 66.32$. The value of $b = 1.1842$ means that for each additional follow-up call made, the salesperson can expect to increase, *on average*, the number of cars sold by about 1.1842 per week. The value of $a = 18.9476$ means that if the salesperson did not make any follow-up calls (i.e., $x = 0$), he or she can expect to sell, *on average*, about 19 cars per week.

While in this particular case, the value of the intercept appears to be meaningful, it is not always meaningful outside the observed range of the sample data. In fact, we should always remain careful in interpreting the *estimated values* of both the intercept and the slope parameters outside the range of observed data. For example, a negative value of intercept in an equation estimating quantity demanded may not make much sense as quantities cannot be negative. Similarly, it would be meaningless to say that, if a salesperson made 1000 follow-up calls per week to possibly 100 customers who may have visited the showroom, the salesperson would increase sales by 1184 cars per week.

Graphically (see Chart 13-15), the value of $b = 1.1842$ indicates the slope of the estimated regression line and the value of the intercept a indicates the value of the point on the line where the line intersects the vertical sales-axis. Since the range of calls does not include $x = 0$, you have to extend the regression line backwards (to the left) to find the point where it intersects the vertical axis.

DRAWING THE REGRESSION LINE

To draw the regression line manually, you need two pairs of values for the two variables, i.e., values for any two points on the line. Thus $\hat{y} = 18.9476$ and $x = 0$ is one pair of values, and $\hat{y} = 66.32$ and $x = 40$ is another pair of values. The values of $\hat{y}$ corresponding to each x value in the observation range are given in column 7 of Table 13-7. You can find all these values using a calculator just as we found the value of $\hat{y}$ for $x = 0$ above. The value of $\hat{y}$ for $x = 0$ of course you can get from the estimated regression equation.

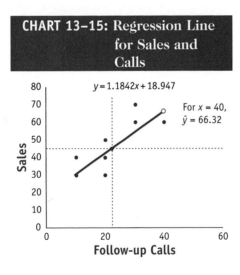

CHART 13–15: Regression Line for Sales and Calls

Stigler, a well known historian of statistics once said, "The method of least squares is the automobile of modern statistical analysis, despite its limitations, occasional accidents, and incidental pollution, it and its numerous variations, extensions and related conveyances carry the bulk of statistical analysis, and are known and valued by all."[4]

PROPERTIES OF THE OLS ESTIMATE OF THE REGRESSION LINE

The regression line obtained by the OLS has some interesting properties. Some of the properties are listed below.

The estimated line passes through the means of the variables X and Y ($\bar{x}$ and $\bar{y}$). Since, the estimated regression line is $\hat{y} = 18.9476 + 1.1842x$, and substituting $\bar{x} = 22$ for x, we get $\hat{y} = 45$, which equals the value of $\bar{y} = 45$ (Verify!). Thus $\bar{y} = a + b\bar{x}$.

We have drawn the lines (dotted lines) for $\bar{x}$ and $\bar{y}$ in the chart above. You can see how the regression line passes through the point where the lines for $\bar{x}$ and $\bar{y}$ intersect with each other.

1. Mean of $\hat{y}$: $(\bar{\hat{y}}) = \bar{y}$. (Hint: Replace $a = \bar{y} - b\bar{x}$ in $\hat{y} = a + bx$, take the sum of both sides, and then divide both sides by n.)

2. The sum and therefore the mean of the error is zero. Another way, $\Sigma e = 0$ (Hint: See the first normal equation.)

3. $\Sigma xe = 0$ (Hint: See the second normal equation.)

4. Estimators a and b are linear functions of the dependent variable Y. (Hint: See the formulae for a and b.)

5. $\Sigma \hat{y}e = 0$ (Hint: Replace $\hat{y} = a + bx$, and expand.)

■ SELF-REVIEW 13-3

We wish to estimate a demand equation for consumption of beer in Canada. Demand for a commodity depends on several variables including real price (nominal price of the commodity divided by the general price level), real per capita disposable income (earned income plus transfer payments minus taxes, in real terms, per capita), prices of substitute commodities, tastes, etc. In this chapter, we assume that the real price of beer is the only variable influencing consumption, and there is a linear relationship between consumption of beer and the real price of beer. The data on per capita consumption of beer by Canadians over 15 years of age (Quantity, Y: the dependent variable) and the real price of beer (Price, X: the independent variable) are given below:

Year	Quantity (Y)	Price (X)	Year	Quantity (Y)	Price (X)
1979	108.1	1.779	1990	97.3	2.546
1980	110.7	1.706	1991	94.5	2.551
1981	105.6	1.762	1992	91.7	2.655
1982	107.8	1.847	1993	87.5	2.765
1983	104.5	1.994	1994	87.1	2.68
1984	104.3	2.16	1995	86.5	2.624
1985	102.8	2.201	1996	85.8	2.622
1986	101.2	2.329	1997	83.6	2.664
1987	100.1	2.448	1998	83.7	2.809
1988	101.3	2.447	1999	85.3	2.837
1989	99.5	2.5			

(a) Estimate the demand equation for beer.
(b) Interpret the values of a and b.
(c) Estimate the consumption of beer at real price = $2.00.

EXERCISES 13-11 TO 13-18

Note: It is suggested that you save your values for Σx, Σx^2, Σxy, Σy, and Σy^2, as these exercises will be referred to later in the chapter.

13-11. Refer to Exercise 13-3. Use asset as the independent variable.
    (a) Determine the regression equation.
    (b) Estimate the likely profit for a company with assets equal to 5 billion dollars.
    (c) Interpret the regression equation.

13-12. Refer to Exercise 13-4. Use IR as the independent variable.
    (a) Determine the regression equation.
    (b) Estimate UR for IR = 1%.
    (c) Interpret the regression equation.

13-13. Refer to Exercise 13-5.
    (a) Determine the regression equation.
    (b) Estimate the selling price of a 10-year-old car.
    (c) Interpret the regression equation.

13-14. As we discussed in Statistics in Action, we are interested in computing the Beta risk for Bell Canada (BCE) stocks from the data for closing prices for BCE stocks and S&P/TSX for the last Friday of each month for 20 months (May 2001 to November 1999). The data are given below:

Date	S&P/TSX (X)	BCE (Y)	Date	S&P/TSX (X)	BCE (Y)
25-May	8 292.84	39.75	29-Jul	10 342.98	34.60
27-Apr	7 967.34	39.38	30-Jun	10 195.45	35.10
30-Mar	7 608.00	35.44	26-May	9 020.88	32.65
23-Feb	8 028.81	39.45	28-Apr	9 347.61	41.66
26-Jan	9 158.19	42.50	31-Mar	9 462.39	43.97
29-Dec	8 933.68	43.30	25-Feb	9 141.17	39.17
24-Nov	9 024.43	42.25	28-Jan	8 390.40	34.56
27-Oct	9 321.89	39.90	31-Dec	8 413.75	31.86
29-Sep	10 377.92	35.05	26-Nov	7 889.94	26.48
25-Aug	11 246.04	33.30			

First, you will need to convert both variables to percent changes to find rates of return for both Bell Canada stock and the S&P/TSX. Remember to use percent changes in Bell Canada stock as the dependent variable and percent changes in S&P/TSX as the independent variable.
    (a) Draw a scatter diagram.
    (b) Determine the regression equation. Interpret the regression equation. What is the value of the Beta risk? Interpret.
    (c) Find the rate of return on Bell Canada stock when the market rate of return (S&P/TSX) is 5 percent.

13-15. In this question, we are interested in estimating the relationship between a company's earned revenue and the profits realized from those revenues.

A random sample of 10 Canadian companies was selected and the revenue and profits, reported in millions of dollars, are reported below.

Company	Profit (Y) ($ million)	Revenue (X) ($ million)
Algoma Central	7.4	257.5
Algonquin Mercantile	5.9	139.3
Budd Canada	8.6	385.6
CFS Group	1.5	81.9
Dover Industries	3.0	135.1
Mark's Work Warehouse	6.4	321.2
Motion International	2.6	125.7
QMedia Services	4.5	101.8
Sleeman Breweries	7.4	96.1
SR Telecom	6.9	195.3
Source: Globe & Mail Interactive Services, May 15, 2001		

Let revenue be the independent variable and profit be the dependent variable.
(a) Draw a scatter diagram.
(b) Determine the regression equation. Interpret the regression equation.
(c) For a company with $150.0 million in revenue, estimate the profit.

13-16. We are studying mutual funds for the purpose of investing in several funds. For this particular study, we want to focus on the assets of a fund and its five-year performance. Ten mutual funds were selected at random, and their assets and annual rates of return over the past five years are shown below.

Fund Assets	Assets (X) ($ millions)	Returns (Y) (%)
AGF World Balanced	89.9	8.9
AIM Canadian Premier	814.3	14.1
Altamira Income	369.1	6.6
Canada Life C'dn Equity S-9	596.2	8.9
Clarica MVP Equity	73.7	10.6
Dynamic Fund of Canada	170.2	10.8
Fidelity Canada Large Cap-A	236.2	8.7
Janus Global Equity	153.8	12.7
RBC Canadian Bond	7.38	5.4
Standard Life Ideal Bond	44.3	6.2
Source: www.globefund.com, May 22, 2001		

(a) Draw a scatter diagram.
(b) Determine the regression equation. Use assets as the independent variable.
(c) Write a brief report on your findings in part (b).
(d) For a fund with $400.0 million in assets (not shown), determine the five-year rate of return (in percent).

13-17. The Alberta Electric Illuminating Company is studying the relationship between kilowatt-hours (thousands) and the number of rooms in a private single-family homes. A random sample of 10 homes yielded the following:

Number of Rooms (X)	Kilowatt-Hours (thousands) (Y)	Number of Rooms (X)	Kilowatt-Hours (thousands) (Y)
12	9	8	6
9	7	10	8
14	10	10	10
6	5	5	4
10	8	7	7

(a) Determine the regression equation.
(b) Determine the number of kilowatt-hours (in thousands) for a six-bedroom home.

13-18. Refer to the data in Excel Chart 13-2.
Use the 20 observations for GDP and the unemployment rate. Use GDP as the independent variable.
(a) Determine the regression line.
(b) Interpret the regression line.
(c) Repeat (a) and (b) above with unemployment as the independent variable.
(d) Comment on the differences in results in (a), (b), and (c).

13.4 HOW GOOD IS THE ESTIMATED REGRESSION LINE?

In the previous section, we noted that, given the population regression model, ordinary least squares estimators have very convincing statistical properties. These properties are based on the possibility of generating probability distributions of the estimators obtained through repeated sampling. That is, if we took a large number of random samples from the same population and used OLS to obtain the estimated regression line for each sample, the estimators (the coefficients a and b) are best linear unbiased. However, in practice, we estimate a regression line based on a single sample of information. How can we be sure that we have achieved the desired result?

One way to evaluate our estimated regression line is to find out how well the estimated line represents or explains the information contained in the sample. In other words, how well does the estimated regression line capture the variation in the dependent variable—indeed the prime objective of the regression analysis. Other methods of evaluation are also based on this idea.

ANALYSIS OF VARIANCE

As we already know, total variability in the values of a variable can be measured by its variance. The variance, as you have seen in Chapter 4, is the average of the squared deviations of the actual values of the variable from its mean. The total variation in the values of the variable Y, in the spirit of the definition of variance, can be written as, $\sum(y - \bar{y})^2$. We call this total sum of squared deviations, SS Total.

In order to decompose this variation into the variation explained by the estimated regression line (SSR) and the error variation (SSE—the variation left unexplained by the regression line), we play a trick. We add and subtract $\hat{y}$ inside the expression for SS Total:

$$= \sum [(y - \hat{y}) + (\hat{y} - \bar{y})]^2$$

and then expand the squared term:

$$= \sum (y - \hat{y})^2 + \sum (\hat{y} - \bar{y})^2 + 2 \sum (y - \hat{y})(\hat{y} - \bar{y})$$

Based on the two normal equations of OLS, we can show that the last term is equal to zero. We therefore have:

$$\sum (y - \bar{y})^2 = \sum (y - \hat{y})^2 + \sum (\hat{y} - \bar{y})^2 \qquad \textbf{13-15}$$

$$\text{Thus,} \quad \text{SS Total} = \text{SSE} + \text{SSR}$$

CHART 13-16

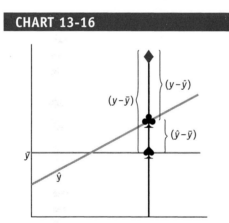

Thus, the total variation in Y can be divided into two parts: the variation SSR is the part that is explained by the sample regression line, and the SSE is the part of the variation in Y that is not explained by the sample regression line. This is illustrated for a single observation in Chart 13-16. You can also see this division in numbers in columns 5, 7, and 9 of Table 13-8 below.

TABLE 13-8

Name (1)	x (2)	y (3)	$\hat{y}$ (4)	$(y - \bar{y})$ (5)	$(y - \bar{y})^2$ (6)	$(\hat{y} - \bar{y})$ (7)	$(\hat{y} - \bar{y})^2$ (8)	$e = (y - \hat{y})$ (9)	e^2 (10)
Tom	20	30	42.63	−15	225	−2.37	5.62	−12.63	159.52
Jeff	40	60	66.32	15	225	21.32	454.54	−6.32	39.94
Brian	20	40	42.63	−5	25	−2.37	5.62	−2.63	6.92
Mary	30	60	54.47	15	225	9.47	89.68	5.53	30.58
Sara	10	30	30.79	−15	225	−14.21	201.92	−0.79	0.62
Yoshimi	10	40	30.79	−5	25	−14.21	201.92	9.21	84.82
Santosh	20	40	42.63	−5	25	−2.37	5.62	−2.63	6.92
Jim	20	50	42.63	5	25	−2.37	5.62	7.37	54.32
Hansa	20	30	42.63	−15	225	−2.37	5.62	−12.63	159.52
Joan	30	70	54.47	25	625	9.47	89.68	15.53	241.18
Totals	220	450	449.99	0	1850	−0.01	1065.84	0.01	784.34
Average	22	45	45	0		0		0	

Dividing each sum of squares by the appropriate degrees of freedom, we can obtain the variances, often called mean squares in the context of regression analysis. The degrees of freedom (df) for SS Total are $n - 1$, for SSR are k, and for SSE are $n - k - 1$. *Here n is the number of paired observations in the sample data and k is the number of independent variables in the regression equation. In our case, we have one independent variable, follow-up calls, therefore k = 1.* MSR is the variance explained by the regression and MSE is the unexplained variation. We can organize our discussion in what is called an Analysis of Variance (ANOVA) table as below:

ANOVA Table

Source of Variation	Sums of Squares	df	Mean Square
Regression	SSR	k	MSR = SSR/k
Error	SSE	$n - k - 1$	MSE = SSE/$(n - k - 1)$
Total	SS Total	$n - 1$	MST = SS Total/$(n - 1)$

Example 13-5 | In order to illustrate the calculations, we use our sales and follow-up calls example. We have already found the estimated values $(\hat{y})$ in Column 3 of Table 13-8. To find SS Total, SSR, and SSE, we first need to find the respective deviations: $(y - \bar{y})$, $(\hat{y} - \bar{y})$, and $(y - \hat{y})$.

We compute these deviations in columns 5, 7, and 9 of Table 13-8. We then find squares of these deviations in columns 6, 8, and 10 respectively. Totals of all columns and averages of some columns are also given in the bottom two rows of the table. From the table, we can easily write our ANOVA Table for the example as below. (Note: numbers may not add up due to rounding.)

ANOVA Table

Source of Variation	Sums of Squares	df	Mean Square
Regression	SSR = 1065.84	1	MSR = 1065.84
Error	SSE = 784.34	8	MSE = 98.04
Total	SS Total = 1850.00	9	MST = 205.56

GOODNESS OF FIT AND THE COEFFICIENT OF DETERMINATION

Now we are ready to evaluate our sample regression. Our question is how well the estimated regression line explains the sample observations. This can be accomplished by simply finding out what proportion of the total variation in the dependent variable is explained by the estimated regression line.

Since, SS Total = SSE + SSR, dividing through by SS Total, we get

$$\frac{\text{SS Total}}{\text{SS Total}} = 1 = \frac{\text{SSE}}{\text{SS Total}} + \frac{\text{SSR}}{\text{SS Total}} \Rightarrow \frac{\text{SSR}}{\text{SS Total}} = 1 - \frac{\text{SSE}}{\text{SS Total}}$$

Thus, the value $\dfrac{\text{SSR}}{\text{SS Total}}$ gives us the proportion of the variation explained by the sample regression line. This proportion is known as the **coefficient of determination**, also called R^2.

Coefficient of Determination	$R^2 = \dfrac{\text{SSR}}{\text{SS Total}} = 1 - \dfrac{\text{SSE}}{\text{SS Total}}$	13-16a

A value of $R^2 = 0.8$ means that the sample regression line (or the independent variable) is successful in explaining 80 percent of the variation in the dependent variable. As the second term in the definition of R^2 suggests, the higher the SSE, the lower will be the value of R^2 and vice versa. Since we normally estimate the regression line and the resulting errors before estimating R^2, it is easier to compute R^2 based on the definition of R^2 in terms of SSE.

Since, $error\ (e) = (y - \hat{y}) = y - (a + bx)$, we can write:

$$\text{SSE} = \sum e^2 = \sum (y - \hat{y})^2 = \sum \{y - (a + bx)\}^2 = \sum y^2 - a\sum y - b\sum xy$$

We can use either the first term or the last term to find the SSE. Hence, we can compute R^2 by

Computational Formula	$R^2 = 1 - \dfrac{\sum e^2}{\sum y^2 - \dfrac{1}{n}(\sum y)^2}$	13-16b
	$= 1 - \dfrac{\sum y^2 - a\sum y - b\sum xy}{\sum y^2 - \dfrac{1}{n}(\sum y)^2}$	13-16c

In passing, we should note that we should not interpret R^2 as the square of the correlation coefficient "r." The concept of the coefficient of correlation is based on the joint distribution of two random variables, whereas the concept of the coefficient of determination is based on the assumptions noted under the population regression model. Algebraically though, the square of the coefficient of correlation in a two-variable model does equal the value of the coefficient of determination. However, the coefficient of correlation computed for variables that involve one or both non-random variables can only be used as a descriptive measure, but not as a statistical measure for drawing inferences about the relationship in the population.

For our example of sales and follow-up calls, we can easily compute R^2 from the ANOVA table.

$$R^2 = \frac{\text{SSR}}{\text{SS Total}} = \frac{1065.84}{1850.00} = 0.576$$

We can also use the computational formulae to find R^2.

For example, from the values in Table 13-7, and the values of $a = 18.95$ and $b = 1.84$, we compute

$$R^2 = 1 - \frac{\sum y^2 - a\sum y - b\sum xy}{\sum y^2 - \dfrac{1}{n}(\sum y)^2} = 1 - \frac{22100 - 18.95(450) - 1.184(10800)}{22100 - \dfrac{1}{10}(450)^2} = 0.576$$

The advantage of using the latter formula is that we do not have to conduct the analysis of variance to compute R^2.

Thus, our estimated regression line explains 57.6 percent of the variation in sales values in the sample data. Alternatively, we could say that 57.6 percent of the variation in sales can be attributed to the follow-up calls. The remaining 42.4 percent of the variation in sales values must be attributed to factors other than follow-up calls. Note, all other factors, by our assumption, include all minor elements that are not worth including as separate variables. If we know, *a priori*, that there is another important variable contributing to sales, we should have included it in the regression equation (this will then become a multiple regression model treated in the next chapter) rather than estimating sales based on follow-up calls only.

STANDARD ERROR OF ESTIMATE

While the coefficient of determination measures the proportion of the variation explained by the sample regression line, the average of the SSE gives us an idea about the spread of the sample observations (the unexplained variation in the dependent variable Y) around the estimated regression line. In other words, the SSE gives us an idea about the precision of the estimated line. The less the variation, the more precise the estimate would be. If the SSE was zero, we would have a perfect fit. The two measures are like two sides of the same coin.

Similar to the idea of standard deviation, we define the standard error of estimate (a measure of the standard deviation around the estimated regression line) as the square root of the average of all squared deviations between the actual values (y) and the estimated values ($\hat{y}$) of the dependent variable (Y). The SSE gives us the total of such deviations. Thus, we can find the standard error of estimate (S_e) as the square root of Mean Square Error (MSE), where MSE is obtained by dividing the SSE by its degrees of freedom ($= n - k - 1 = n - 2$). See the ANOVA Table for details. This is given below along with alternative computational formulae:

Standard Error of Estimate

$$S_e = \sqrt{\text{MSE}} = \sqrt{\frac{\text{SSE}}{n-2}} = \sqrt{\frac{\sum e^2}{n-2}} = \sqrt{\frac{\sum y^2 - a\sum y - b\sum xy}{n-2}} \qquad \textbf{13-17}$$

Both the coefficient of determination and the standard error of estimate can be computed by using SSE. For our example of sales and follow-up calls, we can easily compute S_e either from the ANOVA table or from Table 13-7.

From the ANOVA table, $S_e = \sqrt{\dfrac{\text{SSE}}{n-2}} = \sqrt{\dfrac{784.34}{8}} = \sqrt{98.04} = 9.90$. Alternatively, as we computed R^2, we can compute S_e without conducting the ANOVA from Table 13-8.

What does the value of $S_e = 9.9$ indicate? It is the average of the dispersion of all observations from the estimated regression line. Based on the empirical rule for random observations (see Chapter 4), we expect 68 percent of the observations to fall between $\hat{y} \pm 9.9$ and 95 percent of the observations between $\hat{y} \pm 2(9.9)$. If we check the deviations of observations from the regression line in column 9 of Table 13-8, 7 out of 10 (70 percent) of the observations are within the limits of $\hat{y} \pm 9.9$, and 100 percent observations are within the limits of $\hat{y} \pm 2(9.9)$! Considering the small size of our sample, this is much better than expected.

■ SELF-REVIEW 13-4

Refer to Self-Review 13-3 where we studied the relationship for the Canadian demand for beer. Construct the ANOVA table. Determine the standard error of estimate. Calculate the coefficient of determination. Interpret the results.

EXERCISES 13-19 TO 13-24

13-19. Refer to Exercise 13-11.
    (a) Construct an ANOVA table.
    (b) Determine the coefficient of determination. Interpret.
    (c) Find the standard error of estimate. Interpret.

13-20. Refer to Exercise 13-12.
    (a) Construct an ANOVA table.
    (b) Determine the coefficient of determination. Interpret.
    (c) Find the standard error of estimate. Interpret.

13-21. Refer to Exercise 13-13.
    (a) Construct an ANOVA table.
    (b) Determine the coefficient of determination. Interpret.
    (c) Find the standard error of estimate. Interpret.

13-22. Refer to Exercise 13-14.
    (a) Construct an ANOVA table.
    (b) Determine the coefficient of determination. Interpret.
    (c) Can you identify the reasons for the variation in Bell Canada stocks that is not explained by the market rate of return?
    (d) Find the standard error of estimate. Interpret.

13-23. Refer to Exercise 13-15.
    (a) Construct an ANOVA table.
    (b) Determine the coefficient of determination. Interpret.
    (c) Find the standard error of estimate. Interpret.

13-24. Refer to Exercise 13-16.
    (a) Construct an ANOVA table.
    (b) Determine the coefficient of determination. Interpret.
    (c) Find the standard error of estimate. Interpret.

13.5 INFERENCE

HOW CLOSE IS OUR ESTIMATED REGRESSION LINE TO THE POPULATION REGRESSION LINE?

In the preceding sections, we estimated the regression line based on a sample of observations, we discussed how well the estimated regression line fits the particular *sample observations* and some of the mathematical properties of the estimated line. Now it's time to find out how reliable is our estimate, or how much confidence we can put in our estimated regression line as a representation of the *population regression line*. In other words, what inferences can we draw about the relationship between sales and follow-up calls in the population based on our estimated relationship from a given sample of observations.

In this section, we study the statistical properties of the estimated regression line. Like our studies of the statistical properties of means, proportions, and variances in earlier chapters, we can study the statistical properties of the estimated regression line through the techniques of the confidence interval and test of hypothesis. However, as you learned earlier, these techniques depend on some specific form of probability distribution.

Recall the assumptions (1 to 5) in Section 13.3 specifying the population regression model. We assumed that the independent variable is non-random (and its values fixed in repeated sampling) and linearly related with the random variable Y, and the associated error term (ϵ) in the population regression equation has zero mean, constant variance, zero covariance (and therefore correlation) with other error terms. These assumptions were sufficient for the technique of OLS to yield the Best Linear Unbiased Estimators (BLUE). We did not require any other assumptions about the probability distribution of (ϵ) for the OLS to yield BLUE. Using only the basic population regression model without additional assumptions on the distribution of the error term, it is very difficult to draw useful inferences about the population regression line based on sample observations.

As we saw in chapters 8, 9, and 10, the central limit theorem and normal distribution play an important role in drawing inferences for a variety of populations. We can outright assume that the population error term has a normal distribution (without an appeal to the central limit theorem). Alternatively, given the nature of the population error term that consists of a large number of individually insignificant components, we can apply the central limit theorem to obtain the normal distribution of the error term. In either case, we shall have the normal distribution of the error term. We therefore add the following assumption to the population regression model.

Assumption #6
The error term (ϵ) is normally distributed with zero mean, zero covariance with other error terms, and a constant variance $= \sigma_\epsilon^2$. Since normal distribution is completely specified by its mean and variance, in brief, we write the assumption as $\epsilon \sim N(0, \sigma_\epsilon)$.

Together, these six assumptions about the regression model constitute what is conventionally called the *classical normal linear regression model* (*CNLRM*).

TEST OF HYPOTHESIS FOR REGRESSION COEFFICIENTS

From our earlier discussion, we know that Y, the dependent variable, is a linear function of the error term, and the estimators a and b are linear functions of the dependent variable. We also know that if we repeat our estimation of the regression line for a number of random samples of size n (with some predetermined values of the independent variable, X), the estimators a and b will have a probability distribution. Since the error term is now assumed to have a normal distribution, the estimators a and b will also have normal distributions. Since normal distributions are completely specified by two parameters, mean and variance, we need to find mean and variance of a and b. It can be shown that

$$\text{Mean }(a) = \alpha \qquad \text{Var }(a) = \sigma_a^2 = \sigma_\epsilon^2 \left[\frac{\sum x^2}{n \sum (x - \bar{x})^2} \right] \qquad \text{13-18}$$

$$\text{Mean }(b) = \beta \qquad \text{Var }(b) = \sigma_b^2 = \sigma_\epsilon^2 \left[\frac{1}{\sum (x - \bar{x})^2} \right] \qquad \text{13-19}$$

Similarly, for each given value of X, the mean of $Y(= \mu_{y|x})$ is $\alpha + \beta x$ and its variance is σ_ϵ^2. Note, for each given value of X the variance Y is the same as the variance of ϵ.

As we noted earlier, precision or reliability of an estimator depends on the size of its variance. As is obvious from the formulae for the variances of both a and b, the larger the variance of the error term σ_ϵ^2, the larger will be the variances of a and b. However, the larger the variance of the variable X, the smaller will be the variance of the estimators a and b. This is the reason for the advice to have as much variation in the independent variable as possible. Lastly, a larger sample size, by making the denominator larger, tends to reduce the variation in both the estimators, the reason for advocating as large a sample size as possible.

Given the means and variances, we can standardize the estimators to derive a standard normal distribution for conducting a test of hypothesis. Thus,

Z distribution for estimator a is $\dfrac{a - \alpha}{\sigma_a}$ with mean = zero and variance = 1.

Z distribution for estimator b is $\dfrac{b - \beta}{\sigma_b}$ with mean = zero and variance = 1.

However, we are still one step short of conducting the test of hypothesis. Both σ_a and σ_b depend on the unknown standard deviation of the population error term σ_ϵ. We therefore use S_e in place of σ_ϵ and replace σ_a and σ_b by S_a and S_b.

Our test statistic for a and b therefore are $\dfrac{a - \alpha}{S_a}$ and $\dfrac{b - \beta}{S_b}$ respectively. As explained in Chapter 9, the test statistic for both a and b will now have a flatter distribution, known as t distribution with $n - 2$ degrees of freedom (the degrees of freedom for S_e). Thus,

$$\frac{a - \alpha}{S_a} \sim t_{(n-2)} \qquad \text{13-20}$$

and

$$\frac{b - \beta}{S_b} \sim t_{(n-2)} \qquad \text{13-21}$$

Where

$$S_a = \sqrt{S_e^2 \left[\frac{\sum x^2}{n \sum (x - \bar{x})^2} \right]} \qquad \text{13-22}$$

$$S_b = \sqrt{S_e^2 \left[\frac{1}{\sum (x - \bar{x})^2} \right]} \qquad \text{13-23}$$

Example 13-6

Recall our estimated regression equation for sales and follow-up calls:
$\hat{y} = 18.9476 + 1.1842x$

Where $a = 18.9476$, $b = 1.1842$, and $n = 10$

Let H_0: $\beta \leq 0 \Rightarrow$ follow-up calls do not increase sales. In other words, the difference between b and the hypothesized value of β ($\beta = 0$, in this case) is purely due to chance.
H_1: $\beta > 0 \Rightarrow$ follow-up calls are an effective tool to increase sales.

Now suppose we select a 5 percent level of significance, that is, we are willing to commit a maximum of 5 percent error in rejecting H_0, assuming H_0 is true. The critical value of t for 8 (= 10 − 2) degrees of freedom is $t_{0.05(8)} = 1.86$. We will reject H_0 only if the value of the test statistic from the sample observations is larger than 1.86.

Solution

To compute the value of the test statistic from the sample observations, we still need the value of S_b. Recall, we can write $\sum(x-\bar{x})^2 = \sum x^2 - \frac{1}{n}(\sum x)^2$. We already know the values for $\sum x^2 = 5600$, $\sum x = 220$, and $n = 10$ as given in Table 13-7.

Thus, we get $\sum x^2 - \frac{1}{n}(\sum x)^2 = 5600 - \frac{(220)^2}{10} = 760$ and since $S_e = 9.901$

$S_b = \sqrt{(9.901)^2\left(\frac{1}{760}\right)} = 0.3591$. Thus our sample value of $t = \frac{1.1842 - 0}{0.3591} = 3.2973$.

Since the value of t from our sample data is far larger than the required value from the t distribution for 8 degrees of freedom (1.86), the difference between b and the hypothesized value of β ($\beta = 0$, in this case) cannot be attributed to pure chance. We therefore conclude that there is sufficient evidence against H_0 (or in favour of H_1), and hence reject H_0. If you check the P-value in the t table for 8 degrees of freedom, you would find it close to 0.005. Could you reject H_0, if the true H_0 were $\beta \le 1$ against H_1: $\beta > 1$ at a 5 percent level of significance? Try the challenge!

Also, try conducting the test of hypothesis for H_0: $\alpha = 0$ against H_1: $\alpha \ne 0$ at your selected level of significance. The calculations should now be easier. (Hint: $S_a = S_b\sqrt{\frac{1}{n}\sum x^2}$.) However, as we will show later, we can get these calculations and more by the click of a few buttons in both Excel and Minitab. See Charts 13-17 and 13-18.

TEST OF SIGNIFICANCE FOR THE INDEPENDENT VARIABLE OR THE MODEL

An alternative test of hypothesis procedure in the context of regression analysis depends on the analysis of variance. Here, we test the significance of the variations (in the dependent variable) explained by the independent variable. In other words, how significant are the explanatory variable(s), or the assumed model, in explaining the variation in the dependent variable? In the context of one independent variable, however, the test boils down to the test of hypothesis on the slope parameter β, which we have already conducted. It, however, assumes greater importance in the context of multiple independent variables. This is discussed in the next chapter. Here, for the sake of completeness, we illustrate the procedure below.

H_0: The independent variable (X) is statistically insignificant in explaining variation in the dependent variable (Y), i.e.,

H_0: $\beta = 0$ and

H_1: $\beta \ne 0$

Test statistic is given by the ratio	$F = \dfrac{MSR}{MSE} = \dfrac{SSR/k}{SSE/(n-k-1)}$	**13-24a**

Alternatively, it can be written in terms of R^2 as

	$F = \dfrac{R^2/k}{(1-R^2)/(n-k-1)}$	**13-24b**

Under the same assumptions we made for testing hypotheses on β, this test statistic F has a probability distribution known as F with k degrees of freedom (used in computing MSR) for the numerator and $n - k - 1$ degrees of freedom (used in computing MSE) for the denominator. Therefore, n is the sample size and k is the number of independent variables in the regression equation. For an explanation, see the discussion on the ANOVA table.

Assuming we wish to continue with our decision rule of a maximum 5 percent error in rejecting the null hypothesis, the critical value of $F_{0.05(1,8)} = 5.32$.

The computed value of $F = \dfrac{\text{MSR}}{\text{MSE}} = \dfrac{1065.84}{98.04} = 10.8$. This is far greater than the critical value of 5.32 for our regression line. Thus, there is sufficient evidence that the independent variable, follow-up calls, is effective in explaining variations in sales. In other words, our regression line is a good fit for the hypothesized relation between sales and follow-up calls. Thus, the F ratio provides an alternative method of testing hypotheses on β in a two-variable regression analysis. This is not surprising as we can prove that in a two-variable regression analysis, when H_0: $\beta = 0$ and H_1: $\beta \neq 0$, $F_\alpha = (t_{\alpha/2})^2$. Note, this relationship does not hold in more than two variable regressions or for a one-tailed alternative hypothesis.

■ SELF-REVIEW 13-5

Refer to Self-Review 13-4.
- (a) Conduct a hypothesis test where the null hypothesis (H_0) is that the effect of price is greater than or equal to zero (i.e., $\beta \geq 0$) and the alternative hypothesis (H_1) is that price has a significant effect on the demand for beer ($\beta < 0$). Use a 0.05 level of significance.
- (b) Conduct an F test to test whether the model is statistically significant. Use the 0.05 level of significance.

EXERCISES 13-25 TO 13-28

13-25. Refer to Exercise 13-14.
- (a) Test the null hypothesis that the Beta risk for Bell Canada stock is less than or equal to 1, against the alternative hypothesis that it is greater than 1. Use the 0.05 level of significance.
- (b) Test the overall significance of the model using an F test. Use the 0.05 level of significance.

13-26. Refer to Exercise 13-15.
- (a) Test the null hypothesis that revenue has no effect on profit. Use the 0.01 level of significance.
- (b) Test the overall significance of the model using an F test. Use the 0.01 level of significance.
- (c) Is there any difference between the results of (a) and (b)?

13-27. Refer to Exercise 13-16.
- (a) Use a t test to see if the coefficient for the asset variable is statistically significant. Use the 0.05 significance level.
- (b) Now use an F test to test for the significance of the interest rate variable in the model at the 0.05 level of significance.
- (c) Is there any difference between the results of (a) and (b)? Show that $F = t^2$.

13-28. Refer to Minitab Chart 13-3 for the data on inflation rate and interest rate.
- (a) Determine the regression equation using the rate of inflation as the dependent variable.
- (b) Conduct a hypothesis test to determine if the coefficient for the interest rate is statistically different from zero. Use the 0.05 significance level.

(c) Now use an F test to test for the significance of the interest rate variable in the model at the 0.05 level of significance.

(d) Is there any difference between the results of (b) and (c)? Show that $F = t^2$.

EXCEL CHART 13-17: Regression Analysis of Sales on Calls

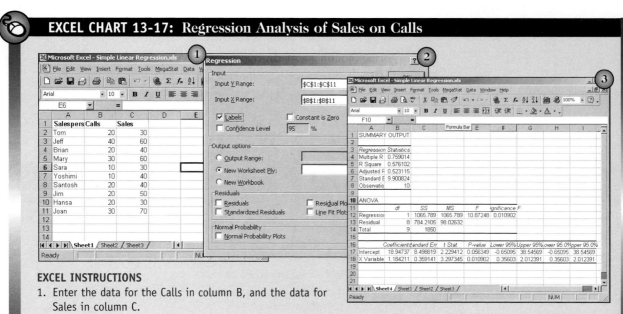

EXCEL INSTRUCTIONS

1. Enter the data for the Calls in column B, and the data for Sales in column C.
2. Look under Tools and click on Data Analysis. Select Regression.
3. In the Regression dialogue box enter C1.C11 to input all the data for your Sales (Y range). Then enter B1.B11 to input all the data for your Calls (X range).
4. Be sure the Labels box is checked, but not the Constant is Zero box.
5. Click OK and your summary output will appear.

MINITAB CHART 13-18: Regression Analysis of Sales on Calls

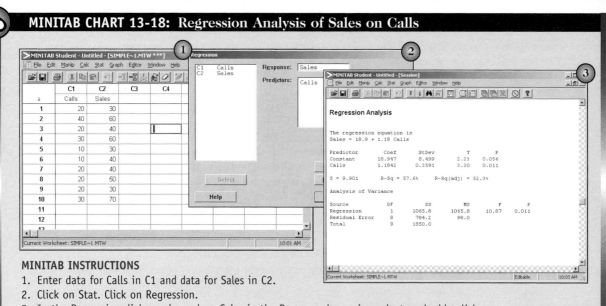

MINITAB INSTRUCTIONS

1. Enter data for Calls in C1 and data for Sales in C2.
2. Click on Stat. Click on Regression.
3. In the Regression dialogue box, place Sales in the Response box using select or double click.
4. Place Calls in the Predictors box.
5. To obtain output, click on OK.

CHAPTER OUTLINE

I. A **scatter diagram** is a graphic tool to portray the relationship between two variables. The diagram displays each pair of observations as one point on the chart, observations on one variable on the X-axis (the horizontal axis) and on another variable on the Y-axis (the vertical axis).

II. **Covariance** is a measure of linear association. It is defined as an average (arithmetic mean) of the product of variations in each of two variables from their mean values. For population it is defined as:

$$\sigma_{xy} = \frac{\sum (x - \mu_x)(y - \mu_y)}{N}$$ **13-1**

and for a sample of n observations:

$$S_{xy} = \frac{\sum (x - \bar{x})(y - \bar{y})}{n - 1}$$

A. A positive value of covariance shows a positive (or direct) relationship between two random variables. A negative value of covariance shows a negative (or inverse) relationship between two random variables.

B. It is not a very popular measure of association due to its heavy dependence on the units in which each variable is measured.

III. **Coefficient of correlation** is a measure of the degree of *linear* relationship between two *random* variables. It is defined as the covariance between two *standardized* random variables. Both variables must be on at least the interval scale of measurement. For a sample of n pairs of observations,

$$r = Cov\left(\frac{(x - \bar{x})}{S_x} \right)\left(\frac{(y - \bar{y})}{S_y} \right)$$ **13-3a**

It can easily be calculated by using the formula:

$$r = \frac{n\sum xy - (\sum x)(\sum y)}{\sqrt{n\sum x^2 - (\sum x)^2}\ \sqrt{n\sum y^2 - (\sum y)^2}}$$ **13-3c**

A. The coefficient of correlation can range from -1.00 to $+1.00$.

B. Like covariance, a positive sign means there is a direct relationship between the variables, and a negative sign means there is an inverse relationship.

C. A value of $+1.00$ indicates perfect positive correlation, and -1.00 indicates perfect negative correlation.

D. A zero value of the correlation coefficient in a sample of observations conveys a lack of linear relationship between two variables in that sample data, but not for the population or other samples.

E. If two variables are statistically independent, then any non-zero value of the coefficient of correlation in the observed data should be interpreted as meaningless.

F. We should exercise caution in using a computed value of correlation coefficient in the presence of outliers, non-linear relationships, and spurious relationships.

G. The coefficient of correlation as defined in statistics is *neutral* with respect to causality between variables.

IV. We can *test for the significance of correlation* in the population by the test statistic

$$t = \frac{r\sqrt{n-2}}{\sqrt{1-r^2}} \text{ with } (n-2) \text{ degrees of freedom.} \qquad \textbf{13-4}$$

V. **Regression analysis** was first developed in the context of controlled experiments, but it is applicable to observational data under certain conditions. Regression analysis enables us to find the direction of relationship, the strength of relationship, as well as the prediction of yet unobserved values of the dependent variable.

A. In classical regression analysis, the random variable (Y) is called the *dependent* (the response or explained) *variable*. Likewise, the non-random variable (X) is called the *independent* (the predetermined or explanatory) *variable*. The random variable has a sub-population of values for each predetermined value of the non-random variable.

B. A *mathematical relationship* $y = \alpha + \beta x$ is deterministic. It gives a unique value of the dependent variable for each value of the independent variable.

C. A *statistical relationship* $y = \alpha + \beta x + \epsilon$ is stochastic or random. It gives us several observed values (a sub-population of values) of the dependent variable for a given value of the independent variable.

D. The *Classical Linear Regression Model* assumes that the dependent variable Y is linearly related to the independent variable X and the error term. The errors are assumed to have a probability distribution with zero mean, a constant variance, and zero covariance between the errors, and zero covariance between errors and the values of the independent variable.

E. The *sample regression equation* is written as $y = a + bx + e$.

F. $\hat{y} = a + bx$ is a sample estimator of the mean value of y in the population $(\mu_{y|x} = \alpha + \beta X)$.

a and b are sample estimators of α and β.

VI. The **Ordinary Least Squares Method (OLS)** is used to compute the values of a and b from a sample of observations by the following formulae:

Slope of the Regression Line
$$b = \frac{n(\sum xy) - (\sum x)(\sum y)}{n(\sum x^2) - (\sum x)^2} \qquad \textbf{13-13}$$

Y-intercept
$$a = \frac{\sum y}{n} - b\frac{\sum x}{n} \qquad \textbf{13-14}$$

A. Given the assumptions of our regression model, the OLS Estimators (OLSE) a and b are Best Linear Unbiased Estimators (BLUE) of α and β. In brief, *OLSE are BLUE*.

VII. *Total variation in the dependent variable Y* (*SS Total*) can be divided into two parts: the variation SSR is the part that is explained by the sample regression line, and the SSE is the part of the variation in Y that is not explained by the sample regression line. We therefore have:

SS Total = SSE + SSR. In terms of the formula, it is written as:

$$\sum (y - \bar{y})^2 = \sum (y - \hat{y})^2 + \sum (\hat{y} - \bar{y})^2 \qquad \textbf{13-15}$$

VIII. The proportion of the total variation in the dependent variable explained by the sample regression line is known as the **Coefficient of determination**, also called R^2. It can be estimated by

$$R^2 = \frac{\text{SSR}}{\text{SS Total}} = 1 - \frac{\text{SSE}}{\text{SS Total}} = 1 - \frac{\sum y^2 - a \sum y - b \sum xy}{\sum y^2 - \frac{1}{n}\left(\sum y\right)^2} \qquad \textbf{13-16}$$

IX. Similar to the idea of standard deviation, we define **standard error of the estimate (S_e)** as the square root of the average of all squared deviations between the sample observations and the estimated values. It is computed by:

$$S_e = \sqrt{\frac{\text{SSE}}{n-2}} = \sqrt{\frac{\sum e^2}{n-2}} = \sqrt{\frac{\sum y^2 - a \sum y - b \sum xy}{n-2}} \qquad \textbf{13-17}$$

A. SSE gives us an idea about precision of the estimated line. The less the variation, the more precise the estimate would be. If the SSE were zero, we would have a perfect fit. The R^2 and S_e are like two sides of the same coin.

X. We can draw *inferences about the relationship between variables* (in a population) through a test of hypothesis. We can conduct a test of hypothesis for individual parameters, as well as the importance of the independent variable(s).

A. A *test of hypothesis for individual parameters* α and β is conducted through:

$$\frac{a - \alpha}{S_a} \sim t_{(n-2)} \qquad \textbf{13-20}$$

and

$$\frac{b - \beta}{S_b} \sim t_{(n-2)} \qquad \textbf{13-21}$$

B. The *test of hypothesis for the model* or *the explanatory power* (importance) of an independent variable(s) depends on the analysis of variance. Here, we test the significance of the explained variation provided by the independent variable(s) in the variation of the dependent variable.

Test statistic is given by the ratio

$$F = \frac{\text{MSR}}{\text{MSE}} = \frac{\text{SSR}/k}{\text{SSE}/(n - k - 1)} \qquad \textbf{13-24a}$$

Or, in terms of R^2, as

$$F = \frac{R^2/k}{(1 - R^2)/(n - k - 1)} \qquad \textbf{13-24b}$$

C. Since, in this chapter, we have only one independent variable ($k = 1$), inferences based on the F test are equivalent to inferences based on the t test (based on H_0: $\beta = 0$ and H_1: $\beta \neq 0$). The F test assumes greater importance in multiple regression analysis discussed in the next chapter.

CHAPTER EXERCISES 13-29 TO 13-45

13-29. A major airline selected a random sample of 25 flights and found that the correlation between the number of passengers and the total weight, in kilograms, of luggage stored in the luggage compartment is 0.94. Using the 0.05 significance level, can we conclude that there is a positive correlation between the two variables?

13-30. A sociologist claims that the success of students in college (measured by their GPA) is related to their family's income. For a sample of 20 students, the coefficient of correlation is 0.40. Using the 0.01 significance level, can we conclude that there is a positive correlation between the variables?

13-31. An Environmental Protection Agency study of 12 automobiles revealed a correlation of 0.47 between engine size and performance. At the 0.01 significance level, can we conclude that there is a positive correlation between these variables? What is the P-value? Interpret.

13-32. A study of college soccer games revealed the correlation between the number of shots attempted and the number of goals scored to be 0.21 for a sample of 20 games. Is it reasonable to conclude that there is a positive correlation between the two variables? Use the 0.05 significance level. Determine the P-value.

13-33. A sample of 30 used cars sold by Northcut Motors in 2000 revealed that the correlation between the selling price and the number of kilometres driven was -0.45. At the 0.05 significance level, can we conclude that there is a negative correlation in the population between the two variables?

13-34. For a sample of 32 Canadian townships, the correlation between the mean number of square feet per office worker and the mean monthly rental rate in the central business district is 0.363. At the 0.05 significance level, can we conclude that there is a positive correlation in the population between the two variables?

13-35. What is the relationship between the amount spent per week on food and the size of the family? Do larger families spend more on food? A sample of 10 families in the Toronto area revealed the following figures for family size and the amount spent on food per week.

Family Size	Amount Spent on Food ($)	Family Size	Amount Spent on Food ($)
3	99	3	111
6	104	4	74
5	151	4	91
6	129	5	119
6	142	3	91

(a) Compute the coefficient of correlation.
(b) Calculate the coefficient of determination.

(c) Can we conclude that there is a positive association between the amount spent on food and family size? Use the 0.05 significance level.

13-36. A sample of 12 homes sold last week in Charlottetown, PEI, is selected. Can we conclude that as the size of a home (reported below in thousands of square feet) increases, the selling price (reported in $ thousands) also increases?

Home Size (thousands of square feet)	Selling Price ($ thousands)	Home Size (thousands of square feet)	Selling Price ($ thousands)
1.4	100	1.3	110
1.3	110	0.8	85
1.2	105	1.2	105
1.1	120	0.9	75
1.4	80	1.1	70
1.0	105	1.1	95

(a) Compute the coefficient of correlation.
(b) Estimate the regression equation.
(c) Can we conclude that there is a positive association between the size of a home and the selling price? Use the 0.05 significance level.

13-37. The manufacturer of Cardio Glide exercise equipment wants to study the relationship between the number of months since the glide was purchased and the length of time the equipment was used last week.

Person	Months Owned	Hours Exercised	Person	Months Owned	Hours Exercised
Rupple	12	4	Massa	2	8
Hall	2	10	Sass	8	3
Bennett	6	8	Karl	4	8
Longnecker	9	5	Malrooney	10	2
Phillips	7	5	Veights	5	5

(a) Plot the information on a scatter diagram. Let hours of exercise be the dependent variable. Comment on the graph.
(b) Estimate the regression equation.
(c) At the 0.01 significance level, can we conclude that there is a negative association between the variables?

13-38. The following regression equation was completed from a sample of 20 observations:

$$\hat{y} = 15 - 5X$$

SSE was found to be 100 and SS Total 400.
(a) Determine the standard error of estimate.
(b) Calculate the coefficient of determination.

13-39. An ANOVA table is:

Source	df	SS	MS	F
Regression	1	50		
Error				
Total	24	500		

(a) Complete the ANOVA table.
(b) How large was the sample?
(c) Determine the standard error of estimate.
(d) Calculate the coefficient of determination.

13-40. The following is a regression equation:

$$\hat{y} = 17.08 + 0.16x$$

This information is also available: $S_e = 4.05$, $\sum x = 210$, $\sum x^2 = 9850$, and $n = 5$.
(a) Estimate the value of $\hat{y}$ when $x = 50$.
(b) Is variable X significant in explaining the variation in Y? Use the 5 percent level of significance.

13-41. The National Highway Association is studying the relationship between the number of bidders on a highway project and the winning (lowest) bid for the project. Of particular interest is whether the number of bidders increases or decreases the amount of the winning bid.

Project	Number of Bidders, X	Winning Bid ($ millions) Y	Project	Number of Bidders, X	Winning Bid ($ millions) Y
1	9	5.1	9	6	10.3
2	9	8.0	10	6	8.0
3	3	9.7	11	4	8.8
4	10	7.8	12	7	9.4
5	5	7.7	13	7	8.6
6	10	5.5	14	7	8.1
7	7	8.3	15	6	7.8
8	11	5.5			

(a) Determine the regression equation. Interpret the equation. Do more bidders tend to increase or decrease the amount of the winning bid?
(b) Estimate the amount of the winning bid if there were seven bidders.
(c) Test the significance of the linear regression model.
(d) Calculate the coefficient of determination. Interpret its value.

13-42. Mr. William Profit is studying companies going public for the first time. He is particularly interested in the relationship between the size of the offering and the price per share. A sample of 15 companies that recently went public revealed the following information.

Company	Size ($ millions) X	Price per share, Y	Company	Size ($ millions) X	Price per share, Y
1	9.0	10.8	9	160.7	11.3
2	94.4	11.3	10	96.5	10.6
3	27.3	11.2	11	83.0	10.5
4	179.2	11.1	12	23.5	10.3
5	71.9	11.1	13	58.7	10.7
6	97.9	11.2	14	93.8	11.0
7	93.5	11.0	15	34.4	10.8
8	70.0	10.7			

(a) Determine the regression equation.
(b) Calculate the coefficient of determination. Do you think Mr. Profit should be satisfied with using the size of the offering as the independent variable? Use R^2 formula to conduct an F test for the model.

13-43. The Bardi Trucking Co., located in Winnipeg, Manitoba, makes deliveries in the Great Lakes region, Southern Manitoba, and Northern Manitoba. Jim Bardi, the president, is studying the relationship between the distance a shipment must travel and the length of time, in days, it takes the shipment to arrive at its destination. To investigate, Mr. Bardi selected a random sample of 20 shipments made last month. Shipping distance is the independent variable, and shipping time is the dependent variable. The results are as follows:

Shipment	Distance (kilometres)	Shipping Time (days)	Shipment	Distance (kilometres)	Shipping Time (days)
1	656	5	11	862	7
2	853	14	12	679	5
3	646	6	13	835	13
4	783	11	14	607	3
5	610	8	15	665	8
6	841	10	16	647	7
7	785	9	17	685	10
8	639	9	18	720	8
9	762	10	19	652	6
10	762	9	20	828	10

(a) Draw a scatter diagram. Based on these data, does it appear that there is a relationship between how many kilometres a shipment has to go and how long it takes to arrive at its destination?
(b) Determine the coefficient of correlation. Can we conclude that there is a positive correlation between distance and time?
(c) Calculate and interpret the coefficient of determination.
(d) Determine the standard error of the estimate.

13-44. Friendly Supermarkets are considering expanding into the Saskatoon area. Ms. Luann Miller, director of planning, must present an analysis of the proposed expansion to the operating committee of the Board of Directors. As a part of her proposal she needs to include information on the amount people in the region spend per month for grocery items. She would also like to include information on the relationship between the amount spent for grocery items and the income. She gathered the following information on a sample of 40 households.

Household	Monthly Amount Spent ($)	Monthly Income ($)	Household	Monthly Amount Spent ($)	Monthly Income ($)
1	555	4388	21	913	6688
2	489	4558	22	918	6752
3	458	4793	23	710	6837
4	613	4856	24	1083	7242
5	647	4856	25	937	7263
6	661	4899	26	839	7540
7	662	4899	27	1030	8009
8	675	5091	28	1065	8094
9	549	5133	29	1069	8264
10	606	5304	30	1064	8392
11	668	5304	31	1015	8414
12	740	5304	32	1148	8882
13	592	5346	33	1125	8925
14	720	5495	34	1090	8989
15	680	5581	35	1208	9053
16	540	5730	36	1217	9138
17	693	5943	37	1140	9329
18	541	5943	38	1265	9649
19	673	6156	39	1206	9862
20	676	6603	40	1145	9883

(a) Let the amount spent be the dependent variable and monthly income, the independent variable. Create a scatter diagram, using a software package.
(b) Determine the regression equation. Interpret the slope value.
(c) Calculate the coefficient of determination. Comment on the estimated relationship for making a decision on the expansion of the store in Saskatoon.

13-45. Below is information on the price per share and the dividend for a sample of 30 companies.

Company	Price per Share ($)	Dividend ($)	Company	Price per Share ($)	Dividend ($)
1	20.00	3.14	16	57.06	9.53
2	22.01	3.36	17	57.40	12.60
3	31.39	0.46	18	58.30	10.43
4	33.57	7.99	19	59.51	7.97
5	35.86	0.77	20	60.60	9.19
6	36.12	8.46	21	64.01	16.50
7	36.16	7.62	22	64.66	16.10
8	37.99	8.03	23	64.74	13.76
9	38.85	6.33	24	64.95	10.54
10	39.65	7.96	25	66.43	21.15
11	43.44	8.95	26	68.18	14.30
12	49.08	9.61	27	69.56	24.42
13	53.73	11.11	28	74.90	11.54
14	54.41	13.28	29	77.91	17.65
15	55.10	10.22	30	80.00	17.36

(a) Calculate the regression equation using the selling price as the dependent variable. Interpret the slope value.

(b) Determine the coefficient of determination. Interpret its value.

(c) Develop an ANOVA table for this problem and interpret.

www.exercises.ca 13-46 TO 13-47

Note: For the next two questions you will be asked to download some specific data sets and answer the questions using statistical software (Excel or Minitab). To retrieve the data you will go to www.statcan.ca → Learning Resources → Σ-Stat → CANSIM II and download the required data and conduct the regression analysis as requested. CANSIM II allows you to download the data in several formats. We have found that saving the data on your diskette in the form of a spreadsheet: WK1 (time as rows) works best in both Excel and Minitab. You can look for the data on a particular variable by using the search procedure or by accessing a particular series by its number. We shall give you both to facilitate your work. In case the series numbers on the Web site change for some reason, you will have to search for the required data.

13-46. In this problem, you are asked to study the relationship between Investment and GDP. We shall use Business Gross Fixed Capital Formation at current prices (series #V498927) as Investment and Gross Domestic Product at current prices (series #V498918) as our GDP variable. These and many other series are part of Table #380-0002. We ask you to use annual data for 1961 onwards (the latest annual figures available). While downloading the required data, you need to specify these dates, the frequency as *annual*, conversion method *annual sum*, and output format as *WK1 with time as rows*. Note, the data are reported in millions of dollars.

(a) Determine the regression equation using Investment as the dependent variable. Interpret the regression equation.

(b) Can you determine if the coefficient on the GDP variable is statistically different from zero? Use the 0.05 significance level.

(c) Estimate what the level of investment would be if GDP were $800 billion. Also construct a 95 percent confidence interval for this estimate.

(d) Calculate the coefficient of determination and interpret.

13-47. In this question, you are asked to study the relationship between Demand for Money and Interest Rates. For Money Demanded, you will use data for M2 (series #V122530, table #176-0043), which is a measure of the amount of money both within and outside of financial institutions. For the Interest Rate you will use the Bank Rate (series #V37128, Table #176-0025), which is the interest rate that the Bank of Canada charges to financial institutions. Download *quarterly* data for the period 1981 onwards (latest quarterly data available) following the instructions in Exercise 13-50 above. The frequency to be used for both variables will be *quarterly*. Since the original series is monthly, the conversion method for M2 will be *quarterly sum*, and the conversion method for the interest rate will be *quarterly average*. Do not forget to specify the output format as spreadsheet: *WK1, time as rows*. M2 is reported in millions of dollars and the interest rate is expressed as percentages.

(a) Determine the regression equation using Money Demanded (M2) as the dependent variable. Interpret the regression equation.

(b) Test the hypotheses that the Interest Rate has no effect on Money Demanded.

(c) Calculate and interpret the coefficient of determination.

(d) Estimate Money Demanded when the interest rate is 8 percent.

COMPUTER DATA EXERCISES 13-48 TO 13-51

13-48. Refer to the data in file 100 of Top 1000 Companies.xls, which reports data on a random sample of 100 top Canadian companies.

(a) Let Profit be the dependent variable and Revenue be the independent variable. Determine the regression equation. Estimate the profit for a company with $150 million in revenue.

(b) Compare your answers in (a) with those you obtained in Exercise 13-15, parts (c) and (e). Can you account for the differences? Why would the regression equation be different?

(c) Test the hypothesis that the coefficient for Revenue is statistically different from zero.

13-49. Refer to the data in file BASEBALL-2000.xls, which reports information on the 2000 Major League Baseball season.

(a) Let the games won be the dependent variable and total team salary (in millions of dollars) be the independent variable. Can you conclude that there is a positive association between the two variables? Determine the regression equation. Interpret the slope, that is the value of *b*. How many additional wins will an additional $5 million in salary bring?

(b) Determine the correlations between games won and ERA and games won and team batting average. Which has the stronger correlation? Can we conclude that there is a positive correlation between wins and team batting average and a negative correlation between wins and ERA? Use the 0.05 significance level.

(c) Assume the number of games won is the dependent variable and attendance the independent variable. Can we conclude that the correlation between these two variables is greater than 0? Use the 0.05 significance level.

13-50. Refer to the data in file OECD.xls on the accompanying CD-ROM, which reports information on 29 countries.

(a) Suppose you wish to use the population as the independent variable to predict the number of people employed (the dependent variable). Develop the appropriate linear regression equation. Use the equation to predict employment in Mexico where the population is 96 582 million.

(b) Find the correlation coefficient between land area and domestic production. Use the 0.05 significance level to test whether there is a positive correlation between these two variables.

(c) Does there appear to be a relationship between the level of manufacturing and energy consumption? Support your answer with statistical evidence.

13-51. Refer to the Income and Well-Being data set (Table 13-1.xls or Table 13-1.MTW on the accompanying CD-ROM), which reports data on per capita income (index) and the well-being (index) of Canadians for the period 1971–1997.

(a) Let Income be the independent variable and Well-Being be the dependent variable. Determine the regression equation and comment on its interpretation. Is income a good determinant of well-being? What other factors may be important in determining well-being?

(b) Test the hypothesis that the coefficient for Income is equal to 1. This would mean that if the income index rises by 1, then the well-being index would also rise by 1.

(c) Estimate the level of well-being if the income level equalled 130 (index). Why does this estimate differ from a time when income actually equalled 130 in 1981?

CHAPTER 13   ANSWERS TO SELF-REVIEW

13-1. (a) The Scatter Diagram:

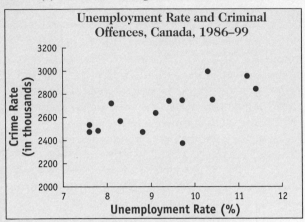

From the scatter diagram, we can see there is a positive relationship between the rate of unemployment and the number of crimes committed in Canada during 1986–99.

(b) In order to compute the coefficient of correlation, we need the following worksheet:

Year	UR (x)	Crimes (y)	xy	x^2	y^2
1986	9.7	2374	23 028	94.09	5 635 876
1987	8.8	2471	21 745	77.44	6 105 841
1988	7.8	2486	19 391	60.84	6 180 196
1989	7.6	2533	19 251	57.76	6 416 089
1990	8.1	2720	22 032	65.61	7 398 400
1991	10.3	2993	30 828	106.09	8 958 049
1992	11.2	2952	33 062	125.44	8 714 304
1993	11.4	2841	32 387	129.96	8 071 281
1994	10.4	2747	28 569	108.16	7 546 009
1995	9.4	2737	25 728	88.36	7 491 169
1996	9.7	2745	26 627	94.09	7 535 025
1997	9.1	2637	23 997	82.81	6 953 769
1998	8.3	2568	21 314	68.89	6 594 624
1999	7.6	2476	18 818	57.76	6 130 576
Totals	129.4	37 280	346 776	1 217.3	99 731 208

$$r = \frac{(14)(346,776) - (129.4)(37,280)}{\sqrt{(14)(1217.3) - (129.4)^2}\sqrt{(14)(99,731,208) - (37,280)^2}}$$

$$r = 0.704$$

Since our coefficient of correlation is close to 0.704, we can conclude there is a strong linear association between Unemployment Rate and number of crimes committed in Canada during the 1986–99 period.

13-2. $$r = \frac{n\sum xy - (\sum x)(\sum y)}{\sqrt{n\sum x^2 - (\sum x)^2}\sqrt{n\sum y^2 - (\sum y)^2}}$$

$H_0: \rho \le 0, H_1: \rho > 0,$

Assume $\alpha = 0.05,$
For $n = 14$, the critical value of t: $t_{\alpha(n-2)} = t_{0.05(12)}$
$= 1.782$
The value of the test statistic

$$t = \frac{r\sqrt{(n-2)}}{\sqrt{1-r^2}} = \frac{0.704\sqrt{(14-2)}}{\sqrt{1-(0.704)^2}} = 3.43$$

Since the value of the test statistic is greater than 1.782, we reject H_0.
The number of crimes in Canada (based on the sample data) is significantly (positively) related to the rate of unemployment.

13-3. First, we prepare the worksheet below. Column x contains the price variable (price of beer deflated by the overall consumer price index) and column y contains the per capita consumption of beer in litres.

(a)

Year	x	y	xy	x^2	y^2
1979	1.779	108.1	192.310	3.165	11 685.61
1980	1.706	110.7	188.854	2.910	12 254.49
1981	1.762	105.6	186.067	3.105	11 151.36
1982	1.847	107.8	199.107	3.411	11 620.84
1983	1.994	104.5	208.373	3.976	10 920.25
1984	2.160	104.3	225.288	4.666	10 878.49
1985	2.201	102.8	226.263	4.844	10 567.84
1986	2.329	101.2	235.695	5.424	10 241.44
1987	2.448	100.1	245.045	5.993	10 020.01
1988	2.447	101.3	247.881	5.988	10 261.69
1989	2.500	99.5	248.750	6.250	9 900.25
1990	2.546	97.3	247.726	6.482	9 467.29
1991	2.551	94.5	241.070	6.508	8 930.25
1992	2.655	91.7	243.464	7.049	8 408.89
1993	2.765	87.5	241.938	7.645	7 656.25
1994	2.680	87.1	233.428	7.182	7 586.41
1995	2.624	86.5	226.976	6.885	7 482.25
1996	2.622	85.8	224.968	6.875	7 361.64
1997	2.664	83.6	222.710	7.097	6 988.96
1998	2.809	83.7	235.113	7.890	7 005.69
1999	2.837	85.3	241.996	8.049	7 276.09
Totals	49.926	2 028.9	4763.020	121.395	197 666.00

Slope of the Regression Line:

$$b = \frac{n(\sum xy) - (\sum x)(\sum y)}{n(\sum x^2) - (\sum x)^2}$$

$$= \frac{21(4763.02) - 42.926(2028.9)}{21(121.395) - (49.926)^2}$$

$$= \frac{100023.42 - 101294.8614}{2549.295 - 2492.6054}$$

$$b = -22.43$$

Y-intercept: $a = \dfrac{\sum y}{n} - b\dfrac{\sum x}{n}$

$$a = \frac{2028.9}{21} + 22.43\left(\frac{49.926}{21}\right)$$

$$= 96.614 + 53.326 = 149.94$$

Thus, the estimated regression equation is:
$\hat{y} = 149.94 - 22.43x$

(b) The estimated value of the intercept indicates that Canadians (age: over 15 years), *on average*, would drink nearly 150 litres of beer if beer were free (zero price). However, since our sample data does not include zero price, we should be cautious to believe this interpretation. Who knows, they might drink much more than 150 litres if it were free!

Slope $b = -22.43$ indicates Canadians, *on average*, would drink 22.43 litres less for every price increase of a dollar. Certainly, the price seems to play a good role in determining the quantity of consumption.

(c) For $x = \$2.00$, the estimated quantity of consumption can be found by replacing $x = 2$ in the estimated regression equation. Thus, $\hat{y} = 149.94 - 22.43(2.00) = 105.08$

13-4. (a) **ANOVA Table**

Source	df	SS	MS	F	Significance F
Regression	1	1358.058	1358.05	89.841	1.23837E-08
Residual	19	287.2074	15.1161		
Total	20	1645.265			

(b)

$$S_e = \sqrt{\frac{SSE}{n-2}} = \sqrt{\frac{287.2074}{19}} = 3.888 \text{ or}$$

$$S_e = \sqrt{\frac{\sum y^2 - a\sum y - b\sum xy}{n-2}}$$

$$= \sqrt{\frac{197666 - 149.94(2028.9) + 22.43(4763.02)}{21-2}}$$

$$= \sqrt{\frac{287.2726}{19}} = 3.888$$

Value of the standard error of the estimate indicates the average of the dispersion of all observations from the estimated regression line.

$$R^2 = \frac{SSR}{SS\ Total} = \frac{1358.058}{1645.265} = 0.825 \text{ or}$$

$$R^2 = 1 - \frac{\sum y^2 - a\sum y - b\sum xy}{\sum y^2 - \frac{1}{n}\left(\sum y\right)^2}$$

$$= 1 - \frac{197666 - 149.94(2028.9) + 22.43(4763.02)}{197666 - \frac{1}{21}(2028.9)^2}$$

$$R^2 = 1 - \frac{287.2726}{1645.276} = 0.825$$

The value of R^2 indicates that our estimated equation explains 82.5 percent of the variations in the consumption of beer.

13-5. (a) $H_0: \beta \geq 0$, $H_1: \beta < 0$. H_0 is rejected if $t < -t_{0.05(19)}$.

$t_{0.05(19)} = -1.729$, the test statistic is found by

$$t = \frac{b - \beta}{S_b}.$$

Where,

$$S_b = \sqrt{S_e^2\left[\frac{1}{\sum(x - \bar{x})^2}\right]}$$

$$\sum(x - \bar{x})^2 = \sum x^2 - \frac{1}{n}\left(\sum x\right)^2$$

$$= 121.395 - \frac{(49.926)^2}{21}$$

$$= 121.395 - 118.695 = 2.7$$

Since $S_e = 3.888$

$$S_b = \sqrt{(3.888)^2\left[\frac{1}{2.7}\right]} = \sqrt{\frac{15.1165}{2.7}} = 2.3661$$

Therefore, $t = \frac{-22.43 - 0}{2.36} = -9.48$.

We therefore reject H_0 and conclude that the sample data provides sufficient evidence for a negative relationship between the consumption of beer and price.

(b) Since the model consists of only one independent variable, the test of the model is the same as the test of the coefficient of the independent variable: $H_0: \beta = 0$, $H_1: \beta \neq 0$. However, the test statistic in this case is F. H_0 is rejected if the test statistic $F > F_{0.05(1,19)}$. $F_{0.05(1,19)} = 4.38$. The test statistic for the sample data is found by $F = \frac{MSR}{MSE}$

$$= F = \frac{1358.1}{15.1} = 89.84$$

We therefore reject H_0, and conclude that the price plays a (statistically) significant role in explaining variations in the dependent variable (quantity of beer).

CHAPTER 14

Multiple Regression Analysis and Regression Diagnostics

GOALS

When you have completed this chapter, you will be able to:

- Understand the importance of an appropriate *model specification* and multiple regression analysis
- Comprehend the *nature* and *techniques* of multiple regression models and the concept of *partial regression coefficients*
- Use the *estimation techniques* for multiple regression models
- Conduct an *analysis of variance* of an estimated model
- Explain the *goodness of fit* of an estimated model
- Draw inferences about the assumed (true) model through a joint test of hypothesis (*F test*) on the coefficients of all variables
- Draw inferences about the importance of each independent variable through *tests of hypothesis (t tests)*
- Identify the problems raised, and remedies thereof, by the presence of multicollinearity in the data sets
- Identify the problems raised, and remedies thereof, by the presence of outliers/influential observations in the data sets
- Identify the violation of model assumptions, including linearity, homoscedasticity, autocorrelation, and normality through *simple diagnostic procedures*
- Use some *simple remedial measures* in the presence of violations of the model assumptions
- Write a research report on an investigation using multiple regression analysis
- 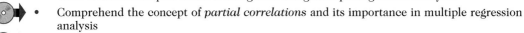 Comprehend the concept of *partial correlations* and its importance in multiple regression analysis
- 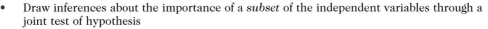 Draw inferences about the importance of a *subset* of the independent variables through a joint test of hypothesis
- 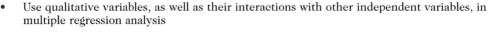 Use qualitative variables, as well as their interactions with other independent variables, in multiple regression analysis
- 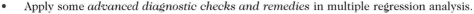 Apply some *advanced diagnostic checks and remedies* in multiple regression analysis.

CARL FRIEDERICH GAUSS (1777–1855)

In the last chapter, we noted that Galton, apparently ignorant of many developments in mathematical statistics, had ingeniously invented his own primitive methods, the concepts of correlation and regression in the context of a bivariate normal distribution. Further, as noted in the last chapter, Legendre and Gauss, working independently on astronomical data, seem to have discovered the method of ordinary least squares (OLS) nearly 100 years earlier! Gauss' later proof (1823) of the so-called "Gauss–Markov Theorem" is certainly the most elegant presentation of the power of the ordinary least squares technique. Gauss' proof of the power of the OLS method is based on sound probabilistic foundations, and its applicability to finite samples and any number of explanatory variables. Andrei Andreevich Markov (1856–1922), a Russian statistician, ignorant of Gauss' proof, discovered it independently; this is the reason why statisticians call it the Gauss–Markov Theorem. However, applications of the OLS method to social sciences had to wait for Udny Yule's synthesis (1897) of the OLS with correlation methods developed by Galton and Pearson, and his interpretation of the multiple regression coefficients as *partial* or *net* regression coefficients.

Gauss was born in Brunswick, Germany, the only child of a bricklayer, Gebhard Dietrich Gauss, and his second wife, Dorothea. He is considered as one of the top two or three mathematicians of all time. While at elementary school, he surprised his teacher by adding numbers from 1 to 100 almost instantly by spotting that the sum was 50 pairs of numbers, each pair summing to 101. The Duke of Brunswick, impressed by Gauss' mathematical talent awarded him a scholarship in 1791 that continued to support Gauss' education for nearly 10 years. Gauss studied at the University of Gottingen, and later held the positions of professor of astronomy and director of the Gottingen observatory.

Gauss made many contributions in mathematics as well as in other disciplines, such as astronomy, physics, and statistics. In statistics, Gauss is known for his contributions to normal distribution (sometimes called *Gaussian distribution*) and the method of ordinary least squares. In January 1801, an Italian astronomer, Piazzi, discovered Ceres, a new "small planet," but he could only observe 9 degrees of its orbit before it disappeared. Gauss calculated the orbit through the OLS technique. When Ceres appeared again at the end of the year, people found Gauss' prediction to be the most accurate. Gauss is believed to have not told anyone at the time that he had used his newly discovered OLS technique.

During the Napoleonic wars, Laplace, a noted mathematician, is said to have told Napoleon to spare Gottingen because one of the foremost mathematicians of his time lived there!

INTRODUCTION

In the previous chapter, we discussed the classical regression model of linear relationship between two variables, and learned the technique of estimating the influence of one (independent) variable on another (dependent) variable. The estimated relationship allowed us to understand the strength of relationship between the variables, as well as to predict (estimate) an average value of the dependent variable for each value of the independent variable. Based on the model assumptions, we learned how to draw inferences about the relationship in a population based on a sample of observations from the population. Lastly, based on the estimated relationship, we were also able to obtain an interval estimate, with a particular level of confidence, for an average or an individual value of the dependent variable conditional on a given value of the independent variable. The entire analysis of the previous chapter was based on the assumption of only one independent (explanatory) variable that has any systematic influence on the dependent variable.

In this chapter, we extend the scope of our analysis to two or more independent variables. *First*, we explore the role of multiple independent variables in regression analysis, including a detailed discussion of specification bias and our increased ability to separate out the effects of simultaneous changes in the independent variables in observational data. *Second*, we outline the general regression model, and use this context to elaborate on the meaning of partial regression coefficients and partial correlation coefficients. *Third*, we conduct analysis of variance of the estimated regression and explain the role of the coefficient of multiple determination and the standard error of estimate for the regression. *Fourth*, we develop tests of hypothesis for each regression coefficient as well as the entire regression model. *Fifth*, we introduce the role of qualitative variables in regression analysis. Finally, we analyze consequences of violation of each of the model assumptions for estimation and inference, conduct simple diagnostic checks to understand how well an estimated model approximates the model assumptions, and suggest simple remedies. Diagnostic tests and remedies of an advanced nature are discussed in Chapter 14 Appendix A on the CD-ROM accompanying this text.

14.1   WHY DO WE NEED MULTIPLE REGRESSION ANALYSIS?

We can think of at least three reasons, though related with each other, why the two variable regression analyses of the last chapter will not be adequate for our understanding of the real world of business and economics.

1. Suppose, based on economic theory, we believe that demand for beer is influenced by the price of beer and income. However, we are interested in studying the influence of only price on the demand for beer. We therefore use the two-variable model, consumption of beer (dependent variable) and price (independent variable), as in the last chapter (see Self-Review 13-3), and estimate the effect of price on consumption. Have we done something wrong? The answer is yes. In general, the estimates of regression parameters based on the two-variable model will be both inaccurate and imprecise due to incorrect specification of our model. We discuss this situation in detail later in this chapter.

2. As in natural sciences, most theoretical models in business and economics hypothesize relationships between any two variables that are conditional on the values of

all other variables. This is known as the *ceteris paribus*, or *the other things remaining the same* clause in theories. For example, economists hypothesize that quantity demanded varies inversely with price, for any fixed or given values of income, prices of substitutes, etc. In business, advertising expenditure is positively related with sales volume, when the values of all other variables influencing the sales volume such as price, quality of the product, etc. are fixed. Thus, to carry out an empirical investigation of these relationships, we need to control the values of the variables that are assumed to be fixed.

However, most of the data gathered in business and economics is the result of observational surveys rather than controlled experiments. In observational data, values of all variables change simultaneously. This makes it very difficult to separate out the effect of one independent variable from the effects of other independent variables on the dependent variable. For example, to study the effect of price on consumption of beer, when both price and income are changing and therefore influencing the consumption of beer at the same time, we need to isolate the effect of income from the effect of price on the consumption of beer.

As we indicated in the last chapter, multiple regression analysis enables us to separate out, to a large extent, the simultaneous influence of several independent variables without conducting a controlled experiment. Thus, through multiple regression analysis, we can study the influence of price on the consumption of beer (without having to conduct a controlled experiment to keep the income level constant) when both price and income are changing. Thus, *multiple regression analysis is an S.O.S. (Save Our Souls) or sine qua non for developing our understanding of the real world of business and economics without worrying too much about our inability to run controlled experiments.*

3. In general, we are interested in understanding the influence of all the major independent variables on a given dependent variable. For example, we may be interested in understanding the influence of not only price, but also other theoretically significant variables such as the prices of substitutes, income and tastes, on the demand for beer.

CONSEQUENCES OF EXCLUSION OF A RELEVANT VARIABLE

Let us assume, as economic theory suggests, that both real price (X_1) and real disposable income per person (X_2) influence (linearly) consumption of beer per person (Y).

In symbols, we can write this in the form of a *statistical regression model* as, Consumption of Beer $= \alpha + \beta_1$ (Real Price of Beer) $+ \beta_2$ (Real Disposable Income) $+ \epsilon$ or,

True Model (Population)	$y = \alpha + \beta_1 x_1 + \beta_2 x_2 + \epsilon$	14-1

The corresponding equation for a sample of observations that is used to estimate the population parameters can be written as:

True Model (Sample)	$y = a + b_1 x_1 + b_2 x_2 + e$	14-1a

We assume that the true model satisfies all the assumptions of a statistical regression model as discussed in the last chapter. In addition, we must assume that the independent variables X_1 and X_2 are not perfectly correlated. If they are perfectly correlated, one variable is sufficient to do the job of both variables! A revised list of assumptions for the general model of k independent variables will be given later.

Now suppose our primary interest is to understand the quantitative response of beer consumption to changes in the price variable. We therefore estimate the following "*wrongly*" *specified* two-variable regression model:

Wrongly Specified Model (Population)	$y = \alpha^* + \beta_1^* x_1 + \epsilon^*$	**14-2**
Wrongly Specified Model (Sample)	$y = a^* + b_1^* x_1 + e^*$	**14-2a**

We have used (*) for the coefficients and the error terms in Equations 14-2 and 14-2a to distinguish them from the correctly specified model, Equations 14-1 and 14-1a.

How serious are the consequences of the omission of the income variable from Equation 14-2, and therefore Equation 14-2a, for estimation and inference? Are the OLS estimators a^* and b_1^* unbiased estimators of true α and β_1? Are the inferences about the true values of α and β_1 based on a^* and b_1^* valid? Answers to these questions depend on the nature of the relationship between the included independent variable(s) and the excluded independent variable(s).

Let us look closely at the differences in models given by Equations 14-1 and 14-2 above. The property of unbiasedness requires that $E(a^*) = \alpha$ and $E(b_1^*) = \beta_1$. Since Equation 14-1 is the true specification of the model, the error term in equation (14-2) can be written as: $\epsilon^* = \beta_2 x_2 + \epsilon$. Thus, ϵ^* includes a systematic component $\beta_2 x_2$. Therefore, ϵ^* is no longer random with zero mean (violating assumption number 3 in the last chapter). Furthermore, when X_1 and X_2 are correlated, X_1 is no longer independent of the error term (ϵ^*), thus violating assumption number 1 of the last chapter. Since the BLUE properties of the OLSE crucially depend on these assumptions, omission of a theoretically relevant variable from the regression has some serious consequences for estimation, inference and prediction. We have summarized the consequences in Table 14-1.

TABLE 14-1: Consequences of the Omission of a Relevant Variable

Consequences for	X_1 and X_2 are not related	X_1 and X_2 are related
Estimation	a^* is a biased estimator of α b_1^* is an unbiased estimator of β_1	a^* and b_1^* are biased and inconsistent estimators of α and β_1
Inference	The estimators of standard errors of a^* and b_1^* are biased. Therefore, the tests of hypothesis for α and β_1 are not valid.	The estimators of standard errors of a^* and b_1^* are biased. Therefore, the tests of hypothesis for α and β_1 are not valid.
Predictions and Interval Estimates	Biased	Biased and inconsistent

We can say something about the direction and size of the bias in a situation where there are only two independent variables (e.g., price and income) in the *true* model.

THE SIZE OF THE BIAS

Let us assume that the explanatory variables X_1 and X_2 are linearly related by the equation:

$$x_2 = a_{21} + b_{21}x_1 + error \qquad \text{14-3}$$

This is a *descriptive regression equation* (also called *auxiliary regression*) between X_2 and X_1 since both variables are non-random. Further, the coefficient b_{21} is a known constant since it is based on the predetermined values of X_1 and X_2 that remain the same in repeated sampling. The coefficient (b_{21}) in Equation 14-3 measures a linear relationship between X_1 and X_2. The size of bias is then given by:

$$\text{Bias} = E(b_1^*) - \beta_1 = \beta_2 b_{21} \qquad \text{14-4}$$

The derivation of this bias is given in Chapter 14 Appendix A on the CD-ROM.

THE DIRECTION OF BIAS

The knowledge of the signs of β_2 and b_{21} in Equation 14-4 enables us to identify the direction of bias. In general, the direction of bias in b_1^* as the estimator of β_1 in the true model can be shown as follows:

TABLE 14-2: Direction of Bias

	$b_{21} > 0$	$b_{21} < 0$
$\beta_2 > 0$	Positive Bias	Negative Bias
$\beta_2 < 0$	Negative Bias	Positive Bias

These consequences also carry over to the estimation of coefficients in a model containing any number of variables. In fact, if an excluded variable is related to any one of the included variables in the regression, the coefficients of all included variables will be biased regardless of their relation to the excluded variable!

What happens is that a change in price, in the absence of an income variable in the wrongly specified model, captures both the direct effect (β_1) of price on consumption, as well as the indirect (or induced) effect ($\beta_2 b_{21}$) of change in price on consumption. The induced effect occurs due to a non-zero relationship between price and income in the sample data. Obviously, if $b_{21} = 0$, the indirect effect disappears and b_1^* becomes an unbiased estimator of β_1. Furthermore, b_1^* is also unbiased when $\beta_2 = 0$, even if price and income are related. This is obvious, since $\beta_2 = 0$ implies that X_2 in Equation 14-1 is not a relevant variable to be included in the model. In other words, Equation 14-1 is no longer a wrongly specified model. We can give a visual effect to these ideas through a diagrammatic representation. See Chart 14-1.

CHART 14-1: Exclusion of a Relevant Variable

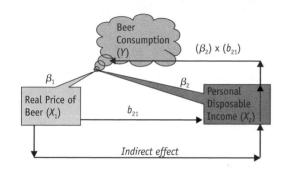

CONSEQUENCES OF INCLUSION OF AN IRRELEVANT VARIABLE

The penalty, however, is much less serious if the true model is given by Equation 14-2, and we, by mistake, estimate Equation 14-1. That is, as mentioned above, we have included an *irrelevant variable* (X_2) in the true model Equation 14-2. In this case, the OLS estimators a and b_1 obtained from sample model (14-1a) are unbiased and consistent estimators of the coefficients a^* and β_1^* in Equation 14-2. The standard errors of the coefficients are, however, larger and therefore t ratios are smaller, which sometimes may lead us *not* to reject a null hypothesis when in fact it should be rejected.

Thus, it is clear that omission of a relevant variable can land us in very serious trouble in terms of both accuracy and precision of the estimates. One should therefore make every effort to include all variables that are based on sound theoretical grounds. However, if we are unsure of sufficient theoretical justification for a variable, *the penalty for including an irrelevant variable is much less serious as compared to the penalty for excluding a relevant variable.*

Example 14-1

Let us examine the bias that we may have had in the demand for beer based on the price variable alone, when *the true model includes both price and income as the independent variables.* Beer consumption is measured in litres per person (15+) per year. Price (real) is the price of beer per litre adjusted by overall inflation. Income (real) is personal income per person (15+) after taxes and adjusted for inflation. The sample consists of observations on these variables for Canada for the 1979–99 period. The values of b_1^*, b_1, b_2 and b_{21} are obtained from the following regressions.

The values in parentheses below the coefficients are values of the t statistic for the coefficients.

The regression equation of Beer Consumption on Price only (Wrong Model) is:

$$\text{Beer Consumption} = 150 - 22.431 \text{ Price (real)}$$
$$(26.4) \qquad (-9.5)$$
$$R^2 = 82.5\% \qquad\qquad\qquad \textbf{14-5}$$

The Regression Equation of Beer Consumption on Price and Income (True Model) is:

$$\text{Beer Consumption} = 98.1 - 26.467 \text{ Price (real)} + 0.00281 \text{ Income (real)}$$
$$(3.5) \quad (-8.6) \qquad\qquad (1.9)$$
$$R^2 = 85.4\% \qquad\qquad\qquad \textbf{14-6}$$

The Regression Equation of Income on Price is:

$$\text{Income (real)} = 18\,456 + 1436.6 \text{ Price (real)}$$
$$(22.5) \quad (4.2)$$
$$R^2 = 45.5\% \qquad\qquad\qquad \textbf{14-7}$$

Thus, we have $b_1^* = -22.431$, $b_1 = -26.467$, $b_2 = 0.00281$, $b_{21} = 1436.6$.

Since b_{21} is positive and we expect β_2 to be positive, we expect a positive bias in b_1^*. From Equation 14-4, an *estimate* (since we would never know the true value of β_2) of the size of bias in this sample $= b_2 b_{21} = (1436.6) (0.00281) = 4.0368$, which is positive. This is verified from the difference in the estimated values of b_1^* and b_1 for this sample:

$$(b_1^* - b_1) = -22.431 - (-26.467) = 4.036$$

As Equation 14-4 indicates, *the seriousness of the problem of under-specifying* (omitting a relevant variable) *a model lies in that, on average, the values of the bias in repeated sampling does not vanish*. Note that a zero value of an estimate of bias obtained in a particular data set does not imply that the estimator b_1^* is unbiased.

14.2 ROLE OF MULTIPLE REGRESSION ANALYSIS IN OBSERVATIONAL DATA

As we mentioned earlier, in the real world, changes in the dependent variable are often the result of simultaneous changes in several independent variables, both by themselves as well as through their interactions with each other. Scientists are often able to run controlled experiments to study the effect of one independent variable at a time by holding values of the other independent variables constant. Students of business, economics and other social sciences do not enjoy that luxury. Most of the data available to us is the result of observational studies of the real world where all independent variables enjoy full autonomy of exerting their influence on the dependent variable through their actions and interactions with other variables. As we mentioned earlier, multiple regression analysis enables us to isolate the effect of each independent variable on the dependent variable from, so to speak, a *potpourri* of the effect of simultaneous changes in several independent variables on the dependent variable. How this is accomplished without a controlled experiment is a feat, and one of the most useful discoveries for empirical research as illustrated in the Statistics in Action on page 601. While a mathematical proof is beyond the scope of this book, we shall nonetheless show you an intuitive proof through an example.

Example 14-2

Let us rewrite Equation 14-1 for demand for beer:

Consumption of Beer = $\alpha + \beta_1$ (Real Price of Beer) + β_2 (Real Disposable Income) + ϵ

Suppose we are interested in the influence of price on consumption of beer. Economists' model of demand says that both price and income influence consumption. However, the effect of price (β_1) assumes that income is kept constant. Likewise, the effect of income assumes that the price is kept constant. We are unable to run a controlled experiment that would keep income constant for a study of price effect and vice versa. The data available to us is observational data where both income and price are changing simultaneously. Based on the observational data and Minitab software, our estimated Equation 14-6 is rewritten below.

Beer Consumption = 98.1 − 26.467 Price (real) + 0.00281 Income (real)

(3.5) (−8.6)   (1.9)

$R^2 = 85.4\%$ **14-6**

How do we know that the estimate of $\beta_1 = b_1 = -26.467$ is the result of changes in price only, holding income constant? One way to prove this is to remove the effect of the income variable from both beer consumption and price variables, and re-estimate the equation between beer consumption and price variables which are free from the effect of income changes.

To achieve this, we proceed in three stages.

Stage 1   We run a regression of beer consumption on income to find the effect of income on beer consumption. This is given by the estimated values of beer consumption based on income alone (Equation 14-8). We then purify the actual values of beer consumption by subtracting the estimated values of beer consumption from the actual values of beer consumption, and call this purified (residual) value of beer consumption, Resid1.

$$\text{Beer Consumption} = 229 - 0.00607 \text{ Income (real)}$$
$$(4.5) \quad (-2.6)$$
$$R^2 = 25.9\% \qquad\qquad 14\text{-}8$$

Stage 2   We run a regression of price on income to find the effect of income on price. This is given by the estimated values of price based on income alone (Equation 14-9). We then purify the actual values of price by subtracting the estimated values of price from the actual values of price, and call this purified (residual) value of price, Resid2.

$$\text{Price (real)} = -4.96 + 0.000336 \text{ Income (real)}$$
$$(4.5) \quad (-2.6)$$
$$R^2 = 48.2\% \qquad\qquad 14\text{-}9$$

Stage 3   In this last stage, we run the regression of purified values of consumption of beer (Resid1) on the purified values of price (Resid2) to find the pure effect of price on consumption (Equation 14-10). The coefficient of Resid2 should now give us the pure price effect on consumption of beer.

$$\text{Resid1} = -0.001 - 26.467 \text{ Resid2}$$
$$(0.0) \quad (-8.8)$$
$$R^2 = 80.3\% \qquad\qquad 14\text{-}10$$

Now compare the coefficient of price in Equation 14-6 and the coefficient of Resid2 (purified price variable) in Equation 14-10. The value of both coefficients equals (-26.467), with approximately the same values of the t statistic given below the estimated values of the regression coefficients. Thus, we have shown, by example, that the regression coefficient of price in the multiple regression (Equation 14-6) yields the *pure* or *net* price effect on consumption of beer without running a controlled experiment (i.e., holding income constant). The pure or net price effect is also called the *partial* effect since it excludes the effect of income from the *total* or *gross* price effect given by the two-variable regression model (Equation 14-2 or 14-5). Likewise, we can show that the coefficient of income in the multiple regression model (Equation 14-6) gives us the net income effect, holding the price variable constant. Thus,

In the multiple regression equation: $y = \alpha + \beta_1 x_1 + \beta_2 x_2 + \epsilon$ 14-1

The expected value of the variable Y (average in repeated sampling) being:
$E(y) = \alpha + \beta_1 x_1 + \beta_2 x_2$

We can interpret the parameters α, β_1, and β_2 as:

α is the intercept term, the value of $E(y)$ then $x_1 = x_2 = 0$.

β_1 measures the *direct* or *net* or *partial* effect, on average, of a unit change in x_1 on y, holding x_2 constant, and is therefore called a *partial regression coefficient* of x_1 on y.

β_2 measures the *direct* or *net* or *partial* effect, on average, of a unit change in x_2 on y, holding x_1 constant, and is therefore called a *partial regression coefficient* of x_2 on y.

Note that the intercept term, in general, represents an average effect of all excluded variables from the model, assuming, as we must, that the effect of these excluded variables is distributed randomly. Why? Mechanically, of course, we can interpret α as an average of y values for $x_1 = 0$ and $x_2 = 0$. But, *we must exercise caution in interpreting an estimated value of α in this manner*.

For the interpretation of all β's from now on, we shall use the phrase *partial effect*, implying that all other independent variables are held constant.

Thus, the estimated regression equation of Beer Consumption on Price and Income can be interpreted as follows:

Beer Consumption = 98.1 − 26.467 Price (real) + 0.00281 Income (real)

                    (3.5)   (−8.6)   (1.9)

         $R^2 = 85.4\%$ 14-6

An increase in price by one unit (a dollar in our case), on average, has a partial effect of reducing consumption of beer by 26.5 litres per person (15 years and over) per year. Alternatively, we could say that a reduction in the price of beer by one unit (a dollar in our case), on average, has a partial effect of increasing consumption of beer by 26.5 litres per person (15 years and over) per year. Likewise, an increase in income by one unit (a dollar in our case) per year, on average, has a partial effect of increasing consumption of beer by 0.00281 litres per person (15 years and over) per year. We could also say that an increase in income by $1000 per person (15 years and over) per year would have, on average, the partial effect of increasing consumption of beer by 2.81 litres per person (15 years and over) per year. The value of the intercept, 98.1 litres per person (15 years and over) indicates the average value of consumption attributable to all excluded variables in the model. However, mechanical interpretation of people drinking 98.1 litres per person (15 years and over) when both price and income equal zero does not make much sense. As mentioned earlier, *the value of the intercept outside the range of sample values of the explanatory variables is often misleading*. Obviously, a zero value for price and income is outside the observed range of values of these variables.

Similar to the concept of the partial regression coefficient is the concept of the **partial correlation coefficient**. This is covered in Section 14A.3 in Chapter 14 Appendix A on the CD-ROM.

14.3   THE GENERAL LINEAR REGRESSION MODEL

SPECIFICATION OF THE POPULATION REGRESSION MODEL

We can generalize the two independent-variable model to include any number of, say k, variables as follows:

$$y = \alpha + \beta_1 x_1 + \beta_2 x_2 + \beta_3 x_3 + \beta_4 x_4 + \cdots + \beta_k x_k + \epsilon \qquad \text{14-11}$$

Where, Y is the dependent variable, and is *linearly* related with k independent variables. α is intercept term, β's are the partial regression coefficients as discussed above, and ϵ is the random error term. Strictly speaking, there are $(k + 1)$ variables, if we include the *invisible* variable related with the intercept term. It is invisible because all values of the variable are equal to one. Textbooks often ignore this complication to simplify the notation. The Regression Model assumptions are given below. We write them a little differently this time to allow us an easy reference to each element of the model for a thorough discussion of the model diagnostics, later in this chapter.

1. **Assumptions about the Relationship**

   (a) *Functional Specification*: The independent variable X's are linearly related with the dependent variable Y.

   This assumption can be relaxed to include some non-linear relations without affecting the properties of the estimators. However, the relationship must be linear in all parameters. For example, we can apply the OLS to an equation such as $y = \alpha + \beta_1 x_1 + \beta_2 x_2 + \beta_3 x_2^2 + \epsilon$ by simply redefining x_2^2 as another variable x_3. However, a relationship such as $y = \alpha + \beta_1 x_1 + x_2^{\beta_2} + \epsilon$ is non-linear in parameter β_2, and is therefore not allowed.

   (b) *Variable Specification*: The relationship has been correctly specified to avoid any possibility of specification bias. That is, all relevant explanatory variables have been included.

2. **Assumptions about the Independent Explanatory Variables**

   (a) *Non-Random*: The explanatory variables are *non-random*, or distributed independently of the error term.

   (b) *Absence of Perfect Multicollinearity*: None of the independent variables is perfectly correlated (linearly related) with any or all other independent variables. A linear relationship between the independent variables is called **multicollinearity**. This assumption rules out perfect multicollinearity between any two or more independent variables. For example, perfect collinearity between two independent variables X_1 and X_2 implies that we can write $x_1 = c_1 + c_2 x_2$, where c_1 and c_2 are any known constants (numbers like 2, 3.7, 50, etc.).

   In the general case of k variables, we define perfect multicollinearity as

   $$c_0 + c_1 x_1 + c_2 x_2 + \cdots + c_k x_k = 0 \qquad \text{14-12}$$

   where, all $c_0, c_1, c_2, c_3, \ldots c_k$ are known constants, not all zero at the same time.

In the presence of perfect multicollinearity, the collinear variable does not contain any additional information that is not already contained in other variables. As we shall show later, we *cannot* estimate parameters in the presence of perfect multicollinearity.

3. **Assumptions about the Error Term (ϵ)**
   (a) *Zero Average*: The average of the error term is zero. $E(\epsilon) = 0$
   (b) *Constant Variance*: The variance of the error term is constant for all sets of values of the explanatory variables. $Var(\epsilon) = \sigma^2$. This is called **homoscedasticity**.
   (c) *Zero Covariance*: The covariance between the various values of the error term is zero. $E(\epsilon_i \, \epsilon_j) = 0$ where i and j are any two different values of the error term. This is referred to as the *absence of* **autocorrelation**.

GAUSS–MARKOV THEOREM

As we discussed in the last chapter, given that a model satisfies the assumptions given above, the Ordinary Least Squares technique will yield the Best Linear Unbiased Estimators of the parameters α and all β's. Thus, OLSE are BLUE. Two important things about the theorem are noteworthy. The theorem does not assume any particular form of probability distribution for the error term or any particular sample size. The BLUE property of the estimators must be understood that OLSE have a minimum variance among the set of all linear and unbiased estimators.

ESTIMATION

We shall illustrate the OLS estimation technique for the case of two independent variables. For a larger number of independent variables, simple algebra becomes a little messy and therefore we will not venture into that. However, the use of matrix algebra, beyond the scope of this book, can give a very neat presentation of most of the aspects of estimation and inference for any number of variables. In most cases, however, you will be using computer software such as Excel or Minitab to solve for the values of the OLS estimators. We shall illustrate the case of two explanatory variables to familiarize you with what is involved in the OLS technique of estimation in a multiple regression model. In fact, as you will soon see, it is not much different from what you learned in the two-variable regression in the last chapter, except an increase in the number of equations, one for the estimation of each parameter involved. We therefore rewrite Equation 14-1 below:

$$y = \alpha + \beta_1 x_1 + \beta_2 x_2 + \epsilon \qquad \text{14-1}$$

To estimate parameters α, β_1, and β_2 from a sample of n observations, we first rewrite the above equation as sample regression Equation 14-13 (which is the same as 14-1a):

$$y = a + b_1 x_1 + b_2 x_2 + e \qquad \text{14-13}$$

In this equation, a, b_1, and b_2 are estimators and e is the random error term in a sample of observations. The OLS technique consists of finding a, b_1, and b_2 such that the sum of the squared errors (differences between the actual values (y) of the variable Y and the estimated values ($\hat{y}$) of the variable Y) are minimum. This is achieved as follows:
Let

$$e = (y - \hat{y}) \qquad \text{14-14}$$

and

$$\hat{y} = a + b_1 x_1 + b_2 x_2 \qquad \text{14-15}$$

Minimize

$$\sum e^2 = \sum (y - \hat{y})^2 = \sum [y - (a + b_1 x_1 + b_2 x_2)]^2 \qquad \text{14-16}$$

with respect to a, b_1 and b_2.

Using calculus, we get the following three equations:

$$\sum e = 0 \qquad \text{14-17}$$

$$\sum x_1 e = 0 \qquad \text{14-18}$$

$$\sum x_2 e = 0 \qquad \text{14-19}$$

Replacing e by $(y - \hat{y}) = (y - a - b_1 x_1 - b_2 x_2)$, and with some algebraic manipulations, we get the following three *normal* (*do not confuse with normal distribution*) equations:

$$\sum y = na + b_1 \sum x_1 + b_2 \sum x_2 \qquad \text{14-20}$$

$$\sum x_1 y = a \sum x_1 + b_1 \sum x_1^2 + b_2 \sum x_1 x_2 \qquad \text{14-21}$$

$$\sum x_2 y = a \sum x_1 + b_1 \sum x_1 x_2 + b_2 \sum x_2^2 \qquad \text{14-22}$$

Solving Equations 14-20, 14-21, and 14-22 simultaneously, and writing

$$y' = (y - \bar{y}), \ x_1' = (x_1 - \bar{x}_1), \ x_2' = (x_2 - \bar{x}_2) \qquad \text{14-23}$$

we get the estimators a, b_1, and b_2, as follows:

$$a = \bar{y} - b_1 \bar{x}_1 - b_2 \bar{x}_2 \qquad \text{14-24}$$

$$b_1 = \frac{\left(\sum x_1' y'\right)\left(\sum x_2'^2\right) - \left(\sum x_2' y'\right)\left(\sum x_1' x_2'\right)}{\left(\sum x_1'^2\right)\left(\sum x_2'^2\right) - \left(\sum x_1' x_2'\right)^2} \qquad \text{14-25}$$

$$b_2 = \frac{\left(\sum x_2' y'\right)\left(\sum x_1'^2\right) - \left(\sum x_1' y'\right)\left(\sum x_1' x_2'\right)}{\left(\sum x_1'^2\right)\left(\sum x_2'^2\right) - \left(\sum x_1' x_2'\right)^2} \qquad \text{14-26}$$

Note that the denominators in Equations 14-25 and 14-26 are the same. By carefully looking at the order of subscripts, you will easily be able to remember the equations. However, with speedy computers and readily available software such as Excel and Minitab, you will not be required to remember them, at least not the equations involving more than two independent variables.

Example 14-3

Let us suppose that the Real Estate Board of Vancouver is very interested in understanding the influence of various characteristics on the price of housing in the eastern part of Vancouver and hires you as an expert statistician for the task. Note prices based on characteristics of a commodity, rather than its cost factors such as wages, interest, etc., are called *hedonic prices*. You have already learned in this course how to go about the task of *estimating* a regression relationship involving one independent variable. We now illustrate estimation in the context of multiple independent variables.

First, you specify the form of the model, such as Equation 14-1 and the associated sample function in Equation 14-13. *Second*, you decide to collect data, for example on a sample of 20 houses up for sale in Vancouver East, on price (the dependent variable called "Price"), number of bedrooms (an independent variable called "Bedrooms"), number of bathrooms (an independent variable called "Baths"), and square footage of built space (an independent variable called "Footage"). This list of independent variables is based on your discussion with the Real Estate Board, prior to your collection of data. The Real Estate Board also believes that all these independent variables are positively associated with price. *Third*, using Excel or Minitab, you enter the data on computer as shown in Screen 1 of Chart 14-2. Following the steps

MINITAB CHART 14-2

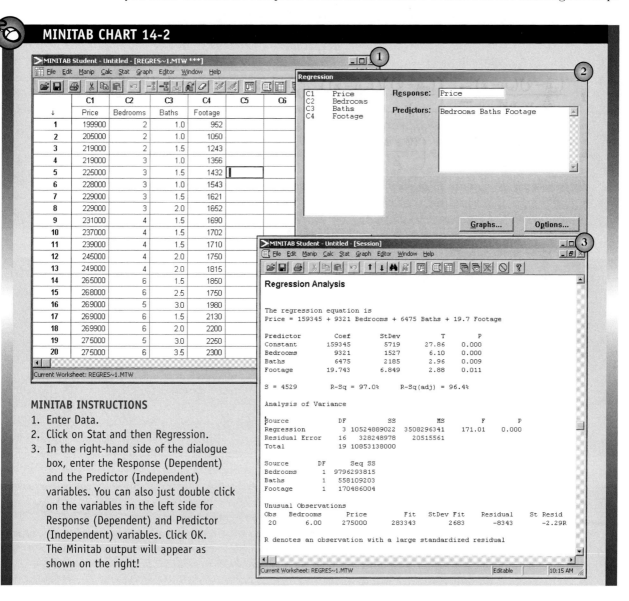

MINITAB INSTRUCTIONS

1. Enter Data.
2. Click on Stat and then Regression.
3. In the right-hand side of the dialogue box, enter the Response (Dependent) and the Predictor (Independent) variables. You can also just double click on the variables in the left side for Response (Dependent) and Predictor (Independent) variables. Click OK. The Minitab output will appear as shown on the right!

for regression analysis for the software you use, you obtain the results of your regression. The detailed results of the regression using Minitab are given in Minitab Chart 14-2. However, first of all, you need to explain the influence of each independent variable on the dependent variable price to the Real Estate Board, i.e., interpret your estimated equation.

The estimated regression equation:

$$\text{Price} = 159\,345 + 9321 \text{ Bedrooms} + 6475 \text{ Baths} + 19.7 \text{ Footage} \qquad \textbf{14-27}$$

INTERPRETATION

Intercept: Mechanically, the value of the intercept measures the average value of the dependent variable, given a zero value of all explanatory variables. It is the average of the random effects of all individually unimportant (theoretically irrelevant) variables excluded from the model. Some statisticians therefore call the **intercept term a garbage collector**. Since, in general, the zero values of the explanatory variables are outside the observable range, *the value of the intercept is often meaningless*. In our case, the value of the intercept term equals $159 345 for a house with no bedroom, no bathroom and no square footage. Obviously, this is a meaningless value. Nevertheless, we should always include the intercept term in the estimating equation, unless the theory behind the relationship tells us otherwise. Exclusion of an intercept term from a relationship implies forcing the regression line from the origin. This might have undesirable effects on the estimates of the coefficients of explanatory variables.

Coefficients of the explanatory variables: Recall that the value of a coefficient associated with each variable measures, on average, the *net* or *partial* effect of unit increase in that particular independent variable on the dependent variable, holding all other independent variables constant. Note the phrases *on average* and *partial effect*. The estimated regression line is an average relationship only, and each of the multiple regression coefficients gives us only the partial effect of the particular independent variable on the dependent variable. Furthermore, we should always remember the units in which each variable is expressed for an accurate interpretation. Thus, an increase of one bedroom in a house increases the price of house, *on average*, by $9321, holding the number of bathrooms and square footage constant. Given that the values of the bedrooms and square footage are constant, an extra bathroom adds, *on average*, $6475 to the value of a house. Likewise, for a house with the same number of bedrooms and bathrooms as any other house, an increase in the size of house by one square foot increases the price of house, *on average*, by nineteen dollars and seventy cents. What is the value of a house with 3 bedrooms, 1 bathroom, and 1400 square footage of built area? You can find this just by replacing the independent variables by these values. It should equal $221 363. Verify the result. Again, the caution against interpreting the value of the intercept outside the observable range of the independent variables applies equally to the value of the partial coefficients. *Accuracy of prediction of a value of the dependent variable outside the observed range of sample values depends on the accuracy of the predicted values of the independent variables outside the observed range as well as the stability of the estimated relationship between the dependent and independent variables outside the observed range.*

■ SELF-REVIEW 14-1

Table 14-3 below and in data file Table 14-3.xls contains quarterly data on investment ($ millions), interest rate (%), Gross Domestic Product (GDP, $ millions), and capacity utilization rate (%) in Canada, and three dummy variables (to be explained later). All variables are in real terms, that is, they are unaffected by changes in overall price level.

　　Estimate a linear regression equation for investment as the dependent variable, and interest rate, GDP, and Capacity as the independent variables. Interpret the values of the regression coefficients of the estimated equation. Estimate the value of investment for Interest = 4 percent, GDP = $200 000 million, and the capacity utilization rate of 82 percent.

TABLE 14-3

YYYYQ	Investment	Interest	GDP	Capacity	D1	D2	D3
1993Q1	22 985	5.967	171 836	79.8	0	0	0
1993Q2	27 341	4.906	176 730	80.0	1	0	0
1993Q3	27 743	4.380	182 222	80.2	0	1	0
1993Q4	27 128	4.105	183 795	80.8	0	0	1
1994Q1	24 787	3.872	177 359	81.0	0	0	0
1994Q2	29 920	6.063	184 497	82.6	1	0	0
1994Q3	29 548	5.549	192 826	83.2	0	1	0
1994Q4	28 703	5.763	193 668	83.6	0	0	1
1995Q1	25 552	7.617	185 087	83.8	0	0	0
1995Q2	29 492	7.147	190 692	81.7	1	0	0
1995Q3	28 359	6.258	196 729	80.8	0	1	0
1995Q4	27 655	5.786	196 574	80.4	0	0	1
1996Q1	26 282	4.967	187 859	80.8	0	0	0
1996Q2	29 898	4.515	191 990	81.4	1	0	0
1996Q3	30 878	3.977	200 003	82.3	0	1	0
1996Q4	32 211	2.841	201 064	81.9	0	0	1
1997Q1	30 365	2.722	193 359	82.0	0	0	0
1997Q2	36 482	2.827	200 795	82.7	1	0	0
1997Q3	37 016	2.909	209 766	83.8	0	1	0
1997Q4	37 065	3.465	211 093	83.5	0	0	1
1998Q1	33 098	4.099	201 701	83.1	0	0	0
1998Q2	38 036	4.363	207 527	82.7	1	0	0
1998Q3	37 164	4.624	215 288	81.9	0	1	0
1998Q4	37 838	4.359	217 486	82.5	0	0	1
1999Q1	34 743	4.364	208 594	82.6	0	0	0
1999Q2	41 418	4.072	216 623	82.7	1	0	0
1999Q3	40 820	4.244	226 572	84.1	0	1	0
1999Q4	42 847	4.326	228 465	84.7	0	0	1
2000Q1	40 055	4.571	219 609	85.6	0	0	0
2000Q2	46 158	4.922	228 581	85.8	1	0	0
2000Q3	45 317	4.911	237 465	85.7	0	1	0
2000Q4	45 200	4.896	235 830	85.1	0	0	1

Source: Statistics Canada, adapted

EXERCISES 14-1 TO 14-4

14-1. Thompson Machine Works purchased several new, highly sophisticated machines. The production department needed some guidance with respect to qualifications needed by an operator. Is age a factor? Is the length of service as a machine operator important? In order to further explore the factors needed to estimate performance on the new machines, four variables were listed:

X_1 is the length of time employee was a machinist (in years)
X_2 is the mechanical aptitude test score
X_3 represents prior on-the-job rating
X_4 represents age (in years)

Performance on the new machine is designated Y.

Thirty machinists were selected at random. Data were collected for each, and their performances on the new machines were recorded. A few results are:

Name	Performance on New Machine Y	Length of Time as a Machinist X_1	Mechanical Aptitude Score X_2	Prior On-the-Job Performance X_3	Age X_4
Andy Kosin	112	12	312	121	52
Sue Annis	113	2	380	123	27

The equation is: $\hat{y} = 11.6 + 0.4x_1 + 0.286x_2 + 0.112x_3 + 0.002x_4$

(a) What is the full designation (name) of the equation?
(b) How many dependent variables are there? How many independent variables?
(c) What is the number 0.286 called?
(d) As age increases by one year, how much does estimated performance on the new machine increase?
(e) Carl Knox applied for a job on a new machine. He has been a machinist for six years, and he scored 280 on the mechanical aptitude test. Carl's prior on-the-job performance rating is 97, and he is 35 years old. Estimate Carl's performance on the new machine.

14-2. A sample of widowed senior citizens was studied to determine their degree of satisfaction with their present life. A special index, called the index of satisfaction, was used to measure satisfaction. Six factors were studied, namely, age at the time of first marriage (X_1), annual income (X_2), number of children living (X_3), value of all assets (X_4), status of health in the form of an index (X_5), and the average number of social activities per week—such as bowling and dancing (X_6). Suppose the multiple regression equation is:

$$\hat{y} = 16.24 + 0.017x_1 + 0.0028x_2 + 42x_3 + 0.0012x_4 + 0.19x_5 + 26.8x_6$$

(a) What is the estimated index of satisfaction for a person who first married at 18, has an annual income of $26 500, has three children living, has assets of $156 000, has an index of health status of 141, and has 2.5 social activities a week on the average?
(b) Which would add more to satisfaction, an additional income of $10 000 a year or two more social activities a week?

14-3. Diane Rusty is interested in a Pizza Delight franchise in Ottawa. She is looking for the best location. To make an informed decision about the location, she decided to estimate sales revenue per month (Y) in other Pizza Delight restaurants based on the number of competitors in business (X_1), number of people living in the area (X_2), and average household income per year (X_3) in the area. The estimated regression equation is $\hat{y} = 120\,000 - 21\,000x_1 + 1.00x_2 + 1.5x_3$

(a) Estimate sales revenue for a Pizza Delight that has three competitors in an area with a population of 10 000 and an average household income of $50 000.

(b) Interpret the coefficients.

(c) Assume Diane has been offered a job worth $10 000 per month. The cost of running a Pizza Delight is about 65 percent of the sales revenue. Paul, her friend suggests opening a Pizza Delight in a location that has five competitors, a population base of 20 000, and an average household income of $40 000. Should she accept her friend's advice?

14-4. A student estimated the United States' demand for Canadian softwood lumber (called Lumber). She chose the housing starts in the US (called House), a ratio of the price of Canadian softwood lumber to the price of US softwood lumber (called Relative Price), and exchange rate (US cents per Canadian dollar, called Exchange Rate). All variables are expressed in percentage changes. The results are given below (with t-values in the parentheses below the coefficients):

Lumber = 20.3395 + 1.5219 House – 0.9902 Relative Price – 1.5338 Exchange Rate

   (5.91)   (6.25)   (–3.16)   (–2.04)

Adjusted $R^2 = 0.7716$ $F = 14.648$ $n = 17$

(a) Are the signs of the regression coefficients in accordance with your expectations?

(b) Interpret each of the regression coefficients. (Hint: when both dependent and independent variables are in percentage changes or logs, the values of the regression coefficients are the same as *elasticities*, i.e,. the percentage change in the dependent variable in response to a one percentage change in the independent variable).

(c) Estimate a percentage change in Canadian exports of softwood lumber to the US, for each of the following: a 3 percent decline in the housing starts in the US, a 20 percent duty imposed by the US on Canadian softwood lumber (assume an equivalent increase in the Relative Price variable), and a 2 percent decline in the exchange rate in year 2001.

14.4 ANALYSIS OF VARIANCE: HOW GOOD IS THE ESTIMATED MODEL?

As we discussed in the last chapter, *analysis of variance* of the estimated model enables us to analyze how well the estimated relationship as a whole represents the sample data *and* how likely it is a good estimate for the assumed relationship in the population. The first question, as in the last chapter, is covered by the analysis of variance and the associated statistics such as R^2 and the standard error of the estimate. The second question is answered by the test of hypothesis for the entire model.

The reasoning behind, and the format of, the analysis of variance in multiple regression analysis resembles the analysis of variance for the two-variable regression analysis discussed in the last chapter. We will therefore discuss only the major aspects here as a review.

In the analysis of variance, we divide the total variation in the dependent variable (SS Total, measured by the sum of squared differences of the observed values of the dependent variable from their mean value) into two parts. One part consists of the variation in the dependent variable *explained* by the estimated regression line (SSR, measured by the sum of squared differences of the estimated values of the dependent variable from the mean of the estimated values). Another part consists of the variation in the dependent variable *not* explained by the estimated regression line (SSE, measured by the sum of squared differences of the observed values of the dependent variable from the estimated values of the dependent variable).

We therefore have

$$\sum(y - \bar{y})^2 = \sum(y - \hat{y})^2 + \sum(\hat{y} - \bar{y})^2 \qquad \textbf{14-28}$$

$$\text{SS Total} = \quad \text{SSE} \quad + \quad \text{SSR}$$

These sums of squared differences are presented in the second column of the ANOVA table. Degrees of freedom for computing each sum of squares (n is sample size and k is the number of explanatory variables in the model) are presented in the third column. The last column is simply the mean of the sum of squares obtained by dividing the sum of squares by its degrees of freedom (df).

ANOVA Table-1

Source of Variation	Sums of Squares	df	Mean Square
Regression	SSR	k	MSR = SSR/k
Error	SSE	$n - k - 1$	MSE = SSE/$(n - k - 1)$
Total	SS Total	$n - 1$	MST = SS Total/$(n - 1)$

Example 14-4

We continue with our example of housing prices in Vancouver East, and write the results of the analysis of variance in the form of an ANOVA table. The Minitab output presents the degrees of freedom in the second column and the sums of squares in the third column. The fourth column is the mean squares. In addition, the Minitab output contains two more columns. The fifth column presents the value of the F statistic calculated from the sample data. The sixth column presents the probability (P) of committing an error (Type I error) in rejecting a *true* null hypothesis of "no relationship between the dependent variable and *all* explanatory (independent) variables." Below the ANOVA table, the Minitab output also gives the values of the standard error of regression (S), the coefficient of determination (R-sq) and the coefficient of determination adjusted for degrees of freedom (R-sq (adj)).

ANOVA Table-2 (from Minitab Output Chart 14-2 page 611)

Housing Prices in Vancouver East					
Source	df	SS	MS	F	P
Regression	3	10 524 889 022	3 508 296 341	171.01	0.000
Residual Error	16	328 248 978	20 515 561		
Total	19	10 853 138 000			

$S = 4529$ R-Sq = 97.0% R-Sq(adj) = 96.4%

As explained in the last chapter, the **coefficient of determination** is defined as:

Coefficient of Determination	$R^2 = \dfrac{\text{SSR}}{\text{SS Total}} = 1 - \dfrac{\text{SSE}}{\text{SS Total}}$	14-29

From ANOVA Table-2, we can find R^2 by dividing the Sum of Squares due to regression by the total sum of squares as

$$R^2 = \frac{\text{SSR}}{\text{SS Total}} = \frac{10\,524\,889\,022}{10\,853\,138\,000} = 0.96976 \qquad \text{14-30}$$

This is reported (rounded to two decimal points and then expressed in percent form) as 97 percent in the Minitab output. Now you can explain the success of your estimation to the Real Estate Board, based on the value of R^2 as follows. Your estimated regression (based on the independent variables Bedrooms, Bathroom, and Footage) explains 97 percent variation in the price of housing (the dependent variable) in Vancouver East. The Real Estate Board is pleased to hear that. This is a great success, so far. However, a member of the Real Estate Board would like to understand your success in terms of the adjusted coefficient of determination ($\bar{R}^2$) and the unexplained variation in prices, that is, the standard error of estimate (S_e).

Adjusted Coefficient of Determination ($\bar{R}^2$) R^2 suffers from one limitation. It does not take into account the degrees of freedom (see Equation 14-29). If we add an independent variable to the multiple regression, the value of R^2, will, in general, increase (at worst, it will remain the same) in spite of a loss of one more degree of freedom in calculating the sums of squares. This would be misleading.

We therefore adjust R^2 for the degrees of freedom and call it adjusted R^2 (written as ($\bar{R}^2$) to provide us with a more accurate picture of the goodness of fit of the estimated equation. Thus, we define

$$\text{Adjusted } R^2 = \bar{R}^2 = 1 - \frac{\text{SSE}/(n-k-1)}{\text{SS Total}/(n-1)} \qquad \text{14-31}$$

As shown, under ANOVA Table-2, $\bar{R}^2$ for our housing example is 96.4 percent, not much different from R^2 of 97 percent. Since $\bar{R}^2$ is R^2 adjusted for degrees of freedom, there is a definite relationship between the two given by

$$\bar{R}^2 = 1 - (1 - R^2)\left(\frac{n-1}{n-k-1}\right) \qquad \text{14-32}$$

Thus, $\bar{R}^2$ will equal R^2 only when $k = 0$ (no explanatory variable) or $R^2 = 1$. Since, regression analysis always has some independent variable(s), $\bar{R}^2$ will, in general, be smaller than R^2. Further, an addition of a variable will increase both $\bar{R}^2$ and R^2. However, if a researcher is on a "fishing expedition" to obtain a maximum possible value of R^2 by adding irrelevant variables to the model, he or she will soon discover a penalty in terms of a lower $\bar{R}^2$. In fact, it can be shown that an addition of a variable will only increase $\bar{R}^2$, if the t statistic for the estimated coefficient of that variable is greater than 1. This is an alternative criterion used by some researchers for adding a variable. Note that, whereas R^2 is always positive, the value of $\bar{R}^2$ can be negative in the presence of low R^2 or low degrees of freedom, or both. For example, if $R^2 = 10\%$, $n = 20$, $k = 5$, $\bar{R}^2 = -22\%$. *Try finding the value of $\bar{R}^2$, if $R^2 = 80\%$, $n = 10$ and $k = 8$.*

CAVEATS ON USING THE COEFFICIENT OF DETERMINATION

In comparing R^2 or $\bar{R}^2$ for two or more models, we must remember the following:

1. The sample size and the dependent variable should be the same in all models. Since the R^2 or $\bar{R}^2$ measures proportional variation in the dependent variable explained by the independent variable(s), a dependent variable measured in different units, such as $\log y$, $\sqrt{y}$ or $1/y$, would give a different result.

2. We cannot compare a model without an intercept to a model with an intercept using R^2 or $\bar{R}^2$.

3. R^2 or $\bar{R}^2$, as a measure of goodness of fit, is not based on any requirements of the model, estimation or inference. It is simply a by-product of the estimation technique and a mechanical measure of the proportion of the sample variation in the dependent variable explained by the independent variable(s). Too much emphasis on the value of R^2 or $\bar{R}^2$ can lead researchers to what is called *data mining*, an all-out effort to find the variables that would produce a high R^2 or $\bar{R}^2$. This can lead researchers to introduce specification bias in their estimators. Researchers are therefore well advised to be concerned more about the theoretical relevance of the variables, appropriate sample information, a correspondence between the actual and the expected sign of the coefficients and statistical significance of the coefficients, rather than indulging in the game of maximizing R^2 or $\bar{R}^2$.

STANDARD ERROR OF ESTIMATE (S_e)

The standard error of estimate and the coefficient of determination (particularly the $\bar{R}^2$) are two sides of the same coin. While $\bar{R}^2$ gives us an idea of the goodness of fit (in terms of percentage), the value of S_e gives us an idea about the *lack* of goodness of fit (in terms of the original units of the dependent variable) from the estimated line. Some researchers, in fact prefer S_e to $\bar{R}^2$, as S_e gives information in terms of the departure of the estimated values from the actual values of the dependent variable. The S_e is simply the positive square root of the Mean Squared Error recorded in an ANOVA table.

For Example 14-4, from ANOVA Table-2, we see that,

$$S_e = \sqrt{\frac{\text{SSE}}{(n-k-1)}} = \sqrt{\frac{328\,248\,978}{16}} = 4529.41 \qquad \textbf{14-33}$$

This is recorded in the Minitab output as 4529. Now, you can tell the Real Estate Board that, *on average*, the actual (observed) prices differ from the estimated prices by only $4529. Based on the empirical rule for random observations (see Chapter 4), we expect 68 percent of all observations to fall between $\hat{y} \pm 4529$ and 95 percent of the observations between $\hat{y} \pm 2(4529)$. In fact, most of the errors are much smaller. For example, the actual value of observation number 12 is under-predicted by only $871 and that of observation number 4 is over-predicted by $1555. Try to verify. While, one could use the S_e for evaluating the *lack* of goodness of fit, the major uses of S_e are in testing hypotheses.

14.5 TESTS OF HYPOTHESIS

HOW WELL THE ESTIMATED LINE REPRESENTS THE TRUE RELATIONSHIP IN THE POPULATION

Given the model assumptions, the Gauss-Markov theorem tells us that the OLS estimators of the coefficients of independent variables in our sample regression line are BLUE. Thus, if we were to obtain data on the dependent variable by taking samples (of the same size and for the same values of the independent variables) a large number of times, from the same population, then, *on average*, the estimated values of the parameters will approach the true values of the parameters (*a statement of accuracy*). In addition, the estimators are guaranteed to have a minimum variance among all possible linear unbiased estimators (*a statement about precision*).

In practice, however, we take only one sample to estimate the values of the parameters. Can we place some confidence (in a probability sense) in our estimates as to their closeness to the unknown values of the parameters? The Gauss–Markov theorem does not assume the exact nature of probability distribution of the estimators beyond its having two parameters, mean and variance. We therefore need to add an assumption to our population relations contained in Equations 14-1 or 14-11. Researchers usually assume that the population error term is normally distributed. Since the dependent variable is a linear function of the error term, the dependent variable is also normally distributed. Furthermore, since the OLS estimators are linear functions of the dependent variable, the OLS estimators are also normally distributed. Now, we are in business. Now, we can, assuming the possibility of repeated sampling, make probabilistic statements about the closeness of sample estimates to parameters.

3. (d) **Assumption about the Probability Distribution of the Error Term (ϵ); it is normally distributed: $\epsilon \sim N(0, \sigma_\epsilon)$**

With this assumption, as noted in the previous chapter, we can now conduct tests of hypothesis either for the entire model or for each regression parameter in the model. In the two-variable model of the previous chapter, the two tests were equivalent. However, this is no longer true in the multiple regression model of this chapter. As a passing note, we mention that the assumption of normal distribution yields a more general class of estimators called Best Unbiased Estimators (BUE). In other words, we do not have to restrict ourselves to the class of linear estimators only.

TEST OF HYPOTHESIS FOR THE POPULATION MODEL

We now conduct the test of hypothesis for the population regression line.

$$E(y|x_1, x_2, x_3, \ldots, x_k) = \alpha + \beta_1 x_1 + \beta_2 x_2 + \beta_3 x_3 + \cdots + \beta_k x_k \qquad \text{14-34}$$

where the left-hand side of the equation is an expectation of all possible values of the Y variable for any given set of values of all X variables in the population regression model.

This is a joint test for all parameters associated with the independent variables in the model. The null hypothesis consists of *no linear relationship* between the dependent variable and all independent variables. An alternative hypothesis is that at least one independent variable is linearly related with Y (at least one of the β's is non-zero) and therefore is significant in explaining the variation in the dependent variable. In symbols:

H_0: $\beta_1 = \beta_2 = \beta_3 = \cdots = \beta_k = 0$ and
H_1: At least one of $\beta_1, \beta_2, \beta_3, \ldots, \beta_k \neq 0$

The test statistic is given by the ratio:

$$F = \frac{\text{MSR}}{\text{MSE}} = \frac{\text{SSR}/k}{\text{SSE}/(n-k-1)} \qquad \textbf{14-35a}$$

Alternatively, it can be written in terms of R^2 as

$$F = \frac{R^2/k}{(1-R^2)/(n-k-1)} \qquad \textbf{14-35b}$$

First, we choose the level of significance (Type I error) that we are willing to tolerate in rejecting the null hypothesis, when, in fact, it is *true*. *Second*, we find the critical value of the F statistic from the F table for the chosen level of α and the degrees of freedom, k for the numerator and $n-k-1$ for the denominator of the F ratio. Note the critical value of F thus obtained assumes that the null hypothesis is true. *Third*, using the sample information on mean square errors for the explained and unexplained variation (given in the ANOVA table), or the values of R^2, we compute the sample value of the F statistic. *Fourth*, we compare the sample value of the F statistic with the F value obtained from the probability distribution of F (the F table). *Fifth*, we reject the null hypothesis if the sample value of the F statistic is greater than the critical value of F. *Lastly*, we conclude whether the evidence from the sample supports or does not support the alternative hypothesis. In passing, we note that the F test statistic can also be used to conduct a test of hypothesis on a subset of parameters in the model. In this context, it is called the **Partial F test**. This is covered in Section 14A.4 of Chapter 14 Appendix A on the CD-ROM.

Example 14-5

In our previous example on housing prices in Vancouver East, we have three independent variables and therefore three β's. Our null and alternative hypotheses for the entire model therefore are:

H_0: $\beta_1 = \beta_2 = \beta_3 = 0$
H_1: At least one of β_1, β_2, $\beta_3 \neq 0$

Let us set $\alpha = 0.05$

The critical value of F (for $\alpha = 0.05$, $k = 3$ in the numerator and $n - k - 1$ (= 20 − 3 − 1) = 16 in the denominator) from the F table in Appendix D = 8.70 (closest to 15 degrees of freedom for the denominator). Thus,

$$F_{0.05\,(3,16)} = 8.70$$

The sample value of F can be computed either from the ANOVA table or from R^2.

From the ANOVA table: the sample value of $F = \dfrac{\text{MSR}}{\text{MSE}} = \dfrac{3\,508\,296\,341}{20\,515\,561} = 171.01$

as recorded in the Minitab output. This can also be calculated from R^2 values as

$F = \dfrac{0.97/3}{(1-0.97)/16} = 172.44$. This value is a little different due to rounding in the value of R^2.

Comparing the critical value of F with the sample value of F, we notice that the sample value is much larger compared to the critical value leading us to reject the null hypothesis. We therefore conclude that *at least one of the β's is not zero*. Alternatively, we say that at least one of the independent variables is significant in explaining the variable, price of housing in Vancouver East. In fact, we can say that there is *practically* zero probability (see the P-value in the Minitab output of ANOVA in Minitab

Chart 14-2) of committing a Type I error in rejecting the entire model. This result may please your Real Estate Board. However, one person on the board is very particular about the significance of each independent variable in the model. This is answered by conducting a test of hypothesis on each independent variable (i.e., each β) in the model.

TEST OF HYPOTHESIS FOR EACH REGRESSION COEFFICIENT IN THE POPULATION MODEL

In order to conduct a test of hypothesis for each regression coefficient in the population model, we need the probability distribution of the estimators of the population regression coefficients. Under Assumption 3(d) stated on page 619, each estimator would have a normal probability distribution with mean β and standard deviation σ_b. However, σ_b involves an unknown parameter σ_ϵ, estimated by S_e from the sample information. Under OLS assumptions, S_e^2 is an unbiased estimator of σ_ϵ^2. Thus, for an estimator b_j of a population regression coefficient β_j, we have the statistic $\dfrac{b_j - \beta_j}{\sigma_{b_j}}$ distributed as Z (normal) distribution with mean equal to zero and variance equal to one. Further, it can also be shown that

$$\sigma_{b_j}^2 = \frac{\sigma_\epsilon^2}{\sum (x_j - \bar{x}_j)^2} \frac{1}{(1 - R_j^2)} \qquad \text{14-36}$$

where, R_j^2 is the coefficient of determination obtained from the regression of the independent variable X_j on the remaining independent variables in the model.

Since σ_ϵ is unknown, we replace it by its estimator S_e and therefore $\sigma_{b_j}^2$ by $S_{b_j}^2$. This yields $\dfrac{b_j - \beta_j}{S_{b_j}}$, which is distributed as t distribution with $(n - k - 1)$ degrees of freedom.

We have shown Equation 14-36 to explain to you what is involved in testing the hypothesis about each individual parameter in the model. In particular, it shows you the importance of having an unbiased estimator S_e^2 of σ_ϵ^2 for conducting the test of hypothesis, and the importance of relationships among the independent variables (R_j^2).

Since the calculations for each estimator S_{b_j} can distract you from studying the important statistical concepts (besides, of course, being too tedious), we use the results given from Minitab or Excel output. Minitab output gives both the t statistic and the standard errors for each regression coefficient. Note that the t statistics for each regression coefficient in both the Minitab and Excel outputs are based on the assumption of a null hypothesis of the corresponding value of the parameter equal to zero against the alternative hypothesis of non-zero value of the parameter. This is a two-tailed hypothesis. If you wish to test a null hypothesis for a non-zero value of the parameter (e.g. β_j = 1), you have to use the standard error S_{b_j} to find the t value for that particular null hypothesis. Given the equation for t, this should be a matter of few seconds with a calculator.

Continuing with our housing example, we first choose the null hypothesis for each of the regression coefficients. Suppose our null hypothesis together with the alternative hypothesis (as expected by the Real Estate Board) for each regression coefficient is that

H_0: $\beta_1 \leq 0$, $\beta_2 \leq 0$, $\beta_3 \leq 0$
H_1: $\beta_1 > 0$, $\beta_2 > 0$, $\beta_3 > 0$

We have written all three pairs of hypotheses at one time, rather than writing them three times. However, they are very different from the hypotheses for the entire model. We next determine the decision rule, that is the level of significance (α). Assume $\alpha = 0.01$. The nature of the alternative hypothesis determines if we are conducting a one-sided or two-sided test. In our case of one-sided tests, we obtain the critical value of t for $\alpha = 0.01$ and the degrees of freedom $= (n - k - 1) = (20 - 3 - 1) = 16$; from the t table the critical value of $t = 2.583$ (i.e., $t_{0.01(16)} = 2.583$). Since, the degrees of freedom and the level of significance are the same for all null hypotheses, we use the same value as a critical value for all null hypotheses.

The values of the coefficients with standard errors (StDev), t statistic (T) and P-values (P) for each coefficient, as shown in Minitab Chart 14-2, are given below:

Test Statistics for Individual Coefficients

TABLE 14-4: Housing Prices in Vancouver East

Predictor	Coeff	StDev	T	P
Constant	159 345	5719	27.86	0.000
Bedrooms	9 321	1527	6.10	0.000
Baths	6 475	2185	2.96	0.009
Footage	19.7	6.8	2.88	0.011

As we see from the table, the t values of the estimated regression coefficients for bedrooms, and bathrooms are larger than the critical value of $t = 2.583$. We therefore reject the null hypotheses for these regression coefficients. Minitab and Excel outputs also give P-values (*the exact value of a Type I error in rejecting the null hypothesis based on the computed value of t statistic*) based on a two-tailed hypothesis. *For a one-tailed test of hypothesis, we should use half of the reported P-value.* The Real Estate Board should now be happy about the results of your investigation.

However, someone on the Board just noticed that you have not included a basement variable in your model. He thinks this is a serious lapse in your analysis. You look for data on basements for each house. The data on basements is, however, recorded only as a presence or absence of a basement: a qualitative variable. How do we satisfy this person on the Board about his presumption that a basement is an important consideration in the buyer's willingness to pay for the house? Obviously, we need to extend our model to include a qualitative variable, Basement; however, we first note some caveats on conducting tests of hypothesis.

A CAVEAT ON TESTS OF HYPOTHESIS

In simple regression analysis, we showed that an individual t test on the coefficient of the explanatory variable was equivalent to the F test for the model. This was possible as there was only one explanatory variable in the model. In multiple regression analysis, when we have more than one explanatory variable, the two tests are no longer equivalent. It is possible for the individual t tests to indicate that each of the regression parameter values is zero, and yet the F test to indicate that all regression parameters (excluding the intercept) are not zero. The reason is that *the test of hypothesis based on the F test for the model is conceptually different from the test of hypotheses for each regression coefficient in the multiple regression model.* The t test concerning, for example, β_2, in the two independent-variable model, is carried out without any assumption about β_1, whereas the F test is based on a joint statement about β_1 and β_2. Recall, this difference between the multiple t tests and F test was also discussed in Chapter 12 in the context of analysis of variance.

In practice, all t tests are conducted based on the same data set, and therefore they are often dependent due to a non-zero covariance among the estimates of the regression coefficients. The F test for the model is a joint test for all regression parameters (excluding the intercept) and thus includes the dependence that may exist between various coefficient estimates. The t tests for individual coefficients on the other hand do not take into account the covariance among the estimated regression coefficients. Further, a high degree of multicollinearity among the explanatory variables also results in very low values of t statistics, though the value of the F statistic is usually very large. The proof of these propositions is, however, beyond the scope of this book. Problems associated with multicollinearity are discussed later in this chapter.

14.6   QUALITATIVE VARIABLES: AN EXTENSION

As we discussed in Chapter 1, variables can be either qualitative or quantitative. Thus far, in our regression model, we have included both dependent and independent variables that are quantitative. The regression model can be extended to include qualitative variables either as a dependent variable or as an independent variable or both. In this book, we wish to extend the regression model to include qualitative variable(s) as one or more independent variable(s). **Qualitative variables**, by their very nature, list attributes of a variable in a number of categories. Examples of qualitative variables are: gender (male and female), seasons or quarters in a year (Fall, Winter, Spring, Summer), house with or without a basement/garage, ethnicity of a person, types of occupations, level of education attained (high-school, graduate, post-graduate), etc. A discussion on the usage of interactions between qualitative and/or quantitative variables is outlined in Section 14A.5 in Chapter 14 Appendix A on the CD-ROM.

TWO CATEGORIES

To illustrate the concept, let us suppose that high school teachers' salaries depend on years of experience and level of education. Thus, we can write the population regression equation as

$$\text{Salary} = \alpha + \beta_1 \text{ Experience} + \beta_2 \text{ Education} + \epsilon \qquad \textbf{14-37}$$

Suppose, the level of education has two categories, a bachelor's degree and a master's degree. Some teachers will have a bachelor's degree and others, a master's degree. We can write zero for the bachelor's degree and 1 for the master's degree. Thus,

$$\text{(Average) Salary} = \alpha + \beta_1 \text{ Experience} + \beta_2 \text{ Education}$$

CHART 14-3

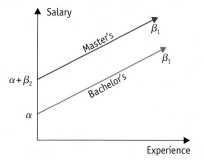

This gives us an average salary of a bachelor's degree holder $= \alpha + \beta_1$ Experience.

The average salary of a master's degree holder $= \alpha + \beta_1$ Experience $+ \beta_2$. This is shown in Chart 14-3 on the previous page.

The salary intercept for bachelor's degree holders is α.

The salary intercept for master's degree holders is $\alpha + \beta_2$.

The slope coefficient β_1 (an increase in salary for each year of experience, regardless of the degree) is the same for both bachelor's and for master's degree holders.

If a qualitative variable has two categories, then we choose one category as a base category with an assigned value equal to zero and represent another category with an assigned value equal to 1. Such variables are called *categorical* or **dummy variables**.

MULTIPLE CATEGORIES

How do we handle a qualitative variable such as seasons with multiple categories? The rule is that one of the categories must be chosen as the base category (the control group), and each of the remaining categories must be assigned one dummy variable. There is no rule as to which of the categories should be the base category. In general, we choose that category as the base category that is more suitable as the basis for comparison for all other categories, or the category whose influence on the dependent variable is not the subject of our investigation. Since we have four seasons, we choose one of the seasons as the base category, and use three dummy variables, one for each of the three remaining seasons. Thus, for example, we choose Fall as the base category, and use one dummy variable (DUM1) for Winter, one dummy variable for Spring (DUM2), and one dummy variable for Summer (DUM3). The variable DUM1 will have a value of 1 for the presence of Winter and zeros otherwise; DUM2 will have a value of 1 for the presence of Spring and zeros otherwise; and DUM3 will have a value of 1 for the presence of Summer and zeros otherwise. We illustrate these multiple categories in Self-Review 14-2.

 If a qualitative variable has m categories, then we choose one category as a base category and use $m - 1$ dummy variables for the remaining $m - 1$ categories.

Example 14-6

In the case of our housing example, the records show that some houses have a basement and others do not. Thus, we have two categories of houses. According to the observation numbers (see Minitab Chart 14-2 on page 611), the records are given below. We write 1 for a house with a basement and 0 for a house without a basement.

Observ. #	1	2	3	4	5	6	7	8	9	10
Basement	0	0	0	0	1	1	0	0	0	1
Observ. #	11	12	13	14	15	16	17	18	19	20
Basement	1	1	1	1	1	1	1	1	1	1

We record the values of basement (0 or 1) for each observation in a column in Minitab or Excel, just like the values for any other independent variable.

Thus, basement in our regression analysis becomes an independent variable. Popularly, in regression analyses, each category (other than the control group) of a qualitative variable is called a **dummy variable**. In the case of the Basement variable, we have two categories, *basement* or *no basement*, and therefore we have one dummy variable, *Basement*. The price of a house without a basement becomes a *comparison group* or *base group* or *control group* with zeros as its values. By default, then, the houses with a basement become the group whose values are being compared with the base

MINITAB CHART 14-4: Regression Analysis: Price versus Bedrooms, Baths, Footage and Basements

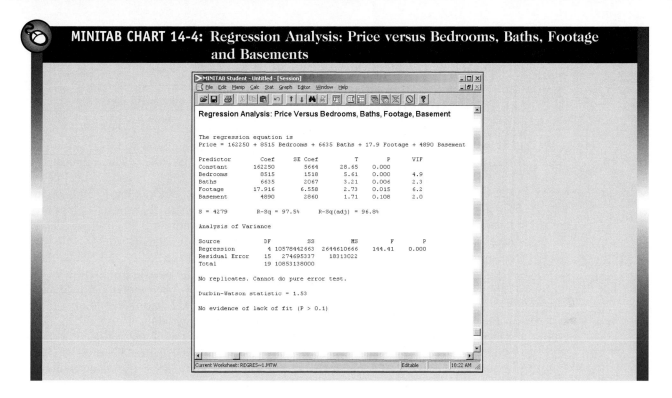

group. Thus, we have one dummy variable. We call it *Basement* in the Regression Equation. Results of a regression analysis of housing prices with an addition of a basement are summarized in Minitab Chart 14-4.

The estimated regression equation is:

$$\text{Price} = 162\,250 + 8515\,\text{Bedrooms} + 6635\,\text{Baths} + 17.9\,\text{Footage} + 4890\,\text{Basement} \qquad \textbf{14-38}$$

The results show that, on average, a basement adds $4890 to the price of a house, given the values of all other features of a house. Note, the addition of the basement variable has the effect of reducing the degrees of freedom by 1. Thus, we now have only 15 degrees of freedom for the t statistic. The critical value of t for 15 degrees of freedom and a 1 percent level of significance is 2.602. Based on this critical value, the basement variable is statistically insignificant. However, based on the *P*-value for a one-tailed test, we see there is 5.4 percent (half of 10.8 percent) probability of committing an error (Type I) in rejecting a true null hypothesis of zero value of the coefficient for the basement. Some may consider this as a high probability of committing an error, others may be willing to tolerate it. However, 5.4 percent seems to be close to the acceptable norm of 5 percent in statistical studies.

Nevertheless, the general rule for including a variable whenever its $|t|$ value exceeds 1 suggests that we should keep the Basement variable in our regression equation. Further, you should note once we know that Basement is a relevant variable, we must not exclude it from the regression equation. As discussed in the beginning of this chapter, an exclusion of a relevant variable from the regression equation will produce biased and inconsistent estimates for all coefficients in the regression equation. You should compare the values of other coefficients in this equation with the values of the coefficients in the regression equation without the Basement variable (Table 14-4).

We have deliberately carried you through the same example to show you how various elements of the multiple regression analysis fit together. You may conclude your report for the Real Estate Board in simple words as follows.

THE CONCLUDING REPORT I

Housing prices in Vancouver East seem to be well represented by the estimated linear relationship between housing prices and the independent variables, number of bedrooms, number of bathrooms, square footage and basement. The value of R^2 (97.5 percent) indicates that the independent variables have been successful in explaining over 97 percent of the variation in housing prices in a random sample of 20 observations. The estimated responses (β's) of housing prices to changes in each of the independent variables seem to accord with *a priori* expectations. The Ordinary Least Squares technique used in estimation of the linear relationship (together with its associated assumptions) guarantees that the estimated responses, on average, in repeated sampling, will be close to the true responses in the population of all houses in Vancouver East. The test statistics for the model as well as each individual response parameter indicate that the probability of committing a Type I error is less than 1 percent in general, and less than 6 percent, for the Basement variable.

Obviously, the Real Estate Board is (or, should be) pleased with your work. However, one member of the Real Estate Board was very observant when she read your report. In particular, she became concerned with a phrase in parentheses, "with associated assumptions," and became anxious to know what those assumptions were. You stated the assumptions for the regression model in the population. This made her uneasy about accepting your results at face value. She persuaded the Board to ask you to verify how your statistical analysis met those assumptions. This is the task to which we now turn.

■ SELF-REVIEW 14-2

Based on the information contained in Self-Review 14-1, extend the multiple regression model by adding dummy variables to four quarters (seasons). Estimate the extended model. Answer the following questions.

(a) Set up an ANOVA table for the problem.
(b) Interpret the standard error of the estimate.
(c) Interpret the values of the coefficient of determination and the adjusted coefficient of determination. Explain why they are different.
(d) Conduct a test of hypothesis for the entire model. ($\alpha = 0.01$)
(e) Conduct a test of hypothesis for each regression coefficient. ($\alpha = 0.01$)
(f) Write a brief report on the findings of the estimated model.

EXERCISES 14-5 TO 14-8

14-5. Refer to the following information:

Predictor	Coef	StDev
Constant	20.00	10.00
X_1	−1.00	0.25
X_2	12.00	8.00
X_3	−15.00	5.00

Source	df	SS	MS	F
Regression	3	7 500.00		
Error	18			
Total	21	10 000.00		

(a) Complete the ANOVA table.
(b) Conduct a global test of hypothesis, using the 0.05 significance level. Can you conclude that any of the net regression coefficients are different from zero?
(c) Conduct a test of hypothesis on each of the regression coefficients. Could you delete any of the variables? ($\alpha = 0.05$)

14-6. Refer to the following information:

Predictor	Coef	StDev
Constant	-150	90
X_1	2000	500
X_2	-25	30
X_3	5	5
X_4	-300	100
X_5	0.60	0.15

Source	df	SS	MS	F
Regression	5	1500.00		
Error	15			
Total	20	2000.00		

(a) Complete the ANOVA table.
(b) Conduct a global test of hypothesis, using the 0.05 significance level. Can you conclude that any of the partial regression coefficients are different from zero?
(c) Conduct a test of hypothesis on each of the regression coefficients. Could you delete any of the variables? ($\alpha = 0.05$)

14-7. Refer to information in Exercise 14-4.
(a) Interpret the adjusted coefficient of determination.
(b) Conduct a test of hypothesis for the entire equation at the 5 percent level of significance.
(c) Conduct a one-tailed test of hypothesis for each of the regression coefficients.
(d) Test the null hypothesis: that elasticity of demand with respect to price equals -1 (at the 5 percent level of significance).

14-8. Linda conducted research on the demand for post-secondary education in Canada for all disciplines together, as well as for each discipline for the period 1970–2001 (32 observations). She used "enrollment" (number of students enrolled) as the dependent variable. The independent variables used are:
(a) *Student Loan* (a variable constructed from the amounts of scholarships and student loans available per student in real value),
(b) *Tuition Fees* (a variable constructed from accommodation costs and relevant tuition fees in real dollars, averaged across Canada),
(c) *Foregone Earnings* (an estimate of foregone earnings in real value while at school),
(d) *Earnings Differential* (a differential in earnings of a high school graduate and a university graduate, in real dollars), and
(e) a *Trend* variable to capture a general rise in demand for education not accounted for by any of the other independent variables included in the model.

Discipline	Constant	Student Loan	Tuition Fees	Forgone Earnings	Earnings Differential	Trend
Education/Phy. Ed.	4.42342	0.518560	−0.483319	−0.522008	1.60179	−0.421400
	(4.01262)	(3.86297)	(−2.56728)	(−1.90047)	(4.54647)	(−0.150400)
		Adj. $R^2 = 0.924128$		$F = 13.2695$	$d = 1.48353$	
Health	6.52070	0.451630	−0.833195	−0.743969	1.49225	−0.027087
	(8.67041)	(4.80857)	(−8.10532)	(−3.95468)	(5.99423)	(−1.31397)
		Adj. $R^2 = 0.955862$		$F = 34.0573$	$d = 1.58896$	
Engineering/Applied Science	8.60237	0.726706	−1.01144	−0.888151	1.15114	−0.022352
	(9.40107)	(6.20861)	(−7.34410)	(−3.59822)	(3.38391)	(−0.818177)
		Adj. $R^2 = 0.934097$		$F = 28.3341$	$d = 1.63214$	
Music/Fine Arts	−10.5437	1.41755	−3.25322	−2.26399	6.74203	−0.057620
	(−4.45074)	(4.93442)	(−8.07627)	(−3.86251)	(8.98713)	(−0.96671)
		Adj. $R^2 = 0.968625$		$F = 39.8210$	$d = 1.44429$	
Arts	8.20078	0.910117	−1.01367	−1.55328	2.01038	−0.054192
	(5.65624)	(5.14654)	(−4.08696)	(−4.28771)	(4.32250)	(−1.46464)
		Adj. $R^2 = 0.917722$		$F = 13.2309$	$d = 1.49376$	
Sciences	4.40083	0.450021	−0.479177	−0.711076	1.86043	−0.566839
	(6.36905)	(5.19377)	(−3.93911)	(−3.89845)	(7.4733)	(−0.029606)
		Adj. $R^2 = 0.964512$		$F = 37.6066$	$d = 1.75660$	
Total Enrollment	8.33147	0.734975	−0.853702	−1.15781	1.81807	−0.030460
	(7.82897)	(5.56232)	(−5.29659)	(−4.31680)	(5.16864)	(−1.06543)
		Adj. $R^2 = 0.942143$		$F = 22.8045$	$d = 1.56323$	

Values for all variables were expressed in terms of percent changes (in fact, in natural logs) before estimation. This conversion makes it possible to interpret the values of regression coefficients as percent change in the dependent variable (on average) in response to a one percent change in each of the independent variables. The results are presented above and t-values are given in parentheses below the coefficients. Answer the following questions. (Conduct all tests of hypothesis at the 5 percent level of significance.)

(a) Compare the values of the adjusted coefficient of determination for all equations. Which equation is the best fit?

(b) Comment on the expected signs of each coefficient versus the actual signs in the estimated equations. Do you find any coefficient wrongly signed in any equation?

(c) Which discipline (including Total) is affected the most by: Student Loan? Tuition? Foregone Earnings? Earnings Differential?

(d) Which disciplines are displaying the least and the most increased/decreased demand for education over time? (Hint: The trend variable represents the value of the coefficient interpreted as an average change in the dependent variable per time period.)

(e) Conduct a test of hypothesis for the entire model for each discipline.

(f) Conduct a test of hypothesis for each of the regression coefficients in any two disciplines of your choice.

(g) Write a brief report on demand for education from these findings.

14.7　REGRESSION DIAGNOSTICS

CONSEQUENCES OF VIOLATIONS OF THE MODEL ASSUMPTIONS

Consequences of violations of the model assumptions are outlined below. Proofs are beyond the scope of this book.

1. There is a *linear* relationship between the dependent variable and all the independent variables. In general, violation of this assumption will yield biased and inconsistent estimators, and invalid inferences.

2. The model includes all *relevant variables*, i.e., the model is correctly specified. In general, violation of this assumption will yield biased and inconsistent estimators, and invalid inferences.

3. All *independent variables are non-random*, or, at least, independent of the error term. Violation of this assumption will not allow us to accurately decompose the total variation into explained variation and the unexplained variation. In general, therefore, violation of this assumption will yield biased and inconsistent estimators, and invalid inferences. Often, this assumption is violated due to misspecification of variables and/or functional form.

4. None of the independent variables is an exact linear function of other independent variables. This is known as the *absence of perfect multicollinearity*. Violation of this assumption would give indeterminate values of the coefficients and infinitely large values of the variances of the coefficients.

5. The *mean of the error term* in the population is zero. Violation of this assumption, in general, will lead to biased and inconsistent estimators, and invalid or inaccurate inferences. Often, this assumption is violated due to misspecification of variables and/or functional form.

6. The variance of the error term is constant. This is known as the assumption of *homoscedasticity* of the error term. Violation of this assumption will lead to biased estimators of the variances of the regression coefficients, inefficient estimators of the regression coefficients and invalid tests of hypotheses.

7. The values of the error are independent of each other. This is known as the assumption of the *absence of autocorrelation*. Violation of this assumption will lead to biased estimators of the variances of the regression coefficients, inefficient estimators of the regression coefficients and invalid tests of hypotheses.

8. The error term is *normally distributed*. This assumption is required for conducting tests of hypotheses. Violation of this assumption will lead to invalid inferences. OLSE are still BLUE.

In general, we will use graphical methods to check violation of these assumptions and supplement them, where possible, with simple quantitative measures. We shall briefly discuss simple remedies when an assumption is violated. However, we should note at the very outset that most of the diagnostic checks and remedies discussed are only of an approximate or "rule of thumb" nature. In most cases, there are no "foolproof" checks or remedies. Additional diagnostic checks and remedies are discussed in Section 14A.1 in Chapter 14 Appendix A on the CD-ROM.

LINEARITY: THE FUNCTIONAL RELATIONSHIP

We have assumed linearity of relationship between the dependent variable (Y) and all independent variables (X's). However, the Ordinary Least Squares technique is applicable to a wide variety of non-linear models that can be transformed into linear relationships. For example, if an independent variable appears in a reciprocal form ($1/X$) or in a power form such as X^2, we can easily transform our data in these forms and run the regression as usual.

There are some relationships such as $y = \alpha x_1^{\beta_1} x_2^{\beta_2} e^{\epsilon}$ or $y = e^{\alpha + \beta_1 x_1 + \epsilon}$. Note "$e$" in this case, is an irrational number approximately equal to 2.71828. This number is used as a base for natural logarithms (ln). Do not confuse this "e" with the error term. These non-linear relationships can easily be transformed into linear relationships by taking logs on both sides of the equation. For example, the former relationship can be written as $ln(y) = ln(\alpha) + \beta_1 ln(x_1) + \beta_2 ln(x_2) + \epsilon$. This is linear in natural log values of the dependent and independent variables. All we have to do is to change the values of the observations to natural logs and estimate the equation. This type of equation is very common in statistical work as the values of estimated coefficients can now be interpreted as partial elasticities (percent change in the dependent variable Y to a one percent change in the associated X variable, holding all other X variables constant). We can similarly transform the other equation as $ln(y) = \alpha + \beta_1 x_1 + \epsilon$. An estimate of β_1 in this case gives percentage change in the dependent variable to a unit change in the independent variable, which is quite useful for estimating instantaneous growth rates ($= \beta_1$) in the dependent variable in response to a unit change in the independent variable (time).

GRAPHICAL METHODS

We can explore the accuracy of a linear model through graphs displaying the relationship between the observed values (y) of the dependent variable and estimated values ($\hat{y}$) of the dependent variable, or the estimated values (e) of the error term against $\hat{y}$. To examine the linearity of the relationship between the price of housing in Vancouver to bedrooms, bathrooms, square footage, and basement variables, we plot observations on the dependent variable *price* against the estimated values $\hat{y}$ (*FITS1*) as shown in Chart 14-5. In Minitab, we can plot this graph along with a fitted line in an option under the regression command. The option is called the *fitted line plot*. Further, we can choose confidence or prediction intervals in an option within the plot. The graph does not indicate any serious departure from linear relationship. The linearly fitted line is very close to the actual observations on price.

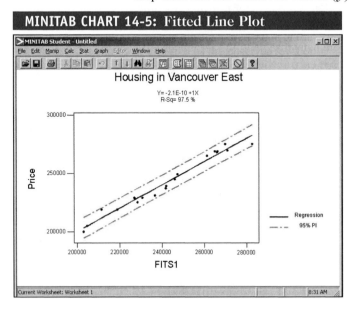

MINITAB CHART 14-5: Fitted Line Plot

QUANTITATIVE METHODS

Another possible approach to see the linearity of relationship of each independent variable with the dependent variable is to look at the partial correlations, a measure of linear relationship, of price with each of the independent variables, holding all other independent variables constant. This is discussed in Section 14A.3 of Chapter 14 Appendix A on the CD-ROM.

Minitab software provides a quantitative test of linear fit, called the **Lack of Fit** test. It is not a popular test and is too complicated to be elaborated on here. However, you can read from the Minitab print out if there is any evidence of lack of fit together with a P-value for it (see Minitab Chart 14-4 on page 625). In our housing example, the P-value is larger than 10 percent, implying *no* sufficient evidence of lack of fit. If the P-value is smaller than a pre-selected level of significance (say 5 percent), you can conclude that the independent variables in only the linear form are *not* sufficient to explain the variation in the dependent variable. In that case, we might wish to use higher order terms (such as squared values) of some of the independent variables. We can experiment with squared terms or the interaction terms (a product of the values of any two independent variables) of the independent variables, one at time, and reanalyze the data for exploring the possibility of non-linear relationships. We discuss a standard test in Section 14A.4 of Chapter 14 Appendix A on the CD-ROM. However, we need to be careful, since we may also observe a lack of fit due to some unusual observations (discussed later in this chapter) in the data set rather than a violation of the linearity assumption in the population.

RELEVANCE AND IRRELEVANCE OF VARIABLES

There are two types of issues involved here. Are the variables included in the model relevant? Have some relevant variables been excluded?

PRESENCE OF IRRELEVANT VARIABLES

The presence of an irrelevant variable in the equation can be answered by (a) theoretical or experiential (if theory is not strong) considerations; (b) the explanatory power of each variable in terms of their partial correlations with the dependent variable; and (c) the P-values for the coefficient of each of the independent variables. In our housing example, all variables included in the equation, except for some doubts about the basement, seem to be relevant. Furthermore, signs of the coefficient of each independent variable are also in agreement with expected signs.

OMISSION OF RELEVANT VARIABLES

The second question of excluding a relevant variable is more difficult to answer. *Theoretically*, from the expectations of real estate, we understand that we have included all important variables influencing housing prices. However, there may be other variables, such as lot size, proximity to public services, locality, etc. that may also be important. We assume that either these variables are fairly correlated with the included variables, or their influence is random, and therefore captured by the error term. However, should an important variable be left out, it should show up in the error term as a systematic component. In general, such a systematic component in the error term would result in under-predicting or over-predicting the values of the dependent variable. To see this possibility *graphically*, we can examine a graph (or a scatter diagram) of the estimated error term (e) or actual values (y) of the dependent variable against the predicted values ($\hat{y}$) of the dependent variable. For our housing example, we can use Chart 14-7, which plots the actual values of price against estimated values of price. There does not seem to be a serious under-prediction or over-prediction.

Statistically, if we look at the R^2 (Minitab Chart 14-4), the R^2 value of 97.5 percent indicates that together these variables are able to explain 97.5 percent of the variation in the price. Not much seems to be left to be explained. Since autocorrelation often results from misspecification of the model, a significant value of the Durbin–Watson d statistic may indicate the possibility of a missing variable. We explain the usage of the d statistic in the context of autocorrelation below. The calculated value of the d statistic (=1.53) is not significant; in fact, it is in an inconclusive range. Based on this additional evidence, we can conclude that we do not have sufficient evidence in favour of any relevant variable omitted from the equation.

OUTLIERS AND INFLUENTIAL OBSERVATIONS: A DIGRESSION

In general, an outlier is an observation that is unusual from the viewpoint of the pattern displayed by the rest of the observations in a data set. In other words, unusually small or large values of a variable that are farther away from the mean value of that variable by about two or more times its standard deviation are called outliers. Since the estimated regression line is based on the OLS technique, it calculates an average response of the dependent variable to a unit change in the independent variable. Therefore, like the simple average (the arithmetic mean), it is unduly affected by the presence of unusually small or large observations in the data set. Some outliers can be so influential that they can succeed in twisting the estimated regression line in their favour. Consequently, we may end up with inaccurate estimates of the regression line and/or the standard error of estimate. This would give us wrong ideas about the values of the regression parameters as well as wrong signals in tests of hypotheses of these parameters.

In Chart 14-6a two influential observations (blue diamonds) have succeeded in twisting the regression line (double arrowhead) in their favour. The regression line without using the influential observations has a much higher slope (single arrowhead line).

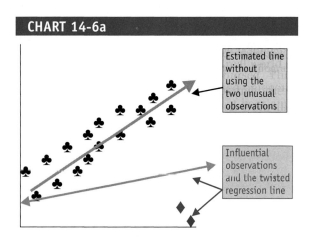

CHART 14-6a

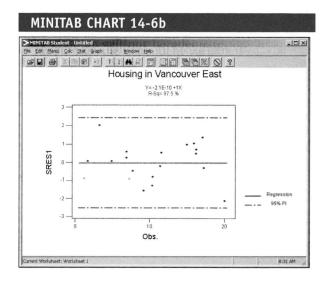

MINITAB CHART 14-6b

Minitab output prints the unusual observations that result in unusually large values of the **standardized residuals**. Standardized residuals are the values of residuals divided by their respective standard errors. These standardized residuals have zero mean and a variance equal to 1. Standardized residuals larger than an absolute value of two (plus or minus) are marked as R on the side in the regression output. Minitab also gives an output of Studentized Deleted Residuals—called *deleted t residuals* in Minitab's dialogue box and noted as TRES in Minitab's worksheet—a special type of standardized residuals that have Students' t distribution with $df = (n - k - 2)$. These residuals are useful for checking the statistical significance of an outlier. Values of these residuals greater than the value of t for $df = (n - k - 2)$ and a level of significance such as 0.05 indicates that the outlier is statistically significant.[1] Observations on the independent variables that are estimated to exert undue influence (*high leverage*: with leverage values larger than $2(k + 1)/n$, where k is the number of independent variables and n is the number of observations) on the estimates are marked as X on the side. Remember to check off standardized residuals and high leverages under the storage option in Minitab. In addition, Minitab also points out the observations that are influential in terms of the combined effect of unusual observations of both dependent and independent variables. This is measured by *Cook's Distance* (called D for short) statistic. As a rule of thumb, a value of D greater than 1 for any observation is considered influential. However, in terms of inference procedures, an observation is considered influential if the value of D is greater than $F_{0.5}$ (with $df = (k + 1)/(n - k - 1)$). Alternatively, a p-value of less than 0.5 for the associated F value mentioned above would imply that the observation is influential.

Both Excel and Minitab outputs give us all the values of the standardized residuals as routine output. For a visual interpretation of outliers, you can plot the standardized residuals (SREs) against the observation numbers (Chart 14-6b), or predicted values of the dependent variable, in either Minitab or Excel (see Solutions to Self-Review).

The existence of outliers should be checked for recording errors, and for their presence from the viewpoint of an inconsistency with the assumed regression model. Outliers should be removed from the data set only if they represent an error in recording and/or inconsistency with the assumed regression model. Since outliers may contain some important information about the underlying population relationship, an automatic removal of outliers from the data set is not advised. For example, if the prices of some houses happen to be unusually large due to some extraordinary design or existence of a swimming pool or some other unique feature, an aspect *not* being modelled, we can remove such observation(s) from the data set and re-estimate the regression equation. However, if some outliers represent houses with unusually high prices that can be justified by unusually large values of the independent variables (included in the model) associated with those houses, such outliers should not be removed. Chart 14-5 does not indicate any problem with reference to outliers. Most of the observations are close to the fitted line, and none of the observations is outside the 95 percent prediction interval. Chart 14-6b presents a chart of standardized residuals against observation numbers. This chart also tells the same story as Chart 14-5. However, we should note that the presence of outliers is a feature of data in a particular sample of observations, which may not exist in another sample of observations. Outliers by themselves therefore do not invalidate any of the assumptions of the regression model.

MULTICOLLINEARITY

As we mentioned earlier, presence of perfect multicollinearity (MC) between independent variables will result in indeterminate estimates. You can convince yourself by replacing, say $x_1' = 5x_2'$ in an equation either for b_1 (Equation 14-25) or for b_2 (Equation 14-26), and see what you get. The result should be 0 divided by 0, an undefined quantity! Likewise, you can see what happens to the variances of b_1 or b_2 by substituting $R_j^2 = 1$ in the equation for variance, Equation 14-36. Here, you will end up dividing a quantity by zero. What is the resulting value? Remember, R_j^2 is the coefficient of determination in the (auxiliary/secondary) regression of the independent variable X_j on the remaining independent variables in the model. Note that the dependent variable Y is not involved in this regression. We rewrite Equation 14-36 for your convenience below:

$$\sigma_{b_j}^2 = \frac{\sigma_\epsilon^2}{\sum(x_j - \bar{x}_j)^2} \frac{1}{(1 - R_j^2)} \qquad \textbf{14-36}$$

CHART 14-7:
Types of
Multicollinearity

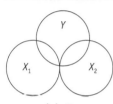

(a) Zero

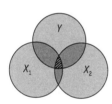

(b) Low

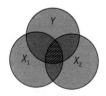

(c) High

(d) Perfect

Perfect multicollinearity occurs rarely in observed data. In general, it would occur in situations where an investigator has mistakenly specified variables that, by chance, are perfectly correlated in the sample of observations. For example, an investigator is trying to estimate consumption of wine (Y) in Canada based on the independent variables nominal GDP (X_1) and inflation (X_2) from 20 quarterly observations over the last 5 years. Now suppose the GDP in *real* terms (GDP adjusted for inflation) remained constant over the sample period implying all changes in nominal GDP occurred due to changes in inflation only. Obviously, GDP and Inflation are perfectly correlated. There is no way of finding separate effects of nominal GDP and Inflation on consumption. The situation is depicted in Chart 14-7(d), where nominal GDP and Inflation affect consumption only simultaneously (the overlaps of X_1 with Y and X_2 with Y are the same) in this particular sample of observations. Note that the overlap of circles for X_1 and X_2 is only illustrative and does not necessarily imply identical sets of values of two variables. Zero MC is depicted in Chart 14-7(a), where, in *another sample* of observations, GDP and Inflation affect consumption only individually (X_1 and X_2 circles have no common overlap with Y).

IMPERFECT MULTICOLLINEARITY

Zero and perfect MC are rare. Observed data, in general, exhibits low to high MC. Thus, MC is a matter of degree, not of kind. The common hatched area in parts (b) and (c) (obtained for two different data sets) of Chart 14-7 depict low MC and high MC cases. Does imperfect MC pose any problem for the OLS method? *Since, the MC is due to correlation between non-random variables, it does not affect BLUE properties of the OLS.* In fact, a low MC in one sample of observations may turn into a high MC in another sample of observations. This, however, does make the estimates of the parameters unstable (dependent on the sample of observations).

Furthermore, the higher the degree of MC among the independent variables, the higher will be the variances of the estimators. You can check this by putting different values of R_j^2 in the equation for variance of the estimators (Equation 14-36). A higher variance of the estimator will make the t statistics for the estimators very small, although the coefficient of determination for the entire equation may be very large. Sometimes, a high degree of MC can result in the wrong signs of the estimates of the regression coefficients. Low t ratios, in turn would falsely lead us not to reject the null hypothesis about the individual regression coefficients.

>   **Imperfect MC** does not violate any OLS assumptions, therefore the OLSE are BLUE regardless of the degree (less than one) of MC present. An MC is essentially a problem underlying the sample of observations used in an investigation.

TABLE 14-5: Simple Correlations R_j^2 and VIF

	Price	Bedrooms	Baths	Footage	R_j^2	VIF
Bedrooms	0.950				0.796	4.9
Baths	0.773	0.628			0.558	2.3
Footage	0.942	0.879	0.744		0.838	6.2
Basement	0.739	0.702	0.467	0.673	0.508	2.0

In the presence of a high degree of MC, in general, the estimated equation will display a high R^2 (the coefficient of determination between Y and all independent variables), low t ratios, and, sometimes, wrong signs of the estimated values of the regression coefficients.

Since MC, in general, is found in all observed data, statisticians have devised some rules of thumb as to a tolerable degree of MC. The rules of thumb about the degree of MC that one can use depend on the degree of correlation among the independent variables. A high degree of sample correlation (say, greater than 0.8) between any two independent variables indicates a high MC. However, in cases of more than two independent variables, a high MC may be present even though sample correlations are low. *Thus, a high sample correlation is sufficient but not a necessary condition for high MC.* A more popular measure is based on what is called the *Variance Inflation Factor (VIF)*. The VIF for an independent variable j is defined as $VIF_j = \dfrac{1}{1 - R_j^2}$. A value of VIF higher than 10 (corresponds to the value of $R_j^2 = 0.9$) is generally considered beyond a tolerable limit. Some statisticians compare the overall R^2 for the regression with R_j^2 for each variable as a guide.

Values of VIF greater than 10, or, values of simple correlation coefficient (r) greater than 0.9, are considered beyond a tolerable limit for the presence of multicollinearity. Another rule of thumb suggested by L.R. Klein, a Nobel Laureate economist, is that a value of R_j^2 greater than the overall R^2 (coefficient of determination in the regression of Y against all X's) may indicate a trouble spot due to the MC problem.

Example 14-7 In our housing example, the sample correlation coefficients between independent variables and the VIF values (see Table 14-5) indicate that the Footage variable is the most troublesome of all from the viewpoint of MC in our model. A VIF value of 6.2 for the Footage variable implies that the variance of the regression coefficient for the Footage variable will be unduly inflated (6.2 times larger) due to the presence of MC of Footage with the remaining independent variables (Bedroom, Bath, and Basement). This would result in a smaller t value or larger P-value for the regression coefficient. In other words, in the absence of MC, we would have a smaller Type I error in rejecting the null hypothesis than indicated by the P-value 0.015 for the Footage variable and 0.108 for the Basement variable. However, using Klein's rule, none of the R_j^2 are higher than the overall R^2 value for the regression (= 0.975) thus indicating MC within tolerable limits.

14.8 ERROR TERM DIAGNOSTICS

We have made several assumptions about the population error term, including zero mean, constant variance, zero covariance, its independence with the explanatory variables, and normal distribution (for a test of hypothesis). The population error term is however an unknown variable. We can check these assumptions only based on the estimated error term obtained from the sample regression line, which, theoretically speaking, will only give us some approximate results. We will focus our attention on the diagnostic methods checking violation of the assumptions of homoscedasticity, autocorrelation, and the normality of the error term. (We have placed model diagnostics of the error (residual) term in this separate section due to its unique character in the population regression model.)

HOMOSCEDASTICITY

Homoscedasticity of the error term implies that the values of the variance of the error term will be equal to each other for all values of the independent variables. In general, this assumption is often violated in the cross-section data (all observations recorded at a given point of time) such as salaries of employees in a firm, rate of return on investment in a number of firms, or GPA of a number of students in a course in a particular year. If the variance of the error term is positively associated with the squared values of an independent variable, the OLSE of the variance of the error term will be biased downward (t ratios higher than they should be), sometimes leading us to reject a null hypothesis when it should not be rejected. The converse is true for a negative association between the variance of the error term and the values of the independent variable.

Graphically, statisticians examine violation of homoscedasticity by plotting values of the error term against values of the independent variable. When there is more than one independent variable, we plot values of the error term against the estimated values of the dependent variable. In multiple regression analysis, however, a more theoretically sound way is to plot the *squared* values of the error term against the estimated values of the dependent variable. Minitab output, however, uses the simple error term instead of the squared error term (see Chart 14-11d). This should also give an approximate idea about the violation of the homoscedasticity assumption.

CHART 14-8

a. Homoscedasticity

b. Heteroscedasticity

c. Minitab Output

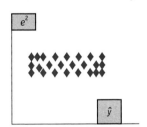

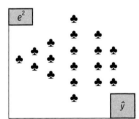

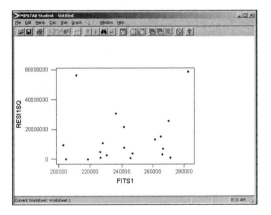

If the error term or the squared error term is homoscedastic, there will be no clear pattern (Chart 14-8a). If the error term is heteroscedastic, the squared error term will have a different spread at different values of the estimated dependent variable (Chart 14-8b), or at least with some of the independent variables.

Example 14-8

In our example of housing prices in Vancouver East, we plotted the squared error term (RES11SQ) against the estimated y values (Chart 14-8c). As is apparent from the chart, there does seem to be some evidence of heteroscedasticity for a few observations, particularly one for a house in the lower price range and another for a house with the highest price. However, there does not seem to be a discernible pattern in terms of a particular type of algebraic relationship. Most of the statistical methods and remedies depend on a discernible pattern of the squared error term with the independent variables. To examine the problem further, as to which independent variable may be causing the problem, we should plot the squared error term against each of the independent variables. In general, if the variances increase or decrease with the values of an independent variable, the usual *remedy* is to transform that variable by giving a lower weight to the values of the independent variable associated with higher variances. However, if unequal variances were due to non-linearity or a missing variable in the regression equation, the remedy would consist of an appropriate model specification.

AUTOCORRELATION

The OLS technique assumes zero covariance between the error term of one observation and the error term of any other observation. In simple words, it means that the error term or the dependent variable in the regression equation, say investment in the year 1995, does not depend on the investment in any other year. In time-series data (observations on all variables recorded over time), this assumption is often violated. Jan Kmenta, a noted statistician, likens the idea of autocorrelation to a lingering sound of a stringed instrument after a taping. In economics and business data, the impact of a change in the dependent variable, such as investment, productivity or costs, does linger on to the values taken by the variable over other time periods. In general, the shorter the length of the time period (monthly/quarterly instead of annually), the larger the possibility of autocorrelation. However, autocorrelation does not have such a pronounced effect in the cross-section data. The rate of return on investment in one company does not, in general, depend on the rate of returns of other companies in the same time period.

Although the presence of autocorrelation does not violate the unbiasedness property of the OLSE, the OLSE are no longer BLUE. The variance of the error term is no longer a minimum in the class of all linear unbiased estimators. A positive autocorrelation in the successive error terms together with a positive association in successive values of the independent variables (a general feature of time-series data) would result in a downward bias in the OLS estimator of the variance of the regression coefficients (higher t ratios). Thus, we sometimes may erroneously reject a null hypothesis when it should not be rejected. The converse is true for a negative association between the variance of the error term and the values of the independent variable.

The assumption of autocorrelation is very general in the sense that it involves all time periods. However, statisticians often focus their ideas on the problem in terms of the correlation of the error term in successive time periods (covariance between values in 1999 and 2000) rather than between the distant time periods. The implications for estimation and inference are the same. When an error term in time period t (ϵ_t) is correlated with the error term in time period (ϵ_{t-1}), we call it a **first-order autocorrelation**. A positive relationship between ϵ_t and ϵ_{t-1} is called a **positive autocorrelation** and a negative relationship between ϵ_t and ϵ_{t-1} is called a **negative autocorrelation**.

Graphically, negative autocorrelation implies that the sign of each successive error term is different (i.e., a movement of the successive error terms in opposite directions: positive followed by the negative and vice versa). Chart 14-9b shows this pattern.

Positive autocorrelation is shown by movement of the successive error terms in the same direction (a kind of cyclical pattern along most up or down phases involving two or more observations). See Chart 14-9c.

CHART 14-9: Autocorrelations

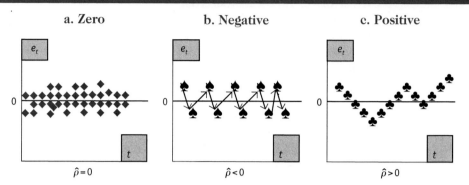

Statistically, a simple test statistic d, designed by Durbin and Watson, can be used, in a majority of circumstances, to find the presence or absence of autocorrelation (ρ). In the context of a first order autocorrelation, the d statistic is defined as

$$d = \sum_{t=2}^{t=n} (e_t - e_{t-1})^2 \bigg/ \sum_{t=1}^{t=n} e_t^2 \qquad \text{14-39}$$

$$d \cong 2(1 - \hat{\rho}) \text{ or } \hat{\rho} \cong 1 - (\tfrac{1}{2}d) \qquad \text{14-40}$$

When $\rho = 0$, the value of d is approximately equal to 2. Since $d = 2(1 - \hat{\rho})$, we can test a null hypothesis of $\rho = 0$ against either a one-sided alternative hypothesis (e.g. $\rho > 0$) or a two-sided alternative hypothesis, $\rho \neq 0$. Durbin and Watson have calculated lower and upper limits of the d statistic for various values of the number of observations in a sample (n) and for various values of the number of independent variables (k) for a set of levels of significance. The values for the 5 percent level of significance are given in table form opposite. Minitab and Excel (MegaStat) print out calculated values of d (as a part of the regression output if you put a check mark for Durbin–Watson in the Options Screen). Given the calculated value of d from the sample and the critical values of d_U and d_L from the Durbin–Watson table, the decision is made according to Chart 14-10.

For example, if you wish to test

H_0: $\rho = 0$ and H_1: $\rho > 0$ and $n = 25$, $k = 3$ and calculated value of $d = 0.95$

From the table, values of $d_U = 1.65$ and $d_L = 1.12$. Decisions are made as follows:

Reject H_0, if $d < d_L$. Do not reject H_0, if $d > d_U$. The test is inconclusive if $d_L \leq d \leq d_U$. Since the calculated value of $d = 0.95$; this implies $d < d_L$. We therefore reject H_0. This indicates a significant (at 5 percent level) positive autocorrelation.

CHART 14-10: Durbin–Watson Test of Autocorrelation

Positive Auto Correlation $\rho > 0$	Incon- clusive Zone	Do not Reject H_0 $\rho > 0$	Incon- clusive Zone	Negative correlation $\rho > 0$

| 0 | d_L | d_U | 2 | $4 - d_U$ | $4 - d_L$ | 4 |

TABLE 14-6: Durbin–Watson d Statistic: Significance points of d_L and d_U at 0.05 level of significance

n	k=1 d_L	d_U	k=2 d_L	d_U	k=3 d_L	d_U	k=4 d_L	d_U	k=5 d_L	d_U	k=6 d_L	d_U	k=7 d_L	d_U	k=8 d_L	d_U
6	0.610	1.400	–	–	–	–	–	–	–	–	–	–	–	–	–	–
7	0.700	1.356	0.467	1.896	–	–	–	–	–	–	–	–	–	–	–	–
8	0.763	1.332	0.559	1.777	0.368	2.287	–	–	–	–	–	–	–	–	–	–
9	0.824	1.320	0.629	1.699	0.455	2.128	0.296	2.588	–	–	–	–	–	–	–	–
10	0.879	1.320	0.697	1.641	0.525	2.016	0.376	2.414	0.243	2.822	–	–	–	–	–	–
11	0.927	1.324	0.658	1.604	0.595	1.928	0.444	2.283	0.316	2.645	0.203	3.005	–	–	–	–
12	0.971	1.331	0.812	1.579	0.658	1.864	0.512	2.177	0.379	2.506	0.268	2.832	0.171	3.149	–	–
13	1.010	1.340	0.861	1.562	0.715	1.816	0.574	2.094	0.445	2.390	0.328	2.692	0.230	2.985	0.147	3.266
14	1.045	1.350	0.905	1.551	0.767	1.779	0.632	2.030	0.505	2.296	0.389	2.572	0.286	2.848	0.200	3.111
15	1.077	1.361	0.946	1.543	0.814	1.750	0.685	1.977	0.562	2.220	0.447	2.472	0.343	2.727	0.251	2.979
16	1.106	1.371	0.982	1.539	0.857	1.728	0.734	1.935	0.615	2.157	0.502	2.388	0.398	2.624	0.304	2.860
17	1.133	1.381	1.015	1.536	0.897	1.710	0.779	1.900	0.664	2.104	0.554	2.318	0.451	2.537	0.356	2.757
18	1.158	1.391	1.046	1.535	0.933	1.696	0.820	1.872	0.710	2.060	0.603	2.257	0.502	2.461	0.407	2.667
19	1.180	1.401	1.074	1.536	0.967	1.685	0.859	1.848	0.752	2.023	0.649	2.206	0.549	2.396	0.456	2.589
20	1.201	1.411	1.100	1.537	0.998	1.676	0.894	1.828	0.792	1.991	0.692	2.162	0.595	2.339	0.502	2.521
21	1.221	1.420	1.125	1.538	1.026	1.669	0.927	1.812	0.829	1.964	0.732	2.124	0.637	2.290	0.547	2.460
22	1.239	1.429	1.147	1.541	1.053	1.664	0.958	1.797	0.863	1.940	0.769	2.090	0.677	2.246	0.588	2.407
23	1.257	1.437	1.168	1.543	1.078	1.660	0.986	1.785	0.895	1.920	0.804	2.061	0.715	2.208	0.628	2.360
24	1.273	1.446	1.188	1.546	1.101	1.656	1.013	1.775	0.925	1.902	0.837	2.035	0.751	2.174	0.666	2.318
25	1.288	1.454	1.206	1.550	1.123	1.654	1.038	1.767	0.953	1.886	0.868	2.012	0.784	2.144	0.702	2.280
26	1.302	1.461	1.224	1.553	1.143	1.652	1.062	1.759	0.979	1.873	0.897	1.992	0.816	2.117	0.735	2.246
27	1.316	1.469	1.240	1.556	1.162	1.651	1.084	1.753	1.004	1.861	0.925	1.974	0.845	2.093	0.767	2.216
28	1.328	1.476	1.255	1.560	1.181	1.650	1.104	1.747	1.028	1.850	0.951	1.958	0.874	2.071	0.798	2.188
29	1.341	1.483	1.270	1.563	1.198	1.650	1.124	1.743	1.050	1.841	0.975	1.944	0.900	2.052	0.826	2.164
30	1.352	1.489	1.284	1.567	1.214	1.650	1.143	1.739	1.071	1.833	0.998	1.931	0.926	2.034	0.854	2.141
31	1.363	1.496	1.297	1.570	1.229	1.650	1.160	1.735	1.090	1.825	1.020	1.920	0.950	2.018	0.879	2.120
32	1.373	1.502	1.309	1.574	1.244	1.650	1.177	1.732	1.109	1.819	1.041	1.909	0.972	2.004	0.904	2.102
33	1.383	1.508	1.321	1.577	1.258	1.651	1.193	1.730	1.127	1.813	1.061	1.900	0.994	1.991	0.927	2.085
34	1.393	1.514	1.333	1.580	1.271	1.652	1.208	1.728	1.144	1.808	1.080	1.891	1.015	1.979	0.950	2.069
35	1.402	1.519	1.343	1.584	1.283	1.653	1.222	1.726	1.160	1.803	1.097	1.884	1.034	1.967	0.971	2.054
36	1.411	1.525	1.354	1.587	1.295	1.654	1.236	1.724	1.175	1.799	1.114	1.877	1.053	1.957	0.991	2.041
37	1.419	1.530	1.364	1.590	1.307	1.655	1.249	1.723	1.190	1.795	1.131	1.870	1.071	1.948	1.011	2.029
38	1.427	1.535	1.373	1.594	1.318	1.656	1.261	1.722	1.204	1.792	1.146	1.864	1.088	1.939	1.029	2.017
39	1.435	1.540	1.382	1.597	1.328	1.658	1.273	1.722	1.218	1.789	1.161	1.859	1.104	1.932	1.047	2.007
40	1.442	1.544	1.391	1.600	1.338	1.659	1.285	1.721	1.230	1.786	1.175	1.854	1.120	1.924	1.064	1.997
45	1.475	1.566	1.430	1.615	1.383	1.666	1.336	1.720	1.287	1.776	1.238	1.835	1.189	1.895	1.139	1.958
50	1.503	1.585	1.462	1.628	1.421	1.674	1.378	1.721	1.335	1.771	1.291	1.822	1.246	1.875	1.201	1.930
55	1.528	1.601	1.490	1.641	1.452	1.681	1.414	1.724	1.374	1.768	1.334	1.814	1.294	1.861	1.253	1.909
60	1.549	1.616	1.514	1.652	1.480	1.689	1.444	1.727	1.408	1.767	1.372	1.808	1.335	1.850	1.298	1.894
65	1.567	1.629	1.536	1.662	1.503	1.696	1.471	1.731	1.438	1.767	1.404	1.805	1.370	1.843	1.336	1.882
70	1.583	1.641	1.554	1.672	1.525	1.703	1.494	1.735	1.464	1.768	1.433	1.802	1.401	1.837	1.369	1.873
75	1.598	1.652	1.571	1.680	1.543	1.709	1.515	1.739	1.487	1.770	1.458	1.801	1.428	1.834	1.399	1.867
80	1.611	1.662	1.586	1.688	1.560	1.715	1.534	1.743	1.507	1.772	1.480	1.801	1.453	1.831	1.425	1.861
85	1.624	1.671	1.600	1.696	1.575	1.721	1.550	1.747	1.525	1.774	1.500	1.801	1.474	1.829	1.448	1.857
90	1.635	1.679	1.612	1.703	1.589	1.726	1.566	1.751	1.542	1.776	1.518	1.801	1.494	1.827	1.469	1.854
95	1.645	1.687	1.623	1.709	1.602	1.732	1.579	1.755	1.557	1.778	1.535	1.802	1.512	1.827	1.489	1.852
100	1.654	1.694	1.634	1.715	1.613	1.736	1.592	1.758	1.571	1.780	1.550	1.803	1.528	1.826	1.506	1.850
150	1.720	1.746	1.706	1.760	1.693	1.774	1.679	1.788	1.665	1.802	1.651	1.817	1.637	1.832	1.622	1.847
200	1.758	1.778	1.748	1.789	1.738	1.799	1.728	1.810	1.718	1.820	1.707	1.831	1.697	1.841	1.686	1.852

A test for an alternative hypothesis of negative autocorrelation can be conducted by the following:

Reject H_0, if $d > 4 - d_L$. Do not reject H_0, if $d < 4 - d_U$.

The test is inconclusive if $4 - d_U \leq d \leq 4 - d_L$.

One of the disadvantages of the test is its inconclusiveness in certain circumstances. An advantage, however, is that you could use the d statistic for specification errors such as non-linearity and omission of a variable, heteroscedasticity (arising due to omission of some variables), etc. *Remedies* for autocorrelation generally consist of transforming variables by removing autocorrelation, introducing a time trend in the equation as a catch-all term for missing variables that may be systematically decreasing or increasing over time, or running a regression in terms of first differences rather than raw values of the variables. See Section 14A.1 in Chapter 14 Appendix A on the CD-ROM for details.

Example 14-9

For our housing example, the Minitab's Residual Model Diagnostics Chart (Chart 14-11b) indicates positive autocorrelation. You can get all of the charts in Chart 14-11 as a part of regression output. While estimating the regression equation, click on the storage option in the dialogue box, and then put a check mark on Residuals and Fits and run the regression. In the second step, go back to Regression, click on the Residual Plots, and enter RESI1 in the Residuals and FITS1 in the FITS. Minitab will give a Chart similar to Chart 14-11.

You can conduct the statistical test of hypothesis for the calculated value of $d = 1.53$ (Minitab Chart 14-11 in our example as follows).

Suppose, your H_0: $\rho = 0$ and H_1 $\rho > 0$ and the level of significance is 5 percent. For $n = 20$, $k = 4$ the values of d from the table are $d_U = 1.83$ and $d_L = 0.90$. Since the calculated value of $d = 1.53$ falls between d_U and d_L, our test of hypothesis is inconclusive. A test that gives conclusive results is discussed in Section 14A.1 in Chapter 14 Appendix A on the CD-ROM.

MINITAB CHART 14-11: Error Term Diagnostics

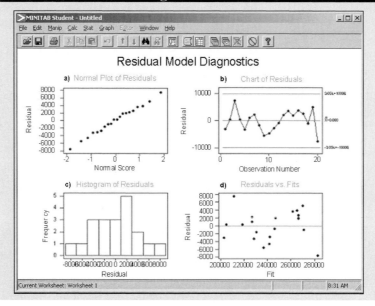

NORMALITY OF THE ERROR TERM

As we have indicated earlier, OLSE of the population regression coefficients are BLUE regardless of the form of the distribution of the error term. Further, unbiasedness of S_e^2, the estimator of σ_ϵ^2, also does not require the assumption of normality. We assume normal distribution of the error term for conducting a test of hypothesis, particularly in the context of small or finite samples. For large samples, we can conduct the tests of hypothesis without imposing the assumption of normal distribution on the error term.

Graphically, we can discover the *non-normality* of the error term by either plotting the residuals against normal scores or by drawing the histogram of residuals. If the error term satisfies the normality assumption, then, in the former case, errors will lie along a straight line, and in the latter case, the shape of the histogram of the error term should resemble the shape of a normal distribution. The Minitab output of Residual Model Diagnostics prints both types of graphs (see Charts 14-11a and 14-11c). There are several statistical tests starting from testing for skewness (= 0) and peakedness (kurtosis = 3) of the distribution of the error term, chi-square test of goodness of fit to mathematically more complicated test statistics. We shall discuss the chi-square test of goodness of fit in the next chapter. A test based on skewness and kurtosis is discussed in Section 14A-1 Chapter 14 Appendix A, as well as, in detail, in the next chapter. Note, both Minitab (under Basic Statistics menu) and MegaStat (under Descriptive Statistics menu) have built-in procedures for testing the normality assumption. The Anderson-Darling procedure of Minitab is popular. MegaStat uses the chi-square test. In general, a p-value of less than 0.05 is used to indicate violation of the normality assumpiton.

Example 14-10

Chart 14-11a displays the distribution of the estimated errors on a normal probability graph and 14-11c displays it as a histogram chart in the housing example. The distribution of the errors in Chart 14-11a seems quite close to a straight line, indicating a close agreement of the estimated errors with a normal distribution. In the histogram (Chart 14-11c), non-normality of the error term seems to be somewhat more pronounced. In particular, we see the distribution is moderately skewed to the left. However, the departure of the error distribution from normality does not seem to be too serious, thus giving us a sense of confidence in the validity of our tests of hypotheses.

THE CONCLUDING REPORT II

In general, given a theoretical relationship between variables, or a relationship between variables based on practical experience where theoretical foundations are not strong, statisticians evaluate adequacy of a model based on a sufficiently high value of the coefficient of determination, an agreement between the signs of the estimated regression coefficients and their expected signs, significant t ratios of the regression coefficients, and a satisfactory distribution of the error term.

You now present the results of your diagnostic checks to the Real Estate Board. While the Board notes that the results of your investigation are not perfect, 9 out of 10 members of the Board are pleased with your work. The voting pattern probably shows the level of perfection of your investigation. The next day, you receive an offer with a handsome salary to work as a statistical adviser to the Board! Would you take the offer? In this chapter, we have taken you step by step as to how one should carry out a statistical investigation involving multiple regression analysis. We hope, if you continued your work in this manner and presented a written report to your supervisors involving all elements discussed in the chapter, you will soon become an expert in this type of investigation. In general, your final report should include the following elements:

WRITING A RESEARCH REPORT

(a) The *Research Agenda* including a statement of the real-world problem/phenomenon that you wish to investigate.

(b) *Model assumptions*: The theory to be used or *a priori* expectations about all variables to be included in the model including the sign of each parameter—behaviour of the dependent variable in response to changes in each of the independent variables, and a justification for your assumptions about the functional form.

(c) *Description of data* on each variable.

(d) A discussion of the *results of estimation*.

(e) *Tests of hypothesis* for each of the regression coefficients and the entire regression.

(f) *Diagnostic Checking*.

(g) *Concluding Remarks* including limitations of the study, if any.

SOME CAVEATS

- **Different types of Correlations:** We have used a number of concepts of correlation coefficients in this and the previous chapter. It is extremely important to remember the differences in their meanings. We have summarized these differences in the chapter outline given below.
- **Interpreting the values of the estimates of the regression coefficients:** The intercept in the regression equation, in general, does not yield any meaningful interpretation. It is a catch-all for an average response of the dependent variable to all minor variables left out from the regression. Units in which variables are measured are extremely important in interpreting the values of the regression coefficient. You must not compare the values of the regression coefficients of variables expressed in different units.
- **Causality and Regression:** Estimated values from a regression equation cannot be used to establish causation between variables. A causal relationship between variables is based on theoretical foundations. Alternatively, in the absence of solid theoretical foundations, you may define causality between variables based on informed guesses, or *a priori* expectations. Further, we assume these causal relations in the population values of the variables. The values of parameters estimated from a sample are only *one* piece of evidence in favour of or against the assumed relationships. It is not the end of the story. Another sample might give very different information about the relationship. In general, we only corroborate or refute a theory or prior expectations if we can consistently do so in the context of a large number of samples, or our sample is close to the population. If a particular theory or prior expectations is refuted in this manner, the theory or prior expectations needs revising and the empirical investigation should again be carried out based on the revised theory or prior expectations.
- **Data Mining:** We must avoid the temptation of trying to get a high value of the coefficient of determination and significant *t* ratios by including or excluding certain variables or massaging the data to yield the desired results. The variables and the associated data must be consistent with theory or prior expectations. Our inferences are valid only for the assumed relationships in the population, and not for the changes in the relationships based on statistical findings.
- **Further References:** While at work, you may need to clarify or better understand some of the issues covered in this chapter. In fact, this chapter covers many of the issues, in a simplified manner, in what is now a full-blown discipline called

econometrics. Any of the following textbooks that cover the subject in a relatively non-mathematical manner will be useful.

Gujarati, Damodar N., *Basic Econometrics*, McGraw-Hill, Inc., Fourth Edition, 2003.

Kmenta, Jan, *Elements of Econometrics*, Second Edition, Macmillan Pub. Co. 1986.

Ramanathan, Ramu, *Introductory Econometrics*, Fourth Edition, Dryden, 1998.

Wooldridge, Jeffrey, *Introductory Econometrics: A Modern Approach*, South-Western Pub., 2000.

■ SELF-REVIEW 14-3

We continue with our Self-Review 14-2 on investment demand in Canada.
(a) Do you see any problems with the specifications of the regression model?
(b) Does the estimated model reveal multicollinearity?
(c) Is the error term autocorrelated? Heteroscedastic?
(d) Check for the normality assumption of the error term.
(e) How serious are the consequences of the above violations, if any, for estimates of the regression coefficients and for inferences?
(f) Write a brief report on this investigation, including your findings from all three Self-Reviews.

■ CHAPTER OUTLINE

I. Multiple regression analysis plays three major roles in understanding the behaviour of a variable. *First*, in the presence of multiple forces affecting a dependent variable, it enables us to better understand the effect of a given independent variable on the dependent variable of interest. *Second*, it enables us to separate out, to a large extent, the simultaneous influence of several independent variables without conducting a controlled experiment. *Third*, it enables us to study the influence of multiple forces (independent variables) on a variable of interest (dependent variable).

II. An omission of a relevant variable can result in very serious problems in terms of both accuracy and precision of the estimates. One should therefore make every effort to include all variables that are based on sound theoretical grounds. However, if we are unsure of a sufficient theoretical justification for a variable, the penalty for including an irrelevant variable is much less serious as compared to the penalty for excluding a relevant variable.

III. The general classical linear regression model is written as:

$$y = \alpha + \beta_1 x_1 + \beta_2 x_2 + \beta_3 x_3 + \beta_4 x_4 + \cdots + \beta_k x_k + \epsilon \qquad \textbf{14-12}$$

where, the dependent variable Y is linearly related with k independent variables X's; α is the intercept term; β's are the partial or net regression coefficients (the effect of one independent variable on the dependent variable, holding all other independent variables constant); and ϵ is the random error term.

The classical linear regression model is based on a set of assumptions, given towards the end of this outline. If a regression model satisfies the assumptions, the Gauss–Markov Theorem states that the OLSE are BLUE.

IV. In a two-independent-variable model,

$$y = \alpha + \beta_1 x_1 + \beta_2 x_2 + \epsilon$$

α, β_1 and β_2 can be estimated by a, b_1 and b_2 through the OLS technique.

Writing $y' = (y - \bar{y})$, $x'_1 = (x_1 - \bar{x}_1)$, $x'_2 = (x_2 - \bar{x}_2)$ **14-23**

$$a = \bar{y} - b_1 \bar{x}_1 - b_2 \bar{x}_2$$ **14-24**

$$b_1 = \frac{(\sum x'_1 y')(\sum x'^2_2) - (\sum x'_2 y')(\sum x'_1 x'_2)}{(\sum x'^2_1)(\sum x'^2_2) - (\sum x'_1 x'_2)^2}$$ **14-25**

$$b_2 = \frac{(\sum x'_2 y')(\sum x'^2_1) - (\sum x'_1 y')(\sum x'_1 x'_2)}{(\sum x'^2_1)(\sum x'^2_2) - (\sum x'_1 x'_2)^2}$$ **14-26**

V. Correlations

The word *correlation* appears in many places in the previous chapter as well as this chapter. However, all uses of the word *correlation* do not have the same conceptual meaning.

Coefficient of correlation between two random variables having a bi-variate probability distribution in the population (as defined in Chapter 13, Section 13.1) is conceptually different from the concept of coefficient of correlation between two or more variables where *at least* one of the variables is non-random. An estimate of the former concept enables us to draw *inferences* about a linear relationship in the population, whereas a computed value of the latter concept merely *describes* the degree of linear relationship in a *sample* of observations.

Partial correlation coefficient is a descriptive measure of linear relationship between the dependent variable and an independent variable, holding the remaining independent variables in the model constant. A detailed discussion of this concept is provided in Section 14A.3 of Chapter 14 Appendix A on the accompanying CD-ROM.

Coefficient of Determination (R^2) in multiple regression analysis (see Equation 14-11) is defined as the ratio of the explained variation to the unexplained variation. The square root of R^2 is called the coefficient of multiple correlation. However, $\sqrt{R^2}$ does not have a useful meaning.

Adjusted Coefficient of Determination ($\bar{R}^2$) is the coefficient of determination (R^2) adjusted for loss in the degrees of freedom.

Coefficient of Determination (R^2_j) is the coefficient of determination in the regression (called an *auxiliary* or a *secondary* regression) of one of the independent variables (say the jth variable) on all other independent variables in a multiple regression model. Although R^2_j is interpreted similarly to R^2, conceptually they are very different.

VI. The reasoning behind, and the format of, the analysis of variance in multiple regression analyses resembles that of the two-variable regression analysis, discussed in Chapter 13.

We therefore have

$$\sum(y - \bar{y})^2 = \sum(y - \hat{y})^2 + \sum(\hat{y} - \bar{y})^2 \qquad \text{14-28}$$

$$\text{SS Total} = \text{SSE} + \text{SSR} \qquad \text{14-28}$$

$$\text{Coefficient of Determination: } R^2 = \frac{\text{SSR}}{\text{SS Total}} = 1 - \frac{\text{SSE}}{\text{SS Total}} \qquad \text{14-29}$$

$$\text{Adjusted } R^2 = \bar{R}^2 = 1 - \frac{\text{SSE}/(n-k-1)}{\text{SS Total}/(n-1)} \qquad \text{14-31}$$

$$\text{The Standard Error of Estimate: } S_e = \sqrt{\frac{\text{SSE}}{(n-k-1)}} \qquad \text{14-33}$$

VII. The test of hypothesis for the regression model is conducted by

$H_0: \beta_1 = \beta_2 = \beta_3 = \cdots = \beta_k = 0$ and
$H_1:$ At least one of $\beta_1, \beta_2, \beta_3, \ldots, \beta_k \neq 0$

The test statistic is given by the ratio: $F = \dfrac{\text{MSR}}{\text{MSE}} = \dfrac{\text{SSR}/k}{\text{SSE}/(n-k-1)}$ **14-35a**

Alternatively, it can be written in terms of R^2 as $F = \dfrac{R^2/k}{(1-R^2)/(n-k-1)}$ **14-35b**

VIII. The test of hypothesis for each regression coefficient β_j is conducted by $\dfrac{b_j - \beta_j}{S_{b_j}}$,

which is distributed as the t distribution with $(n-k-1)$ degrees of freedom.

IX. Qualitative variables, by their very nature, list attributes of a variable in a number of categories. If a qualitative variable has m categories, then we choose one category as a base category and use $m-1$ dummy variables for the remaining $m-1$ categories.

X. Regression Diagnostics: Checking the Model Assumptions
  A. There is a linear relationship between the dependent variable and all independent variables. In general, violation of this assumption will yield biased and inconsistent estimators, and invalid inferences.
  B. Unusually small or large values (farther away from their mean values by about two or more times their standard deviations) of the dependent and/or independent variables are, in general, called *outliers*. Some outliers can be influential in twisting the estimated regression line in their favour. Estimators are still BLUE.
  C. The model includes all relevant variables, i.e., the model is correctly specified. In general, violation of this assumption will yield biased and inconsistent estimators, and invalid inferences.
  D. All independent variables are non-random, or distributed independently of the error term. In general, violation of this assumption will yield biased and inconsistent estimators, and invalid inferences. Often, this assumption is violated due to misspecification of variables and/or functional form.
  E. None of the independent variables is an exact linear function of other independent variables. This is known as absence of perfect multicollinearity.

Violation of this assumption would give indeterminate values of the regression coefficients and infinitely large values of the variances of the coefficients. Estimators are still BLUE.

F. The mean of the error term in the population is zero. Violation of this assumption, in general, will lead to biased and inconsistent estimators. Often, this assumption is violated due to misspecification of variables and/or functional form.

G. The variance of the error term for each set of values of the independent variables is the same. This is known as the assumption of homoscedasticity of the error term. Violation of this assumption will lead to inefficient estimators of the regression coefficients and invalid tests of hypotheses.

H. The values of the error in different observations are independent. This is known as the assumption of absence of autocorrelation. Violation of this assumption will lead to inefficient estimators of the regression coefficients and invalid tests of hypotheses.

I. The error term is normally distributed. This assumption is required for conducting tests of hypotheses. Violation of this assumption will lead to invalid inferences in small samples. OLSE are still BLUE.

Furthermore, in the text we discuss simple diagnostic tests and remedies when an assumption is violated. Diagnostic tests and remedies of an advanced nature are discussed in the appendix to this chapter found on the student CD-ROM accompanying this text.

EXERCISES 14-9 TO 14-15

14-9. Tim LeBlanc estimated the rate of return on investment as the dependent variable for a number of Canadian corporations. The multiple regression equation yields the following partial results.

Source	Sum of Squares	df
Regression	750	4
Error	500	35

(a) What is the total sample size?
(b) How many independent variables are being considered?
(c) Compute the coefficient of determination.
(d) Compute the standard error of estimate.
(e) Test the hypothesis that none of the regression coefficients is equal to zero. Let $\alpha = 0.05$.

14-10. Natasha Durling, a student at Memorial University, estimated a regression equation between the consumption of oranges (dependent variable: Y), and Income (X_1) and Price (X_2) as the independent variables, based on a sample of information on 25 residents in St. John's, NF. The regression coefficients and the standard error are as follows:

$$b_1 = 2.676 \quad s_{b_1} = 0.56$$
$$b_2 = -0.880 \quad s_{b_2} = 0.71$$

Conduct a test of hypothesis to determine whether either independent variable has a coefficient equal to zero. Would you consider deleting either variable from the regression equation? Use the 0.05 significance level.

14-11. Willy Veld, a student at the University of Calgary, estimated a regression equation between the dependent variable profits at a number of local restaurants, and the independent variables—number of parking spaces (X_1), number of hours the restaurant is open (X_2), number of waiters employed (X_3), distance from the centre of town (X_4), and availability of lunch buffets $(X_5 = 1$ for yes). The results are given below:

The following output was obtained

Predictor	Coef	StDev	t ratio
Constant	3.00	1.5	2.00
X_1	4.00	3.00	1.33
X_2	3.00	0.20	15.00
X_3	0.20	0.05	4.00
X_4	−2.50	1.00	−2.50
X_5	3.00	4.00	0.75

Analysis of variance

Source	df	SS	MS
Regression	5	100	20
Error	20	40	2
Total	25	140	

(a) What is the sample size?
(b) Compute the value of R^2.
(c) Compute the multiple standard error of estimate.
(d) Conduct a global test of hypothesis to determine whether any of the regression coefficients are significant. Use the 0.05 significance level.
(e) Test the regression coefficients individually. Would you consider omitting any variable(s)? If so, which one(s)? Use the 0.05 significance level.

14-12. Suman Chawla, the regional manager of Pizza Hut in Atlantic Canada, is investigating why certain stores in her region are performing better than others. She believes that three factors are related to total sales: the number of competitors in the region, the population in the surrounding area, and the amount spent on advertising. From her district, consisting of several hundred stores, she selects a random sample of 30 stores. For each store she gathered the following information.

Y = total sales last year (in $ thousands)
X_1 = number of competitors in the region
X_2 = population of the region (in millions)
X_3 = advertising expense (in $ thousands)

The sample data were run on Minitab software with the following results.

Predictor	Coef	StDev	t ratio
Constant	14.00	7.00	2.00
X_1	−1.00	0.70	−1.43
X_2	30.00	5.20	5.77
X_3	0.20	0.08	2.50

Analysis of variance

Source	df	SS	MS
Regression	3	3050.00	762.50
Error	26	2200.00	84.62
Total	29	5250.00	

(a) What are the estimated sales for the Pizza Hut that has 4 competitors, a regional population of 0.4 (400 000), and an advertising expense of 30 ($30 000)?

(b) Compute the R^2 value.

(c) Compute the standard error of estimate.

(d) Conduct a global test of hypotheses to determine whether any of the regression coefficients are not equal to zero. Use the 0.05 level of significance.

(e) Conduct tests of hypotheses to determine which of the independent variables have significant regression coefficients. Which variables would you consider eliminating? Use the 0.05 significance level.

14-13. Tina Kabir, an undergraduate student working on a summer job with the automobile association in Prince Edward Island (PEI), collected the following data on used truck (half-ton pick-up) prices: *Price* (in dollars), *Age* (in years), *Km* (kilometres driven), and whether the truck is classified as a *King Cab* (additional seating capacity, yes = 1). She maintained the hypothesis that truck prices are normally distributed and linearly related to Age and/or Km (not sure!), and King Cab, with expected signs of regression coefficients for Age as negative, for Km as negative, and for King Cab as positive. Based on a sample of 26 observations she ran three regressions. The Minitab printouts for these regressions as well as the charts for Regression #2 are given on page 650. The data set is given in file Exercise 14-13.xls on the CD-ROM accompanying the text.

Answer the following questions:
(a) Compare all regressions and answer the following:
   (i)   What are the major differences in these regressions? Your answer should include a comparison of the role played by each independent variable and adjusted R^2 in explaining the variation in the dependent variable.
   (ii) Examine Regression #1. Are the signs of the regression coefficients consistent with the expected signs? Is there any reason to suspect a high degree of multicollinearity? (Hint: Check, R^2, t ratios, VIFs and simple correlation coefficients). Which variables seem multicollinear and why? If some variables are multicollinear, which variables should be dropped and why?
   (iii) The researcher chose Regression #2 as the final estimate of the population regression line. Is she justified in her choice? Explain.

(b) Focus on Regression #2 and answer the following:
   (i)   Interpret adjusted R^2 and the values of each of the regression coefficients.
   (ii) Conduct a test of hypothesis for the entire model and for each of the regression coefficients at the 1 percent level of significance. Remember to use the appropriate one-sided or two-sided alternative hypothesis.

(c) Examine the charts (note, these are based on Regression #2) and the d statistic and answer the following:
   (i)   Examine Chart 5. Does the linear regression seem appropriate? Are there any outliers?
   (ii) Examine Chart 4. Is there any evidence of heteroscedasticity?
   (iii) Examine Chart 2 and d statistic. Is there any evidence of autocorrelation?
   (iv) Examine Charts 1 and 3. Is there any evidence that the error term is not normal?
   (v)   From all the charts (1 to 5), can you say anything about the specification bias due to omission of a relevant variable from the model?

(d) Write a brief report on this regression analysis, including what you have learned from this exercise.

Regression Analysis (1): Trucks in PEI

The regression equation is

$$\text{Price} = 19\,116 - 1651\,\text{Age} + 0.00173\,\text{Km} + 3784\,\text{King Cab}$$

Predictor	Coef	StDev	T	P	VIF
Constant	19116	1017	18.80	0.000	
Age	−1651.0	305.7	−5.40	0.000	3.2
Km	0.001727	0.009244	0.19	0.853	2.8
King Cab	3783.6	698.2	5.42	0.000	1.2

$S = 1533$ $R\text{-Sq} = 88.5\%$ $R\text{-Sq(adj)} = 86.9\%$

Analysis of Variance

Source	df	SS	MS	F	P
Regression	3	397 347 255	132 449 085	56.33	0.000
Residual Error	22	51 731 070	2 351 412		
Total	25	449 078 325			

No replicates. Cannot do pure error test.

No evidence of lack of fit ($P > 0.1$)

Durbin–Watson statistic = 2.59

Correlations (Pearson): Trucks in PEI

	Price	Age	Km
Age	−0.852		
Km	−0.640	0.799	
King Cab	0.709	−0.405	−0.248

Regression Analysis (2): Trucks in PEI

The regression equation is

$$\text{Price} = 19\,107 - 1606\,\text{Age} + 3802\,\text{King Cab}$$

Predictor	Coef	StDev	T	P	VIF
Constant	19 107.4	994.2	19.22	0.000	
Age	−1606.0	184.1	−8.72	0.000	1.2
King Cab	3 801.6	676.8	5.62	0.000	1.2

$S = 1501 \qquad R\text{-Sq} = 88.5\% \qquad R\text{-Sq(adj)} = 87.5\%$

Analysis of Variance

Source	df	SS	MS	F	P
Regression	2	397 265 148	198 632 574	88.17	0.000
Residual Error	23	51 813 176	2 252 747		
Lack of Fit	8	31 590 268	3 948 783	2.93	0.035
Pure Error	15	20 222 908	1 348 194		
Total	25	449 078 325			

Durbin–Watson statistic = 2.55

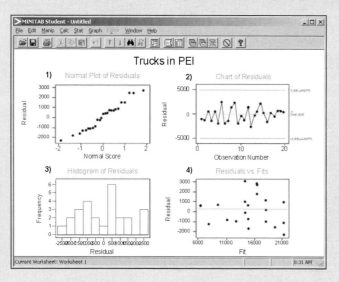

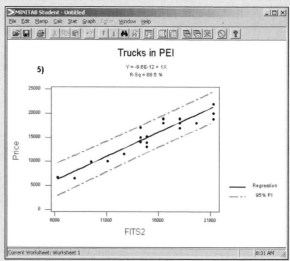

Regression Analysis (3): Trucks in PEI

The regression equation is

$$\text{Price} = 15\,999 - 0.0376\,\text{Km} + 5125\,\text{King Cab}$$

Predictor	Coef	StDev	T	P	VIF
Constant	15 999	1249	12.81	0.000	
Km	−0.037630	0.008484	−4.44	0.000	1.1
King Cab	5 125.1	973.2	5.27	0.000	1.1

$S = 2287 \qquad R\text{-Sq} = 73.2\% \qquad R\text{-Sq(adj)} = 70.9\%$

Analysis of Variance

Source	df	SS	MS	F	P
Regression	2	328 749 571	164 374 786	31.42	0.000
Residual Error	23	120 328 754	5 231 685		
Lack of Fit	22	102 328 754	4 651 307	0.26	0.938
Pure Error	1	18 000 000	18 000 000		
Total	25	449 078 325			

Durbin–Watson statistic = 2.02

14-14. Angela Chou has just finished her undergraduate studies from McGill University. She landed her first job at the Centre for Living Standards in Ottawa. The Centre asked her to investigate the determinants of poverty in Ontario communities. She collected data on 60 communities from surveys of communities conducted by Statistics Canada (Community Profiles: Statistics Canada). She selected the percentage of poor persons living under the poverty line [*Poor (%)*], measured by Low Income Cut-Off, designed by Statistics Canada as a measure of poverty for a community, as the dependent variable. The independent variables selected are percent of single families in each community [*Single Families (%), unemployment rate (%)*], percent of population in the community holding a bachelor's degree as their highest level of education attained [*Bachelor's degree (%)*], and percent of population holding a High School Diploma as their highest level of education attained [*High School (%)*]. She ran two regressions and chose the second regression as her final choice. Refer to the data set in file Exercise14-14.xls on the CD-ROM.

Answer all questions outlined in Exercise 14-13.

Regression Analysis (1): Poverty in Ontario

The regression equation is

$$Poor\ (\%) = -3.81 + 0.798\ Single\text{-}Families\ (\%)$$
$$+ 0.624\ Unemployment\ Rate\ (\%)$$
$$- 0.170\ Bachelor's\ Degree\ (\%) - 0.003\ High\ School\ (\%)$$

Predictor	Coef	StDev	T	P	VIF
Constant	−3.807	3.044	−1.25	0.216	
Single-F	0.79755	0.09503	8.39	0.000	1.5
Unemp. R	0.6241	0.1237	5.05	0.000	1.6
Bach.Deg	−0.17020	0.08463	−2.01	0.049	1.2
High Sch	−0.0034	0.1195	−0.03	0.977	1.1

$S = 2.167$ $R\text{-}Sq = 79.6\%$ $R\text{-}Sq(adj) = 78.1\%$

Analysis of Variance

Source	df	SS	MS	F	P
Regression	4	1009.84	252.46	53.75	0.000
Residual Error	55	258.31	4.70		
Total	59	1268.15			

Durbin–Watson statistic = 2.06

Correlations (Pearson): Poverty in Ontario

	Poor (%)	Single-Fam.	Unemp. Rate	Bach. Deg.
Single-Fam.	0.797			
Unemp. R.	0.730	0.503		
Bach. Deg.	−0.136	0.147	−0.236	
High Sch.	−0.118	−0.164	−0.116	−0.225

Regression Analysis (2): Poverty in Ontario

The regression equation is

$$\text{Poor (\%)} = -3.88 + 0.798 \text{ Single-Fam (\%)} + 0.625 \text{ Unemp. Rate (\%)} - 0.170 \text{ Bach. Degree (\%)}$$

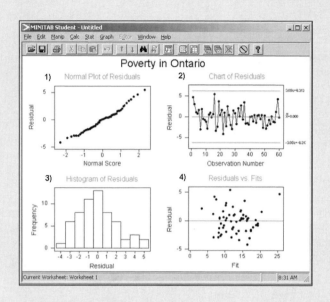

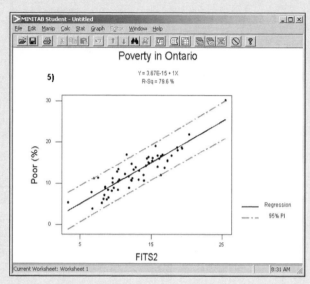

Predictor	Coef	StDev	T	P	VIF
Constant	−3.883	1.502	−2.59	0.012	
Single-F	0.79767	0.09409	8.48	0.000	1.5
Unemp. R	0.6245	0.1216	5.14	0.000	1.5
Bach.Deg	−0.16963	0.08149	−2.08	0.042	1.2

$S = 2.148$ $R\text{-Sq} = 79.6\%$ $R\text{-Sq(adj)} = 78.5\%$

Analysis of Variance

Source	df	SS	MS	F	P
Regression	3	1009.84	336.61	72.97	0.000
Residual Error	56	258.31	4.61		
Total	59	1268.15			

Durbin–Watson statistic = 2.06

14-15. Paul Williams, an undergraduate student at the University of Manitoba, collected data for his research project for Statistics II course from Statistics Canada's Web site on consumption of Beer (*Volume*: in number of litres per adult), Price of Beer (*Price*: in dollars), Personal Disposable Income (*PDI*: income per person after accounting for taxes paid and transfers, such as EI and welfare payments, received). He also speculated some effect of recession years on consumption. He used a dummy variable (*Recession* = 1 for years 1981–1983 and 1991–93). He maintained the hypothesis that the consumption of beer in Manitoba is normally distributed and linearly related to Price, PDI and (possibly) to Recession, with expected signs of regression coefficients for Price as negative, PDI and Recession as positive. Based on a sample of 19 observations, he ran two regressions. The Minitab printouts for these regressions as well as the charts for Regression #2 are given below. The data set is available in file Exercise 14-15.xls on the CD-ROM accompanying the text. Answer all questions outlined in Exercise 14-13.

Regression Analysis (1): Beer in Manitoba

The regression equation is

$$\text{Volume} = -19.8 + 0.00944\ \text{PDI} - 42.6\ \text{Price} + 0.55\ \text{Recession}$$

Predictor	Coef	StDev	T	P	VIF
Constant	−19.75	67.20	−0.29	0.773	
PDI	0.009442	0.003338	2.83	0.013	1.5
Price	−42.560	8.595	−4.95	0.000	1.4
Recession	0.551	4.079	0.14	0.894	1.4

$S = 7.095$ $R\text{-Sq} = 63.8\%$ $R\text{-Sq(adj)} = 56.5\%$

Analysis of Variance

Source	df	SS	MS	F	P
Regression	3	1328.42	442.81	8.80	0.001
Residual Error	15	755.18	50.35		
Total	18	2083.61			

Durbin–Watson statistic = 0.98

Correlations (Pearson): Beer in Manitoba

	Volume	PDI	Price
PDI	0.082		
Price	−0.652	0.491	
Recession	0.134	−0.474	−0.402

Regression Analysis (2): Beer in Manitoba

The regression equation is

$$\text{Volume} = -15.7 + 0.00929\ \text{PDI} - 42.8\ \text{Price}$$

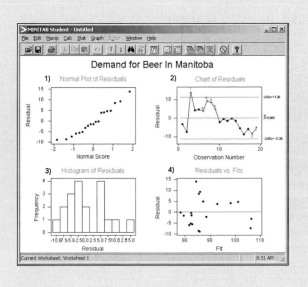

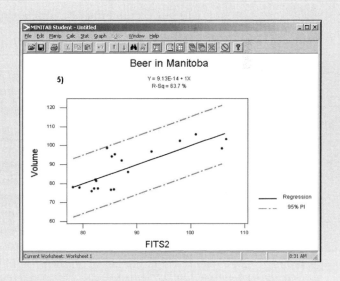

Predictor	Coef	StDev	T	P	VIF
Constant	−15.67	58.15	−0.27	0.791	
PDI	0.009285	0.003032	3.06	0.007	1.3
Price	−42.816	8.122	−5.27	0.000	1.3

$S = 6.874$ $R\text{-Sq} = 63.7\%$ $R\text{-Sq(adj)} = 59.2\%$

Analysis of Variance

Source	df	SS	MS	F	P
Regression	2	1327.51	663.75	14.05	0.000
Residual Error	16	756.10	47.26		
Total	18	2083.61			

Durbin–Watson statistic = 0.97

COMPUTER DATA EXERCISES 14-16 TO 14-27

Note, these exercises in general would require use of a software package such as Excel/MegaStat or Minitab for computations. Data sets for these exercises are available on the CD-ROM.

Use the following questions as a guide for all the remaining exercises (Exercises 14-16 to 14-30):

1. Estimate the multiple linear regression equation. Interpret the values of the regression coefficients of the estimated equation.
2. Set up an ANOVA table for the problem.
3. Interpret the standard error of the estimate.
4. Interpret the values of the coefficient of determination and the adjusted coefficient of determination. Explain why they are different.
5. Conduct a test of hypothesis for the entire model (at the 5 percent level of significance).
6. Conduct a test of hypothesis for each regression coefficient (at the 5 percent level of significance).
7. Do you see any problems with specification of the regression model?
8. Examine your data for outliers.
9. Does the estimated model reveal multicollinearity?
10. Is the error term autocorrelated?
11. Is the error term heteroscedastic?
12. Check for the normality assumption of the error term.
13. Does the model violate any of the assumptions? How serious are the consequences of the above violations, if any, for estimation and inference?
14. Use appropriate remedies for each of the violations in Question 13 above. Re-estimate the most appropriate model and write a brief report on your findings. *This question is optional. Consult your instructor for guidance.*

14-16. The administrator of a new paralegal program at Seagate Vocational College wants to estimate the grade point average in the new program. He thought that the high school GPA (HS-GPA), the verbal score (SAT-Vb) on the Scholastic Aptitude Test (SAT) and the mathematics score (SAT-Math) on the SAT would be good predictors of paralegal GPA (PL-GPA). The data on 18 students can be found in file Exercise 14-16.xls on the CD-ROM.

14-17. The Real Estate Board of Regina is interested in understanding determinants of price of housing in Regina. The Board hires you during the summer to help them conduct this study. Suppose you collect data on a random sample of 20 houses (advertised for sale) in Regina to study determinants of prices. Further, your collected data consists of the selling price for each house (*Price*: the dependent variable, in dollars) and some characteristics of those houses. The housing characteristics (the independent variables) for which data has been obtained, are size of the lot (*Lot*: in square feet), number of bedrooms (*Bedroom*), age of the house (*Age*: in years), square footage of built area (*Footage*: in square feet), *Garage* (= 1, if a house has a Garage) and *location* of the house (three locations *A*1, *A*2 and *A*3). The data set is given in file Exercise 14-17.xls on the CD-ROM accompanying this text. Hint: use one of the locations as the control group.

Conduct a multiple regression analysis and answer the questions outlined at the beginning of the Computer Data Exercises.

14-18. The General Manager of Toyota Limited is interested in understanding the determinants of Canadian demand for Japanese cars. The Toyota Research Department has hired you to conduct the study. Data are available in file Exercise 14-18.xls on the CD-ROM (for 1980–99) on the number of cars imported from Japan (*CARS*: in numbers), Canadian personal disposable income per head (*PDI*: adjusted for inflation), price of Japanese cars (*PR-JP*: in Canadian Dollars), price of competing North American cars (*PR-NA*: in Canadian Dollars), price of gas (*GAS*: in Canadian cents per litre) and Canadian population (*POP*: in thousands).

Conduct a multiple regression analysis and answer the questions outlined at the beginning of the Computer Data Exercises.

14-19. Mr. Steve Douglas has been hired as a management trainee by a large brokerage firm. As his first project, he is asked to study the gross profit of firms in the chemical industry. What factors affect profitability in that industry? Steve selects a random sample of 16 firms and obtains data on the number of employees, number of consecutive common stock dividends paid, total value of inventory at the start of the current year and gross profit for each firm. His findings are available in file Exercise 14-19.xls on the CD-ROM.

Conduct a multiple regression analysis and answer the questions outlined at the beginning of the Computer Data Exercises.

14-20. The Canadian Softwood Lumber Association is interested in understanding the determinants of Canadian exports of softwood lumber to the United States in an attempt to find ways to increase their sales to the US. You have been requested to help the Association in this task. From your education and/or experience you understand that the American demand for Canadian softwood lumber, in general, should depend on the construction activity in the US, mortgage rates (the lower the mortgage rate, the higher the demand for housing, which in turn increases the demand for softwood lumber), and income of Americans (higher income leads to higher demand for housing, which in turn leads to higher demand for softwood lumber). Since it is the real value of the variables that matters, adjust all variables for inflation rates. You have collected the data for your study from Statistics Canada and US government Web sites for the period 1970–1999. (See the data set in file Exercise 14-20.xls on the CD-ROM.)

Lumber: Canadian Softwood Lumber Exports to US (in US dollars, adjusted for inflation), *Housing*: Construction of new housing units in the US (in thousands), *Interest*: US discount rate, adjusted for US inflation, *GDP Real*: Gross Domestic Product of US (billions of US dollars, adjusted for US inflation).

Conduct a multiple regression analysis and answer the questions outlined at the beginning of the Computer Data Exercises.

14-21. A mortgage department of a large bank is studying its recent loans. Of particular interest is how such factors as the value of the home (in thousands of dollars), education level of the head of the household, age of the head of the household, current monthly mortgage payment (in dollars) and sex of the head of the household (male = 1, female = 0) relate to the family income. Are these variables effective predictors of the income of the household? A random sample of 25 percent is obtained. (See the data set in file Exercise 14-21.xls on the CD-ROM accompanying the text.)

Conduct a multiple regression analysis and answer the questions outlined at the beginning of the Computer Data Exercises.

14-22. Alberta Business Association is interested in understanding the determinants of profit of Canadian corporations. The Association has hired you to conduct the study. They have provided you with data on 22 of the top 1000 Canadian corporations (available in file Exercise 14-22.xls on the CD-ROM). The data consists of *Profits* (in $000), *Revenue* (in $000), Market capitalization (*Market Cap*: a measure of the size of the corporation, in $ million), Return on Capital (*Return*: in %) and the number of employees (*Employees*, number) for each corporation.

Conduct a multiple regression analysis and answer the questions outlined at the beginning of the Computer Data Exercises.

14-23. Mr. Fred G. Hire is the manager of human resources at St. Luke's Medical Centre. As part of his yearly report to the president of the medical centre, he is required to present an analysis of the salaried employees. Because there are over 1000 employees, he does not have the staff to gather information on each salaried employee, so he selects a random sample of 30. For each employee, he records monthly salary; service at St. Luke's in months; sex (1 = male, 0 = female); and whether the employee has a technical or clerical job. Those working in technical jobs are coded 1, and those who are in clerical jobs, 0. (See the data set in file Exercise 14-23.xls on the CD-ROM.)

Conduct a multiple regression analysis and answer the questions outlined at the beginning of the Computer Data Exercises.

14-24. Many areas in Southern Ontario have experienced rapid population growth over the last 10 years. It is expected that the growth will continue over the next 10 years. This has resulted in many of the large grocery store chains building many new stores in the region. The Super Grocery Stores chain is no exception. The director of planning for Super Stores wants to study adding more stores in this region. He believes there are several factors that indicate the amount families spend on groceries. The first is their income and the other is the number of people in the family. The director gathered information on 25 households; the data can be found in file Exercise 14-24.xls on the CD-ROM. Food and income are reported in thousands of dollars, and the variable size refers to the number of people in the household.

Conduct a multiple regression analysis and answer the questions outlined at the beginning of the Computer Data Exercises.

14-25. Refer to the file Youth Unemployment in Canada.xls on the CD-ROM. This data includes 100 quarterly observations on the unemployment rate (%) experienced by the Canadian youth (age group: 15–24), an average of the minimum wage rates for each province in Canada (adjusted for inflation) and total unemployment rate. Conduct a detailed investigation of the determinants of quarterly youth unemployment in Canada. (Hint: Use first quarter as the control group and one dummy variable for each of the remaining quarters). (*Source: Statistics Canada*)

14-26. Refer to the file Real Estate Data.xls on the CD-ROM enclosed with the book. The data set includes information on homes sold in Victoria during the last year. The data consists of selling price of homes, number of bedrooms, number of bathrooms, size of house, whether there is a pool, whether there is an attached garage and distance from the centre of the city. Conduct a detailed investigation of the determinants of the selling price of homes in Victoria.

14-27. Refer to the data in file BASEBALL-2000.xls on the CD-ROM, which reports information on 30 Major League Baseball teams. The data consists of number of games won, team batting average, number of stolen bases, number of errors committed, team ERA and whether the team's home field is natural grass or artificial turf. Conduct a detailed investigation of the determinants of winning a game in baseball.

www.exercises.ca 14-28 TO 14-30

14-28. Homestore (www.homestore.ca) is an online real estate Web site advertising houses listed for sale in selected communities across Canada. Go to the homestore Web site and select a province, a town in the province, and then pick one or more sections of the town. A number of options should appear, if you wish you could narrow your search, then select search. Record values of the dependent variable: selling price, and independent variables: rooms, bathrooms, square footage of built area, lot size, age, basement, and any other important characteristic in the area that you wish to model. Your sample should consist of about 30 observations. Analyze the estimated regression equation and conduct diagnostic checks for outliers, multicollinearity, autocorrelation, heteroscedasticity and normality. Write a brief report on your findings.

14-29. As explained in Exercises 13-50 and 13-51 of Chapter 13, go to the Σ-STAT Web site. In this exercise, we ask you to develop a multiple regression for Canadian Demand for Money (*Money*) based on quarterly observations 1981–onwards (the latest quarterly data available for all variables). Recall Exercise 13-51 of Chapter 13. In that exercise, you estimated the demand for money based on only one independent variable, interest rate (*Interest*)—the cost of holding your assets in money. However, households and businesses also need money for day-to-day transactions and precautionary purposes. Use gross domestic product (*GDP*) at current prices as a measure of transactions and precautionary demand for money. Furthermore, we also need more money as the prices of goods and services increase. There are several price indices. We shall use consumer price index (*CPI*). The series numbers for these variables are as follows: Money (M2): V122530; Interest Rate (Bank Rate): V37128; GDP at current prices: V498918; and CPI: P100000. Download data for 1981 onwards (the latest quarterly data available for all variables). Take quarterly averages for Interest Rate and CPI, and quarterly sum for Money and quarterly data for GDP (note GDP data in this series is already quarterly).

Conduct your regression analysis using money as the dependent variable and Interest, GDP and CPI as the independent variables. Interpret the coefficients. Do they have the right signs? Something has happened. Check the correlation matrix and or VIFs. You will see a very high correlation between CPI and other independent variables. There is a very high degree of multicollinearity. Why is this so? Obviously, if you think carefully, you will find that there is something wrong with our model specification. (Hint: All variables are in nominal terms, implying the effect of CPI already built in them, making CPI an irrelevant variable!). This is one of the common types of errors in model specification. Re-estimate the regression equation without CPI, and see the results. Discuss your estimates, conduct all tests of hypotheses and diagnostic checking. Write a brief report on what you learned from this exercise.

14-30. Go to the Σ-STAT Web site as in Exercise 14-29 above. In this exercise, we ask you to develop a multiple regression equation using consumption of all durable goods (series number: V498920) as the dependent variable, Gross Domestic Product (series number: V498918), Consumer loan rate (series number: V122523), household credit (series number: V36408) and quarterly dummies similar to the Self-Reviews on Investment exercise. Select a sample of quarterly observations for the period from quarter 1, 1981 to the latest quarterly data available for all variables. Download data as in Exercise 14-29 above. Discuss your estimated regression equation and comment on the model diagnostics.

Excel and MegaStat for Multiple Regression Analysis: An Explanation

In the chapter examples we have used Minitab software. Minitab is easy to use and much more versatile. In this section, we use Excel and MegaStat to illustrate the use of these packages in regression analysis for the benefit of students who do not have access to Minitab. In addition to some of the details provided by Excel's Data Analysis, MegaStat also gives a reasonably good analysis of the error term, in particular, a graph of residuals and the computed value of Durbin–Watson statistic, Variance Inflation Factors, etc. that are not available in Excel. We therefore use Excel's Data Analysis for Self-Reviews 14-1 and 14-2, and a combination of Data Analysis and MegaStat for Self-Review 14-3. If you wish, you can use MegaStat for all these Self-Reviews. As explained in the chapter text, all results, and more, can be obtained through Minitab. We give the necessary commands and an explanation of output for Excel and MegaStat below.

Excel

Correlation Matrix: *Tools → Data Analysis → Correlation.* Specify the range for values of the required variables and look for the output in a separate worksheet. This can also be obtained in MegaStat.

  Regression Analysis: *Tools → Data Analysis → Regression.* In the *dialogue box*, specify the input *range for values* for the dependent (Input *Y* Range) and all independent (Input *X* Range) variables. Check Labels (if you include the row of variable names in the range of values) and New Worksheet Ply. Check Residuals, Standardized Residuals, Residual Plots, Line Fit Plots and Normal Probability Plots.

  Values of residuals are useful to examine the error term manually or using the residuals to run a secondary regression. **Values of Standardized Residuals** are useful to examine outliers—values that are larger than (plus/minus) two times the standard deviation. *Residual Plots* (charts residuals versus each independent variable) may be used to examine the source of heteroscedasticity due to an independent variable.

  Line Fit Plots (charts for predicted values and the observed values of the dependent variable versus the values of each independent variable) may be used to examine non-linearity, theoretically not a very sound technique.

  Normal Probability Plots (charts that plot a normal probability) can be used to assess the normality assumption of the error term by examining the closeness of the scatter to a straight line. Look for all the output on a separate worksheet. For the reasons explained in the text, we often use some other charts obtained through graphing techniques of Excel for a more accurate diagnostic checking.

MegaStat

Correlation/Regression → Regression Analysis In the dialogue box, specify the *Input Range* for the dependent variable (Y) and all independent variables (X's). Put check marks for **Variance Inflation Factors:** used for checking multicollinearity. **Test Intercept:** if you wish. **Force Zero Intercept:** use this only if zero intercept is required based on the theory underlying your model.

Output Residuals: gives the predicted values of the dependent variable and the residuals; useful for charting residuals against the predicted values to identify specification errors or for charting squares of these residuals against predicted values to identify departures from homosedasticity.

Durbin–Watson: gives value of the "d" statistic for identifying the presence of autocorrelation.

Plot Residuals: produces (1) a chart of *Residuals versus Observation numbers*—useful for checking autocorrelation and outliers, by looking at residuals that are larger than twice the size of standard errors shown as gridlines; (2) a chart of *Residuals vs. Predicted Values*—useful for identifying specification errors; and (3) charts of *residuals vs. each of the independent variable*—useful for, though not conclusive of, identifying trouble spots due to specification errors, heteroscedasticity, etc.

Diagnostics and Influential Residuals: (1) *Leverage values* (noted as *HI* in Minitab) are used to identify an influential observation in the data set on the independent variables; in MegaStat, shaded blue if the observation is influential. (2) *Studentized Residuals* Called *Standardized Residuals* in Minitab and noted as *St Resid* (in session window) or *SRES* (in the worksheet); obtained by dividing each residual by the residual's standard error. Note that the Excel's Data Analysis package gives slightly different values due to a difference in method of computation. (3) *Studentized Deleted Residuals* Called *deleted t residuals* in Minitab and noted as *TRES* in Minitab's worksheet; a special type of standardized residuals that have Student's t distribution with $df = (n - k - 2)$, and therefore useful for checking the statistical significance of an outlier. In MegaStat, shaded light blue if the P-value is ≤ 0.05 and dark blue if the P-value is $\leq$ to 0.01. (4) *Cook's Distance* Noted as *Cook* in Minitab's worksheet, the values of Cook's D statistic are used to identify the combined effect of an outlier and influential observation(s). In MegaStat, shaded light blue if the P-value is ≤ 0.8 and dark blue if the P-value is ≤ 0.5.

Normal Probability Plot of Residuals: gives a chart of residuals plotted against normal scores—can be used to assess the normality assumption of the error term by examining the closeness of the scatter to a straight line.

All **results** of MegaStat are stored in a worksheet called **Output**.

14-1. From the results in Excel, illustrated in the output below, we can write the regression equation as

Investment = −68 271.6 − 590.29 Interest
+ 0.308 GDP + 512.09 Capacity

Interpretation

The Intercept: The mechanical interpretation of the value of intercept equal to an average investment of negative 68 271 (in millions of dollars) when all independent variables are zero is meaningless. This value of intercept is based on the zero values of all independent variables, which, in this case, are obviously very far from the observed range of values of all independent variables in the model. It is practically inconceivable to have zero values of variables like GDP, capacity use, or the interest rate.

Coefficient of Interest Rate: A unit increase in the interest variable (for example, from 5 percent to 6 percent) would lead to a decrease in investment by 590.29 million dollars, assuming no change in the values of all other independent variables (GDP and Capacity). As the cost of borrowing (the interest rate) increases, theoretically we do expect a decrease in investment. Thus, the sign of the interest is consistent with theory.

Coefficient of Capacity: As the capacity use in businesses increases, businesses would experience a need for further investment. In the estimated equation, assuming no change in the values of other independent variables in the equation (GDP and Interest), an increase in capacity by one percentage point (for example, from 80 percent to 81 percent) would increase the need for investment by 512.09 million dollars. The positive sign of the coefficient agrees with the expected sign.

Coefficient of GDP (Real): An increase in real GDP would signal a higher demand for products, and therefore a larger need for investment. In the estimated equation, we find that a dollar increase (in millions) in real GDP would require an increase in investment by 0.308 million dollars, assuming no change in the values of all other independent variables (Interest and Capacity). That is, each dollar increase in GDP leads to an increase in investment by 30.8 cents. The sign of the coefficient is in accordance with our theoretical expectations.

Estimated value of investment for given values of the independent variables: Interest = 4 percent, GDP = 200 000 (in millions) and Capacity = 82 percent can be found by substituting these values in the equation at appropriate places:

Investment = −68 271.6 − 590.29 (4) + 0.308 (200 000)
+ 512.09 (82)

This gives the estimated value of investment = $32 958.02 millions.

14-2. The Excel printout of the regression procedure including three dummy variables for four quarters is given below. Quarter 1 is used as the control group.

(a) The ANOVA table is produced by Excel and illustrated in the tables below. The ANOVA table includes sums of squares (SS) together with degrees of freedom (df) for each sum of squared term, mean square (SS divided by df), the value of the F statistic, and its P-value. As explained in the chapter, the ANOVA table displays the breakdown of the variation in the dependent variable into two parts.

Summary Output Self-Review 14-1

Regression Statistics	
Multiple R	0.96773576
R Square	0.9365125
Adjusted R Square	0.92971026
Standard Error	1746.15446
Observations	32

ANOVA Table Self-Review 14-1

	df	SS	MS	F	Significance F
Regression	3	1 259 356 469	419 785 490	137.677226	7.2653E-17
Residual	28	85 373 551.47	3 049 055.41		
Total	31	1 344 730 020			

Regression Coefficients Self-Review 14-1

	Coefficients	Standard Error	t Stat	P-value	Lower 95%	Upper 95%
Intercept	−68 271.598	21 368.22632	−3.1950054	0.00344843	−112 042.47	−24 500.721
Interest	−590.28848	284.7267825	−2.0731751	0.0474724	−1 173.5255	−7.0514521
GDP(Real)	0.30774581	0.031352404	9.81570058	1.4489E-10	0.24352325	0.37196838
Capacity	512.086644	319.621095	1.60216785	0.12034158	−142.62823	1 166.80151

SS due to regression is the part of variation in the dependent variable that has been explained by the regression model. SS due to Residual is the part that has not been explained by the regression model. The Total sum of squared variations in the dependent variable (from its mean) is 1.34E + 09 = 1 340 000 000 (moving decimal point 9 digits to the right). Of this, 1.32E + 9 (= 1 320 000 000) has been explained by the regression model, and the balance 27 883 090 remains unexplained. Note these figures are in $ millions!

(b) The standard error of estimate, as reported in the **Summary Output for Self Review 14-2** is 1052.337 ($ millions). This indicates that, on average, the actual (observed) values of investment differ from the estimated values of investment by $1052.337 million. Based on the empirical rule, we expect 68 percent of all observed values of investment to fall in the range $\hat{y} \pm 1052.337$ about 95 percent of all observed values of investment to fall in the range $\hat{y} \pm 2(1052.337)$ and about 99 percent of all observed values of investment to fall in the range $\hat{y} \pm 3(1052.337)$.

(c) The values of R^2 *and adjusted* R^2 as displayed under the summary output are 0.979 and 0.974 respectively. Thus, based on the value of R^2, we say that 97.9 percent of the variation in the dependent variable has been explained by the estimated regression model. Based on the value of adjusted R^2, we say that 97.4 percent of the variation in the dependent variable has been

explained by the estimated regression model. The two values are different due to the loss of degrees of freedom (number of independent variables) in estimating the regression model. This loss of degrees of freedom is accounted for by the adjusted R^2, but not by the R^2. The adjusted R^2 is therefore a better representation of the explanatory power of the model.

(d) *Test of hypothesis for the entire model* is based on the F statistic. In the model, we have six variables and therefore six β's. Our null and alternative hypotheses therefore are:

$$H_0: \ \beta_1 = \beta_2 = \beta_3 = \beta_4 = \beta_5 = \beta_6 = 0$$
$$H_1: \ \text{The alternative hypothesis is that at}$$
least one of the six β's is not zero. (In short, H_0 is not true).

Level of Significance: Assume a level of significance is equal to 1 percent.

The critical value of F for 6 and 25 degrees of freedom and a 1 percent level of significance from the F table in Appendix D is equal to 3.63. The calculated value of the F statistic as given in ANOVA Table Self-Review 14-2 is equal to 198.22. This is much larger than the critical value. We therefore reject H_0 and conclude that, based on evidence available from the observations on all variables, the linear regression model with the six independent variables is significant in explaining the variation in the dependent variable. Our conclusion is subject to at most 1 percent error in rejecting a true null hypothesis. As a matter of fact, the exact

Summary Output Self-Review 14-2

Regression Statistics	
Multiple R	0.989652
R Square	0.979412
Adjusted R	0.974471
Standard E	1052.337
Observation	32

ANOVA Table Self-Review 14-2

	df	SS	MS	F	Significance F
Regression	6	1.32E + 09	2.2E + 08	198.2166	7.84E-20
Residual	25	27 685 909	1 107 412		
Total	31	1.34E + 09			

Regression Coefficients Table Self-Review 14-2

	Coefficient	Standard Error	t Stat	P-value
Intercept	− 67 337.4	13 384.37	− 5.03105	3.44E-05
Interest	− 674.153	172.6339	− 3.9051	0.000632
GDP (Real)	0.316606	0.021059	15.03434	4.98E-14
Capacity	475.2099	202.8301	2.342896	0.027394
Quarter 2	3050.719	540.5505	5.643726	7.12E-06
Quarter 3	− 5.2902	574.7603	− 0.0092	0.992729
Quarter 4	− 201.364	576.7215	− 0.34915	0.729899

amount of Type I error, as given by the P-value for F in the ANOVA table is 7.84E-20 (= 0.0000000000000000000784!, moving the decimal point 20 digits to the left).

(e) *Test of hypothesis for each regression coefficient*: Our null hypothesis for each coefficient is:

$$H_0: \ \alpha = 0, \ \beta_1 \geq 0, \ \beta_2 \leq 0, \ \beta_3 \leq 0, \ \beta_4 = 0,$$
$$\beta_5 = 0, \ \beta_6 = 0$$

Our alternative hypotheses for each coefficient should depend on theoretically expected signs of the coefficients, if available. We do not have any theoretically expected signs for the intercept term and the quarterly dummy variables. (To be more accurate, we should conduct a *partial F test* for the seasonal dummies. See the appendix to this chapter on the acompanying CD-ROM, and try another challenge.) However, we do expect interest rates to affect investment negatively and the GDP and capacity use variables to affect investment positively. The alternative hypothesis for each of the regression coefficients therefore is:

$$H_1: \ \alpha \neq 0, \ \beta_1 < 0, \ \beta_2 > 0, \ \beta_3 > 0, \ \beta_4 \neq 0,$$
$$\beta_5 \neq 0, \ \beta_6 \neq 0$$

Thus the intercept and quarterly dummies require two-tailed tests, and GDP, Interest and capacity coefficients require only a one-tailed test.

Level of significance: we assume it to be 1 percent.

The test statistic is t, and its critical value at a 1 percent level of significance and 25 degrees of freedom:

for a one-tailed hypothesis is $t = \pm 2.485$

for a two-tailed hypothesis is $t = \pm 2.787$

Calculated values of t based on sample observations are illustrated in the Regression Coefficients Table Self-Review 14-2. The sample $|t|$ values for the coefficients of intercept, GDP, Interest and Quarter 2 variables are all larger than the required critical values, thus rejecting the null hypothesis in each case. However, Capacity, Quarter 3 and Quarter 4 coefficients are not significant at 1 percent. Since capacity is a theoretically important variable, we worry about the insignificance of the Capacity coefficient. However, if we examine the P-value (the exact amount of Type I error in rejecting the null hypothesis) for the capacity coefficient, we see that this is not too high, merely 1.4 percent (half of the two-tailed hypothesis P-value reported by Excel).

(f) The linear regression model of investment with Interest Rate, GDP, Capacity Use and quarterly dummies together seems to have excellent explanatory power, explaining nearly 98 percent of the variation in investment. The coefficient of the Capacity variable that has the highest Type I error is also within the conventional range of 5 percent. The insignificant dummy variables for Quarter 3 and Quarter 4 however, do not have any theoretical justification and may, therefore, be removed from the model.

14-3. (a) As indicated in Self-Review 14-2, we have removed the dummy variables for Quarters 3 and 4 and re-estimated the model. Note, now we have only one dummy variable with *two* categories: "Quarter 1" and "Rest of Year." The results from Excel are illustrated in the tables and graph opposite. Based on the results, we do not see any problem with model specification. The coefficients of both GDP and Interest are nearly the same and statistically significant. However, the coefficient of capacity shows marked improvement both in the value of the coefficient and the t statistic. Now the coefficient of the capacity variable is significant at less than 1 percent (P-value = 0.0071%). Further, as the illustration of output shows, the scatter diagram of *Actual versus Predicted Investment* (Self Review 14-3 Chart A) appears to approximate a linear relationship fairly well. The graph does not reveal any systematic pattern (under- or over-prediction). This indicates that we have not left out any significant variable from the model. Further, the illustration of Excel output that displays a graph of Residuals versus Predicted Values of Investment (see Self-Review 14-3 Chart B) does not seem to contain any abnormal pattern in the residuals. This corroborates the above conclusion that our model is specified accurately in terms of the linear relationship as well as the inclusion of all relevant variables. However, we should wait for the final comment until we have completed the diagnostic checking of the residuals.

The graph of residuals against the observation numbers in MegaStat output (Self-Review 14-3 Chart C) also includes gridlines, each gridline being equal to 1 standard error. Therefore, the points above or below two gridlines from the zero gridline may be called outliers. The graph reveals that there are few outliers in the beginning of the data (observation numbers 1 and 3) and one in the middle part (observation number 14). Should we remove these outliers from the data set? This is a challenge for you. A hint is given at the end of this review.

Summary Output Self-Review 14-3

Regression Analysis			
0.979	R^2	Adjusted R^2	0.976
0.990	R		
1016.222	std. error of estimate		
32	observations		
4	predictor variables		
Investment	dependent variable		

ANOVA Table Self-Review 14-3

Source	SS	df	MS	F	p-value
Regression	1 316 846 929.698	4	329 211 732.474	318.79	0.000
Residual	27 883 090.102	27	1 032 707.041		
Total	1 344 730 820.000	31			

Durbin–Watson statistic = 0.63

Regression Coefficients Table Self-Review 14-3

Variables	Coefficients	Std. error	t(df-27)	P-value	95% Lower	95% Upper	Beta
					Confidence interval		
Intercept	$b_0 = -68\,040.265$	12 435.857	-5.471	0.000	$-93\,556.519$	$-42\,524.010$	
Interest	$b_1 = -673.576$	166.080	-4.056	0.000	$-1\,014.344$	-322.809	-0.120
GDP (Real)	$b_2 = 0.315$	0.018	17.228	0.000	0.277	0.352	0.848
Capacity	$b_3 = 487.367$	186.042	2.620	0.014	105.642	869.093	0.125
Quarter 2	$b_4 = 3\,115.416$	417.548	7.461	0.000	2 258.678	3 972.153	0.208

SELF-REVIEW 14-3 CHART A: Actual versus Predicted Investment

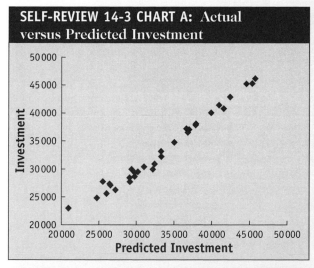

SELF-REVIEW 14-3 CHART C: Plot of Residuals against Observation Number

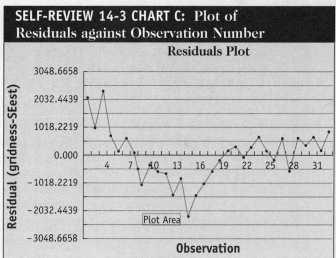

Durbin-Watson = 0.63

SELF-REVIEW 14-3 CHART B: Residuals against Predicted Investment

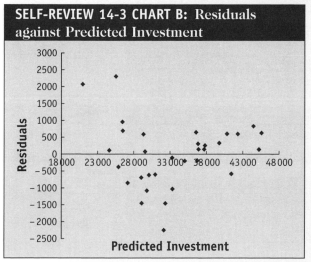

(b) As we discussed in the chapter, *multi-collinearity* can create serious problems in terms of the significance of the regression coefficients. Using the correlation procedure of data analysis in Excel, we generated the values of correlations among all variables in the model. The results from Excel are illustrated in Sample Correlations Table Self-Review 14-3. From the results, it is evident that the Capacity and GDP variables are highly correlated ($r = 0.802$).

Sample Correlations Table Self-Review 14-3

	Correlations				
	Investment	Interest	GDP (Real)	Capacity	Quarter 2
Investment	1				
Interest	−0.3266	1			
GDP (Real)	0.961091	−0.25569	1		
Capacity	0.804115	−0.07467	0.80225	1	
Quarter 2	0.119333	0.092045	−0.08466	−0.0478	1

We can get a better picture of multi-collinearity by running auxiliary regressions (regression of one independent variable on the remaining independent variables) for each independent variable. Based on the R_j^2 for each jth independent variable, as shown in the chapter, we can find the Variance Inflation Factor for each regression coefficient. The VIF for GDP, Capacity and Interest variables were found to be 3.15, 2.96 and 1.13 respectively. See the table below. However, in spite of the inflated variances, the t ratios for each of the coefficients are large enough to reject the null hypothesis for these coefficients. Thus multicollinearity has not posed any serious problem for inferences.

Finding R_j^2 and VIF for Each Independent Variable

Regression Analysis: GDP(Real) versus Interest, Capacity, D1
The regression equation is
GDP(Real) = − 466 613 − 2947 Interest
          + 8269 Capacity − 1177 D1
  R-Sq = 68.3% VIF = 1/(1 − 0.683) = 3.15

Regression Analysis: Capacity versus Interest, GDP(Real), D1
The regression equation is
Capacity = 65.5 + 0.200 Interest
        + 0.000080 GDP(Real) + 0.040 D1
  R-Sq = 66.2%, VIF = 1/(1 − 0.662) = 2.96

Regression Analysis: Interest versus Capacity, GDP(Real), D1
The regression equation is
Interest = − 8.9 + 0.251 Capacity
        − 0.000036 GDP(Real) + 0.169 D1
  R-Sq = 11.7% VIF = 1/(1 − 0.117) = 1.13

Note: The version of MegaStat on your CD will compute the VIF values for you if you check that choice.

(c) *Autocorrelation* can be checked either graphically, from the chart of residuals against the observation number, or through a quantitative test in terms of the Durbin–Watson d statistic. MegaStat output (see Self-Review Chart 14-3A) facilitates both these techniques. The graph of residuals does reveal positive autocorrelation. This is confirmed by the value of the Durbin–Watson statistic equal to 0.63 as placed in the ANOVA table. To find if the positive autocorrelation is statistically significant, we test for the null hypothesis of zero autocorrelation against an alternative hypothesis of positive autocorrelation. The lower and upper limits of the d statistic from the table for $n = 32$ and $k = 4$ (for a 5 percent level of significance) are $d_L = 1.177$ and $d_U = 1.732$. The sample value of $d = 0.63$ obviously falls below d_L. We therefore reject the null hypothesis of zero autocorrelation and conclude that there is sufficient sample evidence in favour of positive autocorrelation.

Heteroscedasticity: We can check for the presence of heteroscedasticity (unequal error variances) by plotting squared residuals against the predicted values of the dependent variable investment; the graph is illustrated in Self-Review 14-3 Chart D. The chart reveals that the scatter of residuals has a larger spread (variance) for smaller values of investment as compared to larger values of investment.

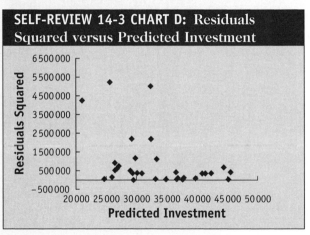

SELF-REVIEW 14-3 CHART D: Residuals Squared versus Predicted Investment

To see which independent variable may be causing this problem, we need to plot squared residuals against each independent variable. These charts were tried but were not conclusive, and therefore are not given here. We ask you to verify for yourself. Quantitative tests of homoscedasticity are given in the appendix to this chapter on the CD-ROM.

(d) *Normality of the Error Term*: A visual check of normality assumption of the residuals can be done through the histogram of residuals. Using the histogram procedure of data analysis in Excel, we have drawn a histogram of the estimated residuals, shown in Self-Review 14-3 Chart E. The distribution of estimated residuals does seem somewhat skewed towards the right of the zero point.

We carry out quantitative tests of normality in brief in the appendix to this chapter and in detail in the next chapter.

SELF-REVIEW 14-3 CHART E: Histogram of Residuals

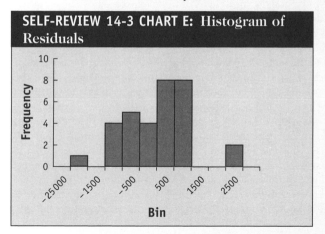

(e) The residual diagnostics indicate the presence of both autocorrelation and heteroscedasticity.

In the presence of both heteroscedasticity and autocorrelation, our estimators of the regression coefficient are still unbiased. However, they are not efficient. In other words, the variances of the estimators of the regression coefficients are biased. Since the tests of hypothesis for the regression coefficients are based on these variances, the results of the tests of hypothesis too, are suspect.

Violation of the assumption of normality also has a similar effect of invalidating the tests of hypothesis. This is certainly a serious matter. However, statisticians have developed advanced techniques, beyond the scope of this book, which can be used to obtain better estimates of the variances and valid tests of hypothesis at least in large samples. Some remedies are discussed in Section 14A-1 on the CD-ROM.

(f) In terms of the coefficients of determination and tests of hypotheses, the regression model for investment appears to have faired well. The regression coefficients are in accordance with the theoretical expectations. Multicollinearity does not seem to have posed any serious problem. Multicollinearity between Capacity and GDP variables may have resulted in higher variances of the regression coefficients and therefore lower t ratios. However, autocorrelation and heteroscedasticity may compromise the reliability of the results.

Since heteroscedasticity is commonly found in cross-sectional rather than time-series data, the reasons for its presence in our regression model are not very obvious. It is possible that our model has omitted some important variable. Alternatively, the dependent variable might have been influenced by some extraneous forces, producing a break in the linear relationship. A closer scrutiny of the data indicates that investment in the early quarters, particularly the four quarters of 1993 were heavily influenced by a recovery following the deep recession of 1990–91. This is also confirmed by some outliers in the early period. Thus, the outliers seem to contain some important information. This has not been explicitly allowed for in our regression model. If we use a dummy variable for this extraordinary period (1 for the four quarters of 1993 and zeros for all other values), the problems of autocorrelation, heteroscedasticity, outliers and, to a large extent, violation of normality, disappear. We leave this to you to as an exercise to verify this claim.

A REVIEW OF   CHAPTERS 13 AND 14

This section is a review of the major concepts and terms introduced in Chapters 13 and 14. In Chapter 13, our focus was on formulating and estimating a *linear* relationship between two variables based on a sample of information, and testing hypotheses about their values in the population.

The degree of *linear* relationship between two *random* variables can be measured by the coefficient of correlation. The coefficient of correlation (r) can assume any value between -1.00 and $+1.00$ inclusive. A negative value of r indicates that, on average, the two variables are inversely related, i.e., an increase in one variable is associated with a decrease in another variable. Positive values of r indicate that the two variables are, on average, directly related. Values of r equal $+1$ or -1 indicate a perfect linear relationship, and 0 indicates an absence of linear relationship. A value near 0, such as -0.15 or 0.15, indicates a weak relationship. A value near -1 or $+1$, such as -0.90 or $+0.90$, indicates a strong relationship. Correlation does not necessarily imply a cause and effect relationship between the variables.

The strength of linear relationship between two variables, where one variable is random (dependent) and another variable is non-random (independent), can be examined through the technique of regression analysis. The two-variable analysis can be extended to multiple variables to study the relationship between one dependent (random) variable and several independent (non-random) variables. An estimated linear relationship in the simple case involving one dependent variable (Y) and one independent variable (X) can be expressed by the equation $\hat{y} = a + bx$. For k independent variables, e.g., $X_1, X_2, \ldots X_k$, the estimated multiple regression equation is: $\hat{y} = a + b_1x_1 + b_2x_2 + \cdots + b_kx_k$. Constants $a, b, b_1, b_2, \ldots b_k$ are the estimated values of the corresponding population parameters.

In simple regression analysis, the coefficient of regression (b) associated with the independent variable measures, on average, the response of the dependent variable to a unit change in the independent variable, regardless of any change(s) in other independent variable(s) absent from the regression model. In multiple regression analysis, the coefficients ($b_1, b_2, \ldots b_k$) associated with independent variables ($X_1, X_2, \ldots X_k$) measure, on average, the response of the dependent variable to a unit change in a particular independent variable, holding the remaining independent variables unchanged. In this sense, multiple regression analysis serves as a powerful tool to separate out the individual effects of several variables without the need of controlled experiments. The regression technique is widely used in policy analysis and forecasting by both private and public sector organizations. However, researchers are well advised to conduct diagnostic checks to see if the particular investigation adequately meets the requirements of techniques of estimation and inference.

Various measures, such as the coefficient of determination, the multiple standard error of estimate, the results of the global test of hypothesis, test of hypothesis for each regression coefficient, and some model diagnostics are reported in the output of most computer software packages.

■ GLOSSARY

Analysis of Variance (ANOVA)   A technique that helps to decompose total variation (SSTotal) in the dependent variable into the variation explained by the regression model (SSR) and the variation that is not explained by the regression model (SSE).

Autocorrelation   A measure of correlation between successive residuals in the population. This condition frequently occurs when variables are measured over time (time-series data).

Best Linear Unbiased Estimators (BLUE)   Estimators that have minimum variance in the class of linear and unbiased estimators.

Coefficient of Correlation   A measure of the degree of linear association between two random variables. It is defined as the ratio of covariance between the variables to the standard deviations of those variables. Its value lies between $+1$ and -1. A value closer to zero indicates an absence of linear association between two variables.

Coefficient of Determination   This is defined as the proportion of total variation in the dependent variable that is explained by the independent variable(s). It can assume any value between 0 and $+1.00$ inclusive. A value of 0.82 indicates that 82 percent of the variation in the dependent variable is accounted for by the linear relation of the dependent variable with the independent variable(s).

Confidence Interval Estimator　A formula that provides an estimate of the interval of values expected to contain the mean value of the dependent variable in the population, with an assumed level of confidence (probability), for a given set of value(s) of the independent variable(s). The farther the value of the independent variable is from its mean, the wider the interval. A particular interval estimate based on a sample of observations is called the *Confidence Interval Estimate*.

Correlation Matrix　A listing of all possible simple coefficients of correlation in a sample data. A correlation matrix includes the correlations between each of the independent variables and the dependent variable, as well as those among all the independent variables. Conceptually, these correlations are not the same as the coefficient of correlation between two random variables defined earlier.

Covariance　A measure of linear association defined as an average of the product of the variations in each of the two random variables from their mean values.

Dummy Variable　A variable with two categories. One category consists of the presence of an attribute and another category, the absence of the same attribute. If a qualitative variable has m categories (attributes), then we choose one category as a *base* category, and use $m-1$ dummy variables for the remaining $m-1$ categories.

Gauss–Markov Theorem　Under certain conditions, the ordinary least squares estimators are Best Linear Unbiased Estimators.

Goodness of Fit　A measure of closeness of fit of the observed data to the regression line. It is measured by the coefficient of determination.

Homoscedasticity　It refers to the property of equality of all variances of the dependent variable or the error term in the population for each value of the independent variable. The case of unequal variances is called *heteroscedasticity*. Heteroscedasticity often occurs when variables are measured at a point of time (cross-section data).

Least Squares Method　A technique used to estimate the response of the dependent variable to changes in the independent variable(s) in a regression equation. The technique consists of minimizing the sum of the squared errors between the observed values and the estimated values of the dependent variable.

Linear Regression Equation　A statistical relationship between two or more variables. For a sample of observations on variables X and Y, it takes the form: $y = a + bx + e$ with an estimated counterpart as $\hat{y} = a + bx$ for one independent variable X, and $\hat{y} = a + b_1 x_1 + b_2 x_2 + \cdots + b_k x_k$ for

multiple independent variables, $X_1, X_2, X_3 \dots X_k$. Estimated values $\hat{y}$ are used to predict y-values based on a set of selected x-values. The variable Y is dependent and the variable X is independent.

Misspecification　An incorrect functional form, or an inclusion of an irrelevant variable, or an omission of a relevant variable in the regression model. Misspecification of a model results in *specification bias in the estimators*.

Multicollinearity　A condition that occurs in a sample of observations in multiple regression analysis when the independent variables are themselves correlated.

Multiple Regression Equation　The estimated relationship in the form of a mathematical equation between several independent variables and a dependent variable. The general form is $\hat{y} = a + b_1 x_1 + b_2 x_2 + b_3 x_3 + \cdots b_k x_k$. It is used to estimate values of Y given selected values of X on each of the k independent variables.

Partial Correlation Coefficient　The coefficient of correlation between any two variables, assuming all other variables remain unchanged.

Partial (Net) Regression Coefficients　The regression coefficients that measure the response of the dependent variable to a unit change in the independent variable, assuming all other variables remain unchanged.

Prediction Interval Estimator　A formula that provides an estimate of an interval of values expected to contain an individual observation of the dependent variable in the population, with an assumed level of confidence (probability), for a given value(s) of the independent variable(s). The farther the value of the independent variable is from its mean, the wider the interval. A particular interval estimate based on a sample of observations is called a *Prediction Interval Estimate*.

Qualitative Variable　A nominal scale variable that records the data on a variable in two or more categories.

Regression Coefficients　The constants that measure the response of the dependent variable to a unit change in the independent variable in the population. Note, an estimated value of the regression coefficient changes from sample to sample, and is therefore a random variable.

Regression Diagnostics　An analysis of how adequately the regression model assumptions are satisfied in a sample of observations.

Residuals　The difference between the actual value of the dependent variable and the expected value of the dependent variable in a population based on a regression model. An *estimated value of the residual* is the difference between the observed value (y) of the dependent variable and the estimated value ($\hat{y}$) of the dependent variable.

Scatter Diagram　A chart that visually depicts the relationship between two variables.

Standard Error of Estimate A measure of the dispersion of the actual Y values about the regression line. It is reported in the same units as the dependent variable.

Test of Significance Techniques of testing null hypotheses about regression coefficients, regression models, independent variable(s) and correlation coefficient.

■ EXERCISES

PART I—FILL IN THE BLANKS AND DISCUSSION

1. The goodness of fit between a set of independent variables X and a dependent variable Y is measured by the _____.

2. A coefficient of correlation was computed to be -0.90. Comment.

3. Pearson's r for a problem involving 60 pairs of data was computed to be 0.40. Comment. Is the correlation in the population zero? Give evidence.

4. The coefficient of determination was computed to be 0.38 in a problem involving one independent and one dependent variable. What does this mean?

5. Distinguish between simple and partial regression coefficients.

Exercises 6 through 10 are based on the following table. The accounting division for a large chain of department stores is trying to predict the net profit for each of the chain's many stores based on the number of employees in the store, overhead cost, and so on. A few statistics from some of the stores are:

Store	Net Profit ($ thousands)	Number of Employees	Overhead Cost ($ thousands)	Average Mark up (percent)	Theft Loss ($ thousands)
1	846	143	79	69	52
2	513	110	64	50	45

6. The dependent variable is _____.

7. The general form of the estimated equation for this problem is _____.

8. The multiple regression equation was estimated at $\hat{y} = 67 + 8x_1 - 10x_2 + 0.004x_3 - 3x_4$. What are the predicted sales for a store with 112 employees, an overhead cost of $65\,000$, a mark up rate of 50 percent, and a loss from theft of $50\,000$?

9. Suppose R^2 was computed to be 0.86. Explain.

10. Suppose that the multiple standard error of estimate was 3 (in $ thousands). Explain what this means in this problem.

PART II—PROBLEMS

11. Quick-print firms in a large downtown business area spend most of their advertising dollars on advertisements on bus benches. A research project involves predicting monthly sales based on the annual amount spent on placing ads on bus benches. A sample of quick-print firms revealed these advertising expenses and sales:

Firm	Annual Bus Bench Advertising ($ thousands)	Monthly Sales ($ thousands)
A	2	10
B	4	40
C	5	30
D	7	50
E	3	20

a. Draw a scatter diagram.
b. Determine the coefficient of correlation.
c. What is the coefficient of determination?
d. Compute the regression equation.
e. Estimate the monthly sales of a quick-print firm that spends $4500 on bus bench advertisements.
f. Summarize your findings.

12. The following output for ANOVA and Regression Coefficients is given:

Source	Sum of Squares	df	MS
Regression	1050.8	4	262.70
Error	83.8	20	4.19
Total	1134.6	24	

Predictor	Coef	St. Dev.	t ratio
Constant	70.06	2.13	32.89
X_1	0.42	0.17	2.47
X_2	0.27	0.21	1.29
X_3	0.75	0.30	2.50
X_4	0.42	0.07	6.00

a. Compute the coefficient of determination.
b. Compute the multiple standard error of estimate.
c. Conduct a test of hypothesis to determine whether any of the partial regression coefficients are different from zero. Use the 5 percent level of significance.
d. Conduct a test of hypothesis on the individual regression coefficients. Can any of the variables be detected? Use the 5 percent level of significance.

■ CASES

A. PROFITS OF MAJOR CANADIAN CORPORATIONS

Refer to the data in file 100 of Top 1000 Companies.xls on the CD. This data set contains information on a randomly selected sample of 100 of the Top 1000 companies in Canada. The data includes information on Profits (in $000), Revenue (in $000), Market capitalization (Market Cap, a measure of the size of the corporation, in $ millions), Return on Capital (Return, in %) and the number of employees (Employees, number) for each corporation. Conduct a detailed investigation of the determinants of profit for major Canadian corporations. *Try to answer all questions given at the beginning of the Computer Data Exercises.*

B. TERRY AND ASSOCIATES: THE COST OF DELIVERING MEDICAL KITS

Terry and Associates is a specialized medical testing centre in Toronto. One of their major sources of revenue is a kit used to test for elevated amounts of lead in the blood.

Workers in auto body shops, those in the lawn care industry and commercial house painters are exposed to large amounts of lead and thus must be randomly tested. It is expensive to conduct the test, so the kits are delivered on demand to a variety of locations throughout the Metro Toronto area and adjacent townships.

Kathleen Terry, the owner, is concerned about appropriate costing of each delivery. To investigate, Ms. Terry gathered information on a random sample of 50 recent deliveries. Review the data in file Case Study B.xls on the CD-ROM. Factors thought to be related to the cost of delivering a kit are:

Prep — The time between when the customized order is phoned into the company and when it is ready for delivery.

Delivery — The actual travel time from Terry's plant to the customer.

Mileage — The distance in kilometres from Terry's plant to the customer.

Conduct a detailed regression analysis of the determinants of delivery costs. *Try to answer all questions given at the beginning of the Computer Data Exercises on page 654.*

CHAPTER 15

Chi-Square Distribution: Tests of Goodness of Fit and Independence

GOALS

When you have completed this chapter, you will be able to:

- Understand the nature and role of chi-square distribution

- Identify a wide variety of uses of the chi-square distribution

- Conduct a test of hypothesis comparing an observed frequency distribution to an expected frequency distribution

- Conduct a test of hypothesis for normality using the chi-square distribution

- Conduct a hypothesis test to determine whether two attributes are independent.

KARL PEARSON (1857–1936)

Karl Pearson, the favourite disciple of Francis Galton, was born in London, England. He is fondly called "the founder of the science of statistics." He is well known for his contributions to the development of statistical concepts such as standard deviation, correlation, regression and frequency curves, and, in general, for his influence in the development of the statistical approach to knowledge.

The earliest incident Pearson could remember from his childhood days characterizes the man and his mission in life. The incident as Pearson remembered, "...I was sitting in a high chair and I was sucking my thumb. Someone told me to stop sucking it and said that unless I did so the thumb would wither away. I put my two thumbs together and looked at them a long time. 'They look alike to me' I said to myself, 'I can't see that the thumb I suck is any smaller than the other. I wonder if she could be lying to me.'" "In this simple anecdote," Walker writes, "we have rejection of constituted authority, appeal to empirical evidence, faith in his own interpretation of the observed data, and final imputation of moral obliquity to a person whose judgement differed from his own. These characteristics were prominent through his entire career."[1]

Prior to Pearson, normal distribution was considered something like a universal law. Most scientists, including Laplace, analyzed their data sets simply by assuming that their data sets followed a normal distribution. Pearson experimented with fitting curves to many data sets, including the data sets used by earlier scientists, and found that most data sets did not resemble normal distribution. But there was no method available to indicate how bad the fit was. This prompted Pearson to discover the χ^2 (pronounced as *chi-square*) statistic, what some statisticians call his "greatest single contribution to statistical theory." He then used his χ^2 statistic on many data sets. Most of them failed the test! Even the runs at roulette occurring at Monte Carlo in July 1892, supposedly random, failed the test. Maybe the game was rigged! The beauty of the χ^2 statistic is that it can be used for any data set regardless of the shape of its distribution or the scale of measurement. Now, the χ^2 statistic is used for a variety of purposes in statistics. We discuss several applications of the χ^2 statistic in this chapter.

Pearson, like Francis Galton, had a multifaceted personality. He received his education in mathematics at Cambridge. The young Pearson was interested in poetry, philosophy, and in the search for a concept of Deity. During his travels to Germany where he studied physics and metaphysics, he was deeply influenced by Marxism and was later seen, upon his return to England, lecturing on socialism, even contributing to the Socialist songbook. In his first publication, at the age of 23, in a book written in the form of letters from a man Arthur to his fiancée, he writes, "I rush from science to philosophy, and from philosophy to our old friends the poets; and then overwearied by too much idealism, I fancy I become practical in returning to science. Have you ever attempted to conceive all there is in the world worth knowing—that not one subject in the universe is unworthy of study?"[2] Later, Pearson, came under the influence of Galton, and devoted much of his lifetime to advancing Galton's theory of natural inheritance though statistical methods. In *Biometrica*, the journal he founded, his choice of the motto for the journal was the one written under Charles Darwin's statue: *Ignoramus, in hoc signo laboremus*. In English, it means, "We are ignorant, so let us work."

1498
1548
1598
1648
1698
1748
1898
1948
2000

INTRODUCTION

We introduced you to the chi-square distribution in Chapter 9. In that chapter, we showed you the derivation of chi-square distribution based on a number of independently distributed normal random variables, and its major properties. There were two reasons for introducing the chi-square so early in the textbook. First, as you would have noticed, chi-square plays a significant role in the derivation of both Student's t distribution, used in Chapter 9 and onwards, and Fisher's F distribution, used in Chapter 12 and onwards. Second, as Chapter 9 shows, chi-square distribution can be used for testing a hypothesis about the variance in the population based on a set of sample data.

In this chapter, we focus on the use of chi-square distribution (1) for comparing an observed frequency distribution with a population distribution—a distribution that we might expect according to some theory or assumptions, and (2) for examining dependence between variables. Since, these tests involve the entire frequency distributions rather than particular parameters, some statisticians call these uses of chi-square as non-parametric tests.[3] For our purpose, however, the beauty of chi-square lies in its applicability to not only quantitative data, but also to qualitative data that we often encounter in business and many non-business related disciplines.

15.1 PEARSON'S PROBLEMS

In Pearson's time, the normal distribution was considered something like a universal law. Pearson looked at several distributions, but many of them did not seem to look like the normal distribution. He did not, however, have any test statistic to draw inferences as to whether a particular distribution was approximately normal or approximately some other type of probability distribution. We illustrate Pearson's problems by the following two examples. Let us suppose that a population can be divided into k groups. The groups are also called cells or categories. Further, let us use,

f_o observed frequency in a group,
f_e expected frequency in a group,
n the total of frequencies, the sample size. Thus, $n = \Sigma f_o = \Sigma f_e$.

Example 15-1

Is the Die Fair?

Meera bought a die to play games with on a weekend. Before starting to play, her friend, Paul looks at the die. By the looks of the die, Paul thinks it is not a fair die. Meera insists, and even bets 20 dollars, that it is a fair die. Who is right?

Solution

If the die is fair, both Paul and Meera agree, since the die has six faces, each number on the die has an equal probability ($p = 1/6$) of occurrence. Thus, if they tossed the die 60 ($n = 60$) times, each number on the die can be expected to show up 10 ($= n \times p = 60 \times 1/6$) times. This is called the *expected frequency*.

When the die is actually tossed 60 times, 1 shows up 10 times, 2 shows up 11 times, 3 shows up 7 times, 4 shows up 9 times, 5 shows up 10 times and 6 shows up 13 times! These are the observed frequencies for each number (face) on the die. The categories, the faces of the die, are recorded in the first column, observed frequencies in the second column, and the expected frequencies in the third column of Table 15-1. Chart 15-1 provides a visual counterpart of the differences in f_o and f_e.

Is The Die Fair?

TABLE 15-1: Observed and Expected Frequencies for Sixty Rolls of a Die

Face	f_o	f_e
1	10	10
2	11	10
3	7	10
4	9	10
5	10	10
6	13	10
Total	60	60

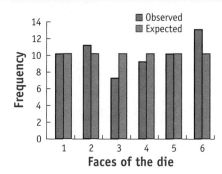

CHART 15-1: Observed and Expected Frequencies for Sixty Rolls of a Die

By looking at the differences between observed and expected frequencies, Paul thinks he is right; the die is not fair. Meera, on the other hand, thinks that the differences between the observed and expected frequencies are small enough that they could be attributed to chance, the sampling error. How can they settle the matter?

Example 15-2

Are All Hockey Players Equally Popular?

Ms. Jan Kilpatrick is the marketing manager for a manufacturer of sports cards. She plans to begin a series of cards with pictures and playing statistics of former professional league hockey players. One problem is the selection of the former players. At the hockey card show at the Southside Mall last weekend, she set up a booth and offered cards of the following six Hall of Fame hockey players: Gordie Howe, Bobby Hull, Bobby Orr, Guy Lafleur, Mike Bossy, and Maurice Richard. At the end of the first day she sold a total of 120 cards. The number of cards sold for each old-time player is shown in Table 15-2. If the six players were equally popular among card lovers, she should expect to sell 20 cards ($n \times p = 120 \times 1/6$) for each hockey player. This gives us the expected frequency of 20 for each player.

If the hockey players are equally popular, we would expect the observed frequencies (f_o) would be equal or nearly equal to expected frequencies (f_e). That is, we would expect to sell as many cards for Mike Bossy as for Bobby Orr. Thus, any discrepancy in the set of observed and expected frequencies could be attributed to sampling (chance). An examination of the set of observed frequencies in Table 15-2 indicates that the cards for Guy Lafleur is sold rather infrequently, whereas the cards for Gordie Howe and Bobby Orr are sold more often. Is the difference in sales due to chance, or can we conclude that there is a preference for the cards of certain players?

Are all Hockey Players Equally Popular?

TABLE 15-2: Hockey Players

Player	f_o	f_e
Mike Bossy	17	20
Bobby Orr	30	20
Bobby Hull	13	20
Guy Lafleur	15	20
Gordie Howe	28	20
Maurice Richard	17	20
Total	120	120

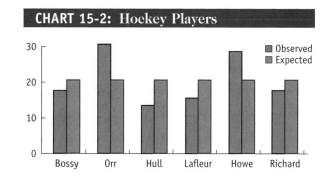

CHART 15-2: Hockey Players

The main features in the above examples can be summarized below:

- There are k categories or cells. The categories are mutually exclusive and include all outcomes (exhaustive) of a random experiment.
- The observed frequency in each category is an outcome of the random experiment in each category. These outcomes are therefore random variables.
- Each category has an assumed value of expected frequency, i.e., an assumed characteristic of the population. The expected frequency in each category equals the number of total observations (the sample size, n) multiplied by the probability of each observation falling in the particular category (p). That is, $f_e = (n) \times (p)$. In the particular examples given above, the value of p ($= 1/6$) is equal for each category.
- Note that the value of p may be different for each category depending on the assumption about the population.
- In this context, the null hypothesis is that hockey stars are equally popular, and the alternative hypothesis is that hockey stars are *not* equally popular.

15.2 PEARSON'S SOLUTIONS

THE TEST STATISTIC

Pearson defined a test statistic for the differences between the observed frequencies and the expected frequencies based on the idea that the smaller the difference, the better the fit.

In order to find the closeness of fit between the distribution of sample data and the assumed distribution in the population, Pearson developed a test statistic based on the differences between the observed frequency/category and the expected frequency in each class interval in the sample of observations. Instead of simple differences, he took the squared differences and standardized them by dividing the squared differences by the expected frequencies. Pearson thus obtained a statistic as a sum of these squared differences divided by the corresponding expected frequencies.

$$X^2 = \sum_{1}^{k} \left[\frac{(f_o - f_e)^2}{f_e} \right]$$

15-1

where
f_o is the observed frequency in a category
f_e is $(n) \times (p)$ = expected frequency in a category
k is the number of categories

Pearson has shown that, for a sufficiently large sample size (n), the test statistic X^2 is distributed approximately as a chi-square (χ^2) distribution. A general rule is that the sample size must be large enough to yield (n) $\times$ (p) *at least equal to* 5 for each category. The condition is required since the chi-square distribution is a continuous distribution, whereas observed frequency distributions are often discrete distributions.

Recall, for binomial approximation to normal distribution, we had imposed the same condition of (n) $\times$ (p) to be *at least equal to* 5. The only difference is that, whereas the binomial distribution had only two categories (success and failure), a goodness of fit test is generally applied to distributions that have more than two categories.

MULTINOMIAL DISTRIBUTIONS

Multinomial distributions can be seen as an extension of binomial distributions for more than two categories. Discrete distributions that satisfy the requirements of a binomial experiment, and where each trial consists of more than two outcomes (categories) are generally called multinomial distributions. For example, if, at the end of this course, we classified all students in two categories: pass and fail, we have a binomial population. On the other hand, if we classified all students into F, C, B, and A grade categories, we have a multinomial population with four categories. Similarly, in a die tossing experiment, if each outcome of a trial can be classified in one of the two categories: getting 5 or 6 in a toss *or* getting 1, 2, 3, or 4 in a toss, we have a binomial population. On the other hand, if each outcome of a trial can be classified in three categories—category one: getting 1 or 2, category two: getting 3 or 4, category three: getting 5 or 6, we have a multinomial population.

A CAVEAT

The reliability of inferences based on a chi-square test statistic crucially depends on the nature of the approximation; the better the approximation, the more reliable the inferences.

WHAT IS THE CHI-SQUARE (χ^2) DISTRIBUTION?

We should note that, theoretically, the X^2 test statistic, as defined above, is not the same thing as the chi-square probability distribution. The test statistic is based on the multinomial distribution, which is a discrete variable with no particular distribution known *a priori*, whereas the chi-square distribution is a continuous probability distribution based on the squares of the independent Z distributions. When the condition $n \times p$ is greater than or equal to 5 is satisfied for each category of the multinomial distribution, the test statistic X^2 is distributed approximately as the chi-square distribution. This enables us to use the chi-square distribution in place of the test statistic X^2 for statistical inferences, i.e., rejecting or not rejecting the null hypothesis at a pre-specified level of significance.

The derivation of **chi-square distribution** from normal distribution was explained in Chapter 9. Pearson derived the chi-square probability distribution to test the closeness of fit between the expected frequencies in the population and the actual frequencies based on a random experiment. We ask you to review the derivation of chi-square distribution in Chapter 9. Some simpler elements of the derivation and the properties of the distribution are given below.

- If a random variable X is distributed normally with a mean μ and a standard deviation σ, then the standardized variable $Z = \dfrac{x - \mu}{\sigma}$ has the standard normal distribution with a mean zero and a standard deviation equal to 1.

- If there are k such independently distributed normal random variables, $Z_1, Z_2, Z_3, \ldots, Z_k$, then the sum of the squares of all normal random variables (Z's) has a definite probability distribution with k degrees of freedom. Pearson called this probability distribution the chi-square distribution.

$$\chi^2 = Z_1^2 + Z_2^2 + Z_3^2 + \cdots + Z_k^2 \text{ is distributed with "}k\text{" degrees of freedom} \qquad \textbf{15-2}$$

- Since the chi-square variable is based on squared Z variables, it takes only the positive values, from zero to infinity. In general, the chi-square distribution is positively skewed.

CHART 15-3: Chi-Square Distributions for Selected Degrees of Freedom

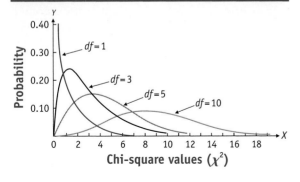

- For a sufficiently large degree of freedom, or as k tends to infinity, the chi-square probability distribution approaches the symmetrical shape of the normal distribution. See Chart 15-3 on the left. Note this requirement is different from the requirement of $n \times p$ is greater than or equal to 5 for the test statistic to be distributed approximately as a chi-square distribution.

- Like the t distribution, we have a different chi-square distribution for each degree of freedom, the number of independent categories. See Chart 15-3.

- The mean of the chi-square distribution is equal to the degrees of freedom (the number of independent Z's in chi-square) and the variance equals twice the value of the mean.

- Pearson tabulated probabilities for a number of interval values of chi-square and degrees of freedom. A modified version given in Appendix E is used to draw statistical inferences.

15.3 GOODNESS-OF-FIT TEST: EQUAL EXPECTED FREQUENCIES

Shape of χ^2 distribution approaches normal distribution as df becomes larger.

The **goodness-of-fit test** is one of the most common uses of the chi-square distribution. The test is appropriate for any level of data. In both examples above, the expected cell frequencies are equal for all categories due to an equal probability of an outcome falling in each of the k categories. Since the probability of an outcome falling in each category is the same ($p_1 = p_2 = p_3 = p_4 = p_5 = p_6 = 1/6$), the goodness-of-fit test in such cases is also called a *test of homogeneity*. Alternatively, we can call it a test of uniform probability distribution. We illustrate the use of the goodness-of-fit test for the hockey player example, and give you a little challenge to settle the dispute between Meera and Paul yourself (Exercise 15-5). We will use the same systematic five-step hypothesis-testing procedure first introduced in Chapter 10. Before we embark on the test of hypothesis procedures, we should note the following two points.

1. The Degrees of Freedom: We have mentioned degrees of freedom (we shall call it df from now on) several times above. How is the df determined in the context of the chi-square test statistic? As in other cases, the df in a data set is determined by the number of independent data points or observations involved in computing a statistic. In the context of a chi-square test statistic for goodness of fit, the number of categories is the number of data points. Since the total number of sample observations is divided into k categories, given the values in any of the $k - 1$ categories, we can find the value in the kth category.

For example, in the case of the sale of hockey cards, suppose the manager knows the total number of cards sold and the number of cards sold for all other players except for Bobby Orr. Does she need to count the cards sold for Bobby Orr? She can easily find the number of cards sold for Bobby Orr by subtracting the number of cards sold for all other hockey stars from the total number of cards sold. Cards sold for Boby Orr therefore, must equal $120 - (17 + 13 + 15 + 28 + 17) = 30$ cards. Thus, we only have five of the six categories free to move, and therefore $6 - 1 = 5$ degrees of freedom in this case. In other words, the total number of all cards sold represents one constraint on our degrees of freedom in the data set arranged in k categories, leaving us with $k - 1$ degrees of freedom.

Degrees of freedom for the chi-square test statistic equals the number of independent categories, which is equal to $k - 1$.

2. The Value of the Test Statistic and the Goodness of Fit Since the value of the test statistic is defined in terms of the difference between the observed frequencies and the expected frequencies, *when the null hypothesis is true*, a closeness of fit implies a smaller value of the test statistic. How much smaller is acceptable, depends on the level of significance, the acceptable level of a Type I error.

 The smaller the value of the test statistic, the better the goodness of fit.

THE FIVE-STEP PROCEDURE: THE HOCKEY PLAYERS EXAMPLE

Step 1 **State the null hypothesis (H_0) and the alternative hypothesis (H_1).** The null hypothesis, H_0, is that the random sample belongs to a population that follows a specified distribution. If H_0 is true, then differences between the observed and expected frequencies can be attributed to sampling (chance). The alternative hypothesis, H_1, is that the random sample does not belong to the population that follows a specified distribution. If there is sufficient evidence against H_0, i.e., there is a large difference between the observed and the expected frequencies that *cannot* be attributed to chance factors alone, H_0 is rejected and H_1 is accepted. In the hockey players example therefore our null hypothesis is that hockey stars are equally popular, and our alternative hypothesis is that they are not equally popular.

Step 2 **Select the level of significance.** We selected the 0.05 level, which is the same as the Type I error probability. Thus, the probability is 0.05 that a true null hypothesis will be rejected.

Step 3 **Select the test statistic.** Since all expected frequencies are greater than 5, we can use the chi-square distribution as our test statistic:

$$\text{Chi-Square Test Statistic: } \chi^2 = \sum \left[\frac{(f_o - f_e)^2}{f_e} \right] \text{ with } k - 1 \text{ degrees of freedom,}$$

where:
k is the number of categories, and
f_o is an observed frequency in a particular category, and
f_e is an expected frequency in a particular category.
In the case of the hockey stars, $df = k - 1 = 6 - 1 = 5$

Step 4 **Formulate the decision rule.** Recall, the decision rule in hypothesis testing requires finding a number that separates the region where we do not reject H_0 from the region of rejection. This number is called the **critical value**. As we have seen above, the chi-square distribution is really a family of distributions. Each distribution has a different shape, depending on the number of degrees of freedom. As explained above, the chi-square test statistic in this case has $k-1$ degrees of freedom, where k is the number of categories. Since there are six categories, there are $k - 1 = 6 - 1 = 5$ degrees of freedom.

The critical value for 5 degrees of freedom and a 0.05 level of significance is found in Appendix E for chi-square. A portion of that table is shown in Table 15-3. The critical value is 11.070, found by locating 5 degrees of freedom in the left margin and then moving horizontally (to the right) and reading the critical value in the 0.05 column.

The decision rule is to reject H_0 if the computed value of chi-square is greater than 11.070. If it is less than or equal to 11.070, do not reject H_0. Chart 15-4 shows the decision rule.

TABLE 15-3: A Portion of the Chi-Square Table				
Degrees of Freedom	**Right-Tail Area**			
df	**0.1**	**0.05**	**0.02**	**0.01**
1	2.706	3.841	5.412	6.635
2	4.605	5.991	7.824	9.21
3	6.251	7.815	9.837	11.345
4	7.779	9.488	11.668	13.277
5	9.236	11.070	13.388	15.086

CHART 15-4: Chi-Square Probability Distribution for 5 Degrees of Freedom, Showing the Region of Rejection, at the 0.05 Level of Significance

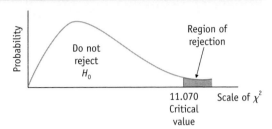

The decision rule indicates that if there are large differences between the observed and expected frequencies, resulting in a computed χ^2 of more than 11.070, the null hypothesis should be rejected. However, if the differences between f_o and f_e are small, the computed χ^2 value will be 11.070 or less, and the null hypothesis should not be rejected. The reasoning is that such small differences between the observed and expected frequencies are probably due to chance.

Step 5 **Compute the test statistic and make a decision.** Of the 120 cards sold in the sample, we counted the number of times Mike Bossy, Bobby Orr, and each of the others were sold. The counts were reported in Table 15-2. The calculations for chi-square follow. (Note again that the expected frequencies are the same for each cell/player.)

Column 1 Determine the differences between f_o and f_e. The sum of these differences for all categories is zero.

Column 2 Square the difference between the observed and the expected frequency for each category. That is $(f_o - f_e)^2$.

Column 3 Divide the result obtained in column 2 by the expected frequency in that category. That is $\dfrac{(f_o - f_e)^2}{f_e}$.

Finally, compute the sum of the values for all categories in column 3. The result is the value of χ^2, which is 12.8 in this case.

The computed value of χ^2 of 12.8 is in the rejection region beyond the critical value of 11.07. *The decision, therefore, is to reject H_0 at the 0.05 level of significance and to accept H_1.* The difference between the observed and the expected frequencies is not

TABLE 15-4: Computing the Value of Chi-Square for Hockey Stars					
Player	f_o	f_e	**(1)** $(f_o - f_e)$	**(2)** $(f_o - f_e)^2$	**(3)** $(f_o - f_e)^2/f_e$
Bossy	17	20	−3	9	0.45
Orr	30	20	10	100	5.0
Hull	13	20	−7	49	2.45
Lafleur	15	20	−5	25	1.25
Howe	28	20	8	64	3.2
Richard	17	20	−3	9	0.45
Total	120	120	0	0	12.8

due to chance. Rather, the differences between f_o and f_e are large enough to be considered statistically significant. The chance that these differences are due to sampling is very small. So we conclude that it is unlikely that hockey players are equally popular. Here is a small *challenge* for you! Could you reject the null hypothesis at 1 percent level of significance?

We can use software to compute the value of chi-square. In this example, we show the use of Excel/MegaStat software. Note in the output window of MegaStat, O stands for f_o and E for f_e, and *% of chi-square* stands for percent contribution made to the total value of chi-square by each category. Thus the difference in the observed and expected frequencies for Bobby Orr makes 39 percent (= 5/12.8) contribution to the chi-square value of 12.8.

EXCEL CHART 15-5: Computing the Value of Chi-Square Using Excel/MegaStat

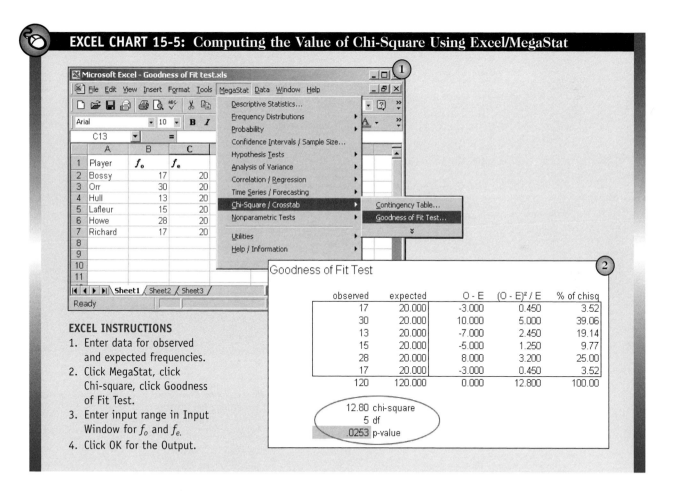

EXCEL INSTRUCTIONS
1. Enter data for observed and expected frequencies.
2. Click MegaStat, click Chi-square, click Goodness of Fit Test.
3. Enter input range in Input Window for f_o and f_e.
4. Click OK for the Output.

■ SELF-REVIEW 15-1

The Human Resources Director at St. John Pulp and Paper is concerned about absenteeism among hourly workers. She decides to sample the records to determine whether absenteeism is distributed evenly throughout the five-day work week. The null hypothesis to be tested is: absenteeism is distributed evenly throughout the week. The

0.01 level is to be used. The sample results are:

Days	Monday	Tuesday	Wednesday	Thursday	Friday
Numbers Absent	8	9	10	11	12

(a) What are the numbers 8, 9, 10, 11, 12 called?
(b) How many categories (cells) are there?
(c) What is the *expected* frequency for each day?
(d) How many degrees of freedom are there?
(e) What is the chi-square critical value at the 1 percent significance level?
(f) Compute the χ^2 test statistic.
(g) What is the decision regarding the null hypothesis?
(h) Specifically, what does this indicate to the resource director?

EXERCISES 15-1 TO 15-8

15-1. In a particular chi-square goodness-of-fit test there are four categories and 200 observations. Use the 0.05 significance level.
(a) How many degrees of freedom are there?
(b) What is the critical value of chi-square?

15-2. The null hypothesis and the alternative hypothesis are:
H_0: The expected frequencies are equal in all categories.
H_1: The expected frequencies are *not* equal in all categories.

Category	f_o
A	10
B	20
C	30

(a) State the decision rule, using the 0.05 significance level.
(b) Compute the value of chi-square.
(c) What is your decision regarding H_0?

15-3. The null hypothesis and the alternative hypothesis are:
H_0: The expected frequencies are equal in all categories.
H_1: The expected frequencies are *not* equal in all categories.

Category	f_o
A	10
B	20
C	30
D	20

(a) State the decision rule, using the 0.05 significance level.
(b) Compute the value of chi square.
(c) What is your decision regarding H_0?

15-4. A six-sided die is rolled 30 times and the numbers 1 through 6 appear as shown in the following frequency distribution. At the 0.10 significance level, can we conclude that the die is fair?

Outcome	Frequency	Outcome	Frequency
1	3	4	3
2	6	5	9
3	2	6	7

15-5. Determine whether Meera's die (in the example in Section 15.1) is biased. How would you convince Paul of your decision?

15-6. The Director of Golf for the Link Group wishes to study the number of rounds of golf played by members on weekdays. He gathered the following sample information for 520 rounds.

Day	Rounds
Monday	124
Tuesday	74
Wednesday	104
Thursday	98
Friday	120

At the 0.05 significance level, is there a difference in the number of rounds played by day of the week?

15-7. A group of department store buyers viewed a new line of dresses and gave their opinions of them. The results were:

Opinion	Number of Buyers	Opinion	Number of Buyers
Outstanding	47	Good	39
Excellent	45	Fair	35
Very Good	40	Undesirable	34

Because the largest number (47) indicated the new line is outstanding, the head designer thinks that this is a mandate to go into mass production of the dresses. The head sweeper (who somehow became involved in this) believes that there is not a clear mandate and claims that the opinions are evenly distributed among the six categories. He further states that the slight differences among the various counts are probably due to chance. Test the null hypothesis that there is no significant difference among the opinions of the buyers. Test at the 0.01 level of risk. Follow a formal approach; that is, the five-step procedure discussed above.

15-8. The safety director of Honda Canada took samples at random from the file of minor accidents and classified them according to the time the accident took place.

Time	Number of Accidents	Time	Number of Accidents
8 a.m. up to 9 a.m.	6	1 p.m. up to 2 p.m.	7
9 a.m. up to 10 a.m.	6	2 p.m. up to 3 p.m.	8
10 a.m. up to 11 a.m.	20	3 p.m. up to 4 p.m.	19
11 a.m. up to 12 p.m.	8	4 p.m. up to 5 p.m.	6

Using the goodness-of-fit test and the 0.01 level of significance, determine whether the accidents are evenly distributed throughout the day. Write a brief explanation of your conclusion.

15.4 GOODNESS-OF-FIT TEST: UNEQUAL EXPECTED FREQUENCIES

The expected frequencies (f_e) in the previous problem involving hockey cards were all equal (20). Theoretically, it was expected that a picture of Mike Bossy would appear 20 times a picture of Bobby Orr would appear 20 times, and so on. The chi-square test can also be used if the expected frequencies are not equal. The following example illustrates the case of unequal expected frequencies and also gives a practical use of chi-square—namely to find out whether a local experience differs from the national experience.

Example 15-3

A national study of hospital admissions during a two-year period revealed these statistics concerning senior citizens who resided in care centres and who were hospitalized anytime during the period: 40 percent were admitted only once in the two-year period; 20 percent were admitted twice; 14 percent were admitted three times, and so on. The complete percentage distribution is given in Table 15-5.

TABLE 15-5: National Study: Admissions of Senior Citizens to Hospitals in a Two-Year Period

Number of Times Admitted	% of Total
1	40
2	20
3	14
4	10
5	8
6	6
7	2
Total	100

TABLE 15-6: Local Study: Admissions to the York County Hospital during a Two-Year Period

Number of Times Admitted	Number of Senior Citizens f_o
1	165
2	79
3	50
4	44
5	32
6	20
7	10
Total	400

The administrator of the local hospital is anxious to compare her York County Hospital experience with the national pattern or distribution. She selected 400 senior citizens in local care centres who needed hospitalization and determined the number of times during a two-year period each was admitted to her hospital. The observed frequencies are listed in Table 15-6.

The chi-square statistic is used to compare this local experience with the national experience. The question is: how can the locally observed frequencies in Table 15-6 be compared with the national percentages in Table 15-5. We will use the 0.05 level of significance.

Solution

Determining expected frequencies

Obviously, the *number* of observed frequencies resulting from the study of local senior citizens cannot be compared directly with the *percentages* given for the nation's hospitals. However, the percentages for the nation in Table 15-5 can be converted to expected frequencies, f_e. Table 15-5 shows that 40 percent of the senior citizens who required hospitalization used hospital services only once in a two-year period. Thus, if there is *no* difference between the experience at York County Hospital and the national experience, then 40 percent (proportion = 0.4) of the 400 sampled by the hospital administrator (160 senior citizens) would have been admitted just once during the two-year period. Further, 20 percent of the 400 sampled (80 people) would have been admitted twice, and so on. The rule for calculating expected frequency from the proportions or probabilities (*p*) for any category (say, *i*th category, where *i* can stand for any category from 1 to *k*) can be written as follows. Expected Frequency in the *i*th category, $(f_e^{\,i})$ = number of total observations (*n*) × probability (or proportion) of an observation(s) falling in the *i*th category (p^i). In symbols, we can write it as,

Expected Frequency	$f_e^i = n \times p^i$	15-3

The observed local frequencies and the expected local frequencies based on the percents in the national study are given in Table 15-7.

TABLE 15-7: Observed and Expected Frequencies for York County Hospital

Number of Times Admitted (Category)	Observed Number of Admissions (f_o)	Expected Number of Admissions (f_e)
1	165	40% × 400 = 160
2	79	20% × 400 = 80
3	50	14% × 400 = 56
4	44	10% × 400 = 40
5	32	8% × 400 = 32
6	20	6% × 400 = 24
7	10	2% × 400 = 8
	400	400

Must be equal

The null and alternative hypotheses are:

H_0: There is no difference between the local experience and the national experience.

H_1: There is a difference between the local experience and the national experience.

To find the decision rule we use Appendix E. There are *seven categories*, each distinguished by the number of times a senior citizen required hospitalization. So the degrees of freedom is *df* = *k* – 1 = 7 – 1 = 6. The *critical value of chi-square*, obtained from the table of chi-square distribution for 6 degrees of freedom and a 0.05 level of significance, is *12.592*.

Therefore, *the decision rule is to reject H_0 if the sample value of $\chi^2 > 12.592$.*

Data from Weldon's Experiment

Dice showing 5 or 6	0	1	2	3	4	5	6	7	8	9	10	11	12	Total
Number of times	185	1149	3265	5475	6114	5194	3067	1331	403	105	14	4	0	26 306

CHART 15-6: Decision Criteria for York County Hospital Research Study

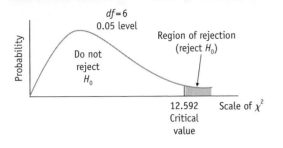

TABLE 15-8: Computing the Value of Chi-Square for the Hospital Study

Times Admitted	f_o	f_e	$f_o - f_e$	$(f_o - f_e)^2$	$(f_o - f_e)^2/f_e$
1	165	160	5	25	0.156
2	79	80	−1	1	0.013
3	50	56	−6	36	0.643
4	44	40	4	16	0.4
5	32	32	0	0	0
6	20	24	−4	16	0.667
7	10	8	2	4	0.5
Totals	400	400	0		$2.379 = \chi^2$

The decision rule is portrayed graphically in Chart 15-6. The details of computations are given in Table 15-8.

The computed value of chi-square (2.379) lies to the left of 12.592 and is, therefore, in the region where we cannot reject H_0. The *null hypothesis*, that there is no difference between the local experience at York County Hospital and the national experience, is therefore *not rejected*. The hospital administrator would conclude that, given the evidence, the local situation with respect to the hospitalization of senior citizens in care centres is similar to that in other parts of the country.

USING CHI-SQUARE WHEN SOME EXPECTED FREQUENCIES ARE SMALLER THAN FIVE

As we have mentioned earlier, if there is an unusually small number of expected frequencies (less than 5) in a cell, chi-square (if applied) might result in an erroneous conclusion due to a very poor approximation of the test statistic to the chi-square distribution. The rule of 5, we should note is a conservative rule that keeps us on the safe side. Recently, researchers have refined the rule to include expected frequencies between 1 and 5, if the number of such categories does not exceed 20 percent of all categories. That is, if there are 10 categories, a maximum of two (20 percent of 10) categories can contain expected frequencies between 1 and 5. There are other similar rules advanced by researchers. However, to be on the safe side, we recommend using the conservative rule of 5. In general, in a situation where we encounter a smaller than expected frequency in any category, we combine the category with the smaller frequency with another **adjacent** category. In combining categories, however, we must remain cautious about not creating a meaningless category.

Example 15-4

A Quebec university is comparing its staffing policy with universities of similar size and offering similar programs. Expected frequencies indicate an average staffing pattern of different levels at other universities. Observed frequencies are for the staffing pattern at the university in Quebec (see Table 15-9). Is there any difference in the size of the administration and the teaching staff at the university in Quebec compared to other universities in the province?

In the data, however, there are 3 categories with expected frequencies less than 5. Furthermore, about 43 percent of the categories (3 out of 7) contain less than 5 under expected frequencies. Either way, it does not seem appropriate to use the chi-square distribution for this data. If we still use the chi-square distribution for inferences, we shall obtain the results shown in part A of Chart 15-7. The calculated value of chi-square is 10.9. The value of chi-square for 6 degrees of freedom and 5 percent

TABLE 15-9: University in Quebec

University Faculty and Staff	f_o	f_e
President	1	1
Vice Presidents	3	2
Assistant Vice Presidents	4	3
Registrar/Admissions Staff	25	15
Professors (full-time)	92	95
Professors (part-time)	85	100
Other Staff	40	34
Total	250	250

CHART 15-7: University in Quebec

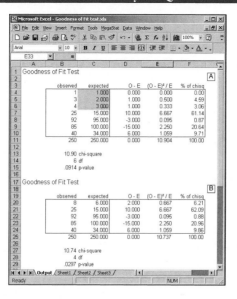

level of significance is 12.59. We thus fail to reject the null hypothesis of no difference.

However, if we combine the first three categories into a senior administration category, thus satisfying the rule of 5, the calculated value of chi-square is 10.74 (See Chart 15-7, part B). The critical value of chi-square for a 5 percent level of significance and 4 degrees of freedom is 9.488. Obviously, now we can reject the null hypothesis of no difference at 5 percent level of significance. In fact, as shown by the *P*-value, the Type I error in rejecting the null hypothesis is only 0.0297 or 2.97 percent as compared to the *P*-value of 9.14 percent (without combining the first three categories).

■ SELF-REVIEW 15-2

Canadian Accounting classifies accounts receivable as "current," "late," and "not collectible." Industry figures show that 60 percent of accounts receivable are current, 30 percent are late, and 10 percent are not collectible. Williams and Sheppard, a law firm in Mississauga, Ontario, has 500 accounts receivable: 320 are current, 120 are late, and 60 are not collectible. Are these numbers in agreement with the industry distribution? Use the 0.05 significance level.

EXERCISES 15-9 TO 15-12

15-9. The following hypotheses are given about student pocket expenses per week divided into three categories: A (over $20), B (between $10 and $20), and C (below $10).

H_0: 40 percent are in category A, 40 percent are in B, and 20 percent are in C.
H_1: The observations are not as described in H_0.

At Concordia, a sample of 60 yielded the following results:

Category	f_o
A	30
B	20
C	10

(a) State the decision rule using the 0.01 significance level.

(b) Compute the value of chi-square.

(c) What is your decision regarding H_0?

15-10. The chief of security for the Calgary Mall was directed to study the problem of missing goods. He selected a sample of 100 boxes that had been tampered with and ascertained that for 60 of the boxes, the missing contents were attributed to shoplifting. For 30 other boxes, he blamed employees for stealing the goods, and the remaining 10 boxes he blamed on poor inventory control.

In his report to the mall management, can he say that shoplifting is *twice* as likely to be the cause of the loss as compared with employee theft or poor inventory control? Use the 0.01 level of significance.

15-11. The credit card department of the Bank of Commerce knows from long experience that 5 percent of the cardholders have had some high school, 15 percent have completed high school, 25 percent have had some post-secondary education, and 55 percent have completed postsecondary education. Of the 500 cardholders whose cards have been called in for failure to pay their charges, 50 had some high school, 100 had completed high school, 190 had some postsecondary education, and 160 had completed postsecondary education. Can we conclude that the sample distribution of cardholders who do not pay their charges is different from the long experience of the bank of such cardholders? Use the 0.01 significance level.

15-12. For many years TV executives used the guideline that 30 percent of the audience was watching each of the three prime-time networks and 10 percent was watching local cable stations on a weekday night. A random sample of 500 viewers in the Halifax, Nova Scotia last Monday night showed that 165 homes were tuned into the CBC affiliate, 140 to the CTV affiliate, 125 to the ABC affiliate, and the remainder were viewing a local cable station. At the 0.05 significance level, can we conclude that the guideline is still reasonable?

15.5 USING THE GOODNESS-OF-FIT TEST TO TEST FOR NORMALITY

The goodness-of-fit test is one of several ways to determine whether a set of observed frequencies matches a set of expected frequencies that conforms to a normal distribution. To put it another way, do the observed values in a frequency distribution coincide with the expected values based on a normal distribution in the population? Recall in earlier chapters we often assumed that the sampled populations followed the normal distribution. This test offers a way to check that assumption.

Example 15-5 | After completing this chapter, one of the authors in his statistics class asked students to form groups of four to conduct a study as their mini-research project of one of the tests of goodness of fit based on primary data. Angela, Martha, Tina and Sara formed a group to investigate whether family incomes of students followed a normal distribution. They collected data on family incomes of 160 (randomly selected) students. They grouped all 160 students according to their family incomes into seven categories, as shown in Table 15-10. Angela's group gave the presentation to their class as follows:

TABLE 15-10: Family Incomes of 160 Students	
Family Income Per Year ($ thousands)	Number of Students
20 up to 30	4
30 up to 40	20
40 up to 50	41
50 up to 60	44
60 up to 70	29
70 up to 80	16
80 up to 90	2
90 and over	4
Total	160

Problem: Do the observed frequencies coincide with the expected frequencies based on the normal probability distribution?

Solution

As you know, expected frequencies in each category are based on probabilities in that category. Probabilities based on a normal distribution can be found from the probability tables for standard normal distribution (the Z variable). In order to find the expected frequencies based on normal distribution, therefore, we need to proceed in three steps:

First,   convert X-values for lower and upper limits of all categories into Z-values.
Second,   find probabilities based on each interval of Z-values for each category.
Third,   find expected frequencies by multiplying probabilities (found in Step 2) for each category by the total number of observations (160).

Step 1

Recall from Chapter 7,

$$Z = \frac{X - \mu}{\sigma}$$

where X is any value of the variable in the sample, such as $70 (thousand). For the data classified in class intervals, X-values refer to lower and upper limits of each class, μ is the mean of the population, and σ is the standard deviation of the population. However, in many cases, such as this one, we do not know the population mean and the standard deviation. In such cases, we use the estimated mean ($\bar{X}$) and the estimated standard deviation (S). The estimated mean and standard deviation from the sample raw data are:

$$\bar{x} = 54.03 \text{ and } S = 13.76$$

We illustrate computations of z-values for the 70 to 80 class interval. The z-values for other class intervals are calculated similarly.

The z-value for 70, the lower limit of the "70 up to 80" class, is 1.16, found by

$$Z_L = \frac{x_L - \bar{x}}{S} = \frac{70 - 54.03}{13.76} = 1.16$$

This indicates that 70 is 1.16 standard deviations above the mean of 54.03.
For the upper limit of the "70 up to 80" class, $z = 1.89$, found by

$$Z_U = \frac{x_U - \bar{x}}{S} = \frac{80 - 54.03}{13.76} = 1.89$$

Thus, 80 is 1.89 standard deviations above the mean of 54.03.

Note, since z_L and z_U are the same for adjacent categories except the first and last category, we only need to find z_L for all categories. Further, given the Z values in the normal table (only up to 3.09) we do not need to find the z_L-values for categories where

$$\frac{x_L - \bar{x}}{S} < -3.09$$

Step 2

Recall Prob. $(1.16 < z < 1.89)$ = Prob. $(0 < z < 1.89)$ – Prob. $(0 < z < 1.16)$. **Probability between 0 and the Upper Limit (1.89).**

To determine the area (probability) between the Z-values from 0 to 1.89, refer to the standard normal distribution table on the back inside cover of this book. Go down the left margin to 1.8, then horizontally to 0.09, and read the area. It is 0.4706. This is also the area under the curve between the mean of 54.03 and 80.00.

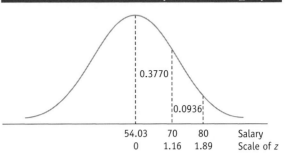

CHART 15-8: Computing the Normal Probability for a Category

Probability between 0 and the Lower Limit (1.16).

Similarly, we find Prob. $(0 < z < 1.16) = 0.3770$.

Thus, Prob. $(1.16 < z < 1.89) = 0.4706 - 0.3770 = 0.0936$.

This is the probability of family incomes falling in the group 70 to 80 (thousands). Thus, we expect 0.0936 or 9.36 percent of the family incomes to be between 1.16 and 1.89 standard deviations from the mean. This information is summarized in Chart 15-8. You can also use Excel or Minitab to compute these probabilities for each category as explained in Chapter 7.

Step 3

The expected frequency in a category, say ith category, is found by multiplying the probability (p^i) in that category with the total number of observations (n) as given by Formula 15-3 on page 683. Our category number (looking from the top, the category for 70 to 80) is $i = 6$. In this 6th category, $n = 160$ and $p^6 = 0.0936$. Note n is the same for all categories. It is the probability that differs from one category to another category. Therefore, expected frequency for the $i = 6$th category is: $f_e^i = (n) \times (p^i) = (160) \times (0.0936) = 14.976$. Please note the superscript i on p and f refers to categories. Do not confuse it with raising p and f to the power i.

Expected frequencies for other categories are found in the same manner. Expected frequencies for all categories are noted in Table 15-11. Note, we have combined the expected frequencies in the last two categories, since they were much smaller than five. (The expected frequencies for all categories, together with details of calculations are listed in Table 15-11.)

Now to compute the value of chi-square, see Table 15-12. Column 2 shows the observed frequency and column 3 the expected frequency for each of the salary categories. Columns 4, 5, and 6 show the computations for the chi-square value. The computed value of chi-square is 2.590.

As usual, the null and the alternative hypotheses are stated as:

H_0: The population follows the normal distribution.
H_1: The population does not follow the normal distribution.

TABLE 15-11: Calculating Expected Frequencies

Salary	Z values	Area (p^i)	Expected Frequency (f_e^i)
Under 30	Under -1.75	0.0401	$0.0401 \times 160 = 6.416$
30 to 40	-1.75 to -1.02	0.1138	$0.1138 \times 160 = 18.208$
40 to 50	-1.02 to -0.29	0.232	$0.2320 \times 160 = 37.120$
50 to 60	-0.29 to 0.43	0.2805	$0.2805 \times 160 = 44.880$
60 to 70	0.43 to 1.16	0.2106	$0.2106 \times 160 = 33.696$
70 to 80	1.16 to 1.89	0.0936	$0.0936 \times 160 = 14.976$
80 or over	1.89 and over	0.0294	$0.0294 \times 160 = 4.704$
Totals		1	160.00

TABLE 15-12: Calculations for Chi-Square

Salary (thousands)	(2) f_o	(3) f_e	(4) $f_o - f_e$	(5) $(f_o - f_e)^2$	(6) $(f_o - f_e)^2/f_e$
Under 30	4	6.416	-2.416	5.837	0.91
30 to 40	20	18.208	1.792	3.211	0.176
40 to 50	41	37.12	3.88	15.054	0.406
50 to 60	44	44.88	-0.88	0.774	0.017
60 to 70	29	33.696	-4.696	22.052	0.654
70 to 80	16	14.976	1.024	1.049	0.07
80 and over	6	4.704	1.296	1.68	0.357
Totals	160	160			$\chi^2 = 2.59$

To locate the critical value of the chi-square, we need to know the degrees of freedom. In this case there are seven categories (see Table 15-11), so $k - 1 = 7 - 1 = 6$. In addition, the values $54.03, the mean salary, and $13.76, the standard deviation of family incomes, were computed from this sample data. When we estimate population parameters from sample data, we lose a degree of freedom for each estimate. So we lose two more degrees of freedom for using the estimated values of the population mean and the population standard deviation in the computation of the chi-square. Thus, the number of degrees of freedom in this problem is 4, found by $(k - 1) - 2 = (7 - 1) - 2 = 4$. In general, when we use sample statistics to estimate population parameters, the number of degrees of freedom is found by $(k - 1) - p$, where "p" represents the number of population parameters being estimated from the sample data.

From Appendix E for chi-square, using the 0.05 significance level, the critical value of χ^2 is 9.488. H_0 is rejected if the computed value of chi-square is greater than 9.488. In this case we computed χ^2 to be 2.590, so the null hypothesis is **not** rejected. We conclude that the distribution of family incomes of students follows the normal distribution. Note, the expected frequency in the last category is 4.704, which is less than 5. But it seems reasonable to keep it rather than combine it with another category, as this is the only category with less than 5, and, in fact, it is quite close to 5.

USING EXCEL AND MEGASTAT TO TEST FOR NORMALITY

We could use Excel to find the expected frequencies and MegaStat to conduct the goodness-of-fit test. To find the expected frequencies in Excel, type in the upper limits of all categories in a column (as shown in Column C of Excel Chart 15-9), except for the last upper limit. The last upper limit for a normal distribution is infinity. Then, use f_x menu on the tool bar and find NORMDIST under Statistical functions. Click it. You will see a dialogue box with four empty rows, asking you the following:

1. *X*: enter the range of *X* values for the upper limits, except for the last category.

2. Mean: enter the value of mean for the population (if known) or calculated from the sample of observations.

3. Standard Deviation: Enter the value of the standard deviation for the population (if known) or calculated from the sample of observations.

4. Cumulative: Enter *True*.

You will see the result as shown in Column D in Chart 15-9 below, except for the last category. Since the cumulative probability for all categories must equal 1, enter 1 yourself in the last category. You can now write down the probability for each interval (as shown in Column E) by subtracting the probability shown for the upper limit in the previous class interval. The probability in the first class interval will remain the same as the cumulative probability in that class interval. Now multiplying Column E of interval probabilities with the number of observations ($n = 160$), you get the expected frequencies shown in Column F.

To conduct the goodness-of-fit test, use MegaStat for Column B (observed frequency) and Column F (expected frequency) as explained in Chart 15-5. The result is slightly different due to rounding.

MegaStat can also be used to test normality through a built-in procedure in the program available under "Descriptive Statistics." All you need to do in this procedure is specify "Input range" and place a check mark in the box "Normal curve goodness of fit"

EXCEL CHART 15-9: Test for Normality

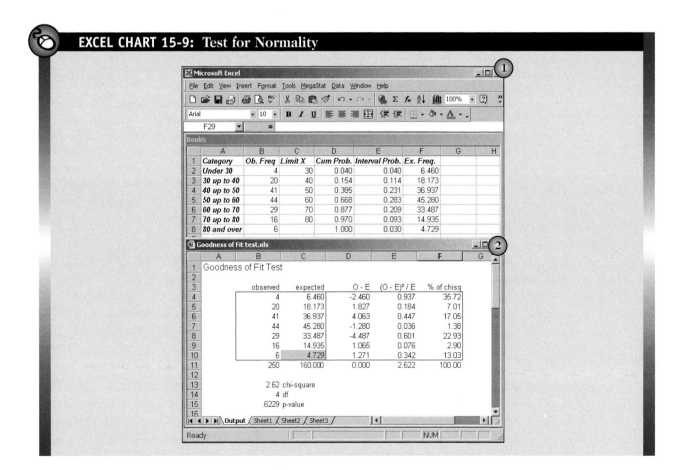

to get the output in terms of the computed value of chi-square and the *P*-value for the test. However, you may not get the same results due to differences in methods of computation.

WORKING WITH MINITAB TO TEST THE GOODNESS OF FIT

Alternatively, we can use Minitab to compute the cumulative probabilities, expected frequencies, and then the chi-square test statistic. Steps are shown in the session window of Minitab in Chart 15-10. However, formulae for these tests are mathematically too involved to be discussed here.

Minitab also has built-in procedures for three different types of tests of normality under "Basic Statistics." The Anderson-Darling test is most popular. To use any of the normality tests in Minitab, click Basic Statistics, Normality Test. Double-click Variable name and check the box for the required test on the Normality Test screen. Click OK. Use the *P*-value to make inferences. In general, a *P*-value of less than 0.05 provides sufficient evidence against normality.

MINITAB CHART 15-10: Test for Normality

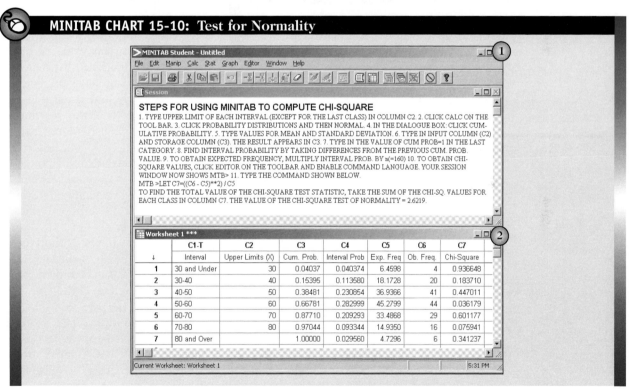

JARQUE–BERA TEST FOR NORMALITY

Since the normal distribution is characterized as symmetric (zero skewness) and as mesokurtic (kurtosis = 3) distribution, one natural way to test for normality is to test whether a frequency distribution in fact has these characteristics. C.M. Jarque and Anil K. Bera have proposed a test statistic built upon these characteristics of the normal distribution.[4] The test statistic is given by:

$$JB = n\left[\frac{S^2}{6} + \frac{K^2}{24}\right]$$

15-4

Where, S is a sample estimate of the coefficient of skewness and K is a sample estimate of the coefficient of kurtosis. Under the null hypothesis, H_0: $S = 0$ and $K = 0$ in the population, the JB test statistic is distributed as a chi-square distribution with 2 degrees of freedom. Note though, the value of kurtosis equals 3 for a normal distribution. However, both Excel and Minitab report a value of kurtosis after subtracting 3. The formula has therefore been adjusted accordingly for consistency with Excel and Minitab outputs.

The JB test statistic has performed well even in small samples. All that the test statistic needs is the sample estimates of S and K easily obtained in both Excel and Minitab. Recall, in Chapter 14, we promised to test the residuals for normality in this chapter. We shall therefore illustrate the test of normality for the data on residuals obtained from the regression analysis in Self-Review Exercise 14-3. The Excel charts 14-3c and 14-3e in the Answers to Self-Review are based on the data on ordinary residuals. Using the data on ordinary residuals, we computed the JB test statistic, as shown in Chart 15-11.

Since, under the null hypothesis, the critical value of chi-square for 2 degrees of freedom and a 5 percent level of significance is 5.99, and the value of JB equals 1.003, we conclude that the residuals are normally distributed.

The obvious advantage of the JB test is, it is extremely simple to apply. It can be applied to raw data as well as grouped data. Unlike the goodness-of-fit test for normality, the JB test is therefore not affected by the arbitrariness of class intervals. The only disadvantage, of course, is that the JB test tracks the specific shape of the distribution (i.e., symmetry and peak), whereas the goodness-of-fit test tracks correspondence between the observed frequencies and the expected frequencies for each class interval. In the Self-Review below, we apply the goodness-of-fit test for normality for its comparison with the JB test results.

EXCEL CHART 15-11: JB Test of Normality

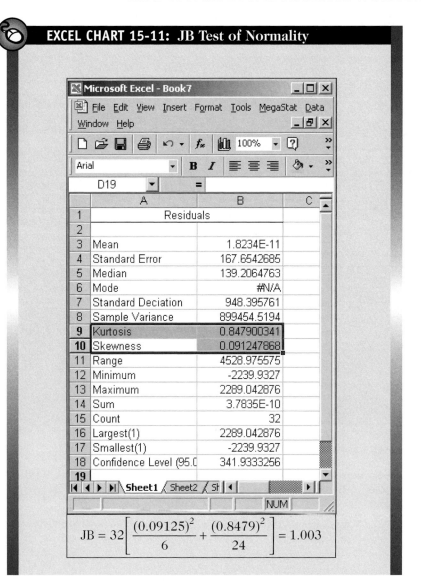

	Residuals
3 Mean	1.8234E-11
4 Standard Error	167.6542685
5 Median	139.2064763
6 Mode	#N/A
7 Standard Deciation	948.395761
8 Sample Variance	899454.5194
9 Kurtosis	0.847900341
10 Skewness	0.091247868
11 Range	4528.975575
12 Minimum	-2239.9327
13 Maximum	2289.042876
14 Sum	3.7835E-10
15 Count	32
16 Largest(1)	2289.042876
17 Smallest(1)	-2239.9327
18 Confidence Level (95.0	341.9333256

$$JB = 32\left[\frac{(0.09125)^2}{6} + \frac{(0.8479)^2}{24}\right] = 1.003$$

■ SELF-REVIEW 15-3

Use the residuals from the regression analysis of Investment in Canada in Chapter 14, Answer to Self-Review 14-3, to test for normality of those residuals based on the goodness-of-fit test. The data on residuals is in file Self-Review 15.3.xls on the CD-ROM.

EXERCISES 15-13 TO 15-14

15-13. A manufacturer of household appliances in Ontario reports in its advertising that the mean life of its washing machines, under normal use, is 6 years, with a standard deviation of 1.4 years. A sample of 90 units sold 10 years ago revealed the following distribution of the lengths of life. At the 0.05 significance level, can the manufacturer conclude that the lives of washing machines are normally distributed?

Length of Life (years)	Frequency
Up to 4	7
4 up to 5	14
5 up to 6	25
6 up to 7	22
7 up to 8	16
8 or more	6

15-14. The commissions for sales of new cars are reported to average $1500 per month with a standard deviation of $300. A sample of 500 sales representatives in Atlantic Canada revealed the following distribution of commissions. At the 0.01 significance level, can we conclude that the population is normally distributed, with a mean of $1500 and a standard deviation of $300?

Commission ($)	Frequency
Less than 900	9
900 up to 1200	63
1200 up to 1500	165
1500 up to 1800	180
1800 up to 2100	71
2100 or more	12
Total	500

15.6 CONTINGENCY TABLE ANALYSIS

The goodness-of-fit tests applied in the previous sections were concerned with only a single variable and a single trait. The chi-square test can also be used for a research project involving *two* traits. For example,

- Is there any relationship between the grade point average students earn in college and their income 10 years after graduation? The two traits measured for each individual are grade point average and income.

- The quality control manager of a company that operates three shifts (24 hours a day) wishes to know if there is a difference in quality on the three shifts. To investigate he selects a sample of 500 parts from this year's production. Each part is classified according to two criteria: whether the part is acceptable or not, and on which of the shifts it was manufactured.

• Does a male released from federal prison make a better adjustment to civilian life if he returns to his hometown or if he goes elsewhere to live? The two traits are adjustment to civilian life and place of residence. Note that both traits are measured on the nominal scale.

Example 15-6

Suppose the Federal Correction Agency wants to investigate the last question cited above: does a male released from federal prison make better adjustments to civilian life if he returns to his hometown or if he goes elsewhere to live? To put it another way, is there a relationship between adjustment to civilian life and place of residence after release from prison?

Solution

As before, the first step in hypothesis testing is to state the null and alternative hypotheses.

H_0: There is no relationship between *adjustment to civilian life* and *where the individual lives after being released from prison*.

H_1: There is a relationship between adjustment to civilian life and where the individual lives after being released from prison.

The 0.01 level of significance will be used to test the hypothesis. Recall that this is the probability of a Type I error (i.e., the probability is 0.01 that a true null hypothesis is rejected).

The Agency's psychologists interviewed 200 randomly selected former prisoners. Using a series of questions, the psychologists classified the adjustment of each individual to civilian life as outstanding, good, fair, or unsatisfactory as shown in Table 15-13. In this case, the Federal Correction Agency wondered whether adjustment to civilian life is *contingent on* (dependent upon) where the prisoner goes after release from prison.

TABLE 15-13: Sample Observations for Adjustment to Civilian Life and Place of Residence

Residence After Release From Prison	Adjustment to Civilian Life				
	Outstanding	Good	Fair	Unsatisfactory	Total
Hometown	27	35	33	25	120
Not Hometown	13	15	27	25	80
Total	40	50	60	50	200

Once we know how many rows (2) and how many columns (4) there are in the contingency table, the critical value and the decision rule can be determined as follows. For a chi-square test of significance where two traits are classified in a contingency table, the degrees of freedom are found by:

Degrees of Freedom (df) for a Contingency Table
= (number of rows − 1)(number of columns − 1) = $(r-1)(c-1)$

In this problem, $df = (r - 1)(c - 1) = (2 - 1)(4 - 1) = 3$.

To find the critical value for 3 degrees of freedom and the 0.01 level (selected earlier), refer to Appendix E for the chi-square table. It is 11.345. The decision rule is to reject the *null hypothesis of independence* if the computed value of χ^2 is greater than 11.345. The decision rule is portrayed graphically in Chart 15-12.

Now we find the computed value of χ^2. The observed frequencies, f_o, are shown in Table 15-14. How are the corresponding expected frequencies, f_e, determined? Note in the "Total" column of Table 15-13 that 120 of the 200 former prisoners (60 percent) returned to their hometowns. *If there was no relationship* between adjustment and residency after release from prison, we would expect 60 percent of the 40 ex-prisoners who made outstanding adjustment to civilian life to reside in their hometowns. Thus, the expected frequency, f_e, for the upper left cell is $0.60 \times 40 = 24$. Likewise, if there was no relationship between adjustment and present residence, we would expect 60 percent of the 50 ex-prisoners (=30) who had a "good" adjustment to civilian life to reside in their hometowns.

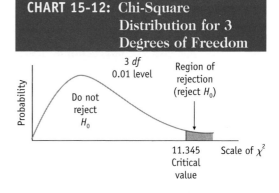

CHART 15-12: Chi-Square Distribution for 3 Degrees of Freedom

Further, notice that 80 of the 200 ex-prisoners (40 percent) did not return to their hometowns to live. Thus, of the 60 considered by the psychologists to have made a "fair" adjustment to civilian life, $0.40 \times 60 = 24$, would be expected not to return to their hometowns.

The expected frequency for any cell can be determined by

$$\text{Expected Frequency for a Cell} = \frac{(Row\,Total)(Column\,Total)}{Grand\,Total} \qquad \textbf{15-5}$$

Using this formula, the expected frequency for the upper left cell in Table 15-13 is:

$$\text{Expected frequency} = \frac{(Row\,Total)(Column\,Total)}{(Grand\,Total)} = \frac{(120)(40)}{200} = 24$$

The observed frequencies, f_o, and the expected frequencies, f_e, for all of the cells in the contingency table are listed in Table 15-14.

TABLE 15-14: Observed and Expected Frequencies

Residence after Release from Prison	Adjustment to Civilian Life								Total (Row)	
	Outstanding		Good		Fair		Unsatisfactory			
	f_o	f_e	f_o	f_e	f_o	f_e	f_o	f_e	f_o	f_e
Hometown	27	24	35	30	33	36	25	30	120	120
Not hometown	13	16	15	20	27	24	25	20	80	80
Total (column)	40	40	50	50	60	60	50	50	200	200

Must be equal

$\dfrac{(80)(50)}{200}$

Must be equal

The test statistic for independence between two variables (residency and adjustment, in this case) is the same as the test statistic X^2 for goodness of fit given by Formula 15-1. For large sample sizes, it is distributed approximately as chi-square distribution with $(r-1)(c-1)$ degrees of freedom under the null hypothesis of independence between the two variables.

The Test Statistic	$$X^2 = \sum_1^k \left[\frac{(f_o - f_e)^2}{f_e} \right]$$	**15-6**

For large sample sizes, X^2 is distributed approximately as a chi-square (χ^2) distribution with $(r-1)(c-1)$ degrees of freedom under the null hypothesis of independence between variables.

Starting with the upper left cell:

$$\chi^2 = \frac{(27-24)^2}{24} + \frac{(25-30)^2}{30} + \frac{(33-36)^2}{36} + \frac{(25-30)^2}{30}$$
$$+ \frac{(13-16)^2}{16} + \frac{(15-20)^2}{20} + \frac{(27-24)^2}{24} + \frac{(25-20)^2}{20}$$
$$= 0.375 + 0.833 + 0.250 + 0.833 + 0.563 + 1.250 + 0.375 + 1.250$$
$$= 5.729$$

Because the computed value of chi-square (5.729) lies in the region to the left of (less than) 11.345, the null hypothesis is not rejected at the 0.01 level. We conclude that there is *no* relationship between adjustment to civilian life and where the prisoner resides after being released from prison. For the Federal Correction Agency's advisement program, adjustment to civilian life is not related to where the ex-prisoner lives.

We can get the same results using either Minitab or Excel. Steps for using Excel and Minitab together with outputs are given in Charts 15-13 and 15-14. Observe the value

EXCEL CHART 15-13: Contingency Test

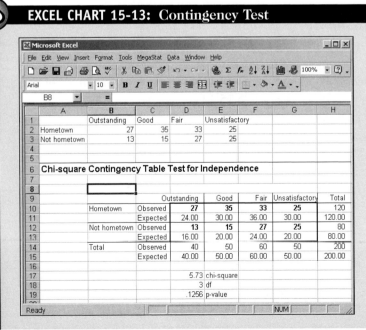

EXCEL INSTRUCTIONS
1. Enter data for observed frequencies in Excel as shown.
2. Click MegaStat.
3. Click Chi-square/Crosstab and select Contingency Table.
4. In the Input dialogue box, include all columns and rows (A1 to E3) and put a check mark for Chi-square and Expected frequencies.
5. Click OK to obtain the output shown on the left.

MINITAB CHART 15-14: Contingency Test

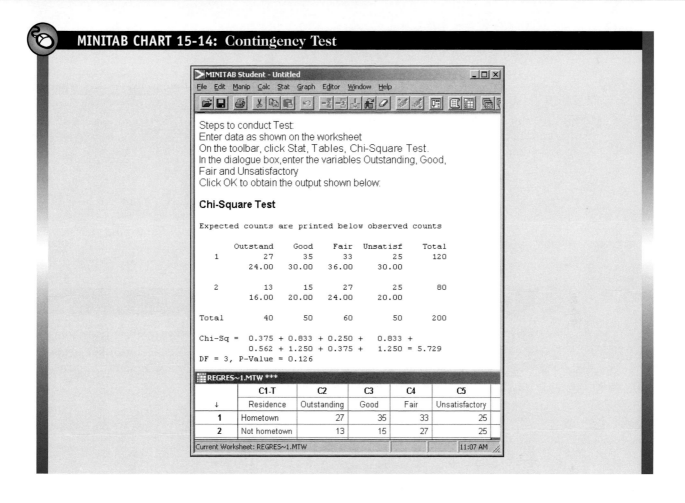

of chi-square is the same as that computed earlier. In addition, the P-value is reported, 0.126. So, the probability (Type I error) of finding a value of the test statistic this large or larger by chance is 0.126, when H_0 is true.

■ SELF-REVIEW 15-4

The "technology-meltdown" in the year 2001 and the terrorists' attacks in the USA on September 11, 2001, have had serious repercussions for both American and Canadian economies. The Government of Canada is considering boosting the Canadian economy through various policies. The Business and Economics Society at a Western Canadian university staged a debate on the issue of policy-effectiveness to boost the economy. The debate on policies seemed to be divided on political party lines. At the end of the debate, therefore, they conducted a poll of 125 students selected randomly and asked them about their support for one of the three debated policies and their affiliations to one of the three political parties. The three policies were (1) to reduce interest rates to boost investment spending (Interest Rate), (2) to reduce personal income taxes (Taxes) to boost consumer spending, and (3) to increase social security spending (Social Security) to increase consumer spending. The party affiliations asked for in the survey were New Democrats (NDP), Liberals, and Canadian Alliance and/or Progressive Conservatives (Alliance/PC).

	NDP	Liberals	Alliance/PC	Total
Social Security	18	12	10	40
Interest Rate	17	15	13	45
Taxes	9	9	22	40
Total	44	36	45	125

(a) What is this table called?
(b) State the null hypothesis and the decision rule. Select a 5 percent level of significance.
(c) Determine the value of the chi-square test statistic. What is your decision regarding the null hypothesis?
(d) Interpret the results.

EXERCISES 15-15 TO 15-18

15-15. The director of advertising for the *Gazette* newspaper in Montreal is studying the relationship between the type of community in which a subscriber resides and the portion of newspaper he or she reads first. For a sample of 1024 readers, she collected the following information.

	National News	Sports	Comics
City	170	124	90
Suburb	120	112	100
Rural	130	90	88

At the 0.05 significance level, can we conclude there is a relationship between the type of community where the person resides and the portion of the paper read first?

15-16. Four brands of light bulbs are being considered for use in a large manufacturing plant in Newfoundland. The director of purchasing asked for samples of 100 from each manufacturer. The numbers of acceptable and unacceptable bulbs from each manufacturer are shown below. At the 0.05 significance level, is there a difference in the quality of the bulbs?

	Manufacturer			
	A	B	C	D
Unacceptable	12	8	5	11
Acceptable	88	92	95	89
Total	100	100	100	100

15-17. The Quality Control Department at Atlantic Superstore, a grocery chain in Atlantic Canada, conducts a monthly check on the comparison of scanned prices to posted prices. The chart below summarizes the results of a sample of 500 items last month. Company management would like to know whether there is any relationship between error rates on regularly priced items and specially priced items in their ads. Use the 0.01 significance level.

	Regular Price	Special Price
Undercharge	20	10
Overcharge	15	30
Correct price	200	225

15-18. The use of cellular phones in automobiles has increased dramatically in the last few years. Of concern to traffic experts, as well as manufacturers of cellular phones, is the effect on accident rates. Is someone who is using a cellular phone more likely to be involved in a traffic accident? What is your conclusion from the following sample information? Use the 0.05 significance level.

	Had an Accident in the Last Year	Did Not Have an Accident Last Year
Cellular phone *not* in use	25	300
Cellular phone in use	50	400

CHAPTER OUTLINE

I. Pearson discovered chi-square distribution to test for goodness of fit between an assumed distribution in the population and an observed frequency distribution. The chi-square distribution is now used in a variety of applications in business and economics, as well as in many other disciplines. It can be used for both qualitative and quantitative data. The characteristics of the chi-square distribution are:
   A. The value of chi-square is never negative.
   B. The chi-square distribution is positively skewed.
   C. It depends on the degrees of freedom. Each time the degrees of freedom change, a new distribution is formed. As the degrees of freedom increase, the distribution approaches the shape of a normal distribution.

II. A goodness-of-fit test shows whether an observed set of frequencies could have come from a hypothesized discrete distribution.
   A. The degrees of freedom are $k - 1$, where k is the number of categories.
   B. The formula for computing the value of chi-square test statistic is

$$\chi^2 = \sum \left[\frac{(f_o - f_e)^2}{f_e} \right]$$

III. A goodness-of-fit test can also be used to determine whether the sample observations came from a continuous distribution such as the normal distribution.
   A. In the case of goodness of fit for a normal distribution, the degrees of freedom are $(k - 1) - p$ where p is the number of parameters estimated to compute the chi-square test statistic.
   B. Test for normality can also be conducted through the Jarque-Bera test statistic.

$$JB = n \left[\frac{S^2}{6} + \frac{K^2}{24} \right]$$ is distributed as chi-square with 2 degrees of freedom.

IV. Chi-square statistic can also be used as a test of independence between two variables (traits). Each variable (trait) is further classified by the number of categories, called rows and columns to form a contingency table. There are (number of rows × number of columns) cells in a contingency table. The total number of rows and columns in the contingency table depends on the number of categories of each variable.

A. Each observation falls in one of the cells of the contingency table.

B. The number of observations in a cell is called the *observed frequency* (f_o).

C. The expected frequency (f_e) in each cell of the contingency table is determined by the product of the total number of observations in the row and in the column corresponding to the cell divided by the number of total observations (grand total) in the table.

$$f_e = \frac{(Row\,Total)(Column\,Total)}{(Grand\,Total)}$$

D. The degrees of freedom for the chi-square for the test of independence are determined by $df = (Rows - 1)(Columns - 1) = (r - 1)(c - 1)$.

CHAPTER EXERCISES 15-19 TO 15-32

15-19. Vehicles heading west on King Street may turn right, left, or go straight ahead on Queen Street. The city traffic engineer believes that half of the vehicles will continue straight through the intersection. Of the remaining half, equal proportions will turn right and left. Two hundred vehicles were observed, with the following results. Use the 0.10 significance level. Can we conclude that the traffic engineer is correct?

	Straight	Right Turn	Left Turn
Frequency	112	48	40

15-20. The publisher of a sports magazine in Alberta plans to offer new subscribers one of three gifts: a sweatshirt with the logo of their favourite team; a coffee cup with the logo of their favourite team; or a pair of earrings also with the logo of their favourite team. In a sample of 500 new subscribers, the number of customers selecting each gift is reported below. At the 0.05 significance level, is there a preference for the gifts or should we conclude that the gifts are equally well liked?

Gift	Frequency
Sweatshirt	183
Coffee cup	175
Earrings	142

15-21. Use Weldon's experimental data in the *Statistics in Action*, Section 15.4, and verify Pearson's conclusion that Weldon's dice were biased. Repeat your calculation again this time with a relative frequency definition of probability of 0.3377. Would you still conclude that the Weldon's dice were biased? Use the 0.05 significance level. (Note your computed value of chi-square will differ from Pearson's computed value due to differences in combining the categories with expected frequencies less than 5.)

15-22. There are four entrances to the Regent Mall shopping complex in Fredericton. The Mall maintenance supervisor would like to know if the entrances are equally utilized. To investigate, 400 people were observed entering the complex. The number of customers using each entrance is reported below. At the 0.01 significance level, is there a difference in the use of the four entrances?

Entrance	Frequency
Main Street	140
King Street	120
Queen Street	90
Walnut Street	50
Total	400

15-23. The owner of a mail-order catalogue in Saskatchewan would like to compare her sales with the geographic distribution of the population. A breakdown of percent of population (% Pop) and the number of orders from a random sample of 1000 orders shipped to each province (Orders) are given in file Exercise 15-23.xls on the CD-ROM.

At the 0.01 significance level, does the distribution of the orders reflect the population?

15-24. The Windsor Mattress and Furniture Company in Windsor, Ontario, wishes to study the number of credit applications received per day for the last 300 days. The information is reported below.

Number of Credit Applications	Frequency (Number of Days)
0	50
1	77
2	81
3	48
4	31
5 or more	13

To interpret, there were 50 days on which no credit applications were received, 77 days on which only one application was received, and so on. Would it be reasonable to conclude that the population distribution is a Poisson distribution with a mean of 2.0? Use the 0.05 significance level. (Hint: to find the expected frequencies use the Poisson distribution with a mean of 2.0. Find the probability of exactly one success given a Poisson distribution with a mean of 2.0. Multiply this probability by 300 to find the expected frequency for this category. Find expected frequencies for other categories in a similer manner.)

15-25. In the 1990s the New Brunswick Mining Company implemented new safety guidelines. Prior to these new guidelines, management expected there to be no accidents in 40 percent of the months, one accident in 30 percent of the months, two accidents in 20 percent of the months, and three accidents in 10 percent of the months. Over the last 10 years, or 120 months, there have been 46 months in which there were no accidents, 40 months in which there was one accident, 22 months in which there were two accidents, and 12 months in which there were 3 accidents. At the 0.05 significance level, can management at the mining company conclude that there has been a change in the monthly accident rate?

15-26. The Canadian Association of Television Broadcasters recently reported that the mean number of television sets per household in Canada is 2.30 sets and that the standard deviation is 1.474 sets. A sample of 100 homes in Winnipeg, Manitoba, revealed the following number of sets per household:

Number of TV Sets	Number of Households	Number of TV Sets	Number of Households
0	7	3	18
1	27	4	10
2	28	5 or more	10

At the 0.05 significance level, is it reasonable to conclude that the number of television sets per household follows the normal distribution based on the
(a) goodness-of-fit test?
(b) Jarque-Bera test?

15-27. Eckel Manufacturing in Edmonton, Alberta, believes that their hourly wages follow a normal probability distribution. To confirm this, 300 workers were sampled and the results organized into the following frequency distribution. At the 0.10 significance level, is it reasonable to conclude that the distribution of hourly wages approximates the normal distribution
(a) based on the goodness-of-fit test?
(b) based on the Jarque-Bera test?

Hourly Wage ($)	Frequency
5.50 up to 6.50	20
6.50 up to 7.50	54
7.50 up to 8.50	130
8.50 up to 9.50	68
9.50 up to 10.50	28
Total	300

15-28. A recent study by a large retailer in Ontario, designed to determine whether there was a relationship between the importance a store manager placed on advertising and the size of the store, revealed the following sample information:

	Important	Not Important
Small	40	52
Medium	106	47
Large	67	32

What is your conclusion? Use the 0.05 significance level.

15-29. Two hundred men selected at random from various levels of management in Quebec were interviewed regarding their concern over environmental issues. The response of each person was tallied into one of three categories: no concern, some concern, and great concern. The results were:

Level of Management	No Concern	Some Concern	Great Concern
Top management	15	13	12
Middle management	20	19	21
Supervisor	7	7	6
Group leader	28	21	31

Use the 0.01 significance level to determine whether there is a relationship between management level and environmental concern.

15-30. A Canadian study regarding the relationship between age and the amount of pressure sales personnel feel in relation to their jobs revealed the following sample information. At the 0.01 significance level, is there a relationship between job pressure and age?

Age (years)	Degree of Job Pressure		
	Low	Medium	High
Less than 25	20	18	22
25 up to 40	50	46	44
40 up to 60	58	63	59
60 and older	34	43	43

15-31. The claims department at the British Columbia Insurance Company in Vancouver believes that younger drivers have more accidents and, therefore, should be charged higher insurance rates. Investigating a sample of 1200 policyholders revealed the following breakdown on whether a claim had been filed in the last three years and the age of the policyholder. Is it reasonable to conclude that there is a relationship between the age of the policyholder and whether or not the person filed a claim? Use the 0.05 significance level.

Age Group	No Claim	Claim
16 up to 25	170	74
25 up to 40	240	58
40 up to 55	400	44
55 or older	190	24
Total	1000	200

15-32. A sample of employees at a large chemical plant was asked to indicate a preference for one of three pension plans. The results are given in the following table. Does it seem that there is a relationship between the pension plan selected and the job classification of the employees? Use the 0.01 significance level.

Job Class	Pension Plan		
	Plan A	Plan B	Plan C
Supervisor	10	12	29
Clerical	19	80	19
Labour	81	57	22

www.exercises.ca 15-33 TO 15-34

(Use the 5 percent level of significance in all Exercises below)

15-33. Collect data on the profile of your community with regard to variables sex and educational characteristics (highest level of schooling for the population age 15 years and over) from the www.statcan.ca Web site.
(a) Are the variables sex and educational characteristics in your county independent?
(b) Use the same data on educational characteristics for your community for either male or female. From the same Web site, collect data on the same variables for Canada as a whole. Test whether the educational character- istics in your community are the same as the national characteristics.

15-34. Collect data on 5-star rated mutual funds from www.globefund.com.
(a) Use the JB test for normality for one-year rate of return for all mutual funds.
(b) Classify all funds into approximately 5 to 7 categories by one-year rate of return. Test for normality using the goodness-of-fit test.
(c) Classify all mutual funds by one-year rate of return (one variable) and asset classes (second variable). Test for the independence of rate of return and asset classes.

■■ COMPUTER DATA EXERCISES 15-35 TO 15-37

15-35. Refer to the file Real Estate Data.xls, which reports information on homes sold in Victoria, B.C. last year.
(a) Develop a contingency table that shows whether a home has a pool and the township in which the house is located. Is there an association between the variables "pool" and "township"? Use the 0.05 significance level.
(b) Develop a contingency table that shows whether a home has an attached garage and the township in which the home is located. Is there an association between the variables "attached garage" and "township? Use the 0.05 significance level.

15-36. Refer to the file BASEBALL-2000.xls, which reports information on the 30 Major League Baseball teams for the 2000 season. Set up a variable that divides the teams into two groups, those that had a winning season and those that did not. There are 162 games in the season, so define a winning season as having won 81 or more games. Next, divide the teams into two salary groups. Let the 15 teams with the largest salaries be in one group and the 15 teams with the smallest salaries in the other. At the 0.05 significance level is there a relationship between salaries and winning?

15-37. Use the data set from file 100 of Top 1000 companies.xls. Use earnings per share for the sample of 100 companies. Are earnings per share in Canadian companies normally distributed? Use both the goodness-of-fit test and the Jarque-Bera test to test for normality at a 0.01 level of significance.

CHAPTER 15   ANSWERS TO SELF-REVIEW

15-1. (a) Observed frequencies.
   (b) Five (Five days of the week).
   (c) 10. Total observed frequencies $\div$ 5 = 50/5 = 10.
   (d) 4; $k - 1 = 5 - 1 = 4$.
   (e) 13.277 (from the chi-square table in Appendix E).
   (f) 1.0.

$$\chi^2 = \sum\left[\frac{(f_o - f_e)^2}{f_e}\right] = \frac{(8-10)^2}{10}$$

$$+\cdots+\frac{(12-10)^2}{10} = 1.00$$

   (g) No. We do not reject H_0.
   (h) Absenteeism is distributed evenly throughout the five-day week. The observed differences are due to sampling variation.

15-2. H_0: $P_C = 0.60$, $P_L = 0.30$, and $P_U = 0.10$.
   H_1: Distribution is not as above.
   Reject H_0 if $\chi^2 > 5.991$.

Category	f_o	f_e	$(f_o - f_e)^2/f_e$
Current	320	300	1.33
Late	120	150	6.00
Uncollectible	60	50	2.00
	500	500	9.33

Reject H_0. The accounts receivable data does not reflect the national average.

15-3. Goodness-of-Fit Test (MegaStat Output).

Observed	Expected	$O - E$	$(O-E)^2/E$	% of chi sq
6	7.372	−1.372	0.255	8.16
5	5.957	−0.957	0.154	4.92
16	11.299	4.701	1.956	62.53
5	7.372	−2.372	0.763	24.39
32	32.000	0.000	3.129	100.00

3.13	chi-square
2	df
0.2092	P-value

Note: O stands for observed frequencies (f_o) and E for expected frequencies (f_e). Although the value of chi-square (3.13) is larger compared to JB (=1), the null hypothesis is still *not* rejected.

15-4. (a) Contingency table.
   (b) There is no relationship between political affiliation and policy option.
      Reject H_0 if sample value of chi-square is greater than 9.488.
   (c) The value of chi-square is completed from the following table.
      The sample value of chi-square is 9.89, so H_0 is rejected at the 5 percent level of significance.
   (d) There is a relationship between policy option and political affiliation.
      Can you reject H_0 at a 1 percent level of significance?

Chi-square Contingency Table Test for Independence (MegaStat Output)

	NDP	Liberal	Alliance/PC	Total
Social Security				
Observed	18	12	10	40
Expected	14.08	11.52	14.40	40.00
$(O - E)^2/E$	1.09	0.02	1.34	2.46
Interest Rate				
Observed	17	15	13	45
Expected	15.84	12.96	16.20	45.00
$(O - E)^2/E$	0.08	0.32	0.63	1.04
Taxes				
Observed	9	9	22	40
Expected	14.08	11.52	14.40	40.00
$(O - E)^2/E$	1.83	0.55	4.01	6.40
Total				
Observed	44	36	45	125
Expected	44.00	36.00	45.00	125.00
$(O - E)^2/E$	3.01	0.89	5.99	9.89

9.89	chi-square
4	df
0.0423	P-value

CHAPTER 16

Nonparametric Methods: Analysis of Ranked Data

GOALS

When you have completed this chapter, you will be able to:

- Conduct the sign test for single and dependent samples using the binomial and standard normal distributions as the test statistics

- Conduct a test of hypothesis for dependent samples using the Wilcoxon signed-rank test

- Conduct and interpret the Wilcoxon rank-sum test for independent samples

- Conduct and interpret the Kruskal-Wallis test for several independent samples

- Compute and interpret Spearman's coefficient of rank correlation

- Conduct a test of hypothesis to determine whether the correlation among the ranks in the population is different from zero.

DR. JOHN ARBUTHNOT (1667–1735)

D r. John Arbuthnot, son of Reverend Alexander Arbuthnot, Principal of King's College Aberdeen, Scotland, was educated at Marischal College, Aberdeen, where he received a master of arts degree at the age of 18. After the death of his father in 1691, he moved to London to teach mathematics and published his first book *Of the Laws of Chance* in 1692. While teaching mathematics, he became a fellow-commoner at Oxford and received his Doctor of Medicine by examination at St. Andrew's, Scotland in 1696. In 1709, he was appointed as Physician Extraordinary to Queen Anne.

In 1710, Dr. Arbuthnot published an essay, *An Argument for Divine Providence*, in which he examined the numbers of male and female births in London for a period of 82 years (1629–1710) and noted that in every year the number of male births exceeded that of female births, though the total number of men and women were approximately equal. Arbuthnot's question was to determine if the ratio of male to female births as compared to the ratio of males and females in the total population (approximately half) could have happened by chance or by some design of the Creator. In Arbuthnot's words,

"Among the innumerable footsteps of Divine Providence to be found in the Works of Nature, there is a very remarkable one to be observed in the exact Ballance that is maintained between the Numbers of men and Women: for by this means it is provided, that the Species may never fail, nor perish, since every Male may have its Female, and of a proportionable Age. This Equality of Males and Females is not the Effect of Chance but Divine Providence, working for a good End, which I thus demonstrate: Let there be a Die of Two sides, M and F... ."[1]

He then calculated the odds of this happening by chance. Based on the binomial distribution, he argued, the odds would be the same as that of obtaining 82 heads in 82 tosses of a coin, i.e., $(1/2)^{82} = 0.000\,000\,000\,000\,000\,000\,000\,000\,0002$, a very small probability indeed. Think of the probability over innumerable number of years since this is happening! Arbuthnot's justification for the Design was that males were the major breadwinners for the family and therefore exposed to greater risks of life. Based on this exercise, Arbuthnot also argued that God exists, and that polygamy is against the laws of Nature and justice! As a small challenge, we ask you to examine the same question in www.exercises.ca in present day circumstances.

Later, Arbuthnot came in contact with great literary figures of his time such as John Gay, Jonathan Swift and Alexander Pope. This seems to have motivated him to write a number of satirical pieces. He is best remembered for his work, *The Law is a Bottomless Pit*, a series of five pamphlets on the Whig war policy, a political satire, in which he introduced the character, John Bull, the typical Englishman. He was called an "unusual genius" by Samuel Johnson, and Pope wrote the famous *Epistle to Dr. Arbuthnot*.

In the 20th century, R.A. Fisher, M.G. Kendall, C. Spearman, F. Wilcoxon, H.B. Mann, D.R. Whitney, W.A. Kruskal and W.A. Wallis have made pioneering contributions to the field of nonparametric statistics.

1498
1548
1598
1648
1698
1748
1898
1948
2000

INTRODUCTION

In Chapters 10 through 14, we learned how to draw inferences about parameters of one or more populations based on a sample of information. In Chapter 15, we learned to draw inferences about the nature of probability distribution in the population. We continue with learning more about the process of inference in this chapter with three major differences.

1. Our testing procedures in Chapters 10 through 15, particularly for small samples, were dependent on the assumption of normal distribution. Alternatively, for large samples, we used the central limit theorem to justify the testing procedures. These assumptions allowed us to use Z, t, F and chi-square testing procedures. In this chapter, we develop methods that require weaker assumptions such as only continuity or continuity with symmetry of the population distributions instead of the stronger assumption of normal distribution. In this sense, they are called *distribution-free* tests.

2. Populations studied in Chapters 10 through 14, in general, required data that was measurable at least on an interval scale. In Chapter 15, we developed testing procedures for population distributions that could apply to data measured on any scale from nominal to ratio level. Like Chapter 15, in this chapter we develop test procedures that are applicable to both quantitative and qualitative data, though most of them assume at least the ordinal scale of measurement. Since the data on the interval scale or ratio scale can be transformed to the nominal/ordinal scale, the methods developed in this chapter can also be applied to higher scales of measurement. The converse is not true.

3. Most of the test procedures developed in this chapter depend merely on signs and/or ranks in the data set. For the data sets available at a higher level of measurement, the tests provide quick and easy methods to conduct a test of hypothesis. However, since the test procedures in such cases do not use all the information contained in the data set, they are less efficient compared to the classical testing procedures.

Thus, **nonparametric tests** require less restrictive assumptions about the populations. This allows us to test characteristics of many populations that are not testable by the classical hypothesis testing procedures (Z, t, F, chi square). However, the nonparametric methods often use less information from the data compared to the parametric test procedures. In this sense, nonparametric test procedures are somewhat weaker compared to their parametric counterparts.

Nonparametric testing procedures are therefore recommended in the following situations:

(a) when the parametric methods do not apply due to a lower scale of measurement; or

(b) when assumptions required for parametric methods such as normal distribution of population(s) happen to be seriously violated; or

(c) as an exploratory device to learn about the nature of the population since the nonparametric methods are very simple to apply.

Six **distribution-free tests** will be considered in this chapter: the sign test, the median test, the Wilcoxon signed-rank test, the Wilcoxon rank-sum test, the Kruskal-Wallis test, and the Spearman coefficient of rank correlation. The sign test is the simplest of all nonparametric test procedures. It serves as an alternative testing procedure for proportions including the median for observations based on single populations as well as observations based on populations of paired observations. The sign test is applicable to data based on any of the four levels of measurement. The Wilcoxon signed-rank test procedure uses both the signs and the magnitude of differences, and is therefore applicable to data measured at least on an ordinal scale. Both of these tests provide a nonparametric alternative to Z and t tests for single and matched pair populations covered in Chapters 10 and 11.

The Wilcoxon rank-sum test provides a nonparametric alternative to a small sample t test for the differences in the means of two populations (Chapter 11). The Kruskal-Wallis test procedure provides a nonparametric alternative to the F test for the differences in the means of more than two populations (Chapter 12). Spearman's rank correlation provides an alternative to Pearson's correlation coefficient for observations based on the ordinal level of measurement (Chapter 13).

16.1 THE SIGN TEST

A FEW SCENARIOS

THE ARBUTHNOT EXPERIMENT

The sign test is based on the sign given to a difference between each sample observation and a hypothesized value in the population, or the sign given to a difference between each paired observation. We usually designate a plus sign for a positive difference and a minus sign for a negative difference. In Arbuthnot's example, male births in London are hypothesized to be ½ of the total births in a year based on equal probability of the birth of a male or female (i.e., due to chance factors). Male births greater than ½ of the total births could then be assigned "+" signs and those lower than ½ "−" signs. Of course, as mentioned in the pioneer vignette, Arbuthnot found male births greater than ½ in all 82 observations (years). In this case, observations are measured at the highest level of measurement (the ratio scale). For the sign test, we are not concerned with the magnitude of the difference, only the direction of the difference.

A PRODUCT-PREFERENCE EXPERIMENT

A product-preference experiment illustrates another use of the sign test. Taster's Choice markets two kinds of coffee in a 4-ounce jar: decaffeinated and regular. Their market research department wants to determine whether coffee drinkers prefer decaffeinated or regular coffee. A randomly selected sample of coffee drinkers is given two small, unmarked cups of coffee, and each drinker is asked his or her preference. Preference for decaffeinated is coded by a "+" sign, and a preference for the regular coffee by a "−" sign. Here again, based on a null hypothesis of no preference for either type of coffee, we would expect half of the sample of coffee drinkers to prefer decaffeinated and the other half regular coffee. We can test this null hypothesis, against the alternative that the decaffeinated coffee is preferred, at a predetermined level of significance, by simply counting the total number of + signs. Since the coffee drinkers were asked only to name their preferred brand of coffee, the observations in this case have been measured at the nominal (the lowest) scale of measurement.

One of the most popular uses of the sign test is for the differences in the means/medians of two populations, dependent in some way on each other. In Chapter 11, we gave a special name, *matched pairs*, to such populations. Matched pair experiments can be viewed in the form of "before/after" type experiments—where the before experiment population serves as a *control group* and the after experiment population as the *treatment group*, or in the form of comparing two treatments on two identical populations.

A BEFORE AND AFTER EXPERIMENT

As an example of the former case, your instructor in this course may be interested in investigating the superiority of a new method of testing your understanding of the course material on weekly take-home assignments as compared to the old method of weekly class tests. You may wish to assume that there is no other influence on the marks except the nature of the tests. The instructor may record the marks of 10 randomly selected students based on past tests (before treatment) and the marks of the same 10 students based on take-home assignments (after treatment). For the sign test, the instructor only needs to record the improvement in performance by a "+" sign and the deterioration in the performance by a "−" sign. Under the null hypothesis, that the new method does not improve performance, the instructor can use a test statistic based on the number of "+" signs to test the null hypothesis.

EXPERIMENTING WITH TWO TREATMENTS

The matched pair situations can also arise in cases where we are interested in comparing the effects of two treatments. One individual from each population is paired with another individual from another population. Both individuals in each pair are assumed to be identical except for the treatment(s). To illustrate, suppose an evaluation is to be made on a new tune-up program for automobiles. For a matched pair example, we take a sample of 20 pairs of cars, each pair being identical except for the want of a tune-up. One car in each pair is randomly assigned for the old tune-up program and another car for the new tune-up program. All cars are given a test drive for 100 kilometres after the tune-ups. Since the sign test uses only the signs, we record the higher performance (less gas consumption) for the car using the new tune-up program (compared to another car in the pair that used the old tune-up program) with a + sign and a lower performance with a − sign. Under the null hypothesis that the two tune-up programs are equal in performance, we expect equal numbers of + and − signs in this experiment. We can test this null hypothesis, against the alternative that the new tune-up program is better, at a predetermined level of significance, by simply counting the total number of + signs.

Given the nature of experiments and the null hypotheses in the above examples, we expect that the test statistic based on the total number of + signs to be distributed as a binomial distribution. By using the binomial distribution, in turn, we can find the probability (*P*-value) of observing the sample value of the test statistic. If the probability (*P*-value) is greater than the predetermined level of significance, we do not reject the null hypothesis.

We will first illustrate applications of the sign test through the use of a before/after experiment in the context of paired observations, and then with an illustration of a test of median of a population based on a single sample of observations. For symmetric populations, the tests for median and mean are equivalent. The test procedure for median can also be used to test any other percentile (quartiles, quintiles, 10th percentiles, etc.) or a proportion.

Example 16-1

A Before and After Experiment

The director of information technology at Samuelson Chemicals recommended that an in-plant computer training program be instituted for managers. The objective was to improve their competence (management efficiency) in operations such as accounting, procurement, production, and so on. Some managers thought it would be a worthwhile program; others resisted it, saying it would be of no value. Despite these objections, it was announced that the computer sessions would commence the first of the month.

A sample of 15 managers was selected at random. The general level of efficiency of each manager was determined by a panel of experts before the program started. Management efficiency was rated as being either outstanding, excellent, good, fair or poor. (See Table 16-1.) After the three-month training program, the same panel of computer experts rated each manager again. The two ratings (before and after) are shown along with the sign of the difference. A + sign indicates improvement, and a – sign indicates that the manager's efficiency had declined after the training program.

TABLE 16-1: Management Efficiency Before and After the Computer Training Program

Name	Before	After	Sign of Difference
T.J. Bowers	Good	Outstanding	+
Sue Jenkins	Fair	Excellent	+
James Brown	Excellent	Good	–
Tad Jackson	Poor	Good	+
Andy Love *(Dropped from Analysis)*	Excellent	Excellent	0
Sarah Truett	Good	Outstanding	+
John Sinshi	Poor	Fair	+
Jean Unger	Excellent	Outstanding	+
Coy Farmer	Good	Poor	–
Troy Archer	Poor	Good	+
V.A. Jones	Good	Outstanding	+
Coley Casper	Fair	Excellent	+
Candy Fry	Good	Fair	–
Arthur Chou	Good	Outstanding	+
Sandy Verma	Poor	Good	+

We are interested in whether the in-plant computer training program was effective in increasing the competence of the managers. That is, are the managers more efficient after the training program than before?

Solution

We will use the five-step hypothesis-testing procedure.

Step 1

State the null hypothesis and the alternative hypothesis.

Hypothesis	Meaning
$H_0: p \leq 0.50$	There is no improvement in efficiency as a result of the in-plant computer training program.
$H_1: p > 0.50$	The efficiency of the managers has improved.

If we *do not reject* the null hypothesis, it will indicate the training program has produced no change in the level of management efficiency, or their competence actually decreased. If we *reject* the null hypothesis, it will indicate that the competence of the managers has improved as a result of the training program.

The binomial distribution discussed in Chapter 6 is used as the test statistic. It is appropriate because the sign test meets all the binomial assumptions, namely:

1. There are only two outcomes: a "success" and a "failure". A manager either increased in computer competence (a success) or did not.

2. For each trial the probability of success is assumed to be 0.50. Thus, the probability of a success is the same for all trials (managers in this case).

3. The total number of trials is fixed (15 in this experiment).

4. Each trial is independent. This means, for example, that T.J. Bowers' performance in the three-month course is unrelated to Sue Jenkins' performance.

Step 2   Select a level of significance. We chose the 0.10 level.

Step 3   Decide on the test statistic. It is the *number of plus signs* (S^+) resulting from the experiment (11 in this case).

Step 4

The "S" statistic has a binomial distribution with parameters n and p.

Formulate a decision rule. Fifteen managers were enrolled in the computer course, but Andy Love showed no increase or decrease in competence. (See Table 16-1). He was, therefore, eliminated from the study, so $n = 14$. From the binomial probability distribution table in Appendix A, for an n of 14 and a probability of 0.50, we copied the binomial probability distribution in Table 16-2. The number of successes is in column 1, the probability of success in column 2, and the cumulative probabilities in column 3. To arrive at the cumulative probabilities, we *add* the probabilities of success in column 2 from the bottom. For illustration, to get the cumulative probability of 11 or more successes, we add $0.000 + 0.001 + 0.006 + 0.022 = 0.029$.

This is a one-tailed test because the alternative hypothesis gives a direction. The inequality (>) points to the right. Thus, the region of rejection is in the upper tail. If the inequality sign pointed toward the left tail (<), the region of rejection would be in the lower tail. If that were the case, we would add the probabilities in column 2 *down* to get the cumulative probabilities in column 3.

Recall that we selected the 0.10 level of significance. To arrive at the decision rule for this problem, we go to the cumulative probabilities in Table 16-2, column 3.

TABLE 16-2: Binomial Probability Distribution for $n = 14$, $p = 0.50$

(1) Number of Successes	(2) Probability of Success	(3) Cumulative Probability	
0	0.000	1.000	
1	0.001	0.999	
2	0.006	0.998	
3	0.022	0.992	
4	0.061	0.970	
5	0.122	0.909	
6	0.183	0.787	
7	0.209	0.604	
8	0.183	0.395	
9	0.122	0.212	
10	0.061	0.090	
11	0.022	0.029	← 0.000 + 0.001 +
12	0.006 ↑	0.007	0.006 + 0.022
13	0.001 Add	0.001	
14	0.000 up	0.000	

We read up from the bottom until we come to the *cumulative probability nearest to but not exceeding the level of significance (0.10)*. That cumulative probability is 0.090. The number of successes (+ signs) corresponding to 0.090 in column 1 is 10. Therefore, the decision rule is: if the number of pluses in the sample is 10 or more, the null hypothesis is rejected and the alternative hypothesis is accepted.

To repeat, we add the probabilities up from the bottom because the direction of the inequality (>) is toward the right, indicating that the region of rejection is in the upper tail. If the number of + signs in the sample is 10 or more, we reject the null hypothesis; otherwise, we do not reject H_0. The region of rejection is portrayed in Chart 16-1.

CHART 16-1: Region of Rejection, $n = 14$, $p = 0.50$

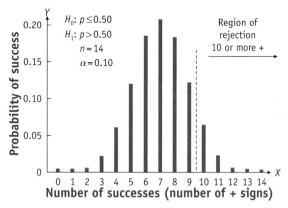

What procedure is followed for a two-tailed test? We combine (add) the probabilities of success in two tails until we come as close to α as possible without exceeding it. In this example α is 0.10. The probability of 3 or fewer successes is 0.029, found by 0.000 + 0.001 + 0.006 + 0.022. The probability of 11 or more successes is also 0.029. Adding the two probabilities gives 0.058. This is the closest we can come to 0.10 without exceeding it. (Had we included the probabilities of 4 and 10 successes, the total would be 0.180, which exceeds 0.10). Hence, the decision rule for a two-tailed test would be to reject the null hypothesis if there are 3 or fewer plus signs, or 11 or more plus signs.

Step 5   Make a decision regarding the null hypothesis. Eleven out of the 14 managers in the computer course improved their efficiency. The number 11 is in the rejection region, which starts at 10, so H_0 is rejected. The three-month computer course was effective. It improved the competency of the managers. Note we can also use Megastat or Minitab to conduct the sign test.

It should be noted again that if the alternative hypothesis does not give a direction—for example, H_0: $p = 0.50$ and H_1: $p \neq 0.50$—the test of the hypothesis is *two-tailed*. In such cases there will be two rejection regions—one in the lower tail and one in the upper tail. If $\alpha = 0.10$ and the test is two-tailed, the area in each tail is 0.05 ($\alpha/2 = 0.10/2 = 0.05$). Self-Review 16-1 illustrates this.

■ SELF-REVIEW 16-1

Recall the Taster's Choice example described earlier, involving a consumer test to determine the preference for decaffeinated versus regular coffee. The null and alternative hypotheses are:

H_0: $p = 0.50$ $n = 12$
H_1: $p \neq 0.50$ $\alpha = 0.10$

(a) Is this a one-tailed or a two-tailed test of hypothesis?
(b) Show the decision rule in a chart.
(c) Letting consumer preference for decaffeinated coffee be a + and preference for regular coffee a −, it was found that two customers preferred decaffeinated. What is your decision? Explain.

EXERCISES 16-1 TO 16-4

16-1. The following hypothesis-testing situation is given: H_0: $p \le 0.50$ and H_1: $p > 0.50$. The significance level is 0.10, and the sample size is 12.
(a) What is the decision rule?
(b) There were nine successes. What is your decision regarding the null hypothesis? Explain.

16-2. The following hypothesis-testing situation is given: H_0: $p = 0.50$ and H_1: $p \ne 0.50$. The significance level is 0.05, and the sample size is 9.
(a) What is the decision rule?
(b) There were five successes. What is your decision regarding the null hypothesis?

16-3. Calorie Watchers (cw) has low-calorie breakfasts, lunches, and dinners. If you join the club, you receive two packaged meals a day. CW claims that you can eat anything you want for the third meal and still lose at least five pounds the first month. Members of the club are weighed before commencing the program and again at the end of the first month. The experiences of a random sample of 11 participants are:

Name	Weight Change	Name	Weight Change
Foster	Lost	Hercher	Lost
Taoka	Lost	Camder	Lost
Lange	Gained	Hinckle	Lost
Rousos	Lost	Hinkley	Lost
Stephens	No change	Justin	Lost
Cantrell	Lost		

We are interested in whether there has been a weight loss as a result of the Calorie Watchers' program.
(a) State H_0 and H_1.
(b) Using the 0.05 level of significance, what is the decision rule?
(c) What is your conclusion about the Calorie Watchers' claim?

16-4. Many new stockbrokers resist giving presentations to bankers and certain other groups. Sensing this lack of self-confidence, management arranged to have a confidence-building seminar for a sample of new stockbrokers and enlisted Career Boosters for a three week course. Before the first session, Career Boosters measured the level of confidence of each participant. It was measured again after the three-week seminar. The before and after levels of self-confidence for the 14 stockbrokers in the course are shown below. Self-confidence was classified as being either negative, low, high, or very high.

Stockbroker	Before Seminar	After Seminar	Stockbroker	Before Seminar	After Seminar
J.M. Martin	Negative	Low	F.M. Orphey	Low	Very high
T.D. Jagger	Negative	Negative	C.C. Ford	Low	High
A.D. Hammer	Low	High	A.R. Utz	Negative	Low
T.A. Jones, Jr.	Very high	Low	M.R. Murphy	Low	High
J.J. Cornwall	Low	High	P.A. Arms	Negative	Low
D.A. Skeen	Low	High	B.K. Pierre	Low	High
C.B. Simmer	Negative	High	N.S. Walker	Low	Very high

The purpose of this study is to find whether Career Boosters was effective in raising the self-confidence of the new stockbrokers. That is, was the level of self-confidence higher after the seminar than before it? Use the 0.05 significance level.

(a) State the null and alternative hypotheses.
(b) Using the 0.05 level of significance, state the decision rule—either in words or in chart form.
(c) Draw conclusions about the seminar offered by Career Boosters.

16.2 USING THE NORMAL APPROXIMATION TO THE BINOMIAL

If the number of observations in the sample is larger than 10, the normal distribution can be used to approximate the binomial. Recall in Chapter 6, we computed the mean of the binomial distribution from $\mu = pn$ and the standard deviation from $\sigma = \sqrt{np(1-p)}$. In this case $p = 0.50$, so the equations reduce to $\mu = 0.50n$ and $\sigma = 0.5\sqrt{n}$, respectively.

The test statistic z is

Sign Test, Large Sample	$Z = \dfrac{(S \pm 0.50) - \mu}{\sigma}$	16-1

If the number of pluses is *more than* $n/2$, we use the following form as the test statistic:

Sign Test, Large Sample, + Signs More Than $n/2$	$Z = \dfrac{(S - 0.50) - \mu}{\sigma} = \dfrac{(S - 0.50) - 0.50n}{0.50\sqrt{n}}$	16-2

If the number of pluses is *less than* $n/2$, the test statistic z is

Sign Test, Large Sample, + Signs Less Than $n/2$	$Z = \dfrac{(S + 0.50) - \mu}{\sigma} = \dfrac{(S + 0.50) - 0.50n}{0.50\sqrt{n}}$	16-3

In the preceding formulae, S is the number of plus signs. The value $+0.50$ or -0.50 is the *continuity correction factor*, discussed in Chapter 7. Briefly, it is applied when a continuous distribution such as the normal distribution (which we are using) is used to approximate a discrete distribution (the binomial).

Example 16-2 | The market research department of Cola, Inc. has been given the assignment of testing a new soft drink. Two versions of the drink are considered—a rather sweet drink and a somewhat bitter one. A preference test is to be conducted consisting of a sample of 64 consumers. Each will taste both the sweet cola (labelled A) and the bitter one (labelled B) and indicate a preference. How will the test of hypothesis be conducted, and what cola, if any, should be marketed?

Solution

Step 1 State the null and alternative hypotheses.

H_0: $p = 0.50$ There is no preference.
H_1: $p \neq 0.50$ There is a preference.

Step 2 Select a level of significance. It is the 0.05 level.

Step 3 The test statistic is selected. It is Z, given in Formula 16-1.

$$Z = \frac{(S \pm 0.50) - \mu}{\sigma}$$

where $\mu = 0.50n$ and $\sigma = 0.50\sqrt{n}$.

Step 4 Formulate the decision rule. Referring to Appendix 3, Areas under the Normal Curve, for a two-tailed test (because H_1, states that $p \neq 0.50$) and the 0.05 significance level, the critical values are $+1.96$ and -1.96. Recall from Chapter 10 that for a two-tailed test we split the rejection region in half and place one half in each tail. That is, $\alpha/2 = 0.05/2 = 0.025$, and continuing, $0.5000 - 0.025 = 0.4750$. Searching for 0.4750 in the body of the table and reading the z value in the left margin gives 1.96, the critical value. Therefore, do not reject H_0 if the computed z value is between $+1.96$ and -1.96. Otherwise, reject H_0 and accept H_1.

Step 5 Compute z, compare the computed value with the critical value, and make a decision regarding H_0. Preference for cola A was given a $+$ sign and preference for cola B a $-$ sign. Out of the 64 in the sample, 42 preferred the sweet cola, A. Therefore, there are 42 pluses. Since 42 *is more than* $n/2 = 64/2 = 32$, we use Formula 16-2 for z:

$$Z = \frac{(S - 0.50) - 0.50n}{0.50\sqrt{n}} = \frac{(42 - 0.50) - 0.50(64)}{0.50\sqrt{64}} = 2.38$$

The computed value of Z equals 2.38. This is larger than the critical value of 1.96. Therefore, the null hypothesis of no difference is rejected at the 0.05 significance level. There is a difference in consumer preference. That is, we conclude consumers prefer one cola over the other.

The P-value is the probability of finding a z value larger than 2.38 or smaller than -2.38. The probability of finding a z value greater than 2.38 is $0.5000 - 0.4913 = 0.0087$. Thus, the two-tailed P-value is 0.0174. So the probability that the null hypothesis is true is less than 2 percent.

■ SELF-REVIEW 16-2

The Human Resources Department in a large automobile assembly plant in Ontario began blood pressure screening and education for the 100 employees in the Paint Department the first of the year. As a follow-up, in July the same 100 employees were again screened for blood pressure and 80 showed a reduction. Can we conclude the education was effective in reducing blood pressure readings?
  (a) State the null hypothesis and the alternative hypothesis.
  (b) What is the decision rule for a significance level of 0.05?
  (c) Compute the value of the test statistic.
  (d) What is your decision regarding the null hypothesis?
  (e) Interpret your decision.

EXERCISES 16-5 TO 16-8

16-5. A sample of 45 overweight men participated in an exercise program. At the conclusion of the program 32 had lost weight. At the 0.05 significance level, can we conclude the program is effective?
  (a) State the null hypothesis and the alternative hypothesis.
  (b) State the decision rule.
  (c) Compute the value of the test statistic.
  (d) What is your decision regarding the null hypothesis?

16-6. A sample of 60 college students in Montreal was given a special training program designed to improve their study and time management skills. One month after completing the course, the students were contacted and asked whether the skills they learned in the program were effective. A total of 42 responded yes. At the 0.05 significance level, can we conclude the program is effective?
  (a) State the null hypothesis and the alternative hypothesis.
  (b) State the decision rule.
  (c) Compute the value of the test statistic.
  (d) What is your decision regarding the null hypothesis?

16-7. Pierre's Restaurant in Calgary announced that on Thursday night the menu would consist of unusual gourmet items, such as squid, rabbit, snails from Scotland, and dandelion greens. As part of a larger survey, a sample of 81 regular customers was asked whether they preferred the regular menu or the gourmet menu. Forty-three preferred the gourmet menu. Using the sign test and the 0.02 level, test whether customers liked the gourmet menu better than the regular menu. Justify your conclusion.

16-8. Assembly workers at Computer Associates (CA) in Vancouver assemble just one or two subassemblies and insert them in a frame. The executives at CA think that the employees would have more pride in their work if they assembled all of the subassemblies and tested the complete computer. A sample of 25 employees was selected to experiment with the idea. The null hypothesis is that the employees have no preference. After a training program, each was asked his or her preference. Twenty liked assembling the entire unit and testing it. At the 0.05 level, use the sign test to arrive at a decision regarding employee preference. Explain the steps you used to arrive at your decision.

16.3   TESTING A HYPOTHESIS ABOUT A MEDIAN

Most of the tests of hypothesis we have conducted so far involved the population mean or a proportion. The sign test is one of the few tests that can be used to test the value of a median. Recall from Chapter 3 that the median is the value above which half of the observations lie and below which the other half lie. For hourly wages of $7, $9, $11, and $18, the median is $10. Half of the wages are above $10 an hour and the other half are below $10.

To conduct a test of hypothesis, a value above the median is assigned a + sign, and a value below the median is assigned a – sign. If a value is the same as the median, it is dropped from further analysis. The procedure is identical to that followed in the small-sample and large-sample cases just discussed.

Example 16-3

A study several years ago by the Customer Research Department of Superior Grocers found the median weekly amount spent on grocery items by young married couples was $123. The CEO would like to repeat the research to determine if the median amount spent has changed. Customer Research's new sample information showed in a random sample of 102 young adult married couples, 60 spent more than $123 last week on grocery items, 40 spent less, and 2 spent exactly $123. At the 0.10 significance level, is it reasonable to conclude that the median amount spent is not equal to $123?

Solution

If the population median is $123, then we expect about half the sampled couples to have spent more than $123 last week and about half less than $123. After discarding the two customers who spent exactly $123, we would expect 50 to be above the median and 50 to be below the median. Is this difference attributable to chance, or is the median some value other than $123? The statistical test for the median will help answer that question.

The null and the alternative hypotheses are:

H_0: Median = $123
H_1: Median ≠ $123

This is two-tailed test because the alternative hypothesis does not indicate a direction, that is, we are not interested in whether the median is less than or greater than $123, only that it is different from $123. The test statistic meets the binomial assumptions. However, the sample size is 100 and p is 0.50, so $np = 100(0.50) = 50$ and $n(1 - p) = 100(1 - 0.50) = 50$, which are both larger than 5, so we use the normal distribution to approximate the binomial. That is we actually use the standard normal distribution as the test statistic. The significance level is 0.10, so $\alpha/2 = 0.10/2 = 0.05$ of the area is in each tail of a normal distribution. From the table for normal distribution which shows the areas under a normal curve, the critical values are -1.645 and 1.645. The decision rule is to reject H_0 if z is less than -1.645 or greater than 1.645.

The median test meets the binomial assumptions. That is:

1. An observation is either larger or smaller than the proposed median, so there are only two possible outcomes.

2. The probability of a success remains constant at 0.50. That is $p = 0.50$.

3. The couples selected as part of the sample represent independent trials.

4. We count the number of successes in a fixed number of trials. In this case we consider 100 couples and count the number who spent more than $123 per week on grocery items.

We use Formula 16-2 for z because 60 is greater than $n/2$ $(100/2 = 50)$.

$$z = \frac{(S - 0.50) - 0.50n}{0.50\sqrt{n}} = \frac{(60 - 0.5) - 0.50(100)}{0.50\sqrt{100}} = 1.90$$

The null hypothesis is rejected because the computed value of 1.90 is greater than the critical value of 1.645. The median amount spent per week on grocery items by young couples is *not* $123. The P-value for this test is 0.0574, found by $2(0.5000 - 0.4713)$.

■ SELF-REVIEW 16-3

After receiving the results regarding the weekly amount spent on grocery items for young couples from the Consumer Research Department the CEO of Superior Grocers wondered if the same was true for senior citizen couples. In this case the CEO wants the Customer Research Department to investigate the question of whether the median weekly amount spent by senior citizens is *greater than* $123. A sample of 64 senior citizen couples revealed 42 spent more than $123 per week on grocery items. Use the 0.05 significance level.

EXERCISES 16-9 TO 16-10

16-9. A trade journal reported that the median starting salary for systems engineers is $80 000. A group of recent graduates believe this amount is too low. In a random sample, of the 205 systems engineers who recently graduated from engineering school, 170 began with a salary of more than $80 000 and five earned a salary of exactly $80 000.
(a) State the null and alternative hypotheses.
(b) State the decision rule. Use the 0.05 significance level.
(c) Perform the necessary computations and interpret the results.

16-10. Suppose Air Canada claims that the median price of a round trip ticket from Montreal to Vancouver is $503. This claim is being challenged by the Association of Travel Agents, who believe the median price is less than $503. To resolve the issue, a random sample of 400 round trip tickets was selected. Of these, 160 tickets were below $503. None of the tickets were exactly $503. Let $\alpha = 0.05$.
(a) State the null and alternative hypotheses.
(b) Reach a decision regarding the controversy.

16.4   WILCOXON SIGNED-RANK TEST

The paired t test, described in Chapter 11 has two requirements. First, the samples must be dependent. Recall that dependent samples are characterized by a measurement, some type of intervention, and then another measurement. For example, a large company began a "wellness" program at the start of the year. Suppose 20 workers enrolled in the weight reduction portion of the program. To begin, all participants were weighed. Next they dieted, did the exercise, and so forth in an attempt to lose weight. At the end of the program, which lasted 6 months, all participants were weighed again. The difference in their weight between the start and the end of the program is the variable of interest.

The second requirement for the paired t test is that the distribution of the differences follows a normal distribution. In the company wellness example in the previous paragraph, this would require that the differences in the weights of the 20 participants follow the normal distribution. In that case this assumption is reasonable. However, there are instances where we want to study the differences between dependent observations where we cannot assume that the distribution of the differences approximates a normal distribution. Frequently we encounter a problem with the normality assumption when the level of measurement in the samples is ordinal, rather than interval or ratio scale. For example, suppose there are 10 surgical patients in the East Wing today. The nursing supervisor asks Nurse Benner and Nurse Jurris to rate each of the 10 patients on a scale of 1 to 10, based on the difficulty of patient care. The distribution of the differences probably would not approximate the normal distribution, and, therefore, the paired t test would not be appropriate.

In 1945, Frank Wilcoxon developed a nonparametric test, based on the differences in dependent samples, where the normality assumption is not required. This test is called the *Wilcoxon signed-rank test*. The Wilcoxon signed-rank test is applicable to any data measured on an ordinal or higher scale of measurement. Further, it assumes only continuous (at least in the vicinity of the median) and symmetrical distributions for the populations, a much weaker requirement than that of normality for the classical test. As compared to the sign test, the Wilcoxon signed-rank test is more powerful as it uses not only the information about the direction of changes (+, −) in the values of a variable but also some information from the magnitude of differences in the values. The price for this power, of course, is the additional requirement of a higher level of measurement (from nominal to ordinal) and a symmetrical distribution of the populations. The following example illustrates its application.

Example 16-4

Maritime Tradition is a family restaurant located primarily in the Maritimes. They offer a full dinner menu, but their specialty is chicken. Recently Bernie Williams, the owner and founder, developed a new spicy flavour for the batter in which the chicken is cooked. Before replacing the current flavour, he wants to conduct some tests to be sure that patrons will like the spicy flavour better.

To begin, Bernie selects a random sample of 15 customers. Each member of the sample is given a small sample of the *current* chicken and asked to rate its overall taste on a scale of 1 to 20. A value near 20 indicates the participant liked the flavour, whereas a score near 0 indicates they did not like the flavour. Next week, the same 15 participants are given a sample of the *new* chicken with the spicier flavour and again asked to rate its taste on a scale of 1 to 20. The results are reported below. Is it reasonable to conclude that the spicy flavour is preferred? Use the 0.05 significance level.

Participant	Spicy Flavour Score	Current Flavour Score	Participant	Spicy Flavour Score	Current Flavour Score
Arquette	14	12	Garcia	19	10
Jones	8	16	Sundar	18	10
Fish	6	2	Miller	16	13
Wagner	18	4	Peterson	18	2
Badenhop	20	12	Boggart	4	13
Hall	16	16	Hein	7	14
Fowler	14	5	Whitten	16	4
Virost	6	16			

Solution

The samples are dependent or related. That is, the same participants are asked to rate both flavours of chicken. Thus, if we compute the difference between the rating for the spicy flavour and the current flavour, the resulting value shows the amount the participants favour one flavour over the other. If we choose to subtract the current flavour score from the spicy flavour score, a positive result is the "amount" the participant favours the spicy flavour. Negative difference scores indicate the participant favoured the current flavour. Because of the somewhat subjective nature of the scores, we are not sure the distribution of the differences follows the normal distribution. We decide to use the nonparametric Wilcoxon signed-rank test.

As usual, we will use the five-step hypothesis-testing procedure. The null hypothesis is that there is no difference in the rating of the chicken flavours in the population. That is, as many participants in the study rated the spicy flavour higher as rated the regular flavour higher. The alternative hypothesis is that the ratings are higher for the spicy flavour. More formally:

H_0: There is no difference in the average ratings of the two flavours.

H_1: The spicy ratings are higher.

This is a one-tailed test. Why? Because Bernie Williams' Maritime Tradition will want to change his chicken flavour only if the sample participants show that the population of customers like the new flavour better. The significance level is 0.05, as stated in the problem above.

The steps to conduct the Wilcoxon signed-rank test are as follows.

1. Compute the difference between the spicy flavour score and the current flavour score for each participant. For example, Arquette's spicy flavour score was 14 and current flavour score was 12, so the amount of the difference is 2. For Jones, the difference is −8, found by 8 − 16, and for Fish it is 4 found by 6 − 2. The differences for all participants are shown in column 4 of Table 16-3.

2. Only the positive and negative differences are considered further. That is, if the difference in flavour score is 0, that participant is dropped from the analysis and the number in the sample reduced. From Table 16-3, Hall, the sixth participant, scored both the spicy and the current flavour a 16. Hence, Hall is dropped from the study and the sample size reduced from 15 to 14.

3. Determine the absolute differences for the values computed in column 4. Recall that in an absolute difference we ignore the sign of the difference. The absolute differences are shown in column 5.

4. Next, rank the absolute differences from smallest to largest. Arquette, the first participant scored the spicy chicken at 14 and the current at 12. The difference of 2 in the two scores is the smallest absolute difference, so it is given a ranking of 1. The next largest difference is 3, given by Miller, so it is given a rank of 2. The other differences are ranked in a similar manner. There are three participants who rated the difference in the flavor as 8. That is, Jones, Badenhop, and Sundar each had a difference of 8 between their rating of the spicy flavour and the current flavour. To resolve this problem, we average the ranks involved and report the average rank for each. This situation involves the ranks 5, 6, and 7, so all three participants are assigned the rank of 6. The same situation occurs for those participants with a difference of 9. The ranks involved are 8, 9, and 10, so three participants are assigned a rank of 9.

TABLE 16-3: Flavour Rating for Current and Spicy Flavours

(1) Participant	(2) Spicy Score	(3) Current Score	(4) Difference in Score	(5) Absolute Difference	(6) Rank	(7) Signed Rank T^+	(7) Signed Rank T^-
Arquette	14	12	2	2	1	1	
Jones	8	16	−8	8	6		6
Fish	6	2	4	4	3	3	
Wagner	18	4	14	14	13	13	
Badenhop	20	12	8	8	6	6	
Hall	16	16	*	*	*	*	
Fowler	14	5	9	9	9	9	
Virost	6	16	−10	10	11		11
Garcia	19	10	9	9	9	9	
Sundar	18	10	8	8	6	6	
Miller	16	13	3	3	2	2	
Peterson	18	2	16	16	14	14	
Boggart	4	13	−9	9	9		9
Hein	7	14	−7	7	4		4
Whitten	16	4	12	12	12	12	
Total						75	30

5. Each assigned rank in column 6 is then given the same sign as the original difference, and the results are reported in column 7. For example, the second participant has a difference score of –8 and a rank of 6. This value is located in the T^- section of column 7.

6. The T^+ and the T^- columns are totalled. The sum of the positive ranks is 75 and the sum of the negative ranks is 30. The Wilcoxon signed-rank test statistic (T) is calculated as the sum of the ranks of either positive differences or the negative differences. Since the sum: $(T^+ + T^-) = 1 + 2 + 3 + \cdots + n = [n(n + 1)/2]$, a constant, we could use either T^+ or T^- as the test statistic. However, the critical values of the test statistic (see, Table 16-4 on page 723) are given in terms of the *smaller* of the two values of the signed rank statistic. For a one-tailed test, therefore, we choose T^+ or T^-, *whichever is expected to be smaller according to the alternative hypothesis.* In our problem, H_1 suggests that T^- should be smaller (fewer persons are expected to prefer the current flavour) and therefore we use T^- as the test statistic. In the case of a two-tailed test, we use T^- or T^+, *whichever is the smaller of the two.* In this way, we are always conducting the test in the left tail of the distribution. The α row is used for one-tailed tests and the 2α row for two-tailed tests.

In this case we want to show that customers like the spicy taste better, which is a one-tailed test, so we select the α row. We chose the 0.05 significance level, so move to the right to the column headed 0.05. Go down that column to the row where n is 14. (Recall that one person in the study rated the chicken flavours the same and was dropped from the study, making the sample size 14.) The value at the intersection is 25, so the critical value is 25. Note that the critical value is the largest value in the rejection area (left tail). Any value of the test statistic larger than the critical value would lead us *not* to reject the null hypothesis. Thus the decision rule is to reject the null hypothesis if the sample value of the test statistic is smaller than or equal to the critical value. In our problem, the value of the test statistic $(T^-) = 30$, so the decision is not to reject the null hypothesis. We cannot conclude there is a difference in the flavour ratings between the current and the spicy. Mr. Williams has not shown that customers prefer the new flavour.

TABLE 16-4: Critical Values of Wilcoxon Signed-Rank Test

	2α						
	0.15	0.10	0.05	0.04	0.03	0.02	0.01
				α			
n	0.075	0.050	0.025	0.020	0.015	0.010	0.005
4	0						
5	1	0					
6	2	2	0	0			
7	4	3	2	1	0	0	
8	7	5	3	3	2	1	0
9	9	8	5	5	4	3	1
10	12	10	8	7	6	5	3
11	16	13	10	9	8	7	5
12	19	17	13	12	11	9	7
13	24	21	17	16	14	12	9
14	28	25	21	19	18	15	12
15	33	30	25	23	21	19	15
16	39	35	29	28	26	23	19
17	45	41	34	33	30	27	23
18	51	47	40	38	35	32	27
19	58	53	46	43	41	37	32
20	65	60	52	50	47	43	37

Source: Abridged from Robert L. McCormack, "Extended Tables of the Wilcoxon Matched-Pair Signed Rank Statistic," *Journal of the American Statistical Association,* September 1965, pp. 866–67.

LARGE SAMPLE APPROXIMATION OF THE WILCOXON SIGNED-RANK TEST

For sample sizes larger than 50, the critical values of the test statistic are not available. However, for a large n, if H_0 is true, as discussed earlier, we can obtain approximate critical values by using normal approximation.

It can be shown that the T statistic is distributed with a

Mean $\mu_T = \dfrac{n(n+1)}{4}$ **Standard Deviation** $\sigma_T = \sqrt{\dfrac{n(n+1)(2n+1)}{24}}$ **16-4**

With continuity correction factor, we define

$$Z = \frac{T \pm 0.5 - \mu_T}{\sigma_T}$$ 16-5

Earlier, we used T equal to T^+ or T^- depending on which is smaller under the alternative hypothesis. With normal approximation this is not necessary. We can now use the value of T as indicated by the alternative hypothesis, T^+ for greater than and T^- for less than alternatives. The normal approximation is good for sample sizes (n) as small as 15. To verify the results using the approximation for the example discussed above, we use $T^+ = 75$, mean of $T = [14(14 + 1)/4] = 52.5$; standard deviation $= \sqrt{(14)(15)(29)/24} = 15.93$. This would give us $z = \dfrac{75 - 0.5 - 52.5}{15.93} = 1.381$. The critical value of Z at a 5 percent level of significance is 1.645, which is larger than the computed value of 1.381. The P-value for 1.381 can be found from the Z table as $0.5 - 0.4162 = 0.084$, which is much larger than the predetermined level of significance of 0.05. Obviously, we cannot reject the null hypothesis.

All of these calculations are easily obtained through Minitab and Excel (MegaStat) programs. The calculations along with instructions for these programs are given below. The results in Minitab are exactly the same as our hand calculations done by using the normal approximation together with the continuity correction factor. MegaStat gives slightly different results, as it does not apply the continuity correction factor. Further, the two packages also differ in adjusting the formula for the test statistic for the ties encountered in ranking the observations. We therefore advise you to exercise caution in comparing results obtained in the two packages. To make life a little simpler, we advise you to stick with one package for this entire chapter.

EXCEL CHART 16-2: Using Excel for Wilcoxon Signed-Rank Test

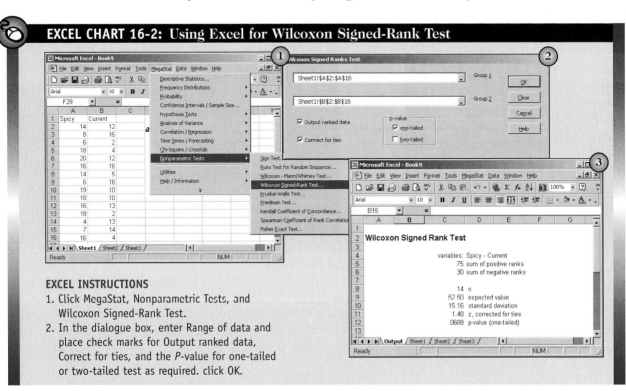

EXCEL INSTRUCTIONS

1. Click MegaStat, Nonparametric Tests, and Wilcoxon Signed-Rank Test.
2. In the dialogue box, enter Range of data and place check marks for Output ranked data, Correct for ties, and the P-value for one-tailed or two-tailed test as required. click OK.

MINITAB CHART 16-3: Using Minitab for Wilcoxon Signed-Rank Test

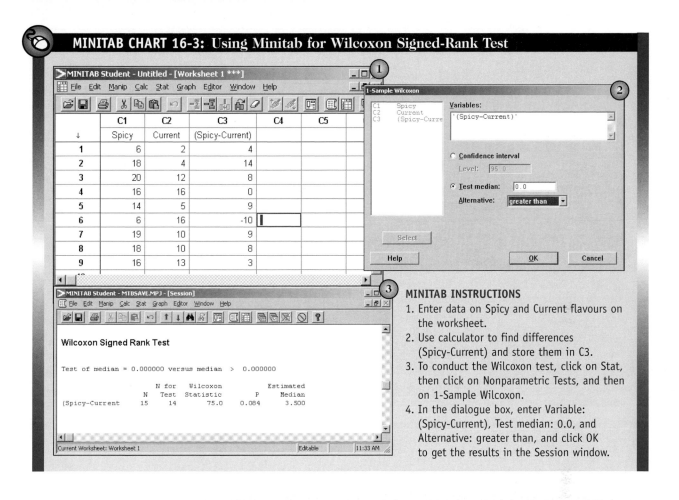

MINITAB INSTRUCTIONS
1. Enter data on Spicy and Current flavours on the worksheet.
2. Use calculator to find differences (Spicy-Current) and store them in C3.
3. To conduct the Wilcoxon test, click on Stat, then click on Nonparametric Tests, and then on 1-Sample Wilcoxon.
4. In the dialogue box, enter Variable: (Spicy-Current), Test median: 0.0, and Alternative: greater than, and click OK to get the results in the Session window.

■ SELF-REVIEW 16-4

A record of the production for each machine operator was kept over a period of time. Certain changes in the production procedure were suggested, and 11 operators were picked as an experimental test group to determine whether the new procedures were worthwhile. Their production rates before and after the new procedures were established are as follows:

Operator	Production Before	Production After	Operator	Production Before	Production After
S.M.	17	18	U.Z.	10	22
D.J.	21	23	Y.U.	20	19
M.D.	25	22	U.T.	17	20
B.B.	15	25	Y.H.	24	30
M.F.	10	28	Y.Y	23	26
A.A.	16	16			

(a) How many usable pairs are there? That is, what is n?
(b) Using the Wilcoxon signed-rank test, determine whether the new procedures actually increased production. Use the 0.05 level and a one-tailed test.

EXERCISES 16-11 TO 16-14

16-11. An industrial psychologist selected a random sample of seven young urban professional couples who own their homes. The size of their home (square feet) is compared with that of their parents. At the 0.05 significance level, can we conclude that the yuppies live in larger homes?

Couple's Name	House size		Couple's Name	House size	
	Professional	Parent		Professional	Parent
Gordon	1725	1175	Kuhlman	1290	1360
Sharkey	1310	1120	Welch	1880	1750
Uselding	1670	1420	Anderson	1530	1440
Bell	1520	1640			

16-12. One of the major car manufacturers is studying the effect of regular versus high-octane gasoline in its economy cars. Ten executives are selected and asked to maintain records on the number of kilometres travelled per litre of gas. The results are:

Kilometres per Litre					
Executive	Regular	High-Octane	Executive	Regular	High-Octane
Bowers	8	9	Rau	13	14
Demars	11	10	Greolke	10	10
Grasser	10	12	Burns	14	12
De Toto	15	14	Snow	14	15
Kleg	14	16	Lawless	10	15

At the 0.05 significance level, is there a difference in the number of kilometres travelled per litre between regular and high-octane gasoline?

16-13. A new assembly-line procedure has been suggested by Mr. Munro. To test whether the new procedure is superior to the old procedure, a sample of 15 men was selected at random. First their production under the old system was determined. Then the new Munro procedure was introduced. After an appropriate break-in period, their production was measured again. The results were:

Employee	Production Old System	Munro Method	Employee	Production Old System	Munro Method
A	60	64	I	87	84
B	40	52	J	80	80
C	59	58	K	56	57
D	30	37	L	21	21
E	70	71	M	99	108
F	78	83	N	50	56
G	43	46	O	56	62
H	40	52			

At the 0.05 significance level can we conclude that the production is greater using the Munro method?

(a) State the null and alternative hypotheses.

(b) State the decision rule.

(c) Arrive at a decision regarding the null hypothesis.

16-14. It has been suggested that daily production of a subassembly would be increased if better portable lighting were installed and background music and free coffee and doughnuts were provided during the day. Management agreed to try the scheme for a limited time. The numbers of subassemblies produced per week by a sample of employees follows.

Employee	Past Production Record	Production after Installing Lighting, Music, etc.	Employee	Past Production Record	Production after Installing Lighting, Music, etc.
JD	23	33	WWJ	21	25
SB	26	26	OP	25	22
MD	24	30	CD	21	23
RCF	17	25	PA	16	17
MF	20	19	RRT	20	15
UHH	24	22	AT	17	9
IB	30	29	QQ	23	30

Using the Wilcoxon signed-rank test, determine whether the suggested changes are worthwhile.

(a) State the null hypothesis.

(b) Arrive at a decision regarding the alternative hypothesis.

(c) Select the level of significance.

(d) State the decision rule.

(e) Compute T and arrive at a decision.

16.5 WILCOXON RANK-SUM TEST

In addition to the signed-rank test for dependent samples discussed in the last section, Wilcoxon also proposed a nonparametric test for comparing the medians of two independent random samples, popularly called *Wilcoxon Rank-Sum* (W) test. The W-test assumes only continuous probability distributions. It is applicable to ordinal or higher scales of measurement. In 1947, an equivalent test was also developed, independently, by H.B. Mann and D.R. Whitney. Many statisticians therefore call this test the Mann-Whitney-Wilcoxon (MWW) test.

The MWW test is a nonparametric alternative to the parametric t test for comparing the locations of two populations by using random samples drawn independently from the two populations. Recall that the t tests, discussed in Chapter 11, require the assumption of a normal distribution, which is much stronger compared to the assumptions required for a MWW test. Further, the MWW test enables us to test hypotheses for data sets measured at ordinal levels of measurement. Thus, when the data is measured at the ordinal level and/or the assumption of a normal distribution is questionable, the MWW test has an advantage over the standard t test. We shall illustrate the usage of the Wilcoxon version of the MWW test below.

To simplify the choice of critical values, we label the two populations as follows. *For a one-tailed test, we use label 1 for the population that is expected to have a smaller median under the alternative hypothesis, and label 2 for the other population. For a two-tailed test we arbitrarily label the two populations as population 1 and population 2.*

Let us assume we have two samples of sizes n_1 and n_2 drawn independently from population 1 and population 2. In order to find the value of the Wilcoxon rank-sum test statistic (W), *first*, we combine all the observations from two samples in a single data set. *Second*, we rank all the observations in the combined data set from the smallest observation receiving rank 1, the next smallest observation receiving rank 2, and so on, to the largest observation receiving rank $n_1 + n_2$. If two or more observations are equal, i.e., tied for ranks, we assign the average of the possible ranks to each of those observations. *Lastly*, we sum the ranks received by each observation for each sample separately.

Thus, we get two sums of ranks: W_1 for the sum of the ranks of all observations in sample 1 and, similarly, W_2 for sample 2. Since the total of both rank-sums ($W_1 + W_2$) is equal to a constant ($= N(N+1)/2$, where $N = n_1 + n_2$), either of them can be used as a test statistic. *For a one-tailed test, we shall use the rank-sum W_1 as our test statistic. In the case of a two-tailed test, we shall use both W_1 and W_2 as our test statistics.* Because of the choice of population labels and the test statistic(s), we are always conducting the test in the left tail of the distribution. Critical values for a few levels of significance have been tabulated for the distribution of the test statistic under the null hypothesis of identical population distributions. We give the necessary critical values (W^*) for sample sizes from 3 to 10 in Table 16-5 below. For samples of larger than 10 observations, we shall use

TABLE 16-5: Critical Values of the Wilcoxon Rank Sum Test for Independent Samples

(a) $\alpha = 0.025$ one-tail; $\alpha = 0.05$ two-tail

Column

Row	3	4	5	6	7	8	9	10
4	6	11	17	23	31	40	50	61
5	6	12	18	25	33	42	52	64
6	7	12	19	26	35	44	55	66
7	7	13	20	28	37	47	58	70
8	8	14	21	29	39	49	60	73
9	8	15	22	31	41	51	63	76
10	9	16	24	32	43	54	66	79

(b) $\alpha = 0.05$ one-tail; $\alpha = 0.10$ two-tail

Column

Row	3	4	5	6	7	8	9	10
3	6	11	16	23	31	39	49	60
4	7	12	18	25	33	42	52	63
5	7	13	19	26	35	45	55	66
6	8	14	20	28	37	47	57	69
7	9	15	22	30	39	49	60	73
8	9	16	24	32	41	52	63	76
9	10	17	25	33	43	54	66	79
10	22	18	26	35	46	57	69	83

Source: From F. Wilcoxon and R.A. Wilcox, "Some Rapid Approximate Statistical Procedures" (1964), p. 28. Adapted and reproduced with the permission of American Cyanamid Company.

normal approximation as explained later. Thus, we can test:

H_0: Probability distribution of population 1 is identical to probability distribution of population 2, against the alternative:

(a) H_1: Population 1 has a smaller median compared to population 2, (use W_1), or

(b) H_1: Median of population 1 is not equal to median of population 2, (use both W_1 and W_2).

Because of our choice of labels, we do not have to consider the case when, under H_1, population 2 has a smaller median compared to population 1.

In case (a): We shall reject the null hypothesis (H_0) when

$W_1 < W^*$ *(corresponding to column equal n_1, and row equal n_2).*

In case (b): We shall reject the null hypothesis (H_0) when

$W_1 < W^*$ *(corresponding to column equal n_1, and row equal n_2), or*

$W_2 < W^*$ *(corresponding to column equal n_2, and row equal n_1).*

Example 16-5

Mr. Dan Thompson, the president of an international airline, recently noted an increase in the number of no-shows for flights out of Dorval. He is particularly interested in determining whether there are more no-shows for flights that originate from Dorval compared with flights leaving Mirabel. Sample data for nine flights from Dorval and eight from Mirabel are reported in Table 16-6. At the 0.05 significance level, can we conclude that there are more no-shows for the flights originating in Dorval?

TABLE 16-6: Number of No-Shows for Scheduled Flights

Mirabel:	13	14	10	8	16	9	17	21	
Dorval:	11	15	10	18	11	20	24	22	25

Solution

If we were to assume the populations of no-shows were normally distributed and had equal variances, the two-sample t tests, discussed in Chapter 11, would be appropriate. In this case Mr. Thompson believes these two conditions cannot be met. Therefore, a nonparametric test, the Wilcoxon rank-sum test, is appropriate.

As per our rule for labelling the populations, let us label the population of no-shows at Mirabel as population 1 and the population of no-shows at Dorval as population 2. If the number of no-shows is the same for Dorval and Mirabel, then in the population we expect the medians of the two ranks to be about the same. If the number of no-shows in the population is not the same, we expect the two sums of ranks to be quite different.

Since Mr. Thompson believes that there are more no-shows for Dorval flights a one-tailed test is appropriate. We use the rank-sum (W_1) for Mirabel as the test statistic. The null and alternative hypotheses are:

H_0: The population distribution of no-shows is the same for Mirabel and Dorval.
H_1: The population distribution of no-shows has a smaller median for Mirabel than for Dorval.

Reject H_0, if the rank-sum for Mirabel: $W_1 < W^*$ *(corresponding to column equal $n_1 = 8$, and row equal $n_2 = 9$) = 54.*

The details of computations are shown in Table 16-7. We rank the observations from *both* samples as if they were a single group. The Mirabel flight with only 8 no-shows had the fewest no-shows, so it is assigned a rank of 1. The Mirabel flight with 9 no-shows is ranked 2, and so on. The Dorval flight with 25 no-shows has the highest no-shows, so it is assigned the largest rank, 17. There are also two instances of tied ranks. There are Dorval and Mirabel flights that each had 10 no-shows and two Dorval flights with 11 no-shows. How do we handle these ties? The solution is to average the ranks involved and assign the average rank to both flights. In the case involving 10 no-shows the ranks involved are 3 and 4. The mean of these ranks is 3.5, so a rank of 3.5 is assigned to both the Dorval and the Mirabel flights with 10 no-shows.

TABLE 16-7: Computing the Rank-Sum

Mirabel (#1)		Dorval (#2)	
No-Shows	Rank	No-Shows	Rank
13	7	11	5.5
14	8	15	9
10	3.5	10	3.5
8	1	18	12
16	10	11	5.5
9	12	20	13
17	11	24	16
21	14	22	15
		25	17
Totals: $W_1 = 56.5$		$W_2 = 96.5$	

If the null hypothesis were true, the medians of two rank-sums should be about equal. Since the value of W statistic (W_1) for Mirabel is expected to be smaller under the alternative hypothesis, we use the rank-sum W_1 as our test statistic. The decision rule requires us to reject H_0 if $W_1 < 54$ ($= W^*$). Since $W_1 = 56.5$, H_0 is not rejected at a 5 percent level of significance. We therefore conclude that there is *insufficient* evidence in favour of the alternative hypothesis.

LARGE SAMPLE APPROXIMATION OF THE WILCOXON RANK-SUM TEST

As mentioned above, for samples sizes 10 or above, the Wilcoxon test statistic can be well approximated by the *normal distribution*.

Earlier, we noted that we use rank-sum W_1 as the test statistic for a one-tailed test, and both W_1 and W_2 as test statistics for a two-tailed test. With normal approximation this is not necessary. We can now use the value of either W_1 or W_2. For simplicity of presentation, we shall continue to use only W_1.

The sampling distribution of the Wilcoxon test statistic W_1 has a mean (μ_{W_1}) and a standard deviation (σ_{W_1}) as follows:

$$\mu_{W_1} = \frac{n_1(n_1 + n_2 + 1)}{2} \quad \text{and} \quad \sigma_{W_1} = \sqrt{\frac{n_1 n_2 (n_1 + n_2 + 1)}{12}} \qquad \textbf{16-6}$$

Thus, the standard normal distribution for W_1 is:

$$Z = \frac{W_1 \pm 0.5 - \mu_{W_1}}{\sigma_{W_1}} \qquad \textbf{16-7}$$

(Use $+0.5$ if $W_1 < \mu_{W_1}$ and -0.5 otherwise.)

For our example of "no-shows" (though samples are smaller than 10) at Mirabel and Dorval airports, $\mu_{W_1} = 72$ and $\sigma_{W_1} = 10.39$. Here is a small challenge for you to verify these calculations! Substitution of these values in the formula for Z would give us $z = (56.5 + 0.5 - 72)/10.39 = -1.444$. The corresponding P-value is $0.5 - 0.4258 = 0.0742$. This indicates that we could reject the null hypothesis at the level of significance of 7.42 percent or higher but not at our predetermined level of significance of 5 percent.

Minitab program, as shown below, uses correction for continuity, and also gives the output for P-value with and without adjustment for "tied" ranks.[2] Excel (MegaStat) does not apply any correction for continuity, though it makes the adjustment for "tied" ranks. For these reasons, results from Minitab and Excel can be different depending on the importance of adjustments for continuity and for "tied" ranks in a particular case. Further, Minitab uses the Mann-Whitney version of the test statistic (called U statistic), which gives equivalent results due to the relationship:

Mann-Whitney Statistic $U_1 = W_1 - \dfrac{1}{2} n_1(n_1 + 1)$ and $U_2 = W_2 - \dfrac{1}{2} n_2(n_2 + 1)$ **16-8**

EXCEL CHART 16-4: Using Excel for M-W-W Rank-Sum Test

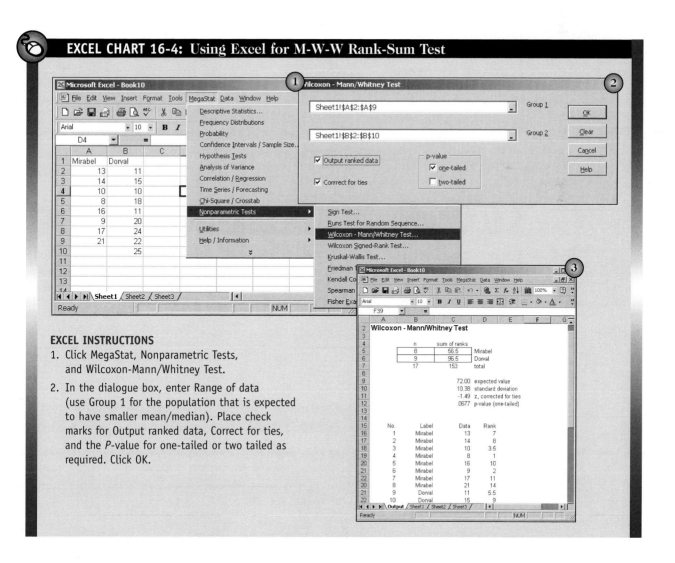

EXCEL INSTRUCTIONS

1. Click MegaStat, Nonparametric Tests, and Wilcoxon-Mann/Whitney Test.

2. In the dialogue box, enter Range of data (use Group 1 for the population that is expected to have smaller mean/median). Place check marks for Output ranked data, Correct for ties, and the P-value for one-tailed or two tailed as required. Click OK.

MINITAB CHART 16-5: Using Minitab for MWW Rank-Sum Test

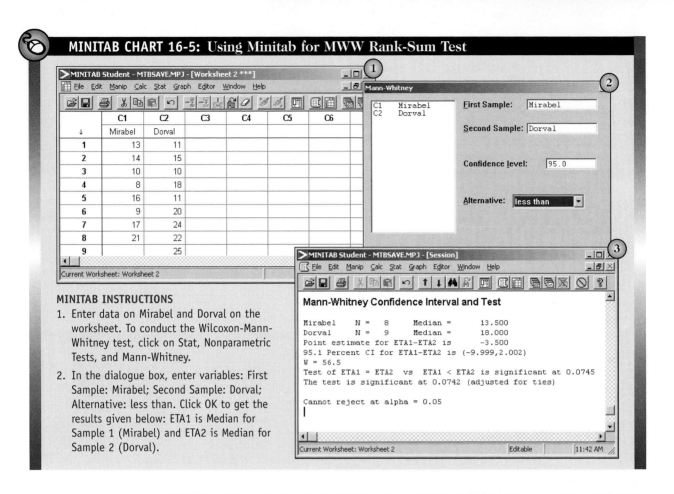

MINITAB INSTRUCTIONS

1. Enter data on Mirabel and Dorval on the worksheet. To conduct the Wilcoxon-Mann-Whitney test, click on Stat, Nonparametric Tests, and Mann-Whitney.

2. In the dialogue box, enter variables: First Sample: Mirabel; Second Sample: Dorval; Alternative: less than. Click OK to get the results given below: ETA1 is Median for Sample 1 (Mirabel) and ETA2 is Median for Sample 2 (Dorval).

■ SELF-REVIEW 16-5

The research director for a golf ball manufacturer wants to know whether there is a difference in the distribution of the distances travelled by two of the company's golf balls. Eight of their Dino brand and eight of their Maxi brand balls were hit by an automatic driver. The distances (in metres) were as follows:

Dino: 252   263   279   273   271   265   257   280
Maxi: 262   242   256   260   258   243   239   265

The nature of population distributions is unknown. At the 0.05 significance level, is there a difference between the two distributions?

EXERCISES 16-15 TO 16-18

16-15. The following observations were randomly selected from populations. The nature of population distributions is unknown. Use the 0.05 significance level, a two-tailed test, and the Wilcoxon rank-sum test to determine whether there is a difference between the two populations.

Population A: 38   45   56   57   61   69   70   79
Population B: 26   31   35   42   51   52   57   62

16-16. The following observations were selected from populations that are not necessarily normally distributed. Use the 0.05 significance level, a two-tailed test, and the Wilcoxon rank-sum test to determine whether there is a difference between the two populations.

Population A: 12   14   15   19   23   29   33   40   51
Population B: 13   16   19   21   22   33   35   43

16-17. Two groups of professional musicians—rock, and country and western—are being studied. One facet of the study involves the age of those in the two groups. Assume the populations of ages are not normally distributed. A sample of 10 rock and 12 country and western musicians revealed the following ages, in years.

Rock: 28   16   42   29   31   22   50   42   23   25
Country and western: 26   42   65   38   29   32   59   42   27   41   46   18

At the 0.05 significance level, can we conclude the country and western singers are older?

16-18. One group was taught an assembly procedure using a standard sequence of steps and another group was taught a new experimental technique. The time to complete the assembly, in seconds, for a sample of workers is shown below.

Current method: 41   36   42   39   36   48   49   38
Experimental: 21   27   36   20   19   21   39   24   22

At the 0.05 significance level, can we conclude the experimental method is faster? Assume that the population distributions of the two methods are not normal.

16.6   KRUSKAL-WALLIS TEST: TEST FOR LOCATIONS OF MULTIPLE POPULATIONS

The analysis of variance (ANOVA) procedure discussed in Chapter 12 was concerned with an investigation of the equality of several population means. The data were interval or ratio level, and it was assumed that the populations were normally distributed and the standard deviations of those populations were equal. What if the data are ordinal scale and/or the populations are not normal, or standard deviations are unequal? W.H. Kruskal and W.A. Wallis introduced a nonparametric test in 1952 requiring only ordinal-level (ranked) data. The test can also be used for higher scales of measurements and thus, in a sense, it is a counterpart of ANOVA, though no analysis of variance is implied by the test. In a way, the Kruskal-Wallis test (called *H* test) is an extension of the Mann-Whitney-Wilcoxon test for multiple populations. The *H test does not require any specific assumptions about the shape of the populations.* Statisticians often assume continuity for theoretical purposes to avoid the problem of ties. However, in practice ties do occur and require an adjustment of the test statistic for deriving an accurate level of significance.

As in the case of ANOVA and the Mann-Whitney-Wilcoxon test, the *Kruskal-Wallis test is applicable to randomly and independently selected samples.* For example, if samples from three groups: executives, staff, and supervisors are to be selected and interviewed, the responses of one group (say, the executives) must in no way influence the responses of the others.

To compute the Kruskal-Wallis test statistic, first all the samples are combined, second the combined values are ordered from low to high, and third the ordered values are *replaced by ranks, starting with 1 for the smallest value.* An example will clarify the procedure.

Example 16-6

A management seminar consists of executives from manufacturing, finance, and trade. Before scheduling the seminar sessions, the seminar leader is interested in whether the three groups are equally knowledgeable about management principles. Plans are to take samples of the executives in manufacturing, in finance, and in trade and to administer a test to each executive. If there is no difference in the scores for the three distributions, the seminar leader will conduct just one session. However, if there is a difference in the scores, separate sessions will be given.

We will use the Kruskal-Wallis test instead of ANOVA because the seminar leader is unwilling to assume that (1) the populations of management scores are normally distributed, or (2) the population standard deviations are the same.

Solution

The usual first step in hypothesis testing is to state the null and the alternative hypotheses.

H_0: The distributions of the management scores for the populations of executives in manufacturing, finance, and trade are identical.

H_1: At least two population distributions are *not* identical.

The seminar leader selected the 0.05 level of risk.

The test statistic used for the Kruskal-Wallis test is designated H. Its formula is:

Kruskal-Wallis Test

$$H = \frac{12}{N(N+1)}\left[\frac{\left(\sum R_1\right)^2}{n_1} + \frac{\left(\sum R_2\right)^2}{n_2} + \cdots + \frac{\left(\sum R_k\right)^2}{n_k}\right] - 3(N+1) \quad \textbf{16-9}$$

with $k-1$ degrees of freedom (k is the number of populations), where:

$\sum R_1, \sum R_2, \ldots, \sum R_k$ are the sums of the ranks of samples $1, 2, \ldots, k$, respectively.

$n_1, n_2, \ldots, n_k$ are the sizes of samples $1, 2, \ldots, k$, respectively.

N is the combined number of observations for all samples.

The distribution of the sample H statistic is very close to the chi-square distribution with $k-1$ degrees of freedom *if every sample size is at least 5.* Therefore, we will use chi-square in formulating the decision rule. In this problem there are three populations—a population of executives in manufacturing, another for executives in finance, and a third population of trade executives. Thus, there are $k-1$, or $3-1=2$ degrees of freedom. Refer to the chi-square table of critical values in Appendix E. The critical value for 2 degrees of freedom and the 0.05 level of risk is 5.991. Do not reject H_0 if the computed value of the test statistic H is less than or equal to 5.991. Reject H_0 if the computed value of H is greater than 5.991, and accept H_1.

The next step is to select samples from the three populations. A sample of seven executives from manufacturing, another sample of eight executives from finance, and the third sample of six executives from trade were selected. Their scores on the test are recorded in Table 16-8. Considering the scores from all three samples as a combined group of data, the trade executive with a score of 35 is the lowest, so it is ranked 1. There are two scores of 38. To resolve this tie, each score is given a rank of 2.5, found by

TABLE 16-8: Management Test Scores for Manufacturing, Finance, and Trade Executives

Manufacturing Executives	Finance Executives	Trade Executives
56	103	42
39	87	38 ←tied for next lowest
48	51	89
38 ←tied for next lowest	95	75
73	68	35 ←lowest
50	42	61
62	107 ←highest score	
	89	

$(2+3)/2$. This process is continued for all scores. The highest score is 107, and that finance executive is given a rank of 21. The scores, the ranks, and the sum of the ranks for each of the three samples are given in Table 16-9.

TABLE 16-9: Scores, Ranks, and Sums of Ranks for Management Test Scores

Manufacturing Executives		Finance Executives		Trade Executives	
Scores	Ranks (R_1)	Scores	Ranks (R_2)	Scores	Ranks (R_3)
56	10.0	103	20.0	42	5.5
39	4.0	87	16.0	38	2.5
48	7.0	51	9.0	89	17.5
38	2.5	95	19.0	75	15.0
73	14.0	68	13.0	35	1.0
50	8.0	42	5.5	61	11.0
62	12.0	107	21.0		
		89	17.5		
	$\Sigma R_1 = 57.5$		$\Sigma R_2 = 121.0$		$\Sigma R_3 = 52.5$

Solving for H:

$$H = \frac{12}{N(N+1)}\left[\frac{(\Sigma R_1)^2}{n_1} + \frac{(\Sigma R_2)^2}{n_2} + \frac{(\Sigma R_3)^2}{n_3}\right] - 3(N+1)$$

$$= \frac{12}{21(21+1)}\left[\frac{57.5^2}{7} + \frac{121^2}{8} + \frac{52.5^2}{6}\right] - 3(21+1) = 5.736$$

Because the computed value of H (5.736) is less than 5.991, the null hypothesis is not rejected. There is no difference among the executives from manufacturing, finance, and trade with respect to their typical knowledge of management principles. From a practical standpoint, the seminar leader should consider offering only one session including executives from all areas.

We can use either Minitab or Excel (MegaStat) to obtain the above results. As shown in the Excel and Minitab charts below, the value of the H statistic is the same as computed above. The programs also report P-values. Minitab reports the P-value with and without adjustment for the ties, which seem to be equal in this case. MegaStat reports P-values adjusted for ties, if requested. The P-value of 0.057 reported by the programs is obviously larger than the predetermined 5 percent level of significance, leading us *not* to reject the null hypothesis.

EXCEL CHART 16-6: Using Excel for Kruskal-Wallis Test

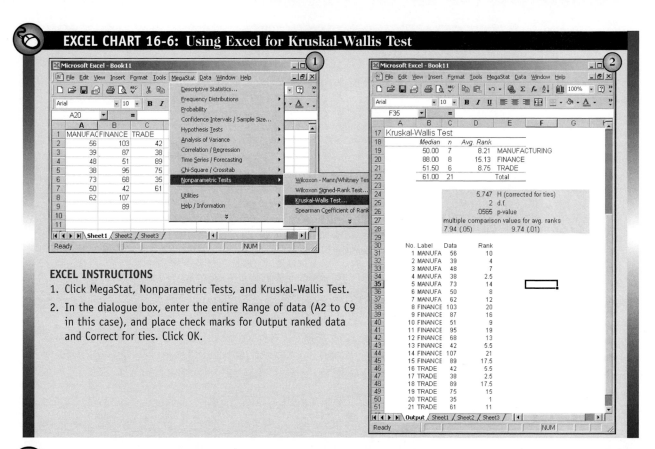

EXCEL INSTRUCTIONS

1. Click MegaStat, Nonparametric Tests, and Kruskal-Wallis Test.

2. In the dialogue box, enter the entire Range of data (A2 to C9 in this case), and place check marks for Output ranked data and Correct for ties. Click OK.

MINITAB CHART 16-7: Using Minitab for Kruskal-Wallis Test

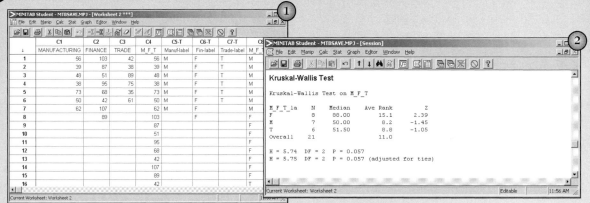

MINITAB INSTRUCTIONS

1. Enter data for each of the three samples in three separate columns (C1, C2, C3).
2. Click Manip on the tool bar and click Stack Columns.
3. In the dialogue box, enter C1, C2, and C3 in Stack the Columns, and C4 for storage.
4. Repeat the same steps for labels for executives in Manufacturing, Finance, and Trade. Labels are arbitrary. You could use numbers 1, 2, and 3.
5. Click Stat, Non-parametric Tests, and Kruskal-Wallis.
6. In the dialogue box, enter C4 in the Response and C8 in the Factor boxes.
7. Click OK to get the Output.

■ SELF-REVIEW 16-6

The regional bank manager of the Royal Bank is interested in the turnover rate of personal chequing accounts in four of the large bank branches. (Turnover rate is the speed at which the money in an account is deposited and withdrawn. An extremely active account may have a rate of 300; if only one or two cheques were written, the rate could be about 30.) The turnover rates of the samples selected from the four bank branches are shown. Using the 0.01 level and the Kruskal-Wallis test, determine whether there is a difference in the turnover rates of the personal chequing accounts among the four branches.

Englewood Branch	West Side Branch	Great Northern Branch	Sylvania Branch
208	91	302	99
307	62	103	116
199	86	319	189
142	91	340	103
91	80	180	100
296			131

EXERCISES 16-19 TO 16-24

16-19. Under what conditions should the Kruskal-Wallis test be used instead of analysis of variance?

16-20. Under what conditions should the Kruskal-Wallis test be used instead of the Wilcoxon rank-sum test?

16-21. The following sample data were obtained from three populations that were not necessarily normal.

Sample 1	Sample 2	Sample 3
50	48	39
54	49	41
59	49	44
59	52	47
65	56	51
	57	

(a) State the null hypothesis.
(b) Using the 0.05 level of risk, state the decision rule.
(c) Compute the value of the test statistic.
(d) What is your decision on the null hypothesis?

16-22. The following sample data were obtained from three populations where the variances were not equal, and you wish to compare the populations.

Sample 1	Sample 2	Sample 3
21	15	38
29	17	40
35	22	44
45	27	51
56	31	53
71		

(a) State the null hypothesis.
(b) Using the 0.01 level of risk, state the decision rule.
(c) Compute the value of the test statistic.
(d) What is your decision on the null hypothesis?

16-23. Anderson Outboard Motors, Inc. recently developed an epoxy painting process for corrosion protection on exhaust components. The Anderson engineers want to determine whether the distributions of the length of life for the paint are equal for three different conditions: salt water, fresh water without weeds, and fresh water with a heavy concentration of weeds. Accelerated-life tests were conducted in the laboratory, and the number of hours the paint lasted before peeling was recorded.

Salt Water	Fresh Water without Weeds	Fresh Water with Weeds
167.3	160.6	182.7
189.6	177.6	165.4
177.2	185.3	172.9
169.4	168.6	169.2
180.3	176.6	174.7

Use the Kruskal-Wallis test and the 0.01 level to determine whether the lasting quality of the paint is the same for the three water conditions.

16-24. The National Turkey Association wants to experiment with three different food mixtures for very young turkeys. Since no experience exists regarding the three food mixtures, no assumptions can be made about the shape of the distribution of weights. The Kruskal-Wallis test must be used to test whether the turkeys are equal in weight after eating the food for a specified length of time. Five young turkeys were given food A, six were given food B, and five were given food C. Test at the 0.05 level whether the mean weights of the turkeys who ate food A, food B, and food C are equal.

Weight (in kilograms)		
Food Mixture A	Food Mixture B	Food Mixture C
11.2	12.6	11.3
12.1	10.8	11.9
10.9	11.3	12.4
11.3	11.0	10.6
12.0	12.0	12.0
	10.7	

16.7 RANK-ORDER CORRELATION

In Chapter 13 we discussed the coefficient of correlation, which measures linear association between two interval- or ratio-scaled variables. For example, the coefficient of correlation reports the association between the salary of executives and their years of experience, or the association between the number of miles a shipment had to travel and the number of days it took to arrive at its destination.

Charles Spearman, a British statistician, introduced a measure of correlation for ordinal-level data. This measure allows us to study the relationship between sets of ranked data. However, the method can also be used to study the relationship between populations measured at a higher scale of measurement. For example, two staff members in the Office of Research at the University of Victoria are asked to rank 10 faculty research proposals. We want to study the association between the ratings of the two staff members. That is, do the two staff members rate the same proposals as the most worthy and the least worthy of funding? Spearman's coefficient of rank correlation, denoted r_s, provides a measure of the association.

The coefficient of rank correlation for a sample of paired observations is computed using the following formula.

Spearman's Coefficient of Rank Correlation	$r_s = 1 - \dfrac{6\sum d^2}{n(n^2 - 1)}$	16-10

where:

d is the difference between the ranks for each pair.

n is the number of paired observations.

Like the coefficient of correlation, the coefficient of rank correlation can assume any value from -1.00 up to 1.00. A value of -1.00 indicates perfect negative correlation and a value of 1.00, a perfect positive correlation among the ranks. A rank correlation of 0 indicates that there is no association among the ranks. Rank correlations of -0.84 and 0.84 indicate a strong association, but the former indicates an inverse relationship between the ranks and the latter indicates a direct relationship.

Example 16-7

A composite rating is given by executives to each college graduate joining a plastics manufacturing firm. The executive rating is an expression of the future potential of the college graduate. The ratings represent, of course, the ordinal level of measurement. The recent college graduate then enters an in-plant training program and is given another composite rating based on tests, opinions of group leaders, training officers, and so on. The executive ratings and the in-plant training ratings are given in Table 16-10.

TABLE 16-10: Executive Ratings and In-plant Training Ratings For a Sample of Recent College Graduates

Graduate	Executive Rating X	Training Rating Y	Graduate	Executive Rating X	Training Rating Y
A	8	4	G	11	9
B	10	4	H	7	6
C	9	4	I	8	6
D	4	3	J	13	9
E	12	6	K	10	5
F	11	9	L	12	9

Calculate the coefficient of rank correlation. Interpret its value.

Solution   It was decided to rank the variables from low to high. The lowest rating given by the executives was a 4 to graduate D, so it was ranked 1. The next lowest was a 7 to graduate H, so it was ranked 2. There were two graduates rated 8. The tie is resolved by giving each a rank of 3.5, which is the average of ranks 3 and 4. The same procedure is followed when there are more than two ratings tied. For example, note that the lowest training rating is 3, and it is given a rank of 1. Then there are three ratings of 4. The average of the three tied ranks is 3, found by $(2 + 3 + 4)/3$. This is illustrated along with the necessary calculations for r_s in Table 16-11.

TABLE 16-11: Calculations Needed for r_s

Graduate	Executive Rating X	Training Rating Y	Rank Executive	Rank Training	Difference between Ranks d	Difference Squared d^2
A	8	4	3.5	3.0	0.5	0.25
B	10	4	6.5	3.0	3.5	12.25
C	9	4	5.0	3.0	2.0	4.00
D	4	3	1.0	1.0	0	0
E	12	6	10.5	7.0	3.5	12.25
F	11	9	8.5	10.5	−2.0	4.00
G	11	9	8.5	10.5	−2.0	4.00
H	7	6	2.0	7.0	−5.0	25.00
I	8	6	3.5	7.0	−3.5	12.25
J	13	9	12.0	10.5	1.5	2.25
K	10	5	6.5	5.0	1.5	2.25
L	12	9	10.5	10.5	0	0
					0.0	78.50

r_s is 0.726, found by:

$$r_s = 1 - \frac{6\sum d^2}{n(n^2 - 1)} = 1 - \frac{6(78.50)}{12(143)} = 0.726$$

The value of 0.726 indicates a strong positive association between the ratings of the executives and the ratings of the training staff. The graduate that received high ratings from the executives also received high ratings from the training staff.

TESTING THE SIGNIFICANCE OF r_s

In Chapter 13 we tested the significance of the coefficient of correlation. For ranked data the question also arises whether the correlation in the population is actually zero. For instance, there were only 12 graduates sampled in the preceding example. In the solution to the example, the rank correlation coefficient of 0.726 indicates a rather strong relationship between the two sets of ranks. Is it possible that the correlation of 0.726 is due to chance and that the correlation in the population is really 0? We will now conduct a test of significance to answer that question.

For a sample of 10 or more, the significance of r_s is determined by computing t using the following formula. The sampling distribution of r_s follows the t distribution with $n - 2$ degrees of freedom.

Hypotheses Test, Rank Correlation	$t = r_s \sqrt{\dfrac{n-2}{1-r_s^2}}$	16-11

The null and alternative hypotheses are:

H_0: The rank correlation between executive rating and in-plant rating is zero.

H_1: The rank correlation between executive rating and in-plant rating is greater than zero.

The decision rule is to reject H_0 if the computed value of t is greater than 1.812 (from Appendix 4 on the CD-ROM, 0.05 significance level, one-tailed test, and 10 degrees of freedom, found by $n - 2 = 12 - 2 = 10$.

The computed value of t is 3.338:

$$t = r_s \sqrt{\frac{n-2}{1-r_s^2}} = 0.726 \sqrt{\frac{12-2}{1-(0.726)^2}} = 3.338$$

H_0 is rejected because the computed t of 3.338 is greater than 1.812. H_1 is accepted. There is a positive correlation between the ranks given by the executives and the ranks assigned by in-plant training staff.

Computations using Excel and Minitab are shown below:

EXCEL CHART 16-8: Using Excel for Rank Correlation

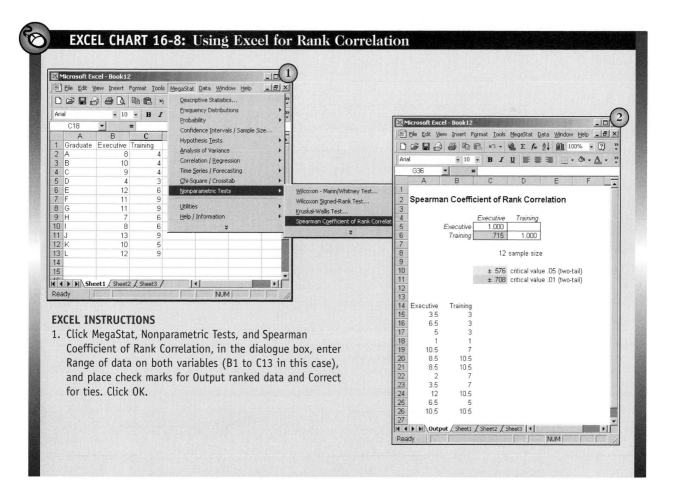

EXCEL INSTRUCTIONS

1. Click MegaStat, Nonparametric Tests, and Spearman Coefficient of Rank Correlation, in the dialogue box, enter Range of data on both variables (B1 to C13 in this case), and place check marks for Output ranked data and Correct for ties. Click OK.

MINITAB CHART 16-9: Using Minitab for Rank Correlation

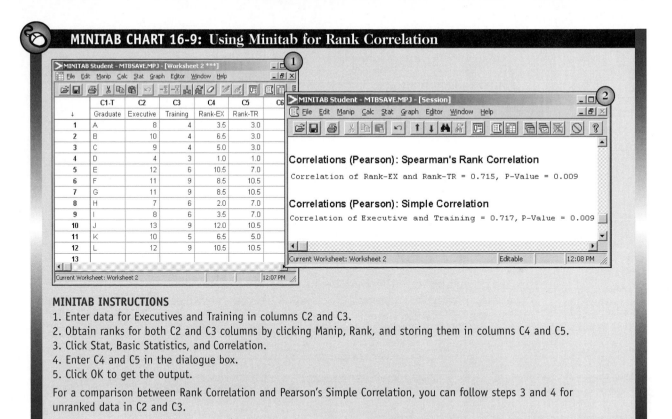

MINITAB INSTRUCTIONS
1. Enter data for Executives and Training in columns C2 and C3.
2. Obtain ranks for both C2 and C3 columns by clicking Manip, Rank, and storing them in columns C4 and C5.
3. Click Stat, Basic Statistics, and Correlation.
4. Enter C4 and C5 in the dialogue box.
5. Click OK to get the output.

For a comparison between Rank Correlation and Pearson's Simple Correlation, you can follow steps 3 and 4 for unranked data in C2 and C3.

■ SELF-REVIEW 16-7

A sample of individuals applying for factory positions at Davis Enterprises revealed the following scores on an eye perception test (X) and a mechanical aptitude test (Y):

Subject	Eye Perception	Mechanical Aptitude	Subject	Eye Perception	Mechanical Aptitude
001	805	23	006	810	28
002	777	62	007	805	30
003	820	60	008	840	42
004	682	40	009	777	55
005	777	70	010	820	51

(a) Compute the coefficient of rank correlation.
(b) At the 0.05 significance level, can we conclude that the correlation in the population is different from 0?

EXERCISES 16-25 TO 16-28

16-25. *The Globe and Mail* research staff wants to pretest a questionnaire to be mailed to several thousand readers. One question involves the ranking of male and female senior citizens with respect to the popularity of certain newspaper sections. The composite rankings of a small group of senior citizens are:

Program	Ranking by Males	Ranking by Females
Major News	1	5
Business Section	4	1
Sports	3	2
Review	2	4
Classified	5	3

(a) Draw a scatter diagram. Let the ranking by males be X.
(b) Compute Spearman's rank-order correlation coefficient. Interpret.

16-26. A university in British Columbia offers both day and evening classes in business administration. One question in a survey of students inquires how they perceive the prestige associated with certain careers. Each student was asked to rank careers from 1 to 8, with 1 having the most prestige and 8 the least prestige. The results were:

Career	Ranking by Day Students	Ranking by Evening Students	Career	Ranking by Day Students	Ranking by Evening Students
Accountant	6	3	Statistician	1	7
Computer programmer	7	2	Marketing researcher	4	8
Bank branch manager	2	6	Stock analyst	3	5
Hospital administrator	5	4	Production manager	8	1

Find the rank coefficient of correlation. Interpret.

16-27. New representatives for the John Ford Metal and Wheel Company attend a brief training program before being assigned to a regional office. At the end of such a program, each representative was ranked with respect to future sales potential. At the end of the first sales year, their rankings were paired with their annual sales:

Representative	Annual Sales ($ thousands)	Ranking in Training Program	Representative	Annual Sales ($ thousands)	Ranking in Training Program
Kitchen	319	3	Arden	300	10
Bond	150	9	Crane	280	5
Gross	175	6	Arthur	200	2
Arbuckle	460	1	Keene	190	7
Greene	348	4	Knopf	300	8

(a) Compute and interpret Spearman's rank correlation coefficient.
(b) At the 0.05 significance level, can we conclude that there is a positive association among the ranks?

16-28. St. Thomas University has five scholarships available for the women's basketball team. The coach provided two scouts with the names of 10 high school players with potential. Each scout attended at least three games and then ranked the players with respect to potential.

Player	Rank by Scout		Player	Rank by Scout	
	Jean Cann	John Cannelli		Jean Cann	John Cannelli
Cora Jean Seiple	7	5	Candy Jenkins	3	1
Bette Jones	2	4	Rita Rosinski	5	7
Jeannie Black	10	10	Anita Lockes	4	2
Norma Tidwell	1	3	Brenda Towne	8	9
Kathy Marchal	6	6	Denise Ober	9	8

(a) Determine Spearman's rank correlation coefficient.
(b) At the 0.05 significance level, can we conclude there is a positive association between the ranks?

CHAPTER OUTLINE

I. The sign test:
   A. No assumptions need be made about the shape of the two populations.
   B. It is based on paired or dependent samples.
   C. For small samples find the number of + or − signs and refer to the binomial distribution for the critical value.
   D. For large samples (more than 10) use the standard normal distribution and the following formula.

$$Z = \frac{(S \pm 0.50) - 0.50n}{0.50\sqrt{n}}$$

II. The median test is used to test a hypothesis about a population median.
   A. Use the normal approximation to the binomial distribution to find μ and σ.
   B. The z distribution is used as the test statistic.
   C. The value of z is computed from the following formula, where S is the number of observations above or below the median.

$$Z = \frac{(S \pm 0.50) - \mu}{\sigma}$$

III. The Wilcoxon signed-rank test:
   A. Data must be at least ordinal scale, and the samples must be dependent.
   B. The steps to conduct the test are:
      1. Rank absolute difference between the related observations.
      2. Apply the sign of the differences to the ranks.
      3. Sum negative ranks and positive ranks.

4. The smaller of the two sums is the computed T value of the test statistic.

5. Find the critical value, and make a decision regarding H_0.

6. For sample sizes larger than 15, we can use the z test.

$$Z = \frac{T \pm 0.5 - \mu_T}{\sigma_T} \quad \text{where} \quad \mu_T = \frac{n(n+1)}{4} \quad \text{and} \quad \sigma_T = \sqrt{\frac{n(n+1)(2n+1)}{24}}$$

IV. The Wilcoxon rank-sum test is used to test whether two independent samples came from identical populations.

A. No assumption about the shape of the population is required.

B. To apply the test, the data must be at least ordinal scale.

C. To determine the value of the test statistic W, all data values are ranked from low to high as if they were from a single population.

D. The sum of ranks for each of the two samples is determined.

E. For small samples, we use the rank-sum as the test statistic depending on the nature of the alternative hypothesis. For a one-tailed test, we use the rank-sum that is expected to be smaller under the alternative hypothesis. For a two-tailed test, we use both rank-sums. We reject the null hypothesis if the test statistic is smaller compared to the critical value for a predetermined level of significance.

F. For samples larger than 10 we use the z statistic.

$$Z = \frac{W_1 \pm 0.5 - \mu_{W_1}}{\sigma_{w_1}}; \quad \text{where} \quad \mu_{W_1} = \frac{n_1(n_1 + n_2 + 1)}{2} \quad \text{and} \quad \sigma_{W_1} = \sqrt{\frac{n_1 n_2(n_1 + n_2 + 1}{12}}$$

V. The Kruskal-Wallis test:

A. No assumptions regarding the shape of the population are required.

B. The samples must be independent and at least ordinal scale.

C. It is used to test whether several populations are identical.

D. The sample observations are ranked from smallest to largest as though they were a single group.

E. The chi-square distribution can be used as the test statistic, provided there are at least 5 observations in each sample.

F. The value of the test statistic is computed from the following:

$$H = \frac{12}{N(N+1)} \left[\frac{\left(\sum R_1\right)^2}{n_1} + \frac{\left(\sum R_2\right)^2}{n_2} + \cdots + \frac{\left(\sum R_k\right)^2}{n_k} \right] - 3(N+1)$$

VI. Spearman's coefficient of rank correlation is a measure of the association between two ordinal-scale variables.

A. It can range from -1 up to 1.

1. A value of 0 indicates there is no association between the variables.

2. A value of -1 indicates perfect negative correlation, and 1 is perfect positive correlation.

B. The value of r_s is computed from the following formula.

$$r_s = 1 - \frac{6 \sum d^2}{n(n^2 - 1)}$$

C. Provided the sample size is at least 10, we can conduct a test of hypothesis using the following formula:

$$t = r_s \sqrt{\frac{n-2}{1-r_s^2}}$$

1. The test statistic is the t distribution.
2. There are $n - 2$ degrees of freedom.

CHAPTER EXERCISES 16-29 TO 16-40

16-29. The program director at CBC is finalizing the prime-time schedule for next fall. She has decided to include a Western but is unsure which of two possibilities to select. She has a pilot called "The Loner" and another called "Cattleman." To help her make a final decision, a random sample of 20 viewers is asked to watch the two pilots and indicate which show they prefer. The results were that 12 liked "The Loner," 7 liked "Cattleman," and one had no preference. Is there a preference for one of the two shows? Use the 0.10 significance level.

16-30. Suppose Merrill Lynch wants to award a substantial contract for fine-line pens to be used nationally in their offices. Two suppliers, Bic and Pilot, have submitted the lowest bids. To determine the preference of office employees, brokers, and others, a personal preference test is to be conducted using a randomly selected sample of 20 employees. The 0.05 level of significance is to be used.
   (a) If the alternative hypothesis states that Bic is preferred over Pilot, is the sign test to be conducted as a one-tailed or a two-tailed test? Explain.
   (b) As each of the sample members told the researchers his or her preference, a "+" was recorded if it was Bic and a "−" if it was the Pilot fine-line pen. A count of the pluses revealed that 12 employees preferred Bic, 5 preferred Pilot, and 3 were undecided. What is n?
   (c) What is the decision rule in words?
   (d) What conclusion did you reach regarding pen preference? Explain.

16-31. Sears Electronics wants to handle just one brand of high-quality compact disc player. The list has been narrowed to two brands: Sony and Pioneer. To help make a decision, a panel of 16 audio experts met. A passage using Sony components (labelled A) was played. Then the same passage was played using Pioneer components (labelled B). A "+" in the following table indicates an individual's preference for the Sony components, a "−" indicates preference for Pioneer, and a 0 signifies no preference.

Expert															
1	2	3	4	5	6	7	8	9	10	11	12	13	14	15	16
+	−	+	−	+	+	−	0	−	+	−	+	+	−	+	−

Conduct a test of hypothesis at the 0.10 significance level to determine whether there is a difference in preference between the two brands.

16-32. The Quebec City Real Estate Association claims that the median rental for three-bedroom houses in the metropolitan area is more than $1200 a month. To check this, a random sample of 149 units was selected. Of the 149 houses, 5 rented for exactly $1200 a month, and 75 rented for more than $1200. At the 0.05 level, test the statement that the median rental is $1200.
(a) State H_0 and H_1.
(b) Give the decision rule.
(c) Do the necessary calculations, and arrive at a decision.

16-33. The Citrus Council wants to find whether consumers prefer plain juice or juice with some orange pulp in it. A random sample of 212 consumers was selected. Each member of the sample tasted a small, unlabelled cup of one kind and then tasted the other kind. Twelve consumers said they had no preference, 40 preferred plain juice, and the remainder liked the juice with pulp better. Test at the 0.05 level that the preferences for plain juice and for orange juice with pulp are equal.

16-34. A research project involving community responsibility is to be conducted. The objective is to find whether women are more community conscious before marriage or after five years of marriage. A test to measure community consciousness was administered to a sample of women before marriage, and the same test was given to them five years after marriage. The test scores are:

Name	Before Marriage	After Marriage	Name	Before Marriage	After Marriage
Beth	110	114	Carol	186	196
Jean	157	159	Lisa	116	116
Sue	121	120	Sandy	160	140
Cathy	96	103	Petra	149	142
Mary	130	139			

Test at the 0.05 level. H_0 is: There is no difference in community consciousness before and after marriage. H_1 is: There is a difference.

16-35. Is there a difference in the annual divorce rates in predominantly rural counties among three geographic regions, namely Atlantic Canada, Central Canada, and Western Canada? Test at the 0.05 level. Annual divorce rates per 1000 for randomly selected counties are:
Atlantic Canada   5.9   6.2   7.9   8.6   4.6
Central Canada   5.0   6.4   7.3   6.2   8.1   5.1
Western Canada   6.7   6.2   4.9   8.0   5.5

16-36. The idle times during the eight-hour day shift and the night shift are to be compared. A time study revealed the following numbers of minutes of idle time for eight-hour periods.
Day shift: 92   103   116   81   89
Night shift: 96   114   80   82   88   91

Is there a difference in the idle times between the two shifts? Test at the 0.05 level.

16-37. The mobility of executives in high tech industries, in service, in heavy construction and in air transportation is to be researched. Samples from each of these industries were selected, and the number of times an executive moved during a 10-year period was converted to an index. An index of 0 would indicate no movement, whereas 100 would indicate almost constant movement from one location to another or one firm to another. The indices for the four groups are shown below as well as in file Exercise 16-37.xls on the CD-ROM.

High Tech	Service	Heavy Construction	Air Transportation
4	3	62	30
17	12	40	38
8	40	81	46
20	17	96	40
16	31	76	21
	19		

We cannot assume that the indices are normally distributed. Thus, we must use a nonparametric test. Using the 0.05 level, determine whether the four populations of mobility indices are identical.

 16-38. A series of questions on sports and world events was asked of a randomly selected group of male senior citizens. The results were translated into a "knowledge" score. The scores were:

Citizen	Sports	World Events	Citizen	Sports	World Events
J.C. McCarthy	47	49	L.M. Zaugg	87	75
A.N. Baker	12	10	J.B. Simon	59	86
B.B. Beebe	62	76	J.Goulden	40	61
L.D. Gaucet	81	92	A.A. Davis	87	18
C.A. Jones	90	86	A.M. Carbo	16	75
J.N. Narko	35	42	A.O. Smithy	50	51
A.F. Nissen	61	61	J.J. Pascal	60	61

(a) Determine the degree of association between how the senior citizens ranked with respect to knowledge of sports and how they ranked on world events.
(b) At the 0.05 significance level, is the rank correlation in the population greater than zero?

 16-39. Early in the basketball season, 12 teams appeared to be outstanding. A panel of sportswriters and a panel of college basketball coaches were asked to rank the 12 teams. Their composite rankings were as follows.

Team	Coaches	Sportswriters	Team	Coaches	Sportswriters
A	1	1	G	7	10
B	2	5	H	8	11
C	3	4	I	9	7
D	4	6	J	10	12
E	5	3	K	11	8
F	6	2	L	12	9

Determine the correlation between rankings of the coaches and the sportswriters. At the 0.05 significance level, can we conclude it is different from zero?

16-40. Professor Bert Forman believes the students who complete his examinations in the shortest time receive the highest grades and those who take the longest to complete them receive the lowest grades. To verify his suspicion, he assigns a rank to the order of finish and then grades the examinations. The results are shown below:

Student	Order of Completion	Score (50 possible)	Student	Order of Completion	Score (50 possible)
Gromney	1	48	Smythe	7	39
Bates	2	48	Arquette	8	30
MacDonald	3	43	Govito	9	37
White	4	49	Gankowski	10	35
Harris	5	50	Bonfigilo	11	36
Cribb	6	47	Hineman	12	33

Convert the test scores to a rank and find the coefficient of rank correlation. At the 0.05 significance level, can Professor Forman conclude there is a positive association between the order of finish and the exam scores?

www.**exercises**.ca 16-41 TO 16-43

16-41. Is there a correlation between the starting position in an auto race and the order of finish? To investigate, use the results of the most recent Canadian auto race. To obtain the results go to http://www.cascar.ca, select race results. For other sports including auto, you can also go through the Web site http://www.Canadiansport.com. All Canadian sports links are listed here.
   (a) Compute the coefficient of rank correlation between the starting position and the order of finish.
   (b) Conduct a test of hypothesis to determine whether the rank correlation is greater than zero.
   (c) Write a brief report summarizing the results.

16-42. Collect data on birth rates of males and females in 30 Canadian counties from community profiles at www.statcan.ca Web site. Test Arbuthnot's proposition.

16-43. Collect data on one-year rate of return on 30 mutual funds from www.globefund.com, 10 funds from natural resources, 10 from global science and technology, and 10 from Canadian balanced category. Answer the following questions.
   (a) Test whether the median rates of return in global science and technology equal the rates of return in the natural resource category. Assume the alternative hypothesis that the tech funds have higher rates of return. Use the 5% level of significance. (Use the Wilcoxon Rank-sum test.)
   (b) Test whether the median rates of return in all three categories are equal, against the alternative hypothesis that they are not equal. Use the 5% level of significance. (Use the Kruskal-Wallis test.)

COMPUTER DATA EXERCISES 16-44 TO 16-46

16-44. Refer to the file Real Estate Data.xls that reports information on homes sold in Victoria, B.C. during the last year.
   (a) Use an appropriate nonparametric test to determine whether there is a difference in the typical selling price of the homes in several townships. Assume the selling prices are not normally distributed. Use the 0.05 significance level.
   (b) Combine the homes with 6 or more bedrooms into one group and determine whether there is a difference in the typical selling prices of the homes. Use the 0.05 significance level and assume that the distribution of selling prices is not normally distributed.
   (c) Assume that the distribution of the distance from the centre of the city is positively skewed. That is, the normality assumption is not reasonable. Compare the distribution of the homes that have a pool with those that do not have a pool. Can we conclude there is a difference in the distributions? Use the 0.05 significance level.

16-45. Refer to the file BASEBALL-2000.xls, which reports information on the 2000 Major League Baseball season.
   (a) Rank the teams by the number of wins and their total team salary. Compute the coefficient of rank correlation between the two variables. At the 0.01 significance level, can you conclude that it is greater than zero?
   (b) Assume that the distributions of team salaries for the American League and National League do not follow the normal distribution. Conduct a test of hypothesis to see if there is a difference in the two distributions.

16-46. Refer to the file OECD.xls, which reports information on census, economic, and business data for 29 countries. Categorize the countries indicating whether they are in Europe, North America, or the Far East. Divide the Gross National Product by the population to determine the per capita GNP. Without assuming normality, test at the 0.05 significance level if there is a difference in the distributions for the three regions. Compare the results to those of Exercise 12-43B in Chapter 12.

CHAPTER 16   ANSWERS TO SELF-REVIEW

16-1. (a) Two-tailed because H_1 does not state a direction.

(b)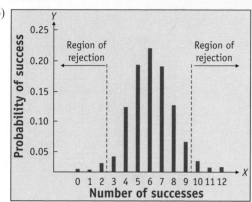

Adding down, $0.000 + 0.003 + 0.016 = 0.019$. This is the largest cumulative probability up to but not exceeding 0.050, which is half the level of significance.

(c) Reject H_0: accept H_1. There is a preference.

16-2. (a) $H_0: p \leq 0.50$, $H_1: p > 0.50$.

(b) Reject H_0 if $z > 1.645$.

(c) Since 80 is more than $n/2 = 100/2 = 50$, we use:
$$z = \frac{(80 - 0.50) - 0.50(100)}{0.50\sqrt{100}} = \frac{29.5}{5} = 5.9$$

(d) H_0 is rejected.

(e) The education was effective.

16-3. (a) H_0: The median $= \$123$, H_1: The median is more than $\$123$.

(b) Reject H_0 if $z > 1.645$.

(c) $z = \dfrac{(42 - 0.50) - 32}{0.50\sqrt{64}} = \dfrac{9.5}{4} = 2.38$

(d) Reject H_0.

(e) The median bill is more than $\$123$.

16-4. (a) $n = 10$ (because there was no change for A.A.)

(b)

Before	After	Difference	Absolute Difference	Rank of Absolute Difference	Negative Ranks	Positive Ranks
17	18	−1	1	1.5	1.5	
21	23	−2	2	3.0	3.0	
25	22	3	3	5.0		5.0
15	25	−10	10	8.0	8.0	
10	28	−18	18	10.0	10.0	
16	16	—	—	—	—	—
10	22	−12	12	9.0	9.0	
20	19	1	1	1.5		1.5
17	20	−3	3	5.0	5.0	
24	30	−6	6	7.0	7.0	
23	26	−3	3	5.0	5.0	
					48.5	6.5

H_0: Production is the same.
H_1: Production has increased.
The sum of the positive signed ranks is 6.5; the negative sum is 48.5. From Table 16–4, one-tailed test, $n = 10$, the critical value is 10. Since 6.5 is less than 10, reject the null hypothesis and accept the alternative. New procedures did increase production.

16-5. H_0: There is no difference in the population of distances travelled by Dino and by Maxi.
H_1: There is a difference.

Dino		Maxi	
Distance	Rank	Distance	Rank
252	4	262	9
263	10	242	2
279	15	256	5
273	14	260	8
271	13	258	7
265	11.5	243	3
257	6	239	1
280	16	265	11.5
Total	89.5		46.5

Maxi is labelled as number 1 and Dino as number 2.

Using small sample Wilcoxon test statistic, our decision rule is to reject H_0, if $W_1 < W^*$ (corresponding to column equals n_1 and row equals n_2) OR $W_2 < W^*$ (corresponding to column equals n_1 and row equals n_2).

Since, in this case, both $n_1 = n_2 = 8$, we have only one critical value of $W = W^* = 52$. $W_1 = 46.5 < 52$. We reject H_0.

If we use a large sample approximation, our decision rule should be:

Do not reject H_0 if the computed z is between 1.96 and -1.96 (from Appendix 3 on the CD-ROM); otherwise, reject H_0 and accept H_1, $n_1 = 8$, the number of observations in the first sample.

$$z = \frac{89.5 - \frac{8(8+8+1)}{2}}{\sqrt{\frac{(8)(8)(8+8+1)}{12}}}$$

$$= \frac{21.5}{9.52} = 2.26$$

Reject H_0; accept H_1. There is a difference in the distances travelled by the two golf balls.

16-6.

	Ranks		
Englewood	West Side	Great Northern	Sylvania
17	5	19	7
20	1	9.5	11
16	3	21	15
13	5	22	9.5
5	2	14	8
18			12
$\sum R_1 = 89$	$\sum R_1 = 16$	$\sum R_3 = 85.5$	$\sum R_1 = 62.5$
$n_1 = 6$	$n_1 = 5$	$n_3 = 5$	$n_1 = 6$

H_0: The distributions are the same.
H_1: The distributions are not the same.

$$H = \frac{12}{22(22+1)}\left[\frac{(89)^2}{6} + \frac{(16)^2}{5} + \frac{(85.5)^2}{5} + \frac{(62.5)^2}{6}\right]$$
$$- 3(22+1)$$
$$= 13.635$$

The critical value of chi-square for $k - 1 = 4 - 1 = 3$ degrees of freedom is 11.345. Since the computed value of 13.635 is greater than 11.345, the null hypothesis is rejected. We conclude that the population distributions are not identical.

16-7. (a) Rank

X	Y	X	Y	d	d^2
805	23	5.5	1	4.5	20.25
777	62	3.0	9	-6.0	36.00
820	60	8.5	8	0.5	0.25
682	40	1.0	4	-3.0	9.00
777	70	3.0	10	-7.0	49.00
810	28	7.0	2	5.0	25.00
805	30	5.5	3	2.5	6.25
840	42	10.0	5	5.0	25.00
777	55	3.0	7	-4.0	16.00
820	51	8.5	6	2.5	6.25
				0	193.00

$$r_s = 1 - \frac{6(193)}{10(99)} = -0.170$$

(b) H_0: $p = 0$; H_1: $p \neq 0$. Reject H_0 if $t < -2.306$ or $t > 2.306$.

$$t = -0.170\sqrt{\frac{10-2}{1-(-0.170)^2}} = -0.488$$

H_0 is not rejected. There is not sufficient evidence for a relationship between the two tests.

A REVIEW OF   CHAPTERS 15 AND 16

Goodness-of-fit test and contingency table analysis applicable to nominal-level data

This section is a review of the major concepts and terms introduced in Chapters 15 and 16. Chapter 15 began the study of *nonparametric*, or *distribution-free* tests by discussing the *chi-square goodness-of-fit test*. This test is applied to a set of observed frequencies, f_0, and a corresponding set of expected frequencies, f_e, to test how well the sets fit. This test involves only one characteristic possessed by an individual such as education. If we are interested in two characteristics, such as a relationship between education level and income, the data are cross-classified into a contingency table, and the chi-square test for independence is applied. For these two lists, no assumption about the shape of the population is needed; they require only that the data be nominal level. The chi-square goodness-of-fit test is also used to determine whether a set of observed frequencies is normally distributed.

Five tests for ordinal-level data

Chapter 16 presented five nonparametric tests of hypothesis and the coefficient of rank correlation, all of which require the ordinal level of measurement. That is, the data must be ranked from low to high. The tests discussed were the *sign test*, the *median test*, the *Wilcoxon rank-sum test*, the *Kruskal-Wallis (analysis of variance) test*, and the *Wilcoxon signed-rank test*.

■ GLOSSARY

Chapter 15

Chi-square distribution A distribution with these characteristics: (1) its value can only be positive, (2) there is a family of chi-square distributions, a different one for each different degree of freedom, and (3) the distributions are positively skewed, but as the number of degrees of freedom increases, the distribution approaches the normal distribution.

Chi-square goodness-of-fit test A test with the objective of determining how well an observed set of frequencies fits an expected set of frequencies. Also called the test of homogeneity.

Contingency table If two characteristics, such as education and income, are cross-classified into a table, the result is called a contingency table. The chi-square test statistic is used to investigate whether the two characteristics are related.

Nominal level of measurement The "lowest" level of measurement. Such data can only be classified into categories, and there is no particular order for the categories. For example, it makes no difference whether the categories "male" and "female" are listed in that order or female first and male second. The categories are mutually exclusive meaning in this illustration, that a person cannot be a male and a female at the same time.

Nonparametric or distribution-free tests Hypothesis tests involving nominal- and ordinal-level data. No assumptions need be made about the shape of the population and in particular we do not assume the population is normally distributed.

Chapter 16

Kruskal-Wallis one-way analysis of variance by ranks A test used when the assumptions for the parametric analysis of variance (ANOVA) cannot be met. Its purpose is to test whether several population medians are equal. Again, the data must be at least ordinal scale.

Sign test A test used for dependent samples. The sign test is used to find whether there is a brand preference for two products or to determine whether performance after an experiment is greater than before the experiment. Also, the sign test is used to test a hypothesis about the median.

Spearman's coefficient of rank correlation A measure of the association between the ranks of two variables. It can range from -1.00 to 1.00. A value of -1.00 indicates a perfect negative association among the ranks and a value of 1.00, a perfect positive association among the ranks. A value of 0 indicates no association among the ranks.

Wilcoxon matched-pair signed-rank test A nonparametric test requiring at least ordinal-level data. Its purpose is to find whether there is any difference between two sets of paired (related) observations. It is used if the assumptions required for the paired t test cannot be met.

Wilcoxon rank-sum test A nonparametric test requiring independent samples. The data must be at least ordinal level. That is, the data must be capable of being ranked. The test is used when the assumptions for the parametric Student t test cannot be met. The objective of the test is to find whether two independent samples can be considered as coming from identical populations.

■ EXERCISES

1. For a chi-square test, what do f_o and f_e stand for?

2. The following is an example of what?

Political Affiliation	Amount Contributed to Campaign		
	$1–$99	$100–$999	$1000 and more
Canadian Alliance	42	87	342
Liberals	596	302	116
New Democrats	42	49	36
All others	19	17	11

3. Refer to Exercise 2 above. What test statistic would be used to find whether there is any relationship between political affiliation and the amount contributed?

4. Refer to Exercise 2. How many degrees of freedom are there?

5. Refer to Exercise 2. Suppose the computed value of χ^2 is 11.248, and the 0.05 level is being used. Should the null hypothesis be rejected?

6. For a goodness-of-fit test, the computed value of chi-square is 8.403, and the critical value is 5.991. The 0.05 level is being used. Is the null hypothesis rejected?

7. Refer to Exercise 6. What is the null hypothesis?

8. What level of measurement is required for the parametric tests of hypotheses discussed in Chapters 11 and 12?

9. What level of measurement is required for the goodness-of-fit test?

10. What level of measurement is required for the Wilcoxon rank-sum test?

11. What is the purpose of the Wilcoxon rank-sum test?

12. What assumptions are made about the shape of the populations in using the Kruskal-Wallis test?

13. What is the objective of the Kruskal-Wallis test?

14. What is the objective of the Wilcoxon signed-rank test?

15. Of the following nonparametric tests (sign test, Wilcoxon rank-sum, Kruskal-Wallis, and Wilcoxon signed-rank), which one deals with three or more samples?

16. Refer to Exercise 15. Which test deals with paired data?

17. Refer to Exercise 15. Can these tests be applied to interval- and ratio-level data?

18. For a Wilcoxon rank-sum test, the alternative hypothesis is: the women have better visual perception than the men. Would a one-tailed or a two-tailed test be applied?

19. The chi-square distribution for 5 degrees of freedom is approximately normally distributed. Is that statement true?

20. How are the degrees of freedom for a goodness-of-fit test determined?

21. Describe the steps followed, using a simple example, to test a hypothesis involving the median.

■ CASES

A. TOP 1000 CANADIAN CORPORATIONS

Use the data set 100 of Top 1000 Companies.xls on the CD-ROM.

(a) Find the rank correlation between the profit rank and the revenue rank.

(b) Classify all companies into three categories: financial, technological, and all others. Test whether the median rates of return on capital are the same in three categories against the alternative that they are different. Use the Kruskal-Wallis test and a 5 percent level of significance.

(c) Select the pairs of categories and test the null hypothesis that the median rates of return are equal in each category against the alternative that they are different. Use the Wilcoxon rank-sum test and a 5 percent level of significance.

(d) Can you compare the results of (b) and (c) above without running the risk of an incorrect Type I error?

B. THOMAS TESTING LABS

John Thomas, the owner of Thomas Testing, has for some time done contract work for insurance companies regarding drunk driving. To improve his research capabilities, he recently purchased the Rupple Driving Simulator. This device will allow a subject to take a "road test" and provide a score, indicating the number of driving errors committed during the test drive. Higher scores indicate more driving errors. Driving errors would include: not coming to a complete stop at a stop sign, not using turning signals, not exercising caution on wet or snowy pavement, and so on. During the road test, problems appear at random and not all problems appear in each road test. These are major advantages to the Rupple Driving Simulator because subjects do not gain any advantage by taking the test several times.

With the new driving simulator, Mr. Thomas would like to study in detail the problem of drunk driving. He begins by selecting a random sample of 25 drivers. He asks each of the selected individuals to take the test drive on the Rupple Driving Simulator. The number of errors for each driver is recorded below. Next, he has each of the individuals in the group drink three 500-ml cans of beer in a 60-minute period and return to the Rupple Driving Simulator for another test drive. The number of driving errors after drinking the beer is also shown below. (These data are also provided in Folder Review 15-16 on the CD-ROM.) The research question is: does alcohol impair the driver's ability and, therefore, increase the number of driving errors?

Mr. Thomas believes the distribution of scores on the test drive does not follow a normal distribution and, therefore, a nonparametric test should be used. Because the observations are paired, he decides to use both the sign test and the Wilcoxon signed-rank test. Compare the results using these two procedures. Which statistical test would you suggest? What conclusion would you make regarding the effects of drunk driving? Write a brief report summarizing your findings.

Subject	Driving Errors		Subject	Driving Errors	
	Without Alcohol	With Alcohol		Without Alcohol	With Alcohol
1	75	89	14	72	106
2	78	83	15	83	89
3	89	80	16	99	89
4	100	90	17	75	77
5	85	84	18	58	78
6	70	68	19	93	108
7	64	84	20	69	69
8	79	104	21	86	84
9	83	81	22	97	86
10	82	88	23	65	92
11	83	93	24	96	97
12	84	92	25	85	94
13	80	103			

CHAPTER 17

Index Numbers

GOALS

When you have completed this chapter, you will be able to:

- Describe the term *index*

- Understand the difference between a weighted and an unweighted index

- Construct and interpret Laspeyres' price index

- Construct and interpret Paasche's price index

- Construct and interpret a value index

- Explain how the Consumer Price Index is constructed and interpreted.

IRVING FISHER (1867–1947)

The experimental use of economic statistics became known in the industrialized world in the 1870s. Etienne Laspeyres (1834–1913) and Hermann Paasche (1851–1925) developed index numbers which are known as Laspeyres' index and Paasche's index respectively. Laspeyres' index overestimates the effect of inflation whereas Paasche's index underestimates the effect of inflation.

The interest in the *Index Number* peaked in the 1890s. Irvine Fisher, the greatest expert on index numbers, wrote: *"Index numbers are a very recent contrivance ... although we may push back their invention a century and three quarters, their current use did not begin till 1869 at the earliest, and not in a general way till after 1900. In fact, it may be said that their use is only seriously beginning today."*[1] He developed the ideal index of prices, known as **Fisher's Ideal Index**, a geometric mean of Laspeyres' index and Paasche's index in which prices are weighted by their base year and year-end quantities respectively. He is known for his contribution to monetary theory (money, interest rates, prices of items, how they are intertwined and how collectively they affect the ecomony). Credit is given to him for making a clear distinction between *stocks* and *flows*. To address the complicated problem of measuring inflation, he explained the theory of the rate of interest, purchasing power of money, and many other pertinent concepts in many of his publications.

Fisher was born in Saugerties, New York, in 1867 and took his B.A. in mathematics and Ph.D. in economics at Yale University in 1899 and 1901 respectively.

Fisher's brilliance in developing economic theories however, did not translate into successful personal investment. During the 1920s, he speculated heavily in stocks. Following the crash of 1929, he still believed in the resurgence of the stock market and borrowed heavily to buy more stocks. Unfortunately, the stock market continued to fall and he lost not only most of his fortune gained earlier but also his reputation as a monetary theorist. He devoted his life to many subjects other than inflation, purchasing power of money, etc., and presented his views forcefully in many of his books. One of his most successful books was *How to Live: Rules For Healthful Living Based on Modern Science*. It was published in 1915 and became a national best-seller.

INTRODUCTION

In this chapter we will examine a useful descriptive tool called an **index**. No doubt you are familiar with indices such as the **Consumer Price Index**, released monthly by Statistics Canada. There are many other indices, such as Dow Jones Industrial Average, Standard & Poor's 500 Stock Average, and Toronto Stock Exchange 300 (S&P/TSX). Indices are published on a regular basis by the federal government, by business publications such as *Business Week*, *Forbes*, and *Canadian Business*, and in most daily newspapers such as *The Globe and Mail*.

Of what importance is an index? Why is the Consumer Price Index so important and so widely reported? As the name implies, it measures the change in the price of a large group of items consumers purchase. The Bank of Canada, consumer groups, unions, management, senior citizens' organizations, and others in business and economics are very concerned about changes in prices. These groups closely monitor the Consumer Price Index as well as the **Producer Price Index**, which measures price fluctuations at all stages of production. To combat sharp price increases, the Bank of Canada raises the interest rate to "cool down" the economy. Likewise, the S&P/TSX, which is published daily, describes the overall changes in stock prices of the major 300 Canadian companies during the day.

A few stock market indices appear daily in the financial section of most newspapers. Some of them are updated every fifteen minutes on many Web sites, such as the business section of *USA Today*. (www.ustoday.com/money/mfront.htm), and the business section of *The Globe and Mail* (www.globeinvestor.com). Shown are the Dow Jones Industrial Average, NASDAQ, and S&P 500 from the *USA Today* Web site and the S&P/TSX Comp from *The Globe And Mail* Web site.

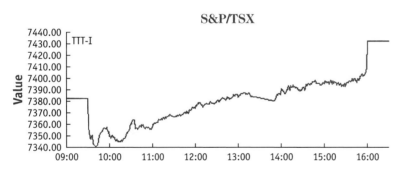

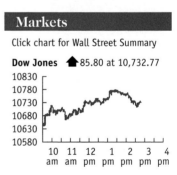

17.1　SIMPLE INDEX NUMBERS

Index Number
A number that expresses the change in the value of a variable such as price, quantity, value over time or place.

WHAT IS AN INDEX NUMBER?

If the index number is used to measure the relative change in just one variable, such as hourly wages in manufacturing, we refer to this as a simple index. It is the ratio of two values of a variable and that ratio converted to a percentage. The following four examples will serve to illustrate the use of index numbers.

Example 17-1 | Minimum hourly wage in Ontario in 1985 was $4 and in 2000 it was $6.85. What is the index of the hourly wage for the year 2000 based on the year 1985?

Solution | The index is $= 171.3$, and is found by:

$$P = \frac{\text{Hourly wage in Ontario in 2000}}{\text{Hourly wage in Ontario in 1985}} = \frac{\$6.85}{\$4}(100) = 171.3$$

where $P =$ price relative for the period.

Thus the hourly wage in 2000 compared to 1985 was 171.3 percent. This means there was an increase of 71.3 percent in hourly wage during the period found by $171.3 - 100 = 71.3$.

Example 17-2 | The number of new motor vehicles sold in Canada increased from 1 280 000 in 1980 to 1 600 000 in 2000. What is the index for the number of new motor vehicles in 2000 based on the number in 1980?

Source: adapted from www.statcan.ca/Daily/English/010215/b.htm

Solution | The index is 125, found by:

$$P = \frac{\text{Total number of new motor vehicles sold in 2000}}{\text{Total number of new motor vehicles sold in 1980}} = \frac{1\ 600\ 000}{1\ 280\ 000} = 125$$

Thus the total number of new motor vehicles sold in 2000 increased by 25 percent during the period.

An index number can also be used to compare the value of one variable with another similar variable at the same point in time.

Example 17-3 | The population of Ontario in 2001 was 11 874 000 and for British Columbia it was 4 095 900. What is the population of British Columbia compared to Ontario?

Solution |

$$P = \frac{\text{Population of British Columbia in 2001}}{\text{Population of Ontario in 2001}} = \frac{4\ 095\ 900}{11\ 874\ 000}(100) = 34.5$$

This indicates that the population of British Columbia is about 34.5 of the population of Ontario, or the population of British Columbia is 65.5 percent less than the population of Ontario $(34.5 - 100) = -65.5$.

Example 17-4 | In January 2001, the average price of two-storey houses in Edmonton, Regina, Vancouver, and Toronto were $125 520, $110 000, $339 500, and $267 083 respectively. What is the index of the average price of two-storey houses in Edmonton, Regina, and Vancouver compared with Toronto?

Solution To find the index in this case, we divide the average price of two-storey houses in Edmonton, Regina, and Vancouver by the average price of two-storey houses in Toronto. Note, Toronto is the base for comparison. The calculations of indices are shown below in tabular form.

City	Price	Index	Calculation
Edmonton	$125 520	47	[($125 520/$267 083) (100)]
Regina	$110 000	41.2	[($110 000/$267 083) (100)]
Vancouver	$339 500	127.1	[($339 500/$267 083) (100)]

We conclude that compared with the average price of two-storey houses in Toronto, the average price of two-storey houses in Edmonton is 53 (100 – 47) percent lower, 58.8 percent lower in Regina, and 27.1 percent higher in Vancouver.

Note from the previous discussion that:

- The index of hourly wage in Ontario (171.3) and the index of the number of new motor vehicles sold (125) are actually percents. However, the percent sign is usually omitted.

- Each index has a base year (or another period such as week, month) or place for comparison. In the example regarding the hourly wage in Ontario, we used 1985 as the base period. The base period should not be a period of economic depression, war, or major calamities. It should be a normal period.

WHY CONVERT DATA TO INDICES?

Indices allow us to express a change in price, quantity, or value as a percent

Compiling index numbers is not a recent innovation. An Italian, G.R. Carli, is credited with originating the first index numbers in 1764. They were incorporated in a report he made regarding price fluctuations in Europe from 1500 to 1750. No systematic approach to collecting and reporting data in index form was evident in the United States until about 1900. The cost-of-living index (now called the Consumer Price Index) was introduced in 1913, and a long list of indices have been compiled since then.

Why convert data to indices? An index is a convenient way to express a change in a heterogeneous group of items. The Consumer Price Index (CPI), for example, includes over 600 separate goods and services items. They range from ground beef to haircuts, and from spark plugs to property taxes. In real life, prices are expressed in dollars per unit weight, boxes, metres, and many other different units. Only by converting the prices of these many diverse goods and services to one index number every month can the federal government and others concerned with inflation keep informed of the overall movement of consumer prices.

Converting data to indices also makes it easier to assess the trend in a series composed of unusually large numbers. For example, gross domestic product (GDP) of all industries in August 2000 and in August 2001 were $936 004 million and $939 786 million respectively. The increase of $3782 million appears significant. However, if the gross domestic product were expressed as an index based on the gross domestic product value of August 2000, the increase would be 0.4 percent!

$$\frac{\text{Gross domestic product in 2001}}{\text{Gross domestic product in 2000}} = \frac{\$939\,786\,000\,000}{\$936\,004\,000\,000}(100) = 100.40$$

CONSTRUCTION OF INDEX NUMBERS

We already discussed the construction of a simple price index. The price in a selected year (such as 2001) is divided by the price in the base year.

The base-period price is designated as p_0, and a price other than the base period is often referred to as the *given period* or *selected period* and designated p_t. To calculate the simple price index P for any given period:

Simple Index	$P = \dfrac{p_t}{p_0} \times 100$	17-1

Suppose that the price of a standard lot at the Shady Rest Cemetery in 1995 was $450. The price rose to $795 in 2001. What is the price index for 2001 using 1995 as the base period? It is 176.7, found by:

$$P = \frac{p_t}{p_0}(100) = \frac{\$795}{\$450}(100) = 176.7$$

Interpreting this result, the price of a cemetery lot increased 76.7 percent from 1995 to 2001.

The base period need not be a single year. In another example note in Table 17-1 if we use 1990–91 = 100, the base price for the stapler would be $21 (found by determining the mean price of 1990 and 1991, ($20 + $22)/2 = $21). The prices $20, $22, and $23 would be averaged if 1990–92 had been selected as the base. The mean price would be $21.67. The indices constructed using the three different base periods are presented in Table 17-1. (Note that when 1990–92 = 100, the index numbers for 1990, 1991, and 1992 average 100.0, as we would expect.) Logically, the index numbers for 2001 using the three different bases are not the same.

TABLE 17-1: Prices of a Benson Automatic Stapler, Model 3, Converted to Indices Using Three Different Base Periods

Year	Price of Stapler	Price Index (1990 = 100)	Price Index (1990–91 = 100)	Price Index (1990–92 = 100)
1985	$18	90.0	$\dfrac{18}{21} \times 100 = 85.7$	$\dfrac{18}{21.67} \times 100 = 83.1$
1990	20	100.0	$\dfrac{20}{21} \times 100 = 95.2$	$\dfrac{20}{21.67} \times 100 = 92.3$
1991	22	110.0	$\dfrac{22}{21} \times 100 = 104.8$	$\dfrac{22}{21.67} \times 100 = 101.5$
1992	23	115.0	$\dfrac{23}{21} \times 100 = 109.5$	$\dfrac{23}{21.67} \times 100 = 106.1$
2001	38	190.0	$\dfrac{38}{21} \times 100 = 181.0$	$\dfrac{38}{21.67} \times 100 = 175.4$

■ SELF-REVIEW 17-1

1. The total revenue in 2000 for a few selected companies is:

Company	Total Revenue ($ millions)
Cominco Ltd.	1 898
Dofasco Inc.	3 217
Maple Leaf Foods	3 977
Molson Inc.	1 924
Future Shop	1 683

   Using the total revenue of Future Shop as the base (denominator), express the total revenue of Cominco, Dofasco, Maple Leaf Foods, and Molson as an index. Interpret.

2. The hourly compensation costs for production workers in manufacturing for selected periods are given below:

Year	Hourly Compensation Costs ($)	Year	Hourly Compensation Costs ($)
1990	15.95	1998	15.60
1995	16.10	1999	15.65
1997	16.47	2000	16.16

   (a) Using 1990 as the base period, determine the index for 1999 and for 2000 data. Interpret the index.
   (b) What is the index for 2000 data using 1995 as the base?

EXERCISES 17-1 TO 17-4

17-1. Retail sales of snowmobiles in Canada for the selected years are given below.

Year	Units	Year	Units
1992	51 665	1999	59 751
1994	58 418	2000	51 995
1995	64 236	2001	46 973

Source: www.snowmobile.org/stats_sales_units_canadian.html

   Develop a simple index for the change in snowmobile sales (units) for the given years based on 1992.

17-2. The following table shows the average annual stock prices of Air Canada from January 1997 to January 2001.

Year	Stock Price
1997	$6.50
1998	14.50
1999	7.50
2000	10.00
2001	14.25

Source: http://finance.yahoo.com

   Develop an index with 1997 as the base, for the change in average annual stock price over the period.

17-3. The following table shows the values of eggs sold for consumption in Ontario from 1994 to 2000.

Year	Value of Eggs Sold ($000)	Year	Value of Eggs Sold ($000)
1994	148 992	1998	174 117
1995	158 318	1999	177 787
1996	182 843	2000	186 923
1997	180 207		

Source: http://estat.statcan.ca/cgi-win/CNSMCGI.EXE

Use the mean sales for the earliest three years to determine the base and then find the index for the years 1997 to 2000. By how much has the value of eggs sold for consumption in 2000 increased from the base period?

17-4. The value of milk and cream sold from farms in New Brunswick in January 1990 was $5.3 million and $5.8 million in January 2001. Using the year 1990 as the base period, develop a simple index for the value of milk and cream sold in New Brunswick in January 2001.
Source: Adapted from www.statcan.ca

17.2 UNWEIGHTED INDICES

In many situations we wish to combine several items and develop an index to compare the cost of a group of items in two different time periods. For example, we might be interested in an index for items that relate to the expense of running and maintaining an automobile. The items in the index might include tires, oil changes, and gasoline prices. Or we might be interested in a college student index. This index might include the cost of books, tuition, housing, meals, and entertainment. There are several ways we can combine the items to determine the index.

SIMPLE AVERAGE OF THE PRICE RELATIVES

Table 17-2 reports the prices for several food items for the years 1996 and 2001. We would like to develop an index for this group of food items for 2001, using 1996 as the base. This is written 1996 = 100.

TABLE 17-2: Composition of Index for Food Price 2001, 1996 = 100

Item	1996 Price ($)	2001 Price ($)	Simple Index
Milk, 1 L	1.33	1.55	116.5
Eggs, dozen	1.63	1.98	121.5
Bread, white, 657 g	1.29	1.41	109.3
Coffee, instant, 200 g	6.52	4.70	72.1
Apples, 1 kg	2.19	2.58	117.8
Soft drink, cola type, 2 L	1.35	1.29	95.6
Total	$14.31	$13.51	

One way of finding the index is to sum the prices for two periods and then determine the index based on the totals.

We could begin by computing a **simple average of the price relatives** for each item, using 1996 as the base year and 2001 as the given year. The simple index for milk is 116.5, found by using Formula 17-1.

$$P = \frac{p_t}{p_0}(100) = \frac{\$1.55}{\$1.33}(100) = 116.5$$

We compute the simple index for the other items in Table 17-2 similarly. In the five-year period, the largest price increase was 21.5 percent for eggs, and a close second was 17.8 percent for apples. For the same period, the largest decrease in price was 27.9 percent for coffee (100 − 72.1), and the next was 4.4 percent for soft drinks. Then, it would be natural to average the simple indices.

Simple Average of the Price Relatives	$P = \dfrac{\sum P_i}{n}$	17–2

Where P_i refers to the index for each of the items and n is the number of items. In our example the index is 105.5, found by:

$$P = \frac{\sum P_i}{n} = \frac{116.5 + 121.5 + 109.3 + 72.1 + 117.8 + 95.6}{6} = 105.5$$

This indicates that the mean of the group of indices increased 5.5 percent from 1996 to 2001.

SIMPLE AGGREGATE INDEX

A positive feature of the simple average of price relatives is that it allows us to obtain the same value for the index regardless of the units of measurement. In the above index, if apples were priced in tonnes instead of kilograms, the impact of apples, on the average, would not change. That is, the commodity "apples" represents one of six items in the index, so the impact of the item is not related to the unit. A negative feature of this index is that it fails to address the relative importance of the items included in the index. For example, milk and eggs receive the same weight, even though a typical family might spend far more over the year on milk than on eggs. Therefore, we need an appropriate way to *weight* the items according to their relative importance. This is called a **simple aggregate index**.

Simple Aggregate Index	$P = \dfrac{\sum p_t}{\sum p_0} \times 100$	17–3

The index for the above food items is found by summing the prices in 1996 and 2001. The sum of the prices for the base period is $14.31 and for the given period it is $13.51. The simple aggregate index is 94.4. This means that the aggregate group of prices had decreased 5.6 percent in the five-year period.

$$P = \frac{\sum p_t}{\sum p_0}(100) = \frac{\$13.51}{\$14.31}(100) = 94.4$$

Since the units of measurement can affect the value of a simple aggregate index, it is not used frequently. In our example the value of the index would differ significantly if we were to report the price of apples in tonnes rather than kilograms. So, we need a way to appropriately "weight" the items according to their relative importance.

17.3 WEIGHTED INDICES

Two methods of computing a **weighted price index** are the **Laspeyres** method and the **Paasche** method. They differ only with respect to the period used for weighting. The Laspeyres method uses *base-period weights*; that is, the original prices and quantities of the items bought are used to find the percent change over a period of time in either price or quantity consumed, depending on the problem. The Paasche method uses *current-year weights*.

LASPEYRES' PRICE INDEX

Etienne Laspeyres developed a method in the latter part of the 18th century to determine a weighted index using base-period weights. Applying his method, a weighted price index is computed by:

Laspeyres' Price Index	$P = \dfrac{\sum p_t q_0}{\sum p_0 q_0} \times 100$	17-4

where:

P is the price index.
p_t is the current price.
p_0 is the price in the base period.
q_0 is the quantity consumed in the base period.

Example 17-5

The prices for the six food items from Table 17-2 are repeated below in Table 17-3. Also included is the number of units of each consumed by a typical family in 1996 and 2001.

TABLE 17-3: Computation of Laspeyres' and Paasche's Indices of Food Price, 1996 = 100

Item	1996 Price ($) ($p_{96}$)	Quantity (q_{96})	2001 Price ($) ($p_{01}$)	Quantity (q_{01})
Milk, 1 L	1.33	156	1.55	180
Eggs, dozen	1.63	26	1.98	20
Bread, white, 657 g	1.29	50	1.41	55
Coffee, instant, 200 g	6.52	12	4.70	12
Apples, 1 kg	2.19	30	2.58	40
Soft drink, cola type, 2 L	1.35	52	1.29	55

Determine a weighted price index using the Laspeyres method. Interpret the result.

Solution

First we calculate the total amount spent for the six items in the base period, 1996. To find this value we multiply the base period price for milk ($1.33) by the base period quantity of 156. The result is $207.48. This indicates that a total of $207.48 was spent on milk in the base period. We continue this for the rest of the items and total the result. The base period total is $528.50. The current period total is calculated in a similar fashion. For the first item, milk, we multiply the quantity in 1996 by the price of milk in 2001, which is $1.55(156). The result is $241.8. We make the same calculation for the rest of the items and total the result. The total is $564.66. Because of the repetitive nature of these calculations, a spreadsheet is effective for carrying out the calculations. Below is a copy of the Excel output. The following menu sequence will generate this output.

The other products and column totals are determined in a similar manner.

EXCEL CHART 17-1: Laspeyres' Index

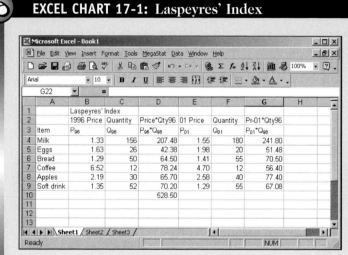

EXCEL INSTRUCTIONS

- Enter the label "item" in Cell A3 and the item names in cells A4 through A9; enter the label "1996 Price" in B2 and prices of items in cells B4 through B9; enter the label "Quantity" in the cell C2 and the quantities in Cells C4 through C9. Enter the label "Price-Qty-96" in the cell D2.
- To determine the product of 1996 prices and quantities, highlight the cells from D4 to D9. With this group of cells still highlighted, type "= B4*C4" in the cell D4 and press Enter. The value "207.48" should appear.
- With Cells D4 through D9 still highlighted, select Edit, then Fill, then Down, and press Enter. The remaining values should appear.
- Move to Cell D10, click on Σ on the tool bar and press Enter. The value 528.50 should appear.

The weighted price index for 2001 is 106.8 and is calculated by:

$$P = \frac{\sum p_t q_0}{\sum p_0 q_0}(100) = \frac{\$564.66}{\$528.50} = 106.8$$

Based on this analysis we conclude that the price of this group of items has increased 6.8 percent in the five-year period. The advantage of this method over the two methods discussed earlier is that the weight of each of the items is taken into consideration. In "simple aggregate index" and "simple average of the price relatives," milk and eggs receive the same weight, even though a typical family might spend far more over the years on milk than on eggs. Similarly the value of coffee is about 46 percent of the total of the base period prices and about 35 percent of the total current year period prices. Thus a change in the price of coffee will drive the index much more than any other item. In the Laspeyres index, the item with the most weight is milk, because the product of the price and the units sold is the largest.

The major disadvantage of the Laspeyres index is that it assumes that the base period quantities are still realistic in the given period. That is, the quantities used for the six items are about the same in 1996 as 2001. In this case, notice that the quantity of eggs purchased has declined by 23 percent, the quantity of milk increased by about 15 percent, and the quantity of cola increased by 5.8 percent.

PAASCHE'S PRICE INDEX

The Paasche index is an alternative. The procedure is similar, but instead of using base period weights, we use current period weights. We use the sum of the products of the 1996 prices and the 2001 quantities. This has the advantage of using the more recent quantities. If there has been a change in the quantities consumed since the base period, such a change is reflected in the Paasche index.

Paasche's Price Index	$P = \dfrac{\sum p_t q_t}{\sum p_0 q_t} \times 100$	17-5

Example 17-6 | Use the information from Table 17-2 to determine the Paasche Index. Discuss which of the indices should be used.

Solution | Again, because of the repetitive nature of the calculations, Excel is used to perform the calculations. The results are shown in the following output.

The Paasche index is 107.5 and is calculated by:

$$P = \frac{\sum p_t q_t}{\sum p_0 q_t}(100) = \frac{\$626.70}{\$583.04}(100) = 107.5$$

This result indicates that there has been an increase of 7.5 percent in the price of this basket of food items between 1996 and 2001. That is, it costs 7.5 percent more to purchase these items in 2001 than it did in 1996. All things considered, because of the change in quantities purchased between 1996 and 2001, the Paasche index is more reflective of the current situation. However, it requires the purchase quantities for every time period, which results in considerable expense in collecting quantity information of the items. Since change in the Paasche index is influenced by changes in both prices and quantities, it is difficult to interpret the change in the index between periods when neither is the base period. The advantages and disadvantages of Laspeyres' index and Paasche's index are summarized on the next page.

STATISTICS IN ACTION

Beginning May 31, 2001, the quarterly Income and Expenditure Accounts use the chain Fisher index formula[2]

$$\sqrt{\left(\frac{\sum P_{t-1}Q_t}{\sum P_{t-1}Q_{t-1}}\right) \times \left(\frac{\sum P_t Q_t}{\sum P_t Q_{t-1}}\right)}$$

as the official measure of real expenditure-based Gross Domestic Product (GDP). It measures the quarter-to-quarter growth rate in GDP and its components accurately. The chain Fisher index formula methodically changes the weighting base from period to period and multiplies the growth rates for the current period by the growth rates for the preceding period. The US quarterly Income and Product Accounts also use the chain Fisher index formula to measure real GDP. Thus, the Canadian measure of real expenditure-based GDP is now in line with the US measure of real GDP.

Laspeyres' Price Index	
Advantages	Requires quantity data from only the base period. This allows a more meaningful comparison over time. The changes in the index can be attributed to changes in the price.
Disadvantages	Does not reflect changes in buying patterns over time. Also, it may overweight goods whose prices increase.

Paasche's Price Index	
Advantages	Because it uses quantities from the current period, it reflects current buying habits.
Disadvantages	It requires quantity data for each year, which may be difficult to obtain. Because different quantities are used each year, it is impossible to attribute changes in the index to changes in price alone. It tends to overweight the goods whose prices have declined. It requires the prices to be recomputed each year.

FISHER'S IDEAL INDEX

As noted above, Laspeyres' index tends to overweight goods whose prices have increased. Paasche's index, on the other hand, tends to overweight goods whose prices have gone down. In an attempt to offset these shortcomings, Irving Fisher, in his book *The Making of Index Numbers*, published in 1922, proposed an index called **Fisher's Ideal Index**. It is the geometric mean of the Laspeyres and Paasche indices. We described the geometric mean in Chapter 3. It is determined by taking the *k*th root of the product of *k* positive numbers.

$$\text{Fisher's Ideal Index} = \sqrt{(\text{Laspeyres' Index})(\text{Paasche's Index})} \qquad \textbf{17-6}$$

Fisher's index seems to be theoretically ideal because it combines the best features of both Laspeyres and Paasche. That is, it balances the effects of the two indices. However, it is rarely used in practice because it has the same basic set of problems as the Paasche index. It requires that a new set of quantities be determined for each year.

Example 17-7

Determine Fisher's ideal index for the data in Table 17-3.

Solution

Fisher's ideal index is 107.1 and is calculated by:

$$\text{Fisher's Ideal Index} = \sqrt{(\text{Laspeyres' Index})(\text{Paasche's Index})}$$
$$= \sqrt{(106.8)(107.5)}$$
$$= 107.1$$

■ SELF-REVIEW 17-2

An index of clothing prices for the year 2001 based on 1996 is to be constructed. The clothing items are dresses and shoes for a random sample of 100 families. The information for prices and quantities for both years is given below where 1996 is used as the base year.

Item	1996		2001	
	Price ($)	Quantity	Price ($)	Quantity
Dresses (each)	65	300	84	400
Shoes (pair)	100	600	140	900

(a) Determine the simple average of the price relatives.
(b) Determine the aggregate price indices for the two years.
(c) Determine Laspeyres' price index.
(d) Determine Paasche's price index.
(e) Determine Fisher's ideal index.

EXERCISES 17-5 TO 17-8

For Exercises 17-5–17-8:
(a) Determine the simple average of the price relatives.
(b) Determine the simple aggregate price indices for the two years.
(c) Determine Laspeyres' price index.
(d) Determine Paasche's price index.
(e) Determine Fisher's ideal index.

17-5.

Item	1996		2001	
	Price ($)	Quantity	Price ($)	Quantity
Laundry detergent (4 L)	5.98	8	6.69	8
Paper Towel (2 rolls)	1.66	20	1.95	25
Facial tissue	1.51	25	1.50	26
Bathroom tissue (4 rolls)	1.99	50	1.88	55

17-6. Fruit prices and the approximate amount consumed by randomly selected 50 families for 1996 and 2001 are below. Use 1996 as the base.

Item	1996		2001	
	Price ($)	Quantity	Price ($)	Quantity
Apples (kg)	2.19	52	2.52	75
Bananas (kg)	1.19	100	1.29	100
Grapefruits (kg)	1.29	25	1.57	25
Oranges (kg)	1.50	100	1.94	75

17-7. Below are the prices of toothpaste (100 mL), deodorant (60 g), and shampoo (300 mL) for 1996 and 2001. Also included is the number of items bought by a person. Use 1996 as the base.

Item	1996		2001	
	Price ($)	Quantity	Price ($)	Quantity
Toothpaste	1.36	6	1.21	6
Deodorant	2.74	3	2.86	4
Shampoo	2.92	4	3.25	5

17-8. Below are the prices of cabbages (kg), carrots (kg), celery (kg), and onions (kg) for 1996 and 2001. Use 1996 as the base.

Item	1996		2001	
	Price ($)	Quantity	Price ($)	Quantity
Cabbages	0.84	10	1.00	16
Carrots	1.18	12	1.16	15
Celery	2.63	10	2.49	12
Onions	1.04	20	1.06	25

VALUE INDEX

Value Index measures percent change in value

A **value index** measures changes in both the price and quantities involved. A value index, such as the index of department store sales, needs the original base-year prices, the original base-year quantities, the present-year prices, and the present-year quantities for its construction. Its formula is:

Value Index
$$V = \frac{\sum p_t q_t}{\sum p_0 q_0} \times 100$$
17-7

Example 17-8

The prices and quantities sold in a Housewares and Small Appliances department of a store for the following items in 1996 and 2001 are given below.

Item	1996		2001	
	Price ($)	Quantity	Price ($)	Quantity
	p_0	q_0	p_t	q_t
CD Player (AM/FM)	115.56	1500	144.45	2000
Covered Roaster	51.98	500	61.65	600
Wall Hair Dryer	33.40	1000	44.60	1500

What is the index of value for the year 2001 using the year 1996 as the base period?

Solution

Total sales in 2001 were $392 790 and the comparable figure for 1996 is $232 730 (see Table 17-4 below). Thus the index of value for 2001 using 1996 = 100 is 168.8. The value of sales in the Housewares and Small Appliances department of the store in 2001 was 168.8 percent of the sales in 1996. That is, the value of sales in the Houswares and Small Appliances department increased 68.8 percent from 1996 to 2001.

$$V = \frac{\sum p_t q_t}{\sum p_0 q_0}(100)$$
$$= (392\,790/232\,730)\,100$$
$$= 168.8$$

TABLE 17-4: Construction of a Value Index for 2001 (1996 = 100)

Item	1996			2001		
	Price ($)	Quantity		Price ($)	Quantity	
	p_0	q_0	$p_0 q_0$ ($)	p_t	q_t	$p_t q_t$ ($)
CD Player (AM/FM)	115.56	1500	173 340	144.45	2000	288 900
Covered Roaster	51.98	500	25 990	61.65	600	36 990
Wall Hair Dryer	33.40	1000	33 400	44.60	1500	66 900
			232 730			392 790

■ SELF-REVIEW 17-3

The following were the prices and quantities of meat sold at a grocery store in 1998 and 2001.

Item	1998		2001	
	Price ($)	Quantity (kg)	Price ($)	Quantity (kg)
Round Steak	9.58	500	11.38	450
Stewing Beef	6.68	900	8.54	1000
Pork	8.63	1000	9.87	1200

Compute the index of value for the grocery store for the year 2001 based on the year 1998.

EXERCISES 17-9 TO 17-10

17-9.   The following were the prices and quantities sold in a men's retail clothing store in 1997 and 2001.

Item	1997		2001	
	Price ($)	Quantity	Price ($)	Quantity
Shirts	70	1500	95	1600
Silk ties	40	450	55	500
Suits	390	800	500	850

Compute the index of value for the retail clothing store for the year 2001 using 1997 as the base period.

17-10.   The prices and quantities sold in a hardware store in 1998 and 2001 were as follows:

Item	1998		2001	
	Price ($)	Quantity	Price ($)	Quantity
Light Bulb (2–150 W)	2.50	15 000	3.40	20 000
Shelf-bracket Screw (5)	7.50	20 000	9.30	25 000
Drain Cleaner (Chemicals)	7.60	1 250	9.30	1 000

Compute the index of value for the hardware store for the year 2001 using 1998 as the base year.

17.4   SPECIAL PURPOSE INDICES

CONSUMER PRICE INDEX (CPI)[3]

The Consumer Price Index (CPI) measures the rate of price change for goods and services bought by Canadian consumers. It is calculated by comparing the cost of a fixed basket of commodities over a period using a given year as a base period. Since the basket includes commodities of unchanging quantity and quality, the CPI indicates the movements in price only. The CPI for *all items* is best known as Laspeyres' index. For many years, the CPI was based on the spending behaviour of urban centres in Canada with a population of at least 30 000. In January 1995, the expenditure weights for 1992 were introduced in the calculation of CPI and since then CPI weights have reflected the spending behaviour of nearly all urban and rural households.

Initially CPI was based on a hypothetical family budget that represented the weekly expenditures of an urban working class family of five. Now it is based on more than 600 separate goods and services used by most urban and rural families. No attempt is made to differentiate between *necessary items* and *luxury items* and nothing is excluded on the basis of moral and social judgment. The goods and services are organized according to a classification system, which forms a hierarchy. The hierarchy of classification includes eight major components. Below are the names and weights attributed to each of them.[4]

1996 CPI Weights (1996 Prices) by Major Component for Canada

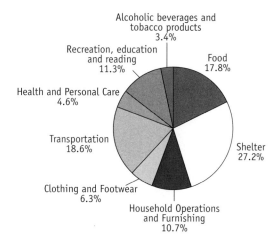

For a given month, the CPI is usually reported in the third week of the following month. Detailed CPIs are published simultaneously for Canada and all provinces and territories. Below is the list of the Consumer Price Indices by province, including Whitehorse and Yellowknife.

The Consumer Price Index by Province including Whitehorse and Yellowknife (1992 = 100) 1996 CPI Weights

October 2001			
Province	CPI	Province	CPI
Newfoundland	114.3	Manitoba	121.5
P.E.I.	115.4	Saskatchewan	121.2
Nova Scotia	116.4	Alberta	121.0
New Brunswick	114.8	British Columbia	115.8
Quebec	113.2	Whitehorse	117.5
Ontario	118.2	Yellowknife	113.5

USES OF CPI

- **Old Age Security Pensions** Canada pension plan payments, and social and welfare payments are adjusted periodically based on the CPI.

Example 17-9

Suppose a person was receiving a Canada Pension payment of $500 per month in January 2000. What would be the payment in January 2001?

Solution

Canada Pension Plan (CPP) payments are indexed once a year in January. The CPP formula averages the indices for twelve consecutive months, divides it by the average of the preceding twelve months, multiplies this result by 100 and then subtracts 100.

The average of CPI values for November 1998 to October 1999 is 110.1; the average of CPI values from November 1999 to October 2000 is 112.9. Thus the Consumer Price Index has increased by 2.5 percent $((112.9/110.1)(100) - 100)$ between these two periods. The Canada Pension payment in January 2001 was $512.5 $((500 + (500 \times 2.5/100))$ (2.5 percent)).

- **Purchasing Power of the Dollar** The Consumer Price Index is also used to determine the *purchasing power of the dollar*.

$$\text{Purchasing Power of Dollar} = \frac{\$1}{\text{CPI}}(100) \qquad \textbf{17-8}$$

Example 17-10

The Consumer Price Index for October 2001 was 116.4 (1996 = 100). What was the purchasing power of the dollar in October 2001?

Solution

Using Formula 17-8, it is $0.86, and is calculated by:

$$\text{Purchasing Power of Dollar} = \frac{\$1}{116.4}(100) = \$0.86$$

The CPI of 116.4 indicates that the purchasing power of the dollar in October 2001 was only $0.86 compared to $1.00 in 1996.

- **Purchasing Power of Money Income** Purchasing power of money (real income) changes as the CPI changes. As prices rise, the CPI increases and consequently the purchasing power of money decreases. Similarly, as prices decrease, the CPI decreases and the purchasing power of money increases. For these reasons, the CPI is widely known as a *deflator*. The purchasing power of money is calculated by:

$$\text{Purchasing Power of Money Income} = \frac{\text{Money Income}}{\text{CPI}}(100) \qquad \textbf{17-9}$$

The following example illustrates the concept of the *deflator*.

Example 17-11

Suppose a person's income has increased from $34 000 to $40 000 during a five-year period. Over the same period, the CPI has also increased from 100 to 115. What is the real value of the increased income of the person?

Solution

$$\text{The purchasing power at the beginning of the period} = \frac{\$34\,000}{100}(100) = \$34\,000$$

$$\text{The purchasing power at the end of the period} = \frac{\$40\,000}{115}(100) = \$34\,783.$$

Thus, with the extra income of 6000 ($40 000 – $34 000), the person can buy only an extra $783 ($34 783 – $34 000) worth of goods and services because the CPI has increased. The CPI has *deflated* the person's income. Another popular term for the deflated income is *income expressed in constant dollars*. In this example, the income expressed in constant dollars for the person is $34 783.

- **Cost of Living Adjustments (COLA)**   Labour unions and management negotiate cost of living allowance (COLA) in collective agreements based on changes in the CPI.

- **The Bank of Canada**   Decisions on the rate of interest and money supply is based on changes in the CPI.

■ SELF-REVIEW 17-4

The take-home pay of Ms. Kusum Singh and the CPI for 1996 and 2001 were:

Year	Take-home Pay	CPI (1992 = 100)
1996	$38 641.40	105.9
2001	$45 265.48	116.8

   (a) What was Ms. Singh's purchasing power of money income in 1996?
   (b) What was her purchasing power of money income in 2001?
   (c) Interpret your findings.

DEFLATING SALES

A price index can also be used to deflate sales or similar money series. Deflated sales are calculated by:

$$\text{Deflated Sales} = \frac{\text{Actual Sales}}{\text{An Appropriate Index}}(100) \qquad \textbf{17-10}$$

Example 17-12   A company sells rubber, leather, and plastic fabricated products. The sales increased from $875 000 in 1992 to $1 245 890 in 1995, and to $1 545 599 in 2000. The Industrial Price Indices for rubber, leather, and plastic fabricated products reported by Statistics Canada were 100, 111.7, and 116.5 respectively, for the years 1992, 1995, and 2000. What are the sales for 1992, 1995, and 2000 expressed in constant dollars?

Solution   Excel is used to calculate the constant dollar sales. The sales are listed in the second column of the Excel worksheet and the Industrial Price Index in the third column.

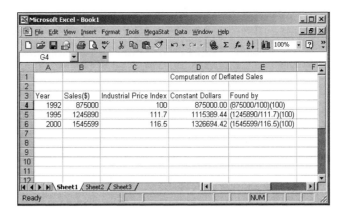

The next column shows the value of sales in constant 1992 dollars. The last column shows the calculations of the constant dollar sales. Actual sales and constant dollar sales have increased over the given period.

■ SELF-REVIEW 17-5

Suppose the Consumer Price Index for the latest month is 118.5 (1996 = 100). What is the purchasing power of the dollar? Interpret.

TORONTO STOCK EXCHANGE S&P/TSX COMPOSITE INDEX[5]

The TSE Composite Index was introduced in 1977 and is a barometer of the rise and fall of stocks of 300 of the most-traded companies in Canada. Since 2000, it has been referred to as the S&P/TSX Composite Index, and it represents about 85 percent of all Canadian stocks. The companies on the S&P/TSX list are divided into fourteen groups representing the different sectors of Canadian industry. Following is the list of groups:

- Consumer products
- Industrial products
- Oil and gas
- Communication and media
- Financial services
- Utilities
- Merchandising

- Real estate
- Conglomerates
- Metals and minerals
- Paper and forest products
- Transportation and environment
- Pipelines
- Gold and precious metals

The movement in stock prices is closely watched by the news media, economists, stock brokers, managers of pension funds, investment analysts, and individuals concerned about their investments.

There are criteria for inclusion of companies in the S&P/TSX Composite Index and Standard & Poor's/TSX Canadian Index Policy Committee reviews them continuously. The criteria are:

- The company must be incorporated under Canadian federal, provincial, or territorial jurisdictions.

- All stocks must be listed on the S&P/TSX for at least 12 full calendar months as of month-end prior to the index stock review meeting.
- The trading value of the stock of the company prior to its consideration must have been at least $1 million.
- The trading volume of the stock prior to its consideration must have been at least 100 000 shares and 100 transactions.

The S&P/TSX Composite Index is a market-weighted index adjusted for major shareholders. The index is calculated by the following formula.

$$S\&P/TSX\ 300\ Index = \frac{Aggregate\ Float\ Quoted\ Market\ Value}{Trade\text{-}weighted\ average\ float\ quoted\ market\ value\ for\ original\ index\ stocks\ for\ the\ year\ 1975}(1000)$$

The aggregate float quoted market value = (outstanding shares − control blocks)(price).

Control blocks = any individual or group of related individuals who control 20 percent or more of the outstanding shares.

1000 = a multiplier chosen so that the start-up index level would be approximately 1000 in 1977. Since adjustments are made periodically to the S&P/TSX composite index and the current year is used to determine the weight for the calculation of the index, it is known as modified Paasche's index.

To find pertinent information about S&P/TSX and the rise and fall in the values of stocks, you can visit www.tse.com

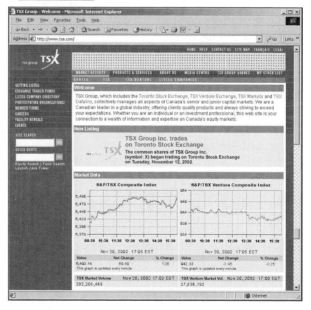

DOW JONES INDUSTRIAL AVERAGE (DJIA)

This is an index of stock prices, but perhaps it would be better described as an "indicator" rather than an index. It is supposed to be the mean price of 30 specific industrial stocks. Today, however, summing the 30 stocks and dividing by 30 does not calculate its value. This is because of stock splits, mergers, and stocks being added or dropped. When changes occur, adjustments are made in the denominator used with the average. Today the DJIA is more of a psychological indicator than a representation of the general price movement on the New York Stock Exchange. The lack of representativeness of the stocks on the DJIA is one of the reasons for the development of the *New York Stock Exchange Index*. This index was developed as an average price of *all* stocks on the New York Stock Exchange. You can find more information about the DJIA by going to the Web site: www.dowjones.com. You can find its current value as well as the 30 stocks that are now a part of its calculation. A history of the DJIA is available at www.dowjones.com/corp/index_average.html. Below is a recent summary.

S&P COMPOSITE INDEX

The full name of this index is the Standard and Poor's Composite Index of Stock Prices. It reports the composite price of 500 common stocks. It, too, is probably a better reflection of the market than is the DJIA. You can access information about the S&P 500 from the Dow Jones Web site. Below is a recent summary.

In the 1920s wholesale prices in Germany increased dramatically. In 1920 wholesale prices increased about 80 percent, in 1921 the rate of increase was 140 percent, and in 1922 it was a whopping 4100 percent! Between December 1922 and November 1923 wholesale prices increased another 4100 percent. By that time government printing presses could not keep up, even by printing notes as large as 500 million marks. Stories are told that workers were paid daily, and then twice daily, so their wives could shop for necessities before the wages became too devalued.

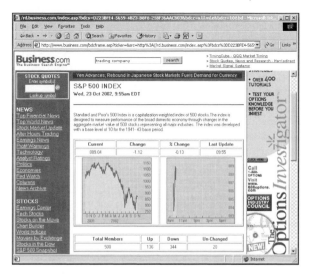

There are many other indices that track business and economic behaviour, such as the NASDAQ, the Russell 2000, and the Wilshire 5000.

CHAPTER OUTLINE

I. An index number measures the relative change from one period to another.
   A. The major characteristics of an index are:
      1. It is a percentage, but the percent sign is usually omitted.
      2. It has a base period.
      3. The base of most indices is 100. However, the base of S&P/TSX is 1000.
   B. The reasons for computing an index are:
      1. It facilitates the comparison of unlike series.
      2. If the numbers are very large, often it is easier to comprehend the change of the index than the actual numbers.

II. There are two types of price indices, unweighted and weighted.
   A. In an unweighted index we do not consider the quantities.
      1. In a simple index, we compare the price in the base period to the price in the given period

$$P = \frac{p_t}{p_0} \times 100 \qquad \textbf{17-1}$$

   where p_t refers to the price in the current period, and p_0 is the price in the base period.
      2. In the simple average of price relatives, we add the simple indices for each item and divide by the number of items.

$$P = \frac{\sum P_i}{n} \qquad \textbf{17-2}$$

      3. In a simple aggregate price index the price of the items in the group are totalled for both periods and compared.

$$P = \frac{\sum p_t}{\sum p_0} \times 100 \qquad \textbf{17-3}$$

   B. In a weighted index the quantities are considered.
      1. In the Laspeyres method the base period quantities are used in both the base period and the given period.

$$P = \frac{\sum p_t q_0}{\sum p_0 q_0} \times 100 \qquad \textbf{17-4}$$

      2. In the Paasche method current period quantities are used.

$$P = \frac{\sum p_t q_t}{\sum p_0 q_t} \times 100 \qquad \textbf{17-5}$$

      3. Fisher's ideal index is the geometric mean of Laspeyres' index and Paasche's index.

$$\text{Fisher's Ideal Index} = \sqrt{(\text{Laspeyres' index})(\text{Paasche's index})} \qquad \textbf{17-6}$$

C. A value index uses both base period and current period quantities.

$$V = \frac{\sum p_t q_t}{\sum p_0 q_0}$$

17-7

III. A. The Consumer Price Index is used to determine the purchasing power of the dollar.

$$\text{Purchasing Power of Dollar} = \frac{\$1}{\text{CPI}}(100)$$

17-8

B. Purchasing Power of Money Income $= \frac{\text{Money Income}}{\text{CPI}}(100)$

17-9

C. A price index can also be used to show deflated sales or a similar money series.

$$\text{Deflated sales} = \frac{\text{Actual Sales}}{\text{An Appropriate Index}}(100)$$

17-10

CHAPTER EXERCISES 17-11 TO 17-46

Exercises 17-11 to 17-16 are based on the Investors Group data set below, and in file Exercise 17-11.xls on the CD-ROM. The following information was taken from Investors Group 2000 Annual Report (75 years Making History). The head office of Investors Group is in Winnipeg, Manitoba.

Year	Sales Mutual Funds ($ millions)	Insurance ($ millions)	Clients (in thousands)
1991	2 270	6 551	426
1992	3 134	7 012	475
1993	3 940	7 600	538
1994	4 240	8 158	706
1995	3 472	9 259	764
1996	5 031	10 327	846
1997	6 513	12 279	940
1998	6 296	14 548	1 053
1999	5 915	18 086	1 138
2000	7 053	20 876	1 167

17-11. Use 1991 as the base period and compute a simple index for mutual fund sales for each year from 1997 to 2000.

17-12. Use the period 1991 to 1993 as the base period to calculate a simple index for mutual funds for each year from 1998 to 2000.

17-13. Use 1992 as the base period and calculate a simple index for insurance sales for each year from 1998 to 2000. Interpret the trend in insurance sales.

17-14. Use the period 1991 to 1993 as the base period to calculate a simple index for insurance sales for each year from 1998 to 2000.

17-15. Use 1992 as the base period and compute a simple index for clients for each year from 1998 to 2000.

17-16. Use the period 1991 to 1993 as the base period and calculate a simple index for clients for each year from 1998 to 2000.

Use the following information, which can also be found in file Exercise 17-17.xls on the CD-ROM, to answer Exercises 17-17 to 17-20. The information is from annual reports of the Royal Bank of Canada.

Year	Revenue ($ millions)	Earnings ($) per Share
1996	7 911	4.09
1997	9 279	5.01
1998	10 049	5.44
1999	10 600	2.55
2000	12 011	3.53

17-17. Calculate a simple index for the gross revenue of Royal Bank. Use 1996 as the base period. What can you conclude about the changes in revenue over the period?

17-18. Calculate a simple index for the revenue of the Royal Bank of Canada using the period 1996–1998 as the base.

17-19. Calculate a simple index for earnings per share of the Royal Bank of Canada. Use 1996 as the base period. What can you conclude about the change in earnings per share over the period?

17-20. Calculate a simple index for earnings per share of the Royal Bank of Canada using the period 1996–1998 as the base.

The following table, which is also found on the CD-ROM in file Exercise 17-21.xls, includes the retail prices of bacon (500 g), milk (1 L), butter (454 g), and bread (675 g) for the years 1996 and 2001 together with an average monthly consumption for a family of four. Use this information to answer Exercises 17-21 to 17-26.

Items	1996		2001	
	Price ($)	Quantity	Price ($)	Quantity
Bacon	3.02	52	3.97	52
Milk	1.33	90	1.50	100
Butter	2.87	26	3.14	30
Bread	1.29	45	1.33	50

17-21. Calculate a simple average of the price relatives of the four items. Use 1996 as the base period.

17-22. Calculate a simple aggregate price index. Use 1996 as the base period.

17-23. Calculate Laspeyres' price index for 2001. Use 1996 as the base period.

17-24. Calculate Paasche's price index for 2001. Use 1996 as the base period.

17-25. Calculate Fisher's Ideal Index using the values of the Laspeyres and Paasche indices computed in the two previous problems. Use 1996 as the base period.

17-26. Calculate a value index for 2001. Use 1996 as the base period.

Use the information below (see also file Exercise 17-27.xls on the CD-ROM) to answer Exercises 17-27 to 17-32. The Chair of a Business Department in a community college asked one of the coordinators to review the cost of the department's supplies of the following items in the year 2000 and 2001. The following table summarizes the cost of the department's supplies.

Item	2000		2001	
	Price ($)	Quantity	Price ($)	Quantity
Pencils (12/pack)	2.20	50	2.54	35
Chalk (dustless)	10.15	100	10.50	75
Coil Notebook (300 pages)	3.50	40	3.56	40
Hi-Liter (10/pack)	10.50	30	10.94	40

17-27. Determine a simple average of the price relatives of the four items using 2000 as the base period.

17-28. Determine a simple aggregate price index for 2001 using 2000 as the base period.

17-29. Determine Laspeyres' price index for 2001 using 2000 as the base period.

17-30. Determine Paasche's price index for 2001 using 2000 as the base period.

17-31. Determine Fisher's Ideal Index for 2001 using the values for the Laspeyres and Paasche indices calculated in the two previous problems.

17-32. Determine a value index for 2001 using 2000 as the base period.

 Prices for selected food items and their quantities sold by a vegetable retail store are given in the table below and in file Exercise 17-33.xls on the CD-ROM. Use this information to answer Exercises 17-33 to 17-38.

Item	1996		2001	
	Price ($)	Quantity	Price ($)	Quantity
Cabbage (1 kg)	0.74	1500	1.00	2000
Carrots (1 kg)	1.07	400	1.16	400
Potatoes (4.54 kg)	2.58	250	3.60	300
Baked beans (398 mL, canned)	0.80	100	0.80	125

17-33. Calculate a simple average of the price relatives of the four items using 1996 as the base period.

17-34. Calculate a simple aggregate price index using 1996 as the base period.

17-35. Calculate Laspeyres' price index for 2001 using 1996 as the base period.

17-36. Calculate Paasche's price index for 2001 using 1996 as the base period.

17-37. Calculate Fisher's Ideal Index, using the values for the Laspeyres and Paasche indices calculated in the two previous problems.

17-38. Calculate a value index for 2001 using 1996 as the base period.

 The prices of selected metals and their quantities[6] for 1996 and 2001 are given below and in file Exercise 17-39.xls on the CD-ROM. Use this information to answer Exercises 17-39 to 17-44.

Item	1996		2001	
	Price ($)	Quantity	Price ($)	Quantity
Gold (kg)	18 860	1000	14 660	1200
Silver (kg)	250	2000	260	3500
Aluminum (kg)	207	1500	226	2000
Platinum (kg)	16 460	800	22 120	1000

17-39. Calculate a simple average of the price relatives of the four items. Use 1996 as the base period.

17-40. Calculate a simple aggregate price index. Use 1996 as the base period.

17-41. Calculate Laspeyres' price index for 2001. Use 1996 as the base period.

17-42. Calculate Paasche's price index for 2001. Use 1996 as the base period.

17-43. Calculate Fisher's Ideal Index using the values of the Laspeyres and Paasche indices computed in the two previous problems.

17-44. Calculate a value index for 2001. Use 1996 as the base period.

17-45. The following table gives information on the Consumer Price Index and the monthly take-home pay of a community college employee.

Year	Consumer Price Index (1996 = 100)	Monthly Take-Home Pay ($)
1996	100	2975
2001	116.8	3600

(a) What is the purchasing power of the dollar for the year 2001 based on the year 1996?

(b) Determine the "real" monthly income of the college employee for the year 1996 and 2001?

17-46. Total retail sales in Canada in May 1999 was $21 398 million; the CPI (all items) for May 1999 was 110.4. For complete information, go to the Web site www.statcan.ca/Daily/English/990618/d990618a.htm

What were the total real retail sales (deflated sales) in Canada in May 1999?

www.exercises.ca 17-47 TO 17-48

17-47. The salaries of Toronto Maple Leaf hockey players in 1997 were:

Player	Salary ($000)	Player	Salary ($000)
Potvin	2500	Prochazka	750
Schneider	2300	Korolev	475
Clark	1728	Warriner	425
Sundin	1450	Hendrickson	414
King	1200	Kypreos	400
Healy	1100	Smith	400
Wolanin	1000	Zettler	400
Yuskevich	925	Modin	400
Adams	850	Sullivan	396
Domi	829	Cousineau	350
Berzin	800	Cooper	299
Johnson	800	Martin	288
McAuley	800	Tremblay	235

Adapted from: www.angelfire.lycos.com/md/MattDurnford/salaries.html

Go to the Statistics Canada Web site: www.statcan.ca/start.html, select *Learning resources, Σ-Stat, Data, Prices and price indexes*, and then *Consumer price index*. Find the Consumer Price Indices for the latest month and year. Calculate Maple Leaf players' real values of their salaries for the latest month and year. Use Excel or Minitab to solve the problem.

17-48. Go to the Statistics Canada Web site: www.statcan.ca/start.html, select *Learning resources, Σ-Stat, Prices and price indexes, Prices*, and then select "326-0012" under Active table. Find the unit prices of the following commodities: cabbage, carrots, potatoes, baked beans, bacon, butter, milk, and bread for January 1996 and December 2000. Enter prices in the price column of January 1996 and December 2000 in the following table.

Item	January 1996		December 2000	
	Price ($)	Quantity	Price ($)	Quantity
Cabbage (kg)		1500		2000
Carrots (kg)		400		400
Potatoes (4.5 kg)		250		300
Baked beans (398 mL, canned)		100		125
Bacon (500 g)		52		52
Homogenized milk (1 L)		90		100
Butter (454 g)		26		30
Bread (675 g)		45		50

Use Excel or Minitab to calculate the following quantities.

(a) Compute Laspeyres' price index for December 2000 using January 1996 as the base period.

(b) Compute Paasche's price index for December 2000 using January 1996 as the base period.

(c) Compute Fisher's Ideal Index using the values for the Laspeyres and Paasche indices computed in (a) and (b).

CHAPTER 17   ANSWERS TO SELF-REVIEW

17-1. 1. For Cominco Ltd.,
$P = (1898/1683)(100) = 112.8$

For Dofasco Inc.,
$P = (3217/1683)(100) = 191.1$

For Maple Leaf Foods,
$P = (3977/1683)(100) = 236.3$

For Molson Inc.,
$P = (1924/1683)(100) = 114.3$

The total revenue of Maple Leaf Foods is 136.3 percent higher than Future Shop. The total revenue of Cominco Ltd is 12.8 percent higher than Future shop.

2. (a) $P = (\$15.65/\$15.95)(100) = 98.1$
$P = (\$16.16/\$15.95)(100) = 101.3$
The hourly compensation costs for production workers in 1999 is 1.9 percent less, and in 2000 it is 1.3 percent more than the base year.
(b) $P = (\$16.16/\$16.10)(100) = 100.4$

17-2. (a) $P_1 = \dfrac{\$84}{\$65}(100) = 129.2$

$P_2 = \dfrac{\$140}{\$100}(100) = 140$

$P = \dfrac{129.2 + 140}{2} = 134.6$

(b) $P = \dfrac{(\$84 + \$140)}{(\$100 + \$65)}(100)$

$= \dfrac{\$224}{\$165}(100) = 135.8$

(c) $P = \dfrac{(\$84(300) + \$140(600))}{(\$65(300) + \$100(600))}(100)$

$= \dfrac{\$109\,200}{\$79\,500}(100) = 137.4$

(d) $P = \dfrac{(\$84(400) + \$140(900))}{(\$65(400) + \$100(900))}(100)$

$= \dfrac{\$159\,600}{\$116\,000}(100) = 137.6$

(e) $P = \sqrt{(137.4)(137.6)} = 137.5$

17-3.

$$V = \frac{\sum p_t q_t}{\sum p_0 q_0}$$

$$= \frac{(\$11.38)(450) + (\$8.54)(1000) + (\$9.87)(1200)}{(\$9.58)(500) + (\$6.68)(900) + (8.63)(1000)}$$

$$\times (100)$$

$$= \frac{\$25\,505}{\$19\,432}(100)$$

$$= 131.3$$

The value index for the grocery store for the year 2001 based on the year 1998 is 131.3.

17-4. (a) Purchasing power on money income in 1996

$$= \frac{\$38\,641.40}{105.9}(100) = \$36\,488.57$$

(b) Purchasing power on money income in 2001

$$= \frac{\$45\,265.48}{116.8}(100) = \$38\,754.69$$

(c) In terms of 1992, Ms. Singh's purchasing power money income has increased by 6.21 percent $(38\,754.69 - 36\,488.57/36\,488.57(100))$; whereas the percentage change in CPI is 10 percent $((116.8/105.9(100)) - 100)$.

17-5. Purchasing Power of Dollar

$$= \frac{\$1}{118.5}(100) = \$0.84$$

The purchasing power of the dollar is $0.84. The dollar in the year 1996 is worth $0.84 today in terms of purchasing power.

CHAPTER 18

Time Series and Forecasting

GOALS

When you have completed this chapter, you will be able to:

• Define the four components of a time series

• Determine a linear trend equation

• Compute a moving average

• Compute the trend equation for a nonlinear trend

• Use trend equations to forecast future time periods and to develop seasonally adjusted forecasts

• Determine and interpret a set of seasonal indices

• Identify cyclical fluctuations

• Deseasonalize data using a seasonal index

• Compute and evaluate forecasts.

JOSEPH ALOIS SCHUMPETER (1883–1950)

Until the 19th century, business cycles were considered the result of some natural events such as a series of bad weather or occurrence of sunspots. Clèment Juglar (1819–1905), a French doctor and statistician, in his book: *A Brief History of Panics,* discovered fairly regular (7–11 year) industrial cycles based mostly on events leading to over-expansion of money supply or squeeze in the availability of funds to industry. Likewise, Wesley C. Mitchell (1874–1948) published a voluminous study, *Business Cycles: The Problem and its Setting,* where he identified 1 to 10 years of simulta-neous recurrence of fluctuations in a number of business related activities through statistical analysis. Mitchell founded the National Bureau of Economic Research (www.nber.org), now a renowned research organization engaged in conducting business cycle analysis in the United States.

Schumpeter developed a theoretical apparatus and conducted statistical analysis of business cycles in his monumental two-volume (nearly 1000 pages) study: *Business Cycles: A Theoretical, Historical, and Statistical Analysis of the Capitalist Process*. He developed a dynamic theory, a self-perpetuating process, of business cycles based on the ebb and flow of innovations and the consequent adjustments by businesses. He clarified regular fluctuations in time series observations that occur within a year as seasonal cycles and those over a period of 7 to 11 years as business cycles (Juglar cycles). He also labelled the "four-phases" of a business cycle as boom-recession-depression-recovery.

Schumpeter, one of the most famous economists of the 20th century, was born in Austria-Hungary (now Slovakia). At the age of 23, he completed a doctorate in law in Vienna. A year later, he married an Englishwoman, the daughter of a high official of the Church of England, and travelled by way of Vienna to Cairo where he practised law at the International Court of Justice. His familiarity with economics and statistics was based on taking some courses during his law degree and his own self-study. Marx and Walras were his favourites. At the age of 28, he published his path-breaking book: *Theory of Economic Development* (1911), where he first outlined his famous theory of entrepreneurship and innovation, the theory that he elaborated later in his book on business cycles. His other major works are his popular *Capitalism, Socialism and Democracy* (1942)—in which he famously predicted the downfall of capitalism in the hands of intellectuals—and his ency-clopaedic *History of Economic Analysis* (1954, published posthumously by his third wife).

Like business cycles, Schumpeter's life, in general, had also been the subject of ebbs and flows. His first marriage was unsuccessful and his second wife whom he loved dearly died in childbirth within a year of marriage (1925). His books could not receive the appro-priate recognition during his lifetime due to the outbreak of the World Wars just after their publications. His entry into political life as Minister of Finance in Austria (1919) and his entry into business as President of a private bank in Austria (1921–24) were also unsuc-cessful through no fault of his own! He was, however, very successful as a teacher at Harvard (1932–50) as evidenced by the success of his students, including Samuelson, Tobin, Bergson, Tsuru, Heilbroner, and Metzler. Some of them are now Nobel laureates. For more details on Schumpeter's life and contributions, please refer to a book written by eighteen distinguished social scientists and edited by S.E. Harris, *Schumpeter: Social Scientist,* Books for Libraries Press, 1951.

INTRODUCTION

Although it is our ignorance about the future that makes life interesting, everyone, whether an individual, business, or government, is interested in knowing what the future will be like. In fact, our everyday life is based on our predictions about the future. Predictions about future values of a variable depend on a number of factors, such as (1) the possibility of occurrence of some unique events such as war, terrorists' attacks on America on September 11, 2001, an invention of a new technology, or a sudden rise in the price of an essential commodity such as oil, (2) future changes in the causal forces, i.e., changes in explanatory variables related with the variable being predicted, (3) nature of past movements in the variable being predicted, (4) people's psychology, (5) national and international policies, and (6) changes in a combination of them.

In general, forecasting is a method of prediction of values that a variable may assume in the near or distant future. Obviously, as is true with prediction in regression analysis, a forecast in the near future (short range) tends to be more reliable than the forecast in the distant future (long range). Nevertheless, forecasting occupies a central role in decision sciences such as business and economics. Government officials, business managers, and individuals require forecasts for decision-making at the current time and for planning for the future.

An analysis of the past values of a variable—a time series—can be used by management to make current decisions and for short- and long-term forecasting and planning. In time series analysis, we usually assume that past patterns will continue into the future. There is no fixed rule about how short or long is the short-term and the long-term. For example, five years may look like a short-term in mineral exploration, a medium-term in the restaurant business, and a long-term in the advertising business. In general, in most business and economics time series, short-term consists of a year or less, medium-term, two to four years and the long-term, five or more years. Short-term forecasts in business are useful for inventory planning, procurement of raw materials, cash-flow management and advertising. Long-range predictions are essential to allow sufficient time for sales, finance, and other departments of a company, and to develop plans for possible new plants, financing, development of new products, and new methods of assembling.

We discussed method of prediction based on possible causal forces in Chapters 13 and 14. In this chapter, we focus on simple methods that use the nature of movements in a variable in the past as a guide to making predictions for values of that variable in the future. In general, this method is called forecasting based on an analysis of time series. An advanced and closely related method of forecasting is based on Auto-regressive Moving Average (ARIMA) technique. Some qualitative methods such as Leading Indicators and the Delphi method are also gaining popularity in recent years. Indeed, forecasting is a multi-billion dollar business in North America. Several universities and private organizations offer separate courses in forecasting, often tailored to the needs of their clients.

18.1   TIME SERIES AND THEIR COMPONENTS

TIME SERIES

A **time series** is a sequential record of observations on a variable over a period of time such as a week, a month, a year or several years. For some variables such as inventories, money supply, savings, and prices, data are recorded at each successive point in time over a specified period. For example, inventories of bread at your local convenience store, prices of Air Canada shares, or the values of the S&P/TSX index at 5:00 p.m. every day over the period of a month or a year, constitute a time series. Variables such as income, investment and business expenses are recorded for each successive period—per day, per week, per month, per year—over a specified time period. For example, annual income of Canadian families, monthly expenses of education, weekly revenues of a Tim Hortons in Fredericton over a specified period, say 1992–2002, constitute a time series of observations on the variable.

Excel Chart 18-1 shows a time series of Canadian gross domestic product per year (the value of all goods and services produced in Canada) in 1992 prices for the 1979 to 2000 period. Chart 18-2 displays a time series of quarterly youth unemployment rate in Canada for the period 1976–2001.

EXCEL CHART 18-1: Canada's Gross Domestic Product (1979–2000, Annual)

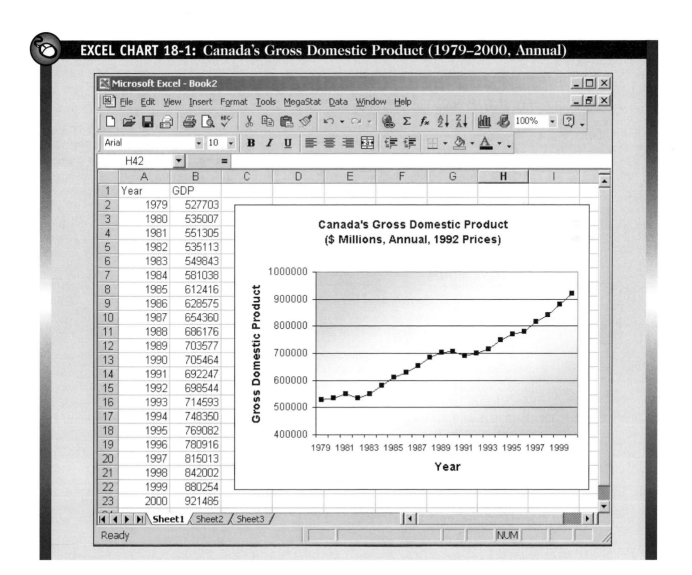

CHART 18-2: Canadian Youth Unemployment Rate
(1976–2000, Quarterly)

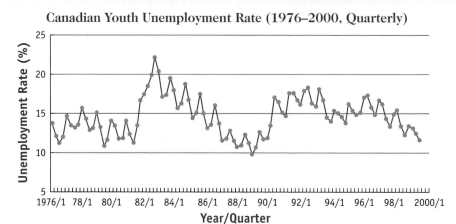

Canadian Youth Unemployment Rate (1976–2000, Quarterly)

COMPONENTS OF A TIME SERIES

In the analysis of time series when values of a variable are recorded at lower than annual frequency (i.e., daily, weekly, monthly, quarterly, etc.), each value of the variable (Y) is assumed to be composed of four components: the trend (T), the cyclical variation (C), the seasonal variation (S), and the irregular variation (I). Since the interest of a researcher may be centred on gaining knowledge of a particular component, the challenge in time series analysis consists of decomposing each value of Y into its various components. The technique of decomposition depends partly on the assumption as to how the various components are related to each other.

ADDITIVE MODEL

In this model, we assume that the various components are additive. Thus,

$$Y = T + C + S + I \qquad\qquad \textbf{18-1}$$

The assumption of additivity implies that the components are independent. In other words, the forces responsible for variation in one component, say T, are unrelated to forces responsible for variation in another component, say S. Thus, for example, a continuous increase in sales (T) of personal computers over the last 20 years is unrelated with an increase in the sales of personal computers in the beginning of the school year or at Christmas (S) or a decrease in sales in the recession years (C) such as 1991–92 or 2000–01.

MULTIPLICATIVE MODEL

In this model, we assume that each component T, C, S, and I are related to each other. So, we could write,

$$Y = T \times C \times S \times I \qquad\qquad \textbf{18-2}$$

In this case, the values of one component are dependent on the values of the other components. For example, we can visualize the values of C, S or I as some proportion of the value of T. This also implies that the forces influencing each component are also related. According to this model, in the above example, the value of increase in sales of personal computers at Christmas (S), or the value of decrease in sales during years such as 1991–92 and 2000–01 (C) is assumed to be related to the long term increase in the level of overall sales (T).

In general, neither of the two models is absolutely accurate for all variables. It is possible that for some variables, the multiplicative model may be more appropriate and for others the additive. For example, in the case of personal computers, it is more accurate to think of the value of sales at a particular Christmas to be proportional, say 125 percent, to the overall value of sales during the year. For variables such as consumption of ice cream in winter, an additive model may provide more accurate results.

However, the traditional techniques of decomposition, the focus of this chapter, are easily explained in terms of the multiplicative model. We shall therefore use the multiplicative model in the rest of the chapter unless the additive model is necessary in particular circumstances.

SECULAR TREND

The long-term behaviour in variables such as national income, retail sales, employment, stock prices, and other business and economic series follow various patterns. Some move steadily upward, others decline, and still others stay the same over time. Variables such as technological change, population growth, and shifts in preferences are major contributors for long-term trends in business and economics time series.

> **_i_ Secular Trend**   A pattern of long-term movement in the values of a variable.

The following are several examples of a secular trend. Chart 18-3 is the same as Excel Chart 18-1 with a trend line inserted on the chart. As the trend line shows, on the whole, the real GDP in Canada during the 1979–2000 period has increased. This is an example of an *increasing trend*. The long-run direction of the time series is increasing. Similarly, Excel Chart 18-4 is an example of declining trend and Chart 18-2 is an example of an (almost) constant trend.

CHART 18-3: An Increasing Trend

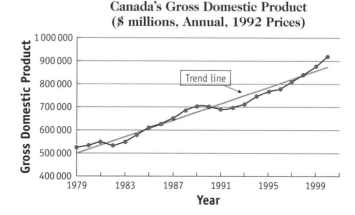

Canada's Gross Domestic Product
($ millions, Annual, 1992 Prices)

EXCEL CHART 18-4: A Declining Trend

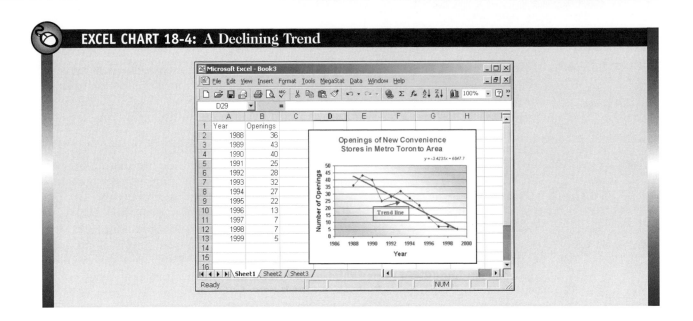

CYCLICAL VARIATION

The second component of a time series is cyclical variation. A typical business cycle consists of a period of prosperity followed by periods of recession, depression, and then recovery. While economists have achieved good success in identifying symptoms of business cycles, they have yet to come to an agreement over its causes. As mentioned in the pioneer's vignette, business cycles in the past have been attributed to a variety of reasons including weather, sunspots, money supply, innovations, underconsumption, unequal distribution of wealth, human psychology, external shocks, inappropriate government policies, etc. In general, business cycles consist of sizable fluctuations unfolding over more than one year in time, above and below the secular trend. In a recession, for example, employment, production, the S&P/TSX Index, and many other business and economic series are below the long-term trend lines. Conversely, in periods of prosperity they are above their long-term trend lines.

> *i* **Cyclical Variation**   Fluctuations in the values of a variable along a long-term trend *over the years* (i.e., periods longer than one year). In general, these fluctuations tend to be repeated every 7 to 11 years.

For example, Chart 18-5 shows the cyclical fluctuations in the time series for before tax profits of Canadian corporations. The number of years taken by a variable from one peak to another peak (or one trough to another trough) defines the duration or period of that cycle. In real life, the duration of each cycle is different, though in the capitalist world, it has been observed to lie between 7 to 11 years (Juglar cycles). The fluctuations in the values of a variable from a trough to a peak or from a peak to a trough (amplitude) need not be the same either. Like the duration of cycles, amplitudes are also different. In Chart 18-5, the troughs seem to have occurred in 1982, 1991, and 2002 (not shown). Peaks seem to have occurred in 1989 and 2000. Note, over a longer period, profits show an upward trend.

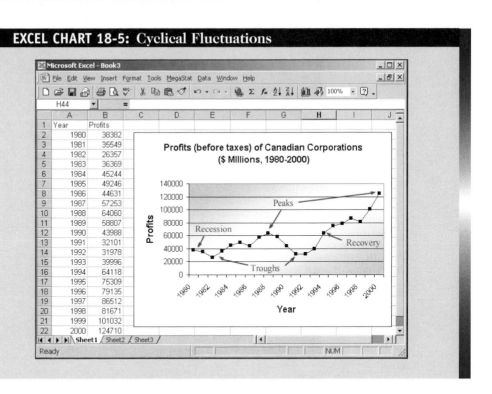

EXCEL CHART 18-5: Cyclical Fluctuations

SEASONAL VARIATIONS

The third component of a time series is the seasonal component. Many sales, production, and other series fluctuate *within* a year. The term season does not necessarily imply Fall, Winter, Spring and Summer.

> **Seasonal Variation**   A regular pattern of fluctuations in a variable *within a year*. In general, these patterns tend to repeat themselves each year.

Almost all businesses tend to have recurring seasonal patterns. Men's and boys' clothing, for example, have extremely high sales just prior to Christmas and relatively low sales just after Christmas and during the summer. Toy sales are another example with an extreme seasonal pattern. More than half of the business for the year is usually done in the months of November and December. Businesses such as lawn care, construction, fishing, logging, and snowploughing are seasonal by nature. Many businesses try to even out seasonal effects by engaging in an offsetting seasonal business. In several Canadian cities, you will see an operator of a lawn care business (in summer) with a snowplough on the front of the truck (in winter) in an effort to earn income in the off-season. In most of the ski areas, you will often find golf courses nearby. The owners of the lodges try to rent to skiers in the winter and to golfers in the summer. This is an effective method of spreading their fixed costs over the entire year rather than a few months. Interestingly, as Chart 18-6 displays, there are fairly regular seasonal fluctuations in the birth of children in Canada. The spring quarter seems to be the most popular season for births. This knowledge can serve as a good planning tool for hospital administrators.

CHART 18-6: Seasonal Pattern of Births

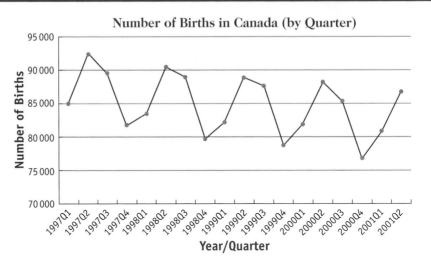

Number of Births in Canada (by Quarter)

IRREGULAR VARIATIONS

Many analysts prefer to subdivide **irregular variations** into *episodic* and *residual variations*. Episodic fluctuations are unpredictable, but they can be identified. The initial impact on the economy of a major strike or a war can be identified, but a strike or war cannot be predicted. The impact of an event such as the terrorist attacks on America on September 11, 2001, on the airline business, stock prices, etc., can be classified as an episodic variation. After the episodic fluctuations have been removed, the remaining variation is called the residual variation. Residual fluctuations, often called chance fluctuations, are unpredictable, and they cannot be identified. Of course, neither episodic nor residual variation can be projected into the future.

18.2 IDENTIFYING A LINEAR TREND BY THE METHOD OF LEAST SQUARES

The long-term trend of many business series, such as sales, exports, and production, often approximates a straight line. If so, the equation to describe this growth is:

Linear Trend Equation	$\hat{y} = a + bt$	18-3

where:

$\hat{y}$ is the estimated value of the Y variable for a selected value of t.

a is the Y-intercept. It is the estimated value of Y when $t = 0$. Another way to put it is: a is the estimated value of Y where the line crosses the Y-axis when t is zero.

b is the slope of the line, or the average change in $\hat{y}$ for each unit increase in t.

t is any value of time corresponding to the value of the variable Y. In time series analysis, for convenience, we usually use the observation numbers 1, 2, 3 and so on to indicate the values of time. There is no fixed rule about this so long as the successive numbers increase by equal amounts.

In Chapter 13 we saw that the **least squares method** of computing the equation for a line through the data gave the "best-fitting" line. Two equations may be solved simultaneously to arrive at the estimates of a and b of the least squares trend equation. They are:

Least Squares (normal) Equations for the Trend Line

$$\sum y = na + b \sum t \qquad\qquad \textbf{18-4}$$

$$\sum ty = a \sum t + b \sum t^2 \qquad\qquad \textbf{18-5}$$

You may recognize these as the normal equations discussed in Chapter 13, with t replacing x in the equations. As we described in Chapter 13, using the normal equations to determine a and b can be tedious. A better approach is to use the following computational equations.

The Slope	$b = \dfrac{n \sum ty - (\sum y)(\sum t)}{n \sum t^2 - (\sum t)^2}$	**18-6**
The Intercept	$a = \dfrac{\sum y}{n} - b\left(\dfrac{\sum t}{n}\right)$	**18-7**

If the number of years is large, say 10 or more, and the magnitude of the numbers is also large, a computer software package is recommended.

Example 18-1

The sales of Jensen Foods, a small grocery chain in Northern Alberta, since 1994 are:

Year	Sales ($ millions)
1997	7
1998	10
1999	9
2000	11
2001	13

Determine the least squares trend-line equation.

Solution

To simplify the calculations, the years are replaced by *coded* values. As mentioned above, we shall let 1997 be 1, 1998 be 2, and so forth. This reduces the size of the values of $\sum t$, $\sum t^2$, and $\sum ty$. (See Table 18-1.)

We can determine the values of a and b using Formulae 18-6 and 18-7:

$$b = \frac{n \sum ty - (\sum y)(\sum t)}{n \sum t^2 - (\sum t)^2} = \frac{5(163) - 50(15)}{5(55) - (15)^2} = 1.30$$

$$a = \frac{\sum y}{n} - b\left(\frac{\sum t}{n}\right) = \frac{50}{5} - 1.30\left(\frac{15}{5}\right) = 6.1$$

TABLE 18-1: Computations Needed for Determining the Trend Equation for Sales

($ millions)

Year	y	t	ty	t^2
1997	7	1	7	1
1998	10	2	20	4
1999	9	3	27	9
2000	11	4	44	16
2001	13	5	65	25
Total	50	15	163	55

The estimated trend equation therefore is: $\hat{y} = 6.1 + 1.30t$.

How do we interpret the equation? The value of 1.30 indicates that sales increased at an average rate of $1.3 million per year. The value 6.1 is the value of estimated sales when $t = 0$. That is, the estimated sales amount for 1996 (the base year) is $6.1 million.

You can plot the least squares trend line by selecting any two points. For example the estimated value of Y for $t = 1$ is $6.1 + 1.3 = 7.4$ and for $t = 3$ is $6.1 + 1.3(3) = 10.0$. By using the values of t on the horizontal axis and the estimated values of Y on the vertical axis and joining these two points (7.4, 1) and (10, 3), we get a line. The line can be extended backward or forward, as needed, simply by using a ruler.

Forecasting with a Linear Trend: if the sales, production, or other data tend to approximate a linear trend, the equation developed by the least squares method can be used to estimate sales for some future period as shown in the example below.

Example 18-2

Refer to the sales data in Table 18-1. The year 1997 is coded 1, and 1998 is coded 2. What is the sales forecast for 2004?

Solution

The year 1999 is coded 3; 2000 is coded 4; 2001 is coded 5; 2002 is coded 6; 2003 is coded 7; and 2004 is coded 8. Thus, in 2004, $t = 8$. Substituting the value $t = 8$ in the equation:

$$\hat{y} = a + bt = 6.1 + 1.30(8) = 16.5$$

Thus, based on past sales, the estimate for 2004 is $16.5 million.

In this time series problem, there were five years of sales data. Based on those five sales figures, we estimated sales for 2004. We should however note that (1) the reliability of the forecast decreases the farther off our projection is from the last actual observation, and (2) the reliability of the forecast will differ from one time series to another depending on the stability of the time series. The forecast is less reliable for less stable time series compared to the forecast for more stable time series.

Estimation of the trend line using Excel and Minitab for the example are given below in Charts 18-7 and 18-8.

EXCEL CHART 18-7: Trend Line

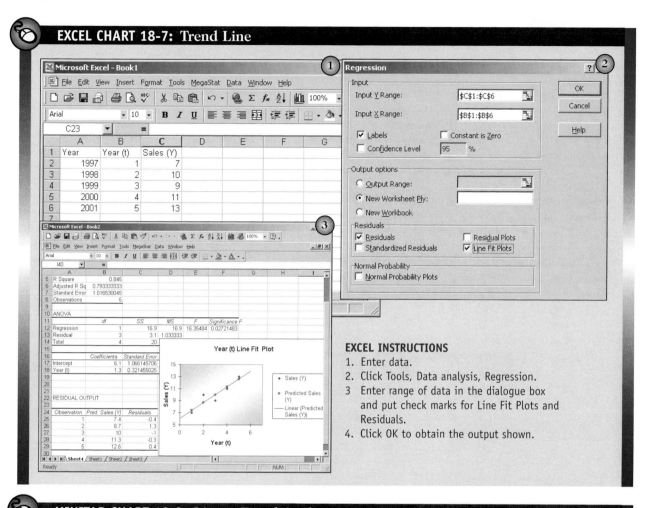

EXCEL INSTRUCTIONS
1. Enter data.
2. Click Tools, Data analysis, Regression.
3. Enter range of data in the dialogue box and put check marks for Line Fit Plots and Residuals.
4. Click OK to obtain the output shown.

MINITAB CHART 18-8: Linear Trend Analysis

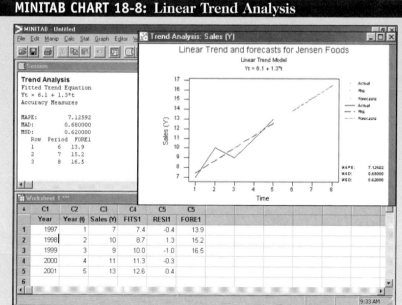

MINITAB INSTRUCTIONS
1. Click Stat, Time Series, and Trend Analysis.
2. In the dialogue box, enter Variable name (Sales), Model type (Linear), Generate forecast (1, 2, or 3 periods from origin; say 5 or any other number you desire).
3. Click Storage and put check marks for the items desired.
4. Click OK.

■ SELF-REVIEW 18-1

Annual production of king-size rockers by Wood Products, Inc. in Winnipeg since 1991 follows.

Year	Production (thousands)	Year	Production (thousands)
1994	4	1998	11
1995	8	1999	9
1996	5	2000	11
1997	8	2001	14

    (a) Plot the production data.
    (b) Determine the least squares equation.
    (c) Determine the points on the straight line for 1994 and 2001.
        Connect the two points to arrive at the line.
    (d) Based on the equation for the line, what is the estimated forecast for 2004?

EXERCISES 18-1 TO 18-4

18-1. The number of business failures in St. John for the years 1997 through 2001 is given below. Determine the least squares equation and estimate the number of failures in 2003.

Year	Code	Number of Failures
1997	1	79
1998	2	120
1999	3	138
2000	4	184
2001	5	200

18-2. Personal consumption expenditures in Canada, in billions of dollars, for the years 1995 to 2000 are given below. Determine the least squares equation, and estimate the expenditure for 2002.

Year	Code	Expenditures ($ billions)
1995	1	460.0
1996	2	482.4
1997	3	512.4
1998	4	532.9
1999	5	558.6
2000	6	591.0

18-3. The following table gives the annual amount of scrap produced by Machine Products, Inc., in Montreal.

Year	Code	Scrap (tonnes)
1997	1	2.0
1998	2	4.0
1999	3	3.0
2000	4	5.0
2001	5	6.0

Determine the least squares trend equation. Estimate the amount of scrap for the year 2003.

18-4. The following table gives the annual amount of net assets ($ millions) in the AGF Canadian Stock Fund. Determine the least squares equation, and estimate the amount of net assets for 2002.

Year	Code	Net assets ($ millions)
1996	1	295.8
1997	2	349.6
1998	3	901.6
1999	4	924.3
2000	5	1401.4

(Source: AGF Mutual Funds Series amended and restated simplified prospectus, March 28, 2001)

18.3 IDENTIFYING TRENDS BY THE MOVING-AVERAGE METHOD

The **moving-average method** is not only useful in smoothing out fluctuations in a time series. It is also the basic method used in measuring seasonal fluctuations, described later in the chapter. In contrast to the least squares method, which expresses the trend in terms of a mathematical equation ($\hat{y} = a + bt$), the moving-average method merely smooths out the fluctuations in the data. This is accomplished by "moving" the arithmetic mean values through the time series.

To apply the moving-average method to a time series, the data should have a definite rhythmic pattern of fluctuations (repeating, say, every three years). The data in the following example is assumed to have three components—trend, cycle, and irregular, abbreviated T, C, and I. There is no seasonal variation, because the data are recorded annually. What the moving-average method does, in effect, is to average out C and I. The residual is trend.

If the duration of the cycles is constant, and if the amplitudes of the cycles are equal, the cyclical and irregular fluctuations can be removed entirely using the moving-average method. The result is a line. For example, in the time series shown in Table 18-2, the cycle repeats itself every seven years. The seven-year moving average, therefore, averages out the cyclical and irregular fluctuations perfectly, and the residual is a linear trend.

The first step in computing the seven-year moving average is to determine the seven-year moving totals. The total sales for the first seven years (1976–82 inclusive) are $22 million, found by $1 + 2 + 3 + 4 + 5 + 4 + 3$. (See Table 18-2.) The total of $22

TABLE 18-2: Computations for the Seven-Year Moving Average

Year	Sales ($ millions)	7-year Total	7-year Mov-Av	Year	Sales ($ millions)	7-year Total	7-year Mov-Av
1976	1			1989	4	32	4.57
1977	2			1990	3	33	4.71
1978	3			1991	4	34	4.86
1979	4	22	3.14	1992	5	35	5.00
1980	5	23	3.29	1993	6	36	5.14
1981	4	24	3.43	1994	7	37	5.29
1982	3	25	3.57	1995	6	38	5.43
1983	2	26	3.71	1996	5	39	5.51
1984	3	27	3.86	1997	4	40	5.86
1985	4	28	4.00	1998	5	41	
1986	5	29	4.14	1999	6		
1987	6	30	4.29	2000	7		
1988	5	31	4.43	2001	8		

million is divided by 7 to determine the arithmetic mean sales per year. The seven-year total (22) and the seven-year mean (3.143) are positioned opposite the middle year for that group of seven, namely, 1976, as shown in Table 18-2. Then the total sales for the next seven years (1977–83 inclusive) are determined. (A convenient way of doing this is to subtract the sales for 1976 ($1 million) from the first seven-year total ($22 million) and add the sales for 1983 ($2 million), to give the new total of $23 million.) The mean of this total, $3.286 million, is positioned opposite the middle year, 1980. Computations using Minitab are given in Chart 18-10.

Sales, production, and other economic and business series usually do not have (1) cycles that are of equal length or (2) cycles that have identical amplitudes. Thus, in actual practice, the application of the moving-average method to data does not result precisely in a line. For example, the production series shown in Excel Chart 18-9 repeats about every five years, but the amplitude of the data varies from one oscillation to another. The trend appears to be upward and is only *somewhat* linear. A five-year moving average is also shown in the Excel Chart 18-9.

Four-year, six-year, and other even-numbered-year moving averages present one minor problem regarding the centring of the moving totals and moving averages. Note that in Table 18-3, there is no centre time period, so the moving totals are positioned *between* two time periods. The total for the first four years ($42) is positioned between 1994 and 1995. The total for the next four years is $43. The averages of the first four years and the second four years ($10.50 and $10.75, respectively) are averaged, and the resulting figure, 10.625, is centred on 1995. This procedure is repeated until all possible four-year averages are computed.

Thus, the technique of using moving averages helps to identify the long-term trend in a time series by smoothing out all fluctuations due to C, S, and I. While using annual data, seasonal fluctuations do not pose a problem, removal of the cyclical component is contingent on the assumption of fairly stable cyclical patterns. Since most cycles do not have the same duration, success in this venture is highly doubtful. In addition, we lose the last few observations in the beginning and end of the series in computing moving average. For example, in a five-year moving average, we lose the observations for the first two and the last two years. This makes forecasting trends in the future based on moving averages even more unreliable.

EXCEL CHART 18-9: Moving Average with Excel

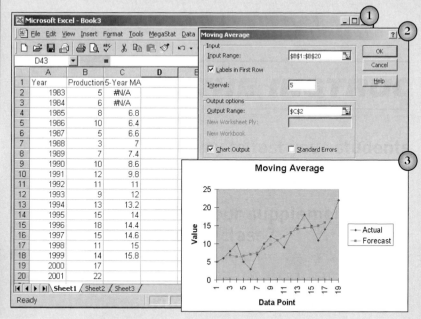

EXCEL INSTRUCTIONS
1. Click Tools, Data Analysis, Moving Average.
2. In the dialogue box, enter data range for the Variable. Put check marks for Labels in First Row and Chart Output. In the Output Range, put the starting cell number.
3. Click OK.
Note: You may have to adjust the MA cells to place the output in the appropriate cells. That is to align your output first moving average number to 1985 by deleting cells.

MINITAB CHART 18-10: Moving Average by Minitab

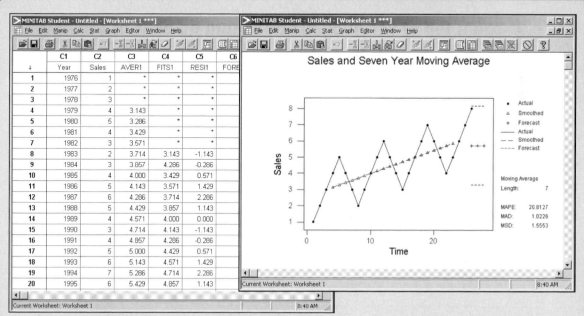

MINITAB INSTRUCTIONS
1. Click Stat, Time series, Moving average.
2. In the dialogue box, enter Sales in Variable box and 7 for MA length.
3. In Generate Forecast (optional), we entered periods beginning observation no. 25.
4. Click Storage and put check marks for Fits, Residuals, Forecasts as desired.
5. Click OK for each dialogue box.

TABLE 18-3: A Four-Year Moving Average

(Average Weekly Sales at Mail-N-Mart, in Thousands)

Year	Sales Y ($000)	4-Year Moving Total	4-Year Moving Average	Centred 4-Year Moving Average
1993	8			
1994	11			
		$42 = (8 + 11 + 9 + 14)$	$10.500 = (42/4)$	
1995	9			10.625
		$43 = (11 + 9 + 14 + 9)$	$10.750 = (43/4)$	
1996	14			10.625
		42	10.500	
1997	9			10.625
		43	10.750	
1998	10			10.000
		37	9.250	
1999	10			9.625
		40	10.000	
2000	8			
2001	12			

■ SELF-REVIEW 18-2

Compute a three-year moving average for the following production series for personal computers for Computech in Toronto. Plot both the original data and the moving average.

Year	Number Produced (thousands)	Year	Number Produced (thousands)
1996	2	1999	5
1997	6	2000	3
1998	4	2001	10

18.4 IDENTIFYING NON-LINEAR TRENDS

The emphasis in the previous discussion was on a time series whose growth or decline approximated a line. A linear trend equation is used to represent a time series when it is believed that the variable is increasing (or decreasing) by a *constant* (*equal*) *amount*, on the average, from one period to another. There are many variables that display a variety of non-linear trends. More common types of non-linearities in business and economics time series can be described by an exponential trend and a parabolic (quadratic) trend. Variables that increase (or decrease) by *increasing* or *decreasing amounts* over a period of time appear *curvilinear* when plotted on paper having an arithmetic scale.

EXPONENTIAL TREND

The variables that increase (or decrease) by *equal percents* or *proportions* over a period of time appear increasing (or decreasing) by a larger amount each period on arithmetic graph paper. (See Excel Chart 18-11 on the following page for a series increasing by increasing amounts each period.)

The estimated version of the trend equation for a time series that does approximate the above description is called an *exponential trend*.[2] This can be written as:

$$\hat{y} = ab^t \tag{18-8}$$

However, using least squares to estimate the trend requires a linear equation. This is easily accomplished in this case by taking the natural logs (*ln*) on both sides of the equation with the following result:

$$ln(\hat{y}) = ln(a) + (t)ln(b) \tag{18-9}$$

where *ln* stands for natural logs.

We should note that, in the above notations, it is the estimated value of *lny* and *not* the *ln* of the estimated value of *y*, and that the coded values of time (*t*) are not in logs. *ln(a)* and *ln(b)* are the estimated values of the parameters for this linear relation between *ln(ŷ)* and time (*t*). We can obtain the value of *ŷ* by taking the inverse of the antilog of *ln(ŷ)*.

If you wish to use a calculator to estimate the log equation, you will need to convert the import values into natural logs for comparison of your results with the results shown in Chart 18-11 and then use the least squares method as you did for estimating the linear trend. The only difference in this case is that we use the *natural log of Y* values instead of the simple *Y* values as the dependent variable. The independent variable is still the same coded value for time (*not* in logs). Actual data for imports of computer chips by a computer store are shown in Chart 18-11. We have also shown the log (natural logs) values of imports and the coded values for time for your information in the same figure. You can also use a calculator to find the natural log values.

Excel Chart 18-11 displays the MegaStat output as a result of estimating the exponential trend in the import data. However, MegaStat uses a different version of the exponential model: $\hat{y} = ae^{rt} \Rightarrow ln(\hat{y}) = ln(a) + rt$. Minitab, on the other hand uses the form $\hat{y} = ab^t \Rightarrow ln(\hat{y}) = ln(a) + (t)ln(b)$ as given above. We can find $b = e^r$ or $r = ln(b)$. Note, $e = 2.71828$. It is used as the base for natural logs. Thus the slope of (*t*) in one form can easily be converted to another form. When using Minitab, follow the instructions in Minitab Chart 18-8 *except* for your choice for the *model type. For the model type, in this case, you choose Exponential instead of Linear*.

The MegaStat output shows estimated regression equation as $ln(\hat{y}) = 2.6137 + 0.1624\ (t)$, where $ln(a) = 2.6137$ and $r = 0.1624$. MegaStat also converts this to $\hat{y} = 13.65\ (1.176)^t$ where $a = 13.65$ and $b = 1.176$. In terms of compound interest formula that you are familiar with, $b = (1 + i)$ where i is the compound interest rate, compounded every period. It can also be interpreted as the average growth rate. Thus, in this example, on average imports grew at the rate of 17.6 percent.

We can also use the logarithmic equation to make estimates of future values. Suppose we want to estimate the imports in the year 2006. The first step is to determine the code for the year 2006, which is 18. How did we get 18? The year 2001 has a code of 13 and the year 2006 is five years later, so $13 + 5 = 18$. The value of imports for the year 2006 is

$$\hat{y} = 13.65(1.176)^{18} = 252.618$$

You can get these values much more easily using computer software.

EXCEL CHART 18-11: Using Excel (MegaStat) for Exponential Trend

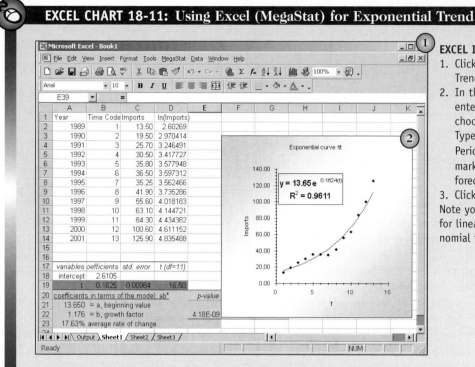

EXCEL INSTRUCTIONS
1. Click MegaStat, Time series, Trendline.
2. In the dialogue box, enter data range for Imports; choose Exponential (*ln*) for Type of Trend Line, Beginning Period = 1, and put a check mark for Scatter plot. Enter forecast period if desired.
3. Click OK.

Note you can also use MegaStat for linear or higher degree polynomial trends.

PARABOLAS AND HIGHER DEGREE POLYNOMIALS

A **parabola** is a second degree polynomial (a line graph is called a first degree polynomial, the degree being determined by the highest number to which an independent variable is raised). Thus, the equation for a parabola is written as:

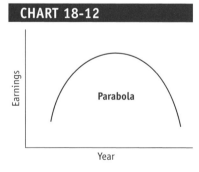

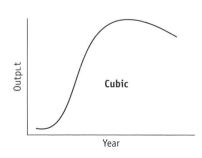

CHART 18-12

Parabola	$y = a + bt + ct^2$ 18-10

and, for a third degree polynomial (the graph of which is a cubic curve) as

Cubic Curve	$y = a + bt + ct^2 + dt^3$ 18-11

In general, a second degree polynomial has one turning point and the graph of a third degree polynomial has two turning points, and so on. Thus a parabola looks like the shape of U (or inverted U). Note that in linear form, values of the variable Y change (per period) by a constant amount (b), in the case of a parabola, they change by the amount $(b + 2ct)$, and in the case of a cubic curve they change by $(b + 2ct + 3dt^2)$.

It is relatively easy to estimate a parabola or higher degree polynomials. All we have to do is to first compute t^2 (for a parabola) and t^2 and t^3 (for a cubic curve) and use them as additional explanatory variables to estimate the equation by least squares. Thus, you will define $y = a + bt + cz$ where $z = t^2$. Thus when you input the range, you will have the data for t and t^2 to estimate a parabola, and data on t, t^2, and t^3 for the cubic curve. You can use MegaStat for estimating these curves by simply choosing 2nd degree or 3rd degree polynomial in place of linear trend. In Minitab, you choose quadratic in place of linear trend analysis. To fit a higher degree polynomial in Minitab you will have to use Stat, Regression analysis, and provide the values of t^2 and t^3 yourself.

A relationship between earnings of an individual and age (in years) may first increase and then decline after some time (an inverted U shape). Likewise, we may observe a cubic relationship, say in fishing, where output in fishing would first increase at an increasing rate and then increase at a decreasing rate (particularly, when the place has not been used for fishing before).

■ SELF-REVIEW 18-3

Sales at Tomlin Manufacturing in P.E.I. since 1997

Year	Sales (millions)
1997	2.13
1998	18.10
1999	39.80
2000	81.40
2001	112.00

(a) Determine the logarithmic equation (the exponential curve) for the sales data.
(b) Sales increased by what percent annually?
(c) What is the projected sales amount for 2002?

EXERCISES 18-5 TO 18-6

18-5. Sally's Software, Inc. is a rapidly growing supplier of computer software to the Toronto area. Sales for recent five-year data are given below.

Year	Sales (millions)
1996	1.1
1997	1.5
1998	2.0
1999	2.4
2000	3.1

(a) Determine the logarithmic (exponential) equation.
(b) By what percent did sales increase, on the average, during the period?
(c) Estimate sales for the year 2003.
(d) Suppose, in the year 2000, sales were incorrectly recorded. The actual sales were in fact $2.1 million. Would a parabola be a better fit to the corrected sales?

18-6. It appears that imports of orange juice have been increasing exponentially.

Year	Imports (thousands/tonne)	Year	Imports (thousands/tonne)
1993	92.0	1997	135.0
1994	101.0	1998	149.0
1995	112.0	1999	163.0
1996	124.0	2000	180.0

(a) Determine the logarithmic (exponential) equation.
(b) By what percent did imports increase, on the average, during the period?
(c) Estimate imports for the year 2003.

18.5   SEASONAL VARIATION

We mentioned that *seasonal variation* is one of the four components of a time series. Business series, such as automobile sales, shipments of soft-drink bottles, and residential construction have periods of above-average and below-average activity within each year.

In the area of production, one of the reasons for analyzing seasonal fluctuations is to have a sufficient supply of raw materials on hand to meet the varying seasonal demand. The glass container division of a large glass company, for example, manufactures non-returnable beer bottles, iodine bottles, aspirin bottles, bottles for rubber cement, and so on. The production scheduling department must know how many bottles to produce and when to produce each kind. A run of too many bottles of one kind may cause a serious storage problem. Production cannot be based entirely on orders on hand, because many orders are telephoned in for immediate shipment. Since the demand for many of the bottles varies according to the season, a forecast a year or two in advance, by month, is essential to good scheduling.

An analysis of seasonal fluctuations over a period of years can also help in evaluating current sales. The typical sales of department stores in Canada, excluding mail-order sales, are expressed as indices in Table 18-4. Each index represents the average sales for a period of several years. The actual sales for some months were above average (which is represented by an index over 100.0), and the sales for other months were below average. The index of 126.8 for December indicates that, typically, sales for December are 26.8 percent above the average for all months; the index of 86.0 for July indicates that department store sales for July are typically 14 percent below the average for all months.

Suppose an enterprising store manager, in an effort to stimulate sales during December, introduced a number of unique promotions, including bands of carollers strolling through the store singing holiday songs, large mechanical exhibits, and clerks dressed in Santa Claus costumes. When the index of sales was computed for that December, it was 150.0. Compared with the typical sales of 126.8, it was concluded that the promotional program was a huge success.

TABLE 18-4: Typical Seasonal Indices for Canadian Department Store Sales, Excluding Mail-Order Sales

Month	Index	Month	Index
January	87.0	July	86.0
February	83.2	August	99.7
March	100.5	September	101.4
April	106.5	October	105.9
May	101.6	November	111.9
June	89.6	December	126.8

DETERMINING A SEASONAL INDEX

Objective: To determine a set of "typical" seasonal indices.

A typical set of monthly indices consists of 12 indices that are representative of the data for a 12-month period. In general, there are four typical seasonal indices for data reported quarterly. Each index is expressed as a percent, with the average for the year equal to 100.0; that is, each monthly index indicates the level of sales, production, or another variable in relation to the annual average of 100.0. A typical index of 96.0 for January indicates that sales (or whatever the variable is) are usually 4 percent below the average for the year. An index of 107.2 for October means that the variable is typically 7.2 percent above the annual average.

Several methods have been developed to measure the typical seasonal fluctuation in a time series. The method most commonly used to compute the typical seasonal pattern is called the **ratio-to-moving-average method**. It eliminates the trend, cyclical, and irregular components from the original data (Y). The numbers that result are called the *typical seasonal index*.

We will discuss in detail the steps followed in arriving at typical seasonal indices using the ratio-to-moving-average method.

The data of interest might be monthly or quarterly. To illustrate, we have chosen the quarterly sales of Toys International. First, we will show the steps needed to arrive at a set of typical quarterly indices. Then we use MegaStat (Excel) and Minitab software to calculate the seasonal indices.

Example 18-3

Table 18-5 shows the quarterly sales for Toys International for the years 1996 through 2001. The sales are reported in millions of dollars. Determine a quarterly seasonal index using the ratio-to-moving-average method.

TABLE 18-5: Quarterly Sales of Toys International ($ millions)

Year	Winter	Spring	Summer	Fall
1996	6.7	4.6	10.0	12.7
1997	6.5	4.6	9.8	13.6
1998	6.9	5.0	10.4	14.1
1999	7.0	5.5	10.8	15.0
2000	7.1	5.7	11.1	14.5
2001	8.0	6.2	11.4	14.9

Solution

Chart 18-13 depicts the quarterly sales for Toys International over a six-year period. Notice the seasonal nature of the sales. For each year the Fall quarter sales are the largest and the Spring quarter sales are the smallest. Also, there is a moderate increase in the sales from one year to the next. To observe this feature, look only at the six Fall quarter sales values. This is the result of a trend.

There are six steps to determine the quarterly seasonal indices.

Step 1

For the following discussion, refer to Table 18-6. The first step is to determine the four-quarter moving total for 1996. Starting with the Winter quarter of 1996, we add $6.7, $4.6, $10.0, and $12.7 (million). The total is $34.0 (million). The four-quarter total is "moved along" by adding the Spring, Summer, and Fall sales of 1996 to the Winter sales of 1997. The total is $33.8 (million), found by 4.6 + 10.0 + 12.7 + 6.5. This procedure is continued for the quarterly sales for each of the six years.

EXCEL CHART 18-13: Toys International Sales (Quarterly)

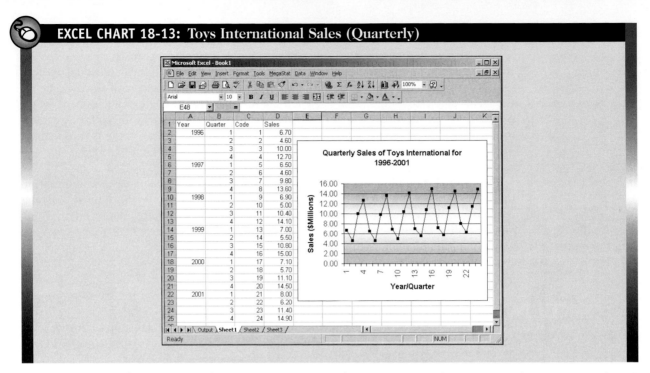

Column 2 of Table 18-6 shows all of the moving totals. Note that the moving total 34.0 is positioned between the Spring and Summer sales of 1996. The next moving total, 33.8, is positioned between sales for Summer and Fall of 1996, and so on. Check the totals frequently to avoid arithmetic errors.

Step 2 Each quarterly moving total in column 2 is divided by 4 to give the four-quarter moving average. (See column 3.) All the moving averages are still positioned between the quarters. For example, the first moving average (8.500) is positioned between Spring and Summer of 1996.

Step 3 The moving averages are then centred (in column 4). The first centred moving average is found by $(8.500 + 8.450)/2 = 8.475$ and centred opposite Summer 1996. The second moving average is found by $(8.450 + 8.450)/2 = 8.45$. The others are found similarly. Note that a centred moving average is positioned on a particular quarter.

Step 4 The **specific seasonal** for each quarter is then computed (in column 5) by dividing the sales in column 1 by the centred moving average in column 4. The specific seasonal reports the ratio of the original time series value to the moving average. To explain further, if the time series is represented by *TSCI* and the moving average by *TCI*, then, algebraically, if we compute *TSCI/TCI*, the result is the seasonal components. The specific seasonal for the Summer quarter of 1996 is 1.180, found by 10.0/8.475.

Step 5 The specific seasonals are then organized by year for all quarters in a table. (See Table 18-7.) This table will help us locate the specific seasonals for the corresponding quarters. The specific seasonal values 1.180, 1.130, 1.141, 1.126, and 1.143 all represent estimates of the typical seasonal index for the Summer quarter. A reasonable method to find a typical seasonal index is to average these values. So we find the typical index for the Summer quarter by $(1.180 + 1.130 + 1.141 + 1.126 + 1.143)/5 = 1.144$. We used the arithmetic mean, but the median or a modified mean can also be used.

TABLE 18-6: Computations Needed for the Specific Seasonal Indices

Year	Quarter	(1) Sales ($ millions)	(2) Four-Quarter Moving Total	(3) Four-Quarter Moving Average	(4) Centred Moving Average	(5) Specific Seasonal
1996	Winter	6.7				
	Spring	4.6				
			34.0	8.500		
	Summer	10.0			8.475	1.180
			33.8	8.450		
	Fall	12.7			8.450	1.503
			33.8	8.450		
1997	Winter	6.5			8.425	0.772
			33.6	8.400		
	Spring	4.6			8.513	0.540
			34.5	8.625		
	Summer	9.8			8.675	1.130
			34.9	8.725		
	Fall	13.6			8.775	1.550
			35.3	8.825		
1998	Winter	6.9			8.900	0.775
			35.9	8.975		
	Spring	5.0			9.038	0.553
			36.4	9.100		
	Summer	10.4			9.113	1.141
			36.5	9.125		
	Fall	14.1			9.188	1.535
			37.0	9.250		
1999	Winter	7.0			9.300	0.753
			37.4	9.350		
	Spring	5.5			9.463	0.581
			38.3	9.575		
	Summer	10.8			9.588	1.126
			38.4	9.600		
	Fall	15.0			9.625	1.558
			38.6	9.650		
2000	Winter	7.1			9.688	0.733
			38.9	9.725		
	Spring	5.7			9.663	0.590
			38.4	9.600		
	Summer	11.1			9.713	1.143
			39.3	9.825		
	Fall	14.5			9.888	1.466
			39.8	9.950		
2001	Winter	8.0			9.888	0.810
			40.1	10.025		
	Spring	6.2			10.075	0.615
			40.5	10.125		
	Summer	11.4				
	Fall	14.9				

TABLE 18-7: Calculations needed for Typical Quarterly Index

Year	Winter	Spring	Summer	Fall	
1996			1.180	1.503	
1997	0.772	0.540	1.130	1.550	
1998	0.775	0.553	1.141	1.535	
1999	0.753	0.581	1.126	1.558	
2000	0.733	0.590	1.143	1.466	
2001	0.801	0.615			
Total	3.834	2.879	5.720	7.612	
Mean	0.767	0.576	1.144	1.522	4.009
Adjusted	0.765	0.575	1.141	1.519	4.000
Index (percent)	76.5	57.5	114.1	151.9	

Step 6 The four quarterly means (0.767, 0.576, 1.144, and 1.522) should theoretically total 4.00 because the average is set at 1.0. The total of the four quarterly means may not exactly equal 4.00 due to rounding. In this problem the total of the means is 4.009. A *correction factor* is therefore applied to each of the four means to force them to total 4.00.

| **Correction Factor for Adjusting Quarterly Means** | $\text{Correction factor} = \dfrac{4.00}{\text{Total of four means}}$ | **18-12** |

In this problem,

$$\text{Correction factor} = \frac{4.00}{4.009} = 0.997755$$

The adjusted Winter quarterly index is, therefore, $0.767(0.997755) = 0.765$. Each of the means is adjusted downward so that the total of the four quarterly means is 4.00. Usually indices are reported as percentages, so each value in the last row of Table 18-7 has been multiplied by 100. So the index for the Winter quarter is 76.5 and for the Fall it is 151.9. How are these values interpreted? Sales for the Fall quarter are 51.9 percent above the typical quarter (the average of all quarters), and for Winter they are 23.5 percent below the typical quarter $(100.0 - 76.50)$. These findings should not surprise you. The period prior to Christmas (the Fall quarter) is when toy sales are brisk. After Christmas (the Winter quarter) sales of toys decline drastically.

Now to summarize briefly the reasoning underlying the preceding calculations, the original data in column 1 of Table 18-6 contain trend (T), cycle (C), seasonal (S), and irregular (I) components. The ultimate objective is to isolate seasonal (S) from the original sales valuation.

Columns 2 and 3 in Table 18-6 were concerned with deriving the centred moving average given in column 4. Basically, we "averaged out" the seasonal and irregular fluctuations from the original data in column 1. Thus, in column 4 we have only trend and cycle (TC).

Next, we divided the sales data in column 1 (*TCSI*) by the centred four-quarter moving average in column 4 (*TC*) to arrive at the specific seasonals in column 5 (*SI*). In symbols, *TCSI/TC* = *SI*.

Then, we took the mean of all specific seasonals, the Winter quarters, the Spring quarters, and so on. This averaging eliminates most of the irregular fluctuations from the seasonals, and the resulting four indices indicate the typical seasonal sales pattern.

Finally, we applied the correction factor to force the average of all indices to equal one with a year. The last row displays the typical indices in percent form.

Both Minitab and Excel (MegaStat) will perform calculations and output the results. The MegaStat output is shown in Chart 18-14. The Minitab output is shown in Charts 18-15 and 18-16. Minitab gives several charts as well as forecasts. However, you should understand the steps in computations outlined in this and the next section. There can be slight differences in answers due to rounding.

EXCEL CHART 18-14: Using MegaStat (Excel) to Compute Seasonal Index

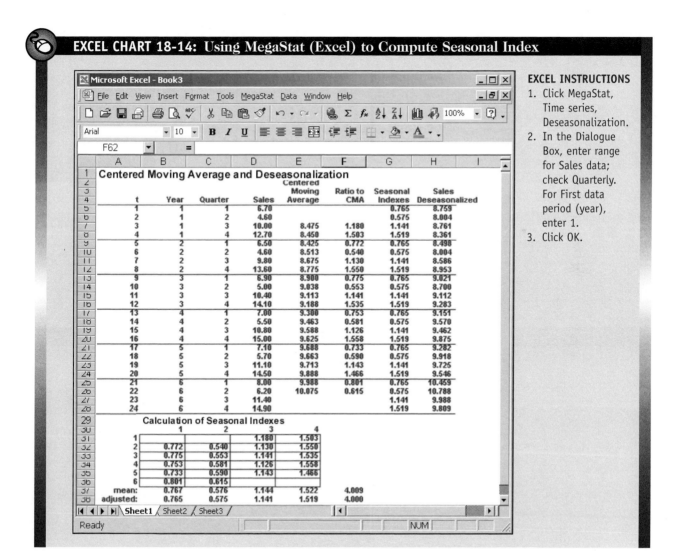

EXCEL INSTRUCTIONS
1. Click MegaStat, Time series, Deseasonalization.
2. In the Dialogue Box, enter range for Sales data; check Quarterly. For First data period (year), enter 1.
3. Click OK.

MINITAB CHART 18-15: Using Minitab for Seasonal Index and Forecasting

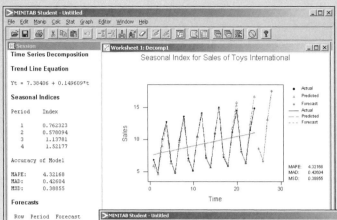

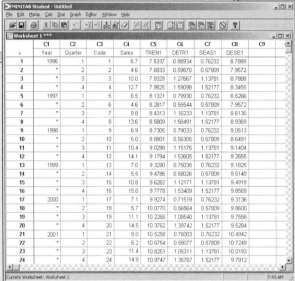

MINITAB INSTRUCTIONS
1. Click Stat, Time Series, Decomposition.
2. In the dialogue box, enter Variable (Sales); Seasonal length (4); Model type (Multiplicative); Model components (choose Seasonal or Trend plus Seasonal); First Obs. (1); Generate Forecasts (enter beginning period and the number of periods to forecast). Click OK.
3. Click Results; put check marks on Display plot and Summary table. Click OK.
4. Click Storage and put check marks for Trend, Seasonals, Seasonally adjusted, De-trended. Click OK.

MINITAB CHART 18-16: Minitab Charts for Seasonal Indices

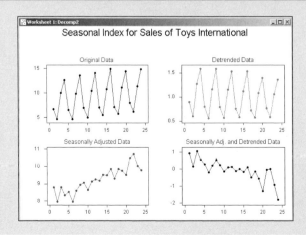

■ SELF-REVIEW 18-4

Banff, Alberta, near Banff National Park, contains shops, restaurants, and motels. Banff has two peak seasons—winter, for skiing on the 3500-metre slopes, and summer, for tourists visiting the parks. The specific seasonals with respect to the total sales volume for recent years are:

Year	Quarter			
	Winter	Spring	Summer	Fall
1997	117.0	80.7	129.6	76.1
1998	118.6	82.5	121.4	77.0
1999	114.0	84.3	119.9	75.0
2000	120.7	79.6	130.7	69.6
2001	125.2	80.2	127.6	72.0

(a) Develop the typical seasonal pattern for Banff using the ratio-to-moving-average method.

(b) Explain the typical index for the Winter season.

EXERCISES 18-7 TO 18-8

18-7. Victor Anderson, the owner of Anderson Belts, Inc., in St. John's NF, is studying absenteeism among his employees. His workforce is small, consisting of only five employees. For the last three years he has recorded the number of employee absences, in days, for each quarter. The data are shown below and in file Exercise 18-7.xls on the CD-ROM.

Year	Quarter			
	I	II	III	IV
1999	4	10	7	3
2000	5	12	9	4
2001	6	16	12	4

Determine a typical seasonal index for each of the four quarters.

18-8. The Appliance Centre in Prince George, B.C., sells a variety of electronic equipment and home appliances. Below and in file Exercise 18-8.xls on the CD-ROM is the data of quarterly sales (in $ millions) reported for the last four years.

Year	Quarter			
	I	II	III	IV
1998	5.3	4.1	6.8	6.7
1999	4.8	3.8	5.6	6.8
2000	4.3	3.8	5.7	6.0
2001	5.6	4.6	6.4	5.9

Determine a typical seasonal index for each of the four quarters.

18.6   DESEASONALIZING DATA

A set of typical indices is very useful in adjusting a sales series, for example, for removing seasonal fluctuations and making seasonally adjusted forecasts. The resulting sales series is called **deseasonalized sales** or **seasonally adjusted sales**. The reason for deseasonalizing the sales series is to remove the seasonal fluctuations so that the trend and cycle can be studied. To illustrate the procedure, the quarterly sales totals of Toys International from Table 18-5 are repeated in column 1 of Table 18-8. The seasonal indices from Table 18-7 (second from the bottom line) in proportional form are reported in column 2 of Table 18-8.

To remove the effect of seasonal variation, the sales amount for each quarter (which contains trend, cyclical, irregular, and seasonal effects) is divided by the seasonal index for that quarter, that is, *TSCI/S*. For example, the actual sales for the first quarter of 1996 were $6.7 million. The seasonal index for the winter quarter is 0.765. The index of 0.765 indicates that sales for the first quarter are

TABLE 18-8

Year	Quarter	(1) Sales ($ millions)	(2) Seasonal Index	(3) Deseasonalized Sales ($ millions)
1996	Winter	6.7	0.765	8.76
	Spring	4.6	0.575	8.00
	Summer	10.0	1.141	8.76
	Fall	12.7	1.519	8.36
1997	Winter	6.5	0.765	8.50
	Spring	4.6	0.575	8.00
	Summer	9.8	1.141	8.59
	Fall	13.6	1.519	8.95
1998	Winter	6.9	0.765	9.02
	Spring	5.0	0.575	8.70
	Summer	10.4	1.141	9.11
	Fall	14.1	1.519	9.28
1999	Winter	7.0	0.765	9.15
	Spring	5.5	0.575	9.57
	Summer	10.8	1.141	9.46
	Fall	15.0	1.519	9.88
2000	Winter	7.1	0.765	9.28
	Spring	5.7	0.575	9.92
	Summer	11.1	1.141	9.72
	Fall	14.5	1.519	9.55
2001	Winter	8.0	0.765	10.46
	Spring	6.2	0.575	10.79
	Summer	11.4	1.141	9.99
	Fall	14.9	1.519	9.81

typically 23.53 percent below the average for all quarters. By dividing the actual sales of $6.7 million by 0.765, we find the *deseasonalized sales* value for the first quarter of 1996. It is $8.76 million or $8 758 170, found by ($6 700 000/0.765). We continue this process for the other quarters in column 3 of Table 18-8, with the results reported in millions of dollars. Because the seasonal component has been removed (divided out) from the quarterly sales, the deseasonalized sales figure contains only the trend (T), cyclical (C), and irregular (I) components. Scanning the deseasonalized sales in column 3 of Table 18-8, we see that the sales of toys showed a moderate increase over the six-year period. Chart 18-17 on page 817 shows both the actual sales and the deseasonalized sales. It is clear that removing the seasonal factor allows us to focus on the overall long-term trend of sales. We will also be able to better determine the regression equation for the trend and use it to forecast future sales.

USING DESEASONALIZED DATA TO FORECAST

The procedure for identifying trend and seasonal adjustments can be combined to yield seasonally adjusted forecasts. To identify the trend, we determine the least squares trend equation on the deseasonalized historical data. Then we project this trend into future periods, and finally we adjust these trend values to account for seasonal factors. The following example will help to clarify.

Example 18-4

Toys International would like to forecast their sales for each quarter of 1999. Use the information in Table 18-8 to determine the forecast.

Solution

The first step is to use the deseasonalized data in column 3 of Table 18-8 to determine the least squares trend equation. The deseasonalized trend equation is:

$$\hat{y} = a + bt$$

where:
$\hat{y}$ is the estimated trend for Toys International sales for period t.
a is the intercept of the trend line at time 0.
b is the slope of the trend line.

The Winter quarter of 1996 is the period $t = 1$, and $t = 24$ corresponds to the Fall quarter of 2001. (See column 1 in Table 18-9.) The sums needed to compute a and b are also shown in Table 18-9.

$$b = \frac{n\sum ty - (\sum y)(\sum t)}{n\sum t^2 - (\sum t)^2} = \frac{24(2873.4) - (221.60)(300)}{24(4900) - (300)^2} = \frac{2481.6}{27\,600.0} = 0.0899$$

$$a = \frac{\sum y}{n} - b\left(\frac{\sum t}{n}\right) = \frac{221.60}{24} - 0.0899\left(\frac{300}{24}\right) = 8.1096$$

TABLE 18-9: Deseasonalized Sales for Toys International: Data Needed for Determining Trend Line

Year	Quarter	(1) t	(2) Y	(3) tY	(4) t^2
1996	1	1	8.76	8.76	1
	2	2	8.00	16.00	4
	3	3	8.76	26.28	9
	4	4	8.36	33.44	16
1997	1	5	8.50	42.50	25
	2	6	8.00	48.00	36
	3	7	8.59	60.13	49
	4	8	8.95	71.60	64
1998	1	9	9.02	81.18	81
	2	10	8.70	87.00	100
	3	11	9.11	100.21	121
	4	12	9.28	111.36	144
1999	1	13	9.15	118.95	169
	2	14	9.57	133.98	196
	3	15	9.47	142.05	225
	4	16	9.87	157.92	256
2000	1	17	9.28	157.76	289
	2	18	9.91	178.38	324
	3	19	9.73	184.87	361
	4	20	9.55	191.00	400
2001	1	21	10.46	219.66	441
	2	22	10.78	237.16	484
	3	23	9.99	229.77	529
	4	24	9.81	235.44	576
Total		300	221.60	2873.40	4900

TABLE 18-10: Quarterly Forecast for Toys International for 2002

Quarter	t	(1) Estimated Sales	(2) Seasonal Index	(3) Quarterly Forecast
Winter	25	10.3571	0.765	7.923
Spring	26	10.4770	0.575	6.024
Summer	27	10.5369	1.141	12.02
Fall	28	10.6268	1.519	16.14

If we assume that the past 24 quarters are a good indicator of future sales, we can use the trend equation to estimate future sales. For example, for the Winter quarter of 2002 the value of t is 25. The estimated sales total for that period is $10 334 000, found by

$$\hat{y} = 8.1096 + 0.0899 \,(25) = 10.3571$$

Using the trend equation, we can forecast sales at Toys International for the four quarters of 2002. These estimates are shown in column 1 of Table 18-10.

Now that we have the trend forecasts for the four quarters of 2002, we can add the seasonal influence. The index for the Winter quarter is 0.765 (column 2), so we can estimate the sales in this quarter by $10.3571(0.765) = 7.923$. The estimates for all four quarters of 2002 are shown in column 3 of Table 18-10. Notice how the seasonal factors drastically increase the sales' estimates for the last two quarters of the year. Again, note the difference in the estimate of the trend line based on actual sales data (Chart 18-15) and on deseasonalized data as well as forecasts. Presumably, forecasts would now be more accurate.

The trend equation, based on deseasonalized sales is:

$$\hat{y} = 8.1096 + 0.0899t \qquad R^2 = 0.785$$

The slope of the trend line is 0.0899. This shows that over the 24 quarters, the deseasonalized sales, on average, increased at a rate of 0.0899 ($ millions) per quarter, or $89900 per quarter. The value of 8.1096 is the intercept ($ millions) of the trend line on the Y-axis (i.e., for $t = 0$).

Note, if we had used actual sales to find the trend line, it would be $\hat{y} = 7.384 + 0.15t$ with an $R^2 = 0.089$. Here is a small challenge for you to verify this claim. Thus, estimating trend based on deseasonalized data provides an accurate picture of trend, and therefore better forecasts with or without the influence of seasonal matters.

Of course, we can use either Excel or Minitab packages to determine the regression equation. Excel Chart 18-17 and Minitab Chart 18-18 display the results. Using a software package will reduce the possibility of an error in arithmetic, differences in Minitab/Excel results are reported below.

EXCEL CHART 18-17

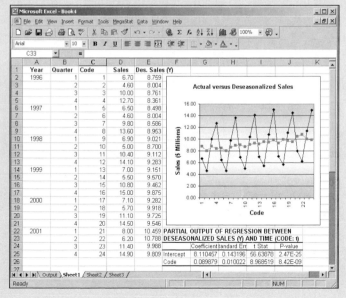

EXCEL INSTRUCTIONS
See Excel Chart 18-7. In this case, we use the Seasonalized Sales (Column E) in place of Actual Sales (Column D) for the Trend line. Alternatively you can use MegaStat's Trend Line procedure to forecast values.

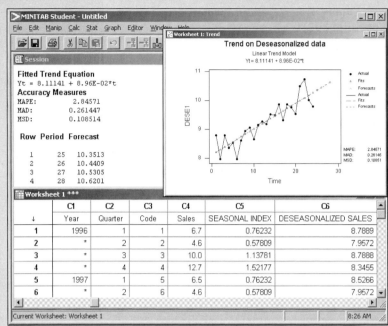

MINITAB CHART 18-18: Trend on Deseasonalized Data and Forecasts

MINITAB INSTRUCTIONS
See Minitab Chart 18-8.
(In this case we use Deseasonalized Sales in Column C6 in place of Actual Sales in Column C4 for Trend line.)

■ SELF-REVIEW 18-5

The Oshawa Electric Company sells electric motors to customers in Ontario. The monthly trend equation, based on five years of monthly data, is

$$\hat{y} = 4.40 + 0.50t$$

The seasonal factor for the month of January is 120, and it is 95 for February. Determine the forecast, including the seasonal effect, for January and February of the sixth year.

EXERCISES 18-9 TO 18-12

18-9. The planning department of Padget and Kure Shoes, the manufacturer of an exclusive brand of women's shoes, developed the following trend equation, in millions of pairs, based on five years of quarterly data.

$$\hat{y} = 3.30 + 1.75t$$

The following table gives the seasonal factors for each quarter.

	Quarter			
	I	II	III	IV
Index	110.0	120.0	80.0	90.0

Determine the forecast for each of the four quarters of the sixth year.

18-10. Team Sports, Inc., in Halifax, sells sporting goods to high schools and colleges via a nationally distributed catalogue. Management at Team Sports estimates they will sell 2000 Wilson Model A2000 catcher's mitts next year. The deseasonalized sales are projected to be the same for each of the four quarters next year. The seasonal factor for the second quarter is 145. Determine the sales including the seasonal effect for the second quarter of next year.

18-11. Refer to Exercise 18-7 regarding the absences at Anderson Belts, Inc. Use the seasonal indices you computed to determine the deseasonalized absences. Determine the trend equation based on the quarterly data for the three years. Forecast the absences including the seasonal effect for 2002.

18-12. Refer to Exercise 18-8, regarding sales at the Appliance Centre. Use the seasonal indices you computed to determine the deseasonalized sales. Determine the trend equation based on the quarterly data for the four years. Forecast the sales including the seasonal effect for 2002.

CHAPTER OUTLINE

I. A time series is a set of data values on a variable over a period of time.
   A. The trend is the long-run direction of the time series.
   B. The cyclical component is the fluctuation above and below the long-term trend line.
   C. The seasonal variation is the pattern in a time series *within* a year. These patterns tend to repeat themselves from year to year for most businesses.
   D. The irregular variation is divided into two components.
      1. Episodic variations are unpredictable, but they can usually be identified. A flood is an example.
      2. Residual variations are random in nature.

II. The linear trend equation is $\hat{y} = a + bt$, where a is the Y-intercept, b is the slope of the line, and t is the time.
   A. The trend equation is determined using the least squares principle.
   B. If the trend is not linear, but rather the increases tend to be a constant percent, the Y values are converted to natural logarithms, and a least squares equation is determined using the natural logs.

III. A moving average can be used to identify the trend and/or the seasonal factors in a time series.

IV. A seasonal factor can be estimated using the ratio-to-moving-average method.
   A. The six-step procedure yields a seasonal index for each period.
      1. Seasonal factors are usually computed on a monthly or a quarterly basis.
      2. The seasonal factor can then be used to adjust forecasts based on trend, i.e., taking into account the effects of the season.

CHAPTER EXERCISES 18-13 TO 18-31

18-13. Refer to the following diagram.
    (a) Is there a decline or increase in the production in the long run?
    (b) Would you use moving average or least squares to estimate the long term trend? Why?
    (c) What is your best guess for the estimated trend in bankruptcies in 2000?

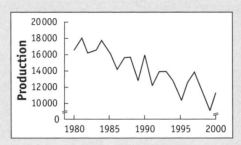

18-14. Refer to the following diagram.
    (a) Does the investment series display a trend? What method would you use to estimate it? Why? Describe the method briefly.
    (b) Does the investment series display cycles? Can you identify them?

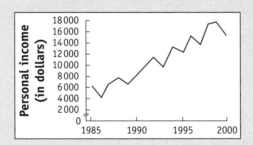

18-15. The asset turnovers, excluding cash and short-term investments, for the RNC Company from 1990 to 2000 are:

1990	1991	1992	1993	1994	1995	1996	1997	1998	1999	2000
1.11	1.28	1.17	1.10	1.06	1.14	1.24	1.33	1.38	1.50	1.65

(a) Plot the data.
(b) Determine the least squares trend equation.
(c) Calculate the points on the trend line for 1993 and 1998, and plot the line on the graph.
(d) Estimate the asset turnover for 2005.
(e) How much did the asset turnover increase per year, on the average, from 1990 to 2000?

18-16. Sales, in billions of dollars, of Atlantic Overhead Door, Inc. for 1995–2000 are:

Year	Sales	Year	Sales
1995	7.45	1998	7.94
1996	7.83	1999	7.76
1997	8.07	2000	7.90

(a) Plot the data.
(b) Determine the least squares trend equation.
(c) Use the trend equation to calculate the points for 1997 and 1999.
    Plot them on the graph and draw the regression line.
(d) Estimate the net sales for 2003.
(e) By how much have sales increased (or decreased) per year on the average
    during the period?

18-17. The number of employees, in thousands, of Atlantic Overhead Door, Inc.
for the years 1995 to 2000 is shown below and in file Exercise 18-17.xls on
the CD-ROM.

Year	Employees	Year	Employees
1995	45.6	1998	39.3
1996	42.2	1999	34.0
1997	41.1	2000	30.0

(a) Plot the data.
(b) Determine the least squares trend equation.
(c) Use the trend equation to calculate the points for 1997 and 1999.
    Plot them on the graph and draw the regression line.
(d) Estimate the number of employees in 2003.
(e) By how much has the number of employees increased (or decreased)
    per year on average during the period?

18-18. Use the import data from Exercise 18-6 on page 805.

(a) Plot the data.
(b) Determine the least squares linear trend equation.
(c) Calculate the points for the years 1994 and 1998.
(d) Estimate the imports in 2003. Does this seem like a reasonable estimate
    based on the historical data?
(e) Compare the quarterly estimates in (d) above with estimates from
    Exercise 18-6, and comment.

18-19. If plotted on arithmetic paper, the following sales series of Infotech Computer
Inc. of Ontario would appear curvilinear. This indicates that sales are
increasing at a somewhat constant annual rate (percent). To fit the sales,
therefore, a logarithmic straight line equation should be used.

Year	Sales ($ millions)	Year	Sales ($ millions)
1991	8.0	1997	39.4
1992	10.4	1998	50.5
1993	13.5	1999	65.0
1994	17.6	2000	84.1
1995	22.8	2001	109.0
1996	29.3		

(a) Determine the logarithmic equation.

(b) Determine the coordinates of the points on the logarithmic straight line for 1994 and 1999.

(c) By what percent did sales increase per year, on average, during the period from 1991 to 2001?

(d) Based on the equation, what are the estimated sales for 2002?

18-20. Reported below (and in file Exercise 18-20.xls on the CD-ROM) are the amounts spent on advertising by Manitoba Manufacturing Limited ($ millions) from 1990 to 2000.

Year	Amount	Year	Amount
1990	88.1	1996	132.6
1991	94.7	1997	141.9
1992	102.1	1998	150.9
1993	109.8	1999	157.9
1994	118.1	2000	162.6
1995	125.6		

(a) Determine the logarithmic trend equation.

(b) Estimate the advertising expenses for 2000.

(c) By what percent per year did advertising expenses increase during the period?

18-21. Listed below (and in file Exercise 18-21.xls on the CD-ROM) is the selling price for a share of Oracle, Inc. stock at the close of the year.

Year	Price	Year	Price
1990	12.9135	1996	29.0581
1991	16.8250	1997	36.0155
1992	20.6125	1998	40.6111
1993	20.3024	1999	35.0230
1994	18.3160	2000	49.5625
1995	27.7538		

(a) Plot the data.

(b) Determine the least squares trend equation. Use both the actual stock price and the logarithm of the price. Which seems to yield a more accurate forecast?

(c) Calculate the points for the years 1993 and 1998.

(d) Estimate the selling price in 2003. Does this seem like a reasonable estimate based on the historical data?

(e) By how much has the stock price increased or decreased (per year) on average during the period? Use your best answer from part b.

18-22. The production of the Reliable Manufacturing Company for 1997 and part of 1998 follows.

Month	1997 Production (thousands)	1998 Production (thousands)	Month	1997 Production (thousands)	1998 Production (thousands)
January	6	7	July	3	4
February	7	9	August	5	
March	12	14	September	14	
April	8	9	October	6	
May	4	5	November	7	
June	3	4	December	6	

(a) Using the ratio-to-moving-average method, determine the specific seasonals for July, August, and September 1997.

(b) Assume that the specific seasonal indices in the following table are correct. Insert in the table the specific seasonals you computed in part (a) for July, August, and September 1997, and determine the 12 typical seasonal indices.

Year	Jan.	Feb.	Mar.	Apr.	May	June	July	Aug.	Sept.	Oct.	Nov.	Dec.
1997							?	?	?	92.1	106.5	92.9
1998	88.9	102.9	178.9	118.2	60.1	43.1	44.0	74.0	200.9	90.0	101.9	90.9
1999	87.6	103.7	170.2	125.9	59.4	48.6	44.2	77.2	196.5	89.6	113.2	80.6
2000	79.8	105.6	165.8	124.7	62.1	41.7	48.2	72.1	203.6	80.2	103.0	94.2
2001	89.0	112.1	182.9	115.1	57.6	56.9						

(c) Interpret the typical seasonal index.

18-23. The sales at Andre's Boutique in Montreal for 1996 and part of 1997 are:

Month	1996 Sales (thousands)	1997 Sales (thousands)	Month	1996 Sales (thousands)	1997 Sales (thousands)
January	78	65	July	81	65
February	72	60	August	85	61
March	80	72	September	90	75
April	110	97	October	98	
May	92	86	November	115	
June	86	72	December	130	

(a) Using the ratio-to-moving-average method, determine the specific seasonals for July, August, September, and October 1996.

(b) Assume that the specific seasonals in the following table are correct. Insert in the table the specific seasonals you computed in part (a) for July, August, September, and October 1996 and determine the 12 typical seasonal indices.

Year	Jan.	Feb.	Mar.	Apr.	May	June	July	Aug.	Sept.	Oct.	Nov.	Dec.
1996							?	?	?	?	123.6	150.9
1997	83.9	77.6	86.1	118.7	99.7	92.0	87.0	91.4	97.3	105.4	124.9	140.1
1998	86.7	72.9	86.2	121.3	96.6	92.0	85.5	93.6	98.2	103.2	126.1	141.7
1999	85.6	65.8	89.2	125.6	99.6	94.4	88.9	90.2	100.2	102.7	121.6	139.6
2000	77.3	81.2	85.8	115.7	100.3	89.7						

(c) Interpret the typical seasonal index.

18-24. The quarterly production of pine lumber, in millions of board feet, by Northwest Lumber, Inc., in B.C. since 1996 is shown below and in file Exercise 18-24.xls on the CD-ROM.

Year	Quarter			
	Winter	Spring	Summer	Fall
1996	7.8	10.2	14.7	9.3
1997	6.9	11.6	17.5	9.3
1998	8.9	9.7	15.3	10.1
1999	10.7	12.4	16.8	10.7
2000	9.2	13.6	17.1	10.3

(a) Determine the typical seasonal pattern for the production data using the ratio-to-moving-average method.
(b) Interpret the pattern.
(c) Deseasonalize the data and determine the linear trend equation.
(d) Project the seasonally adjusted production for the four quarters of 2001.
(e) Forecast production for four quarters of 2001, including seasonal influence.

18-25. Alberta Work Gloves Corp. is reviewing its quarterly sales of Toughie, the most durable glove they produce. The numbers of pairs produced (in thousands) by quarter are shown below and in file Exercise 18-25.xls on the CD-ROM.

	Quarter			
	I	II	III	IV
Year	Jan.–Mar.	Apr.–June	July–Sept.	Oct.–Dec.
1995	142	312	488	208
1996	146	318	512	212
1997	160	330	602	187
1998	158	338	572	176
1999	162	380	563	200
2000	162	362	587	205

(a) Using the ratio-to-moving-average method, determine the four typical quarterly indices.
(b) Interpret the typical seasonal pattern.

18-26. Sales of roof material, by quarter, since 1994 for British Columbia Home Construction, Inc. are shown below and in file Exercise 18-26.xls on the CD-ROM (in $000).

Year	Quarter			
	I	II	III	IV
1994	210	180	60	246
1995	214	216	82	230
1996	246	228	91	280
1997	258	250	113	298
1998	279	267	116	304
1999	302	290	114	310
2000	321	291	120	320

(a) Determine the typical seasonal patterns for sales using the ratio-to-moving-average method.
(b) Deseasonalize the data and determine the trend equation.
(c) Project the sales for 2001, and then add seasonal factors for each quarter.

18-27. The inventory turnover rates for Bassett Wholesale Enterprises in Quebec, by quarter, are:

Year	Quarter			
	I	II	III	IV
1993	4.4	6.1	11.7	7.2
1994	4.1	6.6	11.1	8.6
1995	3.9	6.8	12.0	9.7
1996	5.0	7.1	12.7	9.0
1997	4.3	5.2	10.8	7.6

(a) Arrive at the four typical quarterly turnover rates for the Bassett Company using the ratio-to-moving-average method.
(b) Deseasonalize the data and determine the trend equation.
(c) Project the turnover rates for 1998, and then add seasonal factors for each quarter of 1998.

18-28. Chart 18-1 contains quarterly data for Canada's real Gross Domestic Product for the years 1979–2000.
(a) Identify the years of peaks and troughs in the data, if any.
(b) Determine the least squares trend equation.
(c) Calculate the points on the trend line for 1993 and 1998, and plot the line on the graph.
(d) Estimate the quarterly GDP for 2002. Compare with actual data, if available.
(e) How much did the GDP increase per year, on average, between 1979 and 2000?

18-29. Ray Anderson, owner of the Anderson Ski Lodge in Northern Ontario, is interested in forecasting the number of visitors for the upcoming year. Below and in file Exercise 18-29.xls on the CD-ROM, quarterly data from 1994 to 2000 are available. Develop a seasonal index for each quarter.

How many visitors would you expect for each quarter of 2001, if Ray projects that there will be a 10 percent increase in the total number of visitors in 2000? Determine the trend equation, project the number of visitors for 2001, and add the seasonal factors for the forecast. Which forecast would you choose?

Year	Quarter	Visitors	Year	Quarter	Visitors
1994	1	86	1998	1	188
	2	62		2	172
	3	28		3	128
	4	94		4	198
1995	1	106	1999	1	208
	2	82		2	202
	3	48		3	154
	4	114		4	220
1996	1	140	2000	1	246
	2	120		2	240
	3	82		3	190
	4	154		4	252
1997	1	162			
	2	140			
	3	100			
	4	174			

18-30. The following table (also found in file Exercise 18-30.xls on the CD-ROM) shows Canada's monthly exports of fruits and vegetables (in $ thousands) to all countries from January 1998 to December 2000.

Year/ Month	Exports ($ thousands)	Year/ Month	Exports ($ thousands)	Year/ Month	Exports ($ thousands)	Year/ Month	Exports ($ thousands)
1998/01	18 383	1998/10	83 613	1999/07	23 509	2000/04	23 366
1998/02	17 799	1998/11	25 770	1999/08	54 261	2000/05	21 661
1998/03	16 073	1998/12	22 982	1999/09	39 975	2000/06	18 827
1998/04	15 610	1999/01	19 301	1999/10	62 444	2000/07	29 537
1998/05	16 638	1999/02	18 619	1999/11	36 107	2000/08	49 349
1998/06	15 846	1999/03	20 170	1999/12	26 430	2000/09	33 485
1998/07	22 022	1999/04	17 483	2000/01	27 625	2000/10	53 105
1998/08	32 245	1999/05	15 418	2000/02	24 009	2000/11	41 126
1998/09	25 393	1999/06	15 386	2000/03	25 284	2000/12	21 468

Source: Statistics Canada; Series v192175,
Canada's exports of fruits and fruit preparations to all countries;
Dollars; Monthly, 1968-01-01–2001-04-01) [D402104]

(a) Determine the typical seasonal pattern for the export data using the ratio-to-moving-average method.
(b) Interpret the pattern.
(c) Deseasonalize the data and determine the linear trend equation.
(d) Forecast exports for the twelve months of 2001, including the seasonal effect.

18-31. The following table, which can also be found in file Exercise 18-31.xls on the CD-ROM, gives total value ($ millions) of quarterly retail trade in Canada for 1996–2000.

Year/Quarter	Sales ($ millions)	Year/Quarter	Sales ($ millions)
1996/1	47 287	1998/3	62 976
1996/2	57 047	1998/4	66 674
1996/3	55 731	1999/1	54 843
1996/4	60 805	1999/2	67 126
1997/1	49 709	1999/3	67 456
1997/2	62 155	1999/4	71 355
1997/3	60 623	2000/1	59 192
1997/4	65 349	2000/2	71 428
1998/1	52 235	2000/3	71 831
1998/2	64 791	2000/4	74 582

Table 080-0002—Total retail trade, all stores retail trade,
Canada unadjusted for seasonality, quarterly (Dollars x 1M)
Source: Statistics Canada

(a) Determine the typical seasonal pattern in retail trade in Canada using the ratio-to-moving-average method.
(b) Interpret the pattern.
(c) Deseasonalize the data and determine the linear trend equation.
(d) Forecast retail trade for the four quarters of 2001, including the seasonal effect.

www.exercises.ca 18-32 TO 18-34

18-32. Go to the Statistics Canada Web site (www.statcan.ca). Collect data on monthly sales (excluding concessions) of major department stores in your province for the last five years (Table 076-0002—Major and junior department store sales (excluding and including concessions), Canada, provinces, territories and selected census metropolitan areas, monthly (Dollars)).
(a) Determine the typical seasonal pattern in retail trade in Canada using the ratio-to-moving-average method.
(b) Interpret the pattern.
(c) Deseasonalize the data and determine the linear trend equation.
(d) Forecast retail trade for the next four quarters, including the seasonal effect.

18-33. Collect monthly data on passenger cars (newly manufactured) sold in your province for years 1990 to latest year and quarter; the data is available at www.statcan.ca (Table 079-0001: New motor vehicle sales, Canada, provinces and territories, monthly). Before downloading the data, convert it to quarterly (sum).
(a) Plot the data.
(b) Determine the appropriate (linear or non-linear) trend.
(c) Determine the seasonal index (quarterly).
(d) Deseasonalize the data.

(e) Determine the trend in the deseasonalized data. Does it differ from your answer in part (b) above? Why?

(f) Prepare a quarterly forecast including the seasonal effect for the next four quarters (after the last actual quarterly data).

(g) Write a brief report on your findings.

18-34. Collect monthly (unsmoothed) data on business leading indicators (Composite index of 10 indicators) for Canada for 1980 to the latest month and year available from www.statcan.ca. (Table 377-0003: Business leading indicators for Canada, monthly (1992 Dollars unless otherwise noted) v7687 Canada; Composite index of 10 indicators (Index, 1992 = 100); Unsmoothed (Monthly, D100052).)

Answer all the questions in Exercise 18-33 above.

COMPUTER DATA EXERCISES 18-35 TO 18-36

18-35. Refer to the Baseball 2000 data set, which includes the formation of the 2000 major league baseball season. The data set includes the average player salary since 1976 and the median player salary since 1983. Plot the information and develop a linear trend equation for each. Compare the rate of increase in the median with the rate of increase for the average. Write a brief report on your findings.

18-36. Refer to the Youth Unemployment data set, which includes information on quarterly youth unemployment rate for 1976–2000. Answer all the questions in Exercise 18-33 above.

CHAPTER 18 ANSWERS TO SELF-REVIEW

18-1. (a)

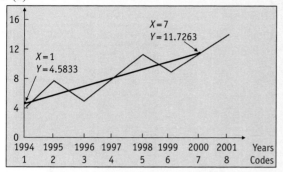

(b) $\hat{y} = a + bt = 3.3928 + 1.905t$ (in thousands)

$$b = \frac{8(365) - 36(70)}{8(204) - (36)^2} = \frac{50}{42} = 1.1905$$

$$a = \frac{70}{8} - 1.1905\left(\frac{36}{8}\right) = 3.3928$$

(c) For 1994:
$$\hat{y} = 3.3928 + 1.1905(1) = 4.5833$$

for 2000:
$$\hat{y} = 3.3928 + 1.1905(7) = 11.7263$$

(d) For 2004, $t = 11$, so
$$\hat{y} = 3.3928 + 1.905(11) = 16.4883$$
or 16 488 king-size rockers.

18-2.

Year	Production (thousands)	Three-Year Moving Total	Three-Year Moving Average
1996	2	–	–
1997	6	12	4
1998	4	15	5
1999	5	12	4
2000	3	18	6
2001	10	–	–

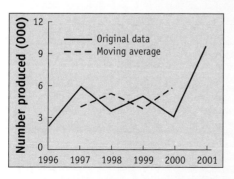

18-3. (a)

Year	Code (t)	Sales (Y)	ln(Y)	t * (ln(Y))	t²
1997	1	2.13	0.756122	0.756122	1
1998	2	18.1	2.895912	5.791824	4
1999	3	39.8	3.683867	11.0516	9
2000	4	81.4	4.399375	17.5975	16
2001	5	112	4.718499	23.59249	25
Total	15	253.43	16.45377	58.78954	55

$$ln(b) = \frac{5(58.79) - (15)(16.454)}{5(55) - (15)^2} = \frac{47.141}{50} = 0.9428$$

$$ln(a) = \frac{16.4538}{5} - (0.9428)\left(\frac{15}{5}\right) = 3.2907 - 2.8284$$
$$= 0.4623$$

(b) About 156.7 percent, obtained as:
$b = e^{ln(b)} = e^{0.9428} = 2.567$
Subtracting 1 from b gives us 1.567 or 156.7 percent.

(c) About 454.4, obtained as
$ln(\hat{y}) = 0.4623 + 0.9428(6) = 6.119$
$\hat{y} = e^{ln(\hat{y})} = e^{6.119} = 454.410$

Note: If your calculator does not have an exponential function, you can get the result by checking Inv (for inverse) and taking *ln* (for natural log) of the number.

18-4. (a) The following values are from a software package. Due to rounding, your figures might be slightly different.

	Winter	Spring	Summer	Fall
Mean	119.35	81.66	125.31	74.24
Typical seasonal	119.35	81.66	125.31	74.24

No correction is needed.

(b) Total sales at a town near Banff for the Winter season are typically 19.35 percent above the annual average.

18-5. The forecast value for January of the sixth year is 34.9, found by
$\hat{y} = 4.40 + 0.5(61) = 34.9$
Seasonally adjusting the forecast, 34.9(120)/100 = 41.88. For February, $\hat{y} = 4.40 + 0.50(62) = 35.4$. Then (35.4)95/100 = 33.63.

APPENDIX A

Binomial Probability Distribution

n = 1
Probability

x	0.05	0.10	0.20	0.30	0.40	0.50	0.60	0.70	0.80	0.90	0.95
0	0.950	0.900	0.800	0.700	0.600	0.500	0.400	0.300	0.200	0.100	0.050
1	0.050	0.100	0.200	0.300	0.400	0.500	0.600	0.700	0.800	0.900	0.950

n = 2
Probability

x	0.05	0.10	0.20	0.30	0.40	0.50	0.60	0.70	0.80	0.90	0.95
0	0.903	0.810	0.640	0.490	0.360	0.250	0.160	0.090	0.040	0.010	0.003
1	0.095	0.180	0.320	0.420	0.480	0.500	0.480	0.420	0.320	0.180	0.095
2	0.003	0.010	0.040	0.090	0.160	0.250	0.360	0.490	0.640	0.810	0.903

n = 3
Probability

x	0.05	0.10	0.20	0.30	0.40	0.50	0.60	0.70	0.80	0.90	0.95
0	0.857	0.729	0.512	0.343	0.216	0.125	0.064	0.027	0.008	0.001	0.000
1	0.135	0.243	0.384	0.441	0.432	0.375	0.288	0.189	0.096	0.027	0.007
2	0.007	0.027	0.096	0.189	0.288	0.375	0.432	0.441	0.384	0.243	0.135
3	0.000	0.001	0.008	0.027	0.064	0.125	0.216	0.343	0.512	0.729	0.857

n = 4
Probability

x	0.05	0.10	0.20	0.30	0.40	0.50	0.60	0.70	0.80	0.90	0.95
0	0.815	0.656	0.410	0.240	0.130	0.063	0.026	0.008	0.002	0.000	0.000
1	0.171	0.292	0.410	0.412	0.346	0.250	0.154	0.076	0.026	0.004	0.000
2	0.014	0.049	0.154	0.265	0.346	0.375	0.346	0.265	0.154	0.049	0.014
3	0.000	0.004	0.026	0.076	0.154	0.250	0.346	0.412	0.410	0.292	0.171
4	0.000	0.000	0.002	0.008	0.026	0.063	0.130	0.240	0.410	0.656	0.815

n = 5
Probability

x	0.05	0.10	0.20	0.30	0.40	0.50	0.60	0.70	0.80	0.90	0.95
0	0.774	0.590	0.328	0.168	0.078	0.031	0.010	0.002	0.000	0.000	0.000
1	0.204	0.328	0.410	0.360	0.259	0.156	0.077	0.028	0.006	0.000	0.000
2	0.021	0.073	0.205	0.309	0.346	0.313	0.230	0.132	0.051	0.008	0.001
3	0.001	0.008	0.051	0.132	0.230	0.313	0.346	0.309	0.205	0.073	0.021
4	0.000	0.000	0.006	0.028	0.077	0.156	0.259	0.360	0.410	0.328	0.204
5	0.000	0.000	0.000	0.002	0.010	0.031	0.078	0.168	0.328	0.590	0.774

APPENDIX A

Binomial Probability Distribution (continued)

n = 6
Probability

x	0.05	0.10	0.20	0.30	0.40	0.50	0.60	0.70	0.80	0.90	0.95
0	0.735	0.531	0.262	0.118	0.047	0.016	0.004	0.001	0.000	0.000	0.000
1	0.232	0.354	0.393	0.303	0.187	0.094	0.037	0.010	0.002	0.000	0.000
2	0.031	0.098	0.246	0.324	0.311	0.234	0.138	0.060	0.015	0.001	0.000
3	0.002	0.015	0.082	0.185	0.276	0.313	0.276	0.185	0.082	0.015	0.002
4	0.000	0.001	0.015	0.060	0.138	0.234	0.311	0.324	0.246	0.098	0.031
5	0.000	0.000	0.002	0.010	0.037	0.094	0.187	0.303	0.393	0.354	0.232
6	0.000	0.000	0.000	0.001	0.004	0.016	0.047	0.118	0.262	0.531	0.735

n = 7
Probability

x	0.05	0.10	0.20	0.30	0.40	0.50	0.60	0.70	0.80	0.90	0.95
0	0.698	0.478	0.210	0.082	0.028	0.008	0.002	0.000	0.000	0.000	0.000
1	0.257	0.372	0.367	0.247	0.131	0.055	0.017	0.004	0.000	0.000	0.000
2	0.041	0.124	0.275	0.318	0.261	0.164	0.077	0.025	0.004	0.000	0.000
3	0.004	0.023	0.115	0.227	0.290	0.273	0.194	0.097	0.029	0.003	0.000
4	0.000	0.003	0.029	0.097	0.194	0.273	0.290	0.227	0.115	0.023	0.004
5	0.000	0.000	0.004	0.025	0.077	0.164	0.261	0.318	0.275	0.124	0.041
6	0.000	0.000	0.000	0.004	0.017	0.055	0.131	0.247	0.367	0.372	0.257
7	0.000	0.000	0.000	0.000	0.002	0.008	0.028	0.082	0.210	0.478	0.698

n = 8
Probability

x	0.05	0.10	0.20	0.30	0.40	0.50	0.60	0.70	0.80	0.90	0.95
0	0.663	0.430	0.168	0.058	0.017	0.004	0.001	0.000	0.000	0.000	0.000
1	0.279	0.383	0.336	0.198	0.090	0.031	0.008	0.001	0.000	0.000	0.000
2	0.051	0.149	0.294	0.296	0.209	0.109	0.041	0.010	0.001	0.000	0.000
3	0.005	0.033	0.147	0.254	0.279	0.219	0.124	0.047	0.009	0.000	0.000
4	0.000	0.005	0.046	0.136	0.232	0.273	0.232	0.136	0.046	0.005	0.000
5	0.000	0.000	0.009	0.047	0.124	0.219	0.279	0.254	0.147	0.033	0.005
6	0.000	0.000	0.001	0.010	0.041	0.109	0.209	0.296	0.294	0.149	0.051
7	0.000	0.000	0.000	0.001	0.008	0.031	0.090	0.198	0.336	0.383	0.279
8	0.000	0.000	0.000	0.000	0.001	0.004	0.017	0.058	0.168	0.430	0.663

n = 9
Probability

x	0.05	0.10	0.20	0.30	0.40	0.50	0.60	0.70	0.80	0.90	0.95
0	0.630	0.387	0.134	0.040	0.010	0.002	0.000	0.000	0.000	0.000	0.000
1	0.299	0.387	0.302	0.156	0.060	0.018	0.004	0.000	0.000	0.000	0.000
2	0.063	0.172	0.302	0.267	0.161	0.070	0.021	0.004	0.000	0.000	0.000
3	0.008	0.045	0.176	0.267	0.251	0.164	0.074	0.021	0.003	0.000	0.000
4	0.001	0.007	0.066	0.172	0.251	0.246	0.167	0.074	0.017	0.001	0.000
5	0.000	0.001	0.017	0.074	0.167	0.246	0.251	0.172	0.066	0.007	0.001
6	0.000	0.000	0.003	0.021	0.074	0.164	0.251	0.267	0.176	0.045	0.008
7	0.000	0.000	0.000	0.004	0.021	0.070	0.161	0.267	0.302	0.172	0.063
8	0.000	0.000	0.000	0.000	0.004	0.018	0.060	0.156	0.302	0.387	0.299
9	0.000	0.000	0.000	0.000	0.000	0.002	0.010	0.040	0.134	0.387	0.630

APPENDIX A

Binomial Probability Distribution (continued)

n = 10
Probability

x	0.05	0.10	0.20	0.30	0.40	0.50	0.60	0.70	0.80	0.90	0.95
0	0.599	0.349	0.107	0.028	0.006	0.001	0.000	0.000	0.000	0.000	0.000
1	0.315	0.387	0.268	0.121	0.040	0.010	0.002	0.000	0.000	0.000	0.000
2	0.075	0.194	0.302	0.233	0.121	0.044	0.011	0.001	0.000	0.000	0.000
3	0.010	0.057	0.201	0.267	0.215	0.117	0.042	0.009	0.001	0.000	0.000
4	0.001	0.011	0.088	0.200	0.251	0.205	0.111	0.037	0.006	0.000	0.000
5	0.000	0.001	0.026	0.103	0.201	0.246	0.201	0.103	0.026	0.001	0.000
6	0.000	0.000	0.006	0.037	0.111	0.205	0.251	0.200	0.088	0.011	0.001
7	0.000	0.000	0.001	0.009	0.042	0.117	0.215	0.267	0.201	0.057	0.010
8	0.000	0.000	0.000	0.001	0.011	0.044	0.121	0.233	0.302	0.194	0.075
9	0.000	0.000	0.000	0.000	0.002	0.010	0.040	0.121	0.268	0.387	0.315
10	0.000	0.000	0.000	0.000	0.000	0.001	0.006	0.028	0.107	0.349	0.599

n = 11
Probability

x	0.05	0.10	0.20	0.30	0.40	0.50	0.60	0.70	0.80	0.90	0.95
0	0.569	0.314	0.086	0.020	0.004	0.000	0.000	0.000	0.000	0.000	0.000
1	0.329	0.384	0.236	0.093	0.027	0.005	0.001	0.000	0.000	0.000	0.000
2	0.087	0.213	0.295	0.200	0.089	0.027	0.005	0.001	0.000	0.000	0.000
3	0.014	0.071	0.221	0.257	0.177	0.081	0.023	0.004	0.000	0.000	0.000
4	0.001	0.016	0.111	0.220	0.236	0.161	0.070	0.017	0.002	0.000	0.000
5	0.000	0.002	0.039	0.132	0.221	0.226	0.147	0.057	0.010	0.000	0.000
6	0.000	0.000	0.010	0.057	0.147	0.226	0.221	0.132	0.039	0.002	0.000
7	0.000	0.000	0.002	0.017	0.070	0.161	0.236	0.220	0.111	0.016	0.001
8	0.000	0.000	0.000	0.004	0.023	0.081	0.177	0.257	0.221	0.071	0.014
9	0.000	0.000	0.000	0.001	0.005	0.027	0.089	0.200	0.295	0.213	0.087
10	0.000	0.000	0.000	0.000	0.001	0.005	0.027	0.093	0.236	0.384	0.329
11	0.000	0.000	0.000	0.000	0.000	0.000	0.004	0.020	0.086	0.314	0.569

n = 12
Probability

x	0.05	0.10	0.20	0.30	0.40	0.50	0.60	0.70	0.80	0.90	0.95
0	0.540	0.282	0.069	0.014	0.002	0.000	0.000	0.000	0.000	0.000	0.000
1	0.341	0.377	0.206	0.071	0.017	0.003	0.000	0.000	0.000	0.000	0.000
2	0.099	0.230	0.283	0.168	0.064	0.016	0.002	0.000	0.000	0.000	0.000
3	0.017	0.085	0.236	0.240	0.142	0.054	0.012	0.001	0.000	0.000	0.000
4	0.002	0.021	0.133	0.231	0.213	0.121	0.042	0.008	0.001	0.000	0.000
5	0.000	0.004	0.053	0.158	0.227	0.193	0.101	0.029	0.003	0.000	0.000
6	0.000	0.000	0.016	0.079	0.177	0.226	0.177	0.079	0.016	0.000	0.000
7	0.000	0.000	0.003	0.029	0.101	0.193	0.227	0.158	0.053	0.004	0.000
8	0.000	0.000	0.001	0.008	0.042	0.121	0.213	0.231	0.133	0.021	0.002
9	0.000	0.000	0.000	0.001	0.012	0.054	0.142	0.240	0.236	0.085	0.017
10	0.000	0.000	0.000	0.000	0.002	0.016	0.064	0.168	0.283	0.230	0.099
11	0.000	0.000	0.000	0.000	0.000	0.003	0.017	0.071	0.206	0.377	0.341
12	0.000	0.000	0.000	0.000	0.000	0.000	0.002	0.014	0.069	0.282	0.540

APPENDIX A

Binomial Probability Distribution (continued)

n = 13
Probability

x	0.05	0.10	0.20	0.30	0.40	0.50	0.60	0.70	0.80	0.90	0.95
0	0.513	0.254	0.055	0.010	0.001	0.000	0.000	0.000	0.000	0.000	0.000
1	0.351	0.367	0.179	0.054	0.011	0.002	0.000	0.000	0.000	0.000	0.000
2	0.111	0.245	0.268	0.139	0.045	0.010	0.001	0.000	0.000	0.000	0.000
3	0.021	0.100	0.246	0.218	0.111	0.035	0.006	0.001	0.000	0.000	0.000
4	0.003	0.028	0.154	0.234	0.184	0.087	0.024	0.003	0.000	0.000	0.000
5	0.000	0.006	0.069	0.180	0.221	0.157	0.066	0.014	0.001	0.000	0.000
6	0.000	0.001	0.023	0.103	0.197	0.209	0.131	0.044	0.006	0.000	0.000
7	0.000	0.000	0.006	0.044	0.131	0.209	0.197	0.103	0.023	0.001	0.000
8	0.000	0.000	0.001	0.014	0.066	0.157	0.221	0.180	0.069	0.006	0.000
9	0.000	0.000	0.000	0.003	0.024	0.087	0.184	0.234	0.154	0.028	0.003
10	0.000	0.000	0.000	0.001	0.006	0.035	0.111	0.218	0.246	0.100	0.021
11	0.000	0.000	0.000	0.000	0.001	0.010	0.045	0.139	0.268	0.245	0.111
12	0.000	0.000	0.000	0.000	0.000	0.002	0.011	0.054	0.179	0.367	0.351
13	0.000	0.000	0.000	0.000	0.000	0.000	0.001	0.010	0.055	0.254	0.513

n = 14
Probability

x	0.05	0.10	0.20	0.30	0.40	0.50	0.60	0.70	0.80	0.90	0.95
0	0.488	0.229	0.044	0.007	0.001	0.000	0.000	0.000	0.000	0.000	0.000
1	0.359	0.356	0.154	0.041	0.007	0.001	0.000	0.000	0.000	0.000	0.000
2	0.123	0.257	0.250	0.113	0.032	0.006	0.001	0.000	0.000	0.000	0.000
3	0.026	0.114	0.250	0.194	0.085	0.022	0.003	0.000	0.000	0.000	0.000
4	0.004	0.035	0.172	0.229	0.155	0.061	0.014	0.001	0.000	0.000	0.000
5	0.000	0.008	0.086	0.196	0.207	0.122	0.041	0.007	0.000	0.000	0.000
6	0.000	0.001	0.032	0.126	0.207	0.183	0.092	0.023	0.002	0.000	0.000
7	0.000	0.000	0.009	0.062	0.157	0.209	0.157	0.062	0.009	0.000	0.000
8	0.000	0.000	0.002	0.023	0.092	0.183	0.207	0.126	0.032	0.001	0.000
9	0.000	0.000	0.000	0.007	0.041	0.122	0.207	0.196	0.086	0.008	0.000
10	0.000	0.000	0.000	0.001	0.014	0.061	0.155	0.229	0.172	0.035	0.004
11	0.000	0.000	0.000	0.000	0.003	0.022	0.085	0.194	0.250	0.114	0.026
12	0.000	0.000	0.000	0.000	0.001	0.006	0.032	0.113	0.250	0.257	0.123
13	0.000	0.000	0.000	0.000	0.000	0.001	0.007	0.041	0.154	0.356	0.359
14	0.000	0.000	0.000	0.000	0.000	0.000	0.001	0.007	0.044	0.229	0.488

APPENDIX A

Binomial Probability Distribution (continued)

$n = 15$
Probability

x	0.05	0.10	0.20	0.30	0.40	0.50	0.60	0.70	0.80	0.90	0.95
0	0.463	0.206	0.035	0.005	0.000	0.000	0.000	0.000	0.000	0.000	0.000
1	0.366	0.343	0.132	0.031	0.005	0.000	0.000	0.000	0.000	0.000	0.000
2	0.135	0.267	0.231	0.092	0.022	0.003	0.000	0.000	0.000	0.000	0.000
3	0.031	0.129	0.250	0.170	0.063	0.014	0.002	0.000	0.000	0.000	0.000
4	0.005	0.043	0.188	0.219	0.127	0.042	0.007	0.001	0.000	0.000	0.000
5	0.001	0.010	0.103	0.206	0.186	0.092	0.024	0.003	0.000	0.000	0.000
6	0.000	0.002	0.043	0.147	0.207	0.153	0.061	0.012	0.001	0.000	0.000
7	0.000	0.000	0.014	0.081	0.177	0.196	0.118	0.035	0.003	0.000	0.000
8	0.000	0.000	0.003	0.035	0.118	0.196	0.177	0.081	0.014	0.000	0.000
9	0.000	0.000	0.001	0.012	0.061	0.153	0.207	0.147	0.043	0.002	0.000
10	0.000	0.000	0.000	0.003	0.024	0.092	0.186	0.206	0.103	0.010	0.001
11	0.000	0.000	0.000	0.001	0.007	0.042	0.127	0.219	0.188	0.043	0.005
12	0.000	0.000	0.000	0.000	0.002	0.014	0.063	0.170	0.250	0.129	0.031
13	0.000	0.000	0.000	0.000	0.000	0.003	0.022	0.092	0.231	0.267	0.135
14	0.000	0.000	0.000	0.000	0.000	0.000	0.005	0.031	0.132	0.343	0.366
15	0.000	0.000	0.000	0.000	0.000	0.000	0.000	0.005	0.035	0.206	0.463

$n = 20$
Probability

x	0.05	0.10	0.20	0.30	0.40	0.50	0.60	0.70	0.80	0.90	0.95
0	0.358	0.122	0.012	0.001	0.000	0.000	0.000	0.000	0.000	0.000	0.000
1	0.377	0.270	0.058	0.007	0.000	0.000	0.000	0.000	0.000	0.000	0.000
2	0.189	0.285	0.137	0.028	0.003	0.000	0.000	0.000	0.000	0.000	0.000
3	0.060	0.190	0.205	0.072	0.012	0.001	0.000	0.000	0.000	0.000	0.000
4	0.013	0.090	0.218	0.130	0.035	0.005	0.000	0.000	0.000	0.000	0.000
5	0.002	0.032	0.175	0.179	0.075	0.015	0.001	0.000	0.000	0.000	0.000
6	0.000	0.009	0.109	0.192	0.124	0.037	0.005	0.000	0.000	0.000	0.000
7	0.000	0.002	0.055	0.164	0.166	0.074	0.015	0.001	0.000	0.000	0.000
8	0.000	0.000	0.022	0.114	0.180	0.120	0.035	0.004	0.000	0.000	0.000
9	0.000	0.000	0.007	0.065	0.160	0.160	0.071	0.012	0.000	0.000	0.000
10	0.000	0.000	0.002	0.031	0.117	0.176	0.117	0.031	0.002	0.000	0.000
11	0.000	0.000	0.000	0.012	0.071	0.160	0.160	0.065	0.007	0.000	0.000
12	0.000	0.000	0.000	0.004	0.035	0.120	0.180	0.114	0.022	0.000	0.000
13	0.000	0.000	0.000	0.001	0.015	0.074	0.166	0.164	0.055	0.002	0.000
14	0.000	0.000	0.000	0.000	0.005	0.037	0.124	0.192	0.109	0.009	0.000
15	0.000	0.000	0.000	0.000	0.001	0.015	0.075	0.179	0.175	0.032	0.002
16	0.000	0.000	0.000	0.000	0.000	0.005	0.035	0.130	0.218	0.090	0.013
17	0.000	0.000	0.000	0.000	0.000	0.001	0.012	0.072	0.205	0.190	0.060
18	0.000	0.000	0.000	0.000	0.000	0.000	0.003	0.028	0.137	0.285	0.189
19	0.000	0.000	0.000	0.000	0.000	0.000	0.000	0.007	0.058	0.270	0.377
20	0.000	0.000	0.000	0.000	0.000	0.000	0.000	0.001	0.012	0.122	0.358

APPENDIX B

Table of Random Numbers

02 711	08 182	75 997	79 866	58 095	83 319	80 295	79 741	74 599	84 379
94 873	90 935	31 684	63 952	09 865	14 491	99 518	93 394	34 691	14 985
54 921	78 680	06 635	98 689	17 306	25 170	65 928	87 709	30 533	89 736
77 640	97 636	37 397	93 379	56 454	59 818	45 827	74 164	71 666	46 977
61 545	00 835	93 251	87 203	36 759	49 197	85 967	01 704	19 634	21 898
17 147	19 519	22 497	16 857	42 426	84 822	92 598	49 186	88 247	39 967
13 748	04 742	92 460	85 801	53 444	65 626	58 710	55 406	17 173	69 776
87 455	14 813	50 373	28 037	91 182	32 786	65 261	11 173	34 376	36 408
08 999	57 409	91 185	10 200	61 411	23 392	47 797	56 377	71 635	08 601
78 804	81 333	53 809	32 471	46 034	36 306	22 498	19 239	85 428	55 721
82 173	26 921	28 472	98 958	07 960	66 124	89 731	95 069	18 625	92 405
97 594	25 168	89 178	68 190	05 043	17 407	48 201	83 917	11 413	72 920
73 881	67 176	93 504	42 636	38 233	16 154	96 451	57 925	29 667	30 859
46 071	22 912	90 326	42 453	88 108	72 064	58 601	32 357	90 610	32 921
44 492	19 686	12 495	93 135	95 185	77 799	52 441	88 272	22 024	80 631
31 864	72 170	37 722	55 794	14 636	05 148	54 505	50 113	21 119	25 228
51 574	90 692	43 339	65 689	76 539	27 909	05 467	21 727	51 141	72 949
35 350	76 132	92 925	92 124	92 634	35 681	43 690	89 136	35 599	84 138
46 943	36 502	01 172	46 045	46 991	33 804	80 006	35 542	61 056	75 666
22 665	87 226	33 304	57 975	03 985	21 566	65 796	72 915	81 466	89 205

APPENDIX C

Percentage Points of the Studentized Range $q_\alpha(K, v)$, $\alpha = 0.05$

	k																		
v	2	3	4	5	6	7	8	9	10	11	12	13	14	15	16	17	18	19	20
1	18.0	27.0	32.8	37.1	40.4	43.1	45.4	47.4	49.1	50.6	52.0	53.2	54.3	55.4	56.3	57.2	58.0	58.8	59.6
2	6.08	8.33	9.80	10.9	11.7	12.4	13.0	13.5	14.0	14.4	14.7	15.1	15.4	15.7	15.9	16.1	16.4	16.6	16.8
3	4.50	5.91	6.82	7.50	8.04	8.48	8.85	9.18	9.46	9.72	9.95	10.2	10.3	10.5	10.7	10.8	11.0	11.1	11.2
4	3.93	5.04	5.76	6.29	6.71	7.05	7.35	7.60	7.83	8.03	8.21	8.37	8.52	8.66	8.79	8.91	9.03	9.13	9.23
5	3.64	4.60	5.22	5.67	6.03	6.33	6.58	6.80	6.99	7.17	7.32	7.47	7.60	7.72	7.83	7.93	8.03	8.12	8.21
6	3.46	4.34	4.90	5.30	5.63	5.90	6.12	6.32	6.49	6.65	6.79	6.92	7.03	7.14	7.24	7.34	7.43	7.51	7.59
7	3.34	4.16	4.68	5.06	5.36	5.61	5.82	6.00	6.16	6.30	6.43	6.55	6.66	6.76	6.85	6.94	7.02	7.10	7.17
8	3.26	4.04	4.53	4.89	5.17	5.40	5.60	5.77	5.92	6.05	6.18	6.29	6.39	6.48	6.57	6.65	6.73	6.80	6.87
9	3.20	3.95	4.41	4.79	5.02	5.24	5.43	5.59	5.74	5.87	5.98	6.09	6.19	6.28	6.36	6.44	6.51	6.58	6.64
10	3.15	3.88	4.33	4.65	4.91	5.12	5.30	5.46	5.60	5.72	5.83	5.93	6.03	6.11	6.19	6.27	6.34	6.40	6.47
11	3.11	3.82	4.26	4.57	4.82	5.03	5.20	5.35	5.49	5.61	5.71	5.81	5.90	5.98	6.06	6.13	6.20	6.27	6.33
12	3.08	3.77	4.20	4.51	4.75	4.95	5.12	5.27	5.39	5.51	5.61	5.71	5.80	5.88	5.95	6.02	6.09	6.15	6.21
13	3.06	3.73	4.15	4.45	4.69	4.88	5.05	5.19	5.32	5.43	5.53	5.63	5.71	5.79	5.86	5.93	5.99	6.05	6.11
14	3.03	3.70	4.11	4.41	4.64	4.83	4.99	5.13	5.25	5.36	5.46	5.55	5.64	5.71	5.79	5.85	5.91	5.97	6.03
15	3.01	3.67	4.08	4.37	4.59	4.78	4.94	5.08	5.20	5.31	5.40	5.49	5.57	5.65	5.72	5.78	5.85	5.90	5.96
16	3.00	3.65	4.05	4.33	4.56	4.74	4.90	5.03	5.15	5.26	5.35	5.44	5.52	5.59	5.66	5.73	5.79	5.84	5.90
17	2.98	3.63	4.02	4.30	4.52	4.70	4.86	4.99	5.11	5.21	5.31	5.39	5.47	5.54	5.61	5.67	5.73	5.79	5.84
18	2.97	3.61	4.00	4.28	4.49	4.67	4.82	4.96	5.07	5.17	5.27	5.35	5.43	5.50	5.57	5.63	5.69	5.74	5.79
19	2.96	3.59	3.98	4.25	4.47	4.65	4.79	4.92	5.04	5.14	5.23	5.31	5.39	5.46	5.53	5.59	5.65	5.70	5.75
20	2.95	3.58	3.96	4.23	4.45	4.62	4.77	4.90	5.01	5.11	5.20	5.28	5.36	5.43	5.49	5.55	5.61	5.66	5.71
24	2.92	3.53	3.90	4.17	4.37	4.54	4.68	4.81	4.92	5.01	5.10	5.18	5.25	5.32	5.38	5.44	5.49	5.55	5.59
30	2.89	3.49	3.85	4.10	4.30	4.46	4.60	4.72	4.82	4.92	5.00	5.08	5.15	5.21	5.27	5.33	5.38	5.43	5.47
40	2.86	3.44	3.79	4.04	4.23	4.39	4.52	4.63	4.73	4.82	4.90	4.98	5.04	5.11	5.16	5.22	5.27	5.31	5.36
60	2.83	3.40	3.74	3.98	4.16	4.31	4.44	4.55	4.65	4.73	4.81	4.88	4.94	5.00	5.06	5.11	5.15	5.20	5.24
120	2.80	3.36	3.68	3.92	4.10	4.24	4.36	4.47	4.56	4.64	4.71	4.78	4.84	4.90	4.95	5.00	5.04	5.09	5.13
∞	2.77	3.31	3.63	3.86	4.03	4.17	4.29	4.39	4.47	4.55	4.62	4.68	4.74	4.80	4.85	4.89	4.93	4.97	5.01

APPENDIX D

Critical Values of the F Distribution at a 1 Percent Level of Significance

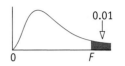

Degrees of Freedom for the Numerator

	1	2	3	4	5	6	7	8	9	10	12	15	20	24	30	40
1	4052	5000	5403	5625	5764	5859	5928	5981	6022	6056	6106	6157	6209	6235	6261	6287
2	98.5	99.0	99.2	99.2	99.3	99.3	99.4	99.4	99.4	99.4	99.4	99.4	99.4	99.5	99.5	99.5
3	34.1	30.8	29.5	28.7	28.2	27.9	27.7	27.5	27.3	27.2	27.1	26.9	26.7	26.6	26.5	26.4
4	21.2	18.0	16.7	16.0	15.5	15.2	15.0	14.8	14.7	14.5	14.4	14.2	14.0	13.9	13.8	13.7
5	16.3	13.3	12.1	11.4	11.0	10.7	10.5	10.3	10.2	10.1	9.89	9.72	9.55	9.47	9.38	9.29
6	13.7	10.9	9.78	9.15	8.75	8.47	8.26	8.10	7.98	7.87	7.72	7.56	7.40	7.31	7.23	7.14
7	12.2	9.55	8.45	7.85	7.46	7.19	6.99	6.84	6.72	6.62	6.47	6.31	6.16	6.07	5.99	5.91
8	11.3	8.65	7.59	7.01	6.63	6.37	6.18	6.03	5.91	5.81	5.67	5.52	5.36	5.28	5.20	5.12
9	10.6	8.02	6.99	6.42	6.06	5.80	5.61	5.47	5.35	5.26	5.11	4.96	4.81	4.73	4.65	4.57
10	10.0	7.56	6.55	5.99	5.64	5.39	5.20	5.06	4.94	4.85	4.71	4.56	4.41	4.33	4.25	4.17
11	9.65	7.21	6.22	5.67	5.32	5.07	4.89	4.74	4.63	4.54	4.40	4.25	4.10	4.02	3.94	3.86
12	9.33	6.93	5.95	5.41	5.06	4.82	4.64	4.50	4.39	4.30	4.16	4.01	3.86	3.78	3.70	3.62
13	9.07	6.70	5.74	5.21	4.86	4.62	4.44	4.30	4.19	4.10	3.96	3.82	3.66	3.59	3.51	3.43
14	8.86	6.51	5.56	5.04	4.69	4.46	4.28	4.14	4.03	3.94	3.80	3.66	3.51	3.43	3.35	3.27
15	8.68	6.36	5.42	4.89	4.56	4.32	4.14	4.00	3.89	3.80	3.67	3.52	3.37	3.29	3.21	3.13
16	8.53	6.23	5.29	4.77	4.44	4.20	4.03	3.89	3.78	3.69	3.55	3.41	3.26	3.18	3.10	3.02
17	8.40	6.11	5.18	4.67	4.34	4.10	3.93	3.79	3.68	3.59	3.46	3.31	3.16	3.08	3.00	2.92
18	8.29	6.01	5.09	4.58	4.25	4.01	3.84	3.71	3.60	3.51	3.37	3.23	3.08	3.00	2.92	2.84
19	8.18	5.93	5.01	4.50	4.17	3.94	3.77	3.63	3.52	3.43	3.30	3.15	3.00	2.92	2.84	2.76
20	8.10	5.85	4.94	4.43	4.10	3.87	3.70	3.56	3.46	3.37	3.23	3.09	2.94	2.86	2.78	2.69
21	8.02	5.78	4.87	4.37	4.04	3.81	3.64	3.51	3.40	3.31	3.17	3.03	2.88	2.80	2.72	2.64
22	7.95	5.72	4.82	4.31	3.99	3.76	3.59	3.45	3.35	3.26	3.12	2.98	2.83	2.75	2.67	2.58
23	7.88	5.66	4.76	4.26	3.94	3.71	3.54	3.41	3.30	3.21	3.07	2.93	2.78	2.70	2.62	2.54
24	7.82	5.61	4.72	4.22	3.90	3.67	3.50	3.36	3.26	3.17	3.03	2.89	2.74	2.66	2.58	2.49
25	7.77	5.57	4.68	4.18	3.85	3.63	3.46	3.32	3.22	3.13	2.99	2.85	2.70	2.62	2.54	2.45
30	7.56	5.39	4.51	4.02	3.70	3.47	3.30	3.17	3.07	2.98	2.84	2.70	2.55	2.47	2.39	2.30
40	7.31	5.18	4.31	3.83	3.51	3.29	3.12	2.99	2.89	2.80	2.66	2.52	2.37	2.29	2.20	2.11
60	7.08	4.98	4.13	3.65	3.34	3.12	2.95	2.82	2.72	2.63	2.50	2.35	2.20	2.12	2.03	1.94
120	6.85	4.79	3.95	3.48	3.17	2.96	2.79	2.66	2.56	2.47	2.34	2.19	2.03	1.95	1.86	1.76
∞	6.63	4.61	3.78	3.32	3.02	2.80	2.64	2.51	2.41	2.32	2.18	2.04	1.88	1.79	1.70	1.59

Degrees of Freedom for the Denominator

APPENDIX D

Critical Values of the F Distribution at a 5 Percent Level of Significance

Degrees of Freedom for the Numerator

	1	2	3	4	5	6	7	8	9	10	12	15	20	24	30	40
1	161	200	216	225	230	234	237	239	241	242	244	246	248	249	250	251
2	18.5	19.0	19.2	19.2	19.3	19.3	19.4	19.4	19.4	19.4	19.4	19.4	19.4	19.5	19.5	19.5
3	10.1	9.55	9.28	9.12	9.01	8.94	8.89	8.85	8.81	8.79	8.74	8.70	8.66	8.64	8.62	8.59
4	7.71	6.94	6.59	6.39	6.26	6.16	6.09	6.04	6.00	5.96	5.91	5.86	5.80	5.77	5.75	5.72
5	6.61	5.79	5.41	5.19	5.05	4.95	4.88	4.82	4.77	4.74	4.68	4.62	4.56	4.53	4.50	4.46
6	5.99	5.14	4.76	4.53	4.39	4.28	4.21	4.15	4.10	4.06	4.00	3.94	3.87	3.84	3.81	3.77
7	5.59	4.74	4.35	4.12	3.97	3.87	3.79	3.73	3.68	3.64	3.57	3.51	3.44	3.41	3.38	3.34
8	5.32	4.46	4.07	3.84	3.69	3.58	3.50	3.44	3.39	3.35	3.28	3.22	3.15	3.12	3.08	3.04
9	5.12	4.26	3.86	3.63	3.48	3.37	3.29	3.23	3.18	3.14	3.07	3.01	2.94	2.90	2.86	2.83
10	4.96	4.10	3.71	3.48	3.33	3.22	3.14	3.07	3.02	2.98	2.91	2.85	2.77	2.74	2.70	2.66
11	4.84	3.98	3.59	3.36	3.20	3.09	3.01	2.95	2.90	2.85	2.79	2.72	2.65	2.61	2.57	2.53
12	4.75	3.89	3.49	3.26	3.11	3.00	2.91	2.85	2.80	2.75	2.69	2.62	2.54	2.51	2.47	2.43
13	4.67	3.81	3.41	3.18	3.03	2.92	2.83	2.77	2.71	2.67	2.60	2.53	2.46	2.42	2.38	2.34
14	4.60	3.74	3.34	3.11	2.96	2.85	2.76	2.70	2.65	2.60	2.53	2.46	2.39	2.35	2.31	2.27
15	4.54	3.68	3.29	3.06	2.90	2.79	2.71	2.64	2.59	2.54	2.48	2.40	2.33	2.29	2.25	2.20
16	4.49	3.63	3.24	3.01	2.85	2.74	2.66	2.59	2.54	2.49	2.42	2.35	2.28	2.24	2.19	2.15
17	4.45	3.59	3.20	2.96	2.81	2.70	2.61	2.55	2.49	2.45	2.38	2.31	2.23	2.19	2.15	2.10
18	4.41	3.55	3.16	2.93	2.77	2.66	2.58	2.51	2.46	2.41	2.34	2.27	2.19	2.15	2.11	2.06
19	4.38	3.52	3.13	2.90	2.74	2.63	2.54	2.48	2.42	2.38	2.31	2.23	2.16	2.11	2.07	2.03
20	4.35	3.49	3.10	2.87	2.71	2.60	2.51	2.45	2.39	2.35	2.28	2.20	2.12	2.08	2.04	1.99
21	4.32	3.47	3.07	2.84	2.68	2.57	2.49	2.42	2.37	2.32	2.25	2.18	2.10	2.05	2.01	1.96
22	4.30	3.44	3.05	2.82	2.66	2.55	2.46	2.40	2.34	2.30	2.23	2.15	2.07	2.03	1.98	1.94
23	4.28	3.42	3.03	2.80	2.64	2.53	2.44	2.37	2.32	2.27	2.20	2.13	2.05	2.01	1.96	1.91
24	4.26	3.40	3.01	2.78	2.62	2.51	2.42	2.36	2.30	2.25	2.18	2.11	2.03	1.98	1.94	1.89
25	4.24	3.39	2.99	2.76	2.60	2.49	2.40	2.34	2.28	2.24	2.16	2.09	2.01	1.96	1.92	1.87
30	4.17	3.32	2.92	2.69	2.53	2.42	2.33	2.27	2.21	2.16	2.09	2.01	1.93	1.89	1.84	1.79
40	4.08	3.23	2.84	2.61	2.45	2.34	2.25	2.18	2.12	2.08	2.00	1.92	1.84	1.79	1.74	1.69
60	4.00	3.15	2.76	2.53	2.37	2.25	2.17	2.10	2.04	1.99	1.92	1.84	1.75	1.70	1.65	1.59
120	3.92	3.07	2.68	2.45	2.29	2.18	2.09	2.02	1.96	1.91	1.83	1.75	1.66	1.61	1.55	1.50
∞	3.84	3.00	2.60	2.37	2.21	2.10	2.01	1.94	1.88	1.83	1.75	1.67	1.57	1.52	1.46	1.39

Degrees of Freedom for the Denominator

APPENDIX E

Critical Values of Chi-Square

This table contains the values of χ^2 that correspond to a specific right-tail area and specific number of degrees of freedom.

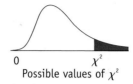

0   χ^2
Possible values of χ^2

Degrees of Freedom, *df*	Right-Tail Area			
	0.10	0.05	0.02	0.01
1	2.706	3.841	5.412	6.635
2	4.605	5.991	7.824	9.210
3	6.251	7.815	9.837	11.345
4	7.779	9.488	11.668	13.277
5	9.236	11.070	13.388	15.086
6	10.645	12.592	15.033	16.812
7	12.017	14.067	16.622	18.475
8	13.362	15.507	18.168	20.090
9	14.684	16.919	19.679	21.666
10	15.987	18.307	21.161	23.209
11	17.275	19.675	22.618	24.725
12	18.549	21.026	24.054	26.217
13	19.812	22.362	25.472	27.688
14	21.064	23.685	26.873	29.141
15	22.307	24.996	28.259	30.578
16	23.542	26.296	29.633	32.000
17	24.769	27.587	30.995	33.409
18	25.989	28.869	32.346	34.805
19	27.204	30.144	33.687	36.191
20	28.412	31.410	35.020	37.566
21	29.615	32.671	36.343	38.932
22	30.813	33.924	37.659	40.289
23	32.007	35.172	38.968	41.638
24	33.196	36.415	40.270	42.980
25	34.382	37.652	41.566	44.314
26	35.563	38.885	42.856	45.642
27	36.741	40.113	44.140	46.963
28	37.916	41.337	45.419	48.278
29	39.087	42.557	46.693	49.588
30	40.256	43.773	47.962	50.892

NOTES

Chapter 1

1. F.N. David, *Games, Gods and Gambling* (New York: Hafner Publishing Company, 1962), p. 9.

2. Ibid.

3. Deborah J. Bennett, *Randomness* (Cambridge, Massachusetts: Harvard University Press, 1998), p. 18.

4. Statistics Canada, *Internet Shopping in Canada*, Catalogue No. 56F0004MIE, February 2001; italics added to excerpt.

5. Joel Best, "Telling the Truth about Damned Lies and Statistics," *The Chronicle Review: The Chronicle of Higher Education*, May 4, 2001.

Chapter 2

1. D.C. Hoaglin, F. Mosteller, and J.W. Tukey, eds., *Understanding Robust and Exploratory Data Analysis* (New York: Wiley, 1983).

2. William S. Cleveland, *The Elements of Graphic Data* (Murray Hill, New Jersey: AT&T Bell Laboratories, 1994), p. 92.

3. Edward R. Tufte, *The Visual Display of Quantitative Information* (Cheshire, Connecticut: Graphic Press, 1998), p. 190.

4. Countries excluding the United States, Japan, and other EU countries.

Chapter 3

1. Commentary on *Nicomachean Ethics* by St. Thomas Aquinas, trans. Henry Regnery Company, Chicago, 1964. Other quotes are from *Book II, Lecture VI*, pp. 237–38.

Chapter 5

1. Blaise Pascal, *Pascal's Pensées* trans. H.F. Stewart, D.D. (New York: Pantheon Books, 1950), p. 3.

2. Source: Adapted from B.L. Bowerman, R.T. O'Connell, and M.L. Hand, *Business Statistics in Practice*, 2nd ed. (New York: McGraw-Hill Irwin, 2001), p. 131.

3. Source: Statistics Canada, 1996.

4. Reverend Thomas Bayes, *An essay towards solving a problem in the Doctrine of Chances*, Phil. Trans., Vol. 53, 1763: 370–418.

Chapter 6

1. A small difference between 4.0 and 4.002 is due to rounded off values of p in Table 6-7.

2. Again, small difference is due to rounded off values of p in Table 6-7.

3. Warren Weaver, *Lady Luck* (London: Heinemann, 1964), p. 265.

Chapter 7

1. Alexander Pope, *Essay on Man*, Epis. III, 140.

2. The probability function $f(x)$ of a normal random variable x with mean μ and standard deviation σ satisfies the equation

$$f(x) = \frac{1}{\sigma\sqrt{2\pi}} \; e^{\frac{1}{2}[(x-\mu)/\sigma]^2}$$

for any value x between $-\infty$ and $+\infty$.

Recall that $\pi = 3.1415\ldots$ and $e = 2.71828\ldots$. Thus, the only unknowns are μ and σ. Once the values of μ and σ are known, we have full information about the curve and can plot it.

3. We can show this directly as follows. If we replace in the equation of normal curve (see the formula in Note 1 for this chapter) the term $\frac{(x-\mu)}{\sigma}$ by z, and scale (multiply) the heights in the resultant curve by σ, we get Formula 7-1. This is just the equation of normal curve with mean 0 and standard deviation 1. (In the formula in Note 1, replace μ by 0, σ by 1, and x by z and verify that we get Formula 7-1.)

4. William G. Cochran, *Sampling Techniques*, 2nd ed. (New York: John Wiley & Sons, Inc., 1963).

Chapter 8

1. William G. Cochran, *Sampling Techniques*, 2nd ed. (New York: John Wiley & Sons, Inc., 1963).

Chapter 9

1. We show this in three steps:

Consider the inequalities $-z_{\alpha/2} \leq \dfrac{\bar{X} - \mu}{\sigma/\sqrt{n}} \leq z_{\alpha/2}$.

(i) Multiplying all terms by $\sigma/\sqrt{n}$, we get $-z_{\alpha/2}\,\sigma/\sqrt{n} \leq (\bar{X} - \mu) \leq z_{\alpha/2}\,\sigma/\sqrt{n}$.

(ii) Now, subtracting $\bar{X}$ from all the terms, we get
$-\bar{X} - z_{\alpha/2}\, \sigma/\sqrt{n} \le -\mu \le -\bar{X} + z_{\alpha/2}\, \sigma/\sqrt{n}$.

(iii) Finally, multiplying all of the terms by (-1), we get $\bar{X} - z_{\alpha/2}\, \sigma/\sqrt{n} \le \mu \le \bar{X} + z_{\alpha/2}\, \sigma/\sqrt{n}$.

(Note that multiplying by a negative number reverses the sign and order of terms. For example, $2 \le 3 \le 4$. Therefore, $-4 \le -3 \le -2$.)

2. A point estimator of a population parameter is said to be consistent if it satisfies the following: for any small numbers ϵ and δ between 0 and 1, we can choose a number n_0 such that for any sample size larger than n_0, the probability of getting a point estimate within a distance of ϵ of the value of the population parameter is at least δ.

3. To state more formally, an unbiased estimator of a population parameter is a consistent estimator if for any small, positive number ϵ, there exists an integer n_0 such that for any sample size greater than n_0, the variance of the estimator is smaller than ϵ.

Chapter 10

1. John Arbuthnot, "An argument for divine Providence, taken from the constant regularity observ'd in the births of both sexes," *Philosophical Transactions of the Royal Society*: London, 1710, pp. 186–90.

2. http://www-groups.dcs.st-andrews.ac.uk/~history/Mathematicians/Pearson_Egon.html

3. G. Gigerenzer, "The superego, the ego, and the id in statistical reasoning," in G. Keren and C. Lewis, eds., *A Handbook for Data Analysis in the Behavioral Sciences* (Hillsdale, N.J.: Lawrence Erlbaum Associates, 1993).

Chapter 11

1. S.M. Stigler, *The History of Statistics: The Measurement of Uncertainty Before 1900* (London, England: Harvard University Press, 1986).

2. John Creedy, "F. Y., Edgeworth, 1845–1926," in D.P. Obrien and J.R. Presley, eds., *Pioneers of Modern Economics in Britain* (New Jersey: Barnes & Noble Books, 1981).

3. S.M. Stigler, *The History of Statistics: The Measurement of Uncertainty Before 1900* (London, England: Harvard University Press, 1986).

4. Ibid.

5. B. Barber and T. Odean, "Trading is Hazardous to Your Wealth: The Common Stock Investment Performance of Individual Investors," *The Journal of Finance*, Vol. LV, No. 2 (2000), pp. 773–805.

6. Using the rule of expected value, discussed in Chapter 6, we get
$E(\bar{X}_1 - \bar{X}_2) = E(\bar{X}_1) - E(\bar{X}_2) = \mu_1 - \mu_2$

Since the two samples are drawn independently, using the rule of variance (see Chapter 6), we get,
$V(\bar{X}_1 - \bar{X}_2) = V(\bar{X}_1) + V(\bar{X}_2) = \dfrac{\sigma_1^2}{n_1} + \dfrac{\sigma_2^2}{n_2}$

7. This is shown by F.E. Satterwaite, in "An Approximate Distribution of Estimates of Variance Components," *Biometrics Bulletin*, 2 (1946), pp. 110–14.

8. B. Jacobsen and S. Bouman, "The Halloween Indicator, 'Sell in May and Go Away': Another Puzzle," Working Paper, University of Amsterdam, 1998.

9. *R.O.B. Report on Business Magazine*, November 2001, p. 111.

10. We give details in Chapter 11 Appendix A on the CD-ROM accompanying the text.

11. We know from Chapter 8 that,
$E(\hat{p}_1) = p_1, \quad E(\hat{p}_2) = p_2,$
$V(\hat{p}_1) = \dfrac{p_1(1-p_1)}{n_1}, \quad \text{and} \quad V(\hat{p}_2) = \dfrac{p_2(1-p_2)}{n_2}.$

Using the rules of expected value and variance, discussed in Chapter 6, Formulae 11-19 and 11-20 follow as in Note 1 of Chapter 6.

Chapter 12

1. For precise definition of F distribution, refer to Chapter 12 Appendix B on the CD-ROM accompanying the textbook.

2. For details, refer to Chapter 12 Appendix B on the CD-ROM.

3. Ibid.

Chapter 13

1. Pearson, 1914: plate II.

2. (Pearson, 1930, p. 386.) For a detailed biography and references cited above, see James W. Tankard Jr., *The Statistical Pioneers*, Schenkman Publishing Co., 1984.

3. Legendre, 1805, pp. 72–73. For more details and the references cited, see S.M. Stigler, *The History of*

Statistics, (London, England: Harvard University Press, 1986).

4. S.M. Stigler, "Gauss and the Invention of Least Squares," *The Annals of Statistics*, Vol. 9, No. 3, pp. 465–74.

Chapter 14

1. Studentized deleted residual for each ith observation is calculated as the ratio of the predicted value of the residual $e_i^* = (y_i - \hat{y}_i^*)$ divided by the standard error of that residual, where $(\hat{y}_i^*)$ is the predicted value of the ith observation (y_i) obtained from running the regression on all observations except the ith observation, i.e., by *deleting* the ith observation from the data set. Alternatively, if adding a Dummy variable (= 1 for the ith observation and zero for all other observations) in a regression on all observations, then the estimate of the coefficient of the Dummy variable equals the predicted value of residual (e_i^*) and the value of t for that coefficient equals the value of the Studentized deleted residual for the ith observation.

Chapter 15

1. Helen M. Walker, "The Contributions of Karl Pearson," *Journal of American Statistical Association*, Volume 53, Issue 281 (March 1958), pp. 11–22.

2. Ibid.

3. The majority of statisticians use the phrase "non-parametric tests" for the test procedures that are "distribution free" in the sense that the test statistics do not require stringent assumptions such as normal distribution on the part of populations. As we shall see shortly, the chi-square test procedure, even for the purposes used in this chapter, does depend on normal distribution in the limit (recall the central limit theorem) for its validity. We have therefore preferred not to place it in the group of "non-parametric" test statistics. For the reason mentioned above, some statisticians have dubbed chi-square as a "semi-non-parametric" test statistic! We elaborate more on these issues in the next chapter devoted to non-parametric tests.

4. C.M. Jarque and A.K. Bera, "A Test for Normality of Observations and Residuals," *International Statistical Review*, Vol. 55, 1987, pp. 163–72. Also see D.N. Gujarati, *Basic Econometrics* (New York: McGraw-Hill, 1995), p. 143.

5. Source: Statistics Canada, Autumn 2001, Catalogue No. 11008.

Chapter 16

1. John Arbuthnot, "An argument for the divine Providence, taken from the constant regularity observ'd in the births of both sexes," *Philosophical Transactions of the Royal Society*, London, 1710, pp. 186–90.

2. An adjustment for a tie is somewhat complicated. It has the effect of changing the standard deviation of the test statistic. The standard deviation

$$\text{adjusted for ties} = \sqrt{\frac{n_1 n_2 (N^3 - N - T)}{12N(N-1)}}, \quad \text{where}$$

$N = n_1 + n_2$ and $T = T_1 + T_2 + T_3 \ldots T_k$. $T_i = (g_i^3 - g_i)$, where "gi" is the number of observations in a tied group i. Thus, if we have two groups: T_1 and T_2, where T_1 has with three tied observations and T_2 has two tied observations, then $T_1 = (3)^3 - 3 = 24$, and $T_2 = (2)^3 - 2 = 6$. Thus $T = 24 + 6 = 30$. Note, if T is zero, the above formula reduces to the uncorrected version of the standard deviation.

Chapter 17

1. I. Fisher, *The Making of Index Numbers: A Study of Their Varieties, Tests and Readability*, 2nd ed. (London: Pickering & Chatto, 1927), p. 460.

2. www.statcan.ca/english/concept/chain/fisher/index.htm

3. Statistics Canada, Catalogue No. 62-557-XPB.

4. Statistics Canada SDDS Catalogue No. 2301.

5. www.tse.com/investor/index.html

6. Usually the weights of these metals are indicated by oz. and pound.

Chapter 18

1. *The Economist*, December 22, 2001.

2. *APEC E-Bulletin*, Atlantic Provinces Economic Council, December 14, 2001.

3. Suppose you deposit $100 (= a) in your bank account, and assume for simplicity, that the bank pays 5 percent ($i = 0.05$) interest per year. Then your principal of $100 would grow geometrically as: $a(1+i)^0$, $a(1+i)^1$, $a(1+i)^2$, $a(1+i)^3$, $a(1+i)^4 \ldots$. The exponents over $(1+i)$ denote the number of periods covered in compounding (receiving interest on the principal plus the accumulated interest). If we write $b = (1+i)$ as the base in an exponential expression, then the above sequence can be summarized as ab^t that would equal the accumulated amount (y_t) at the end of

year t. Thus, we can write $y_t = ab^t$. The annual rate of interest, or an annual growth rate in some other variable, equals $(b - 1)$. Now imagine if the bank compounded the interest rate more frequently, say every month, or every day, or every instant in the limit, then we would get the above formula in a *continuous* form as $y_t = ae^{rt}$ where r is called *instantaneous* rate of growth. Note that $b = e^r$, or $ln(b) = r$. Further, note that a value of $b > 1$ implies a positive growth rate whereas a value $b < 1$ would imply a negative growth rate.

The number, e, in mathematics is obtained as a limit of the series: $\left(1 + \dfrac{1}{m}\right)^m$ as m approaches infinity. You can think of investing \$1 at 100 percent ($r = 1.0$) interest per year compounded "m" times in a year approaching \$1 at the end of the year. An interest rate of r (say, 0.05) per year with continuous compounding would give you e^r dollars at the end of the year. Note that for a value of r other than, 1, $1/m$ inside the bracket becomes r/m.

ANSWERS

to Odd-Numbered Chapter Exercises

Chapter 1

1-1. a. Ordinal   b. Nominal   c. Ordinal

1-3. a. Ratio   b. Ratio   c. Ratio   d. Ratio

1-5. a. Sample   b. Population   c. Population
d. Sample

1-7. Nominal, ordinal, interval, and ratio. Examples will vary.

1-9. a. Lie factor equals % change in graphic elements divided by the % change in the actual quantities represented by those graphical elements. The lie factor in Chart 1-8a is calculated as

$$\left[\frac{(2 \times 4) - (2 \times 1)}{(2 \times 1)} \times 100 \right]$$
$$\div \left[\frac{(200 - 100)}{100} \times 100 \right] = \frac{300}{100} = 3$$

b. See text, Section 1-7.

1-11. Based on these sample findings, we can infer that 270/300 or 90 percent of the executives would move to another location if the other location offered better opportunities for promotion.

1-13. Educational attainment is a nominal scale variable. Percent of employment and growth rate are both ratio scale variables. Thus, vertical axes on both graphs contain the same nominal scale variable and the horizontal axes on both graphs contain (different) ratio scale variables. Information at the bottom of the graphs contains a brief description.

1-15. a. Pool, township, and garage are qualitative variables. Others are quantitative.

b. Pool, township, and garage are nominal level variables. Others are ratio level.

1-17. a. Company names and group names are qualitative. Others are quantitative.

b. Company names and group names are nominal, ranks are ordinal, and other variables are ratio scale.

Chapter 2

2-1. 6 classes.

2-3. Interval of 42.

2-5. a. 5 classes. Using the formula, $2^k = 16$, $k = 4$. However, a minimum of five classes is usually preferred.

b. 3

c. 22

2-7. a.

Number of Visits	Frequency	Relative Frequency
0 up to 3	9	0.176
3 up to 6	21	0.412
6 up to 9	13	0.255
9 up to 12	4	0.078
12 up to 15	3	0.059
15 up to 18	1	0.020
Total	51	1.000

b. The data tends to cluster at the 3 up to 6 times per two-week period.

c. See the last column of the above table.

2-9. a. 8   b. 5   c. 621, 623, 623, 627, 629

2-11. a. 25   b. 1   c. 38, 106

d. 60, 61, 63, 63, 65, 65, 69.   e. No values.

f. 9   g. 9   h. 16

2-13.

0	5
1	2 8
2	
3	0 0 2 4 7 8 9
4	1 2 3 6 6
5	2

There were a total of 16 calls studied. The number of calls ranged from 5 to 52 received. Seven of the 16 subscribers received between 30 and 39 calls. The largest and smallest values are 52 and 5 respectively.

2-15. a. Histogram   b. 100   c. 5   d. 28   e. 0.28

f. 12.5   g. 13

2-17. a.

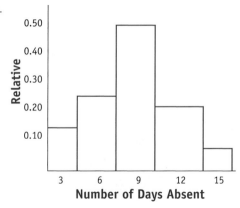

b. 4% of the total area lies above the interval 3 up to 12.

2-19. a. See below.   b. See below.   c. 5

d. 48 000

Salary	Frequ- ency	Cumulative Frequency	Cum. Rel. Freq.
28 000 up to 33 000	5	5	0.20
33 000 up to 38 000	6	11	0.44
38 000 up to 43 000	4	15	0.60
43 000 up to 48 000	3	18	0.72
48 000 up to 53 000	7	25	1.00

2-21. a. 5, 17

b.

Days Absent	Frequency	Cum. Freq.
0 up to 3	5	5
3 up to 6	12	17
6 up to 9	23	40
9 up to 12	8	48
12 up to 15	2	50

c.

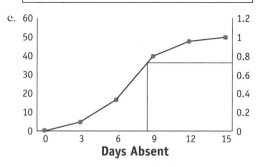

d. About 8.7 days.

2-23. Maxwell Heating and Air Conditioning had the greatest fourth quarter sales of all the companies compared.

Fourth-Quarter Sales ($ thousands)

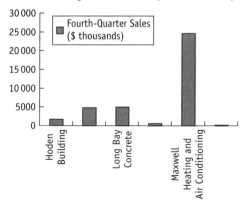

2-25. **Long-Term Business Credits ($ millions)**

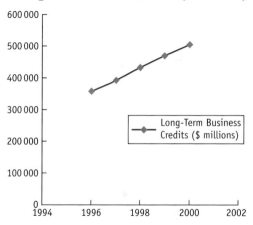

2-27. **Change in GDP at Market Prices ($ millions)**

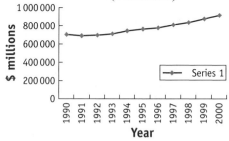

The highest GDP at market prices is approximately $920 000 and the lowest GDP value is approximately $692 000.

2-29. 7 classes.

2-31. a. 5   b. 7   c. 15

d.

Minutes	Frequency
15 up to 22	3
22 up to 29	8
29 up to 36	7
36 up to 43	5
43 up to 50	2
Total	25

e. The majority of observations are at 22 up to 29 and 29 up to 36 classes.

2-33. a. 70 b. 1 c. 0, 145 d. 30, 30, 32, 39
e. 24 f. 21 g. 77.5 h. 25

2-35. a. 56 b. 10 c. 55 d. 18

2-37. a. $37 b. $40

c.

$ Spent	Frequency
80 up to 120	8
120 up to 160	19
160 up to 200	10
200 up to 240	6
240 up to 280	1
Total	44

d. The majority of the spending was in the $120 up to $160 class.

2-39. Below is the bar chart but a pie chart can also be an appropriate chart.

Bar Graph: Top-Selling Drug

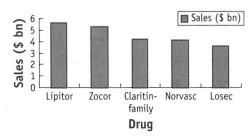

2-41. a. Stem-and-Leaf Display: Grades
Stem-and-leaf of Grades $N = 38$
Leaf Unit = 1.0

```
 2   1 0 3
 4   2 1 8
 5   3 0
14   4 0 1 2 7 7 7 8 8 9
19   5 5 6 7 7 8
19   6 0 1 4 4
15   7 2 3 7
12   8 0 1 4 4 6 6 7 8 8
 3   9 5 5 9
```

b. There are two noticeable peaks at the 40s and 80s.

2-43. a. 7 classes are recommended.

b.

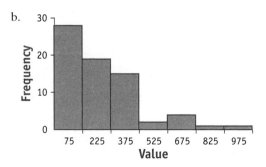

2-45.

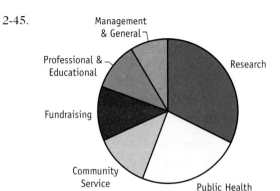

More than half of the expenses are concentrated in the categories Research and Public Health Education.

2-47. a.

b. The USA was our major trading partner in the year 2000.

2-49.

Cash Receipts

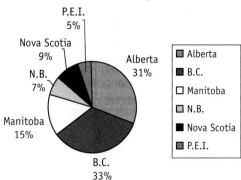

Volume of Milk and Cream Sold from Farms (KL)

2-51.

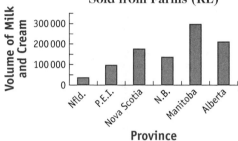

2-53.   Answer will depend on the latest data from the Web site.

2-55.   Stem-and-Leaf Display: Weekly Amounts

Stem-and-Leaf of Weekly Amounts $N = 45$

Leaf Unit = 10

```
   1   0 4
   3   0 5 7
   6   1 0 1 2
  15   1 5 5 6 7 7 8 8 9 9
  21   2 0 2 3 3 4 4
 (10)  2 5 6 7 7 7 7 7 9 9 9
  14   3 0 0 1 2 2 2 3 3 4
   5   3 6
   4   4 2 3
   2   4 7
   1   5
   1   5 7
```

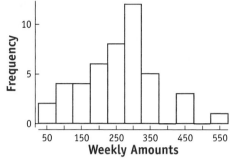

Stem-and-leaf diagram is more informative than the histogram for the same data set. In stem-and-leaf diagram, we do not lose the identity of each value. We know the frequency of each number.

2-57.   a.   **Histogram**

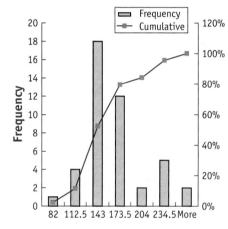

b. 52% (approximately).   c. 35

Chapter 3

3-1. $\mu = 5.4$

3-3.   a. Mean = 7.0

b. $(5 - 7) + (9 - 7) + (4 - 7) + (10 - 7) = 0$

3-5.   14.58

3-7.   a. $888.46   b. Statistic

3-9.   a. Mean of food expenses in Toronto = $5992, in Ottawa = $7226.6

b. The means are statistics.

c. Toronto

d. Mean of the food expenses in Toronto may not be an appropriate average because the range of Toronto data is $4000 ($8000 – $4000) whereas the range of Ottawa data is only $1575 ($8075 – $6500).

3-11. $22.91

3-13. $23.58

3-15. a. No mode.

     b. The given value would be the mode.

     c. 3 and 4, bimodal.

3-17. a. Median = 0.6   b. Modes are 0.2 and 0.6

3-19. a. Median = 23   b. Mode = 22

3-21. 11.18

3-23. 12.16

3-25. Average annual percent decrease = -8.8%

3-27. a. Geometric mean. Profits are in percent.

     b. GM = 15.13%

3-29. No

3-31. Mean of frequency distribution = 47.3

3-33. Mean age of the listeners = 44.8

3-35. Median $= 10 + \dfrac{\frac{30}{2} - 9}{12}(5) = 12.5$

     Mode = 12.5   Median = 12.5

3-37. a. Median = $4888.89   b. Mode = $5000

3-39. Median = $52.5

3-41. a. Mean = 5 Median is 5   b. Population

     c. Yes

3-43. Mean = 34.06 Median = 37.50

3-45. a. $4075.53 million.   b. $2786.5 million.

3-47. Mean = $8.28

3-49. Mean = 23.49

3-51. a. 40 hours.   b. 38 hours.   c. 45 hours.

3-53. a. Mean = $817.2 million.

     b. Highest expenditure = $8401 million, lowest expenditure = $91 million.

3-55. a. GM = 12.57 percent.

     b. $\bar{X}$ = 12.85 percent.   c. Yes

3-57. Average Annual Percent Increase = 5.7%

3-59. a. $\bar{X}$ = $1669.59

     b. Median payment = $1983.08

3-61. a. Mean = 4.2   b. Median = 3.69

3-63. a. Mean = 382.75   b. Median = 383.3 mm

     c. Mode = 387.5

3-65. a. Mean = 125 306.45, median = 117 173.5 (average of two middle numbers of ordered data set), Mode (NA: no modal value).

     b. The median value means that half of the years had more than this many immigrants and half of the years had less than this many immigrants.

     c. 1995 (assuming the data was to be read left to right and down).

3-67. Answers will vary.

3-69. a. Japan, nominal.

     b. Mean = $93 881.6 million
Median = $8920.7 million (Excel).

     c. Median. Range of the sales values is high (Range = $10 1243 million).

     d. Frequency distribution will vary depending on bin size.

3-71. a. $\bar{X}$ = 78, Median = 79.5, Mode = 94 (Excel software).

     b Skewed to the left.

     c. In test #1, the majority of students will do well enough to at least pass and score high (say a class average of 70). There is an upper limit of 100 on a test, which is generally not as far away from the mean as the score of 0.

Chapter 4

4-1. a. 7 b. 6 c. 2.4

     d. The difference between the highest number sold (10) and the smallest number sold (3) is 7. On average the number of service reps on duty deviates by 2.4 from the mean of 6.

4-3. a. 51.32   b. 7.07   c. 11.20

     d. The difference of 29.56 and -21.76 is 51.32. On average, one-year returns on common equity deviate 11.2 percent from the mean of 7.1 percent.

4-5. a. 6.7   b. 38.4   c. 1.51

     d. The difference of 41.35 and 34.65 is 6.7. On average, the weekly share prices deviate $1.51 from the mean share price of $38.4.

4-7. a. 56 928   b. S = 15 393.35

4-9. a. $2.77   b. Variance = 1.26

4-11. Range = 7.3, Arithmetic mean = 6.94, Variance = 6.59, Standard Deviation = 2.57

4-13. a. Variance = 5.5   b. Variance = 5.5

     c. s = 2.35

4-15. a. Variance = 208.89   b. Variance = 208.89

     c. Standard deviation = 14.45

4-17. a. Variance = 4.67   b. Variance = 4.67

     c. s = 2.16

4-19. a. 25   b. 5.33   c. 28.42

4-21.   a. $821 million   b. $209.42 million

c. 43 858.25

4-23.   69.1%

4-25.   a. 95%   b. 47.5%, 2.5%

4-27.   78.52%

4-29.   a. There are two different measurements of the performance of the stocks.

b. CV(PE) = 51.80%, 37.17%

4-31.   a. Mean = 11.58, standard deviation = 5.45

b. 0.74   c. 0.65

d. Skewed to the right. The value of the mean is greater than the value of median.

4-33.   a. Mean = 21.93, Median = 15.8, standard deviation = 21.18

b. 0.87

4-35.   Median = $20 041 million, Q_1 = $14 897.5 million, Q_3 = $29 653 million.

4-37.   a. Q_1 = 33.25, Q_3 = 50.25

b. D_2 = 27.8, D_8 = 52.6   c. P_{67} = 47

4-39.   a. Median = 300, Q_1 = 175, Q_3 = 875

b. IQR = 700   c. 1925 = (875 + 1.5*700)

d. Positive

4-41.

4-43.   Line 1 and Line 3

4-45.   103.2 to 104.8, found by 104 ± 2(0.4)

4-47.   103.9, 104.1

4-49.   3.7

4-51.   9

4-53.   Negatively skewed. The mean is smaller than the median. The longer tail is to the left. There are very few employees at the lower part of the age range with the highest concentration from the median to the upper part of the ages.

4-55.   a. 55   b. 43.2   c. 17.62

4-57.   a. Population

b. Population standard deviation = 185.4. On average, the number of volumes held in libraries deviates from the mean by 185.4 thousand.

c. CV = 60.95%. It allows a comparison if two groups have different scales/means.

4-59.   a. 40 km. The difference between the highest and the lowest distance travelled by employees is 40 km.   b. 10.01 km

4-61.   a.

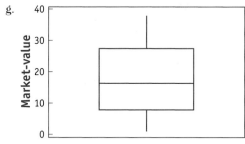

b. Skewed   c. 4

d. IQR = 10.7 (15.77 – 5.07) (Minitab software). It measures the variation of the middle 50% of the observations.

4-63.   a. The median is approximately ≈ 75 000, Q_1 ≈ 600 000, and Q_3 ≈ $950 000

b. Yes; more extreme points on the right.

4-65.   a. 38.06 to 93.53   b. 28.10 percent

c. Pearson's Coefficient of Skewness = – 0.60

4-67.   a. Mean = 17.16,   Median = 16.35

b. Standard deviation = 10.58   c. 0.44, 33.88

d. – 4.0, 38.3   e. CV = 61.66%   f. sk = 0.23

g.

h. The distribution is nearly symmetrical. The mean is 17.16, the median is 16.35 and the standard deviation is 10.58. At most 75 percent of the companies have a value less than 27.4 and at most 25 percent have a value less than 7.825.

4-69.   a. Mean = $72.12, Median = $71.40, and standard deviation = 21.67

b. 45th percentile = $64.76

80th percentile = $95.9

c. See below.

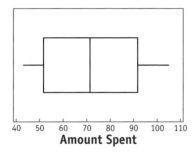

40 50 60 70 80 90 100 110
Amount Spent

d. The data distribution is almost symmetrical. At most 25% of the data are below 7.83 and at most 75% of the data are above it.

4-71. a. Mean = 19 086 323 (Minitab)

Median = 18 209 000(Minitab)

Q_1 = 15 267 000 (Minitab)

Q_3 = 22 377 000 (Minitab)

b. 0.41, yes.

c. See below. No outliers.

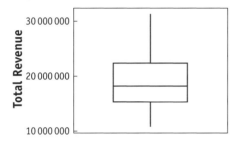

4-73. a. See below. No. Median is not at the centre.

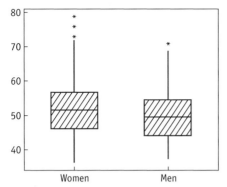

b. The standard deviation of life expectancy for women is 11.10 years and for men is 9.62 years. Therefore, there is more variation in the life expectancy distribution for women than men.

c. Median life expectancy for women = 51.5 years; median life expectancy for men is 49.5 years.

4-75. Answer will depend on the latest data on the Web site.

4-77. Answer will depend on the latest data on the Web site.

Chapter 5

5-1.

Outcomes	Resident 1	Resident 2
1	Yes	No
2	Yes	Yes
3	No	Yes
4	No	No

5-3. 0.76

5-5. a. Empirical   b. Classical

c. Classical   d. Subjective

5-7. a. 0.25   b. 0.019   c. Classical

5-9. a. The survey of 40 randomly selected executives about environmental issues. The sample space is collection of all such strings of possible 40 yes/no answers.

b. Event 1: *26 or more respond yes*; Event 2: *only 10 or less respond yes*.

c. Event 1: *26 or more respond yes*; Event 2: *only 30 or less respond yes*.

d. 0.25   e. Empirical

5-11. a. 0.60   b. 0.40   c. Empirical

5-13. a. 0.52   b. 0.14

5-15. $P(A \text{ or } B) = 0.50$ $P(\text{neither}) = 0.50$

5-17. a. 0.80   b. 0.80

5-19. Events A and C, and events B and C are mutually exclusive. Events B and C are complements

5-21. $P(A \text{ or } B) = 0.83$

5-23. Zero

5-25. a. 0.65   b. No. $P(A \text{ and } C) = 0.1$. So, an executive might read both of them.

c. No

5-27. a. 0.90   b. 0.10   c. 0.30   d. 0.30   e. 0.40

5-29. $P(A \text{ and } B) = 0.12$

5-31. 0.625

5-33. 0.265

5-35. a. A contingency table.   b. 0.668

5-37. Probability the 1st presentation wins = 0.60

Probability the 2nd presentation wins = 0.30

Probability the 3rd presentation wins = 0.10

5-39. 0.4286

5-41. 0.5645

5-43. 0.1053

5-45. a. 78 960 960   b. 840   c. 10

5-47. 142 506

5-49. 120

5-51. 76 904 685

5-53. a. {(M1, M2), (M1, NM2), (NM1, M2), (NM1, NM2)}.

b. (i) {(M1, M2), (M1, NM2), (NM1, M2)},
(ii) {(NM1, NM2)},
(iii) {(M1, NM2), (NM1, M2), (NM1, NM2)}.

c. Not mutually exclusive, but collectively exhaustive.

5-55. Subjective; it is someone's opinion.

5-57. 3/6 or 1/2

5-59. a. The likelihood an event will occur, assuming that another event has already occurred.

b. The collection of one or more outcomes of a random experiment.

c. A measure of the likelihood that two or more events will happen concurrently.

5-61. a. 0.8145   b. Special rule of multiplication.

c. $P(A \text{ and } B \text{ and } C \text{ and } D)$
$= P(A) \times P(B) \times P(C) \times P(D)$

5-63. a. 0.4056   b. 0.39

5-65. a. 0.27   b. 0.12   c. 0.39   d. 0.61

5-67. a. 0.000001   b. 0.97

5-69. a. 0.94   b. 0.06

5-71. a. 0.02   b. 0.63

5-73. a. 0.3818   b. 0.6182

5-75. a. 0.40   b. 0.17   c. 0.12

5-77. 0.0294

5-79. a. 0.35   b. 0.65

5-81. 24

5-83. 0.4545

5-85. Yes

5-87. 2520

5-89. 0.9744

5-91. a. 0.185   b. 0.0075

5-93. a. 0.4375; 0.1875   b. 0.33   c. 0.8125

5-95. 5005

5-97. a. 0.30   b. 0.96

5-99. a. 495   b. 0.002

5-101. a. $P(B) = 0.00525$ b. $P(S \mid B) = 0.0952$

c. $P(S \mid NB) = 0.0498$

5-103. Answer will depend on the latest values on the Web site.

5-105. a. 0.002   b. 0.338   c. 0.15   d. 0.365

e. 0.015

Chapter 6

6-1. Mean = 1.3; Variance = 0.81

6-3. a. The second or middle one.

b. 0.20, 0.40, 0.90

c. $\mu = 14.5$; Variance = 27.25; $\sigma = 5.22$

6-5. 4 g pill with the standard deviation of 0.2. The other option gives a standard deviation of 0.89 for the 4 pills.

6-7. a. 0.6612   b. $\mu = 3.0402$

c. $\sigma^2 = 1.25$; $\sigma = 1.12$

d.

6-9. a. $P(2) = 0.2109$ b. $P(3) = 0.0469$

6-11. a.

x	$P(X)$
0	0.064
1	0.288
2	0.432
3	0.216

b. Mean = 1.8; Variance = 0.72; Standard deviation = 0.8485

6-13. a. 0.2824   b. 0.3765   c. 0.2301   d. $\mu = 1.2$

6-15. $\dfrac{n!}{x!(n-x)!} p^x (1-p)^{(n-x)}$

$= \dfrac{25!}{10!(25-10)!} 0.2^{10}(1-0.20)^{(25-10)}$

$= 0.0118$

6-17. a. $P(X \le 5) = P(X = 0) + P(X = 1)$
$+ \cdots + P(X = 5)$

$= 0.122 + 0.270 + 0.285 + 0.190 + 0.090$
$+ 0.032) = 0.989$

b. $P(X \geq 2) = 1 - [P(X = 0) + P(X = 1)]$
$= 1 - [0.122 + 0.270] = 0.608$

6-19.   a. 0.0008   b. 0.315

6-21.   a. $\mu = 10.5$ b. 0.2061
c. 0.4247   d. 0.5154

6-23.   a. 0.6703   b. 0.3297

6-25.   a. $P(3) = 0.0521$ b. $P(0) = 0.0009$

6-27. $P(x \geq 4) = 0.3528$

6-29.   A random variable is a quantitative or qualita-tive outcome that results from a chance exper-iment. A probability distribution includes the likelihood of each possible outcome.

6-31.   The characteristics of a binomial experiment are: (1) the experiment consists of n Bernoulli trials; (2) the two possible outcomes of each trial are generally denoted as success (S) or failure (F); (3) the outcome of any trial is inde-pendent of the outcome of any other trial; and (4) the probability of success (p) remains the same from trial to trial.

6-33. $\mu = 2; \sigma = 1$

6-35. $\mu = 1.3; \sigma = 1.345$

6-37.   a. 0.001   b. 0.002

6-39.   Profit = 27 600

6-41.   a. 0.8486   b. 0.1703
c. 4.5 found by 30 (0.15)

6-43.   a. 0.3679   b. 0.2316   c. 1.35

6-45.   a. 0.1311   b. 2.4   c. 0.2100

6-47.   a.
0	0.0025
1	0.0207
2	0.0763
3	0.1665
4	0.2384
5	0.2340
6	0.1596
7	0.0746
8	0.0229
9	0.0042
10	0.0003

b. $\mu = 4.5$ and $\sigma = 1.5732$ c. 0.2384
d. 0.5044

6-49.   a. 1.4   b. 0.2466   c. $P(X > 2) = 0.938$

6-51.   a. $P(X = 0) = 0.0025$ (From Poisson table, $\mu = 6$ and $X = 0$).
b. $0.9875 = (1 - 0.0025)^5$

6-53. $\mu = 4$, the following answers are based on Poisson Distribution Table.
a. 0.0183   b. 0.1954   c. 0.6289
d. 0.5665

6-55.   a. 0.1086   b. 0061   c. 0.9939

6-57. $\mu = 8$, $x = 3$

a. $P(X = 3) = \dfrac{8^3 \bar{e}^8}{3!} = 0.0286$

b. $P(X < 3) = P(X = 0) + P(X = 1) + P(X = 2)$

$P(X = 0) = \dfrac{8^0 \bar{e}^8}{0!} = 0.0003$

$P(X = 1) = \dfrac{8^1 \bar{e}^8}{1!} = 0.0027$

$P(X = 2) = \dfrac{8^2 \bar{e}^8}{2!} = 0.0107$

$P(X < 3) = 0.0003 + 0.0027 + 0.0107$
$= 0.0137$

c. $P(X > 4) = 1 - [P(X = 0) + P(X = 1)$
$+ P(X = 2) + P(X = 3) + P(X = 4)]$

$P(X = 4) = \dfrac{8^4 \bar{e}^8}{4!} = 0.0573$

$P(X > 4) = 1 - [0.0003 + 0.0027 + 0.0107$
$+ 0.0286 + 0.0573]$
$= 1 - 0.0996$
$= 0.9004$

6-59.   a. $\mu = 0.7$ b. $P(X = 3) = 0.0284$
c. $P(X \geq 1) = 0.5034$

6-61.   Answer will depend on latest data on the Web site.

Chapter 7

7-1.   It must be non-negative. The total area under the curve must equal 1.

7-3.   For each combination of values of mean and standard deviation, we get a different normal distribution with a different shape.

7-5.   a. 0.6062   b. 0.0674   c. 0.4345
d. 0.0262   e. 0.7939

7-7.   a. 1.96   b. 1.645   c. 1.281

7-9.   a. 0.6826   b. 0.9544   c. 0.9974

7-11.   a. -0.88 and 0.84   b. 0.2995   c. 0.1894

7-13.   a. 0.4332   b. 0.1915   c. 0.3085

7-15.   a. Approximately 0.4017   b. Approximately 0.3606   c. Approximately 0.2007

7-17.   a. Approximately 0.5210   b. Approximately
0.0041   c. Approximately 0.1259

7-19.   a. 0.2038   b. 0.0062   c. 0.7888

7-21.   Approximately $80 - (0.842)(14) = 68.212$

7-23.   Approximately $3100 - (1.88)(250) = \$2630$

7-25.   a. Approximately $(1000)(0.3174) = 317.4$

b. $360 - (1.736)(3) = 354.792$ ml.

c. σ_{new} should be no greater than 2.34.

7-27.   a. $\mu = 22;\ \sigma = 3.15$

b. Approximately 0.2136

c. Approximately 0.0196

d. Approximately 0.858

7-29.   a. $(50)(0.2) = 10$ b. Approximately 0.1886

c. 0.2981   d. Approximately 0.1095

7-31.   a. Approximately 0.96

b. Approximately 0.6968

c. Approximately 0.6568

7-33.   a. -0.4 and 2.9167.   b. 65.54% and 0.18%
of fabricators have, respectively, greater net
sales and more employees compared with
Interline.

7-35.   a. 0.4088   b. Approximately 0.0912

c. Approximately 0.0899

d. Approximately 0.6293

e. Approximately $4.2 + (1.75)(0.6) = 5.25$

7-37.   a. 0.5328   b. 0.3085   c. 0.6247

d. 0.2857

e. $100 - (1.645)(20) = 67.1$ minutes

7-39.   a. Approximately 0.2659

b. Approximately 0.8640

c. Approximately 0.1991

d. Approximately $50\,000 + (0.842)(8000)$
$= \$56\,736$

7-41. $4000 + (1.645)(60) = 4098.7$

7-43.   a. His income is more than that of 97.72% of
the supervisors.

b. Only 2.28% of the supervisors have length of
service less than that of John.

c. Approximately $48\,000 - 1.405(1200)$
$= \$46\,314$

7-45.   a. Approximately 0.1534

b. Approximately 0.1747

c. The chance is very, very small (probability
is almost 0).

7-47.   a. $\mu = 5$ $\sigma = 2.18$

b. Total number of bottles is 100, a fixed
number. Every bottle is either defective or
non-defective; every bottle has the same
probability $(= 0.05)$ of being defective; and
one bottle being defective has no effect on
probability of another bottle being defective.
Thus, the trials are independent of each
other.

c. 0.1251   d. 0.1192   e. 0.0714

f. 0.0197

7-49.   a. $\mu = 8$ $\sigma = 2.6833$

b. Approximately 0.1123

c. Approximately 0.9039

7-51.   Approximately 0.1611

7-53.   a. Approximately 0.3707.   b. Almost 0

c. 228   d. $3.10 + (1.282)(0.3) = 3.4846$

7-55.   a. 0.3085

b. If μ is increased, required probability
$= 0.2266$; if σ is decreased, required probability is 0.1587. Hence, σ should be decreased.

7-57. $\mu = 462\,623.9$ $\sigma = 29\,154.52$

7-59.   Approximately 0.0546

7-61.   Approximately 0.0631

7-63.   Approximately 0.9745

7-65.   Approximately 940.08 kg

7-67.   a. $\mu = 3.363;\ \sigma = 5.077$

b. Using normal approximation, we get probability $= 0.394$; from actual data, we get
fraction $= 0.448$

7-69. $\mu = 9.5$ and $\sigma = 59.81$

Using normal approximation, we get (from
Excel) probability (that the one-year percentage return on common equity of a randomly
chosen company in the list will be greater than
2 percent) equal to 0.55.

In actual data, $(71/100 =)\ 0.71$ fraction of
the companies have a one-year percentage
return on common equity more than 2 percent.
Thus, use of normal distribution did not yield a
good approximation in this case.

Chapter 8

8-1.   See page 327 of the text.

8-3.   a. $\mu = 13.5;\ \sigma = 1.6583$ b. 64

c.

Value of Sample Mean $\bar{x}$	No. of Occurrences	Probability
12	4	0.25
13	4	0.25
14	5	0.3125
15	2	0.125
16	1	0.0625

d. $\mu_{\bar{x}} = 13.5$; $\sigma_{\bar{x}} = 1.1726$

e. Values of μ, and $\mu_{\bar{x}}$ are the same.

f. $\sigma_{\bar{x}} = \dfrac{\sigma}{\sqrt{2}}$

8-5. a. $\mu = 4$; $\sigma = 1.581$

b.

Sample Mean ($\bar{x}$)	No. of Occurrences	Probability
2	1	1/16 = 0.0625
2.5	2	2/16 = 0.125
3	1	1/16 = 0.0625
3.5	2	2/16 = 0.125
4	4	4/16 = 0.25
4.5	2	2/16 = 0.125
5	1	1/16 = 0.0625
5.5	2	2/16 = 0.125
6	1	1/16 = 0.0625

c. $\mu_{\bar{x}} = 4$; $\sigma_{\bar{x}} = 1.118$ d. Values of μ and $\mu_{\bar{x}}$ are the same; $\sigma_{\bar{x}} = \dfrac{\sigma}{\sqrt{2}}$

8-7. a. It is reasonable to conclude that the claim is incorrect.

b. The sample data does not provide us sufficient evidence to doubt the claim.

8-9. a. Approximately 0.0139

b. Approximately 0.0045

8-11. We conclude that the sample data does not provide us with sufficient information to doubt the claim.

8-13. It is reasonable to conclude that the manager's claim is incorrect.

8-15. a. Approximately 0.3311

b. The sample does not provide us with evidence against the Statistics Canada report. We have insufficient evidence to doubt the report.

8-17. Use your telephone directory; choose ten pages from telephone directory using SRR and choose a telephone number from each selected page using random numbers.

8-19. 1. Destructive nature of the test. For example, testing life of battery.

2. Physically impossible to check all items. For example, measure weight of all the fish in a lake.

3. Costly and time consuming to check all items. For example, collecting political opinion of all the voters in Canada.

8-21. A simple random sample would be appropriate. A more convenient method would be to randomly select a pipe from the first say, 20 pipes produced, and then select every 20th pipe produced thereafter and measure their inside diameters.

8-23. a. 048, 133, 224, 218, 217, 248, 195, 069, 186, 240.

b. 17, 42, 67, 92, 117, 142, 167, 192, 217, 242.

c. Since passengers board according to seat numbers, the sample will be uniformly divided across seat numbers if systematic sampling is used. There is, however, a possibility of sampling only windows customers or only aisle customers.

d. (i) Cluster sampling—treat passengers seated in the same row as a cluster.

(ii) Stratified random sampling—divide passengers into males and females or into different age groups or into different fare classes.

8-25. a. $5^2 = 25$

b.

Value of Sample Mean $\bar{x}$	No. of Occurrences	Probability
2	1	0.04
2.5	4	0.16
3	4	0.16
3.5	4	0.16
4	8	0.32
5	4	0.16

c. $\mu = 3.6$; $\mu_{\bar{x}} = 3.6$; $\sigma = 1.2$; $\sigma_{\bar{x}} = 0.8485$; μ and $\mu_{\bar{x}}$ are the same; $\sigma_{\bar{x}} = \dfrac{\sigma}{\sqrt{2}}$

8-27. a. $6^4 = 1296$

b.

Value of Sample Mean $\bar{x}$	No. of Occurrences	Probability
48	1	0.0278
49	4	0.1111
50	8	0.2222
51	10	0.2778
52	8	0.2222
53	4	0.1111
54	1	0.0278

c. $\mu = 51$; $\mu_{\bar{X}} = 51$; $\sigma = 1.9149$; $\sigma_{\bar{X}} = 1.354$;
μ and $\mu_{\bar{X}}$ are the same; $\sigma_{\bar{X}} = \dfrac{\sigma}{\sqrt{2}}$

8-29. a. Almost normal, with mean 135 seconds and standard deviation $\dfrac{8}{\sqrt{40}}$ seconds.

b. $\dfrac{8}{\sqrt{40}} = 1.2649$

c. Approximately 0.89%

d. Approximately 94.3%

e. Approximately 93.41%

8-31. Approximately 0.0066

8-33. a. It will be reasonable to conclude that the claim is incorrect.

b. $u = 1.396$

8-35. Approximately 0.0379

8-37. a. For sheer physical convenience, we should use cluster sampling.

b. It is reasonable to conclude that the average farm size has decreased.

8-39. a. Frontier Airlines Inc., British Airways, Ryanair Holdings Inc., America West Holdings, Air Canada Inc., Midway Airlines Corp.

b. The data will vary according to the date on which you search the Web.

c. Answer will vary according to the data.

d. Alaska Air Group Inc., China Eastern Airlines, Frontier Airlines Inc., Lan Chile S. A., Northwest Airlines Corp., Trans World Airlines Inc.

8-41. a. $\mu = 1871.9$; $\sigma = 652.5544$

b. It is generally accepted that there has been a change in weather pattern in the Halifax area during the last 40 years. Also, distributions of snowfall during different winter days do not really seem to be independent or identical. Hence, Central Limit Theorem does not exactly apply. The final distribution may not be normal.

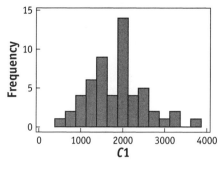

c. The shape of the histogram is not exactly normal though it is not too non-normal either. This is not inconsistent with expectation in part b.

d. Approximately 0.0925

e. The answer will vary according to the sample obtained.

8-43. a. $\sigma = 5.076689$

b. Answer will vary according to the sample chosen.

Chapter 9

9-1.   See definition on page 362 of text.

9-3.   See definition on page 363 of text.

9-5.   a. $\sigma/\sqrt{8}$; $\pm 1.645(\sigma/\sqrt{8})$; $\bar{X} \pm 1.645(\sigma/\sqrt{8})$

b. $\sigma/\sqrt{50}$; $\pm 2.24(\sigma/\sqrt{50})$; $\bar{X} \pm 2.24(\sigma/\sqrt{50})$

c. $\sigma/\sqrt{60}$; $\pm 2.575(\sigma/\sqrt{60})$; $\bar{X} \pm 2.575(\sigma/\sqrt{60})$

9-7. $26 \pm 1.645(6/\sqrt{16}) = (23.5325,\ 28.4675)$

9-9.   a. 1.31   b. 3.707   c. -1.318.   d. 1.356
e. -2.977

9-11. a. $\bar{x} \pm 2.201(s/\sqrt{12})$ b. $\bar{x} \pm 1.729(s/\sqrt{20})$.
c. $\bar{x} \pm 3.499(s/\sqrt{8})$

9-13. $49.353 \pm (2.861)(9.013/\sqrt{20})$
$= (43.587,\ 55.119)$. The analysis does not provide evidence against the probability that $\mu = 50$. It is reasonable to infer that the value of μ is not 60.

9-15. a. 21.9 eggs/month.

b. $(21.9 \pm (2.539)(2.1/\sqrt{20}))$
$= (20.708,\ 23.092)$

c. The population is normally distributed, but population standard deviation is unknown. In this case $\dfrac{\bar{X} - \mu}{S/\sqrt{n}}$ has a t-distribution.

d. The analysis does not provide evidence against the probability that $\mu = 22$; It will be reasonable to infer that μ is not 24.

9-17. a. $\hat{p} = 0.75$ b. 0.022
c. $0.75 \pm (2.575)(0.022) = (0.693, 0.807)$.

d. The technique used in (c) for finding the confidence interval estimate has 99% probability of producing an interval containing p. Hence, it is reasonable to expect the interval obtained to contain the value of p.

9-19. a. $\hat{p} = 0.05$
b. $0.05 \pm (1.96)(\sqrt{(0.05)(0.95)/300})$
$= (0.025, 0.075)$

c. The value 0.1 lies above the interval (0.025, 0.075). Hence, he should not return the lot.

9-21. At least 60.

9-23. An approximate lower bound is 165.

9-25. An approximate lower bound is 62.

9-27. a. An approximate lower bound is 5683.

b. Choose a new estimate of p using a pilot study. Also consider increasing allowable margin of error or decreasing the confidence level.

9-29. $40 \pm 2.68\left(\dfrac{9}{\sqrt{49}}\right)\left(\sqrt{\dfrac{451}{499}}\right)$

$= (36.724, 43.276)$

9-31. $0.6 \pm 1.96\left(\dfrac{\sqrt{(0.6)(0.4)}}{\sqrt{30}}\right)\left(\sqrt{\dfrac{270}{299}}\right)$

$= (0.433, 0.767)$.

9-33. An approximate lower bound for n is 2185.

9-35. a. 54. The best choice of a single value as an estimate of μ is 54.

b. $54 \pm 2.01\left(\dfrac{10}{\sqrt{49}}\right) = (51.13, 56.87)$.

9-37. An approximate lower bound on n is 97.

9-39. a. 1.01 kg.
b. $1.01 \pm 2.031\left(\dfrac{0.02}{\sqrt{36}}\right) = (1.003, 1.017)$.

9-41. a. $0.64 \pm 2.68\left(\dfrac{0.01}{\sqrt{50}}\right) = (0.636, 0.644)$.

b. 0.63 does not lie in the interval in (a). Hence, it will be reasonable to conclude that the value of μ is not 0.63.

9-43. a. $0.63 \pm 1.96\left(\sqrt{\dfrac{(0.63)(0.37)}{1000}}\right) = (0.6, 0.66)$

b. The interval in (a) lies above 0.6. Hence, it is reasonable to conclude that the claim is false.

9-45. $32\,000 \pm 1.69\left(\dfrac{8200}{\sqrt{36}}\right)$

$= (29\,690.33, 34\,309.67)$

9-47. a. An approximate lower bound for n is 709.
b. At least 1068.

9-49. An approximate lower bound for n is 865.

9-51. a. $\bar{x} = 89.4667$. This is the best point estimate of μ.

b. $89.4667 \pm 2.145\left(\dfrac{8.08}{\sqrt{15}}\right) = (84.99, 93.99)$.

c. The interval in (b) lies entirely above 80. Hence it is reasonable to conclude that the mean stress level is in the dangerous level.

9-53. $2.76 \pm 2.39\left(\dfrac{0.75}{\sqrt{60}}\right) = (2.53, 2.99)$.

9-55. a. $\bar{x} = 2408.8$

b. $2408.8 \pm 2.262\left(\dfrac{304.4276}{\sqrt{10}}\right)$

$= (2191.04, 2626.56)$.

9-57. a. $\bar{x} = 62.583$

b. $62.583 \pm 1.796\left(\dfrac{3.942}{\sqrt{12}}\right) = (60.539, 64.627)$.

c. \$60 lies in the interval in (b). Hence, we have no reason to doubt the claim.

9-59. $0.22 \pm 1.96\left(\sqrt{\dfrac{(0.22)(0.78)}{1001}}\right) = (0.194, 0.246)$.

9-61. a. $0.54 \pm 1.96\left(\sqrt{\dfrac{(0.54)(0.46)}{1400}}\right)$

$= (0.514, 0.566)$.

b. The entire interval lies above 0.5. Hence, it is reasonable to conclude that a majority of Canadians favour moderate user fees and charges.

9-63. Select a sample of size 10; calculate

$\bar{x} \pm 2.262\left(\dfrac{s}{\sqrt{10}}\right)$. The answer will vary

according to the sample chosen.

9-65. a. (211.99, 230.22).   b. (0.249, 0.399)
c. (3.45, 4.15).   d. (0.601, 0.751)
e. (0.779, 0.916)

9-67. a. (9503.47, 10\,048.79)   b. (36.08, 40.32)
c. (16.427197, 18.347803)

Chapter 10

10-1. a. Two-tailed.

b. Reject H_0 if $z < -1.96$ or if $z > 1.96$

c. -1.2

d. We do *not* have sufficient evidence to reject H_0.

e. P-value = 0.2302. We would reject H_0 only if the value of α chosen were greater than 0.2302

10-3. a. One-tailed.

b. Reject H_0 if $z > 1.645$

c. 1.167

d. We do not have sufficient evidence to reject H_0.

e. P-value = 0.1216. We would reject H_0 only if the value of α chosen were greater than 0.1216

10-5. a. $H_0: \mu \geq 80\,000$, $H_1: \mu < 80\,000$

b. Reject H_0 if $z < -1.645$ c. $z = -0.693$

d. There is insufficient evidence to reject H_0.

e. P-value = 0.2423. We would reject H_0 if the value of α were greater than 0.2423

10-7. a. $H_0: \mu = 6.0$; $H_1: \mu \neq 6.0$ b. $\alpha = 0.05$

c. $Z = \dfrac{\bar{X} - 6}{0.5/\sqrt{n}}$

d. Reject H_0 if $z < -1.96$ or if $z > 1.96$

e. (i) The computed z-value is -2.56. There is sufficient evidence to reject H_0.

(ii) P-value = $2(0.5 - 0.4948) = 0.0104$. We would reject H_0 for any value of α greater than 0.0104

(iii) β = approximately 0.6406; $(1 - \beta)$ = approximately 0.3594

10-9. a. Reject H_0 if $t > 1.833$

b. $t = 2.108$

c. There is sufficient evidence to reject H_0.

10-11. a. $H_0: \mu \geq 6.8$; $H_1: \mu < 6.8$

b. Reject H_0 if $t < -1.69$ c. $t = -7.2$

d. There is sufficient evidence to reject H_0.

10-13. $H_0: \mu \leq 305$; $H_1: \mu > 305$; decision rule: reject H_0 if $t > 1.729$. $t = 2.236$. Hence, there is sufficient evidence to reject H_0.

10-15. $H_0: \mu \geq 42.3$; $H_1: \mu > 42.3$; decision rule: reject H_0 if $t < -1.319$; $t = -3.085$. There is sufficient evidence to reject H_0.

10-17. $H_0: \mu \leq 15$; $H_1: \mu > 15$; decision rule: reject H_0 if $t > 1.725$; $t = 13.748$. There is sufficient evidence to reject H_0.

10-19. $H_0: \mu \leq 1.9$; $H_1: \mu > 1.9$; decision rule: reject H_0 if $t > 2.821$; $\bar{x} = 1.934$, $s = 0.05$, $t = 2.15$; there is insufficient evidence to reject H_0. P-value is between 0.025 and 0.05

10-21. $H_0: \mu \leq 4.0$; $H_1: \mu > 4.0$; decision rule: reject H_0 if $t > 1.796$

$\bar{x} = 4.5$; $s = 2.68$; $t = 0.65$. There is insufficient evidence to reject H_0. P-value is greater than 0.1

10-23. Decision rule: reject H_0 if $z > 1.645$; $z = 1.09$; there is insufficient evidence to reject H_0.

10-25. $H_0: p \leq 0.52$; $H_1: p > 0.52$; decision rule: reject H_0 is if $z > 2.326$; $z = 1.62$; there is insufficient evidence to reject H_0.

10-27. $H_0: p \geq 0.90$; $H_1: p < 0.90$; decision rule: reject H_0 is if $z < -1.281$; $z = -2.67$; there is sufficient evidence to reject H_0.

10-29. $H_0: \mu \geq 5$; $H_1: \mu < 5$; decision rule: reject H_0 if $t < -1.678$; $t = -2.176$; there is sufficient evidence to reject H_0. P-value is between 0.01 and 0.025

10-31. $H_0: \mu \leq 90$; $H_1: \mu > 90$; decision rule: reject H_0 if $t > 1.291$; $t = 1.818$; there is sufficient evidence to reject H_0.

10-33. $H_0: \mu \geq 3.1$; $H_1: \mu < 3.1$; decision rule: reject H_0 if $t < -1.671$; $t = -0.968$; there is insufficient evidence to reject H_0. P-value is greater than 0.1

10-35. a. $H_0: \mu \geq 25$; $H_1: \mu < 25$; decision rule: reject H_0 if $z < -2.326$; $z = -1.1595$; there is insufficient evidence to conclude that the mean weight is less than 25 kg.

b. The population distribution is approximately normal and σ is known.

Hence $\dfrac{(\bar{X} - 25)}{\sigma\sqrt{10}}$ is approximately Z.

c. P-value = 0.123

10-37. $H_0: \mu \geq 2.6$; $H_1: \mu < 2.6$; decision rule: reject H_0 if $t < -1.895$; $\bar{x} = 2.488$

$s = 0.155$; $t = -2.044$. There is sufficient evidence to reject H_0.

10-39. $H_0: \mu = 4.8$; $H_1: \mu \neq 4.8$; decision rule: reject H_0 if $t < -2.201$ or if $t > 2.201$; $\bar{x} = 4.978$; $s = 0.374$; $t = 1.649$. There is insufficient evidence to reject H_0.

10-41. H_0: $\mu \geq 6.5$; H_1: $\mu < 6.5$; decision rule: reject H_0 if $t < -2.718$; $\bar{x} = 5.1667$; $s = 3.1575$; $t = -1.463$. There is insufficient evidence to reject H_0.

10-43. H_0: $\mu = 0$; H_1: $\mu \neq 0$; decision rule: reject H_0 if $t < -2.11$ or if $t > 2.11$; $\bar{x} = -0.2322$; $s = 0.312$; $t = -3.158$. There is sufficient evidence to reject H_0. P-value = 0.0058.

10-45. a. (247.26, 252.74)   b. 0.0875   c. 0.438

10-47. n should be at least 33.

10-49. H_0: $\mu \geq 8$; H_1: $\mu < 8$; decision rule: reject H_0 if $t < -1.714$; $t = -0.77$. There is insufficient evidence to reject H_0.

10-51. H_0: $\mu \leq 367$; H_1: $\mu > 367$; decision rule: reject H_0 if $t > 2.681$; $t = 3.421$. There is sufficient evidence to reject H_0. P-value is between 0.005 and 0.0005

10-53. H_0: $p \leq 0.6$; H_1: $p > 0.6$; decision rule: reject H_0 if $z > 2.326$; $z = 2.89$. There is sufficient evidence to reject H_0.

10-55. H_0: $p \leq 0.44$; H_1: $p > 0.44$; decision rule: reject H_0 if $z > 1.645$; $z = 2.55$. There is sufficient evidence to reject H_0.

10-57. H_0: $\mu \leq 1\,483\,949$; H_1: $\mu > 1\,483\,949$;   decision rule: reject H_0 if $t > 1.725$

Select a random sample of size 20, compute $\bar{x}$, s, and t. If $t > 1.725$, conclude that there is sufficient evidence to reject H_0. Otherwise, conclude that there is insufficient evidence to reject H_0.

10-59. H_0: $\mu = 18.6$; H_1: $\mu \neq 18.6$

From MegaStat output, P-value = 0.0021. We have sufficient evidence to reject H_0 for value of α greater than 0.0021. For given value of α (= 0.05), we reject H_0.

Chapter 11

11-1. H_0: $\mu_1 = \mu_2$; H_1: $\mu_1 \neq \mu_2$; $df \approx 88$; decision rule: reject H_0 if $t < -2.64$ or if $t > 2.64$; $t = 2.59$. There is insufficient evidence to reject H_0.

11-3. H_0: $\mu_1 = \mu_2$; H_1: $\mu_1 \neq \mu_2$; decision rule: reject H_0 if $t > 2.12$ or if $t < -2.12$; $t = -1.416$; there is insufficient evidence to reject H_0.

11-5. H_0: $\mu_1 \geq \mu_2$; H_1: $\mu_1 < \mu_2$; $df \approx 34$; decision rule is: reject H_0 if $t < -1.691$; $t = -0.581$; there is insufficient evidence to reject H_0. 99% confidence interval estimate = (-1.14, 0.74).

11-7. H_0: $\mu_1 = \mu_2$; H_1: $\mu_1 \neq \mu_2$; $df \approx 77$; decision rule is: reject H_0 if $t < -2.641$ or if $t > 2.641$; $t = -2.66$; there is sufficient evidence to reject H_0.

11-9. H_0: $\mu_m \geq \mu_f$; H_1: $\mu_m < \mu_f$; decision rule: reject H_0 if $t < -2.624$; $t = -0.234$. There is insufficient evidence to reject H_0.

11-11. H_0: $\mu_D \leq 0$; H_1: $\mu_D > 0$; decision rule: reject H_0 if $t > 2.353$; $t = 7.35$. There is sufficient evidence to reject H_0.

11-13. H_0: $\mu_D \geq 0$; H_1: $\mu_D < 0$; decision rule: reject H_0 if $t < -2.764$; $t = -2.894$. There is sufficient evidence to reject H_0. 95% confidence interval estimate = (0.795, 6.114).

11-15. H_0: $\mu_D \geq 0$; H_1: $\mu_D < 0$; decision rule: reject H_0 if $t < -2.821$; $t = -0.885$. There is insufficient evidence to reject H_0.

11-17. H_0: $p_1 \leq p_2$; H_1: $p_1 > p_2$; decision rule: reject H_0 if $z > 1.645$; $z = 1.614$; there is insufficient evidence to reject H_0. 98% confidence interval estimate = (-0.041, 0.241).

11-19. H_0: $p_1 - p_2 \leq 0.02$; H_1: $p_1 - p_2 > 0.02$; decision rule: reject H_0 if $z > 1.645$; $z = 1.045$; there is insufficient evidence to reject H_0.

11-21. H_0: $p_s - p_m = 0$; H_1: $p_s - p_m \neq 0$; decision rule: reject H_0 if $z < -1.96$ or if $z > 1.96$; $z = 1.745$. There is insufficient evidence to reject H_0. 95% confidence interval estimate = (-0.0067, 0.1067).

11-23. H_0: $\mu_1 = \mu_2$; H_1: $\mu_1 \neq \mu_2$; $df \approx 73$; decision rule: reject H_0 if $t < -2.651$ or if $t > 2.651$; $t = -2.839$; there is sufficient evidence to reject H_0.

11-25. H_0: $\mu_1 = \mu_2$; H_1: $\mu_1 \neq \mu_2$; $df \approx 21$; decision rule: reject H_0 if $t < -2.08$ or if $t > 2.08$; $t = 1.2013$; there is insufficient evidence to reject H_0.

11-27. H_0: $\mu_1 = \mu_2$; H_1: $\mu_1 \neq \mu_2$; $df \approx 20$; decision rule: reject H_0 if $t < -2.086$ or if $t > 2.086$; $t = 0.8985$; there is insufficient evidence to reject H_0.

11-29. H_0: $\mu_1 = \mu_2$; H_1: $\mu_1 \neq \mu_2$; decision rule: reject H_0 if $t < -2.819$ or if $t > 2.819$; $t = -2.374$; there is insufficient evidence to reject H_0.

11-31. H_0: $\mu_1 \leq \mu_2$; H_1: $\mu_1 > \mu_2$; decision rule: reject H_0 if $t > 2.65$; $t = 0.819$; there is insufficient evidence to reject H_0.

11-33. H_0: $\mu_D \leq 0$; H_1: $\mu_D > 0$; decision rule: reject H_0 if $t > 1.833$; $t = 0.321$; there is insufficient evidence to reject H_0.

11-35. H_0: $\mu_1 = \mu_2$; H_1: $\mu_1 \neq \mu_2$; $df \approx 126$; decision rule: reject H_0 if $t < -1.979$ or if $t > 1.979$; $t = -5.587$; there is sufficient evidence to reject H_0.

11-37. H_0: $\mu_D \leq 0$; H_1: $\mu_D > 0$; decision rule: reject H_0 if $t > 1.895$; $t = 3.02$; there is sufficient evidence to reject H_0.

11-39. H_0: $p_1 - p_2 \leq 0$; H_1: $p_1 - p_2 > 0$; decision rule: reject H_0 if $z > 1.645$; $z = 1.019$; there is insufficient evidence to reject H_0.

11-41. H_0: $p_1 - p_2 = 0$; H_1: $p_1 - p_2 \neq 0$; decision rule: reject H_0 if $z < -1.96$, or if $z > 1.96$; $z = 1.636$; there is insufficient evidence to reject H_0.

11-43. H_0: $\mu_D = 0$, H_1: $\mu_D \neq 0$; decision rule: reject H_0 if $t < -2.262$ or if $t > 2.262$; calculate $\bar{d}$, s_D, t, and draw the conclusion.

11-45. a. μ_1 = without pool; μ_2 = with pool; H_0: $\mu_1 = \mu_2$; H_1: $\mu_1 \neq \mu_2$.

   From computer output: P-value. 0.001; there is sufficient evidence to reject H_0.

   b. μ_1 = without garage; μ_2 = with garage; H_0: $\mu_1 = \mu_2$; H_1: $\mu_1 \neq \mu_2$.

   From computer output: P-value. 0; there is sufficient evidence to reject H_0.

   c. μ_1 = township 1; μ_2 = township 2; H_0: $\mu_1 = \mu_2$; H_1: $\mu_1 \neq \mu_2$.

   From computer output: P-value. 0.031; there is sufficient evidence to reject H_0.

11-47. μ_1 = mean for year 2000; μ_2 = mean for year 1999; H_0: $\mu_1 \leq \mu_2$; H_1: $\mu_1 > \mu_2$.

   From computer output: P-value. 0.107; there is insufficient evidence to reject H_0.

Chapter 12

12-1. H_0: $\mu_1 = \mu_2 = \mu_3$; H_1: treatment means are not all the same; decision rule: reject H_0 if $F > 4.26$. $F = 21.94$; reject H_0.

12-3. H_0: $\mu_1 = \mu_2 = \mu_3$; H_1: μ's are not all the same; decision rule: reject H_0 if $F > 4.26$. $F = 14.18$; reject H_0.

12-5. H_0: $\mu_1 = \mu_2 = \mu_3$; H_1: treatment means are not all the same; decision rule: reject H_0 if $F > 4.26$. $F = 50.96$; reject H_0.

   Using Fisher's LSD, a 95% confidence interval estimate for $(\mu_1 - \mu_2)$ is (5.275, 9659). There is significant evidence that population means of treatments 1 and 2 are different.

12-7. a. H_0: $\mu_1 = \mu_2 = \mu_3 = \mu_4$; H_1: The treatment means are not all equal; decision rule: reject H_0 if $F > 3.71$. $F = 2.36$; do not reject H_0.

   b. We do not have to conduct the Tukey's test.

12-9. **For treatments**: H_0: $\mu_1 = \mu_2$; H_1: $\mu_1 \neq \mu_2$; decision rule: reject H_0 if $F > 18.5$. $F = 43.75$; reject H_0.

For blocks: H_0: $b_1 = b_2 = b_3$; H_1: the block means are not all equal; decision rule: reject H_0 if $F > 19.0$. $F = 8.14$; do not reject H_0.

12-11. **For treatments**: H_0: $\mu_1 = \mu_2 = \mu_3$; H_1: The treatment means are not all equal; decision rule is: reject H_0 if $F > 4.46$. $F = 5.75$; reject H_0.

For blocks: H_0: $b_1 = b_2 = b_3 = b_4 = b_5$; H_1: The block means are not all equal; decision rule: reject H_0 if $F > 3.84$. $F = 1.55$; do not reject H_0.

12-13. H_0: $\mu_1 = \mu_2 = \mu_3 = \mu_4$; H_1: treatment means are not all equal; decision rule: reject H_0 if $F > 3.10$. $F = 1.667$; do not reject H_0.

12-15. H_0: $\mu_1 = \mu_2 = \mu_3$; H_1: the means are not all equal; decision rule: reject H_0 if $F > 3.89$. $F = 13.38$; reject H_0.

12-17. H_0: $\mu_1 = \mu_2 = \mu_3 = \mu_4$; H_1: the means are not all equal; decision rule: reject H_0 if $F > 3.10$. $F = 9.12$; reject H_0.

12-19. H_0: $\mu_1 = \mu_2$; H_1: $\mu_1 \neq \mu_2$;

   a. decision rule: reject H_0 if $F > 4.75$ $F = 23.097$; reject H_0.

   b. decision rule: reject H_0 if $t < -2.179$ or if $t > 2.179$. $t = -4.806$; reject H_0.

   c. $(-4.806)^2 \approx 23.097$; $(-2.179)^2 \approx 4.75$. Both the tests give the same result.

12-21. **For colour**: H_0: $\mu_1 = \mu_2 = \mu_3 = \mu_4$; H_1: the means are not all equal; decision rule: reject H_0 if $F > 4.76$. $F = 5.88$; reject H_0.

For size: H_0: $b_1 = b_2 = b_3$; H_1: the means are not all equal; decision rule: reject H_0 if $F > 5.14$. $F = 7.59$; reject H_0.

12-23. H_0: $\mu_1 = \mu_2 = \mu_3 = \mu_4$; H_1: the means are not all equal; decision rule: reject H_0 if $F > 3.49$. $F = 0.67$; do not reject H_0.

12-25.

For Gasoline	**For Automobile**
H_0: $\mu_1 = \mu_2 = \mu_3$	H_0: $\mu_1 = \mu_2 = ... \mu_7$
H_1: The population means are not the same; reject H_0 if $F > 3.89$	H_1: Mean mileage is not the same reject H_0 if $F > 3.00$
$F = 17.10$; so, reject H_0	$F = 9.60$; so, reject H_0

12-27. Answers will vary.

12-29. a. H_0: $\dfrac{\sigma_1^2}{\sigma_2^2} = 1$; H_1: $\dfrac{\sigma_1^2}{\sigma_2^2} \neq 1$; P-value = 0.984; we do *not* have sufficient evidence to reject H_0.

   For each of (b), and (c), H_0: $\mu_1 = \mu_2 = \mu_3$; H_1: The μ's are not all equal.

   For (b), P-value = 0.039; we have sufficient evidence to reject H_0.

For (c), P-value = 0.231; we do *not* have sufficient evidence to reject H_0.

12-31. a. $H_0: \dfrac{\sigma_1^2}{\sigma_2^2} = 1$; $H_1: \dfrac{\sigma_1^2}{\sigma_2^2} \ne 1$ P-value ≈ 0.009;

we have sufficient evidence to reject H_0.

b. $H_0: \dfrac{\sigma_1^2}{\sigma_2^2} = 1$; $H_1: \dfrac{\sigma_1^2}{\sigma_2^2} \ne 1$ P-value ≈ 0.004;

we have sufficient evidence to reject H_0.

c. $H_0: \mu_1 = \mu_2 = \mu_3$; H_1: the population means are not all equal. P-value ≈ 0.201; we do *not* have sufficient evidence to reject H_0.

Chapter 13

13-1. $s_{xy} = \dfrac{\sum(x - \bar{x})(y - \bar{y})}{n - 1} = \dfrac{19.4}{4} = 4.85$

Tips received by Mary and Will are positively (linearly) related.

13-3. a.   **Profits and Assets (in $ millions)**

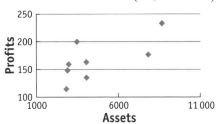

b. $r = 0.697737$

c. Yes. We expect assets and profits to be positively associated.

d. Because of 1. a small sample 2. a non-linear relation, or 3. confounding factors.

13-5. a.   **Relation between Age (X) and Selling Price (Y, $000) of Cars**

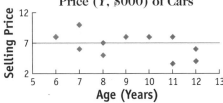

$S_{xy} = -2.18182$

b. $r = -0.512$

c. Yes. An older (higher age) car is likely to command a lower price.

13-7.   Reject H_0 if $t > 1.812$ $df = 10$

$t = \dfrac{0.32\sqrt{12 - 2}}{\sqrt{1 - (0.32)^2}} = 1.07$

Do not reject H_0. There is no significant relationship.

13-9. $H_0: \rho \le 0$ $H_1: \rho > 0$ Reject H_0 if $t > 2.552$
$df = 18$

$t = \dfrac{0.78\sqrt{20 - 2}}{\sqrt{1 - (0.78)^2}} = 5.288$. Reject H_0.

There is a positive correlation between litres sold and the pump price.

13-11. a. Profits = 114.8 + 0.0112 Assets.

b. $170.8 million.

c. Profits and assets are positively (linearly) related. A one million dollar increase in assets is related with, *on average*, an increase of $11.2 (thousands) in profits. The value of the intercept (profits = $114.8 million) for Assets = zero dollars is obviously meaningless.

13-13. a. Price = 10.69 – 0.437 Age.   b. $6327

c. Selling Price and Age are negatively (linearly) related. A one-year increase in the age is related with, *on average*, a decrease of $437 in the selling price of cars. The value of the intercept (= 10 690 for age = zero) is not meaningful since new cars are not included in the range of observations.

13-15. a.   **Relationship between Revenue (X, $ millions) and Profits (Y, $ millions)**

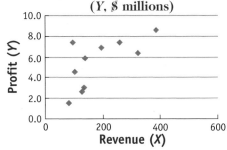

b. Profit = 2.593872 + 0.015364   Revenue (Based on a linear relation between profits and revenue, a million $ increase in revenue, on average, leads to an increase in profits by 15 364 dollars.)

c. Estimated profit = $4.898472 million.

13-17. a. $\hat{y} = 1.333 + 0.667x$

b. Estimated KW Hours (in thousands) $= 5.335$

13-19. a. ANOVA

	df	SS	MS	F	Significance F
Regression	1	4733.296	4733.296	5.692201	0.054334
Residual	6	4989.243	831.5405		
Total	7	9722.539			

b. Coefficient of Determination:

$$R^2 = \frac{SSR}{SS\,Total} = \frac{4733.296}{9722.5} = 0.487$$

The independent variable asset explains about 48.7% variation in the dependent variable profits.

c. The Standard Error of Estimate:

$$S_e = \sqrt{\frac{SSE}{n-2}} = \sqrt{\frac{4989.243}{6}} = 28.84$$

On average, actual (observed) values of profits deviate from the profits estimated by the regression line by about $28.84 million.

13-21. a. ANOVA

	df	SS	MS	F	Significance F
Regression	1	10.48862	10.48862	3.544485	0.08913
Residual	10	29.59138	2.959138		
Total	11	40.08			

b. Coefficient of Determination:

$$R^2 = \frac{SSR}{SS\,Total} = \frac{10.489}{40.08} = 0.262$$

The independent variable Age explains about 26.2% variation in the dependent variable Price.

c. The Standard Error of Estimate:

$$S_e = \sqrt{\frac{SSE}{n-2}} = \sqrt{\frac{29.5914}{10}} = 1.72$$

On average, actual (observed) values of the selling price of cars deviate from the price estimated by the regression line by about $1720

13-23. a. ANOVA

	df	SS	MS	F	Significance F
Regression	1	23.05918	23.05918	6.519227	0.034001
Residual	8	28.29682	3.537103		
Total	9	51.356			

b. Coefficient of Determination:

$$R^2 = \frac{SSR}{SS\,Total} = \frac{23.059}{51.356} = 0.449$$

The independent variable Revenue explains about 44.9% variation in the dependent variable Profit.

c. The Standard Error of Estimate:

$$S_e = \sqrt{\frac{SSE}{n-2}} = \sqrt{\frac{28.297}{8}} = 1.88$$

On average, actual (observed) values of profit deviate from the values of profit estimated by the regression line by about $1.88 million.

13-25. a. $H_0: \beta = 1$ and $H_1: \beta < 1$

The sample value of $t = \frac{b-1}{S_b} = \frac{0.5115-1}{0.3525}$

$= -1.39$ is less than the critical value $t_{0.05(16)}$ $= -1.746$ We therefore do not reject H_0 at 5% level of significance, and conclude that the Beta risk for BCE stock is *not* different from the level of risk in the TSE 300 stocks as a whole.

b. Note, the result of the F test in this chapter of only one independent variable are equivalent to the t test of the coefficient of the independent variable: $H_0: \beta = 0$ against the alternative $(H_1)\ \beta \neq 0$).

H_0: The explanation provided by the model is *not* significant. H_1: the explanation provided by model is significant. Reject H_0 if the sample value of F is greater than the critical value of $F_{0.05(1,16)} = 4.49$

Sample value of $F = \frac{MSR}{MSE} = \frac{207.47}{98.50} = 2.11$.

H_0 is not rejected. The model does not provide statistically significant explanation for the variation in the dependent variable.

13-27. a. $H_0: \beta = 0$ and $H_1: \beta \neq 0$; Reject H_0 if the sample value of the t statistic is greater (in absolute value) than $t_{0.05(8)} = 2.306$

From Exercise 13-14, the estimated value of β is 0.005160. Therefore, the sample value

of $t = \frac{b-0}{S_b} = \frac{0.00516-0}{0.003304} = 1.56$. We there-

fore do not reject H_0 at 5% level of significance, and conclude that the coefficient of the independent variable asset is *not* different from zero.

b. Critical value of $F_{0.05(1,8)} = 5.32$. Sample

value of $F = \frac{MSR}{MSE} = \frac{16.663}{6.833} = 2.44$. H_0 is

not rejected. The model does not provide statistically significant explanation for the variation in the dependent variable.

c. The conclusions reached in (a) and (b) are same. $(1.56)^2 = 2.434$

13-29. $H_0: \rho \le 0$ $H_1: \rho > 0$; $n = 25$; $r = 0.94$; $t_{0.05(23)}$

$= 1.714$; Reject H_0 if $t > 1.714$ $t = \dfrac{0.94\sqrt{25-2}}{\sqrt{1-(0.94)^2}}$

$= 13.213$; Reject H_0. There is sufficient evidence for a positive correlation between passengers and weight of luggage.

13-31. $H_0: \rho \le 0$; $H_1: \rho > 0$; $n = 12$; $r = 0.47$; $t_{0.01(10)}$

$= 2.764$; Reject H_0 if $t > 2.764$ $t = \dfrac{0.47\sqrt{12-2}}{\sqrt{1-(0.47)^2}}$

$= 1.684$

Do not reject H_0. The sample does *not* provide sufficient evidence for a positive correlation between engine size and performance. p-value is greater than 0.05, but less than 0.10.

13-33. $H_0: \rho \ge 0$; $H_1: \rho < 0$; $n = 30$; $r = -0.45$; $t_{0.05(28)}$

$= 1.701$; Reject H_0 if $t < -1.701$ $t = \dfrac{-0.45\sqrt{30-2}}{\sqrt{1-0.2025}}$

$= -2.67$

Reject H_0. There is a negative correlation between the selling price and the number of kilometres driven.

13-35. a. $r = 0.589$.   b. $H_0: \rho \le 0$; $H_1: \rho > 0$; $n = 10$; $t_{0.05(8)} = 1.86$; Reject H_0 if $t > 1.86$

$t = \dfrac{0.589\sqrt{10-2}}{\sqrt{1-(0.589)^2}} = 2.062$

H_0 is rejected. There is sufficient evidence for a positive association between family size and the amount spent on food.

13-37. a. There is an inverse relationship between the variables. As the months owned increases the number of hours exercised decreases.

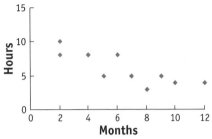

b. The regression equation is: $\hat{y} = 9.94 - 0.637x$, where x is number of months owned and y is the number of hours exercised. On average, the number of hours exercised decreases by 0.637 hours for each month past the purchase of the equipment.

	Coefficients	Standard Error	t Stat	P-value
Intercept	9.939303	1.107151	8.97737	1.89E-05
Months	−0.63682	0.153093	−4.15966	0.003167

c. Yes. The value of t statistic $= -416$. The critical value of t for one tailed test for $t_{0.01(df=8)} = 2.896$. We therefore reject the H_0 of zero association and conclude in favour of negative association.

13-39. a.

Source	df	SS	MS	F
Regression	1	50		2.56
Error	23	450		19.57
Total	24	500		

b. $n = 25$

c. $S_e = \sqrt{19.5652} = 4.4233$

d. $r^2 = 50/500 = 0.10$ or 10%

13-41. For this exercise, we do computations manually:

a. $\hat{y} = 11.2358 - 0.4667x$. On average, an increase in the number of bidders by one decreases the winning bid by $466 700

b. $\hat{y} = 11.2358 - 0.4667(7.0) = 7.9689$

c. $7.9689 \pm (2.160)(1.114)$

$$\sqrt{1 + \frac{1}{15} + \frac{(7 - 7.1333)^2}{837 - \dfrac{(107)^2}{15}}}$$

$= 7.9689 \pm 2.4854$

$[5.4835, 10.4543]$

d. $r^2 = 0.499$. The number of bidders explains nearly 50% of the variation in the amount of the bid.

13-43. a. There appears to be a relationship between the two variables. As the distance increases, so does the shipping time.

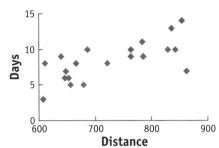

b. $r = 0.692$ $H_0: \rho \le 0$ $H_1: \rho > 0$; $n = 20$; $t_{0.05(18)} = 1.734$; Reject H_0 if $t > 1.734$.

$t = \dfrac{0.692\sqrt{20-2}}{\sqrt{1-(0.692)^2}} = 4.067$

H_0 is rejected. There is a positive association between shipping distance and shipping time.

c. $r^2 = 0.479$, nearly half of the variation in shipping time is explained by shipping distance.

d.

$$S_e = \sqrt{\frac{1550 - (-7.126)(168) - (0.0214)(125\,051)}{20 - 2}}$$
$$= 1.987$$

13-45. a. The regression equation is: Price per share $= 26.8 + 2.41$ Dividend

For each dollar increase in dividend, on average, the price per share increases by $2.41

b. $R^2 = 65.8\%$. In words, the variable dividend explains 65.5% variation in share prices.

c. ANOVA table is given below:

Analysis of Variance

Source	df	SS	MS	F	P
Regression	1	5049.5	5049.5	53.87	0.000
Residual Error	28	2624.4	93.7		
Total	29	7673.9			

13-47. Answers will vary depending on the data collected.

13-49. a. Pearson correlation of Wins and Salary $= 0.498$

$H_0: \rho \le 0$ $H_1: \rho > 0$

At the 5% level, reject H_0 if $t > 1.701$

$$t = \frac{0.498\sqrt{30 - 2}}{\sqrt{1 - (0.498)^2}} = 3.04 \text{ Reject } H_0. \text{ The}$$
population correlation is positive.

The regression equation is Wins $= 69.4 + 0.203$ Salary. An additional $5 million would increase the wins by 1.015, found by 0.203(5).

b. The correlation between games won and ERA is -0.66; and between games won and batting average 0.357. ERA has a stronger correlation. Critical values of t are -1.701 for ERA and 1.701 for batting average.

$$t = \frac{-0.66\sqrt{30 - 2}}{\sqrt{1 - (-0.66)^2}} = -4.65$$

$$t = \frac{0.357\sqrt{30 - 2}}{\sqrt{1 - (-0.357)^2}} = 2.02$$

So both conclusions are supported.

c. The correlation between wins and attendance is 0.591.

$H_0: \rho \le 0$ $H_1: \rho > 0$

At the 5% level, reject H_0 if $t > 1.701$

$$t = \frac{0.591\sqrt{30 - 2}}{\sqrt{1 - (0.591)^2}} = 3.21$$

Reject H_0. The population correlation is positive.

13-51. a. The regression equation is Well-Being $= 82.24 + 0.198$ Income. An increase in income index by 1 unit increases well-being index by about 0.2 units. While income and well-being are positively related, the income variable explains only about 55% (see value of R^2) variation in well-being. The remaining variation in well-being may depend on factors such as wealth and income inequality, economic and social security, poverty, etc.

b. $H_0: \beta = 1$ against $H_1: \beta \ne 1$; $n = 27$; $t_{0.05(25)} = 2.06$; Reject H_0 if $|t| > 2.06$

$$t = \frac{0.198 - 1}{0.0358} = -22.4. \text{ Reject } H_0.$$

c. The level of well-being for index of income equal 130 is found by $82.24 + 0.198 (130) = 107.98$. An increase in income index from 100 (in 1971) to 130 would be accompanied by an increase in the index well-being to 107.98. Thus, a 30% increase in income is capable of increasing the well-being by about 8% only. It differs from the actual well-being of 106.46 in 1981 due to factors other than income (that may be responsible for well-being but not included in the mode) and chance errors.

d. The point estimate of well-being index is found by $82.24 + 0.198 (120) = 106$. The confidence interval estimate
$$= 106 \pm 6.17\sqrt{0.037 + 0.02356} = 106 \pm 1.52$$

Chapter 14

14-1. a. Multiple regression equation.

b. One dependent, four independent.

c. A partial regression coefficient.

d. 0.002

e. 105.014 found by $\hat{y} = 11.6 + 0.4 (6) + 0.286 (280) + 0.112 (97) + 0.002 (35)$

14-3. a. 142 000, found by $\hat{y} = 120\,000 - 21\,000(3) + 1.0 (10\,000) + 1.5 (50\,000)$

b. Assuming values of other variables are held constant, an increase in one competitor, on average, results in reduction of sales by $21 000. Interpret other coefficients similarly.

c. Estimated sales revenue = 95 000. Cost of running Pizza Delight = 95 000 (0.65) = 61 750. Profit = 95 000 – 61 750 = $33 250, which is much larger than the salary of $10 000. Diane should accept her friend's advice.

14-5. a.

Source	df	SS	MS	F
Regression	3	7 500	2500	18
Error	18	2 500	138.89	
Total	21	10 000		

b. H_0: $\beta_1 = \beta_2 = \beta_3 = 0$ H_1: Not all β's are 0; $F_{0.05(3,18)} = 3.16$; Reject H_0.

c.

For X_1	For X_2	For X_3
H_0: $\beta_1 = 0$	H_0: $\beta_2 = 0$	H_0: $\beta_3 = 0$
H_1: $\beta_1 \neq 0$	H_1: $\beta_2 \neq 0$	H_1: $\beta_3 \neq 0$
$t = -4.00$	$t = 1.50$	$t = -3.00$

Reject H_0 if $t > 2.101$ or $t < -2.101$

In the absence of a theoretical reason for the variables, variable X_2 may be deleted.

14-7. a. The value of adjusted $R^2 = 0.7716$ indicates that all independent variables together explain 77.16% variation in the dependent variable, after an adjustment has been made for the loss of degrees of freedom due to the number of coefficients (four including the constant term) estimated by the model.

b. H_0: $\beta_1 = \beta_2 = \beta_3 = 0$ and

H_1: At least one of β_1, β_2, and $\beta_3 \neq 0$

The sample value of the test statistic is $F = 14.648$. $F_{0.05(3,13)} = 3.41$; Reject H_0.

c. The critical value of for a one-tailed test of hypothesis at 5% level of significance ($df = 13$) is 1.771. Reject H_0 if $t > 1.771$ or $t < -1.771$

H_0: $\beta_1 = 0$	H_0: $\beta_2 = 0$	H_0: $\beta_3 = 0$
H_1: $\beta_1 > 0$	H_1: $\beta_2 < 0$	H_1: $\beta_3 < 0$
$t = 6.25$	$t = -3.16$	$t = -2.04$

All variables are statistically significantly at 5% level of significance.

d. H_0: $\beta_2 = -1$; H_1: $\beta_2 < -1$. The sample value of t for H_0: $\beta_2 = -1$ is $(-0.9902 - (-1))/0.313 = 0.031$. Do not reject H_0 (at 5% level of significance). See detailed answer.

14-9. a. $n = 40$ b. 4   c. $R^2 = 750/1250 = 0.60$

d. $S_e = \sqrt{500/35} = 3.7796$

e. H_0: $\beta_1 = \beta_2 = \beta_3 = \beta_4 = 0$. H_1: Not all β's equal 0

$F_{0.05(4,35)} = 2.65$; H_0 is rejected if $F > 2.65$

$F = \dfrac{750/4}{500/35} = 13.125$ H_0 is rejected. At least one β_i does not equal zero.

14-11. a. $n = 26$ b. $R^2 = 100/140 = 0.7143$

c. 1.4142, found by $\sqrt{40/20}$

d. H_0: $\beta_1 = \beta_2 = \beta_3 = \beta_4 = \beta_5 = 0$. H_1: Not all β's are 0. $F_{0.05(5,20)} = 2.71$; Reject H_0.

e. H_0: $\beta_1 = 0$ and $H_1 \neq 0$. H_0 is rejected in each case if $t < -2.086$ or $t > 2.086$. In the absence of a theoretical reason, X_1 and X_5 may be dropped.

14-13. a. (i) Model #1 has all three variables, but Model #2 and Model #3 have only two variables. Model #2 has the largest value of the adjusted R^2 indicating that one of the variables (Km) does not contribute at all to the explanation in Model #1. However, when price is regressed on Km (without Age, Model #3) Km does provide a good explanation to variation in price, though not as well as the Age variable (Model #2).

(ii) The negative sign of the coefficient of Km variable is not consistent with expected sign (positive). We have a high R^2 but a very low t ratio for the coefficient of Km. Although VIF is not very high, simple correlation between Age and Km variables is about 0.8. Since in Model #3, Km does have the expected sign, we can conclude that a high degree of multicollinearity between Age and Km variable is responsible for the wrong sign of the coefficient of the Km variable in Model #1.

(iii) Based on the explanation given in (i) and (ii) above, the researcher is justified in her choice in dropping Km from Model #1.

b. (i) Model #2: The variables Age and Kingcab together explain nearly 88.5% variation in price. Coefficient of Age indicates that as trucks get older by a year, they lose, on average, $1606 in price, holding the Kingcab variable constant. Similarly, holding Age constant, Kingcab style trucks command, on average, a higher price by $3801.6.

(ii) P-values for the model (based on F-statistic) as well as each coefficient (based on t-statistic) are zero. Therefore, we reject the null hypothesis for model as well as the null hypotheses for each coefficient at 1% level of significance.

c. (i) All observations are within the 95% prediction interval indicating absence of any major outliers. A linear regression line seems to provide a good fit.

(ii) In both charts 4 and 5, the spread of observations seem larger in the approximate mid-price range. However, there is not sufficient evidence of heteroscedasticity.

(iii) Chart (#2) does not show sufficient evidence of autocorrelation. Further, since the sample value of d-statistic (2.55) is smaller than the critical value of $d = (4 - d_U)$ = 2.688, we *do not* reject the null hypothesis of *zero* autocorrelation.

(iv) Visually, from the charts 1 and 3, there does seem to be some departure from normality. However, it does *not* appear to be serious.

(v) Considering all charts together, there does not seem to be any serious problem with estimation or inference.

14-15. a. (i) Model #1 has all three variables, but Model #2 does not include the dummy variable for recession. However, Model #2 has a higher value of the adjusted R^2 (59.2% compared to 56.5%) indicating that the recession variable does not contribute significantly to the explanation in Model #1.

(ii) Coefficients of both PDI and Price have expected signs. A positive sign of the coefficient of the Recession variable indicates as if people tend to drink more during recession, possibly due to longer hours at home (fewer jobs during recession)! Both simple correlations among the independent variables and the VIF do not provide any indication of multicollinearity among the independent variables.

(iii) Yes. There is no *a priori* theoretical reason to include the Recession dummy in the model. Since the dummy variable is not significant, the researcher is justified in choosing Model #2.

b. (i) Model #2: The variables PDI and Price together explain nearly 59.1% variation in Volume. Coefficient of PDI indicates that a $1000 increase in PDI results in a 9.29-litre increase in consumption of beer (per adult,

per year), on average, holding the price of beer constant. Similarly, holding PDI constant, a dollar increase in price of beer, on average, results in a decrease in consumption of beer by 42.8 litres (per adult, per year).

(ii) P-values for the model (based on F-statistic) as well as each coefficient (based on t-statistic) are zero. Therefore, we reject the null hypothesis for model as well as the null hypotheses for each coefficient at 1% level of significance.

c. (i) No. All observations are within the 95% prediction interval indicating absence of outliers. A linear regression model seems to provide a good fit.

(ii) In both charts 4 and 5, the spread of observations seem larger in the lower to mid-volume range. However, there is not sufficient evidence of heteroscedasticity. See detailed solution for a quantitative test.

(iii) Chart (#2) shows evidence of autocorrelation. Further, the sample value of d-statistic is smaller than the critical value of $d = 1.074$, we reject the null hypothesis of *zero* autocorrelation.

(iv) Visually, from charts 1 and 3, there does seem to be some departure from normality. It does *not* appear to be serious.

(v) Except for the problem of autocorrelation, there does not seem to be any serious problem with estimation. Although the estimators are unbiased, presence of autocorrelation would lead to wrong inferences. We were successful in removing autocorrelation by an addition of a Trend variable in the model. See detailed answer.

14-17. Results of the regression analysis on the data set are given below:

(1) The estimated regression equation is:

Price = −1580 + 0.44 Lot + 10 148 Bedroom
(*t-values*)   (2.13)   (1.31)

−613.7 Age + 66.2 Footage + 19 509 Garage
  (1.03)   (3.4)   (2.15)

+ 20 266 A_1 + 21 620 A_2.
  (1.81)   (1.79)

Interpretation: An increase in one square foot in lot size, on average, increases price of a house by 44 cents, assuming all other independent variables (bedroom, age, ...) are held constant. An additional bedroom, on average, increases price of house by $10 148, assuming the rest of the independent variables in the equation are held constant. Other coefficients are interpreted in similar manner.

(2) **ANOVA table**

Source	SS	df	MS	F	p-value
Regression	11 245 744 466	7	1 606 534 923	5.58	0.0048
Residual	3 453 365 034	12	287 780 419		
Total	14 699 109 500	19			

(3) The value of Standard Error of Estimate (S_e) = 16 964 indicates that, *on average*, the estimated price of houses deviate from the actual prices by nearly $16 964. Using the empirical rule of thumb for symmetric distributions, we expect actual prices of about 95% of all houses to lie within an interval: $\hat{y} \pm 2(16\,394)$.

(4) The value of R^2 is 0.765 and the value of Adj. R^2 is 0.628. The value of R^2 indicates that 76.5% of the sample variation in the dependent variable is explained by the independent variables in the model. The value of Adj. R^2 is different from the value of R^2 because the value of Adj. R^2 takes in to account the loss of degrees of freedom due to the number of coefficients estimated by the OLS technique and thus cautions the researcher against placing too much emphasis on the R^2.

(5) H_0: $\beta_1 = \beta_2 = \cdots = \beta_7 = 0$, H_1: At least one of the β's is *not* equal to zero. As shown in the ANOVA Table, the P-value for F is 0.0048 (= 0.48%), which is smaller than 5% level of significance. We reject H_0 in favour of H_1.

(6) Based on expected signs for each of the coefficients, our null and alternative hypotheses are as given below:

H_0: $\beta_1 = 0$, H_1: $\beta_1 > 0$; H_0: $\beta_2 = 0$, H_1: $\beta_2 > 0$; H_0: $\beta_3 = 0$, H_1: $\beta_3 < 0$; H_0: $\beta_4 = 0$, H_1: $\beta_4 > 0$; H_0: $\beta_5 = 0$, H_1: $\beta_5 > 0$; H_0: $\beta_6 = 0$, H_1: $\beta_6 > 0$; H_0: $\beta_7 = 0$; H_1: $\beta_7 > 0$

The (absolute) critical value of t-statistic for one-tailed test of hypothesis for 12 degrees of freedom and 5% level of significance is 1.782. Thus, using this critical value of t, we would reject a null hypothesis if the sample value of t is greater than 1.782. Except for the regression coefficients of Bedroom and Age variables, all other regression coefficients are statistically significant.

(7) Given the R^2 value and the information in other parts of this question, we do not have sufficient reason to justify any problem with model specification.

(8) Examining the plot of residuals, all (except one) observations seem to be within 2 times the standard error limits.

(9) Based on the simple correlations, we do not see sufficient evidence of multicollinearity. The largest value of simple correlation coefficient is 0.487 between Bedroom and Lot variables.

(10) The Graph of residuals does not seem to show any autocorrelation. The Durbin-Watson (d) statistic for the regression 2.13 implies an estimated value of autocorrelation = $1 - 1/2d = 1 - 1.065 = -0.065$, which is negligible for all practical purposes.

(11) The graph of the squared error term against the predicted price does reveal that variance is increasing with higher priced houses. Based on the quantitative test, we do not reject the null hypothesis of homoscedasticity.

(12) A histogram of residuals does not indicate any serious departure from normality.

(13) Based on all findings in (1) to (12), we think that the estimated values of parameters and the inferences are fairly reliable.

(14) Write a descriptive report by combining all features from (1)–(13).

14-19. Results of the regression analysis on the data set are given below:

(1) The regression equation (#1) is

Profit = 965 + 2.87 Employees
(t-values):   (1.81)

+ 6.8 Dividends + 0.287 Inventory
(0.66)   (2.59)

Interpretation: An increase in one employee, on average, increases gross profit by $2.87, assuming dividends and inventories are held constant. Other coefficients are interpreted similarly.

(2) ANOVA Table shows the F-value of 14.90 with a P-value of 0.000

Analysis of Variance

Source	df	SS	MS	F	P
Regression	3	45510101	15170034	14.90	0.000
Residual Error	12	12215892	1017991		
Total	15	57725994			

(3) The value of Standard Error of Estimate (S_e) = 1009 indicates that, *on average*, the gross profits of companies deviate from the actual profits by nearly $1009. Using the empirical rule of thumb for symmetric distributions, we expect actual prices of about 95% of all houses to lie within an interval: $\hat{y} \pm 2(1009)$

(4) The value of R^2 is 0 78.8% and the value of Adj. R^2 is 73.5%. See Exercise 14–17 part (4) above for further explanation.

(5) $H_0: \beta_1 = \beta_2 = \beta_3 = 0$, H_1: At least one of the β's is *not* equal to zero. As shown in the ANOVA Table, the *P*-value for *F* is 0.000 is smaller than 5% level of significance. We reject H_0 in favour of H_1.

(6) Based on expected influence of each variable, we write our null and alternative hypotheses as below:

$H_0: \beta_1 = 0$, $H_1: \beta_1 > 0$; $H_0: \beta_2 = 0$, $H_1: \beta_2 \neq 0$; $H_0: \beta_3 = 0$, $H_1: \beta_3 \neq 0$. For a one-tailed hypothesis: $t_{0.05,12} = 1.782$ and for two-tailed $t_{0.05,12} = 2.179$. Reject H_0 for β_1 and β_3. H_0 for β_2 is not rejected.

(7) Given the R^2 value of 78.8%, model seems to perform well.

(8) Examining the plot of residuals against observation numbers, all observations seem to be within 3 times the standard error limits (upper and lower control limits).

(9) Based on the simple correlations, we do not see sufficient evidence of multicollinearity. The largest value of simple correlation coefficient is 0.699 between employees and inventory variables.

(10) The Graph of residuals against observation numbers does not seem to show sufficient evidence of autocorrelation. The Durbin-Watson (*d*) statistic for the regression 2.41 leads us to suspect negative autocorrelation. But the test is inconclusive.

(11) The graph of the squared error term against the predicted price does reveal a larger spread around smaller profit levels.

(12) The histogram of residuals does not indicate any serious departure from normality. The Normal plot of residuals is also very close to a straight line implying no serious departure from normality.

(13) Based on all findings in 1 to 12, we think that a re-estimated model excluding the dividend variable would provide a better picture of the estimated values of parameters and the inferences.

(14) Write a descriptive report by combining all features from (1)–(13).

14-21. REGRESSION ANALYSIS #1

(1) The Estimated Equation is:

Income = 28.24 + 0.0287 Value
(*t*-values)(9.46)   (5.77)

+ 0.65 Education – 0.049 Age
(2.69)   (–1.57)

–0.0004 Mortgage + 0.723 Sex
(–0.32)   (2.90)

Interpretation: An increase in a year of education is related, on average, with an increase of $650, assuming all other independent variables are held constant. Males, on average, earn $723 more compared to Females, assuming all other independent variables are held constant. As people get older by a year, they earn, on average, less by $49, all other independent variables are held constant. Other coefficients are similarly interpreted.

(2) ANOVA Table is given below:

ANOVA

	df	SS	MS	F	Significance F
Regression	5	19.89143	3.978287	**11.38542**	**3.47E-05**
Residual	19	6.638967	0.349419		
Total	24	26.5304			

(3) The standard error of estimate equals 0.591. It indicates, on average, the observed values of the dependent variable income deviate from the estimated income by $591. Using the empirical rule of thumb for symmetric distributions, we expect actual family incomes (in thousands) of about 95% of all households to lie within an interval: $\hat{y} \pm 2(0.591)$.

(4) The value of R^2 is 0.75 and the value of Adj. R^2 is 0.684. See answer to Exercise 14-17 for further interpretation.

(5) $H_0: \beta_1 = \beta_2 = \beta_3 = \beta_4 = \beta_5 = 0$, H_1: At least one of the β's is *not* equal to zero. As shown in the ANOVA Table, the *P*-value for *F* is close to 0.000, which is much smaller than 5% level of significance (0.05). We reject H_0 in favour of H_1.

(6) Based on the expected influence of each independent variable, we write our null and alternative hypotheses as below:

$H_0: \beta_1 = 0$, $H_1: \beta_1 > 0$; $H_0: \beta_2 = 0$, $H_1: \beta_2 > 0$; $H_0: \beta_3 = 0$, $H_1: \beta_3 \neq 0$, $H_0: \beta_4 = 0$, $H_1: \beta_4 \neq 0$; $H_0: \beta_5 = 0$, $H_1: \beta_5 > 0$. $t_{0.05,19}$ (one tail) = 1.729 and

$t_{0.05,19}$ (two-tail) = 2.093. We reject H_0 for β_1, β_2, and β_5. H_0 for β_3 and β_4 are not rejected.

(7) Since the signs of the age coefficient and mortgage payments are both counter-intuitive and statistically insignificant, they seem like irrelevant variables and therefore could be dropped from the model.

(8) There are no outliers. The Chart of (standardized) Residuals versus Fitted values indicates that all residuals are within two times the standardized values.

(9) There is no evidence of multicollinearity.

(10) The chart of residuals against observation number does not display sufficient evidence of autocorrelation. The value of d statistic = 2.18 indicates a value of autocorrelation of only 0.09

(11) The chart of squared residuals against the fitted values does not display sufficient evidence of heteroscedasticity.

(12) The chart of histogram of residuals does not reveal any serious departure from normality.

(13) The model does not violate any of the assumptions except for presence of some irrelevant variables.

(14) The re-estimated equation after dropping the variable mortgage payments provide equally satisfactory relationship. The regression equation is

Income = 28.1 + 0.0281 Value
t-values   (6.17)

              + 0.659 Years of Education
                          (2.81)

              − 0.0490 Age + 0.739 Sex
                  (−1.6)   (3.1)

$S = 0.5777$ R-Sq = 74.8%
R-Sq(adj) = 69.8% $F = 14.87$ $d = 2.27$

14-23. (1) The regression equation is

Monthly Salary = 652 + 13.4 Length of Service
(t-values)   (1.89)   (2.62)

−6.71 Age + 206 Sex − 33.5 Job
(− 1.06)   (2.28)   (− 0.37)

Interpretation: An increase in a length of service by a month, on average, is related with an increase of monthly salary of $13.4, assuming all other independent variables are held constant. Other coefficients are similarly interpreted.

(2) **Analysis of Variance**

Source	df	ss	ms	f	p
Regression	4	1 066 830	266 708	4.77	0.005
Residual Error	25	1 398 651	55 946		
Total	29	2 465 481			

(3) The standard error of estimate equals 236.5. It indicates, on average, the observed values of the dependent variable salary deviate from the estimated salary by $236.5. Using the empirical rule of thumb for symmetric distributions, we expect actual family incomes (in thousands) of about 95% of all households to lie within an interval: $\hat{y} \pm 2(236.5)$.

(4) The value of R^2 is 0.433 and the value of Adj. R^2 is 0.342. The value of R^2 indicates that 43.3 % of the sample variation in the dependent variable is explained by the independent variables in the model. See answer to Q. 17 for further interpretation.

(5) $H_0: \beta_1 = \beta_2 = \beta_3 = \beta_4 = 0$, H_1: At least one of the β's is *not* equal to zero. As shown in the ANOVA Table, the P-value for F is close to 0.005, which is much smaller than 5% level of significance (0.05). We reject H_0 in favour of H_1.

(6) Based on the expected influence of each independent variable on the dependent variable, we write our null and alternative hypotheses as below:

$H_0: \beta_1 = 0$, $H_1: \beta_1 > 0$; $H_0: \beta_2 = 0$, $H_1: \beta_2 > 0$; $H_0: \beta_3 = 0$, $H_1: \beta_3 > 0$, $H_0: \beta_4 = 0$, $H_1: \beta_4 \neq 0$. $\beta_5 > 0$. $t_{0.05,19}$ (one tail) = 1.708 and $t_{0.05,19}$ (two-tail) = 2.06. We reject H_0 for β_1, and β_3. H_0 for β_2 and β_4 are not rejected.

(7) The value of R^2 is low indicating a poor explanation of variation in the Salary. A better set of variables is required. Sign of the Age coefficient is counter-intuitive. This may be due to multicollinearity between Age and Service variables (see Part (9) below). The Job dummy is highly insignificant. Thus, Age and Job variables may be dropped.

(8) I Chart of Residuals and the output of unusual observations show that there are 3 unusual observations beyond $2S_e$ limits, but none beyond $3S_e$ limits. Further, Minitab does not record X beside any of these outliers implying that they are not influential in changing the relationship. See the Output below.

(9) The degree of multicollinearity between Age and Service is beyond tolerable limits.

(10) Minitab's I Chart of residuals against observations does not show sufficient evidence of autocorrelation. The value of d statistic is very close to 2 (= 2.03) also indicates absence of autocorrelation.

(11) The chart of squared residuals against the fitted values does not display sufficient evidence against homoscedasticity.

(12) Minitab's both Normal plot and the Histogram of residuals do not reveal any serious departure from normality.

(13) The model does not violate any of the assumptions except for presence of multicollinearity between age and service variables and doubtful (and insignificant) nature of the contribution made by the Technical dummy variable. We should therefore re-estimate the model without Age and Technical dummy variable.

(14) We re-estimated the model after dropping the variable Age and the technical Dummy.

The regression equation is

Monthly Salary = 784 + 9.02 Length of Service
(t-value)   (2.48)   (2.90)

                + 224 Sex
                    (2.57)

R-Sq = 40.5% R-Sq(adj) = 36.1%;
Durbin-Watson statistic = 2.09

We still have a poor model, as it does not explain more than 40.5% of the variation in the dependent variable Salary.

14-25. (1) The regression equation is

Youth U.I. = -1.18 + 0.602 Min-Wages
(t-values)   (-0.96)   (3.92)

                + 1.38 Total U.I. + 0.280 Q2
                    (23.41)   (1.12)

                -0.344 Q3 -0.124 Q4
                (-1.32)   (-0.47)

Interpretation: An increase in Minimum Wages by a dollar increases the youth unemployment rate, on average, by 0.6, assuming all other independent variables are held constant. Unemployment rate, on average, is higher (by 0.28%) in the second quarter as compared to the first quarter. Other coefficients are similarly interpreted.

(2) **Analysis of Variance**

Source	df	SS	MS	F	P
Regression	5	523.00	104.60	138.90	0.000
Residual Error	94	70.79	0.75		
Total	99	593.79			

(3) The standard error of estimate equals 0.8678. It indicates, on average, the observed values of the dependent variable youth unemployment rate deviate from the estimated youth unemployment rate by 0.8678. Using the empirical rule of thumb for symmetric distributions, we expect, on average, 95% of all actual values of youth unemployment rate (in %) to lie within an interval: $\hat{y} \pm 2(0.8678)$.

(4) The value of R-Sq = 88.1% and the value of R-Sq(adj) = 87.4%.

See answer to Q. 17 for further interpretation.

(5) $H_0: \beta_1 = \beta_2 = \beta_3 = \beta_4 = \beta_5 = 0$, H_1: At least one of the β's is *not* equal to zero. As shown in the ANOVA Table, the P-value for F is 0.000 is smaller than 5% level of significance. We reject H_0 in favour of H_1.

(6) Based on our expectations, we write our null and alternative hypotheses as below:

$H_0: \beta_1 = 0, H_1: \beta_1 > 0; H_0: \beta_2 = 0, H_1: \beta_2 > 0; H_0: \beta_3 = 0, H_1: \beta_3 > 0$

$H_0: \beta_4 = 0, H_1: \beta_4 \neq 0; H_0: \beta_5 = 0, H_1: \beta_5 \neq 0$

Critical value of t for 5% level of significance and 94 df is for a one-tailed test is approximately 1.66 and for a two tailed-test is 2.0. We therefore reject H_0 for β_1 and β_2. H_0 for the quarterly dummies are not rejected.

(7) Given the R-Sq = 88.1%, overall model seems to perform well and the coefficients have the major variables minimum wages and total unemployment have expected signs and are significant. The graph does not reveal any significant departure from linearity.

(8) There are few outliers but none significant enough to exert an undue influence on the estimated relationship.

(9) Simple correlations between independent variables are sufficiently low (the highest being 0.35) to warrant any concern about multicollinearity.

(10) The Graph of residuals (see the Residuals against observations Plot) seems to show good evidence of autocorrelation. The Durbin-Watson (d) statistic for the regression 0.26 leads us to suspect a strong positive autocorrelation. Since

the critical value of d_L for 5 independent variables and 100 observations at 5% level of significance equals 1.57, we *reject* the null hypothesis of no positive autocorrelation.

(11) The graph of the squared error term against the predicted Youth Unemployment does reveal heteroscedasticity, larger variances between 10 to 15% unemployment rates. Based on a quantitative test, we *reject* the null hypothesis of homoscedasticity.

(12) Both the histogram of residuals and the normal plot do not reveal any significant departure from normality. However, based on the JB Test, we *reject* the null hypothesis of normality!

(13) As noted above, we have several problems with our regression including autocorrelation, heteroscedasticity and non-normality.

(14) Since autocorrelation seems to be quite a serious problem in regression #1, a regression in terms of the first differences of all variables (where prefix D before each variable stands for first differences) gives satisfactory results.

D-Youth = $-0.145 + 2.08$ D-MW $+ 1.68$ D-TUI
(t-values) (-2.42) (2.46) (28.25)

$+ 0.743$ Q2
(5.5)

S = 0.4901   R-Sq = 90.6%   R-Sq(adj) = 90.3%
Durbin-Watson statistic = 2.37

The results of regression in first differences seems to have removed the problem of not only autocorrelation but also heteroscedasticity as well as non-normality!

14-27. (1) The regression equation is:

Games won = 34.8 + 528 Batting
(t-values)   (1.69)   (7.23)

-0.0044 Stolen $- 0.0178$ Errors
(-0.26) (-0.40)

-19.5 ERA $- 4.47$ Surface.
(-10.49) (-2.47)

Interpretation: For each additional "point" that the team batting average increases, the number of wins, on average, goes up by 0.528, found by 528(0.001), holding other variables constant. Other coefficients are interpreted similarly.

(2) Analysis of Variance

The ANOVA table gives $F = 33.68$ with P-value very close to zero. See table below.

ANOVA Table

Source	SS	df	MS	F	p-value
Regression	2,531.1683745	5	506.2336749	33.68	4.28E$-$10
Residual	360.6982922	24	15.0290955		
Total	2,891.8666667	29			

(3) The standard error of estimate equals 3.877. It indicates, on average, the observed values of the dependent variable youth unemployment rate deviate from the estimated youth unemployment rate by 0.8678. Using the empirical rule of thumb for symmetric distributions, we expect, on average, 95% of all actual values of youth unemployment rate (in %) to lie within an interval: $\hat{y} \pm 2(3.877)$.

(4) The value of R-Sq = 87.5% and the value of R-Sq(adj) = 84.9%.

The value of R^2 indicates that 87.5% of the sample variation in the dependent variable games won explained by the independent variables in the model. For further interpretation, see Exercise 14-17.

(5) H_0: $\beta_1 = \beta_2 = \beta_3 = \beta_4 = \beta_5 = 0$, H_1: At least one of the β's is *not* equal to zero. As shown in the ANOVA Table, the p-value for F (= 33.68) is close to 0.00. We reject H_0 in favour of H_1.

(6) We write our null and alternative hypotheses as below:

H_0: $\beta_1 = 0$, H_1: $\beta_1 \neq 0$; H_0: $\beta_2 = 0$, H_1: $\beta_2 \neq 0$; H_0: $\beta_3 = 0$, H_1: $\beta_3 \neq 0$

H_0: $\beta_4 = 0$, H_1: $\beta_4 \neq 0$; H_0: $\beta_5 = 0$, H_1: $\beta_5 \neq 0$

Critical value of t for 5% level of significance and 24 df is for a two-tailed test is 2.064. We therefore do not reject H_0 for β_2 and β_3.

(7) Given the R-Sq = 87.5%, overall model seems to perform well except for variables stolen bases and error. The graph does not reveal any significant departure from linearity.

(8) There are no outliers (beyond ± 2 S_e limits), to warrant our concern. See the residual plot.

(9) Simple correlations between independent variables are sufficiently low (the highest being 0.361) to warrant any concern about multicollinearity. The same is true about the variance inflation factors. Verify.

(10) The Graph of residuals (see the Residuals Plot) does not show sufficient evidence of autocorrelation. The Durbin-Watson (d) statistic for the regression (=1.91) is close to 2 and is larger than the critical value of $d_U = 1.83$

(based on 5% level of significance and 30 observations), and therefore we *fail to reject* the null hypothesis of *no* positive auto-correlation.

(11) The graph of the squared error term against the predicted values of games won does not reveal sufficient evidence of heteroscedasticity.

(12) The histogram of residuals does not reveal any significant departure from normality.

(13) As noted above, the variables stolen bases and Errors are highly insignificant. In the absence of a theoretical justification, we may re-estimate the model without these variables as given in 14 below.

(14) *The Re-Estimated Equation excluding variables Stolen Bases and Errors:*

Games won = 29.5 + 537 Batting Average
(*t*-values)   (1.76)   (7.93)

$$- 19.48\ \text{ERA} - 4.35\ \text{Surface}$$
$$(-10.94)\qquad (-2.51)$$

$R^2 = 0.874$;   Adj $R^2 = 0.86$;   DW = 1.88

Chapter 15

15-1. a. 3

b. 7.815

15-3. a. Reject H_0 if $\chi^2 > 7.815$ ($df = 3$, $\alpha = 5\%$)

b. $\chi^2 = \dfrac{(10-20)^2}{20} + \dfrac{(20-20)^2}{20} + \dfrac{(30-20)^2}{20}$

$+ \dfrac{(20-20)^2}{20} = 10.0$

c. Reject H_0. The categories are not equal.

15-5. H_0: Each face of the die is equally likely.

H_1: Each face of the die is not equally likely.

Reject H_0 if $\chi^2 > 11.07$ (for $df = 5$ and $\alpha = 5\%$)

$\chi^2 = \dfrac{(10-10)^2}{5} + \dfrac{(11-10)^2}{5}$

$+ \cdots + \dfrac{(13-10)^2}{5} = 4.00$

Do not reject H_0. The die is fair.

15-7. H_0: There is no difference in the proportions.

H_1: There is a difference in the proportions.

Reject H_0 if $\chi^2 > 15.086$ ($df = 5$, $\alpha = 1\%$)

$\chi^2 = \dfrac{(47-40)^2}{40} + \cdots + \dfrac{(34-40)^2}{40} = 3.400$

Do not reject H_0. There is no difference in the proportions.

15-9. a. Reject H_0 if $\chi^2 > 9.210$ ($df = 2$, $\alpha = 1\%$)

b. $\chi^2 = \dfrac{(30-24)^2}{24} + \dfrac{(20-24)^2}{24}$

$+ \dfrac{(10-12)^2}{12} = 2.50$

c. Do not reject H_0.

15-11. H_0: The proportions are as stated.

H_1: The proportions are not as stated.

Reject H_0 if $\chi^2 > 11.345$ ($df = 3$, $\alpha = 1\%$)

$\chi^2 = \dfrac{(50-25)^2}{25} + \dfrac{(100-75)^2}{75} + \dfrac{(190-125)^2}{125}$

$+ \dfrac{(160-275)^2}{275} = 115.22$

Reject H_0. Proportions are not as stated.

15-13. H_0: Distribution is normally distributed.

H_1: It is not normally distributed.

Reject H_0 if $\chi^2 > 7.815$ ($df = 3$, $\alpha = 5\%$)

Computed $\chi^2 = 0.469$. Do not reject H_0, the distribution is normal.

15-15. H_0: There is no relationship between community type and section read. H_1: There is a relationship.

Reject H_0 if $\chi^2 > 9.488$ ($df = (3-1) \times (3-1) = 4$, $\alpha = 5\%$))

$\chi^2 = \dfrac{(170-157.50)^2}{157.50} + \cdots + \dfrac{(88-83.62)^2}{83.62}$

$= 7.340$

Do not reject H_0. There is no relationship between the community type and section read.

15-17. H_0: No relationship between error rates and item type.

H_1: There is a relationship between error rates and item type.

Reject H_0 if $\chi^2 > 9.21$ ($df = (3-1) \times (2-1) = 2$, $\alpha = 1\%$))

$\chi^2 = \dfrac{(20-14.1)^2}{14.1} + \dfrac{(10-15.9)^2}{15.9}$

$+ \cdots + \dfrac{(200-199.75)^2}{199.75} + \dfrac{(225-225.25)^2}{225.25}$

$= 8.033$

Do not reject H_0. There is no relationship between error rates and item type.

15-19. H_0: $B_{(\text{Straight})} = 0.50$, $B_{(\text{Left})} = B_{(\text{Right})} = 0.25$;
H_1: Distribution is not as given by H_0.
$df = 2$; $\alpha = 10\%$; Reject H_0 if $\chi^2 > 4.605$

The computed value of $\chi^2 = 3.52$, which is less

than the critical value of 4.605. H_0 is not rejected. The proportions are as given in the null hypothesis.

15-21. H_0: The dice are fair. H_1: The dice are not fair.

$df = 10$; $\alpha = 5\%$;   Reject H_0 if $\chi^2 > 18.307$.

Goodness of Fit Test: $P(x) = 0.3333$
(Based on the Classical Definition of Probability)

35.94	chi-square
10	df
0.0001	p-value

Goodness of Fit Test: $P(x) = 0.3377$
(Based on the Relative Frequency Definition of Probability)

8.18	chi-square
10	df
0.6113	p-value

H_0 is rejected (P-value = 0.0001) for the definition of fairness based on the classical definition of probability. H_0 is not rejected (P-value = 0.6113) for the definition of fairness based on the relative frequency definition of probability!

15-23. H_0: The distribution of mail orders by province is the same as the distribution in the population by province.

H_1: The H_0 is not true.

We combined the last three provinces in one category.

$df = 10$; $\alpha = 1\%$; Reject H_0 if $\chi^2 > 23.209$

The computed value of $\chi^2 = 9.54$. H_0 is not rejected (P-value = 0.4820).

15-25. H_0: $\pi_0 = 0.4$; $\pi_1 = 0.3$; $\pi_2 = 0.2$; $\pi_3 = 0.1$

H_1: The proportions are not as given

$df = 3$; $\alpha = 5\%$; Reject H_0 if $\chi^2 > 7.815$

The computed value of $\chi^2 = 0.694$. Do not reject H_0.

Evidence does not show a change in the accident distribution.

15-27. a. H_0: The distribution is normal.

H_1: The distribution is not normal.

Reject if $\chi^2 > 4.605$ ($df = 5 - 1 - 2 = 2$; $\alpha = 10\%$).

$$\bar{X} = \frac{2430}{300} = 8.10 \qquad s = \sqrt{\frac{19\,994 - \frac{(2430)^2}{300}}{300 - 1}} = 1.02$$

Wage	f_o	Area	f_e	$(f_o - f_e)^2/f_e$
5.50 up to 6.50	20	0.0582	17.46	0.370
6.50 up to 7.50	54	0.2194	65.82	2.123
7.50 up to 8.50	130	0.3741	112.23	2.814
8.50 up to 9.50	68	0.2630	78.90	1.506
9.50 up to 10.50	28	0.0853	25.59	0.227
	300			7.04

Reject H_0. We cannot conclude that the distribution is normal.

b. $\text{JB} = n\left(\dfrac{S^2}{6} + \dfrac{K^2}{24}\right)$

$\qquad = 300\left(\dfrac{(-0.0492)^2}{6} + \dfrac{(-0.277)^2}{24}\right)$

$\qquad = 1.079$

Based on JB test, we cannot reject the null hypothesis of normality!

15-29. H_0: Level of management and concern regarding the environment are not related.

H_1: Level of management and concern regarding the environment are related.

Reject H_0 if $\chi^2 > 16.812$ ($df = (4 - 1)(3 - 1) = 6$; $\alpha = 1\%$)

$$\chi^2 = \frac{(15 - 14)^2}{14} + \cdots + \frac{(31 - 28)^2}{28} = 1.550$$

Do not reject H_0. Levels of management and environmental concerns are not related.

15-31. H_0: Whether a claim is filed and age is not related.

H_1: Whether a claim is filed and age is related.

Reject H_0 if $\chi^2 > 7.815$

$$\chi^2 = \frac{(170 - 203.33)^2}{203.33} + \frac{(74 - 40.67)^2}{40.67}$$

$$+ \cdots + \frac{(24 - 35.67)^2}{35.67} = 53.639$$

Reject H_0. Age is related to whether a claim is filed.

15-33. Answers will vary.

15-35. a. H_0: There is no relationship between pool and township.

H_1: There is a relationship between pool and township.

Reject H_0 if $\chi^2 > 9.488$ ($df = 4$; $\alpha = 5\%$)

$$\chi^2 = \frac{(9 - 5.43)^2}{5.43} + \cdots + \frac{(13 - 10.21)^2}{10.21}$$
$$= 6.680$$

Do not reject H_0. There is no relationship between pool and township.

b. H_0: There is no relationship between attached garage and township.

H_1: There is a relationship between attached garage and township.

Reject H_0 if $\chi^2 > 9.488$ ($df = 4$; $\alpha = 5\%$)

$$\chi^2 = \frac{(6 - 4.86)^2}{4.86} + \cdots + \frac{(12 - 10.82)^2}{10.82}$$
$$= 1.980$$

Do not reject H_0. There is no relationship between attached garage and township.

15-37. a. Goodness of Fit Test (1): 8 categories: chi-square = 49.01; $df = 4$; p-value = 5.82E-10

Combining the first two and the last two categories in (1) above:

Goodness of Fit Test (2): 5 categories: chi-square = 11.47; $df = 2$; p-value = 0.0032

Both, goodness of Fit test lead to rejection of normality assumption.

Jarque-Berra Test		
Skewness1	Kurtosis1	N1
0.762389	3.85110	100

JB = 71.49, which is greater than 5.99 and therefore we reject the normality assumption at 5% level of significance.

The Result from **MegaStat procedure** of normal curve of goodness of fit (based on the result of 8 categories → $df = 5$) gives the value of chi-square = 49.76 with a p-value = 1.55E-09 (close to zero).

Note the expected frequency is the same, 12.5 for all categories and the value of chi-square is 49.76 with a p-value close to zero.

The Result from **Mintab's Anderson-Darling test** for normality are given in graph format together with a value of $A^2 = 4.297$ and a p-value of 00.00

Thus, all tests of normality reject the null hypothesis of normality in this example!

Chapter 16

16-1. a. If the number of pluses (successes) in the sample is 9 or more, reject H_0.

b. Reject H_0 because the cumulative probability associated with nine successes (0.073) does not exceed the significance level (0.10).

16-3. a. H_0: $p \leq 0.50$ H_1: $p > 0.50$ $n = 10$

b. H_0 is rejected if there are nine or more plus signs. A "+" sign represents a loss.

c. There are nine + signs with a cumulative probability = 0.032. We reject H_0. It is an effective program.

16-5. a. H_0: $p \leq 0.50$ (There is no change in weight.)

H_1: $p > 0.50$ (There is a loss of weight.)

b. Reject H_0 if $z > 1.645$ (for 5% level of significance)

c. $z = \dfrac{(32 - 0.50) - (0.50)(45)}{0.50\sqrt{45}} = 2.68$

d. Reject H_0. The weight loss program is effective.

16-7. H_0: $p \leq 0.50$; H_1: $p > 0.50$ Reject H_0 if $z > 2.054$ (at 2% level of significance)

$z = \dfrac{42.5 - 40.5}{4.5} = 0.44$ Since the computed value of z (= 0.44) is less than the critical value of z (= 2.054) we do not reject H_0. There is no sufficient evidence for a preference between two menus.

16-9. a. H_0: Median $\leq \$80\,000$ H_1: Median $> \$80\,000$

b. Reject H_0 if $z > 1.645$ (for 5% level of significance)

c. $z = \dfrac{(170 - 0.50) - 0.5(205 - 5)}{0.5\sqrt{200}} = 9.83$

H_0 is rejected. The median income is higher than $\$80\,000$

16-11. Sums $T^- = 4$ and $T^+ = 24$. We use T^- as the test statistic, as suggested by the alternative hypothesis (parents have smaller homes). For a 0.05 level, one-tailed test, $n = 7$, the critical value is 3. Since the probability value of $T = 4$ is greater than the probability value of $T = 3$, we do not reject H_0 (one-tailed test). There is no difference in the square footage. Yuppies do not live in larger homes.

16-13. a. H_0: The production is the same for the two systems.

H_1: Production using the Munro method is greater.

b. H_0 is rejected if $T \leq 21$, $n = 13$

c. The sum of the negative ranks is 6.5. Since 6.5 is less than 21, H_0 is rejected. Production using the Munro method is greater.

16-15. H_0: The distributions are the same.

H_1: The distributions are not the same.

Reject H_0 if $z < -1.96$ or $z > 1.96$

$$z = \frac{86.5 - \dfrac{8(8+8+1)}{2}}{\sqrt{\dfrac{(8)(8)(8+8+1)}{12}}} = 1.943$$

H_0 is not rejected. There is no difference in the two populations.

16-17. H_0: The distributions are the same.

H_1: The distribution of country is to the right.

Reject H_0 if $z > 1.65$

$$z = \frac{158.5 - \dfrac{12(12+10+1)}{2}}{\sqrt{\dfrac{(12)(10)(12+10+1)}{12}}} = 1.35$$

H_0 is not rejected. There is no difference in the distributions.

16-19. ANOVA requires that we have two or more populations, the data are interval or ratio-level, the populations are normally distributed, and the population standard deviations are equal. Kruskal-Wallis requires only ordinal-level data, and no assumptions are made regarding the shape of the populations.

16-21. a. H_0: The three population distributions are equal.

b. Reject H_0 if $H > 5.991$

c. $H = \dfrac{12}{16(16+1)}\left[\dfrac{(64)^2}{5} + \dfrac{(53)^2}{6} + \dfrac{(19)^2}{5}\right]$
$- 3(16+1) = 59.98 - 51 = 8.98$

d. Reject H_0 because $8.98 > 5.991$. The three distributions are not equal.

16-23. H_0: The distributions of the lengths of life are the same.

H_1: The distributions of the lengths of life are not the same.

H_0 is rejected if $H > 9.210$

$H = \dfrac{12}{15(16)}\left[\dfrac{(46)^2}{5} + \dfrac{(39)^2}{5} + \dfrac{(35)^2}{5}\right]$
$- 3(16) = 0.62$

H_0 is not rejected. There is no difference in the three distributions.

16-25. a.

Males

b. $r_s = 1 - \dfrac{6(34)}{5(5^2 - 1)} = -0.7$ Fairly strong negative correlation among the ranks.

16-27. a. $r_s = 1 - \dfrac{6(83.5)}{10(10^2 - 1)} = 1 - 0.506 = 0.494$

A moderate positive correlation.

b. H_0: No correlation among the ranks.

H_1: A positive correlation among the ranks.

Reject H_0 if $t > 1.860$

$t = 0.494\sqrt{\dfrac{10-2}{1-(0.494)^2}} = 1.607$

H_0 is not rejected. We conclude that the correlation in population among the ranks could be 0.

16-29. H_0: $\pi = 0.50$ H_1: $\pi \neq 0.50$ $n = 19$

H_0 is rejected if there are either 5 or fewer "+" signs, or 14 or more. The total of 12 "+" signs falls in the acceptance region. H_0 is not rejected. There is no preference between the two shows.

16-31. H_0: $\pi = 0.50$ H_1: $\pi \neq 0.50$

H_0 is rejected if there are 12 or more or 3 or fewer "+" signs. Since there are only 8 plus signs, H_0 is not rejected. There is no preference with respect to the two brands of components.

16-33. H_0: $\pi = 0.50$ H_1: $\pi \neq 0.50$

Reject if $z > 1.96$ or $z < -1.96$

$z = (159.5 - 100)/7.071 = 8.415$

Reject H_0. There is a difference in the preference for the two types of orange juice.

16-35. H_0: The rates are the same. H_1: The rates are not the same.

H_0 is rejected if $H > 5.991$ $H = 0.082$
Do not reject H_0.

16-37. H_0: The populations are the same.

H_1: The populations are different.

Reject H_0 if $H > 7.815$ $H = 14.30$

Reject H_0, accept H_1.

16-39. $r_s = 1 - \dfrac{6(78)}{12(12^2 - 1)} = 0.727$

H_0: There is no correlation between the rankings of the coaches and the rankings of the sports writers.

H_1: There is a positive correlation between the rankings of the coaches and the rankings of the sports writers.

Reject H_0 if $t > 1.812$

$t = 0.727\sqrt{\dfrac{12 - 2}{1 - (0.727)^2}} = 3.348$

H_0 is rejected. There is a positive correlation between the sports writers and the coaches.

16-41.   Answers will vary.

16-43.   Answers will vary.

16-45.   Notice the sample sizes are smaller than 5, but we show the calculations anyway.

H_0: The distributions are the same.

H_1: The distributions are not the same.

Reject H_0 if $H > 5.991$

$H = \dfrac{12}{29(29 + 1)}\left[\dfrac{(337)^2}{22} + \dfrac{(37)^2}{3} + \dfrac{(61)^2}{4} \right]$
$- 3(29 + 1) = 0.328$

Do not reject H_0. The distributions are the same.

Chapter 17

17-1.   113.1

124.3

115.7

100.6

90.9

17-3.   1997: 110.3

1998: 106.6

1999: 108.8

2000: 114.4

14.4%

17-5.   a. $P = 105.8$

b. $P = 107.9$

c. $P = 102.6$

d. $P = 102.8$

e. $I = 102.7$

17-7.   a. $P = 101.6$

b. $P = 104.3$

c. $P = 102.8$

d. $P = 103.2$

e. $I = 103.2$

17-9. $I = 139.0$

17-11.   The index for selected years is

Year	1997	1998	1999	2000
Index	286.9	277.4	260.6	310.7

Year	Simple Index
1997	$\dfrac{6513}{2270}(100) = 286.9$
1998	$\dfrac{6296}{2270}(100) = 277.4$
1999	$\dfrac{5915}{2270}(100) = 260.6$
2000	$\dfrac{7053}{2270}(100) = 310.7$

17-13.   The index for selected years is

Year	1998	1999	2000
Index	207.5	257.9	297.7

Insurance sales have increased since 1998. The insurance sales have almost tripled over the period.

Year	Simple Index
1998	$\dfrac{14548}{7012}(100) = 207.5$
1999	$\dfrac{18086}{7012}(100) = 257.9$
2000	$\dfrac{20876}{7012}(100) = 297.7$

17-15.   The index for selected years is

Year	1998	1999	2000
Index	221.7	239.6	245.7

Year	Simple Index
1998	$\dfrac{1053}{475}(100) = 221.7$
1999	$\dfrac{1138}{475}(100) = 239.6$
2000	$\dfrac{1167}{475}(100) = 245.7$

17-17. The index for selected years is

Year	1996	1997	1998	1999	2000
Index	100	117.3	127	134	151.8

The gross revenue of Royal Bank of Canada has increased about 52% over the period.

Year	Simple Index
1997	$\dfrac{9279}{7911}(100) = 117.3$
1998	$\dfrac{10049}{7911}(100) = 127.0$
1999	$\dfrac{10600}{7911}(100) = 134.0$
2000	$\dfrac{12011}{7911}(100) = 151.8$

17-19. The index for selected years is

Year	1996	1997	1998	1999	2000
Index	100	122.5	133	62.3	86.3

Earnings per share of Royal Bank of Canada has increased in 1997 (22.5%) and 1998 (33%) but has decreased in 1999 (37.7%) and in 2000 (13.7%).

Year	Simple Index
1997	$\dfrac{5.01}{4.09}(100) = 122.5$
1998	$\dfrac{5.44}{4.09}(100) = 133.0$
1999	$\dfrac{2.55}{4.09}(100) = 62.3$
2000	$\dfrac{3.53}{4.09}(100) = 86.3$

17-21. $P = 114.2$

17-23. $P = 118$

17-25. $I = 117.7$

17-27. $P = 106.2$

17-29. $P = 104.3$

17-31. $I = 104.4$

17-33. $P = 120.8$

17-35. $P = 130.1$

17-37. $I = 130.5$

17-39. $P = 106.3$

17-41. $P = 101.1$

17-43. $I = 101.4$

17-45. a. Purchasing power of dollar = $0.86

b. Real monthly income for the year 1996 = $2975; Real monthly income for the year 2001 = $3082.19

17-47. Answer depends on the latent value of CPI.

Chapter 18

18-1. $b = \dfrac{2469 - (721)(15)/5}{55 - (15)^2/5} = \dfrac{306}{10} = 30.6$

$a = \dfrac{721}{5} - 30.6\left(\dfrac{15}{5}\right) = 52.4$ for 2003, $t = 8$

$\hat{y} = 52.4 + 30.6t = 52.4 + 30.6(8) = 297.2$

18-3. $b = \dfrac{69 - (20)(15)/5}{55 - (15)^2/5} = \dfrac{9}{10} = 0.90$

$a = \dfrac{20}{5} - 0.90\left(\dfrac{15}{5}\right) = 1.30$

$\hat{y} = 1.30 + 0.90t = 1.30 + 0.90(7) = 7.6\text{(tonnes)}$

18-5. a. The logarithmic equation is: $ln(\hat{y}) = -0.1235 + 0.2545(t)$

Note: $a = e^{ln(a)}$ $b = e^{ln(a)}$ gives $a = 0.884$; $b = 1.289$

And, hence the equation in exponential form as $\hat{y} = (0.884)(1.289)^t$

b. The average percentage growth rate is found as: $(b - 1)*100 = (1.289 - 1)*100 = 28.9\%$

c. Sales for the year 2003 are found as sales for $t = 8$

For $t = 8$: $ln(\hat{y}) = -0.1235 + 0.2545(8) = 1.9125$. Since, $\hat{y} = e^{ln(\hat{y})}$, $\hat{y} = e^{1.9125} = 6.769$

d. Quadratic (parabola) trend provided a better fit. This can be judged in two ways. (1) Graphically the fitted points are closer to the actual points. (2) Accuracy measures such as MAPE, MAD, or MSD that measure the errors, on average, between the actual and the fitted values. A lower value of these measures indicates a better fit.

18-7.

Quarter	Seasonal Indexes
1	0.690
2	1.666
3	1.168
4	0.476

18-9.

Estimated Pairs		Quarterly Forecast	
t	(millions)	Seasonal Index (%)	(millions)
21	40.05	110.0	44.055
22	41.80	120.0	50.160
23	43.55	80.0	34.840
24	45.30	90.0	40.770

18-11. $\hat{y} = 5.5528 + 0.3787\ (t)$. The following are the sales estimates.

Estimate	Index	Forecast
10.097	0.690	6.967
10.476	1.666	17.452
10.854	1.168	12.678
11.233	0.476	5.347

18-13. a. A decline, as shown by the linear trend.

b. Least square is preferable for estimating long-term trend on the deseasonalized series obtained by an application of the moving average method on the raw data.

c. 11 200, approximately.

18-15. a.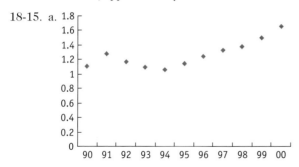

b. $\hat{y} = 1.00455 + 0.04409t$, using $t = 1$ for 1990.

c. For 1993, $\hat{y} = 1.18091$; and for 1998 $\hat{y} = 1.40136$.

d. For 2005, $\hat{y} = 1.70999$.

e. Each asset, on average, turned over 0.044 times.

18-17. a.

b. $\hat{y} = 49.140 - 2.9829t$

c. for 1997, $\hat{y} = 40.1913$ and for 1999, $\hat{y} = 34.2255$

d. for 2003 $\hat{y} = 22.2939$

e. The number of employees decreases, on average, at a rate of 2983 per year.

18-19. a. $ln(\hat{y}) = 1.8196 + 0.2617(t)$

b. For $t = 4$: $ln(\hat{y}) = 1.8196 + 0.2617(4) = 2.8264$;

$\hat{y} = Inv(ln(\hat{y})) = 16.8846$

For $t = 9$: $ln(\hat{y}) = 1.8196 + 0.2617(9) = 4.1749$

$\hat{y} = Inv(ln(\hat{y})) = 65.033$

c. 29.92%, which is the $Inv(ln)$ of 0.2617 minus 1 (in percent form).

d. for 2002, $t = 12$ and $ln(\hat{y}) = 1.8196 + 0.2617(12) = 4.96$

$\hat{y} = Inv(ln(\hat{y})) = 142.59$

18-21. a.

TSE 300:1990–2001

b. Linear Trend: $\hat{y} = 1976.12 + 547.29(t)$

Logarithmic Trend: $ln(\hat{y}) = 7.91 + 0.0987(t)$

Logarithmic trend is more accurate.

c. For 1993: $t = 4$:

Linear Trend: $\hat{y} = 1976.12 + 547.29(4) = 4164.6$

Logarithmic Trend: $ln(\hat{y}) = 7.9148 + 0.0987(4) = 8.3096$

$\hat{y} = Inv(ln(\hat{y})) = 4062.69$

For 1998: $t = 9$:

Linear Trend: $\hat{y} = 1976.12 + 547.29(9) = 6901.73$

Logarithmic Trend: $ln(\hat{y}) = 7.9148 + 0.0987(9) = 8.8031$

$\hat{y} = Inv(ln(\hat{y})) = 6654.84$

d. For 2003, $t = 14$

Linear Trend: $\hat{y} = 1976.12 + 547.29(14) = 9638.18$

Logarithmic Trend: $ln(\hat{y}) = 7.9148 +$
$0.0987(14) = 9.2966$

$\hat{y} = Inv(ln(\hat{y})) = 10\,900.89$

e. Based on the Logarithmic trend: 10.37%, which is the $Inv(ln)$ of 0.0987 minus 1 (in percent form).

Note: Answers may differ from computer output due to rounding.

18-23. a. July 87.5, August 92.9, September 99.3, October 109.1 (all in %).

b.

Month	Total	Mean	Seasonal
July	348.9	87.225	86.777
Aug.	368.1	92.025	91.552
Sept.	395.0	98.750	98.242
Oct.	420.4	105.100	104.560
Nov.	496.2	124.050	123.412
Dec.	572.3	143.075	142.340
Jan.	333.5	83.375	82.946
Feb.	297.5	74.375	73.993
March	347.3	86.825	86.379
April	481.3	120.325	119.707
May	396.2	99.050	98.541
June	368.1	92.025	91.552
	1206.200		

Correction = 1200/1206.2 = 0.99486

c. April, November, and December are periods of high sales, while February is low.

18-25. a.

	Seasonal Index by Quarter	
Quarter	Average SI Component	Seasonal Index
1	0.5014	0.5027
2	1.0909	1.0936
3	1.7709	1.7753
4	0.6354	0.6370

b. The production is the largest in the third quarter. It is 77.5% above the average quarter. The second quarter is also above average. The first and fourth quarters are well below average, with the first quarter at about 50% of a typical quarter.

18-27. a.

	Seasonal Index by Quarter	
Quarter	Average SI Component	Seasonal Index
1	0.5549	0.5577
2	0.8254	0.8296
3	1.5102	1.5178
4	1.0973	1.1029

b. $\hat{y} = 7.667 + 0.0023t$

c.

Period	Production	Index	Forecast
21	7.7153	0.5577	4.3028
22	7.7176	0.8296	6.4025
23	7.7199	1.5178	11.7173
24	7.7222	1.1029	8.5168

18-29.

	Seasonal Index by Quarter	
Quarter	Average SI Component	Seasonal Index
1	1.1962	1.2053
2	1.0135	1.0212
3	0.6253	0.6301
4	1.1371	1.1457

The regression equation is: $\hat{y} = 43.611 + 7.21153t$

Period	Visitors	Index	Forecast
29	252.86	1.2053	304.77
30	260.07	1.0212	265.58
31	267.29	0.6301	168.42
32	274.50	1.1457	314.50

In 1997 there were a total of 928 visitors. A 10% increase in 1998 means there will be 1021 visitors. The quarterly estimates are 1021/4 = 255.25 visitors per quarter.

Period	Visitors	Index	Forecast
Winter	255.25	1.2053	307.65
Spring	255.25	1.0212	260.66
Summer	255.25	0.6301	160.83
Fall	255.25	1.1457	292.44

The regression approach is probably superior because the trend is considered.

18-31. a.

Q1	Q2	Q3	Q4
86.4	104.7	101.6	107.4

b. Sales are higher in quarter 2 and 4 and lower in quarters 1 and 3.

c. Estimated sales on deseasonalized data:
$\hat{y} = 53.252.7 + 843.11(t)$

d.

t	Forecast
21	70\,958.05024
22	71\,801.16235
23	72\,644.27445
24	73\,487.38656

18-33. Answers will vary.

18-35.

Trend Analysis for Average
Linear Trend Model
$Yt = -240330 + 70063.3*t$

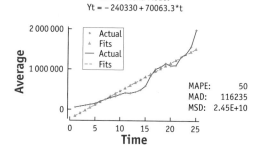

MAPE: 50
MAD: 116235
MSD: 2.45E+10

Trend Analysis for Median
Linear Trend Model
$Yt = 50603.2 + 18150.6*t$

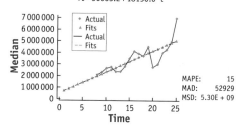

MAPE: 15
MAD: 52929
MSD: 5.30E + 09

The median is increasing $18 150 per year, while the average is increasing much more rapidly ($70 000 per year).

ANSWERS

to Odd-Numbered Review Exercises

Section Review of Chapters 1–4

1. a. Sample

    b. Ratio

    c. $11.60, found by
    $$\frac{9.5 + 9.00 + \cdots + 13}{5} = \$58/5$$

    d. $11.70 Half the employees earn below $11.70 an hour and the other half earn above $11.70 per hour.

    e. $s^2 = 5.85$, found by
    $$s^2 = \frac{696.18 - \dfrac{(58)^2}{5}}{5 - 1} = 5.845$$

    f. $sk = \dfrac{3(11.60 - 11.70)}{2.42} = -0.123$

    A small amount of negative skewness

3. a.

Rolls	Frequency
3 up to 6	2
6 up to 9	6
9 up to 12	8
12 up to 15	3
15 up to 18	1

    b.

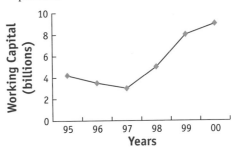

    c. $\bar{X} = \dfrac{186}{20} = 9.3$

    d. 9

    e. 8, 9 each occurs 4 times

    f. 13, found by (16-3)

    g. $s^2 = 9.27$, found by
    $$s^2 = \frac{1906 - \dfrac{(186)^2}{20}}{20 - 1} = 9.2736$$

    h. $s = 3.05$, found by $\sqrt{9.2736}$

i. The limits are 3.2 up to 15.4, found by $9.30 \pm 2(3.05)$

5. a. 8.82%, found by $\dfrac{\sum x_i}{n} = 44.1/5$

    b. 7.48%, found by $\sqrt[5]{5.2 * 8.7 * 3.9 * 6.8 * 19.5}$

    c. Geometric mean, since the growth rates are in percent.

7.

9. Ordinal

11. Less-than-cumulative frequency polygon. About 45; about 35; 10, 35, found by 55 − 20.

13. 9.375%, found by $\dfrac{6}{64}(100)$

15. Coefficient of variation.

17. 92 and 108, found by $100 \pm 2(4)$

19. & 20.

    a. The following histogram is from MINITAB

Histogram of C1		N = 50
Midpoint	**Count**	
0	1	*
40	7	******
80	3	***
120	8	*******
160	15	***************
200	10	**********
240	3	***
280	3	***

    b. & c.

N	MEAN	MEDIAN	TRMEAN	STDEV	SEMEAN
50	147.90	148.50	146.11	69.24	9.79
MIN	**MAX**	**Q1**	**Q3**		
14.00	299.00	106.00	186.25		

The distribution is fairly symmetrical because the mean (147.90) and the median (148.50) are quite close. The mean is ± 2s indicates that the middle 95% of the deposits are between $147.90 \pm 2(69.24) = 9.42$ and 286.38 Range = 299.00 − 14 = 285.00. There is a very slight negative skewness (because the mean is less than the median).

21. a. **Stem-and-Leaf Display: Grades**

   Stem-and-leaf of Grades $N = 54$

   Leaf Unit = 1.0

2	2	36
2	3	
4	4	47
10	5	478999
21	6	01123466669
(17)	7	01122233445556788
16	8	003556799
7	9	1111357

   b. 17 (Minitab) 70 and 78 inclusive.

   c. Skewed to the left.

23. a. **Stem-and-Leaf Display: Age**

   Stem-and-leaf of Age $N = 30$

   Leaf Unit = 1.0

2	2	88
9	3	0023345
(8)	4	44455568
13	5	24566679
5	6	01334

   b. Median 45.5, found by (45 + 46)/2

Section Review of Chapters 5–7

1. Subjective

3. An observation.

5. Complement rule: $1 - P(X) = 0.999$

7. Discrete

9. Discrete

11. Bell-shaped, symmetrical, asymptotic

13. a. 0.10, found by 20/200

   b. 0.725, found by 145/200

   c. 0.925, found by 1 − 15/200

15. a. 0.0183, found from Appendix C, where $\mu = 40$

   b. 0.9817, found by 1 − 0.0183

17. a. 0.2713, found by 379/1397

   b. 0.1346, found by 188/1397

   c. 0.6696, found by (230/802) + (307/802)

19. 6404.16, found by 21736*(0.06) + 34000*(0.15)

Section Review of Chapters 8–9

1. b.

3. c.

5. d.

7. a.

9. a, b, c.

11. Approximately 0.277.

13. (154.0475, 165.9525).

15. (890.49, 1080.51).

17. The value 250 lies inside the 95 percent confidence interval estimate (221.3538, 258.6463). We do not have significant evidence to conclude that the mean daily production of widgets has increased.

19. At least 151.

21. At least 996.

23. a. $(0.62 \pm 0.014) = (0.606, 0.634)$

   b. It will be reasonable to conclude that the statement that "p is less than 0.6" is incorrect.

Section Review of Chapters 10–12

1. e.

3. b.

5. b.

7. a.

9. c.

11. The computed t-value ($= -0.759$) is less than the critical value ($= -1.684$). There is sufficient evidence to infer that the population mean bounce is less than 90 cm.

13. The computed t-value ($= -0.759$) is between critical values (−2.947 and 2.947). We do *not* have sufficient evidence to infer that mean holding powers of Epox and Holdtite are different.

15. **ANOVA Table**

Source of Variation	Sum of Squares	Degrees of Freedom	Mean Square	F
Treatments	20.74	3	6.91	1.04
Error	100.00	15	6.67	
Total	120.74	18		

   1.04 is less than the critical value ($= 3.29$). We do *not* have sufficient evidence to conclude that the population means are not all equal. The choice of location does not impact average.

Section Review of Chapters 13–14

1. The coefficient of determination.

3. H_0: $\rho \le 0$; H_1: $\rho > 0$. Critical value of t is 1.671; computed $t = 3.324$. H_0 rejected. There is positive correlation.

5. Simple regression coefficient measures the total response of the dependent variable to a unit change in the independent variable. The partial regression coefficient measures a (partial) response of the dependent variable to a unit change in an independent variable, holding all other independent variables (in the regression model) constant.

7. $\hat{y} = a + b_1 x_1 + b_2 x_2 + b_3 x_3 + b_4 x_4$.

9. About 86% of the variation in net profit is explained by the four variables.

11. a.

b. $r = \dfrac{5(740) - 21(150)}{\sqrt{[5(103) - (21)^2][5(5500) - (150)^2]}}$

c. $r^2 = (0.9042)^2 = 0.8176$

d. $b = \dfrac{5(740) - 21(150)}{5(103) - (21)^2} = \dfrac{550}{74} = 7.4324$

$a = \dfrac{150}{5} - (7.4323)\left(\dfrac{21}{5}\right) = -1.2161$

$\hat{y} = -1.2161 + 7.4324X$

e. $\hat{y} = -1.2161 + 7.4324(4.5) = \$32.23$ (in thousands).

f. Strong positive association between amount spent on advertising and monthly sales. For each additional $1000 spent on advertising, sales increases $7432.40.

Section Review of Chapters 15–16

1. Frequency observed and frequency expected.

3. Chi-square distribution.

5. Not rejected because 11.248 is less than 12.592.

7. There is no difference between the observed and the expected set of frequencies.

9. Normal level.

11. To determine whether two independent populations come from the same populations.

13. To determine whether three or more populations have equal medians.

15. Kruskal-Wallis

17. Yes

19. No. It is positively skewed.

21. H_0: Median = \$27 000; H_1: Median ≠ \$27 000. Use 0.05 significance level and the sign test. The critical values are -1.96 and 1.96. Count the number of values above the median, compute z, assuming a large sample, and make a decision.

INDEX

Areas under the Normal Curve

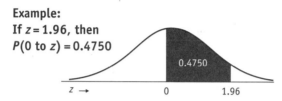

Example:
If $z = 1.96$, then
$P(0 \text{ to } z) = 0.4750$

z	0.00	0.01	0.02	0.03	0.04	0.05	0.06	0.07	0.08	0.09
0.0	0.0000	0.0040	0.0080	0.0120	0.0160	0.0199	0.0239	0.0279	0.0319	0.0359
0.1	0.0398	0.0438	0.0478	0.0517	0.0557	0.0596	0.0636	0.0675	0.0714	0.0753
0.2	0.0793	0.0832	0.0871	0.0910	0.0948	0.0987	0.1026	0.1064	0.1103	0.1141
0.3	0.1179	0.1217	0.1255	0.1293	0.1331	0.1368	0.1406	0.1443	0.1480	0.1517
0.4	0.1554	0.1591	0.1628	0.1664	0.1700	0.1736	0.1772	0.1808	0.1844	0.1879
0.5	0.1915	0.1950	0.1985	0.2019	0.2054	0.2088	0.2123	0.2157	0.2190	0.2224
0.6	0.2257	0.2291	0.2324	0.2357	0.2389	0.2422	0.2454	0.2486	0.2517	0.2549
0.7	0.2580	0.2611	0.2642	0.2673	0.2704	0.2734	0.2764	0.2794	0.2823	0.2852
0.8	0.2881	0.2910	0.2939	0.2967	0.2995	0.3023	0.3051	0.3078	0.3106	0.3133
0.9	0.3159	0.3186	0.3212	0.3238	0.3264	0.3289	0.3315	0.3340	0.3365	0.3389
1.0	0.3413	0.3438	0.3461	0.3485	0.3508	0.3531	0.3554	0.3577	0.3599	0.3621
1.1	0.3643	0.3665	0.3686	0.3708	0.3729	0.3749	0.3770	0.3790	0.3810	0.3830
1.2	0.3849	0.3869	0.3888	0.3907	0.3925	0.3944	0.3962	0.3980	0.3997	0.4015
1.3	0.4032	0.4049	0.4066	0.4082	0.4099	0.4115	0.4131	0.4147	0.4162	0.4177
1.4	0.4192	0.4207	0.4222	0.4236	0.4251	0.4265	0.4279	0.4292	0.4306	0.4319
1.5	0.4332	0.4345	0.4357	0.4370	0.4382	0.4394	0.4406	0.4418	0.4429	0.4441
1.6	0.4452	0.4463	0.4474	0.4484	0.4495	0.4505	0.4515	0.4525	0.4535	0.4545
1.7	0.4554	0.4564	0.4573	0.4582	0.4591	0.4599	0.4608	0.4616	0.4625	0.4633
1.8	0.4641	0.4649	0.4656	0.4664	0.4671	0.4678	0.4686	0.4693	0.4699	0.4706
1.9	0.4713	0.4719	0.4726	0.4732	0.4738	0.4744	0.4750	0.4756	0.4761	0.4767
2.0	0.4772	0.4778	0.4783	0.4788	0.4793	0.4798	0.4803	0.4808	0.4812	0.4817
2.1	0.4821	0.4826	0.4830	0.4834	0.4838	0.4842	0.4846	0.4850	0.4854	0.4857
2.2	0.4861	0.4864	0.4868	0.4871	0.4875	0.4878	0.4881	0.4884	0.4887	0.4890
2.3	0.4893	0.4896	0.4898	0.4901	0.4904	0.4906	0.4909	0.4911	0.4913	0.4916
2.4	0.4918	0.4920	0.4922	0.4925	0.4927	0.4929	0.4931	0.4932	0.4934	0.4936
2.5	0.4938	0.4940	0.4941	0.4943	0.4945	0.4946	0.4948	0.4949	0.4951	0.4952
2.6	0.4953	0.4955	0.4956	0.4957	0.4959	0.4960	0.4961	0.4962	0.4963	0.4964
2.7	0.4965	0.4966	0.4967	0.4968	0.4969	0.4970	0.4971	0.4972	0.4973	0.4974
2.8	0.4974	0.4975	0.4976	0.4977	0.4977	0.4978	0.4979	0.4979	0.4980	0.4981
2.9	0.4981	0.4982	0.4982	0.4983	0.4984	0.4984	0.4985	0.4985	0.4986	0.4986
3.0	0.4987	0.4987	0.4987	0.4988	0.4988	0.4989	0.4989	0.4989	0.4990	0.4990